Veterinary
Bacteriology
and
Virology

Veterinary
Bacteriology and Virology

by

I. A. MERCHANT, D.V.M., Ph.D., C.P.H.
**Dean, Division of Veterinary Medicine
and Professor of Veterinary Bacteriology
Iowa State College**

R. A. PACKER, B.S., D.V.M., Ph.D.
**Professor and Head
Department of Veterinary Hygiene
Iowa State College**

FIFTH EDITION

The Iowa State College Press, Ames, Iowa

First Edition, 1940
Second Edition, 1942
Third Edition, 1946
Fourth Edition, 1950
Second Printing, 1953
Fifth Edition, 1956
Reprinted, 1958

Library of Congress Catalog Card Number: 56–7380

Preface

This textbook, which is to serve as an introduction of bacteriology to students in Veterinary Medicine, emphasizes the general morphological and physiological characteristics of bacteria. It is concerned primarily with those species of bacteria, yeasts, molds, and filtrable viruses that are pathogenic to animals. An elementary introduction to the principles of infection and immunity is included to establish a working basis for the study of pathogenic forms.

A complete description of a pathogenic organism embraces more than the morphology and physiology of the organism; consequently, this text includes the description of each organism as follows: synonyms and history, distribution and transmission, morphology and staining, culture requirements and characteristics, resistance, biochemical properties, antigenic structure and toxins, pathogenicity, immunity, and laboratory diagnosis.

It is imperative that the student acquaint himself with bacteria which are pathogenic only to animals—with those which are pathogenic to both man and animals—and with certain of those which are pathogenic only to man. The intimate relationship of man with animals and the consumption of animal products emphasize the fact that all students of Medical Bacteriology must be familiar with the infectious agents found in man and animals if they are to understand the diseases produced.

Some textbooks of bacteriology include sections which have been omitted purposely from this one. A section on pathogenic protozoa has not been included because such microorganisms are logically studied in courses of animal parasitology in Colleges of Veterinary Medicine; therefore these organisms are discussed in textbooks of parasitology. The inclusion of such a section in a bacteriology book usually minimizes the importance of this significant group.

Although this textbook is intended primarily for undergraduate students, it is believed that the information given will be of value to research workers, livestock disease control officials, and to those who are engaged in the field of private practice. An attempt has been made to include all significant data concerning the various microorganisms, but some of the details which would be of interest to those in advanced research have not been included.

The assistance of authorities on individual organisms is freely enlisted so that controversial statements may be eliminated from subsequent editions. The references listed at the end of each chapter are for the benefit of the student; they have been chosen to assist him in becoming more familiar with the subject. The listing of a complete bibliography is not considered a necessary function of this textbook.

Many advancements in Veterinary Bacteriology and Virology continue to be made each year. It is hoped that most of the pertinent literature has been included in this revision, but it is acknowledged that some may have been inadvertently overlooked.

All of the book has been revised to some extent but certain chapters should be mentioned specifically. The chapter on antibiotics has been brought as up-to-date as possible for this rapidly changing field. The chapter on the pleuropneumonia group has been completely rewritten by our colleague W. P. Switzer. The chapter on the Pasteurellae has been again revised by G. R. Carter. The section on Virology has been increased.

The authors are deeply grateful for many helpful suggestions from numerous sources and again solicit the continuation of such support.

The efficient service of Marshall Townsend, William H. Van Horn, W. E. Holmes, and many other members of the technical staff of the Iowa State College Press is appreciatively acknowledged.

I. A. Merchant
R. A. Packer

May, 1956

Contents

PART IV

The Filtrable Viruses

PART I

General Biology of Microorganisms

1. The Scope and History of Bacteriology

Bacteriology is one of the youngest of the sciences. Its life is little longer than that of a normal man. Its importance in the field of biology was recognized with its inception, and in 1893 Theobald Smith forecast its future when he wrote, "In the study of the microscopic forms known as bacteria we have what might be fitly called the focal point of the various branches of biological science." The development of bacteriology during the years since that statement was made has revealed the truth of it. This has been true particularly of the relationship of bacteria to disease; for the entire conception of infectious disease, its prevention, and its treatment have been developed during the past seventy years. Bacteriology, as a science, has had a phenomenal growth, yet, the knowledge which is included in all the branches of the subject is so commonplace today, one wonders why its development was delayed so long. Even today, however, in scrutinizing the volumes written about bacteria it is observed that these microscopic forms have been known more for *what they do* than for *what they are*. This is understandable in light of the important changes that bacteria produce in materials in which they live. During recent years the trend of investigation has been toward the determination of the nature of bacteria, their chemical composition, and their variations in morphology and physiology. With this added knowledge we shall understand more clearly *why* bacteria bring about the changes by which they have been recognized for years.

Bacteriology is the branch of biology which deals with four different types of minute living organisms: the *bacteria,* the *filtrable viruses,* the *yeasts,* and the *molds.*

Bacteriology, as a science, has numerous divisions, all of which have a common technical foundation, but each division is distinctive because different types of bacteria are found in various habitats. There are definite lines marking some of the divisions while others merge into one another. Any classification of the entire subject would be an arbitrary one, but the one given here is considered appropriate. Bacteriology may be divided into the following: *General Bacteriology, Systematic Bacteriology, Industrial Bacteriology, Agricultural Bacteriology, Dairy Bacteriology, Sanitary Bacteriology,* and *Medical Bacteriology.*

General Bacteriology is the study of the general characteristics of all bacteria. It is of academic importance and probably does not deserve the distinction of a separate division; yet, it is an important part of the science, because students of this subject become acquainted with the entire field of bacteriology. Research in general bacteriology is of value because it is usually directed toward the nature of bacteria regardless of their origin.

Systematic Bacteriology embraces the classification and nomenclature of bacteria. It also is of academic value and gives order and organization to the entire field. There has been an unfortunate tendency on the part of workers in all branches of bacteriology to disregard the sincere attempts to classify bacteria which have been made by systematic bacteriologists. It is freely admitted that methods which are used in classification may be faulty and at times confusing, but it is hoped that as the nature of bacteria becomes fully known, a satisfactory classification may be accomplished and adopted by all.

Industrial Bacteriology includes all the procedures which involve the action of bacteria in the various industries. In the utilization of agricultural by-products bacteria are playing an important role. The function of yeasts in the manufacture of alcohols and gases used in beverages is common knowledge. Bacterial action is fundamental in the manufacture of many organic acids, of which vinegar is the best example. The use of bacteria in the fermentation of corn to prepare alcohols of value as motor fuel is a promising industrial venture. The curing of tobacco, the retting of hemp, and the tanning of leather all depend on bacteria in various stages of the process. The discovery of penicillin initiated the development of a tremendous industry, the manufacture of antibiotics, which is included in this category.

Agricultural Bacteriology is the study of any of the forms of bacteria relating to agriculture and may be divided very appropriately into *soil bacteriology* and *plant bacteriology;* the former embraces the study of those bacteria which are found in the soil and which are of value in maintaining fertility; the latter is the study of bacteria found in plants and is an important part of the subject *Plant Pathology.*

Food Bacteriology includes the various processes which are used in the preparation of foods in the canning industry. This usually is confined to the control of those procedures which prevent spoilage of food and the elimination of conditions of bacterial origin which may impart undesirable flavors to foods.

Dairy Bacteriology embraces the study of all the bacteria, yeasts, and molds which are found in the manufacture of dairy products. This subject includes all bacteria which are harmful as well as those which are useful. In the sanitary control of milk and milk products this field overlaps those of sanitary and medical bacteriology.

Sanitary Bacteriology is so closely allied with Medical Bacteriology that there has been constant hesitation in placing it in a separate division; yet, certain bacteriologic technics sufficiently definite to be placed in a separate category have been developed which aid man in the control of his environment. The bacteriology of water, foods, and sewage makes up the most important part of this subject. It is the study of all bacteria, significant to health, which are found in the environment of man and animals.

Medical Bacteriology embraces the study of those bacteria, yeasts, and molds which are detrimental to the health of man and animals, primarily by their ability to produce disease. This division may be subdivided into *Human Bacteriology* and *Animal Bacteriology,* the latter commonly called *Veterinary Bacteriology.* Accumulated research reveals, however, that the division of these two subjects is becoming increasingly indistinct. Many bacteria are capable of producing disease in both man and animals, and although we are more familiar with the ones transmissible from animals to man, evidence points to the fact that the reverse occurs in some instances. No doubt much overcrossing of infection would be present if man and animals lived in close contact with one another. *Human Bacteriology* may be defined as that portion of medical bacteriology which concerns those microorganisms (bacteria, yeasts, molds, and filtrable viruses) which affect the health of man only and those which are transmitted from animals to man, or from man to animals either directly or in food products. *Veterinary Bacteriology* includes that portion of Medical Bacteriology which concerns those microorganisms (bacteria, yeasts, molds, and viruses) which affect the health of animals only, and those which are transmitted from animals to man, either directly or in food products. Both branches of Medical Bacteriology have as their very able ally, *Immunology,* which considers the resistance of the body to disease and the means which may be used to increase such resistance.

During recent years the study of the filtrable viruses which affect man and animals has progressed so much that the study of such agents is embraced under the general term *Virology.*

THE HISTORY OF MEDICAL BACTERIOLOGY

The development of bacteriology has been due to the true scientific curiosity and energy of great men, aided in many instances by their fortitude in standing for what they knew to be true in the face of apparent disproof and the disdain of their associates. The history of Medical Bacteriology is a story of the evolution of knowledge concerning the causes of disease. It is a most fascinating story, particularly as revealed by Bullock in "The History of Bacteriology," which every student is urged to read. Space allotted to the discussion of this subject in this book permits only a brief review of the significant discoveries of the foremost contributors to the subject.

Early Theories of the Cause of Disease. The life of early man was governed by superstition. It is not surprising that such an affliction as disease, often followed by death, was attributed to the wrath of divine spirits for the punishment of individual sins. This is known as the *Theurgical Theory of Disease*. The Bible gives several interesting accounts of contagious disease. One of the most significant is the discussion of the treatment of lepers as given in Leviticus, Chapters XIII and XIV. The fact that the Jews required leprous people to be segregated indicates that they were aware that the disease was spread by contact, but the cause always was considered to be supernatural. That the infected were required to shield their faces with their hands and to cry "unclean" also indicated a knowledge of transmission. Sometimes an enraged Deity was credited with transmitting evil spirits on poisoned darts as was described in the great classic, "The Iliad," when Appolo apparently became angry and supposedly inflicted the army before Troy with epidemic sickness by means of darts. The Theurgical Theory of Disease persisted through many centuries. The belief in supernatural inflictions of disease is still observed among uncivilized peoples, and occasionally vestiges of it are evident among races considered civilized.

This belief was replaced by the *Miasmatic Theory of Disease* which taught that all disease was due to the emanations from the earth, the influence of the stars, the moon, the winds, the waters, and the seasons. This explanation of the cause of disease was enhanced by the teachings of Hippocrates (460–370 B.C.) who is commonly given the credit of being the originator of the theory. In his treatise, "On Airs, Waters and Places," Hippocrates stressed the relationship of disease to different waters, to the direction of the wind, and to the slope of the land. He also postulated that the four elements—fire, air, water, and earth, and the four qualities—heat, cold, moisture, and dryness, corresponded to the four fluids, or humors, of the body—blood, phlegm, yellow bile, and black bile.

All were closely related according to Hippocrates, and the different types of disease were caused by the changes in temperature and moisture during the various seasons of the year. Hippocrates did not think of disease as being caused by transmissible agents; consequently, he did not advance knowledge a great deal from the early ancient beliefs. He did free medicine from superstition, however, and his clear method of analysis of cases of disease and his description of them certainly make him worthy of the great honor accorded him in his title "The Father of Medicine."

The teachings of Hippocrates were the starting point for theorizing on disease by all medical minded individuals. This resulted in discarding the Miasmatic explanation for a period. The *Pore Theory* came into vogue and was supported by Asclepiades (124 B.C.), Themison (143–23 B.C.), and Thessalus (60 A.D.). Although each of these men based his conception on the function of pores, their resulting theories varied somewhat. The first two investigators believed that a symmetry of proportion of the pores resulted in health and a disproportion of pores caused disease. Thessalus, on the other hand, believed that the pores should be changed in afflicted parts to assure recovery from disease. So positive was he of his theory that he vigorously denounced Hippocrates' Miasmatic Theory.

The close relationship of disease to nature was too apparent for the Miasmatic Theory to be discarded for long. Galen (120–200 A.D.) revived all the medical teachings of the master, Hippocrates, and embellished them with his own observations and imagination. He recognized the four elements, qualities, and humors as postulated by Hippocrates and taught that an excess or deficiency of these humors resulted in disease. Based upon his observation of the individual humoral capacity of each person, Galen classified the temperaments of people as (1) sanguine, (2) phlegmatic, (3) bilious, or (4) melancholic. In order to equalize humors, Galen often found it necessary to draw what he considered excess blood. He advocated blood-letting as one of the cures of disease. No advance in the knowledge of contagion was made during this period. The Miasmatic Theory was accepted whole-heartedly.

The teachings of Hippocrates and Galen were accepted during the Medieval period (1096–1438); however, most scientific investigation and teachings were dominated by the rise of Christianity and its power in the State. Great powers of healing were attributed to the Saints, and fortunate indeed was he who had in his possession, as a charm for healing, a bone or any other article reputed to have come from a Saint. During this period pandemics of plague, epidemic chorea (St. Vitus' dance), and other epidemics swept the civilized world. Ample material was available for the observation of the contagiousness of disease. If such observations were made at that time, very few of them found their way into the medical literature of the period; however, some interesting observations were made by laymen such as Boccaccio (1313–75) who tells an interesting story concerning the transmission of plague in his "Decameron" (1358). He wrote: [1]

> A marvellous thing to hear is that which I have to tell and one which, had it not been seen of many men's eyes and of mine own, I had scarce dared credit, much less set down in writing, though I had heard it from one worthy of belief. I say, then, that of such efficience was the nature of the pestilence in question in communicating itself from one to another, that, not only did it pass from man to man, but this, which is much more, it many times visibly did; to wit, a thing which pertained to a man sick or dead of the aforesaid sickness, being touched by an animal foreign to the human species, not only infected this latter with the plague, but in a very brief space of time killed it. Of this mine own eyes (as hath a little before been said) had one day, among others, experience on this wise; to wit, that the rags of a poor man, who had died of the plaque, being cast out into the public way, two hogs came up to them and having first, after their wont, rooted amain among them with their snouts, took them in their mouths and tossed them about their jaws; then, in a little while, after turning round and round, they both, as if they had taken poison, fell down dead upon the rags with which they had in an ill hour intermeddled.

Science rose with the Renaissance, and during the period (1400–1600) made tremendous advances. The conception of the causes of disease, however, was still retarded by beliefs in divine powers and miasms. Paracelsus (1493–1541) speculated that diseases arose from five main causes: (1) the effect of the stars, (2) the poisons in foods, (3) natural phenomena controlled by the stars and moon, (4) spirits and demons, and (5) effects of the acts of God.

The speculations of Fracastorius (1478–1553) represent the earliest doctrine of infection that came close to the truth. He based his observations on epidemics of plague, syphilis, and typhus of man and of foot-and-mouth disease of cattle which were known to be prevalent in Italy at the time. Contagion was attributed to three possible sources: (1) contagion by contact, (2) contagion by fomites (clothes, wooden things, etc.), and (3) contagion at a distance. He wrote of *seminaria*, or seeds, of disease, showing that he did believe that some seed or living agent was involved. This represented the greatest advance toward solving the actual cause of infection until the most important barrier to the real discovery, the minuteness of bacteria, had been overcome.

The Influence of the Microscope. Although the early Greek physicians had conjectured that invisible living plants existed, the discovery of them awaited the development of the microscope.

Sir E. Ray Lankester has written most appropriately, "The microscope is the means by which our modern understanding of the

---

[1]Giovanni Boccaccio. *The Decameron*, 1358. Trans. John Payne, The Modern Library, New York, p. 9.

structure and nature of living things has been gained, as contrasted with the baseless fancies and blank ignorance of three centuries ago."

Among the early believers in the existence of invisible forms, was Athanasius Kircher (1602–80). He is given the credit of using a microscope of about 32-power magnification with which he saw "worms" in the blood of plague patients. His descriptions were so embellished by imagination that most of his observations are discounted. The first compound microscope is believed to have been made in Holland by Cornelius Drebbel and by Hans and Zaccharias Janssen at about 1590–1610. Galileo, in 1609, is also credited with being one of the first to place a series of lenses in a tube to produce higher magnifications. Toward the end of the seventeenth century two Englishmen, Robert Hooke and Nehemiah Grew, used a microscope in the study of natural objects and the structure of plants. An Italian, Marcello Malpighi (1628–94), who is known as the founder of histology, obviously used a microscope in order to see the detailed cellular structures of the lungs which he described in 1661. The description of the red blood cells by Jan Swammerdam in 1658 was made possible by the use of a microscope.

The manufacture and use of a microscope of a higher magnifying power than any formerly used is credited to Antony von Leeuwenhoek, of Delft, Holland, who lived during the period 1632–1723. The story of the life of this true scientist and of his discoveries has been perpetuated by Dobell. Every student of science dealing with microscopy should read this fascinating account. There is little doubt that Leeuwenhoek should be credited as being the Father of Bacteriology. His letters to the Royal Society of London and the illustrations (Fig. 1.1) which accompanied them prove conclusively that he had seen bacteria of various shapes and sizes in a variety of substances. His microscopes revealed that he was a craftsman of ability, although his interest in his instruments was based upon what they allowed him to see, rather than his ability in manufacturing them. The microscopes of Leeuwenhoek were rough and unfinished although they were mechanically efficient (Fig. 1.2). He made 247 microscopes, very few of which have been handed down to posterity. The highest

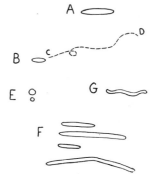

FIG. 1.1 — Leeuwenhoek's figures of bacteria: A and B, probably Bacilli; C–D, path of motile form; E, cocci; F, Leptothrix; G, spirochete.

magnification which he was able to obtain was about 200 diameters. He guarded his instruments jealously, and very few persons were privileged to see them.

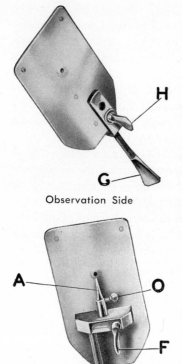

Observation Side

Specimen Side

FIG. 1.2 — Replica of Leeuwenhoek's microscope. A, needle on which to mount specimen; F, screw for focusing specimen; G, screw for raising and lowering specimen; H, clamp screw; O, handle for rotating specimen. (Courtesy Bausch and Lomb.)

The microscope passed through a gradual series of developments until it has become the splendid instrument of the present day (Fig. 1.3). In 1739, J. N. Lieberkühn perfected the solar microscope of Leeuwenhoek. The light transmitted through the glass lenses of the early microscope was broken into its component colors. Chester Moor Hall and John Dollond (1733) are given the credit for independently preparing achromatic lenses which corrected this dispersion. The use of a combination of lenses is attributed to Chevalier of Paris in 1824. Joseph Jackson Lister developed important detailed principles of the modern microscope in 1830. From that date the microscope has been improved by many mechanical innovations. An advance in the knowledge of microorganisms has followed each improvement in the microscope. The compensating ocular, the Abbe condenser and the oil immersion objective enables us to see objects magnified 1,500 diameters; however, there does appear to be a limit to the visibility of highly magnified objects. Physicists agree that the resolving power of the microscope is limited by the length of the waves of light used for illumination. J. E. Barnard has shown that, by using ultraviolet light for dark ground illumination, and suitable quartz lenses, extremely small objects can be recorded by photography.

The development of the electron microscope during very recent years has opened an entirely new invisible world for man to observe. With this instrument, objects which are magnified 25,000 times are photographed and made available for study.

Spontaneous Generation. The spontaneous origin of life (heterogenesis or abiogenesis) among all living things, other than animals

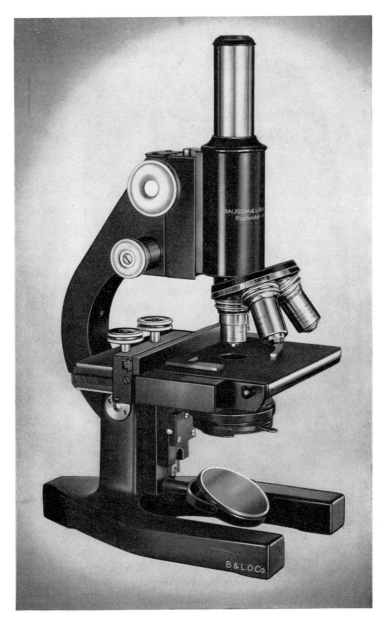

FIG. 1.3 — A modern student microscope. (Courtesy Bausch and Lomb.)

manifestly the result of the act of creation, was the firm conviction of early scientists. The origin of maggots from decaying flesh, and rats from filthy clothing are examples of early beliefs. It is obvious that microscopic living things were believed to arise spontaneously. The proof that such was not the case removed one of the serious barriers to the development of knowledge of the nature of bacteria. Francisco Redi (1626–97) was one of the first to show that maggots did not develop in meat when the meat was covered with fine gauze. Louis Joblot (1647–1723) demonstrated in 1711 that heated infusions were not able to produce animalcules, whereas cold infusions soon teemed with living things. The belief in the theory of spontaneous generation persisted, however, largely due to the efforts of such men as Needham who was an ardent believer in this theory. The experimental work of Spallanzani in 1756 and 1776, which disproved the theory conclusively, served to fan the flame of controversy over the subject. The experiments of Theodore Schwann (1810–82), published during the first part of the nineteenth century, definitely established that fermentation and decay were results of microorganisms rather than the creation of them. Schröder and Dusch in 1854 demonstrated that cotton-wool satisfactorily protected a freshly boiled infusion from fermentation, thereby establishing the use of the cotton plug in laboratory procedures. A staggering blow to the theory of spontaneous generation was dealt by Louis Pasteur in a series of experiments the results of which were published in 1860. In these experiments he demonstrated that the dust in the air was laden with microbes, and when it was prevented from entering flasks containing infusions, the infusions remained sterile.

The results of these experiments were of great practical value. Joseph Lister (1827–1912), a Scottish surgeon, found that infection following surgery was prevented by the application of a dressing containing some material (carbolic acid) capable of destroying the life of floating particles. Thus the use of antiseptics in surgery originated and was the forerunner of the aseptic surgery of today. The heat resistant stages of the various microorganisms were not considered, however, and it was not until the experiments of John Tyndall in 1877 that the final decisive blow was given to heterogenesis. He demonstrated that infusions were made absolutely sterile by repeated heating, allowing intervals for the development of spores, thereby originating the method of fractional sterilization (Tyndallization) which is used so commonly in laboratories of today. At the same time he demonstrated the heat resistance of bacterial endospores.

Fermentation. The action of the leaven in making bread and the fermentation and decay of fruits and vegetables were magic to ancient people. The discovery of the nature of the processes really laid the foundation to the discovery of the relationship of microorganisms to disease. Early chemists conceived that fermentation was the same as other chemical reactions.

Fabbroni (1787) apparently was the first to suggest that fermentation of wine was due to the action of a glutinous substance contained in grapes. The biological nature of fermentation was made obvious by the discovery of yeast cells. This important contribution was shared by Cagniard-Latour (1836), Schwann (1837), and Kutzing (1837). Of these Schwann is credited with being the one to explain alcoholic fermentation and is known as the Father of Fermentation.

The role of microorganisms in fermentation was definitely shown by Louis Pasteur (1822–95). His exactness in experimentation and his enthusiastic support of his results epitomize the character of Pasteur. These characteristics explain why his results were accepted when the results of others were not. As a chemist, it was natural that he should become involved in the subject of fermentation. During the period 1854–80 he demonstrated and explained most of the processes of fermentation. His results were opposed, however, by the German chemist, Liebig, who believed that fermentation was due to a ferment formed by the action of air on the sugar molecule. Spurred on by this controversy, Pasteur conclusively proved that yeast cells produced a ferment which in turn caused the reactions characteristic of fermentation, that lactic acid in milk was produced by ferments of bacteria, and that acetic acid was formed as a result of bacterial ferments. He was hailed as the savior of the wine industry of France when he showed that undesirable organisms caused sour wine. He showed that the proper sterilization of vats eliminated these undesirable organisms.

The Development of the Germ Theory of Disease. In the discussion of the ancient conceptions of the cause of disease it was observed that a glimmering of the truth existed in some of the literature during the fifteenth and sixteenth centuries. In general, however, the scientific world did not accept the belief that contagion was due to living things which grow and multiply in the body of the infected. This hesitance of scientific workers is substantiated by the fact that a very significant book on the nature of consumptions, written by Benjamin Martin in 1720, was comparatively unknown to his contemporaries. He theorized that consumption was caused by some species of animalcula which were inimical to the nature of man; that they were able to exist in the juices and vessels of the body and be carried to the lungs where they localized and wounded or gnawed the tender vessels, thereby producing the disease. It was the adherence to accepted dogma, no doubt, that explained why the discovery of small animalcula by Leeuwenhoek was of so little significance in the understanding of the cause of disease. It is surprising that the keen mind of Bretonneau (1778–1862), who is known as the first to believe in the specificity of disease, did not grasp the significance of animalcula as an aid in explaining specificity of disease.

An Italian layman, Agostino Bassi, discovered in 1835 that a disease of silkworms, known by the Italians as "calcino" and by the French as "muscardine," was caused by a fungus. He demonstrated that the organism could be transmitted from diseased to healthy silkworms by contact and by infected food.

The real basis for the foundation of the *Germ Theory of Disease* was laid by Jacob Henle in 1840 when he speculated "On Miasmata and Contagia." George Rosen has translated this treatise into English which makes it more available to students of this continent. Henle based his theories upon Bassi's discovery of the cause of silkworm disease and the discovery of the relationship of yeast cells to fermentation by Cagniard-Latour, and Schwann. These definite findings, in addition to his own observations, led Henle to give the following reasons which to him proved the individual life of the contagions: [2]

1. The ability to multiply by assimilating foreign materials is known to us only in living organic beings.
2. The action of contagia was also compared with fermentation in that the quantity of the effect is in no relation to the quantity of ferment used. A needle dipped into diluted chicken-pox material having been mixed with a half dram of water is still capable of infecting. This action depends on the ability of the agent to multiply, as has been demonstrated in fermentation and putrefaction; consequently, this is a further proof of the animate nature of the contagia.
3. The precise, typical course of the miasmatic-contagious diseases, and the relations in the course of the corresponding epidemics themselves seem to speak for an independent, temporal development of the disease cause, which occurs only among organic beings.

Although Henle recognized that his theory needed experimental substantiation, he realized that in order for the experiments to develop they needed the light of reasonable theory. The experiments did develop, and it was one of his pupils, Robert Koch, who later expanded the theory into fact which proved the relationship of germs to disease.

The discovery of the fungus of silkworms by Bassi opened the way for the discovery of numerous fungus diseases of man and animals. Some of the discoveries were based on fact, but most of them were without value.

---

[2] Jacob Henle. *On Miasmata and Contagia*, 1840. Trans. George Rosen, Johns Hopkins Press, Baltimore, 1938, p. 19.

In 1849, John Snow observed epidemic cholera was water-borne; this added proof to the germ theory. The classic, "Typhoid Fever," by William Budd, illustrated his conception of the relationship of living, growing germs to that disease.

The discovery of small filiform bodies in the blood of anthrax infected sheep and the subsequent proof of the relationship of these bodies to the disease was conclusive evidence that germs could cause disease. The discovery of the bacilli was made, independently, by P. F. O. Rayer and his associate, C. J. Davaine, in 1850 and by F. A. A. Pollender in 1855. F. A. Brauell established the transmissibility of the disease in 1857 by infecting sheep and horses with anthrax blood. During the period 1863 to 1868, Davaine established the definite relationship of the "bacteria," as he called them, to the disease by observing that they were present in blood of animals having the disease and, also, by observing that when they were not present anthrax did not occur. He demonstrated that the disease could be produced by the injection of one-millionth of a drop of anthrax blood.

Pasteur added materially to the formulation of the Germ Theory of Disease by his discovery, in 1870, that pebrine, a disease of the silkworm, was caused by a protozoan parasite. The crystallization of the Germ Theory of Disease during the 1860's came as a result of a converging of numerous approaches to the nature of microorganisms which may be summarized as follows: First, fermentation had been shown to be due to the action of yeasts. Second, spontaneous generation had been exploded. Third, wound infection following surgical operations had been prevented by the use of antiseptics. Fourth, epidemiological observations by Henle, Snow, Budd, and a host of others substantiated the particulate and living nature of contagion. Fifth, the injection of putrid blood from a case of septicemia reproduced the disease. Sixth, the discovery of the following specific causes of disease: fungi were present in the disease of silkworms; fungi were found in skin infection of man; bacteria were always present in cases of anthrax.

The absolute proof of the Germ Theory came as a result of the classical work of Robert Koch (1843–1910) on anthrax in 1876. Working with crude equipment Koch succeeded in tracing the development of the anthrax bacillus through the sporeforming stage to the germination of the spore and the formation of the bacterial cell. He demonstrated the capacity of the organism to kill mice and to produce the same type of lesions repeatedly. He found that other similar types of bacteria did not produce disease, thereby establishing the specific nature of infectious disease and forming the basis of his postulates or laws for which he has become famous. Koch's discovery was lauded and abetted by Ferdinand Cohn, a botanist, to whom great credit is given for classifying the species of bacteria known at that time and forming a basis of classification and nomenclature on which subsequent systems have been built.

Pasteur had deserted the field of fermentation when he investigated the cause of silkworm disease. Koch's definite discovery of the anthrax organism stimulated Pasteur to delve into the causes of animal and human diseases. He confirmed Koch's work on anthrax and in 1877 clarified the relationship of another organism to an acute and fatal disease. He established the cause of malignant edema as being due to an anaerobic organism which he termed *Vibrion septique*. Pasteur then turned his attention to the nature of disease and to immunity. His classical studies on anthrax immunity laid the foundation of prophylactic treatment of infectious diseases. Koch turned his attention to the perfection of laboratory procedures during the course of which he made monumental discoveries of bacteria, the most important of which was the tubercle bacillus which he demonstrated in 1882. So it was due largely to the efforts of Koch and Pasteur that the Germ Theory of Disease became a fact, the science of medical bacteriology became established, and the field of medicine became revolutionized.

The Development of Laboratory Methods. The perfection of the microscope, the discovery that cotton plugs protect culture media from air-dust contamination, and the conclusion that intermittent boiling kills bacterial spores are three very important contributions to laboratory technic previously discussed. Progress in bacteriology was delayed, however, by the lack of proper methods of staining bacteria and of separating one type of microorganism from another in a pure culture.

Dyes, such as carmine, had been used for the staining of tissues until aniline and the coal-tar dyes were prepared in 1856. Herman Hoffman is given first credit for using carmine and fuchsin in staining bacteria in 1869. The practical use of dyes in bacteriology dates from 1875 when Carl Weigert used methyl violet to stain cocci in tissues. Koch turned his attention to the use of stains which he perfected in 1877 enabling him to stain the flagella of bacteria. He used heat to fix the bacterial film to the slide in 1881. On March 24, 1882, Koch read his first paper on the cause of tuberculosis, a discovery brought about by staining the films of tuberculosis matter with alkaline methylene blue and subsequent treatment with vesuvin and Bismarck brown. Paul Ehrlich, a cousin of Weigert, contributed to the chemical knowledge of stains, introduced the technic of staining blood-films in 1881, and in 1882 improved on the technic of Koch for staining tubercle bacilli. Christian Gram of Denmark introduced the technic now known as the "Gram stain" in 1884; by this method all bacteria are separated into two groups, Gram-negative and Gram-positive.

Numerous methods were employed by the early bacteriologists to separate different species of bacteria and obtain pure cultures. The most popular and successful method was by multiple dilution. Raw potato, however, was commonly used as a solid medium. To Robert Koch goes the credit of first using solid media in 1881. He added gelatin to meat infusion and poured the liquid medium on a glass plate to harden; the medium was protected from dust contamination by placing a bell jar over it. The medium was inoculated by streaking the surface with a platinum wire charged with the material containing bacteria. The use of agar-agar in culture media was introduced by Frau Hesse, the wife of Walther Hesse, one of Koch's early co-workers. Koch used coagulated blood serum for a culture medium in 1882. The value of solid media which enabled bacteriologists to obtain pure cultures cannot be overestimated. It was one of the most valuable contributions to the development of the science. It enabled Koch to fulfill his postulates by isolating organisms in pure culture; accordingly, most of the discoveries of the causes of the various infections were made possible by the use of solid media. It served to stimulate all bacteriological research, for it enabled workers to study the action of pure cultures.

New advances in laboratory technic have aided in the discovery of new organisms and of additional knowledge concerning old ones. The technic of filtration, first employed as a method of purifying media and to test the toxicity of bacteria-free filtrates, lead to the discovery of the large group of disease agents known as filtrable viruses. Constant improvements in methods of sterilization were to reduce the hazards of contamination. Various tests for the metabolic products of bacterial growth were devised to aid in differentiating and classifying bacteria. Methods of culturing bacteria in the absence of free air revealed a large group of anaerobic bacteria and increased knowledge concerning bacterial respiration. Out of all the laboratory procedures, however, three stand out as being the most significant in the development of the science of bacteriology. Those three are: *use of the microscope, sterilization,* and *use of solid media.*

The Development of Theories of Immunity. A resistance to a second attack of the same disease after recovery from the first was an observation by early physicians. This was thought to be the result of magic as was disease itself. The development of immunology, as a science, closely followed that of bacteriology and cannot be separated from it.

Methods of immunizing against disease were practiced long before the Germ Theory of Disease was formulated. In 1798, Edward Jenner described his method of immunizing against smallpox by using attenuated virus. His method was an outgrowth of the commonly known fact that milkmaids became immune to smallpox because of their contact with cows suffering with cowpox. Almost 100 years later, 1877–80, Pasteur accidentally found that cultures of the fowl cholera organism lost their ability to produce disease after they had been grown on artificial media in contact with air. These cultures did have the property, however, of producing an immunity in chickens which rendered them resistant to virulent cultures of the same organism. The triumphant entry of artificial immunization into the field of medicine resulted from Pasteur's classical work on anthrax at Pouilly-le-Fort in 1881. In those experiments he demonstrated that cultures of the anthrax bacillus, attenuated by growing at 42°C., were able to cause the development of a marked immunity in sheep against highly virulent anthrax organisms. His subsequent work on swine erysipelas and rabies were almost as noteworthy, for they substantiated his earlier work and opened the way for other applications of his methods. In the United States, Theobald Smith and D. E. Salmon demonstrated the use of heat-killed cultures of an organism then thought to be the cause of hog cholera. Although the use of the heat-killed cultures of *Salmonella choleraesuis* was of no value in hog cholera immunization, it was of great value in initiating the technic of bacterin therapy which has been widely practiced since that time.

About 1881, Elie Metchnikoff, a Russian zoologist, observed that motile cells in the body of the water flea were able to engulf invading microorganisms. This led to further observations of the phenomenon in man and animals and the formulation of the *Phagocytic, or Cellular Theory of Immunity.*

A few years later, 1888, G. H. F. Nuttall demonstrated that blood of various animals possessed a bactericidal action for anthrax bacilli. This fact was confirmed and explained further by Hans Buchner in 1889. In 1890 E. Fraenkel and E. Behring produced an immunity against diphtheria by injecting old broth cultures. In the same year Behring and Kitasato revealed that the immunity in rabbits against the tetanus organism was due to a material in the blood stream capable of neutralizing the toxin formed by the bacillus. This fact was demonstrated also for the diphtheria bacillus. From these discoveries arose the *Humoral Theory of Immunity* which contends that immunity is due to the action of specific substances in the blood and not due to the action of phagocytic cells entirely.

In attempts to explain the methods by which the pathogenic organisms and their toxins were neutralized by blood serum, other discoveries were made which, for the most part, were results of test-tube experimentation. In 1895 Jules Bordet contended that neutralization was due to a physical sensitization process and a subsequent lytic process. Paul Ehrlich in 1897 insisted that the neutralization process was chemical in nature and upon this premise he formulated his *Side-Chain Theory of Immunity*. He visualized that the body cell produced receptors which were superabundant in immune serum and which caused a chemical neutralization of the invading organism or its toxins when they came in contact. Although Ehrlich's side-chain theory has been relegated to the "historic background" of the subject of immunity, it has served a useful purpose. It has stimulated research out of which have grown more plausible explanations of the phenomenon and has been useful in explaining to the beginning student the intricacies of the various reactions. Ehrlich's terminology is still used to a great extent and some of his fundamental theories linger with a vestige of truth in them.

In 1896 Herbert Durham and Max Gruber demonstrated that a suspension of organisms was agglutinated by a specific immune serum. The practical application of the phenomenon in the diagnosis of typhoid fever was made by F. Widal in 1896. This test, known as the "Widal microscopic test," has been modified during the years until the "Macroscopic Tube Test" is now one of the most common diagnostic methods for certain diseases. R. Kraus demonstrated in 1897 that immune serum also had a specific reaction for a bacterial filtrate which caused it to precipitate. This gave origin to the precipitation test which is used for the diagnosis of disease and for the study of immune reactions.

Simon Flexner demonstrated in 1894 that "animals that had withstood one dose of dog serum would succumb to a second dose given after the lapse of some days or weeks, even when this dose was sublethal for a control animal." Thus he clearly demonstrated that a hypersensitive condition, the exact opposite of immunity, was produced. This reaction was observed also by C. Richet and J. Hericourt in 1898 when eel serum was injected into dogs after allowing a lapse of approximately two weeks from the time the first injection was given. In 1903 M. Arthur observed a skin necrosis in rabbits which followed successive injections of horse serum. In 1904 Theobald Smith found that guinea pigs became hypersensitive to subsequent injections of horse serum during the course of diphtheria antitoxin standardization. From these original observations a mass of data was accumulated about the subject of anaphylaxis and allergy, a study which today is still in its formative stage.

REFERENCES FOR FURTHER STUDY

Adams, F. The Genuine Works of Hippocrates. The Williams & Wilkins Co., Baltimore, 1939.

Bullock, W. The History of Bacteriology. Oxford University Press, New York, 1938.

Clendening, Logan. Source Book of Medical History. Paul B. Hoeber, New York, 1942.

Dobell, C. Antony von Leeuwenhoek and His "Little Animals." John Bale, Sons & Danielsson, London, 1932.

Duclaux, E. Pasteur, A History of a Mind. English Translation by E. F. Smith and Florence Hedges. W. B. Saunders Co., Philadelphia, 1920.

Holmes, W. H. Bacillary and Rickettsial Infections: Black Death to White Plague. The Macmillan Co., New York, 1940.

Metchnikoff, Olga. Life of Elie Metchnikoff. Houghton Mifflin Co., Boston, 1921.

Oliver, Wade W. Stalkers of Pestilence. Paul B. Hoeber, New York, 1930.

Rosen, George. Jacob Henle: On Miasmata and Contagia. Translation. The Johns Hopkins Press, Baltimore, 1938.

2. Morphology and Colony Characteristics of Bacteria, Yeasts, and Molds

The characteristics by which plants and animals are differentiated become less significant among the microscopic forms of life; therefore, it is necessary to understand the factors that are considered in assigning a particular microorganism to the animal or plant kingdom. Difficulty arises particularly in the differentiation of the bacteria and the protozoa. All bacteria probably have a cell membrane which, in function, is closely related to that of plants, and in some species cellulose and chitin may be found. The cell membrane of protozoa is not so well defined and may be described more aptly as a limiting membrane. In shape, habit of growth, and reproduction the bacteria resemble the blue-green algae and molds much more than they do the protozoa. Motility is of no value in placing the bacteria in either kingdom, inasmuch as flagellated forms are found in both the plant and animal kingdoms. Although there is no particular reason why bacteria might not represent a position intermediate to the plants and animals, the evidence, on the whole, is in favor of the classification of true bacteria with plants.

THE PLANT KINGDOM

The position of bacteria in relationship to other plants should be understood. The plant kingdom is divided into four great groups or phyla according to the following classification:

PHYLA

Scientific Names	Common Names
SPERMATOPHYTA	
Gymnospermae	Conifers and Related plants
Angiospermae	Flowering plants
PTERIDOPHYTA	
Lycopodineae	Club mosses
Equisetineae	Horse-tails
Filicineae	Ferns
BRYOPHYTA	
Hepaticae	Liver-worts
Musci	Mosses

THALLOPHYTA

Algae
   Myxophyceae   Blue-green algae
   Chlorophyceae   Green algae
   Phaeophyceae   Brown algae
Fungi
   Basidiomycetes   Club fungi
   Ascomycetes   Sac fungi
   Phycomycetes   Algae fungi
   Myxomycetes   Slime fungi
   Schizomycetes   Bacteria
   Fungi Imperfecti   Imperfect forms

The Thallophyta are those plants devoid of leaves, stems, or true roots but otherwise have very little in common. Many of the different forms of Thallophyta have developed a parasitic capacity for plants, animals, and man. Most of them are found among the bacteria (*Schizomycetes*), a few among the Fungi Imperfecti, commonly called Yeasts (*Saccharomycetes*), and Molds (*Hyphomycetes*). The discussion of the general morphology of these three different types follows.

MORPHOLOGY OF BACTERIA

Shape. The bacteria are grouped according to shape into spherical forms, straight rods, curved or spiral rods, and filamentous forms (Fig. 2.1).

The spherical bacteria are called *cocci* (sing. *coccus*).

The straight rods are called *bacilli* (sing. *bacillus*).

The curved or spiral rods are represented by cells which may vary from a comma shape to a tightly twisted, corkscrew-like cell.

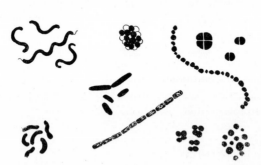

The more loosely curved cells are known as *spirilla* (sing. *spirillum*), and the more tightly coiled forms are called *spirochetes* (sing. *spirochete*).

Many of the bacteria resemble the molds in morphology. These forms are elongated and threadlike, and some of them are branched. They are known as the *filamentous bacteria* and are sometimes called *trichobacteria*.

FIG. 2.1 — Types of bacteria: cocci, bacilli, and spirilla.

The different morphologic groups of bacteria are well defined and on that basis may be classified into various subgroups. As a result of certain stimuli or when grown under unfavorable conditions, however, many bacteria assume unusual and abnormal shapes. Cells of this type have been called involution forms or pleomorphic types, and more recently variant and dissociative forms.

For many years little significance was attached to such changes, and they were thought to be due, in many cases, to contamination. Eventually, however, the changes were recognized and at the present time are considered to represent normal

FIG. 2.2 — Various groups of cocci.

characteristics of bacteria. Most of the variations which occur are of a temporary nature, and are due to a change in the environment of the organism; nevertheless, changes occur where the resulting type is permanent. The student must not be too alarmed when extremely long rods are found in a culture which is supposed to be composed of short plump rods; nor should he be surprised to find coccoid forms in the same culture. Some investigators explain that this variation is due to a cyclic development of the organism. In some species of bacteria such cyclic changes may occur, but bacteriologists in general are not ready to accept such explanations for all the organisms, nor for all the morphologic dissociative changes which have been described.

Cell Grouping. Bacterial cells divide by simple fission, and after division some remain attached to one another while others quickly break apart. Those that remain in groups or chains are held together by *plasmodesma*, a protoplasmic bridge between cells. The cell grouping is so constant that it, also, is used to differentiate various genera from each other and in some cases the species.

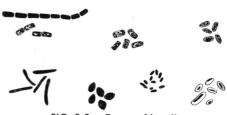

Bacteria divide normally at right angles to the longest axis of the cells. This permits little variation in the cell arrangement of the bacilli, spirilla, and fila-

FIG. 2.3 — Types of bacilli.

mentous forms, but the cocci have no longest axis; hence they may divide in various planes. On this basis the cocci are divided into the following groups.

The *streptococci* (chain-cocci) divide in a constantly parallel plane, forming chains.

The *diplococci* remain in pairs after division, and it is not unusual to see such paired cocci among the streptococci and the staphylococci.

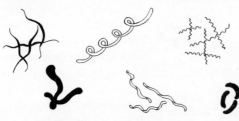

The *staphylococci* divide at various angles forming grapelike clusters of cells.

The *sarcina* divide in three planes at right angles to each other, resulting in the formation of cubes or packets shown in Figure 2.2.

FIG. 2.4 — Types of spirilla.

Bacilli grow either singly or in chains (Fig. 2.3).

Occasionally, the spirilla form short chains of two or three cells, but usually occur singly (Fig. 2.4).

The filamentous types of bacteria occur singly and in tangled masses or in clumps, and occasionally in palisade arrangement (Fig. 2.5).

Size of Bacteria. The size of bacteria is altogether dependent upon the type of morphology. The cocci range from 0.8μ to 1.2μ in size, although some as small as 0.5μ may be found. (The micron, designated by the letter μ, is used for the measurement of bacteria; 1μ = 1/1,000 mm. = 1/25,000 inch.) The rod-shaped microorganisms vary in size. The smallest representative is the influenza organism which is about 0.2μ x 0.5μ. The typhoid bacillus, 0.5μ x 2 to 3μ, represents the medium-sized bacilli. The tetanus bacillus is slender, 0.3μ, but rather long, 3 to 5μ. The spirilla vary in size from 3μ to 50μ, and some of the largest bacteria are found in this group. The filamentous bacteria can be described only according to the diameter of the cell which is usually 0.5μ to 1μ. Measurements for all types of bacteria must be based upon the average of normal cells because variation in size always exists.

FIG. 2.5 — Types of filamentous bacteria.

The Capsule and Cell Membrane of Bacteria. The cell membrane of bacteria is similar in many respects to that of plants, serving as an envelope to give the organism form and to permit the permeation of nutrient substances. There is little doubt that such a membrane exists because bacterial cells have been shown to undergo *plasmoly-*

sis, the shrinking of the protoplasm and subsequent pulling away from the cell membrane. The composition of this membrane in bacteria is not cellulose, as in higher plants, nor chitin as in fungi. Polysaccharide substances are concentrated in the cell membrane, and it is probable that the membrane is composed of a carbohydrate-protein substance.

A capsule composed of a mucoid or mucilagenous substance covers the cell membrane of some bacteria. Many bacteriologists believe it is present to some extent on all bacteria, but in the majority the substance is too thin to be detected by the usual staining procedures. The capsule may be easily demonstrated on certain species of bacteria by suitable staining methods and is recognized on some by the nature of the growth, for example, the "mother of vinegar" and slimy milk and bread. Capsular substance is an extension of the cell membrane and probably produced by it. It is chemically different for the various bacteria. In some it is composed of mucin, a slimy material made up of a protein-like substance united with a carbohydrate, resembling the mucus secreted by the cells of the mucous membrane. In others the capsule is composed of pure carbohydrates and is closely allied to certain of the vegetable gums, such as gum arabic. In still others the material is lipoid in nature forming a compact, waxy coating over the organism. The complex polysaccharide capsular materials found in some of the bacteria have been used extensively during recent years in determining the antigenic relationships of closely related strains of bacteria. These substances seem to be responsible for the specific reactions which are obtained in the serologic study of bacteria.

A relationship apparently exists between capsular substance and virulence, largely due to the resistance of the capsulated organism to phagocytosis; furthermore, the capsulated organism is not as virulent when devoid of its capsule. Many of the capsulated bacteria lose the capsule when grown on artificial media. The anthrax bacillus, for example, is always found to be capsulated when smears of blood from an anthrax infected animal are examined, but organisms grown on laboratory media are without capsules. This is not a permanent loss, however, for the capsules are formed when such organisms are injected into a susceptible animal.

Flagella. Fine threads of protoplasm, called *flagella,* extend from the cell membrane of certain of the bacteria. Such organisms are actively motile and, when viewed in a hanging drop, will be seen to pass quickly across the field of the microscope. This motility is easily distinguished from *Brownian movement* which is thought to be due to molecular bombardment on the surface of the particle and produces a vibrating or oscillating motion. Flagellated bacteria in large numbers are inhibited in their movement, however, and may give a picture similar to Brownian movement; hence, it is necessary to examine motility in dilute suspensions.

The presence of flagella is almost entirely limited to the spirilla and bacilli. Motility has been observed among the cocci, *Sarcina agilis,* but that group of organisms may be generally considered as nonmotile. Filamentous bacteria are nonflagellated.

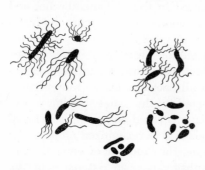

FIG. 2.6 — Arrangement of flagella on bacteria.

Motility may be seen by viewing an organism in a suspended drop, but the flagella cannot be seen in such a preparation. Special fixing and staining technic are required to make the flagella visible. The arrangement of flagella (Fig. 2.6) on the surface of the bacterial cell varies among the different types and is used as a basis of classifying them in the following groups:

1. *Atrichous* bacteria possess no flagella.
2. *Monotrichous* bacteria have a single flagellum on one end.
3. *Lophotrichous* bacteria have a group of flagella at one pole.
4. *Amphitrichous* bacteria have flagella at both poles.
5. *Peritrichous* bacteria are completely surrounded by flagella.

Flagella are usually present on young cells grown in fluid media. Older cells are devoid of flagella, and an organism grown on artificial media for some time may lose its ability to form flagella. This is one type of bacterial variation which must be remembered in forming a complete description of the organism. The flagella also enter into the antigenic composition of the organism as will be observed in a later chapter.

Cell Protoplasm. The small size of bacterial cells makes it difficult to determine the composition of the cell substance or endoplasm. The complex chemical reactions initiated by bacteria make it obvious that they contain protoplasm similar to other cells. Food material diffuses through the cell membrane, is converted into simpler substances which may be utilized by the bacterium for energy, and the end products are eliminated from the cell into the surrounding medium.

The type of nucleus which is possessed by the bacterial cell has been a subject of much controversy and it cannot be said that the problem is settled even today. Three different theories of the nature of *chromatin,* or nuclear material, have been advanced. *First,* the reaction of bacteria with basic dyes has been suggested as proof that the cell is composed of one large nucleus surrounded by very little cytoplasm. *Second*, some of the larger types of bacteria have been shown to have a small nucleus surrounded by cytoplasm; therefore, it has been assumed that all bacteria possess nuclei, even though they are too small to be visible by maximum magnification. Barnard has shown that microphotographs of bacteria taken with dark-field illumination and ultraviolet light show structures highly suggestive of nuclei. Furthermore, the electron microscope has made it possible to learn more about the internal structure of cells. Cell particles suggestive of nuclei are clearly seen in electron micrographs of bacteria. *Third*, a reticular network is present in the bacterial cytoplasm, and chromatin granules lie in the spaces of this network. It has been suggested that in sporeforming bacteria this granular material is concentrated into the spore which functions as the resistant state of the organism and which germinates under favorable conditions to form the bacterial cell. The refractibility of bacteria makes it extremely difficult to study their internal structure in the usual unstained preparation. So far no satisfactory differential staining technics have been perfected to demonstrate the different structures in bacterial cells. The fractionation of the various nucleoproteins of bacterial cells has indicated that true nuclear material does exist. It is not wise to generalize concerning all the various types of cells which are included under the term, bacteria; it may be possible that some bacteria are composed of one large nucleus, that some of the larger and more highly developed types of bacteria have one small nucleus similar to those found in plant and animal cells, and that still others may have a primitive, diffuse nuclear material.

In some species of bacteria, notably those belonging to the diphtheria group or *Corynebacteria,* small granules are found to be stained more intensely than the surrounding protoplasm by the basic aniline dyes. Because of the resemblance of these granules to chromatin they are called *metachromatic granules,* otherwise known as *Babes-Ernst granules* (Fig. 2.7). The nature and function of these granules are not known. They are not associated with the nuclear apparatus; they do not represent the resting stage of the organism; they are not associated with the virulence of the organism. It has been assumed that they represent a reserve food supply for the organism.

Many of the different species of bacteria present a granular, irregular appearance when stained with the basic aniline dyes. The *Pasteurella* organisms commonly associated with hemorrhagic septicemia of animals present a *bipolar* appearance. The protoplasm appears to be concentrated at both poles of the organism, leaving a vacuole-like, unstained space in the center. The various members of the *Clostridium* group, especially the blackleg bacillus, are stained unevenly, showing that the protoplasm accumulates in various parts of the cell.

Among the species of bacteria that live in water are found some that contain sulphur granules in the protoplasm. Fat globules and glycogen granules are found in some bacteria.

Reproduction of Bacteria. Under standard conditions normal multiplication of all bacteria is a simple process. The cell elongates or enlarges, a cell wall develops across the middle, and the two cells either separate completely or remain attached forming the different arrangements described previously. This process is known as *binary fission*. It may occur with considerable rapidity; some organisms in a favorable

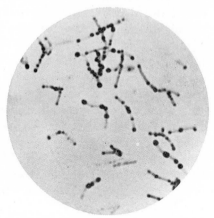

FIG. 2.7 — Metachromatic granules in diphtheria bacilli. (From Nowak: Documenta Microbiologica, courtesy Gustav Fischer.)

medium may grow to their full size and divide to form two individuals in as short a time as twenty minutes. If the organism multiplies at this rate for a short time, the number of resultant organisms is extremely high. For example, if a bacterium divides every half-hour, at the end of two days the progeny is represented by 2^{96}, a number having twenty-eight figures. Such rapid multiplication is never long continued, for food supply is not favorable over a long period of time, and waste products of the bacterial growth tend to accumulate and diminish the rate. The rapidity of bacterial multiplication accounts, in a large measure, for the many changes produced in a short time, such as in the souring of milk and the invasion of the body causing disease.

While the most common mode of reproduction among bacteria is binary fission, other methods have been observed. Buds have been seen in some of the true bacteria, members of the typhoid-dysentery group. Branching has also been noted, although it is difficult to differentiate from budding. After the branches are formed, they segment, giving rise to new cells. This process has been observed among many of the more filamentous types of bacteria as well as in the organism causing typhoid fever.

The filamentous bacteria, or trichobacteria, produce arthrospores, *conidia*, by the disintegration of some of the filaments into short rods or spheres which are capable of reproducing the parent type. In many cases the threads which break up into the arthrospores are somewhat differentiated from the normal cells of the plant, and are serial, resembling closely some of the molds.

It has been suggested by numerous workers that gonidia, which function as part of the reproduction process in higher living things, are formed by certain bacteria. *Gonidia* are formed within the cell, two, four, or more in each cell, and they escape through the cell wall or are liberated upon the disintegration of the cell. Development of mature bacterial cells from these minute granules has been described by numerous workers, many of whom have suggested that the gonidia are filtrable; so it is possible that the filtrable stages of bacteria may be represented by these forms.

Sexual reproduction has been described by some investigators but doubted by others. By demonstrating conjugation and showing that gonidia result from actual contact, a very interesting life cycle for bacteria may be constructed, but conclusive evidence to show that such a procedure exists is still lacking.

Many bacteria produce spores. Although spores, strictly speaking, cannot be considered a part of reproduction, yet they do play a part in the continuity of the life of the organism, and it is well to discuss spore development in connection with reproduction.

Endospores, commonly referred to as *spores,* are produced definitely by bacilli and possibly by some spirilla. The cocci and filamentous forms do not produce spores. The factors which are responsible for the formation of spores are not thoroughly understood. The process appears to be a natural one for those species in which it occurs, but when the period of spore formation in the life of the organism is reached, environmental conditions appear to hasten spore development. These environmental factors are: accumulation of waste products, change in the reaction of the medium, and a decrease for some species or increase for others in oxygen tension. The spore is essentially a portion of the protoplasm of the cell, almost devoid of water, and shrunken in size until it occupies only a portion of the space within the cell; it is surrounded by a heavy wall, probably chitinous in nature. In practically all cases there is but one spore in a cell. The spore may be equatorial or polar in position, and may be of smaller or greater diameter than the cell which produces it (Fig. 2.8). The position and size of the spore are used in the classification of sporeforming bacilli. The term *Clostridium* is used to indicate a spore-bearing rod in which the spore is equatorial and greater in diameter than that of the cell, resulting in a spindle-shaped cell. Tennis racket or drumstick-shaped cells are produced by spores that are polar and are greater in diameter than the cell.

Endospores contain only about 20 per cent of water as compared with 80 to 90 per cent in the cells which produce them. An organism without a spore is usually differentiated by the term *vegetative rod* or *vegetative cell.* Spores are much more resistant to desiccation, heat, light, and chemicals than the vegetative cells. They are of use in carrying the organism over unfavorable conditions, but it must not be assumed that this is their main function.

Spore-bearing bacteria are abundant in the soil, where they are exposed to great ranges of moisture, temperature, and light. When a spore again comes under favorable conditions for growth, it germinates and produces a cell typical of its species. Germination is accomplished by an elongation of the spore with a resulting stretching and bursting of the spore wall (Fig. 2.9). Spores may germinate equatorially in the same manner.

FIG. 2.8 — Types of bacterial spores.

COLONY CHARACTERISTICS OF BACTERIA

When a single bacterial cell is allowed to grow upon the surface of nutrient agar or nutrient gelatin, the newly formed cells accumulate and form the bacterial colony. The different forms of bacteria produce various types of colonies. The streptococci grow in minute, dewdrop-like colonies. The staphylococci produce larger, more opaque, smooth, glistening colonies. The sporeforming bacilli form irregular, greyish, lusterless colonies. The nonsporeforming rods are found in colonies that are whitish-grey, smooth, and glistening. Filamentous bacteria form a thin, transparent, spreading growth on the surface of the medium (Figs. 2.10, 2.11, 2.12, 2.13, and 2.14).

The colonies of closely related species of bacteria may differ in some characteristics; yet many of the colonies of closely related species, and even genera, may be practically alike.

External conditions, such as moisture, temperature, oxygen, and pressure, exert an effect upon the appearance

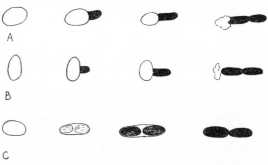

FIG. 2.9 — Diagram showing spore germination.

of the colonies of bacteria; hence, standard conditions for growth must be maintained.

Pigmentation of the colony, also, is often used as a distinguishing feature. Bacterial pigments are water soluble or water insoluble. The water-soluble pigments are of no value in colony differentiation. The water-insoluble pigments, however, impart definite colors to

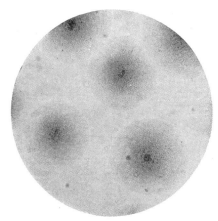

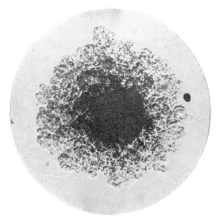

FIG. 2.10 — Colonies of streptococci. (From Nowak: Documenta Microbiologica, courtesy Gustav Fischer.)

FIG. 2.11 — Colony of bacilli. (From Nowak: Documenta Microbiologica, courtesy Gustav Fischer.)

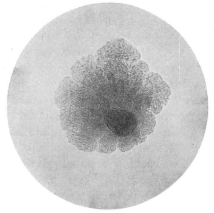

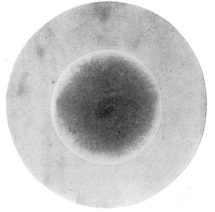

FIG. 2.12 — Colony of bacilli. (From Nowak: Documenta Microbiologica, courtesy Gustav Fischer.)

FIG. 2.13 — Colony of bacteria. (From Nowak: Documenta Microbiologica, courtesy Gustav Fischer.)

colonies. Some of the colors found in bacterial colonies are white, cream, gold, yellow, orange, brown, violet, and red. Varying shades of each color are present in different species. The color of the colony has been used often in naming bacteria, for example: *Staphylococcus albus*, the white staphylococcus; *Staphylococcus aureus*, the golden staphylococcus. Environmental conditions also exert an effect upon pigment production, and when pigment-producing organisms are grown for some time under artificial conditions, some of the bacteria lose the power to form color.

Early bacteriologists believed that only one type of colony could be produced by a given species of organism. This has been proven to be true in general, but certain strains of bacteria have been found to undergo a process known as dissociation or variation, in which a colony entirely different from the original one may be produced. The most common type of dissociation is that from a round, convex, smooth, finely granular, and entire type of colony, commonly designated S, (Fig. 2.15), to an irregular, flat, rough, coarsely granular, undulate, and dull type of colony, commonly designated R, (Fig. 2.16). The organism in the S colony shows many characteristics of physiology and virulence which may be absent in organisms in the R colony. This dissociation may be caused by some environmental effect, such as lack of nutrition, which may be temporary, or it may be caused by factors not understood, which cause a permanent variation. The newly formed dissociative types of colonies may be observed growing as small daughter colonies in the original mother colony or many appear as a sector of the mother colony. Mucoid variants, which may be so viscid that the growth flows over the surface of the agar when the plate is tilted, have been described also. The discovery that dissociation is a normal characteristic of some strains of bacteria has necessitated the inclusion of the dissociative types in the description of organisms.

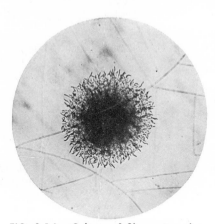

FIG. 2.14 — Colony of filamentous bacteria. (From Nowak: Documenta Microbiologica, courtesy Gustav Fischer.)

Colonies having a moth-eaten appearance have been described. This is caused by the action of bacteriophage, a virus which grows in bacteria, resulting in the lysis and disappearance of sections of the colony.

MORPHOLOGY OF YEASTS OR SACCHAROMYCETES

The yeasts are generally characterized by their morphology and their reproduction by budding. They represent a type of plant more complete than bacteria, although some of the various types resemble some of the bacteria. Yeasts, *Saccharomycetes,* are divided into two groups, the true yeasts and the false yeasts. The former are recognized by the formation of a sporangium in which spores develop. This spore case is commonly called an *ascus,* and as a result the term *Ascomycetes* has been given this group of microorganisms. The false yeasts do not produce spores, but otherwise are similar to the true yeasts.

Shape, Size, and Grouping. Yeasts are unicellular organisms which may be spherical, elliptical, or cylindrical in shape. The size of yeasts vary with the different types of morphology. In general, they are larger than bacteria, although some of the larger bacteria and the average yeast cells may be the same size, 4 to 5µ in diameter. Most of the true yeasts occur as individual cells; however, the newly formed daughter cell having developed by the budding process may cling to the mother cell for some time. Some species of yeast form into long threads giving rise to a mycelium when a mass of them becomes tangled together. These yeasts are much like the molds in this respect. Yeasts grow in a variety of

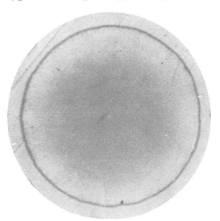

FIG. 2.15 — **Salmonella pullorum**, normal smooth S colony, ✕ 125. (Courtesy Van Roekel.)

types of colonies. The pathogenic varieties, however, form opaque, viscid colonies on solid media.

Structure of the Yeast Cell. The usual structures found in plant and animal cells are found in the yeast cells, as can be seen in Figure 2.17. The ectoplast, or limiting membrane of the cell

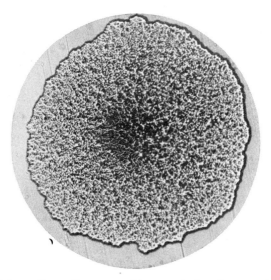

FIG. 2.16 — **Salmonella pullorum**, variant rough R colony, ✕ 25. (Courtesy Van Roekel.)

protoplasm, forms first and from it the cell membrane develops. In old cells it is quite distinct. The cell wall is composed of a car-bohydrate-nitrogenous substance to which the name *yeastcellulose* has been given. Capsules are found covering some species of yeast. Yeasts are nonflagellated.

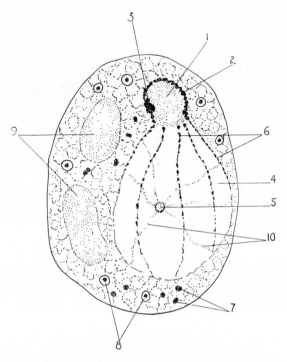

FIG. 2.17 — Detailed structure of the yeast cell. (After Wager.) 1.—Nucleolus. 2.—Peripheral layer of chromatin. 3.—Chromatin on side of nucleolus. 4.—Nuclear vacuole. 5.—Central volutin granule in the vacuole. 6.—Chromatin network. 7.—Granules of fatty substance. 8.—Volutin granules. 9.—Glycogen vacuoles. 10.—Suspending threads for the central volutin granule.

The nucleus of the yeast cell is rather large, and together with the nuclear vacuole takes up considerable space in the cell. The nucleus undergoes division during the budding process, and part of it goes with the newly developed bud or cell.

Vacuoles are frequent in yeasts and may be recognized as highly refractive bodies. They increase in size and number as the food supply of the cell diminishes. Glycogen granules are found in the cytoplasm and have been observed in the vacuoles. Fat droplets are commonly seen in certain yeast cells; in fact, such cells are known to be able to convert simple substances into fat. Glycogen and fat represent the reserve food material of yeasts.

Reproduction of Yeasts. The majority of the yeasts multiply by budding. In this process, a small bud develops from the cell wall of the mother cell, containing all the essential structures of the mother cell; it gradually increases in size, develops a cell wall, and is constricted off as a distinct individual. Mature yeast cells may produce numerous buds when the environment and food supply are favorable.

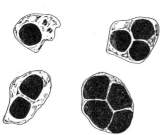

FIG. 2.18 — Ascospores of the yeast cell.

The production of ascospores by yeasts is different from the production of endospores by bacteria. A typical yeast cell produces eight spores while only one spore develops in the individual bacterial cell. The formation of the ascospores in yeasts does not appear to be influenced by the factors operative in stimulating spore development in bacteria; therefore, it would appear to represent a reproductive process more than a resting stage in the life of the cell. Ascospores are formed only when water is present, when the cell is well nourished, and when the temperature is around 25°C. The ascus may result from the fusion of two mature yeast cells which act as gametes; the contents of one cell pass into the other through a minute tube or copulation canal. The nucleus of the newly formed cell divides into the required number of parts to form ascospores, each of which, together with its surrounding protoplasm, becomes surrounded by a membrane (Fig. 2.18).

MORPHOLOGY OF THE MOLDS OR HYPHOMYCETES

All of the fungi that grow in a colony composed of loose cottony threads are classed under the general term of molds, and are grouped together as *Hyphomycetes.* Some of these forms are related to the blue-green algae and are placed with the *Phycomycetes;* others are grouped with the *Ascomycetes;* others are related to the smuts, rusts, and toadstools or *Basidiomycetes;* others are not well defined in morphology and are put with the imperfect forms, the *Fungi Imperfecti.*

Molds are multicellular organisms and, consequently, are easily distinguished from the bacteria and yeasts. The mold plant is made up of a tangled mass of threads called a *mycelium* (Fig. 2.19). Each thread of the mycelium is called a mycelial thread or *hypha* (plural, *hyphae).* The hyphae are designed for two purposes: The vegetative hyphae are for the purpose of supplying nutrition to the mold plant, and the fertile hyphae are differentiated for the purpose of reproduction in the process of spore formation. The hyphae of most of the common molds have numerous cross walls, known as *septa,* dividing one cell from another. Certain species of molds, however, are nonseptated. All molds may be classified upon the basis of this characteristic into *septated* and *nonseptated* molds.

The cells of the mold are much like the higher plants. The cell wall is composed of chitinous material. The protoplasm of the cell

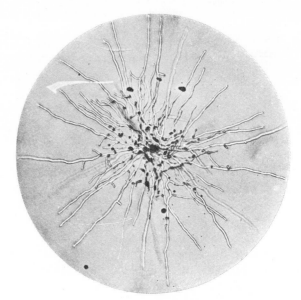

FIG. 2.19 — Developing mycelium of **Aspergillus fumigatus.** (From Nowak: Documenta Microbiologica, courtesy Gustav Fischer.)

contains one or more nuclei, depending upon whether the hyphae of the mold are septate or nonseptate. In the septate type of mold the cell is well defined by the separating walls, and each cell contains a nucleus. In the nonseptate molds, numerous nuclei are suspended in the cytoplasm throughout the hypha. The cytoplasm of the mold cell presents a granular appearance, probably due to the presence of granules and vacuoles similar to those found in yeasts.

In the molds, reproduction is primarily a process of spore formation with subsequent germination and branching of the growing plant. Spores may result from *asexual* and also from *sexual* reproduction. Asexual reproduction is more common among the molds. The morphology of the sporeforming parts differs among the molds. Among the asexually produced spores there are three different types: those formed in a spore case or *sporangium;* those not incased, *conidia;* those that result from breaking-up of the hypha into segments, *oidia* and *chlamydospores* (Fig. 2.20).

The *sporangium* is formed on the tip of a branch, *sporangiophore,* from a specialized hyphal thread designated for reproductive purposes. The tip gradually increases in size, forming the columella, and the spores are formed and are held in the spore case until maturity. When fully ripened, the sporangium breaks open, as does a pea or bean pod, liberating the spores.

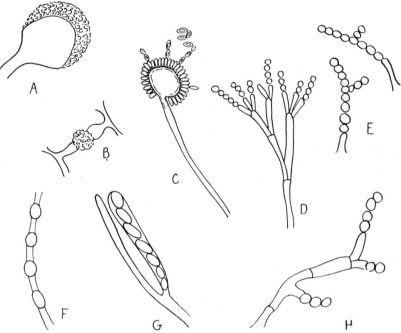

FIG. 2.20 — Types of spore-bearing organs of molds and types of spores. A.—Sporangium of Mucor. B.—Zygospore of Mucor. C.—Conidiophore of Aspergillus. D.—Conidiophore of Penicillium. E.—Oidium type of spore formation. F.—Chlamydospores in the hypha of Chlamydomucor. G.—Ascospore of Peziza. H.—Differentiation of hypha into spores.

In the formation of *conidia* the hypha designated for reproduction is called a *conidiophore.* The conidia or spores are formed at the tip of the conidiophore. Two morphologic types of conidiophores are observed in the common molds (Fig. 2.20). In the *Penicillium* molds the conidiophore branches at the end, and from the tip of each branch the conidia develop, forming long chains. The branches of this conidiophore are close together so these and the long chains of spores of the fully developed conidiophore give a brushlike appearance. The term *Penicillium* comes from the Latin word meaning small brush. In the *Aspergillus* molds a bulblike enlargement, the *basidium,* forms at the tip of conidiophore; small projections, *sterigmata,* are formed, completely covering the basidium, and from these the conidia are formed. These spores, likewise, cling together and form in long chains which completely cover the end of the conidiophore. Great numbers of spores, or conidia, are formed by each of the above methods. This fact explains why molds are so prolific.

Oidia are formed by the breaking up of the hypha into sporelike segments. These segments are considered by some to represent resting stages of the cell, although they seem to possess all the properties of spores. Some of the fungi, particularly the fungus of grain smut, form spores known as *chlamydospores*. There is no strict line of distinction between the *oidia* and *chlamydospores*; however, the latter are dark brown in color and thickwalled. They are formed at irregular points along the hyphae and do not appear to be the result of a segmentation process.

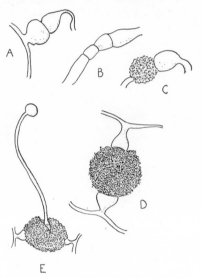

FIG. 2.21 — Diagram of sexual fertilization of **Mucor mucedo.** (After Brefeld.)

Sexual reproduction in molds is formed only among the non-septated varieties, of which *Mucor mucedo* is an excellent example. In this method of reproduction sexual spores, known as *zygospores*, form as the result of the fusion of two hyphae or sexually differentiated parts of the mold plant, (A in Fig. 2.21). After this fusion occurs, articulation into two gametes and two suspensors takes place, B. The cell wall then begins to develop and thicken, forming the zygospore, C and D, still held in place by the suspending parts of the mold plant. The zygospore ripens, may become free of the parent cell, and may function as any mold spore. If it is in a favorable medium, the zygospore may germinate, forming a sporangium stem, E.

The colonies of the various types of molds are different. Some grow in loose cottony masses which will quickly cover any object upon which the mold is growing. Others grow in moderately cottony colonies. Some form low, flat, velvety colonies and a few chalky colonies. All of the mold colonies have color which is imparted to them by the color of the spores; some of the colors found are black, blue, green, and brown. Color is used as a differentiating criterion in classification and is used in some cases in naming the mold, for example, *Aspergillus niger*.

Molds are not of any great significance as causes of disease. One species, *Aspergillus fumigatus,* is found in numerous species of mammals and birds where it causes a pulmonary condition known as aspergillosis. A few of the ill-defined species of molds are parasitic on the skin of man and animals where they produce a condition commonly known as ringworm.

REFERENCES FOR FURTHER STUDY

Bessey, E. A. A Textbook of Mycology. P. Blakiston's Son & Co., Inc., Philadelphia, 1935.

Boltjes, T. Y. Kingma Jour. Path. and Bact. 60:275–87, 1948.

Buchanan, R. E., and Buchanan, Estelle D. Bacteriology. 5th Ed. The Macmillan Co., New York, 1951.

Burrows, Wm., Textbook of Microbiology. 16th Ed. W. B. Saunders Co., Philadelphia, 1954.

Clements, F. E., and Shear, C. H. The Genera of Fungi. The H. W. Wilson Co., New York, 1931.

Conn, H. W., and Conn, H. J. Bacteriology. 4th Ed. The Williams & Wilkins Co., Baltimore, 1929.

Dubos, René J. The Bacterial Cell. Harvard University Press, Cambridge, 1945.

Giltner, W. An Elementary Textbook of General Microbiology. P. Blakiston's Son & Co., Philadelphia, 1928.

Guilliermond, A. The Yeasts. Translated by F. W. Tanner. John Wiley & Sons, Inc., New York, 1920.

Gwynne-Vaughan, H. C. I., and Barnes, B. The Structure and Development of the Fungi. The Macmillan Co., New York, 1927.

Henrici, A. T. Molds, Yeasts, and Actinomyces. John Wiley & Sons, Inc., New York, 1930.

Marshall, C. E. Microbiology. P. Blakiston's Son & Co., Philadelphia, 1921.

Medical Research Council, Various Authors. Volume I, A System of Bacteriology. His Majesty's Stationery Office. London, 1930.

Salle, A. J. Fundamental Principles of Bacteriology. 4th Ed. McGraw-Hill Book Co., Inc., New York, 1954.

Tanner, F. W. Bacteriology. John Wiley & Sons, Inc., New York, 1928.

Thomas, S. J., and Grainger, T. H. Bacteria. The Blakiston Co., New York, 1952.

Zinsser, H., and Bayne-Jones, S. A Textbook of Bacteriology. 9th Ed. D. Appleton-Century Co., New York, 1948.

3. The Physiology of Microorganisms

The simple morphology of microorganisms may lead to the assumption that their physiology is not particularly complex. This is not true because a single species of organism may produce a number of varied changes in a number of varied food substances. If it is assumed that the physiology of a microorganism includes all the interrelationships between it and its environment, it must be concluded that its physiology is a most complex study.

Bacteria are composed of various organic substances and enzymes. The interrelationship of these with nutrient materials initiate complicated chemical reactions. As a result of these chemical reactions, microorganisms are supplied with energy which enables them to reproduce. Numerous immediate environmental influences may affect the growth and metabolic activity of the organism; consequently, bacteria and related forms of life are able to cause numerous and varied types of changes in the medium in which they grow. Many of these changes are complex and not completely explained; others are well understood and are used by man as an aid to better living. The assimilation of simple inorganic substances, the fermentation of carbohydrates, the splitting of proteins, and the conversion of fats are all used in a variety of ways and for different purposes. Diseases are the expressions of specialized types of chemical changes produced by bacteria and their products in living tissues.

In the discussion which follows, the physiology of microorganisms will be considered under the following heads: Chemical, Composition, Growth Rates and Death Rates, Physico-chemical Factors Influencing Growth, Food Relationships, Changes Produced.

CHEMICAL COMPOSITION OF MICROORGANISMS

The food needs and metabolism of bacteria are better understood when the chemical composition of the cell is known. The food utilized by bacteria must contain the elements needed for the building of cell substance which will be used to maintain the structure of the cell or serve as a source of energy.

The size of microorganisms and their close association with the media in which they are grown have been the most difficult barriers to overcome in the determination of their actual chemical composition. Two general methods of studying the chemical composition of bacteria are followed. *Microscopic methods* employ the use of reagents which give definite color reactions when in contact with certain cell constituents; selective action of dyes reveals the presence of various substances within the cell; *chromolysis,* as proposed by Unna, includes the use of dyes that stain the various cell parts which may then be dissolved. In *macroscopic methods,* masses of cells are collected and subjected to chemical analysis. Masses of cells are collected from the surface of solid media or sedimented or centrifuged from liquid media. It is obvious that large numbers of cultures must be made in order to yield a harvest great enough for qualitative chemical analysis, and even more cultures are necessary to determine the proportions of the various chemicals in the bacterial mass. The factor of the medium in which, or on which, the organisms have grown must be considered. Thorough washing may remove the medium from the outside of the cell, but will not remove that which has been absorbed and which is not a necessary part of the cell.

Washing presents a problem in that some of the substances may be removed from the cell by the process, especially when distilled water is used. Results of chemical analysis should always be accompanied by the composition of the medium in which the organism has been grown, and the organism should be grown on various media in order to obtain its definite chemical composition.

Water. Bacteria, in common with other cells, have a high water content. Most of the species which have been examined have a moisture percentage between 75 and 85. A low of 73.3 per cent for *Bacterium coli* has been reported by Nicolle and Alilaire, and a high of 98.3 per cent for Acetobacter (mother of vinegar) by Löw.

Fulmer found the average moisture content of yeast cells to be approximately 73 per cent. Molds contain about 88 per cent moisture. The spores of molds contain about 40 per cent water, and the spores of bacteria approximately 20 per cent.

Total Ash. Apparently the ash content of different types of microorganisms is subject to considerable variation. Bacteria range in ash content from 2 to 30 per cent; tubercle bacilli possess 2.6 to 6.0 to 12.2 per cent. Most of the inorganic constituents of plant life have been found in bacteria. Phosphorus (phosphorus pentoxide P_2O_5) is present in higher percentages than any of the other constituents such as soda (Na_2O), magnesia (MgO), lime (CaO), silica (SiO_2), sulphur trioxide (SO_3), chlorine (Cl), and iron oxide (FeO).

Proteins. The total protein content of microorganisms is also subject to wide variations, depending upon the type of organism, the medium, and the method of determination. Percentages as low as 11.2 for Acetobacter and as high as 87.76 to 92.55 for the glanders organism have been recorded. It is rather difficult to fix an average for bacteria, in general. Yeasts, likewise, have been recorded as varying between 28 to 63 per cent and molds from 19 to 38 per cent.

As in plants, the bacterial protein is of several types which may be divided for the sake of discussion into simple proteins, amino acids, and nucleoproteins.

The simple proteins which are present in bacteria are relatively unknown. In only a few instances have certain species been investigated. Salkowski reported the presence of two proteins in a gelatin-decomposing organism, one a proteose (albumose) and the other a globulin. Greater consideration has been given to the chemical analysis of yeasts and molds than to that of bacteria. Yeast cells contain globulin and albumin and contain, also, protamins, albuminoids, histines, glycoproteins, phosphoproteins, nucleoproteins, lecithoproteins and their derivatives, proteoses, peptones and polypeptids.

Many of the amino acids have been found to be present in bacteria. Some have been found in one type of organism and some in another. Those which have been reported are arginine, histidine, lysine, ammonia, tyrosine, leucine, iso-leucine, l-proline, valine, tryptophane, and l-phenylalinine. Most of the amino acids have been found in yeasts, although numerous ones have been found in molds.

The nucleoproteins of bacteria have been the object of much investigation because the nuclear apparatus of those cells is unknown, and because immunologic specificity is partially determined by such substances. One of the most important hydrolytic products of nucleoprotein is nucleic acid, the presence of which can be shown in most bacterial cells by staining procedures. Nucleic acid, in turn, hydrolyzes to various purine and pyrimidine bases. The hydrolytic products, adenine, guanine, xanthine, and hypoxanthine, of the base nucleotinic acids have been found in certain species of bacteria. In a study of the protein-nucleates of the Brucella groups of organisms, Stahl, Pennell, and Huddleson found the purine and pyrimidine fractions present in the nucleic acid. They further confirmed the fact that carbohydrate is present in nucleic acid which is of great significance in the field of immunology.

Carbohydrates and Related Compounds. Bacterial cells have been found to contain quite a uniform carbon percentage (45–55) in a variety of different substances. Although the nature of the cell walls of bacteria suggest that cellulose may be present, exact chemical studies have failed to reveal it. The cell walls of bacteria, yeasts, and molds are composed, however, of polysaccharide materials which, for the most part, are pentosans.

Various species of bacteria produce a slimy covering when grown in suitable substances, such as milk. This slimy material is composed of carbohydrate in the nature of gum. Although it is of definite importance in various industrial processes, it has not been responsible for great interest until recent years.

The polysaccharide substance in bacterial membranes, and especially in the capsules, is becoming the basis upon which many organisms are differentiated. The pneumococci of man are divided into approximately 32 types on the basis of antigenic specificity, which undoubtedly is caused by the variety of polysaccharides present in the capsules of those organisms. Then, too, the problem of virulence apparently is allied closely with the carbohydrate substance of the bacterial cell. The exact chemical structure of this polysaccharide (soluble specific substance) is not known; it is allied with the polymers of glucose-glucuronic acid, some of which contain nitrogen while others do not.

Fats, Waxes, and Lipoids. A large group of fats, waxes, and lipoids, with their related substances, are extracted from bacteria by the use of various fat solvents. The presence of such substances in bacteria may also be shown by using osmic acid, Sudan III, or other chemicals which stain the fat in the bacterial cell.

The percentage of fat varies considerably with the species of microorganism. Figures ranging from 1.56 to 40.8 per cent, dry weight, have been recorded. The tubercle bacillus has been thoroughly studied because of its waxy covering; hence, much of the information concerning this type of chemical substance is based on the analysis of this organism. The glanders organism has also been shown to contain a high percentage of ether extracts. The presence of such substances in these two species of microorganisms is of pathological interest because of the nature of the lesions produced in diseased tissue. The injection into animals of fatty acids obtained from the phosphatides of the tubercle bacillus has produced the formation of tubercles and an increase of mononuclear leucocytes. The tubercle bacillus also contains a polysaccharide in the phosphatide fraction which appears to serve as an antigenic substance. The injection of phosphatide has been shown to produce typical tuberculous tissue in normal animals.

The wax in acid-fast bacilli has been thoroughly studied also. Tamura found it contained an alcohol which he named mykol. This material is acid-fast and stains Gram-positive. Upon saponification it yields an unknown substance and crotonic and isocrotonic acids.

An increase in fibrous connective tissue has been reported following its injection into animals.

Bacterial Pigments. Most of the species of bacteria possess coloring matter of some type which is manifest when large numbers of cells are together in colonies, and when they are grown on certain types of media, such as potato.

The exact chemical structure of these pigments is not known because the collection and purification of them is very difficult. The pigments which have been studied have been grouped with similar materials, on the basis of chemical tests, which are obtained from animals and plants. One of the most common pigments found in bacteria, especially the cocci, is a carotin-like substance which is *insoluble in water* but is soluble in fat extractives. Many of the red, orange, and yellow pigments belong to this group. A second type of pigment is *water soluble* and belongs to the anthocyanins so abundant in fruits and plants.

Pigments may be *cellular,* that is, an integral part of the cell protoplasm, such as bacteriopurpurin in sulphur bacteria, and sulphur granules in *Beggiatoa.* The coloring matter also may be present in the cell walls of certain bacteria and in molds, or it may be present in the sheaths which surround the cells. Some bacteria produce *extracellular* pigments, some of which accumulate about the cell as in the case of *Serratia marcescens,* or they may diffuse into the surrounding media. This latter type, excreted by *Pseudomonas aeruginosa,* is a leuco compound which is oxidized to a green color and then to brown in the media.

Many bacteria produce pigments which appear to change in color under reflected light. Such colonies of bacteria are called *fluorescent.* Fluorescence, as was noted concerning the color of pigments, is used in the classification of microorganisms. It often is a normal characteristic of smooth (S) colonies as contrasted to the rough (R), and there is some evidence that it is a factor associated with virulence.

Other Substances. The presence of growth-stimulating substances in bacteria has been reported; of these *bios* is the oldest and most thoroughly studied. Little is known of the substance, however, except the fact that it is a material which does stimulate growth, especially in yeasts from which it has been commonly extracted.

The presence of vitamins in microorganisms has been carefully investigated. Vitamin B is the only one which has been observed. It has been found in a number of species of yeasts and in a few species of bacteria.

Free sulphur globules are found in many of the *Thiobacteriales,* in the filaments of *Beggiatoa* and certain spirilla. Iron oxides are found in the sheaths of the so-called "iron bacteria" which are often present in water supplies with a high iron content. Crystals of calcium carbonate and calcium oxalate have been found on the sporangia of molds.

Enzymes are a part of the chemical composition of microorganisms. These substances are better known by what they do than by what they are; therefore, a discussion of them is given later in the chapter.

GROWTH RATES AND DEATH RATES OF MICROORGANISMS

The various physical and chemical agencies manifest their action upon microorganisms by their effect upon the rate of growth and death. Before these agencies can be discussed adequately, certain general considerations concerning rates of growth and death must be presented.

Rates of Growth. When bacteria, or other organisms, are planted in a suitable culture medium and optimum conditions for growth are maintained, the bacteria soon reach a maximum rate of growth. This can be measured best by determining the average length of time required for an organism to grow to its full size, divide, and form two individuals. This has been termed the *generation time*. It is the average time elapsing between cell divisions. It may be most conveniently determined in any given case, not by watching the bacteria under the microscope, but by counting the number of living cells present in a given amount of culture after varying lengths of time. It is evident that the shorter the generation time, the more rapid is the rate of multiplication. Any factor, therefore, which tends to shorten the generation time increases the rate of growth.

The actual length of the generation time may be determined if the bacteria are definitely multiplying at a uniform rate, that is, that the cultures are not too young or too old; this may be determined by counting the bacteria at the beginning and at the end of a given period. It is evident that if one starts with a single organism, at the end of the first generation period there will be two, at the end of the next four (2^2), at the end of the next eight (2^3) and so on. If n represents the number of generations, then there will be at the end of the nth generation period 2^n bacteria. If B represents the number of bacteria at the beginning, and b the number at the end, then

$$b = B2^n$$

If b and B are known, their values may be substituted into the equation, and the value of n may be determined by solving the equation.

Careful studies of bacteria growing in culture media show that the length of the generation time does not remain a constant throughout the time of cultivation. When bacteria are first planted in a culture, particularly if they have been taken from an old culture, they frequently grow slowly at first. As they become accustomed to their environment, they multiply more rapidly. After a time the maximum rate of growth occurs. Still later the bacteria become crowded and the rate of growth diminishes, and finally the bacteria cease to grow and begin to die.

Rates of Death. It is equally important to know something of the laws which govern the rates at which bacteria die under unfavorable conditions. In most of the cases which have been carefully studied, the bacteria die in accordance with a definite law which may be stated as follows: With a given kind of organism under uniform unfavorable conditions, the number of bacteria present in a culture will always be reduced one-half in equal periods of time; that is, regardless of how many bacteria there are at the beginning of a definite period of time, one-half that number will always be alive at the end of the proper interval. For example, suppose that two cultures of the same organism, one containing a million bacteria and the other a thousand bacteria, are subjected

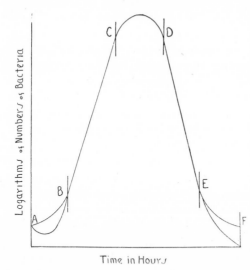

to the same unfavorable conditions. It is found that at the end of a definite period of time, possibly ten minutes, the bacteria in the less concentrated suspension number five hundred. It will be found that in the same period of time there are one-half the number of bacteria in the other culture also, that is, there are 500,000 bacteria. Obviously, *during each equal interval of time a definite percentage of those bacteria living at the beginning of the period will be killed.* The effect of unfavorable conditions upon

FIG. 3.1 — Growth curve of a bacterial culture. A–B, phase of adjustment; B–C, phase of increase; C–D, phase of crisis; D–E, phase of decrease; E–F, phase of readjustment.

the death of microorganisms is compared to the length of time required to reduce the numbers of bacteria by a definite percentage. If at one temperature, for example, half of the bacteria are killed in ten minutes, and at another temperature one-half are killed in five minutes, it is evident that the second temperature is far more destructive than the first. It will be noted that the time required to kill half the bacteria is mathematically converse to the generation time.

In summary, all effects of environment upon microorganisms are manifest in growing cultures by changes in the length of the generation time, changes in morphology, and in the physiological and cultural reactions. Likewise, the effect of environment will be noted upon the death rate by observing the length of time necessary to kill a definite percentage of the microorganisms present.

The Growth Curve. When a bacterial culture is observed carefully from the time that it is removed from a stock culture until it has passed through its growth in the new culture, it will be found to pass through a number of definite phases of growth. These *growth phases* have been the basis of much investigation, for knowledge of them aids in the study of the morphology and physiology of the organism. Various interpretations have been given concerning the different phases of growth in a bacterial culture. The curve presented in Figure 3.1 representing the phases of growth is considered typical by most authorities.

PHYSICO-CHEMICAL FACTORS INFLUENCING THE GROWTH OF MICROORGANISMS

Moisture. Since a high percentage of the bacterial protoplasm is composed of water, it is apparent that moisture is one of the most important substances for the optimum growth of bacteria. The optimum condition for growth in most cases is saturation; however bacteria vary in their response to moisture. The streptococci grow only when the medium is moist, while tubercle bacilli grow abundantly on a medium which is quite dry.

The morphology of some microorganisms and the arrangement of the cells may be different in fluid media and on solid media. Streptococci grow in long chains in fluid media while the chains are short on agar surfaces; and some types of bacteria are elongated rods in fluids and more coccoid on solid surfaces.

The amount of moisture in solid media is important in the study of the colonies of bacteria. When the medium is very moist, the colony has a tendency to spread, but it remains quite compact when the medium is dry.

Temperature. The *optimum* growth temperature is that which most favors the development of the microorganism, that is, that temperature which gives the shortest generation time. The optimum varies with the species. A few organisms found in the ocean, in cold waters, and in alpine regions prefer a low temperature from $0°$ to $15°C$. These are called *psychrophilic*. Those which prefer a somewhat higher temperature are called *mesophilic;* these may be again subdivided into those that prefer a "room" temperature of 18° to 25°C., and those that prefer blood heat (man, 37.5°C.) for the most parasitic forms. Temperatures such as are found in hot springs, interior of compost heaps, and in milk pasteurizers, ranging from 50° to 70°C., favor the development of *thermophilic* bacteria. Fischer has summarized the relationships of bacteria to temperature as given in Table 3.1.

The lowest temperature at which an organism will continue growth is said to be its *minimum*. This temperature varies for different species. Some organisms multiply in brine held at temperatures lower than the freezing point of water.

The highest temperature at which an organism will multiply is called its *maximum* and varies for the three general classes of organisms previously defined. Obviously, the maximum temperature of a psychrophilic organism may be the minimum temperature of a mesophile, while the maximum temperature of the thermophile may be high enough to cause the death of the other two.

The differences between the minimum and maximum growth temperatures vary within rather wide limits. Those organisms which exhibit considerable adaptability and are able to grow through a wide range of temperature are called *eurythermic*. Most of the saprophytic organisms belong in this class. The parasitic

TABLE 3.1
TEMPERATURE RELATIONSHIPS OF BACTERIA

Groups	TEMPERATURE CHANGES IN DEGREES CENTIGRADE			Types
	Minimum	Optimum	Maximum	
Psychrophilic	0	15-20	30	Many water bacteria Cold storage growth
Mesophilic	15-20	37	43	Most pathogens
Thermophilic	25-45	50-55	85	Bacteria from soils, water, thermal springs

types which have minimum and maximum varying but little from the optimum are *stenothermic*.

Harmful effects of temperature will be discussed in the chapter on disinfection and disinfectants.

Light. A few bacteria possessing bacteriopurpurin require light for their development. Some types of microorganisms, particularly the molds, are stimulated by diffuse light. They grow toward a light source in much the same way as do plants, showing the phenomenon known as *phototropism*. The sulphur bacteria grow in the presence of light. All of the pathogenic types of bacteria and most of the other types grow best in the absence of light. Light, especially sunlight, has an extremely harmful effect on bacteria, as will be discussed in detail later.

Oxygen Relationship. Up to 1861, when Pasteur discovered that bacteria grew without air, it was assumed that bacteria, as plants and animals, must have a supply of free oxygen for growth. This discovery marked a point of departure from many theories in biochemistry, especially the biochemistry of microorganisms. Respiration had been considered to be the process by which oxygen was taken up and carbon dioxide was given off in the body and was intimately connected with the formation of energy from food used by living cells. This conception did not altogether fit the respiration of plants nor did it fit the process whereby bacteria which grew without air obtained a source of food which they could utilize for energy. Respiration, then, was defined to mean the process whereby growth energy was obtained from food by oxidative processes. It is apparent that all organisms secure energy through the interactions of chemical compounds. Oxidation appears to be the most important of the reactions whereby energy is released and made a part of cells. This may take place in the presence of free oxygen or in the absence of it. Buchanan and Buchanan aptly state: [1]

. . . most cellular oxidations involve the removal of hydrogen from compounds rather than the addition of oxygen to compounds. Biological oxidations, in other words, are dehydrogenations. But it is a chemical axiom that whenever an oxidation occurs there is a simultaneous reduction. In other words, if cells oxidize their food by removing hydrogen from it, they must at the same time reduce something else by adding the hydrogen to it. Any substance, such as food, which the cell oxidizes by removal of hydrogen is called a *hydrogen donator;* any substance to which the cell transfers the hydrogen is called the *hydrogen acceptor.* The cell secures the energy for growth and movement by this continuous process of hydrogen transfer.

Microorganisms may be divided into three groups on the basis of oxygen relationship. The *first* group is composed of all those which grow only in the presence of free oxygen; in other words, they use oxygen as the acceptor for the hydrogen taken from food materials in direct oxidation. These microorganisms are *aerobes.* The *second* group is composed of those forms which grow in the total absence of free oxygen. They are known as *anaerobes.* This group of microorganisms must use some material other than oxygen as the hydrogen acceptor. This material must be one that may be reduced. Some bacteria are able to utilize carbohydrates for this purpose, others proteins, others nitrates, and some sulphates. The exact reason for this is not known, although two plausible explanations have

[1] R. E. Buchanan and Estelle Buchanan. *Bacteriology,* 4th Ed. The Macmillan Co., New York, 1938, p. 183.

been advanced. Hydrogen peroxide is formed when oxygen serves as an hydrogen acceptor. This is known to be toxic to bacteria. The reason why aerobic forms are not affected is due to the formation of catalase, an enzyme, which breaks H_2O_2 to oxygen and water. The strictly anaerobic bacteria do not form catalase; hence they are unable to live in the presence of free oxygen due to the formation of hydrogen peroxide. The other explanation is based upon the oxidation-reduction potential of the medium in which the organisms are growing, that is, the ratio of oxidized and reduced substances. This potential may be measured electrometrically or by indicators. The most common indicator is methylene blue which is colorless in the reduced form. Anaerobes grow in a medium with a low oxidation-reduction potential, whereas aerobes grow in a medium with a high potential produced by the presence of free oxygen. The *third* group of organisms are those which are able to grow under anaerobic conditions if certain materials are present, such as a carbohydrate. These types are thought to produce catalase; therefore they are not affected by oxygen; in fact, in the absence of fermentable carbohydrate, they grow abundantly in free oxygen. They have a wide range of adaptability in reference to oxidation-reduction potentials. Such microorganisms are called *facultative*.

Most of the organisms which cause disease in animals are aerobic, a few are anaerobic, and some are facultative. The best examples of the anaerobic forms are those which cause tetanus, blackleg, malignant edema, and botulism.

Carbon Dioxide. Certain types of bacteria, notably those belonging to the genus Brucella, grow more abundantly upon initial isolation in a medium which is placed in an atmosphere of 10 per cent carbon dioxide. It has been observed that tubercle bacilli are inhibited in growth when the carbon dioxide is removed by an alkali. The production of toxin by *Micrococcus pyogenes* is enhanced by the presence of the gas. At present no justifiable reason is known to explain why carbon dioxide is able to produce these effects.

Hydrogen-ion Concentration. Many organisms are quite exacting in their requirements as to the reaction of the medium in which they are grown. Some bacteria grow best in a medium which is slightly alkaline. Most pathogenic bacteria belong to this group. Other bacteria grow best in a medium which is slightly acid, and a few species grow abundantly in a very acid medium. Most bacteria have a rather narrow hydrogen-ion range in which they grow best. In media from which acid may be produced by fermentation, the growth of bacteria is inhibited and sometimes entirely halted as the acidity increases. The reverse is also true; increased alkalinity inhibits bacterial multiplicaton as the food substances are changed by the organisms to alkaline products. Since bacteria are so sensitive to hydrogen-ion concentration, the medium in which they are to be grown should be carefully adjusted to the desired reaction.

The Effect of Chemicals. Microorganisms may be influenced in movement and growth by the various chemicals in their immediate environment.

The effect of a chemical upon the movement of organisms is called *chemotaxis.* This effect may be of two different types. When an organism is attracted in its movement toward a chemical substance, the reaction is known as *positive chemotaxis.* An example frequently given to illustrate this is the movement of organisms toward a bubble of air in a medium held between a glass slide and cover glass. In case the organisms are repelled from a chemical, it is known as *negative chemotaxis.*

Organisms which are not motile, those which grow in a colony or mycelium, may be affected in their direction of growth by chemicals. This phenomenon is known as *chemotropism.* Numerous examples of specific types of chemotropism may be observed in nature. Plants which require sunlight for maximum growth, but are grown in the shade, will grow toward the optimum light source. This is known as *heliotropism.* Molds, growing in an enclosed dish will grow toward a source of moisture. This is an example of *hydrotropism.* Many of the sporeforming hyphae of molds, however, will distinctly grow away from a source of moisture, *negative hydrotropism.*

Since chemicals are the basis of all the effects upon the growth processes of microorganisms, and act as foods, it is logical to consider the subject under a separate heading.

THE FOOD RELATIONSHIPS OF MICROORGANISMS

General Discussion. Bacteria are able to use the most diverse substances for food. Different types of organisms have adapted themselves to utilize some foods more than others. Some are able to live on comparatively simple foods; others utilize carbohydrates; still others prefer proteins. Many live upon lifeless foods, and a few grow only on living protoplasm in which they bring about changes known as disease.

Some bacteria, classed under the general term *autotrophic,* are able to manufacture their own food out of simple chemicals. The utilization of simple foods by bacteria is brought about in two ways. Some are able to oxidize various inorganic compounds, such as sulphites, nitrites, and ammonia, into substances which are used as a source of energy. Such organisms are called *chemosynthetic.* Other bacteria, those which contain a red or purple coloring matter known as *bacteriopurpurin*, are able to use light as a source of primary energy and, like the plants containing chlorophyll, are able to synthesize their own food. These organisms are called *photosynthetic*. The sulphur bacteria (Thiobacteriales) are typical of this group.

Most of the microorganisms which are of any significance in commerce or in disease are able to convert the complex organic materials, which have been built up by other living things, to simple substances which may be used as a source of energy. They are *heterotrophic*. It has been shown that autotrophic bacteria are able to cause carbon-to-carbon linkage when the source of both carbons is inorganic while the heterotrophic bacteria are able to do so when the carbon source is organic or when one of the carbons is organic. The heterotrophic bacteria may be divided into two groups on the basis of the nature of their food. Those which live on dead organic matter are known as *saprophytes*. Those which utilize the living tissue of a host for food are called *parasites*. A distinction must be made between living at the *expense* of the host and living *on* or *in* the host. Many microorganisms may live in the intestinal tract, for example, utilizing the food which is there but not upon the tissues of the host. The host and the organism are eating at the same table, living a life of *commensalism*. In the sense that the host might use the food if the bacteria did not, the process may be termed parasitism. In some cases the organisms aid in the conversion of foods to simpler substances which are used by the host as food. This is known as *symbiosis*. In plant life, a good example is found in the fixation of nitrogen by bacteria which makes it available to plants as food. One marked expression of the parasitic nature of microorganisms is disease. The organisms which cause disease, recognized by a change which they produce in the living tissues, are known as *pathogenic* microorganisms.

From the viewpoint of students in veterinary medicine, the microorganisms of importance are those which produce disease; however, it would give a false impression of the place and function of microorganisms in nature to neglect a brief consideration of some of the other changes which they are capable of producing. Microorganisms are widely distributed in nature. They are present in soil to considerable depths where they bring about the decay of organic matter and a change in inorganic substances so that such foods may be utilized by plants. They are present in water where they cause the conversion of organic and inorganic materials into substances used by plant life. They are present in air, largely due to the movement of air, which has taken them from the surface of the earth. When plants die, bacteria aid in their disintegration. When animals die, bacteria aid in their decomposition. We find microorganisms, therefore, acting as a governing force to the chemical changes which take place on and just under the surface of the earth. They serve to maintain the equilibrium between the plant and animal kingdoms which is so essential to both. The changes brought about are considered so important that both plant and animal life would quickly cease to exist if all bacteria should perish. Life then, of necessity, would be required to begin, as it once probably did, with the primitive forms, the autotrophic forms, and again build up a complex system of living things.

Enzymes and Their Action. The majority of the metabolic processes of bacteria are due to the action of enzymes. Although the general characteristics of bacterial enzymes are the same as those of other types of living cells, it is expedient to review them briefly.

An *enzyme* is an organic catalyst secreted by a living cell which initiates a chemical reaction without being a part of the resulting product or being consumed during the reaction. Enzymes have not been sufficiently separated from proteins to have their chemical composition determined; some are colloidal; most are soluble in water; they are precipitated by ammonium sulphate; they are adsorbed by solid particles; their optimum temperature for action lies between 35° and 50°C.; they are destroyed by temperatures above 70°C. in a short time; they are inactivated by light; strong acids and alkalies are destructive to enzymes. Many enzymes survive the concentration of a disinfectant which may destroy the parent cell; hence, antiseptics may be used to inhibit the growth of the parent cell and allow the study of the enzyme.

Enzymes may be *intracellular* or *extracellular*. Many of the food substances used by microorganisms cannot be utilized in the native form. The extracellular enzymes diffuse from the cell and convert such foods into simpler materials which may be assimilated by the cell. Such food substances may not be in a form readily used by the cell as a source of energy and growth; consequently, they must be converted by intracellular enzymes into material which immediately becomes a part of cell protoplasm. Extracellular enzymes which diffuse from the cells and accumulate in the medium may be separated from the cells by filtration. This allows the study of the specific action of certain enzymes. Intracellular enzymes, however, cannot be separated from the cell except by mechanical or natural disintegration of living cells.

Some enzymes are both *anabolic* and *catabolic* in action. They are able to synthesize chemical compounds into complex substances which form cell protoplasm; they then cause a reverse action and bring about the disintegration of that which they have constructed.

Enzymes may be divided into two groups on the basis of the type of chemical reaction which they are able to initiate. The first group, known as *hydrolases*, acts either by the addition or removal of water. The second group, called *oxidases*, acts by oxidation or reduction. Each group is subdivided into numerous subgroups on the basis of the material upon which the enzymes act. Enzymes are named in two general ways. One method is to use the name of the type of action produced. The ending -*ase* is always used. For example, an enzyme may cause the decomposition of saccharose by the addition of water:

$$C_{12}H_{22}O_{11} + H_2O + Invertase = C_6H_{12}O_6 + C_6H_{12}O_6 + Invertase$$

saccharose   dextrose   levulose

The enzyme *invertase* is a *hydrolase* given a specific name in this instance because it causes an inversion of saccharose. Another method of naming an enzyme is to give it the name of the material affected by the enzyme; hence the terms *protease, carbohydrase,* and *lipase* are familiar.

General types of enzymes are classified as follows:

I. Those which add or subtract water (*hydrolases* and *anhydreses*).
   A. Those which hydrolize esters and fats (esterases and lipases).
   B. Those which hydrolize carbohydrates (carbohydrases).
   C. Those which hydrolize proteins (proteases).
   D. Those which cause coagulation (coagulases).
II. Those which cause oxidation and reduction (oxidases and reductases).
   A. Those in which oxygen acts as the hydrogen acceptor (aereases).
   B. Those in which substances, other than oxygen, act as the hydrogen acceptor (anaereases); those which catalyze intramolecular oxidation and reduction (zymase).

Enzymes are highly specific in their action, and each individual species of microorganism produces specific enzymes; since this is true, the various metabolic activities of bacteria, carried on by enzyme action, are used in identifying and classifying bacteria. The hydrolysis of proteins, the fermentation of carbohydrates, and the reduction and oxidation of inorganic compounds are all used as a basis for differentiating closely related types of bacteria. One species of microorganism may produce a number of different types of enzymes. One of the molds, for example, will split starch by the action of one enzyme to yield maltose which is converted to glucose by a second enzyme, and a third changes the glucose to alcohol and carbon dioxide. These "batteries of enzymes" are capable of forming numerous compounds from one substance. In some cases the reaction may be arrested at a desired point, and in others, the products formed are very unstable and are quickly converted into other substances. By discovering the various unstable products formed during a process of fermentation, the complexity of various reactions has been revealed.

Many of the metabolic reactions produced by bacterial enzymes are used in the study of pathogenic bacteria. The products of such reactions are useful in the classification of bacteria, and many of the products play an important role in industry.

Types of Food Materials. The action of enzyme systems on various compounds has been determined for different industrial processes. However, the complexity of the food materials found in the animal body makes it difficult to ascertain the various nutrient materials utilized by pathogenic bacteria. The chemical structure of these bacteria, the various enzymes produced by them, and the products of their growth make it evident that their food necessities do not differ greatly from other living cells.

Reference has been made previously to the oxidizing ability of simple forms (autotrophic). There is little doubt that oxidation provides an important means by which all bacteria make certain food materials more suitable for their source of energy; therefore, any carbon or nitrogen compound can serve as a source of food for most pathogenic bacteria. From these foods the essential building stones, carbon, nitrogen, oxygen, and phosphorus are obtained and are reconstructed by the metabolic processes of the bacterial cell into individual protoplasm. Since each species of bacterium has its own enzyme system, the chemical composition of the protoplasm is specific for each species. The importance of this composition will be evident in the discussion on immunity.

All pathogenic bacteria do not require media in which the essential elements are present. Tissues, tissue extracts, blood serum, and whole blood are universally used to support the growths of most of the bacteria producing disease in man and animals.

Growth Accessory Substances. The stimulation produced by tissues and tissue fluids has been a subject of considerable investigation. This has been particularly true since the importance of the vitamins in the growth of animals has been proven. The substances commonly called growth accessory substances may be termed *bacterial vitamins.* Most materials which are stimulating to bacterial growth are those of the Vitamin B complex, especially thiamin, riboflavin, pantothenic acid, and nicotinic acid. However, such substances as glutamine, pimelic acid, adenine, and uracil have been found effective.

In the early studies of the influenza bacillus it was found that whole blood was essential for growth, hence, the genus name Hemophilus. It is now recognized that two factors, one, called "X" factor, is associated with hemoglobin, probably in hematin, and the second, called "V" factor, is found in yeast extract and in many vegetables. Both are essential for maximum growth.

The role of these growth accessory substances in bacterial metabolism has not as yet been clarified completely. Sufficient evidence has been revealed to indicate that they act as catalysts and in some instances as precursors of respiratory enzymes, forming a link in the molecule needed for cell metabolism.

CHANGES PRODUCED BY MICROORGANISMS

Fermentation of Carbohydrates. The fundamental discovery of the process of fermentation by Schwann and the elucidation of the reaction by Pasteur stimulated research upon all types of fermentative processes. Bacteria, yeasts, and molds all may produce alcohols of various types. The yeasts, however, are most commonly used in the commercial production of alcohols. The enzyme, *zymase*, appears to be the enzyme most active in causing the fermentation of dextrose, the most common sugar found in fruits which are used in the wine industry. Grains used as a source of carbohydrate in fermentation must first undergo the process of malting and mashing in which starch is converted into dextrin and sugar; these are then fermented by yeasts and the resulting "beer" is placed in casks for aging. In bread making the utilization of carbon dioxide, the product of fermentation other than alcohol, is common knowledge.

Various kinds of organic acids are produced by the action of bacteria, yeasts, and molds. In the laboratory, acid production is commonly used as a basis of identification of the different bacteria. Numerous carbohydrates are used in the process. One species of bacteria may ferment dextrose, lactose, and sucrose; another species may ferment only sucrose. Some bacteria produce only acids, while others are able to continue the process until carbon dioxide and hydrogen are produced. The kind of acid produced by bacteria in this routine differential technic is not usually determined.

The fermentation of carbohydrates in the formation of acids is of economic importance. This is true of certain acids more than of others. Some acids may be desirable in many cases and totally undesirable in others.

The fermentation of the lactose in milk into lactic acid is one of the most common types of fermentation. This process may be desirable or undesirable. It is desirable in the preparation of "culture" milk. It is undesirable from the point of view of market milk production because it produces an unpalatable food and interferes with preservation. Lactic acid is formed in the manufacture of sauerkraut where its presence is essential; likewise, in the fermentation of silage, lactic acid is one of the most important acids formed.

The fermentation of the sugars of fruit juices, particularly apples, to form acetic acid, or vinegar, is of common use. The bacterium responsible for the oxidation of the alcohol, formed in the initial step of fermentation, is called *Acetobacter aceti*. The organism is widely distributed in nature, which explains why fruit juices sour quickly when exposed to the air. In the commercial manufacture of vinegar, the juice is inoculated with a culture of the organism known as "mother of vinegar," a mass of organisms held together by the capsule which surrounds each cell.

Butyric acid is formed by the action of certain sporeforming anaerobic bacteria on carbohydrates. These organisms are prevalent in soil; so there is ample opportunity for them to contaminate most food materials. Butyric acid imparts a disagreeable odor to the medium in which the organisms are grown, and for that reason is of economic significance. The spores of the organism enable it to resist heat which usually kills other forms of bacteria. Bacteria which form lactic acid and acetic acid inhibit the growth of butyric acid bacteria, but both lactic and acetic bacteria are killed by heat; this permits the growth of butyric acid bacteria which are found in canned peas, beans and corn, milk, and in milk products where the flavor produced is totally undesirable. The butyric acid bacteria may be used, however, in certain industrial fermentation processes in which the by-products of the organism are desired. Other anaerobic organisms similar to the butyric acid bacillus are able to produce butyl alcohol from starch.

Other acids, such as citric, formic, oxalic, fumaric, and valeric are produced by the action of various microorganisms on carbohydrates.

Fermentation of Fats. The fats, as a general rule, are not acted upon by the enzymes of bacteria. Hydrolytic changes do occur in certain fats, notably butter, where the enzyme *lipase* causes the conversion of butterfat into glycerol and fatty acids. These in turn, particularly glycerol, may be converted into butyric acid and related compounds which impart the rancid flavor found in butter manufactured under insanitary conditions. The salt in butter inhibits the growth of these microorganisms and serves as a preservative.

Hydrolysis of Proteins. Proteins in the solid or colloidal state cannot be utilized by microorganisms as a source of food; consequently, they must be converted into simple substances which are easily assimilated. Most proteins are decomposed by a series of hydrolytic changes brought about by various types of microorganisms. Proteins may be split into *peptones,* these in turn into *peptids,* and these into *amino acids.* The amino acids may be hydrolyzed into a number of end products such as CO_2, NH_3, and CH_4. Other products of protein cleavage are commonly recognized as hydrogen sulphide, phenol, skatol, mercaptans, and indol. The process by which proteins are disintegrated is called *proteolysis.* The hydrolysis of proteins to peptones is known as *peptonization.* This process is commonly recognized in the laboratory by the digestion of gelatin or litmus milk. The enzyme *pepsin* brings about peptonization of proteins in the stomach. In nature the process is observed in the decay and putrefaction of all organic material. The splitting of peptones to ammonia is called *ammonification.* All of the above steps in the decompositions of proteins are of great importance in the nitrogen cycle as will be shown later.

All bacteria are not able to use proteins as a source of food, but may use peptones, amino acids, and nitrogen. Many of the pathogenic bacteria are not able to grow except in the presence of proteins, but they do not produce any marked change in the medium. Still others not only grow in proteins but convert them into the various products described above. These organisms may be aerobic or anaerobic; most of them are sporeforming. *Bacillus subtilis* is a typical example of the aerobic, sporeforming, proteolytic bacilli. The action of this organism is easily demonstrated in the laboratory by the hydrolysis of gelatin and milk. Many of the anaerobic bacilli are actively proteolytic. Probably the most active, on animal tissue at least, are *Clostridium histolyticum* and *Clostridium sporogenes.* Cultures of these organisms may be used to advantage in macerating tanks where tissues are removed from bones. Such organisms are active in decomposition of dead animals and other organic matter.

Some anaerobic bacteria are able to utilize amino acids and in the process of *decarboxylation,* in which carbon dioxide is eliminated, form an amine. Such amines are commonly called *ptomaines.* Some of the amines, such as *putrescine* and *cadaverine,* have extremely disagreeable odors. Odors of decomposition have been connected with disease since the time of Hippocrates, and it is apparent that such products as ptomaines would be incriminated; hence, the term ptomaine poisoning is a familiar one. A few amines are poisonous, for example, *histamine,* which is derived from the amino acid, *histidine.* Histamine is incriminated in anaphylactic reactions and, according to present-day theory, is responsible for the reaction. Most of the ptomaines, however, do not reach a sufficient concentration in food materials to cause the severe illness commonly called ptomaine poisoning.

The proteolytic activity of bacteria is used as a basis for differentiation and classification. Many of the end products of protein cleavage, such as phenol, skatol, and indol, are detected by suitable tests and are useful in identifying bacteria.

Reduction of Inorganic Compounds. Many of the inorganic compounds which are common in nature are reduced by various types of bacteria. One of the best examples of this type of bacterial action is found in the reduction of nitrates under anaerobic conditions, and in the presence of organic matter such bacteria are able to utilize nitrates as a source of oxygen. Nitrates are reduced to nitrites, and the nitrites in turn into free nitrogen gas. This process, known as *denitrification,* is one of the processes by which plant food is made available. In the laboratory it may be shown to be a function of many different species of bacteria; the nitrate reduction test, in which nitrite is detected, is one of the common methods used as an aid in differentiating organisms.

In a similar manner, sulphates are reduced to sulphides. This process is observed frequently in sewage disposal plants if the water of the city contains a large percentage of sulphates.

Oxidation of Inorganic Compounds. Some of the inorganic compounds, notably those of sulphur and iron, are oxidized by bacteria for the purpose of obtaining energy for growth. Hydrogen sulphide, which is common in mineral springs of many regions, is oxidized by a type of sulphur bacteria, Beggiatoa, with the formation of free sulphur and sulphuric acid. The small sulphur granules may be seen in such bacteria when the slimy deposit in mineral springs is examined microscopically.

The oxidation of ferrous carbonate or other iron salts by the iron bacteria is commonly observed. This is true particularly in water which has a high iron concentration. Two general types of bacteria are found to be able to oxidize iron compounds with the formation of ferric hydrate which is deposited in the sheaths of the organisms. One type forms long filamentous masses which may reach a size sufficient to clog water pipes. The other type forms a crustlike deposit on the inside of water pipes which, also, may accumulate to such a size that the pipe is closed. The large iron ore deposits found in Sweden, and probably those in Minnesota, were formed by the action of such bacteria.

Oxidation of Ammonia and Nitrites. In the discussion of the decomposition of protein material, it was observed that ammonia is one of the important end products. Ammonia is not readily utilized by plants as food. Two types of bacteria, the Nitrosococcus and Nitrosomonas, are able to oxidize ammonia to nitrites, which in turn are oxidized by the Nitrobacteria into nitrates. The process of oxidation of ammonia to nitrites and then to nitrates is called *nitrification.* The organisms are prevalent in soil and constitute the most important group of soil microorganisms. Nitrification occurs in sewage which is often allowed to pass into streams. By measuring the relative proportion of ammonia, nitrites, and nitrates in water, the degree of self-purification which polluted water undergoes may be determined.

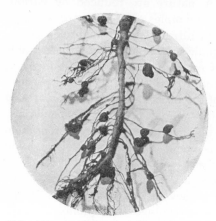

FIG. 3.2 — Nodules on the root of a legume. (From Nowak: Documenta Microbiologica, courtesy Gustav Fischer.)

Nitrogen Fixation. In the process of denitrification, free nitrogen is formed. Approximately 80 per cent of the air is nitrogen. It is an inert gas, and its function in air appears to be one of dilution. Green plants are not able to utilize it for growth. Certain bacteria and molds which grow in the soil are able to fix free nitrogen, however, and make it available to plants. Microorganisms which are able to fix nitrogen may be divided into two groups: those which grow free in the soil, and those which grow on the roots of certain trees and plants.

Both aerobic and anaerobic bacteria which live free in the soil are able to fix nitrogen. The aerobic bacteria of the genus Azotobacter are of the greatest importance because conditions are usually more favorable for the growth of this type of organism.

Various species of bacteria which belong to the genus Rhizobium grow on the roots of plants of the legume family, such as clover, alfalfa, peas, and beans (Fig. 3.2). These organisms cause the formation of nodules along the roots of such plants in which the bacteria may be found in large numbers. These organisms consume free nitrogen from the air, and upon their disintegration, it is used by the host plant.

Certain molds which live upon the roots of trees, such as the alder and Russian olive, are able to fix nitrogen. Nodules are sometimes found upon the roots of these trees, but usually the mold growth is uniformly distributed over the young roots.

The Nitrogen Cycle. The nitrogen cycle is the most important cycle in nature and is largely due to the action of a wide variety of microorganisms. All of the fundamental reactions which complete this cycle have been described previously; in addition, a general summary in the form of an illustration is given in Figure 3.3.

It is observed that the nitrogen cycle is completed by the normal activity of plant and animal life. Plant proteins are converted into animal proteins by the process of digestion and assimilation. Animal proteins are converted into waste products and flesh. The waste products, as represented by ammonia, urea, and amino acids are utilized by bacteria and converted into substances which are available to plants as food. In many instances plant and animal proteins

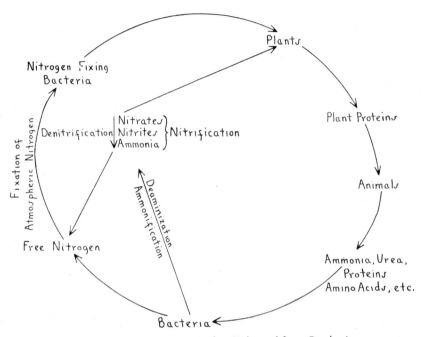

FIG. 3.3 — The Nitrogen Cycle. (Adapted from Fowler.)

return to simple forms as a result of death and decay. Decomposition of proteins may be brought about by autolytic enzymes, but the process is assisted by proteolytic bacteria. In this case nitrogen is either liberated as free nitrogen or becomes a part of the soil and is used by plants. The free nitrogen is fixed by various nitrogen-fixing bacteria and also used by plants as food.

It is apparent that the nitrogen cycle illustrates one of the important functions of bacteria in nature; that is, to maintain an equilibrium between plant and animal life and to assist both forms in the process of living.

REFERENCES FOR FURTHER STUDY

Buchanan, R. E., and Buchanan, Estelle D. Bacteriology. 5th Ed. The Macmillan Co., New York, 1951.

———, and Fulmer, E. I. Physiology and Biochemistry of Bacteria. Vol. I. Williams & Wilkins Co., Baltimore, 1928.

Burrows, Wm. Textbook of Microbiology. Chap. 4, 16th Ed. W. B. Saunders Co., Philadelphia, 1954.

Dubos, René J. The Bacterial Cell. Harvard University Press, Cambridge, 1945.

Gay, F. P., and Associates. Agents of Disease and Host Resistance. Charles C. Thomas, Baltimore, 1935.

Hammer, B. W. Dairy Bacteriology. 3rd Ed. John Wiley & Sons, Inc., New York, 1948.

Henrici, A. T. The Biology of Bacteria. 2nd Ed. D. C. Heath & Co., Boston, 1939.

Jordan, E. O., and Falk, I. S. The Newer Knowledge of Bacteriology and Immunology. University of Chicago Press, Chicago, 1928.

Knight, B. C. J. B. Bacterial Nutrition. Medical Research Council, Special Report Series No. 210. His Majesty's Stationery Office, London, 1938.

Michaelis, L. Oxidation-Reduction Potentials. J. B. Lippincott Co., Philadelphia, 1930.

Porter, J. R. Bacterial Chemistry and Physiology. John Wiley & Sons, Inc., New York, 1946.

Rahn, O. The Physiology of Bacteria. P. Blakiston's Son & Co., Philadelphia, 1932.

Stephenson, M. Bacterial Metabolism. Longmans, Green & Co., London and New York, 1930.

Topley, W. W. C., Wilson, G. S., and Miles, A. A. Principles of Bacteriology and Immunity. 3rd Ed. Wm. Wood Co., New York, 1946.

Waksman, S. A. Principles of Soil Microbiology. 2nd Ed. The Williams & Wilkins Co., Baltimore, 1932.

Werkman, C. H., and Wilson, P. W. (eds.) Bacterial Physiology. Academic Press Inc., New York, 1951.

Zinsser, H., and Bayne-Jones, S. Textbook of Bacteriology. 9th Ed. D. Appleton-Century Co., New York, 1948.

4. | Bacteriological Technics and Methods

The details of technical procedures which are used in the study of microorganisms are found in texts entirely devoted to the subject, but a brief discussion of some of the technics is desirable in this text also. This discussion is based upon the reasons for and the results of the various laboratory procedures, as well as upon the technics themselves.

The most fundamental technic in the study of bacteria is the procedure whereby a pure culture is obtained. Since bacteria, yeasts, molds, and filtrable viruses are able to produce such varied changes in the food on which they live, it is evident that each species must play a part in the process. All knowledge of bacterial metabolism as represented by chemical changes in inanimate material and by disease in living plants and animals is built upon the *specificity* of microorganisms for the particular kind of food from which they obtain the essentials for life. It is obvious, therefore, that the study of any metabolic process involving microorganisms, or their products, must be based upon the *pure culture.*

The morphology of bacteria is used as a basis for recognition and differentiation. It also reveals something of the nature of the various types of cells which aids in the understanding of metabolic processes. The microscope is an essential instrument in microbiology, and a knowledge of the manipulation of the instrument facilitates the work of the student and assures his success in learning. Living microorganisms suspended in a fluid medium are so refractive for light rays that their structure is not easily seen when examined under the microscope; in fact, their exact shape and size are difficult to obtain in an unstained preparation. Methods of staining the various cells have added definitely to the knowledge concerning them. Bacteria react differently to the various staining processes. Their varied reactions are of value in classifying them into groups.

Most of the knowledge concerning microorganisms is based upon a study of them under artificial conditions, that is, in captivity.

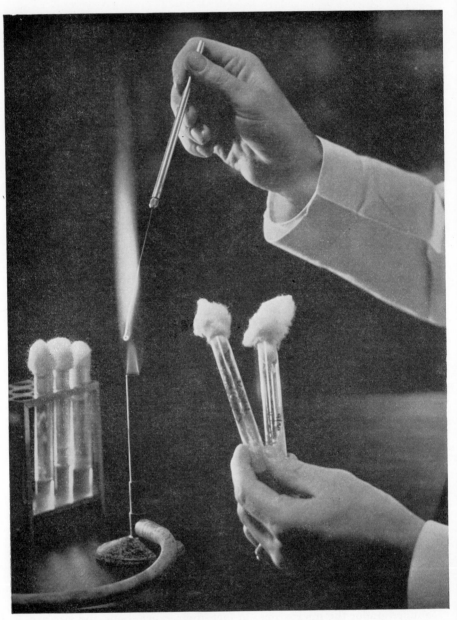

FIG. 4.1 — Technic of media inoculation. (Photo by John Barry, courtesy The Iowa
State College Veterinarian.)

The effect of large numbers of them upon a particular medium is different from the effect of just a few, as well might be expected. The effect of large numbers in an environment of optimum conditions for growth is different from the effect of small numbers in a natural environment surrounded by all of the hazards of normal life. The study of the natural life of bacteria is difficult because of their small size and their association with different bacterial species. Our knowledge, therefore, out of necessity, is based upon the results obtained from the study of bacteria in captivity.

The methods used for bacteriological analyses are varied. An assortment of special equipment, tubes, dishes, flasks, etc., is peculiar to bacteriology. Many different foods are concocted for microorganisms. These foods are changed by the action of bacteria so that numerous tests are necessary to detect the resulting products.

The discussion of bacteriological technics and methods is divided into the following parts: *Isolation and Cultivation Technics, Microscopic Examination, Stains and Staining Methods,* and *Culture Media and Tests.*

ISOLATION AND CULTIVATION TECHNICS

Cultures of bacteria and materials suspected of containing pathogenic bacteria are transferred to culture media by means of a platinum wire or other wire which is not easily disintegrated by the flame (Fig. 4.1). In cases where a large amount of inoculum is transferred, a sterile glass pipette is used. In the collection of material for bacteriological examination, care must be used to eliminate contamination. Fluids must be collected in sterile glass tubes; tissue surfaces must be seared with a hot spatula before a specimen is taken. Even when all precautions are taken, material such as water, urine, milk, tissues, and tissue exudates may contain more than one species of bacteria. In some cases the organism may be present in pure culture, but this cannot be depended upon as being a general rule.

Methods of Securing Pure Cultures. Prior to the use of solid media by Koch, pure cultures of bacteria were obtained by the dilution method. This method is rarely, if ever, used today for that purpose, although it is commonly employed to decrease the number of bacteria in material previous to the use of other technics, whereby the organism is obtained in pure culture.

The method most commonly used for isolating bacteria in pure culture is known as the *plating method;* "plating" because Koch used a glass plate in his original technic. The *Petri dish* or *Petri plate* (Fig. 4.2) is now used for that purpose. The Petri dish is composed of two circular glass plates, one slightly smaller than the other so that it fits into the outer one tightly enough to inhibit the passage of air and sufficiently tight to prevent the passage of dust particles. After the dishes are once sterilized they remain so when they are given reasonable care, but they should be stored in metal or cardboard containers to assure sterility. Two methods are used in the plating technic, the streak plate and the pour plate. The objective of both methods is to obtain the growth of the desired organism in pure culture in well-isolated colonies. In the streak plate the material from which the organism is to be isolated is streaked across the surface of solid medium in parallel lines; the organisms grow in separated colonies along the end of the last few streaks. In making a pour plate, a solid medium contained in a test tube is melted, cooled to 45°C., and inoculated with the organism.

FIG. 4.2 — The Petri culture dish.

The medium and organism are mixed by rapidly rotating the tube between the palms of the hands. The lid of a sterile Petri dish is elevated just enough to permit the insertion of the open end of the test tube from which the medium is poured into the dish. The medium in the dish is allowed to cool. The organisms grow throughout the medium in well-isolated colonies from which the desired organism is "fished" and transferred to a tube of medium in a pure culture. In case the material to be examined is heavily seeded with bacteria, preliminary dilution in sterile water or bouillon is necessary in order to diminish the number of organisms. It is obvious that if bacteria are too numerous, one colony grows over another, and isolation of a pure culture is impossible.

Barber has devised a capillary pipette method whereby it is possible to pick up a single bacterial cell from a drop of suspended medium and transfer it into another drop of medium. This method has been found useful in the study of bacterial dissociation and essential in the study of bacterial cyclogeny. Modifications of the Barber method have been made by many investigators.

A sporeforming organism may be isolated from a nonsporeproducing one by heating the medium in which both are contained to 80°C. for 15 minutes. The spores will resist that temperature while all other cells are killed.

Some chemicals such as crystal violet, inhibit the growth of certain bacteria but permit the growth of others. When these chemicals, in correct proportions, are added to media, the isolation of organisms in pure cultures is obtained. Crystal violet inhibits the growth of Gram-positive bacteria but permits the growth of Gram-negative forms. Antiformin permits the growth of tubercle bacilli, but inhibits the growth of other species. The various inhibiting agents will be discussed more fully in chapters devoted to specific organisms.

A pure culture of a pathogenic microorganism can be obtained in many cases by the injection of the suspected mixture of bacteria into a susceptible experimental animal. Tissues from a suspected case of blackleg may be contaminated with putrefactive bacteria before they are submitted to the laboratory for diagnosis. Since many putrefactive bacteria, as well as the blackleg organism, are anaerobic the isolation of the latter is at times difficult. It may be accomplished by plating the material and incubating the plates anaerobically. Fluid from the suspected material, however, is often injected into a guinea pig. The putrefactive contaminating bacteria do not multiply in the tissues of the guinea pig, whereas *Clostridium chauvoei* grows freely and causes the death of the animal. A pure culture of the organism can be obtained from the infected tissues.

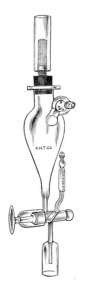

FIG. 4.3 — Filtering apparatus for small amounts of fluid.

The filtrable viruses can be isolated in pure culture by the process of passing the fluid containing the virus through a sterile filter and collecting it in a sterile test tube or flask. An illustration of an apparatus suitable for filtering small amounts of fluids is given in Figure 4.3.

In a previous chapter the factors, such as temperature and oxygen, which influence the growth of microorganisms, were discussed. A brief description of the technics for obtaining those conditions follows.

Incubation of Cultures. Cultures of various kinds of microorganisms are grown in an incubator which is well insulated, assuring a constant temperature. Incubators vary in size and in the material with which they are constructed. Usually heat is supplied from two sources, the gas flame and the electric element. Temperature is controlled by means of a thermostat.

The usual temperature at which pathogenic bacteria are grown is 37.5°C. Gelatin cultures, however, are liquefied at this temperature; consequently, they are usually kept in an incubator regulated to 20°C. Many of the nonpathogenic organisms grow more abundantly at temperatures ranging from 25–30°C. Since various microorganisms have an optimum temperature for growth, the thermostat of the incubator must be adjusted to the desired temperature. In laboratories, where different varieties of organisms are studied, it is obvious that an incubator for each desired temperature must be available.

Anaerobic Methods. In the cultivation of anaerobic bacteria two general principles are involved, the reduction of oxygen tension and the maintenance of the reduced tension. Hall has outlined the anaerobic methods under those two principles as follows:

I. Reduction of oxygen tension
    A. Biological reduction
        Aerobic-anaerobic symbiosis
            Symbiont in the medium
            Symbiont in the air chamber
            Use of animal and plant tissues
    B. Physical reduction
        Boiling
        Evacuation
        Use of inert gases
    C. Chemical reduction
        Agent in air chamber
            Catalytic ignition of hydrogen and residual oxygen
            Reduction by phosphorus
            Reduction by iron compounds
            Reduction by alkaline pyrogallol
        Agent in the medium

II. Maintenance of reduced oxygen tension
    A. Portion of medium sealed off
        Deep medium seals
        Insoluble liquid seals
        Mechanical seals
    B. Air chamber sealed
        Fusion of glass outlet
        Mechanical seals

The biological reduction of oxygen tension is nature's way of producing optimum conditions for the growth of anaerobic bacteria inasmuch as they grow in the presence of aerobic forms or in tissues which absorb oxygen. In the laboratory two common methods are patterned after this process. Aerobic bacilli, such as *Bacillus subtilis*, are grown symbiotically in the same tube with an anaerobe, such as *Clost. tetani*. The growth and toxin production of the latter can be demonstrated in the filtrate of the medium. If the two organisms are grown in separate tubes or flasks, these results are not obtained.

One of the most common media used in laboratories is the minced meat medium. Liver, spleen, brain, or any other tissue may be finely divided and added to a suitable liquid medium. Fresh, sterile tissues are more suitable than the ground, cooked tissues, but the latter are satisfactory for general use.

When the oxygen is driven from a medium with the aid of heat the anaerobic condition must be maintained. The paraffin oil or petrolatum seal is commonly used in the case of fluid media. The oil is put in the medium prior to sterilization; the oxygen is driven out by heating, and the oil forms a perfect seal against air. The oils of heavier consistency, such as vaseline, are better than oils of the light type. If a light oil is used, it should be at least an inch deep over the medium in order to inhibit the permeation of oxygen into the medium.

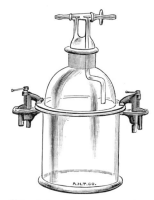

FIG. 4.4 — Novy anaerobic apparatus.

The air may be evacuated from suitable containers, such as the Novy or Smillie apparatus (Fig. 4.4); or inert gases, hydrogen and carbon dioxide, may be passed into them. In the McIntosh-Fildes culture apparatus, oxygen is removed by the oxidation of hydrogen due to the catalytic action of palladinized asbestos wool under the influence of heat generated by the electric current. A source of hydrogen must be available for this method.

The absorption of oxygen by alkaline pyrogallol is commonly used in the student laboratory. This method is based upon the principle that alkaline pyrogallol absorbs oxygen. Pyrogallic acid powder is placed in a container which is absolutely sealed, and 30 per cent sodium hydroxide is added to the powder for alkalinization. The resulting fluid is light brown in color and becomes almost black with continued absorption of oxygen. Test tubes and culture jars may be used in this method. Spray has devised a culture dish which may be used to advantage (Fig. 4.5). The bottom dish is separated into two parts by an elevation. Pyrogallic acid is put on one side and sodium hydroxide on the other. The culture is prepared in the usual way in the top inverted dish which is sealed in a groove provided for the purpose. The two chemicals are mixed by tipping the dish. The resulting effect is the same as described above.

The Rosenthal chromium-sulphuric acid method is another chemical method for producing anaerobic conditions. This method is based upon the addition of sulphuric acid to chromium with the resulting evolution of hydrogen and the subsequent utilization of oxygen according to the following reactions:

$$Cr + H_2SO_4 = CrSO_4 + H_2$$
$$4\ CrSO_4 + 2H_2SO_4 + O_2 = 2\ Cr_2(SO_4)_3 + 2\ H_2O$$

Any of the containers used in anaerobic work can be used in this method if suitable amounts of the ingredients are used; in fact, any container which is sealable and which is provided with a gas outlet may be used.

The Technic. Place in the container 100 cc. of 15 per cent sulphuric acid per liter of capacity and add 5 grams of chromium per liter of capacity. Place the lid on the container, leaving a gas outlet open until the initial reaction has subsided and only slight evolution of hydrogen is observed. The container is then incubated. Since hydrogen is present, the culture apparatus must not be opened close to a flame.

MICROSCOPIC TECHNIC

The use of the microscope is indispensable in the study of bacteria. The student must understand the mechanism of magnification and the essentials of correct illumination if he is to study cultures of bacteria with success. The student in veterinary medicine has had previous courses in which he has become familiar with the manipulation of the microscope and with the general technic of microscopy, and for this reason it is not necessary to repeat these procedures; however, a few minimum essentials of technic which are used in the study of microorganisms are outlined.

Oil Immersion Objectives. The small size of bacteria requires the use of the highest powers of magnification possible. The total magnification of a microscope is obtained by multiplying the magnification due to the objective by the magnification due to the eyepiece. The magnification of the usual student microscope is the total of a $91\times$ objective and a $10\times$ eyepiece or $910\times$. The higher the power of the objective, the smaller is the opening through which the light may reach the eye. It is necessary, therefore, that all possible light shall enter the lens in order to assure a well-illuminated field. This means that light must not be lost by refraction as it passes through the glass slide. For this reason, immersion contact is made between the objective and glass slide or cover glass with cedar oil. This oil is specially prepared so as to have the same refractive index as the oil immersion lens. The lower powers of the microscope are used for studying bacterial colonies, general motility, and the morphology of yeasts and molds, but the oil immersion objective must be used to study the morphology of bacteria if details are to be seen. Much time is saved, therefore, if the student learns to use the oil immersion objective quickly. Bausch describes this technic as follows: [1]

> Apply a small quantity of oil to the front lens of the objective or to the cover glass, using for this purpose the rod in the oil bottle. Lower the objective very carefully with the coarse adjustment until contact is made. This can best be determined by watching the space between objective and slide with the eye well down to the level of the stage. At the instant contact is made, a flash of light will illuminate the oil. When this flash is seen, the objective will be near enough to focus by means of the fine adjustment.

The presence of dust or air bubbles in the immersion oil may destroy the definition of the best objective; therefore, it is very essential to keep the oil bottle stoppered at all times. If bubbles are trapped between objective and slide, it may be necessary to apply fresh oil and to re-focus in order to get rid of them.

Special care must be observed if a low power objective is used after an oil immersion. The oil must invariably be removed from the top of the cover glass by wiping with lens paper. The front of the objective should always be

FIG. 4.5 — Spray culture dish for anaerobic bacteria.

cleaned in the same manner immediately after it has been used. If oil does dry, it may be removed by using lens paper moistened with a *minute* amount of *xylol*.

Illumination. The regulation of the light which illuminates the object is of great importance in microscopic work of all kinds and is of utmost importance in the study of bacteria.

Natural and artificial light are used. Natural light from a north window is an excellent source but has the disadvantage of variability due to cloudy weather. Direct sunlight is too bright for microscopic use. The electric light is the most common source of illumination. A variety of lamps are available for this purpose. Blue and white, frosted and nonfrosted bulbs are used. When the white bulb is used the light is most satisfactory when filtered through a blue glass in the form of a shade or a disc placed in the microscope substage condenser. The light is adjusted after the object has been brought into focus by manipulation of the mirror and the condenser.

The mirror on the microscope is double, plane on one side and concave on the other. When skylight is used as a light source,

[1] E. Bausch. *The Use and Care of the Microscope.* p. 9. Bausch and Lomb Optical Co., Rochester, 1948.

either side may be used, but the plane side gives a more even light. The plane mirror is always used with the substage condenser (Fig. 4.6).

The substage condenser, frequently called the Abbe condenser, is used to concentrate light rays on the object. It is a system of lens

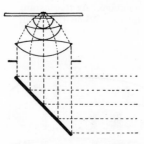

so arranged that the light is refracted, and the rays converge a short distance above the top lens (Fig. 4.6). The intensity of light is governed by lowering or elevating the condenser. For oil immersion magnification the condenser is raised near the level of the stage in order to assure a maximum amount of light.

The substage iris diaphragm is also used to adjust illumination. It should not be used to control the density of illumination but to bring out details in the object which is being studied.

FIG. 4.6 — The path of light reflected from the mirror through the substage condenser. (Courtesy Bausch and Lomb.)

Dark-Field Illumination. Some types of microorganisms, such as the spirochetes, are not stained by the usual methods but are made visible by the dark-field method. Details of the structure of some of the large bacteria, as well as yeasts and molds, are demonstrated by this technic. Various methods are available to demonstrate dark-field illumination. All of them depend on the blocking of the central rays of light but allowing the pasage of a ring of rays around the outer edge of the condenser. These light rays do not enter the microscope unless they are reflected from the object which appears brightly illuminated against a dark background. The three common condensers which are used for this method of illumination are illustrated in Figure 4.7. The dark ground stop is a metal disc which is inserted into the slot in the lower part of the Abbe condenser. It is used satisfactorily to demonstrate the principle of dark-field illumination with the lower powers of magnification. In the paraboloid condenser the central light rays are blocked out by means of an enamel disc on the lens of the condenser. There is no disc in the cardioid condenser since the rays are reflected as they enter the object from the side.

In dark-field illumination, water or immersion oil is placed between the condenser and the object slide. When the higher power of magnification is used, a funnel stop, or a special objective, must be inserted in the oil immersion objective to prevent direct rays from entering the margin of the lens.

Measuring Microorganisms. In order to measure microscopic objects a micrometer scale is used in the eyepiece of the microscope. Since the object to be measured is magnified, the magnification factor must be determined before the size of the object is known. A stage micrometer is used to determine the distance between the lines of the eyepiece micrometer scale. When the microscope has been calibrated, the eyepiece may be used to measure objects. The procedure for measuring bacteria is as follows:

1. Insert eyepiece micrometer in microscope.

2. Examine bacteria on the slide and record their size in terms of divisions of the eyepiece micrometer.

3. Remove the slide of bacteria and insert the stage micrometer.

4. Determine the relation of the division of the eyepiece micrometer to that of the stage micrometer.

5. Compute the size of the bacteria.

The divisions on the stage micrometer are usually 0.01 mm. The unit of measurement of bacteria is the micron (0.001 mm); therefore, the divisions are 10μ in size. If the calibration of the eyepiece shows that two divisions of the eyepiece micrometer are equal to one division of the stage micrometer, then each eyepiece division represents 5μ. The size of the bacteria which have been measured are computed on that basis.

The Hanging Drop. The motility of bacteria is observed best by examining a hanging drop in which the organisms are able to move about freely. A special glass slide with a hollow depression in the center is used for this purpose. The technic is as follows:

Place a thin layer of petrolatum or vaseline around the rim of the hollow-ground slide. Transfer a loopful of broth containing the bacteria to the center of a cover slip. Lower the slide onto the cover slip and press it firmly in place in the rim of petrolatum. Invert it quickly and handle carefully so as not to disturb the drop which is hanging from the cover slip into the hollow of the slide. Examine the preparation with the lower power objective in order to locate the edge of the drop. The organisms may be studied for detail with the higher powers of magnification. The glass slide and cover slip must be absolutely free of dust and finger prints to assure clear vision.

STAINS AND STAINING METHODS

Bacteria are generally so transparent when they are examined in the living condition that the details of their morphology are difficult to discern. It is customary to stain these organisms with various aniline dyes which render them distinctly visible. Some progress has been made in differential staining of the various parts of bacterial cells. Bacteria react differentially to some strains. This is an aid in classifying them.

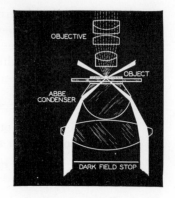

The stains used in biologic work for the most part are known as "coal-tar" dyes because most of them are derivatives of the hydrocarbon, benzene (C_6H_6). "Coal-tar" dyes are non-acid salts of color bases or alkali salts of color bases. "Acidic" and "basic" as applied to dyes refer to the affinity of the chromogenic radicle for acidic and basic groups. The dye is acidic or basic according to the character of its auxochromes. Acidic or basic as applied to dyes has no reference to the hydrogen-hydroxyl-ion reaction and is not to be interpreted in the true chemical sense. Both acidic and basic dyes are more potent in alkaline media. Basic dyes are sold as salts of a colorless acid such as hydrochloric, sulphuric, oxalic, or acetic. Acid dyes are sold as sodium, potassium, calcium, or ammonium salts.

The present-day conception of dyes is based on molecular structure. The basis of the structure is the benzene ring of Kekule. If derivatives, with this structure, contain groups of elements known as "chromophores," they impart the property of color. Chromogenes, although colored, are not dyes. They may coat the cells superficially, but the color can be easily removed by the mechanical process of washing. To become a dye the chromogen derivative must contain, in addition to the chromophore, other groups knowns as "auxochromes." These auxochromes impart to the compound the property of electrolytic dissociation, furnishing it with salt-forming properties, and thus converting it into a dye.

Dyes probably fulfill their function

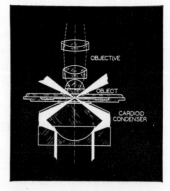

FIG. 4.7 — Condensers used for dark-field illumination. (Courtesy Bausch and Lomb.)

by both chemical and physical processes. The chemical process of staining is thought to be enhanced by the number of auxochromic groups in the dye, as well as the number and adequacy of the chromophilic groups in the cells to be stained. The physical process depends on surface attraction, osmosis, diffusion, and adsorption. Factors which no doubt promote these processes are the size of the dye molecule and adequate pore-volume of the material to be stained.

The abundance of nucleoprotein in bacteria appears to explain their affinity, at least, for basic "coal-tar" dyes. In their staining reactions bacteria behave as if they are composed largely of protein. The amount of dye taken up by bacteria and the firmness with which it is held doubtless depends, in a large part, on the hydrogen-ion concentration of the bacterial protein. The general rule is that the larger the number of hydrogen atoms that have been replaced by methyl, ethyl, or phenyl groups, the deeper the color. A dye retains its color only as long as its affinities for hydrogen are not completely satisfied. Since the pH of bacterial protein changes with age, this may account for the variations in staining between young and old cultures of the same organism.

Mordants and Decolorizing Agents. When bacteria are present in tissues or exudates, they may not be observed because of their small size unless correct staining methods are used. Various methods are available whereby the organisms are stained more deeply than the tissue cells, or the stain in the tissue cells is removed by decolorizing agents, leaving the bacteria as previously colored. Chemical agents which fix the stain, or cause it to penetrate more deeply in the organism, are called *mordants*. Aniline oil, phenol, potassium iodide, tannic acid, and various metallic salts are all used as mordants for different organisms and in various staining procedures. Prolongation of the period of staining and heating increases the intensity with which bacteria and their spores are stained. After the organism has been stained deeply and the stain has been fixed by the action of a mordant, the dye is not removed easily; however, bacteria vary in this respect. Tissue cells also vary which makes differential staining possible. The stain is removed from certain bacteria and tissue cells by decolorizing agents, such as dilute alcohols, acetone, ether, dilute mineral and organic acids, and hot water. The decolorized cells are counterstained with a dye of a contrasting color.

Method of Preparing a Bacterial Film for Staining. A glass slide is cleaned until it is perfectly free from grease. If a drop of water does not spread evenly over the slide, it is not suitable for use. Hot water and alkaline washing powder usually clean the slide satisfactorily. It is necessary to place some slides in dilute acid or alcohol in order to remove the film which prevents the even spread of a drop of water. When the slide is clean, place a drop of bouillon containing the culture on the slide with the loop of the inoculating needle and smear it over a surface about the size of the small finger nail. When it has dried, fix the smear to the slide by passing it through the flame a few times.

In making smears from cultures which have grown on solid media, an inoculating loop full of water is placed on the slide. Into this is mixed a small amount of the culture which has been removed from the growth with the tip of the straight inoculating needle. Too much of the culture must not be transferred or the smear will be too thick to be studied satisfactorily. Films of blood, pus, lymph, milk, and urine are prepared in the same manner. Tissue cells must be spread thinly, however, or the cells will obscure the bacteria which may be present, even when a differential stain is used.

The smears are allowed to dry in the air and are then passed through the Bunsen flame which fixes the film to the slide. Fixation by chemicals, such as methyl alcohol, saturated aqueous mercuric chloride, or formalin, is often used for tissue smears.

The preparation is then stained with the method which is most applicable to the particular organism.

The excess stain is removed by washing the slide with water which is removed by placing the slide between two layers of blotting paper. To assure the removal of all water the slide is passed through the flame.

Immersion oil may be placed directly on the stained film, or a glass cover slip mounted in oil may be placed upon the film.

In summary, the technic of preparing a bacterial film for examination consists of the following steps: (1) preparing the film; (2) drying in air; (3) fixing; (4) staining; (5) washing with water; (6) blotting; (7) drying; (8) mounting.

STAINING METHODS

The Gram Stain: Christian Gram, a Dane, devised a method of staining bacteria in 1884. This method, universally called the Gram stain, has become the most common staining technic used in bacteriology. It consists of staining a prepared bacterial smear with gentian violet, mordanting with Lugol's iodine solution, washing with alcohol or acetone until all of the violet stain is removed, and counterstaining with a contrasting dye such as basic fuchsin or safranin. Those bacteria which retain the gentian violet stain are called Gram-positive, and those which are decolorized and stained red by the counterstain are Gram-negative.

The detailed technic for the staining process is as follows:

1. Stain the film 2 minutes with Hucker's gentian violet prepared as follows:
   1 ml. saturated alcoholic solution of gentian violet or crystal violet (4 grams dye in 20 ml. of 95% ethyl alcohol).
   10 ml. of 1% ammonium oxalate.
2. Wash with water and apply Gram's iodine 1 minute. Gram's iodine is prepared as follows:
   Iodine   1 gm.
   Potassium iodide   2 gms.
   Water distilled   300 ml.
3. Pour off excess fluid and wash with acetone (30 parts) and 95% alcohol (70 parts) until the smear ceases to lose color.
4. Wash with water.
5. Counterstain with 2% aqueous solution of safranin.
6. Wash with water, blot, dry, and examine.

Various theories have been advanced to explain the Gram-staining reaction. Benians contends that the iodine forms a large alcohol-soluble molecule with the gentian violet which is removed from the Gram-negative bacteria but retained by those which stain Gram-positive; the difference is due to the permeability of the cell walls of the two types. Churchman believes that Gram-positive cells possess an outer cortex which is responsible for the retention of the gentian violet stain. Stearns and Stearns have shown that the proteins of Gram-positive bacteria have an isoelectric point more toward the acid side than the Gram-negative bacteria, which explains why Gram-positive bacteria show a greater affinity for basic dyes. Deuszen has explained that Gram staining is due to a chemical reaction resulting from the compound-forming properties of the nucleoprotein of the bacterial cells.

The theory of Churchman has been upheld recently by Henry and Stacey, who have been able to "strip" Gram-positive bacteria of an essential part of their Gram-positive material, leaving Gram-negative cytoskeletons and a Gram-negative extract. These investigators were able to obtain this result by extracting washed bacterial cells at 60° C. with a 2 per cent aqueous solution of a bile salt in the presence of oxygen. The material in the extract can be precipitated by alcohol and consists of magnesium ribonucleate, inert polysaccharides, and traces of protein. It was possible to reconstitute the Gram-positive cell by "plating" the extract back on the cytoskeleton. Those bacteria which are fundamentally Gram-negative do not respond to such technic.

As further proof, Henry and Stacey were able to produce Gram-negative bacteria from known Gram-positive species, such as *Streptococcus salivarus*, by growing in a medium completely devoid of magnesium.

The most plausible explanation of the Gram process is that the Gram-positive material is a high-molecular complex formed by the combination of a reduced basic protein substrate with magnesium ribonucleate.

Alkaline Methylene Blue Stain. In some cases it is desirable to stain a bacterial smear without the use of a differential technic. Methylene blue has been one of the old "standby" stains for this purpose in bacteriology. It is also of value as a counterstain in many methods.

SOLUTION A

Methylene blue (90% dye content) .... 0.3 gm.
Ethyl alcohol (95%) .... 30.0 ml.

SOLUTION B

KOH (0.01% by weight) .... 100 ml.

Solutions A and B are mixed, and the mixture is allowed to stain the smear 3–5 minutes. The preparation is then thoroughly washed with water.

Carbol Fuchsin. This stain is often used in differential staining methods but is effective when used alone.

Basic fuchsin .... 1 ml.
Ethyl alcohol (absolute) .... 10 ml.
5% aqueous carbolic acid .... 90 ml.
The stain is allowed to act 1 to 2 minutes.

Spore Stains. The compact nature of the bacterial spore prevents stains from penetrating to a depth which imparts color. The penetrability of the stain is usually increased by heat or prolonged contact. When once stained, the spore is not decolorized easily.

HANSEN'S METHOD

1. Prepare the film containing the sporeforming bacteria as usual.
2. Stain with steaming carbol fuchsin 5 minutes.
3. Decolorize with 5% acetic acid until the film is a light pink and then wash with water.
4. Counterstain 3 minutes with methylene blue.

The spores will be stained a bright red, and the vegetative part of the cell will be blue.

SCHAEFFER AND FULTON'S METHOD

1. Flood the slide with malachite green (5% aqueous solution allowed to stand ½ hour and filtered) and heat to steaming three or four times within ½ a minute.
2. Wash off excess stain and continue washing ½ minute.
3. Apply 0.5% aqueous safranin for ½ minute.

The spores will retain the green stain, and the vegetative cells will stain red.

Flagella Stains. The flagella of bacteria are not visible in ordinary stained mounts and can be demonstrated only by a special technic. Young, 12- to 18-hour cultures of bacteria should be used to demonstrate flagella. A tube containing 5 ml. of bouillon is inoculated with sufficient quantity of the growth removed from the agar surface to produce a slight turbidity. Incubate for an hour at 37°C. Drop two or three drops without mixing or spreading on a slide which is absolutely clean. When dry, fix in the flame and stain by the following methods:

CASARES-GIL'S METHOD

1. Flood the smear with the mordant prepared as follows:

   Tannic acid .... 10 gms.
   Aluminum chloride ($Al_2Cl_6 \cdot 12H_2O$) .... 18 gms.
   Zinc chloride .... 10 gms.
   Rosaniline hydrochloride .... 15 gms.
   Alcohol (60%) .... 40 ml.

   The solids are dissolved in the alcohol by trituration in a mortar, adding 10 cc. of the alcohol first, and then the rest slowly. For use, dilute with two parts of distilled water, filter, and use the filtrate on the slide. The mordant should act 1 to 2 minutes.
2. Wash carefully with distilled water.
3. Cover the smear with carbol fuchsin for 1 to 2 minutes. Wash with distilled water and allow to dry without blotting.

LOEFFLER'S METHOD

1. Prepare film, fix and apply the following mordant, heating for 5 minutes over a water bath:

   Tannic acid (25% aqueous solution) .... 10 parts
   Saturated solution ferrous sulphate .... 5 parts
   Fuchsin (saturated alcoholic solution) .... 1 part
2. Wash and blot with filter paper.
3. Stain with hot aniline-gentian violet or carbol fuchsin over a water bath for 5 minutes.
4. Wash carefully, let dry, and examine.

Capsule Stains. The capsules of bacteria are fragile and cannot be stained by the usual methods.

HISS'S METHOD

1. Prepare film, dry, and fix.
2. Stain with aniline oil gentian violet, or carbol fuchsin for 5 seconds, or until steam rises.
3. Wash off the stain with 20% aqueous copper sulphate solution.
4. Blot and dry in air. Do not wash.

JOHNE'S METHOD

This is particularly suited for the demonstration of the capsules of the anthrax bacillus in smears from blood or tissues.

1. Dry the smear in air, and fix.
2. Stain with 2% aqueous gentian violet, heating slightly for ¼ to ½ minute.
3. Wash quickly in water.
4. Wash in 1% to 2% acetic acid 6 to 10 seconds.
5. Wash in water; mount in water under a cover slip to examine.

Stains for Metachromatic Granules.

NEISSER'S STAIN

1. The smear of the organism is prepared in the usual way.
2. Flood the smear 10 to 30 seconds with Solution 1 prepared as follows:

   Methylene blue .... 0.1 gm.
   Absolute alcohol .... 20.0 ml.
   Glacial acetic acid .... 5.0 ml.
   Distilled water .... 100.0 ml.
3. Wash in water.
4. Counterstain with Bismarck brown or dilute safranin (preferably the latter) for a few seconds.
5. Blot, dry, and examine.

The granules will be a blackish-blue, and the body of the cells will be brown or pink, depending upon the counterstain.

ALBERT'S STAIN

1. Prepare the smear as usual.
2. Stain for 1 minute with Solution 1 which is prepared as follows:

   Toluidin blue .... 0.15 gm.
   Methyl green .... 0.20 gm.
   Acetic acid (glacial) .... 1.00 ml.
   Alcohol (95%) .... 2.00 ml.
   Distilled water .... 100.00 ml.

   After standing for one day the solution is filtered and is ready for use.
3. Stain for 1 minute with Solution 2 prepared as follows:

   Iodine .... 2.0 gms.
   Potassium iodide .... 3.0 gms.
   Distilled water .... 300.0 ml.
4. Wash with water, blot, dry, and examine.

The granules stain black, the cross striations blue, and the intermediate portions a light green.

Stains for Acid-fast Organisms. Bacteria of a certain group, of which the tubercle bacillus is the most important member, are spoken of as being acid-fast. It is difficult to stain them, but when they are once stained, the color is retained after a treatment with dilute acid. The cause of this acid-fast property is supposedly due to the lipoids which are present on the surface of the organism and also within the cell.

ZIEHL-NEELSEN'S METHOD

1. Smears are fixed with heat as usual.
2. Flood with carbol fuchsin and heat gently to steaming for 3 minutes.
3. Decolorize with acid alcohol composed as follows:

   Hydrochloric acid .... 2.0 ml.
   Alcohol (95%) .... 98.0 ml.

   The smear is decolorized until the thinner parts are decolorized, and the heavier portions remain pink.
4. Counterstain with methylene blue for 1 minute.
5. Wash in water, blot, and dry.

The acid-fast bacteria are stained red, and the tissue cells and other bacteria are blue.

GABBETT'S METHOD

1. Prepare a film and stain as above with carbol fuchsin.
2. Stain for 1 minute with Gabbett's methylene blue prepared as follows:
   Methylene blue (dry .... 2.0 gms.
   Sulphuric acid (sp. gr. 1.84) .... 25.0 ml.
   Distilled water .... 75.0 ml.
3. Wash in water and examine.

The acid-fast organisms will be red in a blue field.

Stains for Blood Cells. Many special stains have been devised for demonstrating blood cells, some of which are used in bacteriologic and immunologic studies. A reliable blood stain is necessary in the study of phagocytosis and in studying bacteria which cause septicemic conditions. The stains most commonly used are the Romanowsky and Giemsa, each with numerous modifications. These stains may be purchased in tablet or powder form from a reliable dealer and are ready for use when mixed with the proper diluent.

WRIGHT'S STAIN

One of the most satisfactory blood stains for routine work is that of Wright. This stain can be purchased in liquid form ready for use, or in powder form from which a saturated solution is made as a stock solution. The stain is prepared for use by adding to 20 ml. of the filtered stock solution 5 ml. of methyl alcohol. This is applied to a blood smear and allowed to stand 1 minute. Distilled water is then added drop by drop until a metallic luster appears on the surface. The stain is allowed to act for 5 minutes; then it is washed off with distilled water, dried, and examined with or without oil immersion. *Care must be taken in washing to float off the metallic sheen, for it forms a precipitate on the smear if allowed to settle there.*

GIEMSA'S STAIN

1. Apply the following fixing agent to moist films for 12 hours.
   95% ethyl alcohol .... 1 part
   Saturated aqueous $HgCl_2$ .... 2 parts
2. Wash in water for a few seconds.
3. Apply Lugol's solution for 5 minutes.
4. Wash in water, then in 0.5% sodium thiosulphate.
5. Stain with Giemsa stain 8 to 10 hours.
6. Wash and mount.

A modification of this method consists of mixing 1 drop of concentrated Giemsa in 20 drops of distilled water. After fixing the smear for 5 minutes in methyl alcohol, it is immersed in dilute stain and placed in a 37.5° incubator for 10 to 12 hours. It is then washed off with distilled water until the film has a slight pink tinge. This method is recommended for staining brain tissue for Negri bodies.

Stain for Negri Bodies.

LENTZ'S METHOD

Impression smears are made upon clean glass slides from (a) Ammon's horn, (b) the cerebellum, or (c) the cerebral cortex. Without allowing to dry, the smears are fixed for about 10 seconds in neutralized methyl alcohol (alcohol 500 ml. to which 0.25 gm. of sodium carbonate has been added) to which 0.1% picric acid has been added. The excess of fixative is removed by blotting with fine filter paper. The smears are stained in the following solution:

Saturated alcoholic solution of fuchsin .... 0.3 ml.
Saturated alcoholic solution of methylene blue .... 2.0 ml.
Distilled water .... 30.0 ml.

This solution, which is a modification of the one proposed by Van Gieson, changes rather quickly at room temperatures and should be prepared in small quantities for immediate use. The stain is poured on the smear and held over the flame until it steams. The smear is then washed in tap water and dried with fine filter paper. Negri bodies appear magenta, the nerve cells blue, and red blood cells yellow or salmon.

CULTURE MEDIA AND TESTS FOR METABOLIC PRODUCTS

Many different types of foods must be available for bacteria which are to be cultivated artificially; however, culture media are used for purposes other than supplying bacteria with the food essential for life. Microscopic examination alone is insufficient to differentiate closely related species of bacteria. For example, it is microscopically impossible to detect the difference between an organism which causes a specific intestinal infection such as typhoid fever and one which is a normal inhabitant of the intestinal tract such as *E. coli*. It is essential, therefore, to use different media in the differentiation of morphologically closely related types of bacteria.

Many different kinds of media which demonstrate the metabolism of the various species of microorganisms can be prepared, as was explained in the discussion of physiology in Chapter 2.

A few standard types of media are commonly used in the laboratory for the growth of bacteria, and a great variety of special types of media have been devised for growing certain species and for demonstrating the formation of particular metabolic products. Some of the tests for metabolic products and the formulae for preparing common media are as follows:

Meat Infusion Broth. This is a medium commonly used in the laboratory, and serves as a basis for the preparation of many others.

Fresh lean meat, beef or horse, is finely ground. Place 500 gms. in 1 liter of distilled water. Place in refrigerator over night. Boil vigorously for ½ hour, maintaining the volume throughout by adding water. Filter through gauze and then paper to remove all meat particles. To each 1,000 ml. of infusion add 10 gms. peptone and 5 gms. of sodium chloride, then heat to dissolve. Adjust to pH 7.4-7.6. Boil for ½ hour and allow to cool. Filter through paper. Dispense in test tubes or flasks and sterilize 15 minutes at 15 pounds pressure.

Meat infusion broth is usually used to determine the type of growth produced in a fluid medium. Growth characteristics noted are (1) abundance and pellicle formation, (2) growth throughout the medium, and (3) the mucoid or granular character of the sediment.

Beef Extract Broth. In much of the routine work, particularly in student laboratories, beef extract is substituted for meat infusion broth.

```
Formula: beef extract  .....................................   5 gms.
         peptone  .........................................  10 gms.
         sodium chloride  .................................   5 gms.
         distilled water  ....................... ...............1,000 ml.
```

The ingredients are mixed together and heated until dissolved. The medium is then filtered, tubed, and sterilized.

Sugar-free Broth. In all meat infusion and meat extract media, there is always a small percentage of sugar. Such media cannot be used for exact fermentation studies unless the sugar has been removed. In order to render a medium sugar-free, the meat infusion is inoculated with a culture of *E. coli* and incubated at 37°C. for 18 hours. The infusion is then sterilized and filtered, and is ready for use.

Carbohydrate Broth. Any desired carbohydrate is added to sugar-free broth in preparing a medium for testing the fermenting ability of an organism. A 1% solution of the carbohydrate is usually used although a 0.5% solution is sufficient in some cases. A suitable indicator is commonly added to such a medium to detect acid formation. Sugar media are sterilized at lower temperatures or for shorter periods than most media because heat is apt to cause the decomposition of some of the carbohydrates. Sterilization with flowing steam for 30 minutes on three consecutive days is the usual procedure. The carbohydrates may be sterilized by filtration through a porcelain filter and then added to the basic medium. In addition to heat sterilization the medium with the carbohydrate may be sterilized by filtration.

Two products of carbohydrate disintegration which are useful in the differentiation of bacteria are *acid* and *gas*.

The formation of acid is usually detected by the use of an indicator in the medium. If the total acidity or the final pH of the medium is desired, it is necessary to titrate the medium or to use a suitable indicator or potentiometer. The kind of acid which is formed is rarely determined in the study of the pathogenic species of bacteria.

In order to detect the formation of gas in carbohydrate fermentation special tubes are used in which the gas collects. Two types of tubes commonly used are the Smith tube and the Durham tube. In the Smith tube the gas collects in the closed arm of the tube. In the Durham tube the gas collects in the small inverted vial. A considerable amount of gas escapes from both tubes since both have portions open to the air. The type of gas which is formed by fermentation is of use in the study of some bacteria. Two of the gases commonly produced are *carbon dioxide* and *hydrogen*. The approximate amount of each of these gases present in a Smith fermentation tube is determined by the following technic:

Fill the open arm of the tube with normal sodium hydroxide and securely close the opening with the thumb. Allow the gas to mix with sodium hydroxide by passing it from one arm to the other several times but finally returning it to the closed arm. The thumb is removed and the medium rises in the closed arm. The gas which has been removed due to the chemical action of sodium hydroxide is carbon dioxide. The volume which is absorbed is measured by using a Frost gasometer. The composition of the remaining gas is determined by passing it into the open arm and removing the thumb when a flame is applied. Hydrogen is indicated by a slight explosion. The relative proportion of carbon dioxide to hydrogen is of value in the recognition of certain species of bacteria.

Voges-Proskauer Test. Acetyl methyl carbinol is a product of dextrose cleavage which is formed by some bacteria in the presence of peptone. It is recognized by the addition of 1 ml. of a 10% solution of sodium hydroxide to approximately 5 ml. of the medium, then adding three or four drops of a 2% solution of ferric chloride. An eosin pink or red color develops near the surface of the medium when it is allowed to stand a few hours.

Serum Broth. Many of the pathogenic bacteria grow more abundantly when the medium is enriched with blood serum. Blood serum is poured or aspirated from blood which has been taken under aseptic conditions and allowed to coagulate in flasks. The sterile serum is added to the basic meat infusion medium by means of a special filler pipette which has been sterilized. Serum may be poured directly into culture tubes if due caution is observed. Serum is added to the ratio of 1 ml. to 10 ml. of medium.

Hiss Serum Water. Horse or cow serum is dialyzed to remove the salts and sugars which are normally present, diluted with three times its volume of distilled water, tubed, and sterilized at 100°C. for 20 minutes on three consecutive days. A 1% peptone water or sugar and salt-free nutrient broth may be used instead of distilled water. For fermentation tests an indicator and 1% of the desired carbohydrate is added. Acid formation is indicated by a change in reaction and a resulting coagulation of the serum. Gas production is apparent by bubbles of gas in the coagulated mass.

Dunham's Solution. Peptone water is prepared by mixing 10 gms. of peptone and 5 gms. of sodium chloride in 1,000 ml. of distilled water. The medium is boiled for 5 minutes, adjusted to pH 7.6–7.8, cooled, and filtered through paper.

This medium is used as a basic medium to which carbohydrates may be added for fermentation studies, and for indol production.

Tryptophane Broth. This medium is prepared by using tryptone instead of peptone in the method described above. It is used almost exclusively to detect the formation of indol by bacteria.

The Indol test. The medium is inoculated and incubated for two days. Various reagents may be used to detect the presence of indol but Kovac's reagent is considered very reliable.

KOVAC'S REAGENT

Amyl alcohol	75 ml.
Hydrochloric acid, conc.	25 ml.
p–dimethyl–aminobenzaldehyde	5 gms.

The test is conducted by overlaying the medium with 2 ml. chloroform followed by 2 ml. Kovac's reagent. The medium and test reagents are not agitated. A positive test is apparent by the formation of a pink to deep red color in the chloroform layer.

Strips of filter paper may be soaked with saturated oxalic acid solution and suspended in the test tube above the medium. Indol formation is noted by the formation of a pink color in the paper strip during incubation.

Milk. Most bacteria grow in milk, so it is used alone, or as an enriching substance for other media. Litmus milk is prepared by adding aqueous litmus solution to fresh skimmed milk until a deep purple color is obtained. Bromcresol purple milk is rapidly replacing litmus milk in many laboratories. It is prepared by adding 10 ml. of a 1.6% alcoholic solution of bromcresol purple to 1,000 ml. of milk.

The changes which bacteria are able to cause in milk are quite varied; this makes it an important differential medium. Milk is coagulated by a rennet-like enzyme or by the formation of acid produced by the fermentation of lactose. The coagulum may be soft or hard. Lactose may be fermented to gas which can be observed in the curd. Milk casein is peptonized by some bacteria but not by others. Casein may be digested but not coagulated. Many species of bacteria grow in milk without causing any physical change in the medium.

Nutrient Gelatin. A good grade of granulated gelatin is added to meat broth or beef extract broth. Twelve to 15% is usually added; it is advisable to use 15% during hot weather whereas 12% is satisfactory during cold weather. To dissolve the gelatin, the medium is heated over an asbestos pad or in a double boiler. The medium is then adjusted to pH 7.4–7.6. After the medium has cooled, the white of egg which is added for clearing is thoroughly stirred into the medium. It is again heated to the boiling point and then filtered through a cotton pad. The medium is tubed and then sterilized in flowing steam for 20 minutes on three consecutive days. It is cooled at once upon removal from the sterilizer.

In addition to being a medium which produces a solid surface, gelatin is of value because it is liquefied (hydrolyzed) by some types of bacteria. Since the medium becomes liquid at about 25°C., it is necessary to incubate it at a lower temperature; 20°C. is usually used. The gelatin liquefying bacteria produce different types of liquefaction when stab cultures are made (Fig. 4.8).

Nutrient Agar. Agar-agar is a carbohydrate-like material which comes from seaweed found in Japanese and Chinese seas. It is used in the granulated form in the laboratory; 2% is the usual amount added to a fluid medium. The mixture must be boiled vigorously 10–15 minutes to melt the agar. Egg white is then added for clearing, and the medium is filtered through a cotton pad, after which it is tubed and sterilized in the autoclave at 15 pounds for 15 minutes.

Agar-agar is not utilized by bacteria as food and is not liquefied by any of the usual temperatures of incubation; consequently, it is an ideal solidifying agent for many different types of media.

Blood-Serum Agar. Sterile blood serum (10%) is mixed with sterile melted nutrient agar which has been cooled to 45°C. The medium is then solidified and is ready for use. Ascites fluid may be substituted for serum.

Blood Agar. Whole blood is often used in the cultivation of pathogenic bacteria. It not only serves as an excellent nutritive medium but as a diagnostic one, for some bacteria are able to reduce hemoglobin.

Under *strictly aseptic* conditions blood is removed from the jugular vein of one of the larger animals (horse, cow, sheep) and collected in a sterile flask containing glass beads. The flask is shaken during the bleeding process and is continually shaken until the fibrin has been removed. The red blood cells are then poured into another sterile flask. Add 1% of the blood to any suitable carbohydrate-free agar base which has been melted and cooled to 45°C. After the addition of the blood, the tube is rotated carefully to prevent the formation of bubbles. The medium contained in the test tubes is then slanted for hardening. Petri dishes may be poured after the blood has been added to the medium. To insure a perfectly smooth surface and medium free of bubbles, the lid of the dish is raised and the surface of the medium is heated momentarily with the Bunsen flame. It is best to incubate blood agar for 24 hours to determine sterility.

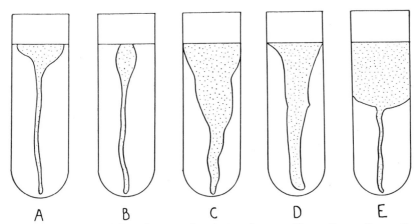

A   B   C   D   E

FIG. 4.8 — Types of liquefaction of gelatin. A, crateriform; B, napiform; C, infundibuliform; D, saccate; E, stratiform.

Edwards' Medium. The examination of milk samples to detect the presence of streptococci is facilitated by the use of special media. Edwards has suggested the following media which are helpful in the diagnosis of bovine mastitis.

Liquid medium.

Meat infusion broth pH 7.4	950 ml.
Sterile ox or horse serum	50 ml.
Dextrose	10 gms.
Crystal violet q.s.	1:200,000 concentration

Solid medium.

Meat extract agar pH 7.4	1,000 ml.
Defibrinated ox blood	50 ml.
Esculin	1.0 gm.
Crystal violet (0.1%)	2 ml.

Put esculin in solution by boiling in a small amount of water and then add last three ingredients to melted agar at 50°C.

The crystal violet inhibits the staphylococci, colonies of *E. coli* and related species are black, due to the reaction with esculin. Colonies of *Streptococcus agalactiae* are made purple by the absorption of gentian violet.

Sodium Azide, Crystal Violet Blood Agar. Streptococci, staphylococci, micrococci, and the swine erysipelas organisms are not inhibited by weak dilutions of sodium azide, whereas most of the other species of bacteria fail to grow. During the study of udder streptococci, Packer has found the following medium valuable in routine examination of milk samples for the presence of *Str. agalactiae* and as an aid in the isolation of streptococci from various sources.

Meat infusion	500	ml.
Tryptose	15	gms.
Sodium chloride	5	gms.
Agar-agar	18	gms.
Sodium azide	0.5	gms.
Crystal violet (dye cont. 94%) 0.1% aqueous solution	2.	ml.
Dist. H₂O q.s.	1,000	ml.

Adjust to pH 7.0
Sterilize by autoclaving 20 min. at 15 lbs. pressure.
Cool to 50°C.
Add 50 cc. sterile citrated or defibrinated blood.
Pour into petri dishes or test tubes for slants as desired.

The final concentration of sodium azide in the above formula is 1:2,000 and of crystal violet 1:500,000.

Some species of streptococci, especially *Str. agalactiae,* absorb the crystal violet from the medium producing violet colored colonies. Hemolysis is more distinct and the zones of hemolysis around the colonies of streptococci are wider when the above medium is used as compared to those on ordinary blood agar. Certain species classified as non-hemolytic upon ordinary blood agar are distinctly beta hemolytic when grown upon this medium.

A selective medium on which only *Erysipelothrix rhusiopathiae* may be grown can be obtained by increasing the concentration of sodium azide to 1:1,000 and of crystal violet to 1:100,000.

Chocolate Agar. To a suitable nutrient agar heated to about 90°C., 5 to 10% sterile defibrinated blood is added. The tubes, or flasks, are shaken gently to mix the blood thoroughly with the agar, and then they are cooled. The medium will have a decided chocolate color. It is not suitable for the isolation of bacteria but serves admirably for a stock medium for species which require blood as a source of food.

Hormone Agar (Huntoon). Filtration through cotton or paper is supposed to remove certain growth-stimulating substances (hormones) from media. In order to avoid this, Huntoon has suggested the following medium:

Chopped beef meat, free from fat and finely ground	500	gms.
Tap water	1,000	ml.
Peptone	10	gms.
Agar flakes	25	gms.
Sodium chloride	5	gms.
Whole egg	1	

All of these ingredients are placed in an ordinary enameled vessel and heated over an open flame with constant stirring until the red color of the meat infusion changes to brown which is at a temperature of about 68°C. Care should be taken not to run the temperature much above this point as the medium will begin to clot, which is undesirable at this time. The medium is now titrated by the addition of normal sodium hydroxide until it is slightly alkaline, and then 1 ml. per liter is added. The vessel is covered and placed in the Arnold sterilizer or in a water bath at a temperature of 100°C. for 1 hour; it is then removed, and the firm clot which has formed is separated from the sides with a glass rod, and the vessel is returned to the sterilizer at 100°C. for 1½ hours. It is removed and allowed to stand at room temperature for about 10 minutes in a slightly inclined position. During this time the fluid separates and may be removed by pipetting or simply by pouring off carefully. The product is allowed to stand in tall cylinders (glass graduates) for 15 to 20 minutes until the fat has risen to the surface when it can be removed. The medium is now tubed and sterilized by the intermittent method. Autoclaving is avoided. If the medium, although clear enough for all practical purposes, seems too turbid, further clearing is obtained by filtration through glass wool, asbestos wool, sedimentation or centrifugation. Under no circumstances should the medium come in contact with cotton, wool, or filter paper.

Liver Infusion Agar. Boil 500 gms. of finely chopped beef liver in 1,000 ml. of water for 2 hours and then filter through glass wool. Add 20 gms. of peptone and 1 gm. of dipotassium phosphate. Adjust reaction to pH 6.8. To this add 15 gms. agar and heat until thoroughly melted. The medium is again filtered and is then tubed and sterilized at 15 pounds pressure for 15 minutes.

Potato-Glycerin Agar. Grind 500 gms. of potato and place in an open vessel. Two liters of distilled water are added and the vessel is placed in a water bath and heated at 60°C. for 12 to 16 hours. The mixture is then filtered through cheesecloth and again made up to 2 liters by the addition of distilled water. By this method the finely ground potato is removed, leaving the clear extract. To the extract are added 50 gms. of shredded or powdered agar, 10 gms. of beef extract, 20 gms. of dextrose, and 40 ml. of glycerin. The mixture is then subjected to 15 pounds of pressure for 30 minutes to dissolve the agar. Following this the pH is adjusted to 6.8 and the medium is placed in tubes or stored in flasks which are sterilized for 15 minutes at 15 pounds pressure in the autoclave.

Brilliant Green-Bile Medium.

Bacto-peptone	10	gms.
Bacto-lactose	10	gms.
Bacto-oxgall	20	gms.
Bacto-brilliant green	0.0133	gm.
Distilled water	1,000	ml.

This medium is used in milk and water analysis as a presumptive test for the presence of *E. coli*. The presence of bile and brilliant green in the medium inhibits the growth of many contaminating types of bacteria. After the above ingredients have been dissolved in the distilled water, the medium is placed in fermentation tubes and sterilized for 15 min. at 15 lbs. pressure. The final pH should be 7.2.

Formate Ricinoleate Broth

Bacto-peptone	5 gms.
Bacto-lactose	5 gms.
Sodium formate	5 gms.
Sodium ricinoleate	1 gms.
Distilled water	1,000 ml.

This medium is used in milk and water analysis as a selective medium for the colon group. The sodium formate increases acid and gas formation by *E. coli*, while sodium ricinoleate inhibits the growth of gram-postive types of bacteria.

The medium is prepared by dissolving the ingredients in boiling distilled water, distributing in fermentation tubes, and autoclaving 15 minutes at 15 pounds pressure.

Desoxycholate Agar

Proteose peptone	10	gms.
Bacto-lactose	10	gms.
Sodium desoxycholate	1	gm.
Sodium chloride	5	gms.
Dipotassium phosphate	2	gms.
Ferric ammonium citrate	2	gms.
Bacto-agar	15	gms.
Bacto-neutral red	0.03	gm.
Distilled water	1,000	ml.

This medium is used for the isolation and direct enumeration of coliform bacteria in milk and water. It is of value also in the isolaton of Salmonella and Shigella species. In this medium Salmonella colonies are colorless and Shigella are colorless but somewhat opaque.

After the ingredients are dissolved in boiling water the medium is cooled to 45–50°C. to be added to the petri plate used for counting. When the medium in this inoculated plate has solidified, the surface is covered with a thin layer of the medium. The final pH of the medium is 7.3. It must not be autoclaved during preparation.

Tetrathionate Broth Base

Proteose peptone	5 gms.
Bacto-bile salts	1 gm.
Calcium carbonate	10 gms.
Sodium thiosulphate	30 gms.
Distilled water	1,000 ml.

The medium is prepared by dissolving the ingredients in the hot distilled water. It is then dispensed in 100 ml. flasks and sterilized in the autoclave 15 minutes at 15 pounds pressure. The day the medium is used 2.0 ml. of iodine solution is added to each 100 ml. of medium. The iodine solution is prepared by dissolving 6 gms. iodine crystals and 5 gms. potassium iodide in 20 ml. of water. The medium is thoroughly shaken and distributed in test tubes for inoculation.

Tetrathionate broth is used as a selective enrichment medium for the isolation of Salmonella from feces or intestinal contents. After inoculation the medium is incubated 24 hours and then streaked out on differential plates for positive selection and indentification.

Selenite Broth

Bacto-tryptone	4 gms.
Bacto-lactose	4 gms.
Disodium phosphate	10 gms.
Sodium acid selenite	5 gms.
Distilled water	1,000 ml.

The medium is prepared by dissolving the above ingredients in the boiling water. It is then dispensed in sterile culture tubes. Excessive heating must be avoided and the medium must not be autoclaved.

Selenite broth is used as a preliminary enrichment medium for the isolation of Salmonella. It inhibits coliform bacteria and enterococci. After 24 hours incubation of the inoculated tubes, plates of SS agar are streaked in order to isolate the Salmonella.

Endo's Agar (Modified). A basic medium is prepared by adding 5 gms. of beef extract, 10 gms. of peptone, and 30 gms. of agar to 1,000 ml. of distilled water. The mixture is heated and adjusted to a pH of 7.8–8.2, is then filtered and placed in 100 ml. lots in small flasks, to which are added 10 gms. of lactose. The medium is then sterilized 15 minutes at 10 pounds. Just before the medium is to be used, add aseptically 10 ml. of a 2.5% solution of sodium sulphite and 0.5 ml. of an alcoholic solution of basic fuchsin which is decolorized to a light straw by the sodium sulphite. The medium is then poured into Petri dishes and incubated overnight to test sterility.

This medium is used as a confirming medium for the presence of *Escherichia coli* and related microorganisms. The colonies of colon bacilli are vermilion in color and color the surrounding medium. Colonies of the typhoid-dysentery group are grayish; and streptococci are deep red. The reactions are due to the fermentation of lactose and the formation of acetaldehyde which is fixed by sodium sulphite; this reaction in turn restores the color to basic fuchsin.

SS (Salmonella Shigella) Agar

Bacto-beef extract	5	gms.
Proteose peptone	5	gms.
Bacto-lactose	10	gms.
Bacto-bile salts no. 3	8.5	gms.
Sodium citrate	8.5	gms.
Sodium thiosulfate	8.5	gms.
Ferric citrate	1	gm.
Bacto-agar	13.5	gms.
Bacto-brilliant green	0.00033	gm.
Bacto-neutral red	0.025	gm.
Distilled water	1,000	ml.

This medium is employed to differentiate those bacteria which ferment lactose from those which do not. It likewise is designed to inhibit the coliform bacteria yet allowing the growth of the more delicate types.

On this medium the Salmonella and Shigella, as well as other bacteria not fermenting lactose, grow in transparent or translucent uncolored colonies. The lactose fermenting bacteria which may grow in the medium form red colonies.

The medium is prepared by placing the ingredients in cold distilled water and then boiling to completely dissolve. It must not be sterilized in the autoclave. Petri dishes are poured with the medium which is allowed to harden and stand for 2 hours with the lids partly removed. This allows the surface of the medium to dry which is important for maximum results. The final pH of the medium is 7.0.

Urea Agar Base

Bacto-peptone	1	gm.
Dextrose	1	gm.
Sodium chloride	5	gms.
Monopotassium phosphate	2	gms.
Urea-Difco	20	gms.
Phenol red	0.012	gm.

The medium is prepared by dissolving all the above ingredients, 29 grams, in 100 ml. distilled water, and *filter sterilizing*. In 900 ml. distilled water dissolve 15 grams agar and sterilize in the autoclave for 15 minutes at 15 pounds. This medium is then cooled and the concentrated urea base medium is added under aseptic conditions. The completed medium is then dispensed in test tubes and allowed to solidify in the slanted position. Inasmuch as this medium cannot be reheated it is essential that slants are made at the time of preparation. For this reason smaller batches are desirable. This can be done by adding 10 ml. of urea base to 90 ml. agar.

Urea base agar is used for the detection of Proteus and to differentiate these organisms from other enteric species. It may be used for any species of bacteria able to hydrolize urea. Proteus cultures are able to hydrolize urea rapidly producing a marked alkaline reaction within 4 hours after inoculation. While aerobacter and paracolon types do hydrolize this medium they do so more slowly, requiring 3–5 days to completely alkalinize the medium. Salmonella and Shigella are not able to produce alkalinity in this medium.

Nitrate Agar

Beef extract	3 gms.
Peptone	5 gms.
Potassium nitrate	1 gm.
Agar	12 gms.
Distilled water	1,000 ml.

The above ingredients are heated thoroughly to melt the agar, and the pH adjusted to about 6.8. The medium is tubed and sterilized in the autoclave 15 pounds, 15 minutes, and the tubes are then slanted. Inoculation with the test organism is made by streaking the slant and stabbing into the butt of the medium. The cultures are incubated 24 to 48 hours.

The above medium is used to detect the reduction of nitrate to nitrite. It is tested for the presence of nitrite by the following reagents:

SOLUTION A

5/N Acetic acid	1,000 ml.
Sulphanilic acid	8 gms.

SOLUTION B

5/N Acetic acid	1,000 ml.
Alpha-amidonaphthylene	5 gms.

Add 2 ml. of each solution (A and B) to the tube to be tested. A red rose color will indicate the presence of nitrite. A control in check tubes of uninoculated agar should always be tested at the same time.

Lead Acetate Agar

Agar	15	gms.
Bacto-tryptone	20	gms.
Dextrose	1	gm.
Lead acetate	0.2	gm.
Distilled water	1,000	ml.

The ingredients are boiled until the agar is melted and the pH is then adjusted to 6.8. The medium is tubed and sterilized at 15 pounds pressure for 15 minutes. The tubes are slanted leaving generous butts. Inoculation is made by streaking the slant and a stab into the butt.

The ability of some species of bacteria to form hydrogen sulphide is used as a differential criterion. In the above medium those species which form H_2S cause a blackening of the medium adjacent to the culture, both on the surface of the slant and along the needle track of the stab inoculation.

The formation of hydrogen sulphide by bacteria may also be detected by placing strips of paper soaked in lead acetate solution in the test tube with a medium which does not contain lead acetate. Some authorities contend that even a trace of lead is inhibitory to some bacteria; therefore, the incorporation of the chemical in the medium may explain why growth is not obtained in some instances. The amount of lead acetate in a medium should be below 0.02% which is considered nontoxic.

Kligler Iron Agar

Bacto-beef extract	3	gms.
Bacto-yeast extract	3	gms.
Bacto-peptone	15	gms.
Proteose-peptone	5	gms.
Lactose	10	gms.
Dextrose	1	gm.
Ferrous sulfate	0.2	gm.
Sodium chloride	5	gms.
Sodium thiosulfate	0.3	gm.
Agar	12	gms.
Phenol red	0.024	gm.
Distilled water	1,000	ml.

The medium is prepared by dissolving the ingredients in boiling distilled water, dispensing in tubes or flasks as desired and sterilizing in the autoclave 15 minutes at 15 pounds pressure (120°C.).

Kligler iron agar is used in the study of the Gram-negative enterobacteria. It differentiates the lactose fermenting species from those which do not ferment lactose. It detects those which ferment dextrose. The fermentation reactions on this medium are noted by the change of phenol red to yellow in case of lactose fermentation; gas is apparent by bubbles which form in the medium. In dextrose fermentation the butt of the slant is changed to yellow but the slant remains red. Hydrogen sulfide production is noted by the blackening of the medium.

SIM Medium

Bacto-beef extract	3	gms.
Peptone	30	gms.
Peptonized iron Difco	0.2	gm.
Sodium thiosulfate	0.025	gm.
Bacto-agar	3	gms.
Distilled water	1,000	ml.

This medium is prepared by dissolving the above ingredients in the boiling distilled water. It is then dispensed in tubes at a depth of 1½ inches. After sterilization for 15 minutes at 15 pounds pressure the medium is allowed to solidify by placing the tubes in a vertical position.

SIM medium serves the triple function of detecting hydrogen sulphide, indol, and motility. The medium is inoculated by the stab method. A small amount of blackening along the needle tract is considered positive for hydrogen sulfide production due to the small amount of sodium thiosulfate in the medium. Motility is noted by the formation of a test tube brush type of growth around the central needle tract. Nonmotile bacteria do not penetrate into the semisolid agar in this manner. Indol production can be detected by placing paper strips soaked with saturated oxalic acid into the tubes hanging below the cotton plug about one inch. Kovac's reagent may also be used, following the same procedure as is used in Dunham's peptone or tryptophane broth.

Russell's Double Sugar Agar. Add to 1,000 ml. beef extract agar 10 gms. lactose, 1 gm. dextrose, and 10 ml. Andrade's indicator. Tube, sterilize intermittently, and slant, leaving generous butts. Inoculate by streaking the slant and by stabbing into the butt of the agar.

This medium is used to differentiate the species of the genera Escherichia, Salmonella, and Eberthella. The first produces marked acid and gas, the second slight acid and gas, and the third slight acid only.

Hibler's Brain Medium. Boil either sheep or beef brain in equal amounts of water. Decant the fluid and press the brain through a potato ricer. Add to the decanted water 2% peptone and 0.1% dextrose. Mix the brain and fluid together and adjust to pH 7.2. Tube in large tubes, filling them one-half full. Sterilize in the Arnold for 30 minutes on three consecutive days.

Dorset's Egg Medium. Wash eggs with 5% phenol solution, allow to dry partially, pierce the ends and blow into sterile flasks. Add 10% water by volume to the weight of the eggs. Mix gently, filter through cheesecloth, tube, and slant in an inspissator. Coagulate by heating to 70°C. 2 to 2½ hours on three consecutive days. Incubate 4 days to determine sterility.

Loeffler's Blood Serum Medium

Fresh ox serum .... 3 parts
1 % dextrose broth .... 1 part

Tube and sterilize either by inspissating as above or by sterilizing in the autoclave. To prevent the formation of bubbles the following procedure must be followed: The steam is turned on suddenly with *all* outlets tightly closed until the pressure records 15 pounds. The mixture of air and high pressure prevents boiling. After the medium has been heated in this manner for 15 minutes, the steam is turned on slowly until the safety valve is slightly open. Heating is continued under this condition for 20 minutes. All outlets must remain closed tightly until pressure has been entirely reduced and medium has had an opportunity to cool. Under the above conditions an entirely smooth and absolutely sterile medium is produced.

Glycerin Agar-Egg Medium. To a basic meat infusion agar add 3% glycerin. Add one egg yolk to each 150 ml. of this medium. A sterile egg yolk is obtained as follows: place the eggs in 80% ethyl alcohol for 30 minutes, remove one end with a flamed forceps, and pour out the egg white. The yolk is then placed directly into the medium which has been melted and cooled to 45–50°C. Shake until the egg yolk and medium are completely mixed. Under aseptic conditions the medium is tubed, slanted and then incubated for sterility. Incubation is essential because the yolks of some eggs are known to be infected.

The medium is used for the cultivation of tubercle bacilli, but is an excellent medium for the cultivation of most of the pathogenic bacteria. The addition of 10% blood serum to the medium increases its nutritive qualities.

Dorset's Synthetic Medium. Dorset devised the following medium for the preparation of tuberculin which is free of meat protein.

l-asparagin	14	gms.
Dipotassium phosphate C.P.	1.80	gms.
Sodium citrate C.P.	0.90	gm.
Magnesium sulphate U.S.P.	1.50	gms.
Ferric citrate U.S.P. scales	0.30	gm.
Dextrose (cerelose)	10	gms.
Glycerol C.P.	100	ml.
Distilled water to	1,000	ml.

The medium is adjusted to pH 7.0 and sterilized in the autoclave at 15 pounds for 15 minutes. It is usually placed in large flasks.

Blood Glucose Cystine Agar (Francis). *Pasteurella tularensis* is most easily grown on a medium in which cystine has been incorporated. For the cultivation of the organism, Francis devised the following medium: To a meat infusion agar add 0.1% cystine and 1% glucose. This is placed in the Arnold and heated long enough to melt the agar and sterilize the cystine and glucose. The medium is cooled to 60°C. and 5% to 8% of defibrinated or whole rabbit blood is added. The medium is then sterilized in a water bath for 2 hours at 60°C.

Mannitol Salt Agar

Bacto-beef extract	1	gm.
Proteose peptone no. 3, Difco	10	gms.
Sodium chloride	75	gms.
d-mannitol	10	gms.
Bacto agar	15	gms.
Bacto-phenol red	0.025	gm.
Distilled water	1,000	ml.

The above ingredients are heated to boiling to completely dissolve, then sterilized for 15 minutes at 15 pounds pressure. The final reaction is pH 7.4.

This medium is used for the isolation of pathogenic staphylococci which ferment the mannitol forming yellow zones around the colonies. It is especially useful in examining milk samples for mastitis and other exudates containing staphylococci but heavily contaminated with other bacteria.

Staphylococcus Medium No. 110

Bacto-yeast extract	2.5	gms.
Bacto-tryptone	10	gms.
Bacto-gelatin	30	gms.
Bacto-lactose	2	gms.
d-mannitol	10	gms.
Sodium chloride	75	gms.
Dipotassium phosphate	5	gms.
Bacto-agar	15	gms.
Distilled water	1,000	ml.

The ingredients are heated in boiling water until completely dissolved and then sterilized in the autoclave 15 minutes at 15 pounds pressure. Plates are poured while the medium is still hot at which time the flask is agitated to resuspend the precipitate which usually forms upon sterilization.

The above medium is used for the selective isolation of pathogenic staphylococci but also may be used to detect those strains which produce gelatinase. In order to detect the latter characteristic, the inoculated plate is flooded with 5 ml. saturated solution of ammonium sulfate and let stand in the incubator 10 minutes. Those organisms which are gelatinase producing are surrounded by a clear zone while the rest of the medium is opaque due to the precipitation of the non-liquefied gelatin by the ammonium sulfate.

Chapman Stone Medium

Bacto-yeast extract	2.5	gms.
Bacto-tryptone	10	gms.
Bacto-gelatin	30	gms.
d-mannitol	10	gms.
Sodium chloride	55	gms.
Ammonium sulfate	75	gms.
Dipotassium phosphate	5	gms.
Bacto agar	15	gms.
Distilled water	1,000	ml.

The medium is prepared by dissolving the above ingredients in boiling distilled water and then distributing it into 100 ml. flasks. It is sterilized in the autoclave at 15 pounds pressure for 15 minutes.

Chapman Stone medium is used for the selective isolation of pathogenic staphylococci and those which are gelatinase producing. It is different from medium no. 110 in that the ammonium sulfate is incorporated in its formula; consequently the reaction is obtained after sufficient incubation and the addition of ammonium sulphate solution is not necessary. Colonies of pathogenic and gelatinase-producing staphylococci are usually pigmented and surrounded by a clear zone. The part of the plate not affected by gelatinase is opaque due to the precipitation of the gelatin by the ammonium sulphate.

Micrococcus Toxin Medium. The following medium has been found very satisfactory for the cultivation of *Micro. aureus* for toxin formation:

Sugar-free veal infusion broth 1,000	ml.
Proteose peptone 40	gms.
Sodium chloride 4	gms.
KH₂PO₄ 2	gms.
MgSO₄ 0.3	gm.
Glycerol 100	ml.
Agar 6	gms.

The above ingredients are heated in the Arnold for 30 minutes, filtered, and the pH is adjusted to 7.6. It is then distributed into flat-bottomed flasks or medicine bottles to a depth of 5 mm. and then autoclaved. The medium is inoculated with a pipette allowing the inoculum to flow entirely over the surface. The cultures are placed in a suitable jar or other container and the air volume is adjusted to 20% CO_2. The organism is incubated at 37°C. for six to eight days. To each 10 ml. of medium is added 1 ml. of 0.8% NaCl solution and medium is thoroughly broken by shaking. The liquid is then squeezed through cheesecloth and passed through a porcelain filter. The filtrate contains the toxin.

Thioglycollate Medium

Bacto-yeast extract 5	gms.
Bacto-casitone 15	gms.
Dextrose 1	gm.
Sodium chloride 2.5	gms.
1-cystine, Difco 0.05	gm.
Thioglycollic acid 0.3	ml.
Agar 0.75	gm.
Distilled water 1,000	ml.

The medium is prepared by dissolving the ingredients in boiling distilled water. It is then dispensed in tubes or flasks as desired and sterilized in the autoclave 15 minutes at 15 pounds pressure.

Thioglycollate medium is used for the growth of facultative anaerobic and anaerobic bacteria without placing the medium under anaerobic conditions. It is used also for testing biologics and antibiotics for sterility.

Potato. Cylinders are cut from potatoes by means of an apple corer or special potato borer. They are then divided by a diagonal longitudinal cut so that each half has one long, sloping surface. It it well to soak the pieces in running water for a few hours to prevent their turning dark when sterilized. They are placed with the sloping surface up in test tubes with a bit of saturated absorbent cotton or any solid object (glass tubing) in the bottom or in special potato tubes. The space below the potato is filled with water to prevent undue desiccation of the potato. The tubes are sterilized in the autoclave for 15 minutes at 15 pounds pressure.

The appearance of bacterial growth on potato is manifest by abundance, pigmentation, and the changes produced in the medium, such as blackening.

Other Vegetable Media. Carrots and other vegetables may be prepared in the same manner as potato. Tomato juice is often used in the same proportions as meat infusion and has been found to be a satisfactory medium for certain of the organisms used in the manufacture of milk products.

REFERENCES FOR FURTHER STUDY

Conn, H. J. Biological Stains. 2nd Ed. Biological Stain Commission, Geneva, New York, 1929.

Difco Laboratories. Manual of Dehydrated Culture Media and Reagents. Detroit, Michigan, 1954.

Gage, S. H. The Microscope. The Comstock Publishing Co., Ithaca, New York, 1941.

Henry, H., and Stacy, M. Histochemistry of the Gram-staining Reaction for Microorganisms. Nature, London. 151:671, 1943.

Levine, Max, and Schoenlein, H. W. A Compilation of Culture Media. Williams & Wilkins Co., Baltimore, 1930.

Mackie, T. J., and McCartney, J. E. Handbook of Practical Bacteriology. E. & S. Livingstone, Edinburgh, 1938.

Packer, R. A. The use of sodium azide (NaN$_3$) and crystal violet in a selective medium for streptococci. Master of Science Degree Thesis. Iowa State College Library, Ames, 1942.

Salle, A. J. Fundamental Principles of Bacteriology. 4th Ed. McGraw-Hill Book Co., New York, 1954.

Stitt, E. R., Clough, P. W., and Branham, S. E. Practical Bacteriology, Haematology and Animal Parasitology. 10th Ed. P. Blakiston's Son & Co., Philadelphia, 1948.

Society of American Bacteriologists. Manual of Methods for Pure Culture Study of Bacteria. Geneva, New York.

5. Sterilization and Disinfection

In the study of bacteria it is necessary that one deals with pure cultures, that is, that only one kind of organism be present in the material which is to be studied, because it is quite impossible to determine from mixed cultures which of the organisms present bring about observed changes. Bacteria are present upon the surface of all laboratory apparatus, in the dust, and upon the hands; they are ubiquitous. Hence, sterilization is a necessity. The use of sterile instruments and dressings in surgical operations emphasizes the need of various procedures for killing bacteria. The preparation of operative fields, the treatment of wounds, the sterilization of milking equipment, and the disinfection of poultry houses and cattle barns are examples of the use and need of methods to destroy bacteria.

The destruction of microörganisms may be accomplished by physical and chemical means. The former method is often called *sterilization* while the latter is termed *disinfection;* this is not a set rule, however, for the ultimate action which kills the organism may be the same when either a physical or a chemical method is employed. Boiling coagulates bacterial protoplasm, and so does a salt of a heavy metal. Natural desiccation removes water from the bacterial cell, so does a dehydrating chemical. It cannot be said that sterilization refers to the destruction of nonpathogenic bacteria, and disinfection refers to the pathogenic bacteria. Sterilization is always aimed at both types, while disinfection, in its true sense applies only to the pathogenic varieties.

Many general terms, such as *bacteriacide*, are used to designate methods of destroying bacteria. Anything that kills germs is a *germicide;* that which kills algae is known as an *algacide;* that which kills fungi is called a *fungicide;* that which kills a virus is a *virucide.* The term *antiseptic* is commonly applied when chemicals are used to inhibit the growth of bacteria. This inhibition of growth is often referred to as *bacteriostasis.* The chemical does not need to be the type nor the concentration to actually kill organisms which are present. The term antiseptic is used in the true meaning of the word, *anti* = against and *sepsis* = decay. When no pathogenic bacteria are present the term *aseptic* is often used. Asepsis may be brought about by physical or chemical methods. Certain disinfectants and antiseptics are added to *sera* and bacterial suspensions in small quantities which act as *preservatives;* organisms which accidentally may be present are inhibited in growth and in time actually perish. A *deodorant* is anything, usually a chemical, which removes or masks odors. It is not to be inferred that a deodorant is always a disinfectant; frequently it is not. People have associated disinfectants with odor, however, and they often judge the killing power of a chemical mixture by its odor. It is an unfortunate circumstance in the practice of medicine when a disinfectant with a disagreeable odor is used. Undesirable professional odors should be avoided; especially since many disinfectants with pleasant odors and high efficiency are available.

For convenience of presentation the physical agencies which cause the destruction of bacteria will precede the discussion of the chemical compounds.

PHYSICAL DISINFECTION

Light. It was noted in Chapter 3 that most bacteria require an environment of darkness for optimum growth. Light is probably the most effective germicide in the universe. In judging the effect of sunlight and other radiations on bacteria, a number of factors must be considered: (1) the wave length and intensity of the radiation, (2) the kind of organism, (3) the medium in which the organism is contained, and (4) the time of exposure.

Early in the study of the action of sunlight on bacteria it was found that various portions of the spectrum were more germicidal than others. A review of a portion of the spectrum (Fig. 5.1) will emphasize that it is divided into various portions based upon the wave length of the radiation. Wave length is expressed in Ångstrom units, Å., (1Å = 1 x 10⁻⁷ mm. or 1/10,000,000 mm.).

The most germicidal rays are those ranging from 2,540 Å to 2,800 Å, but those from 2,100 Å to approximately 3,200 Å possess high bacteriacidal properties. It is seen that these rays are found in the ultraviolet section of the spectrum. The other rays, however, are not without effect in inhibiting bacterial life. Light from which the ultraviolet rays have been filtered is inhibitory to the multiplication of bacteria. Infrared heat radiation is a valuable adjunct to the action of ultraviolet rays, for it has been shown in tropical countries that the increased action of ultraviolet light is partially due to increased heat.

The Cooper-Hewitt and other mercury vapor arc lights and carbon arc lamps are used to produce ultraviolet light. The glass usually used in lamps does not permit the passage of ultraviolet rays; so it is replaced by quartz. Artificial ultraviolet radiation may be used for a variety of purposes, chief among which in bacteriology is the sterilization of water and the study of the germicidal effect of the intensity and length of such rays.

Bacteria vary in their resistance to the action of light. Obviously, the sporeforming types are the most resistant due to the compact nature of spore protoplasm. The vegetative cells of the

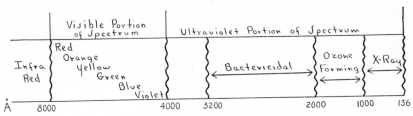

FIG. 5.1 — A portion of the spectrum showing the position of the ultraviolet rays.

different types of pathogenic microorganisms do not differ a great deal in the length of time they are destroyed by direct sunlight; this is within 5 minutes for the majority. It has been observed, however, that fluorescent bacteria are not as easily destroyed as the nonfluorescent. This is explained by the supposition that the short germicidal waves may be converted by fluorescent pigments into longer ones which are without so much effect.

The medium in which the organism is suspended is an important factor in judging the effect of light. A turbid, opalescent, or opaque medium does not permit the penetration of light. In nature, bacteria are protected from sunlight by many materials in which they live. It has been shown, however, by numerous scientists that an uninoculated medium which has been exposed to ultraviolet light becomes definitely inhibitory to the growth of bacteria. Just what change occurs in the medium has not been conclusively explained. Some claim hydrogen peroxide is increased by radiation while others believe that the effect is due to oxidation. It is of little practical significance because most media are contained in glass which does not permit the passage of ultraviolet radiation and, moreover, they are commonly stored in the dark.

Light apparently produces the death of microorganisms in a variety of ways. The accumulation of inhibitory substances in the medium, as suggested above, may be one factor. The most common explanation, however, is that the surface colloids of bacterial cells are coagulated, thereby rendering the cell wall more permeable, which enhances the action of surrounding ions and may also bring about the dissolution of the organism. A more recent explanation is that of Buckholz and Jeney who claim that the energy produced by waves 2,530 to 2,650 Å displace sufficient electrons from the bacterial protoplasm to produce irreversible photochemical changes and subsequent death of the cell.

Electricity. Currents of both low-frequency and high-frequency electricity have been used in order to detect their effect on bacteria. The effect of such currents is difficult to evaluate, however, since many varied conditions are used in the experiments. Most investigators report that bacteria are rendered nonmotile in some cases, and in other instances they are killed. Death is due to the action of chemicals liberated by electrolysis, such as chlorine from sodium chloride, or to the heat generated by the electric current. No practical use has been made of the destructive action of electricity upon microorganisms, as the method is difficult to apply and, as yet, is considered quite inefficient.

Other Rays and Waves. The action of roentgen ray (X rays) upon bacteria has been subjected to much study, but the reports which have been made are too contradictory to conclude that such rays are detrimental to bacteria or are of practical significance. The same is true of cathode rays, radium, sonic, and supersonic waves.

Heat. Another effective physical agency which is commonly used to destroy bacteria is heat. It was noted in Chapter 4 that temperature is an important factor in the growth of bacteria and that different types of microorganisms react differently to temperature variations. This must be stressed again here, for it is obvious that the maximum growth temperature of a thermophilic organism may be the thermal death point of a mesophilic organism. The *thermal death point* of an organism may be defined as that temperature which, under given conditions, will certainly destroy all the cells. The accurate determination of the exact temperature that is necessary to destroy various species of bacteria is frequently of great economic importance. Efficient sterilization and pasteurization can be accomplished only when facts are known. Many methods have been suggested. In the laboratory the determination is frequently made by subjecting freshly inoculated tubes of broth to different temperatures in a water bath for ten minutes each. For reliable results more accurate methods are needed. One of the most common and best is the use of a long, slender, glass vial. A definite amount of culture is introduced into the vial, and the open end is sealed in the flame. The vial is completely immersed in a water bath and suspended by wires or by some other method, so that it does not come in contact with the walls or bottom of the bath as it is heated. A number of vials are prepared. One is heated five minutes, another 10 minutes, at 50°C. The temperature is raised two degrees and two more vials are exposed. This procedure of heating two vials with each increase of two degrees is continued up to 70° for the sporeless bacteria. The vials are cooled quickly, and after exposure, their contents are mixed with agar in a Petri dish, or are added to a tube of other suitable medium. This is then incubated several days. The minimum temperature required to destroy the bacteria can readily be determined by a comparison of the tubes. Bacteria do not die instantaneously even under the action of heat. The following factors must be taken into consideration in determining the thermal death point of bacteria and the rate of death:

1. *The Specific Character of the Organism.* The intrinsic variations in the character of protoplasm of different species make it necessary to determine the thermal death point for each species. Young cultures of bacteria are more quickly killed than old ones.

2. *The Absence or Presence of Spores.* Spores are much more resistant to high temperatures than are the vegetative cells. Forms having spores, therefore, have two rates of death, one for the vegetative cell and the other for the spores.

3. *Presence or Absence of Moisture.* Bacteria are more resistant to dry than to moist heat. The thermal death point is probably the temperature at which *incipient coagulation of the albuminous protoplasm* occurs, resulting in an inability to function. Water is necessary for this coagulation. The following table from Frost and McCampbell illustrates this point:[1]

Egg albumen plus 50 per cent water coagulates at 56°C.
Egg albumen plus 25 per cent water coagulates at 74–80°C.
Egg albumen plus 18 per cent water coagulates at 80–90°C.
Egg albumen plus 6 per cent water coagulates at 145°C.
Egg alubmen plus no water coagulates at 160–170°C.

The action of water is emphasized by the laboratory methods of sterilization discussed below. The autoclave, with live steam at a temperature of 120°C., will destroy in ten minutes the most resistant spores, while in the hot-air oven a temperature of 150° to 170°C. for an hour is necessary.

4. *Reaction and Composition of Medium.* The reaction and composition of the medium have been found to exert a marked influence on the thermal death point; the hydrogen-ion concentration of the medium, that is, the actual acidity, should be noted particularly. It is a well-known fact, for example, that acid fruits are more easily sterilized than are the more nearly neutral vegetables. The composition of the medium may also alter the rate at which heat diffuses through it and comes in contact with the bacteria.

---

[1] William D. Frost and Eugene F. McCampbell. *A Textbook of General Bacteriology.* The Macmillan Co., New York, 1910, p. 140.

5. *Time of Exposure.* In general, the higher the temperature the shorter is the period required to destroy life in the cells. Ten minutes exposure is the usual standard. When the thermal death point of an organism is mentioned, it is without meaning unless the time is given.

Sterilization by the Flame. The destruction of microorganisms by the use of the flame is highly effective when the material to be sterilized is either indestructible or is to be destroyed. The platinum wire used in the laboratory in the transfer of bacteria is sterilized by heating to a red heat in the flame of the Bunsen burner. The open flame is also used to kill bacteria smeared on slides preparatory to staining. The destruction of infected clothing, bedding, buildings, etc., by flame during an epidemic of disease is effective. The burning of carcasses of animals having died with infectious diseases is practiced. The flame also has been used as a means of disinfecting concrete floors and the surfaces of ground.

Sterilization by Hot Air. Glassware is commonly sterilized by subjecting it to a temperature of 150°C. to 170°C. in a hot-air oven for an hour. All bacteria will be destroyed at this temperature providing the material to be sterilized is of such nature that heat can penetrate readily to all parts. This method cannot be used, however, in the sterilization of liquids or of any organic material which might be decomposed at such a temperature.

Sterilization at Temperatures Lower Than the Boiling Point. It is sometimes necessary to sterilize a medium, particularly blood serum, at a temperature lower than the boiling point of water. This is accomplished by placing the material to be sterilized in an apparatus where it may be heated to the desired temperature. usually 70° to 80°C. for 1 to 2 hours on each of five or more consecutive days. When it is known that only vegetative cells are present this method of sterilization is effective, but if large numbers of spores of certain organisms, such as *Bacillus subtilis,* are present, it is almost impossible to sterilize efficiently by this method. The inspissation of certain culture media, especially egg and blood serum media, should be done at temperatures lower than boiling in order to obtain a uniformly smooth-surfaced product.

Pasteurization. A practical use of lower-than-boiling temperatures for the killing of bacteria is in the process generally known as *pasteurization.* In the pasteurization of milk two methods are employed. The holding method requires the heating of milk to 142°F. to 145°F. for a period of 30 minutes. The flash method requires the milk to be held for 15 seconds at 160°F. Both temperatures are high enough to kill the vegetative cells of pathogenic bacteria, but not high enough to kill spores or heat resistant forms. It is a process intended to make milk more safe for human consumption and to prolong its keeping period, but is not intended for a substitute for sanitation in the production and handling of milk. Pasteurization is also used in the treatment of antisera used for the immunization of animals, for the canning of fruits and vegetables, and for the preparation of wines and other beverages.

Sterilization by Steam. It is well known that live steam is an efficient sterilizing medium. Steam is used in the surgery for sterilizing instruments, in the milk plant and dairy for sterilizing equipment, and in canning procedures and for many other purposes. Steam under atmospheric pressure at sea level has a temperature of about 100°C. Some type of apparatus should be used so that the live steam comes in direct contact with the material to be sterilized. One type of apparatus used in the laboratory is called the Arnold steam sterilizer (Fig. 5.2).

A single exposure to live steam for 15 minutes is sufficient to kill all vegetative bacteria, but spores are not thus destroyed. It is customary, therefore, to heat for 30 minutes on one day, keep the medium for 24 hours at a temperature suitable for the germination and development of any spores present, then heat again for 30 minutes in the same manner. Those spores which have germinated will be destroyed by this second heating. A third heating, 24 hours later will certainly destroy all the bacteria which may have been present. This process is called *intermittent sterilization,* or *fractional sterilization,* or *tyndallization.* It finds its principal application in the sterilization of materials which may be changed or broken down by heating at a higher temperature. Among such materials are media containing sugars which undergo incipient caramelization when heated for too long a time or at too high a temperature.

Sterilization by Steam Under Pressure. In order to have complete and rapid destruction of bacterial spores, it is necessary to have temperatures higher than boiling point. This is accomplished in the autoclave (Fig. 5.3), which consists of a chamber into which steam may be introduced and maintained under pressure.

Live steam under pressure unmixed with air has a constant temperature; therefore, if the pressure of the live steam is known, one can determine easily the temperature as well. A technical difficulty often presents itself in the use of the autoclave. It is necessary that all the air in the chamber first be eliminated. This is usually accomplished by allowing the stopcock, which is always present upon the steam chamber of the autoclave, to remain open until all the air has escaped and the steam issues in a constant stream. It is much more satisfactory, however, to use an autoclave equipped with a temperature control device on the steam discharge outlet. This means that sterilization is controlled by temperature rather than by pressure. When the required temperature is reached, the steam pressure is adjusted to maintain the temperature for the required length of time. Material to be sterilized should be allowed to remain 15 minutes in most cases. If large bulks, such as flasks of media and packages of dressings are to be sterilized, a longer period must be allowed for the heat to penetrate into the center of the objects. Material wrapped in cloth or paper should be placed on edge, instead of flat, so steam will circulate through the packages more easily. When properly carried out, sterilization by this method will certainly destroy all the bacteria present. Its principal disadvantage is that certain organic substances may be decomposed at such high temperatures.

FIG. 5.2 — The Arnold sterilizer.

Freezing. Freezing cannot be depended upon as an effective method to destroy microorganisms. Alternate freezing and thawing cause a marked decrease in a bacterial population. Death probably occurs with the solidification of the bacterial protoplasm and, no doubt, is mechanical in nature. Bacteria kept frozen in ice, however, remain alive for considerable periods of time.

Desiccation. Since water is so essential to the life of microorganisms, it is apparent that the removal of it would be detrimental. Drying is one of nature's most effective means of controlling the growth of all bacterial life. We see it active in the preservation of fruits and meat and in the prevention of the decay of trees and other vegetation.

A number of factors must be considered in evaluating the effects of desiccation on bacteria. The various species of microorganisms differ in their ability to survive drying. The cocci and actinomyces, in general, are more resistant than the rod-shaped bacteria. Whether the organism produces an endospore is of great significance in the maintenance of life. It will be recalled that spores are compact, dehydrated bodies of bacterial protoplasm and for this reason are able to resist desiccation for indefinite periods. A young actively growing culture of an organism is more readily killed by drying than one which has passed through the different growth phases and survived into a resistant state. The conditions under which the water is removed from bacteria play an important role. This is particularly true of temperature, rapidity of drying, and the gases present. Generally, the higher the temperature the more rapid is the death of bacteria. It has been shown that bacteria dehydrated at nearly freezing temperatures and kept at that tempera-

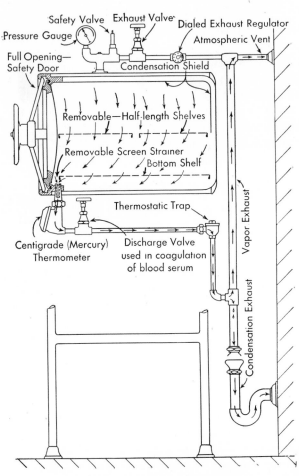

FIG. 5.3 — Cross-section of autoclave sterilizer showing path of steam. (Courtesy American Sterlizer Company.)

ture will remain viable for some time. This process, known as *lyophilization,* is a technical process whereby water is extracted from the bacterial cell by vacuum; the moisture being condensed by drawing it into a chamber kept frigid by a dry ice-alcohol mixture. The small tubes containing the bacteria are then completely sealed and stored at cold temperatures. This method may be used for the preservation of various immunizing substances such as vaccines, bacterins, and immune sera. Organisms dried rapidly are not as apt to be killed as quickly as those dried slowly.

The death of microorganisms by desiccation is probably due to any or all of the following factors: concentration of salts producing plasmolysis, denaturation of proteins, destruction of intracellular enzymes, and the germicidal effect produced by oxidation.

Filtration. Bacteria may be removed from a liquid by passing the liquid through a filter with pores so fine that the organism cannot enter. Such filters are made up in a great variety of shapes and densities. They are extensively used in the isolation of *filtrable viruses* in pure culture; therefore, a more complete discussion of filters and filtration will be found in a later chapter. A laboratory "setup" of a filter apparatus is given in Figure 5.4. This method of sterilization is often used in the sterilization of media which may be altered by heat sterilization.

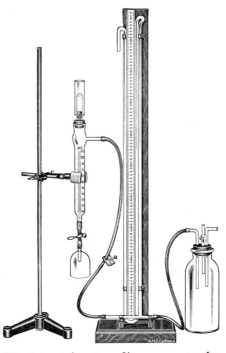

FIG. 5.4 — Laboratory filter apparatus for removing bacteria from fluids.

Filtration is also used for the removal of bacteria from culture media when it is necessary to study their soluble metabolic products as well as in the removal of bacteria from sera which contain antitoxins and other antibodies. Filters of this character have been used for the filtration of a limited supply of drinking water. When first installed they are quite efficient, but it has been observed that the organisms rapidly penetrate through the filter walls, and in the course of time are found in the filtrate; consequently, such filters must be sterilized at intervals if they are to remain efficient.

Although it cannot be considered a method of sterilization, it should be noted here that nature purifies water by filtration. The seeping of water through the ground and the various rock strata underlying it serves as a most effective way of removing bacteria. This process is used extensively by man in an artificial way, by passing water through sand filters in order to remove bacteria and organic materials. It is true that biological action occurs in the surface of the earth and in the top layer of sand which, also, aids in the destruction of bacteria, but filtration is the most important step of the process.

CHEMICAL DISINFECTION

The destruction of bacteria by chemicals is most important to anyone wishing to control the growth of bacteria, and is of special interest to students of medicine. The process of disinfection by the use of chemicals in a practical way dates from the time of Lister. Since that time volumes of literature have accumulated about the subject. Only a brief discussion of some of the common chemicals and a summary of some of the factors pertaining to the process of chemical disinfection, the mode of action, and the methods of evaluating the relative efficiency of disinfectants can be given here.

Factors Affecting Chemical Disinfection. The factors which influence the process of chemical disinfection are extremely varied. Zinsser and Bayne-Jones have summarized them under three separate heads as follows:[2]

A. Factors relating to the chemical disinfectant.
    1. Chemical nature of the substance, inorganic, organic, structure.
    2. Ionization constant.
    3. Concentration
    4. Solubility in the menstruum and in bacterial cellular constituents.
    5. Affinities for bacterial cell protoplasm or constituents.
    6. Mode of action, oxidation, precipitation, etc.
B. Factors relating to the bacteria.
    1. Species of organism.
    2. Chemical composition of the organism.
    3. Growth phase, especially in relation to differences in susceptibility of young cells as compared with old cells or differences between cells of same age. Young cells are often more susceptible than older ones.
    4. Special structures, spores, capsules.
    5. Previous history of the culture. Resistant forms can be selected or produced by gradually increased exposure to toxic agents.
    6. Dissociation in relation to differences in susceptibility.
    7. Number of bacteria in test mixture.
C. General factors affecting both components and the process as a whole.
    1. Temperature. The temperature coefficient of disinfection is high, $Q_{10} = 2$ to 5.
    2. Surface phenomena, especially adsorption and surface tension, and the relationship of these to changes in concentration of substances in interfacial films, changes in permeability and diffusion.
    3. Hydrogen-ion concentration.
    4. Presence of other electrolytes, which influence both ionization of the chemical and the properties of the cells. This is especially true of sodium chloride as shown by numerous investigators.

[2] H. Zinsser and S. Bayne-Jones, *A Textbook of Bacteriology*, D. Appleton-Century Co., New York, 1949.

5. Presence of organic substances, especially proteins, which may react with the substance or form protective films on the organisms, usually reducing the action of the disinfectant.
6. Pressure. Important in some cases, especially in reference to gaseous substances.
7. Time.

It is obvious that since so many factors influence the process of killing bacteria by chemicals, it is rather difficult to choose the best disinfectant or set of conditions for disinfection. It must be remembered, also, that these factors apply to the use of chemicals *in vitro,* and that many more must be considered when chemicals are applied to live tissues.

Characteristics of an Ideal Disinfectant. Certain characteristics may be listed as belonging to an ideal disinfectant. If a particular disinfectant measures up to the characteristics of the ideal, it is valuable for general use. The most important of these characteristics are as follows:

1. *Germicidal power.* The ideal disinfectant should possess high germicidal power, that is, it should kill bacteria in dilute solution. The ability of a disinfectant to kill microorganisms is usually compared with that of phenol. In making such comparisons it is customary to use *Eberthella typhosa,* the cause of typhoid fever, as the test organism. Most commercial disinfectants, particularly the coal-tar products, are sold upon the basis of their phenol coefficient.

2. *Stability.* A disinfectant to be most valuable should be relatively stable in the presence of organic matter. Some of the most powerful of the disinfectants combine with organic matter, forming insoluble compounds, and pass out of solution quite completely. The strength of the disinfectant thereby may be rapidly decreased to a point where it no longer destroys microorganisms.

3. *Homogeneity.* Disinfectants should be homogeneous in composition. Substances which may be bought in pure condition or in crystalline form, such as mercuric chloride, are ideal from this point of view. Many of the commercial disinfectants, particularly those prepared from coal tar, may vary considerably in their composition from time to time, and consequently in their germicidal value.

4. *Solubility.* The ideal disinfectant is one which will dissolve in all proportions in water, of which alcohol is a typical example.

5. *Nontoxic to higher life.* An ideal disinfectant is nonpoisonous to man and to the higher animals. Obviously, disinfectants which will kill one kind of cell and not injure another are not very common. Most of the valuable disinfectants are somewhat injurious to tissues. Certain disinfectants, however, may be injected into the blood stream exerting a more harmful influence upon microorganisms than upon tissues of the body, destroying the former without

seriously injuring the latter. A true example of this type is the arsphenamine used in the treatment of syphilis.

6. *Noncorrosive.* Inasmuch as disinfectants must frequently be used in contact with metals, fabrics, and other materials, it is highly desirable that they should not attack metal, injure fabrics, leave stains, or bleach color.

7. *Penetration.* Disinfectants differ decidedly in their power to penetrate materials to be sterilized. An ideal disinfectant is one which penetrates rapidly and efficiently.

8. *Economy.* The ideal disinfectant should be low in cost. Cost must not be judged by volume but by killing power. One disinfectant may cost more per gallon than another; yet it may have twice the killing power. Since certain effective chemicals are very expensive, they can be used only in limited quantities and for special purposes. The high cost of salts of silver for example, practically limits silver to medicinal uses. If the entire water supply of a city is to be sterilized, a disinfectant must be chosen which is relatively inexpensive. This also applies to the disinfection of public stock yards.

9. *Power to remove dirt and grease.* A film of oil or grease over the surface of certain materials may wholly prevent the action of many disinfectants. Those which have power to dissolve or remove grease and all kinds of dirt are naturally more efficient.

10. *Deodorizing power.* A disinfectant which can combine with and destroy malodorous substances is preferable to one which does not, provided, of course, it does not have a disagreeable odor.

The Action of Chemical Disinfectants. Chemicals destroy microorganisms in a variety of ways. A few of the chemicals have only one type of action, while others bring about death by a number of different types of chemical action.

Probably the most varied of any of the chemicals are the inorganic salts. It has been observed previously that salts of various kinds in low concentrations are stimulating to the growth of bacteria and are of importance as buffers in media. In high concentrations, however, most salts are definitely toxic and hasten death. Salts vary in toxicity; sodium chloride is toxic only in high concentrations while mercury bichloride is toxic in low concentrations. It has been shown, however, that the toxic action of many salts and other types of disinfectants may be increased by the addition of sodium chloride. This is due to the increased dissociation and dispersion of the disinfectant, and as a result there is an increased effect upon the bacterial cells. This is not true of other salts. The addition of NaCl to $HgCl_2$ definitely lowers the toxicity of the latter. Salts do not produce bacterial death by osmotic effects. Bacteria are quite resistant to changes in osmotic pressure, living in distilled water as well as in rather high salt concentrations. Salts do, however, exert a dehydrating action upon the media in which bacteria grow, and thereby cause inhibition of growth and eventual death. Due to the dissociation of salts, most of the germicidal action is caused by the effect of ions (ion effect) upon the bacterial cell. This effect may be the result of the influence upon cell permeability, the lyotropic action upon cell protoplasm altering cell metabolism, and the inactivation of enzymes on which the cell depends for the synthesis of food substances.

Oxidation is one of the most common methods by which chemicals cause death. Many of the salts, for example, potassium permanganate and sodium perborate, are active oxidizing agents. The halogen compounds also are noted for this kind of chemical action.

Some chemicals which are used in sterilization are active reducing compounds. These, it is true, are not as commonly used as the oxidizing agents. The ferrous salts, sulphites, and thiosulphites are good examples of this type of chemical.

Many of the most effective chemicals form irreversible compounds with bacterial protoplasm by the coagulation of the protein. The salts of the heavy metals, i. e., silver, mercury, zinc, copper, and bismuth, are active in this manner. The derivatives of benzene, the coal-tar products, chief among which are phenol and cresol, are used widely as the basis of many commercial disinfectants. These chemicals in their pure state, saponified or altered by the replacement of an H atom by another chemical, cause the death of bacteria by the coagulation of bacterial protein.

Bacteriostatic Compounds. The bacteriostatic effect of dyes, and other chemicals not classed as dyes, is commonly employed to control the growth of bacteria. Since many of the dyes are specific for certain species of bacteria, this method of control has three definite uses. First, it is possible to incorporate dyes in media to inhibit the growth of undesirable species, for example, the addition of gentian violet to media inhibits the growth of Gram-positive bacteria but permits the growth of Gram-negative types. Second, the bacteriostatic action of dyes is used to differentiate closely related species of bacteria, which is best illustrated by the use of basic fuchsin, thionin, and pyronin in differentiating the members of the brucella group. Third, dyes are used in the treatment of disease. Skin infections caused by Gram-positive cocci may be controlled by the use of gentian violet. The acridine dyes, acriflavine and proflavine, are used internally as general antiseptics. Chemicals not classed as dyes may be used in the same manner as has been demonstrated by sodium cacodylate which has been used for years as a pulmonary and general antiseptic. It has always been the hope of those interested in chemotherapy that chemicals which would inhibit the growth of bacteria in vivo would be discovered. Ehrlich's discovery of salvarsan resulted from such investigations. The subsequent use of arsenicals and compounds of bismuth and antimony in treating spirochaetal infections has stimulated the search for other agents which would be effective against bacteria.

The discovery by Domagk in 1932 that prontosil was an effective chemotherapeutic agent against experimental streptococcal infection in mice, opened the pathway for the subsequent development of the sulfonamide compounds. The most significant contribution to this development was the discovery by Tréfouëls and his associates, that the active part of the prontosil was para-amino-benzene-sulfonamide, commonly known as *sulfanilamide;* subsequently, other compounds have been prepared by attaching other radicals to the nitrogen of the sulfonamide group. These compounds possess different solubilities, toxicities, and specific chemotherapeutic effects. The period between 1935 and 1942 may be called the "sulfonamide era" in chemotherapeutic research.

It is quite likely that this era has not entirely ended for new compounds are being created, each claiming lesser toxicity for animal tissues and greater specificity for the various types of pathogenic bacteria.

The sulfonamide compounds which have been developed and found to be therapeutically useful are as follows: sulfanilamide, sulfathiazole, sulfapyridine, sulfadiazine, sulfasuxidine (succinylsulfathiazole), sulfaguanidine, sulfathaladine, sulfamethazine, sulfamerazine, and promin. To this list also must be added the parent compounds prontosil and neoprontosil. The sulfonamides are incorporated in many different types of vehicles for therapeutic purposes. They are prepared as water-soluble jellies, fatty ointments, oil-in-water emulsions, pastes, powders, and solutions. These drugs are frequently used in combination with other drugs for specific purposes. The discussions of the specificity of each of the above compounds for certain species of bacteria and the toxicity of each is beyond the scope of this brief summary.

The method by which the sulfonamides produce bacteriostasis is a subject of interest. It must be emphasized that this action is not a sterilization of fluids and tissues which are infected. These compounds inhibit the reproduction of bacteria; hence the living ones either perish because of their inability to convert food to energy or they become phagocytized by body cells. Numerous theories have been proposed to explain the mechanism by which these compounds act, but the most accepted one at present is known as the *Woods-Fildes theory of competitive inhibition.* In 1940 Woods reported that the action of sulfanilamide is neutralized by *p*-aminobenzoic acid. This compound is required by most bacteria as an essential growth accessory substance, many being able to synthesize it. The structural formula of *p*-aminobenzoic acid is similar to sulfanilamide and it has been postulated by Woods and Fildes that sulfanilamide replaces *p*-aminobenzoic acid in cellular metabolism. The explanation for the specificity of the various sulfonamide compounds has not been developed as yet.

"Furacin" is another type of bacteriostatic agent which has been recently developed. In 1944 Dodd and Stillman observed that several investigators had recorded the bacteriostatic action of furan compounds. Following the study of 42 different furan compounds they found that the nitro group was essential in activating the furans to produce greater bacteriostasis. Later Cramer and Dodd found that the most effective agent was nitrofurazone N.N.R.: *5-nitro-2 furaldehyde semicarbazone,* known now by the trademark, Furacin.[3] Numerous reports have been made showing that this compound is quite effective against skin infections in man particularly those caused by *Micrococcus aureus.* Reports of the value of Furacin in animal infections are not numerous. Kaplan has shown that external infections in dogs and cats responded quickly to the drug and Knowles, Knowles, and Knowles reported it of definite value in treating cases of otitis externa of dogs and cats. In addition to its bacteriostatic qualities Furacin may be used in wounds and incisions without fear of interference with healing.

During very recent years the value of all bacteriostatic agents has been overshadowed by the antibiotics. The latter substances are discussed in detail in the next chapter.

THE EVALUATION OF DISINFECTANTS

The many chemicals which have germicidal power have made desirable the adoption of methods which determine the effectiveness of such chemical substances. In order to make wise selections of disinfectants, the user must have some value to which he may refer; furthermore, the testing of antiseptics and disinfectants is required by the federal government because all chemicals offered for interstate shipment or for import into or export from the United States are subject to the provisions of the Federal Insecticide Act and the Federal Food and Drugs Act, or both.

Various methods of testing the germicidal value of chemicals have been devised. In 1881 Koch saturated silk threads with cultures of bacteria, treated them with the disinfectant and then transferred them into tubes of sterile broth in order to detect the growth of surviving cells. Krönig and Paul (1897) introduced the use of garnets which were submerged in the test culture, then transferred to the disinfectant, and then washed in sterile water.

---

[3] Eaton Laboratories, Inc., Norwich, Conn.

The wash water was cultured to determine the effect of the treatment. Rideal and Walker (1903) were the first to use phenol as a standard with which the action of other disinfectants was compared under standard conditions. Chick and Martin (1908) believed that the addition of 3 per cent dried human feces to the test solution would give a more natural condition for the test because most disinfectants were commonly used in the presence of organic matter. Subsequent tests which have been developed to measure disinfectants have been based largely upon the technic outlined by Rideal and Walker. The comparison of all chemicals to phenol has been criticized justly, however, and for that reason other methods which give a truer picture of the value of nonphenol compounds have been advocated. The real test of the ability of a chemical to kill bactera, and its value as a disinfectant for use on skin and other tissues is not obtained by its action on bacteria suspended in distilled water in a test tube; therefore, toxicity tests have been devised which measure the effect of the disinfectant or antiseptic on live tissue along with its ability to kill bacteria.

It is not desirable in this book to outline in detail the various tests used in the testing of disinfectants and antiseptics. The student is referred to more complete treatises for further information, a list of which is given at the end of this chapter. Only a brief description of each method will be given here.

The Phenol Coefficient. The *phenol coefficient* of a disinfectant may be defined as the ratio of the killing power of the disinfectant to the killing power of pure phenol when determined under standard conditions. It is obvious, therefore, that the most important factors in such a determination are the conditions under which the test is made. The conditions under which phenol coefficients and other germicide tests are determined are given in Circular No. 198 by Ruehle and Brewer, of the United States Department of Agriculture and form the basis for the following discussion.

1. Choice of microorganism: *Eberthella typhosa* (Hopkins strain) and *Micrococcus aureus.*

2. Composition of medium: 5 gms. of Liebig's beef extract, 5 gms. of chemically pure sodium chloride, and 10 gms. of Armour's peptone (for disinfectant testing) in 1,000 ml. of distilled water.

3. Acidity of medium: pH 6.8.

4. Amount of culture medium in tube: 10 ml.

5. Phenol: Must meet the requirements of the United States Pharmacopoeia, and in addition, the congealing point must not be below 40°C. A 5% stock solution is required.

6. Amount of culture added to diluted disinfectants: 0.5 ml. to 5.0 ml.

7. Resistance of test culture to phenol (dilutions killing in 10 minutes, but not in 5 minutes): 1–90.

8. Condition of tube in test: plugged with cotton.

9. Temperature of test: 20°C.

10. Time intervals of the test: 5, 10, and 15 minutes.

11. Amount of medication mixture transferred (size of loop): 4 mm. loop (of No. 23 B. and S. gage wire).

12. Calculation of phenol coefficient: highest dilution not killing in 5 minutes but killing in 10 minutes divided by same for phenol.

The calculation of the phenol coefficient will be clarified by the following example:

	5 minutes	10 minutes	15 minutes
Disinfectant (X)			
1-300	0	0	0
1-325	+	0	0
1-350	+	0	0
1-370	+	+	0
1-400	+	+	+
Phenol:			
1- 90	+	0	0
1-100	+	+	+

It is apparent that the highest dilution of disinfectant (X) not killing in 5 minutes, but killing in 10 minutes, is 1:350; likewise the dilution for phenol is 1:90.

The phenol coefficient is $350/90 = 3.89$.

In order to avoid an impression of assumed accuracy, the phenol coefficient is calculated to the nearest 0.1, unless the coefficient is less than 1.0, which in the above case would be 3.90.

The Wet Filter-Paper Method. The wet filter-paper method is a germicidal test rather than a test of inhibitory properties. It is used when the substance to be tested is not soluble or completely miscible with water, or for substances that are to be used in high concentration, such as soaps, tooth pastes, suppositories, dyes, dusting powders, salves, and ointments. If the substance is to be used in the body cavities the test is carried out at 37°C.; if not, the test is carried out at 20°C. or at room temperature.

No. 2 Whatman filter paper is cut into pieces about 0.5 cm. square, and sterilized in a plugged test tube at temperatures below 170°C. to prevent charring. A suitable number of the paper squares are then impregnated with *Micrococcus aureus,* or other test organisms, by immersion in a 24-hour broth culture of the organism. The culture must have the standard resistance required for phenol coefficient testing. The wet inoculated squares are then placed in the liquid or solid substance to be tested, arranged in intimate contact, and completely covered. At the end of 5 minutes, 10 minutes, 15 minutes, or 1 hour, or any other desired length of time, the wet papers are removed with a sterilized, stiff, platinum wire bent at a sharp angle to form a hook and placed in 10 ml. of sterile broth. After all possible disinfectant has been removed (in the case of sticky substances, the needle must be used to aid in freeing the squares of adherent germicide) the squares are retransferred to a fresh tube of sterile broth (10 ml.) and the tubes are incubated at 37° for 48 hours; they are then observed for evidence of growth.

Resubcultures are always required in this test because the first tube of broth to which the filter-paper squares have been added frequently contains sufficient antiseptic to exhibit inhibition of growth. Both tubes of broth are usually incubated.

The Dry Filter-Paper Method. The dry filter-paper method is used in tests of fumigants and of oils that are to be used where moisture is absent. It is similar to the wet filter-paper test, using squares of paper that have been impregnated as described under the test above, with the exception that squares are dried for two days in a sterile Petri dish in the 37°C. incubator. This test can be used successfully only with organisms capable of resisting the drying. *Eberthella typhosa* will not withstand the drying. *Micro. aureus* is the usual test organism. The inoculated, dried-paper squares may be used at any time up to 30 days after the drying period, but the resistance of the organism at no time should fall so low that it is incapable of withstanding a 1-80 dilution of phenol for 5 minutes at 20°. It should be emphasized that control tests with nonmedicated squares should always be carried out to test the viability of the test organism. As is true in the wet filter-paper method, resubcultures are always necessary.

The Agar-Plate Method. The agar-plate method is a test for inhibitory properties and is used for substances remaining in contact with the body in the absence of serous body fluids. Examples of substances which may be tested by this method are salves, dusting powders, creams, plasters, pads, adhesive tape, catgut, and suppositories. The test organism ordinarly used is *Micro. aureus*, but for special purposes the test may be used with any organism capable of growing on agar. The agar is of the same composition as that previously described for carrying stock cultures of the test organism.

Fifteen to 20 ml. of agar are melted and cooled to 42°–45°C. To this is added 0.1 ml. of a 24-hour broth culture of the test organism. The inoculated agar is then poured into a sterile Petri plate and allowed to harden. As soon as the agar has hardened, the test substance is placed in intimate contact with the surface of the agar. If it is a salve, it is first warmed sufficiently to soften and thus secure a complete peripheral contact. As a control, warmed sterile petrolatum may be placed on another portion of the plate. The plates are incubated 24–48 hours under unglazed porcelain tops at 37°C. and are then examined for evidence of inhibition. If the preparation is antiseptic or inhibitory, a zone of clear agar will be observed around the portion where the substance has been in contact with the agar and the width of the zone will indicate the diffusibility of the inhibitory (antiseptic) agent. If there is no inhibition, growth of the test organism will be observed adjacent to and even under the test substance.

The Serum Agar-Plate Method. Preparations recommended for use on open wounds, cuts, and abrasions are effective only if they exhibit activity in the presence of serous fluids. In testing such preparations the agar-plate method is modified by the addition of 10 per cent sterile horse serum to the agar.

The Agar Cup-Plate Method. The agar cup-plate method is merely a variation of the agar-plate method. It is used on products liquid at the temperature of the test. The agar, or serum agar, is inoculated as in the agar-plate method. Before the agar cools, a depression or cup is made in the medium by standing a sterile flat-bottomed glass tube, 1.5 cm. in diameter, in the liquefied agar; after hardening, the glass tube is removed by slightly twisting and pulling at the same time. Insertion of a sterile wire down the side of the tube for the introduction of air will eliminate much of the cracking of the agar. Another method of preparing the agar cup plate is to allow the medium to harden and then cut out a disk in the agar, by means of a cork borer, 1.5 cm. in diameter. Several drops of melted agar are placed in the cup to seal cracks or crevices. After the agar cup plate is prepared, 6 drops of the test liquid are placed in the cup, and the plate is incubated under an unglazed porcelain top for 24 to 48 hours. If there is a clear zone about the cup, the substance under test has inhibitory properties. Here, as well as in the agar-plate test, the agar in the clear zone may be tested for growth by subculture in broth to indicate whether the action is germicidal or merely inhibitory.

Tests in the Presence of Organic Matter. In general, the tests outlined above will take care of most of the preparations; however, special tests may be required to determine the value of products recommended for certain purposes. For example, recommendations on the label may make advisable the use of various additions of organic matter, such as increased amounts of peptone or the addition of gelatin, blood, ascitic fluid, saliva, urine, or feces, depending upon the information desired.

The Toxicity Index. The use of various chemicals to disinfect skin and other tissues prior to surgical operations and for the treatment of infections has prompted the development of methods which measure the toxicity of such antiseptics for tissues. An ideal antiseptic, obviously, would be one which would kill bacteria but would not injure tissue cells. Numerous investigators have devised methods which may be used to measure the *toxicity index* of a disinfectant, that is, *the highest dilution of disinfectant required to prevent the growth of embryonic tissue divided by the highest dilution to kill the test organism.*

Lambert exposed fragments of human connective tissue to a saline suspension of *Micro. aureus* and transferred them to different disinfectants. After an hour of exposure the fragments were placed in physiologic salt solution where they were washed for a few minutes and then embedded in plasma. The tissue was examined after several days of incubation for evidence of growth of bacteria and tissue cells. The chemicals tested included alcohol, argyrol, iodine, hydrogen peroxide, hypochlorites, mercuric chloride, phenol, potassium cyanide, potassium mercuric iodide, and tricresol. Since iodine killed the cocci in strengths that did not injure the connective tissue cells, it was found to be the best disinfectant.

Lambert and Meyer subsequently modified the above technic by using rabbit spleen which was bathed for 1 minute in a culture of *Micro. aureus* followed by 20-minute exposures to various germicides before embedding in plasma. Acriflavine, albargin, alcohol, iodine, gentian violet, hexylresorcinol, mercuric chloride, Mercurochrome, neosalvarsan, and protargol were tested. Iodine, again, gave the best results.

German submerged fragments of chick tissues in broth cultures of *Streptococcus hemolyticus, Micro. aureus,* and *E. coli* and then transferred them to the disinfectants. After periods of 1 to 5 minutes exposure they were transferred to agar plates. Chick tissues were also bathed in the various dilutions of disinfectants, washed in Locke's solution, and embedded in plasma in order to detect growth. The efficiency of the antiseptic was considered to be directly proportional to its bacteriostatic effect and inversely to its harmful action on the tissues.

Buschbaum and Bloom devised a test employing periosteum of 12-day embryonic chicks cultured in 2 parts of chicken plasma, one part of embryonic chick extract, and one part of various strengths of the antiseptic dissolved in Tyrode's solution. *Micro. aureus* was used as the test organism. Five types of cultures were made: (1) antiseptic and bacteria; (2) antiseptic and tissue; (3) antiseptic, bacteria, and tissue; (4) bacteria; (5) tissue. Various concentrations of the antiseptics were used in the cultures which were observed after 24 and 48 hours for evidence of tissue growth. They considered as the index of relative toxicity the ratio resulting by dividing the greatest concentration in which cells showed normal growth by the greatest dilution that killed the bacterium used, which would be 1.0 or more. The antiseptics which were tested had the following ratios: phenol 0.2, iodine 0.5, Mercurochrome 0.5, Metaphen 0.6, and Merthiolate 0.9, the latter being the least toxic of the group.

The most recent technic introduced to determine the *toxicity index* of antiseptics is that of Salle and associates. Fundamental to the test is the determination of the *Micro. aureus* phenol coefficients for various antiseptics by using the technic which has been described previously. Heart tissue fragments from 9-day-old chick embryos embedded in guinea pig plasma diluted with three parts of Tyrode's solution and one part of embryonic fluid are used as the test-tissue cultures. Various dilutions of the disinfectants are made in chick embryonic fluid and added to the flasks containing the tissue cultures and examined for evidence of growth after 48 hours incubation. The toxicity index for the antiseptics is determined by dividing the highest dilution showing no tissue growth by the highest dilution showing no growth of *Micro. aureus*. The most efficient antiseptic is the one having the lowest toxicity index. Table 5.1 shows results of the testing of several germicides obtained by Salle and Lazarus. Note that iodine appears to be the most ideal antiseptic as measured by the tissue culture technic as well as by the phenol coefficient methods.

DISINFECTANTS AND ANTISEPTICS IN COMMON USE

Space does not permit the listing of all chemicals which are available as disinfectants and antiseptics, nor is it the function of this book to discuss the chemical structure and the application of chemicals in the field or laboratory. Chemicals used as antiseptics and disinfectants are classed in definite groups, such as acids and alkalies. Various combinations of one group of chemicals with another (mercuric iodide) may be utilized in preparing more ideal disinfectants. Certain chemicals may be treated in specific ways, saponification of the cresols for example, to make a more ideal compound. It is obvious that these combinations are almost limitless; hence it is easily understood why so many preparations are available to the user with each individual compound making its claim to being the most suitable for all types of disinfection. It is doubtful if there is a universal "ideal disinfectant," nor is it essential that there should be such a substance. Different chemicals should be chosen for different types of disinfection. One may excel in one situation where another is entirely inapplicable.

Acids. The addition of acid to any solution containing bacteria, with the consequent increase in hydrogen-ion concentration, in-

TABLE 5.1

Toxicity Index of Various Germicides

Germicide	Highest Dilution Showing No Tissue Growth = A	Highest Dilution Showing No Growth of *Micro. aureus* = B	Toxicity Index = A/B	*Staph. aureus* Phenol Coefficient
Iodine	1- 1,800	1-20,000	0.09	308
Iodine trichloride ..	1- 2,400	1- 6,000	0.4	92
Mercuric chloride..	1- 45,000	1-16,000	2.8	246
Hexylresorcinol	1- 21,000	1- 7,000	3.0	108
Metaphen	1- 76,000	1- 6,000	12.7	92
Phenol	1- 840	1- 65	12.9	....
Potassium mercuric iodide	1- 12,000	1- 900	13.3	13.8
Merthiolate	1-176,400	1- 4,000	35	71
Mercurochrome ...	1- 10,500	1- 40	262	0.6

creases the rate of death. Some bacteria, termed the *acidophiles,* will grow well in relatively high hydrogen-ion concentrations. The ability of these organisms to grow in the presence of high concentrations of acid is sometimes utilized in their isolation. Some types of bacteria are able to survive the hydrogen-ion concentration of gastric juice, which makes them of greater consequence in intestinal infections.

Acids are most commonly used as preservatives. The most important are the acetic (usually in the form of vinegar) and the lactic acids, the latter the preservative agent in sour milk, sauerkraut, and silage. Benzoic acid, salicylic acid, sulphurous acid, formic acid, pyroligneous acid, carbonic acid, and citric acid have been used, and some continue to be used as preservatives for fruits and meats. They are not active germicides but do prohibit the growth of microorganisms.

Boric acid is used extensively as an antiseptic wash for mucous membranes, particularly of the conjunctiva. It is a poor germicide but does have antiseptic qualities.

Alkalies. High alkalinity, that is, high concentration of hydroxyl ions, likewise exerts a destructive action upon microorganisms. Sodium hydroxide is one of the most widely used chemicals of this group. In a 0.5 per cent concentration it is valuable as a germicide for mechanical milking equipment. In stronger solutions it is used in the disinfection of stanchion floors, maternity stalls, and farrowing pens. It has been shown to be almost a specific viricide, especially for the virus of foot and mouth disease. McBryde, Niles, and Cole have also called attention to its use in destroying the virus of hog cholera.

Unslaked lime (quick lime) added to water is converted into calcium hydroxide, and when used in strong solutions, as in white-wash, it has a marked disinfecting action.

Various detergents, chief among which is trisodium phosphate, are used in the dairy industry in washing milk equipment, in the washing of dishes, and in washing bottles for beverages. While they are not as active as the hydroxides, such compounds are definitely germicidal when used in hot solutions.

Salts of Heavy Metals. The salts of silver, mercury, arsenic, copper, and zinc are all used in a variety of combinations as disinfectants and antiseptics.

Silver nitrate is one of the most commonly used compounds containing silver. It is objectionable, however, because of its corrosive and irritating action on tissue. Silver proteinates such as argyrol, silvol, and neosilvol are not as irritating to live tissue and are frequently used to disinfect surfaces of mucous membranes.

The mercury compounds are well known for their germicidal value. Mercuric chloride is the most widely used of these chemicals. The biniodide of mercury is also quite popular. Because of the toxic and corrosive action of simple mercury compounds, various complex mixtures have been prepared. Mercurochrome has had periods of popularity. Metaphen and Merthiolate are two comparatively new mercury compounds which appear to be satisfactory germicides.

Arsenic compounds are not used to a great extent as germicides because they are toxic to human and animal life; however, the value of the complex salts of arsenic in the treatment of spirochetal infections is well known.

The salts of copper cannot be depended upon for their germicidal action. As an algacide, however, copper sulphate has no equal and is used extensively in the control of algae in water supplies.

Zinc salts are practically devoid of germicidal activity, but zinc oxide is widely used in the treatment of many conditions where infection may exist. The beneficial results are due to an astringent action which promotes healing.

Phenols and Related Compounds. Phenol, or carbolic acid C_6H_5OH, either pure or in mixtures with alcohol, glycerin, or various oils, ranks among the most efficient of the disinfectants. Weak dilutions, 0.5 per cent, are used in the preservation of antigens, viruses, and antisera used in immunizing procedures. The methyl phenols or cresols, $C_6H_4CH_3OH$, either pure or in trade mixtures— tricresol, creolin and liquor cresolis—are also effective germicides.

They are most frequently used in 1 to 5 per cent solutions and will destroy bacteria even in the presence of quantities of organic matter. For this reason they are universally used for the disinfection of barns, pens, railway cars, trucks, and many other places where infected animals have been kept.

Orthophenylphenol is an odorless disinfectant which has rather wide use as a barn disinfectant. It is effective against *Mycobacterium tuberculosis,* hence is useful as a disinfectant for barns after tuberculin reactors have been removed. This disinfectant is much more satisfactory for dairy barn use because it does not impart odors to milk as is the case when the phenolic compounds are used.

The Halogens. The halogens and the variety of compounds which are prepared by mixing them with other chemicals have the distinction of being the most widely used of any of the disinfectants. Halogens are not effective in the presence of organic matter, and for that reason their use is limited.

Chlorine is used more than any other chemical of the group. Chlorine gas, or the various mixtures, such as hypochlorite prepared by the action of chlorine on lime, all exert a germicidal action on bacteria by oxidation resulting from the union of chlorine with hydrogen in water. Chlorine is used in the sterilization of water supplies, in the treatment of sewage water, for the sterilization of all dairying equipment used in the transfer of milk from the farm to the consumer, and for sterilizing dishes and glassware and many other articles. Some of the more stable chlorine compounds are used in the treatment of wounds and other disease processes; among these are chloramine-T, dichloramine-T, Javelle water, Dakin's solution, and azochloramide.

Iodine is one of the most efficient disinfectants for use on skin surfaces. Usually it is used in alcoholic solutions with potassium iodide, and for that reason is irritating to tissue. The value of low concentrations, such as 1 per cent of iodine, as antiseptics has been proven during recent years. Reference was made to this fact in the preceding discussion of the toxicity index, which the student should review at this point. Colloidal iodine is used as an intestinal antiseptic and a parasiticide. Iodine is commonly used in combination with other chemicals, biniodide of mercury, for example, forming stable and effective disinfectants. Iodoform is one of the iodine compounds which is used in wounds and other septic processes; it is valuable for this purpose, but to some the odor of the compound is disagreeable, and for that reason the use of it in medicine is objectionable.

Fluorine is too reactive and toxic to be of great use as a disinfectant. Sodium fluoride is a valuable insecticide and may be added in small quantities, 10 mg. per ml. of blood, for the preservation of blood intended for laboratory examination. Bromine is too reactive to be of any use as a disinfectant or antiseptic.

Miscellaneous Compounds. Alcohol, especially ethyl alcohol, is considered by many to be a most effective antiseptic, and is credited by some as a disinfectant. The efficacy of this alcohol is dependent upon the concentration. Investigation and experience have shown that 70 per cent alcohol is most efficient. Concentrations above and below that concentration are ineffective. Alcohols in general are more bactericidal in the higher molecular weight. This fact is shown clearly by the *Eb. typhosa* phenol coefficients of various alcohols tested by Tilley and Schaffer given in Table 5.2.

Isopropyl alcohol has been shown to be a more effective germicide than the more commonly used ethyl alcohol. It is used in the 98–99 per cent pure state and is noncorrosive to instruments. The pungent odor of this alcohol is objectionable and for that reason it has not come into wide use.

TABLE 5.2

PHENOL COEFFICIENTS OF VARIOUS ALCOHOLS *
Primary Normal Alcohols

	Phenol Coefficients
Methyl	0.026
Ethyl	0.040
Propyl	0.102
Butyl	0.237
Amyl	0.78
Hexyl	2.30
Heptyl	6.80
Octyl	21.00
Secondary Alcohols	
Propyl	0.064
Butyl	0.152
Amyl	0.38
Hexyl	1.00
Tertiary Alcohols	
Butyl	0.081
Amyl	0.182
Hexyl	0.45

* Tilley and Schaffer, Jour. Bact. 12:303, 1926.

Chloroform is used as an attenuating agent for vaccines. It may be added as a preservative to blood serum which is to be used in the preparation of Loeffler's medium or to enrich other media; likewise, ether is used for the above purposes.

Formaldehyde gained great popularity as a disinfectant when it was popular to fumigate infected dwellings. Its value as a disinfectant in that procedure was due to its solubility in water; on account of this characteristic it is usually sold commercially as Formalin, an aqueous alcoholic solution containing approximately 40 per cent formaldehyde. Formalin is an effective germicide and is used not only in the killing of animal and human pathogenic bacteria, but also for treating seeds and potato tubers in order to kill fungi with which they may be contaminated. This chemical is used as an attenuating agent for bacteria, toxins, and viruses which are to be used as immunizing agents. Formaldehyde forms hexamethylenamine with ammonia, a compound which is used extensively as a urinary antiseptic.

Potassium permanganate is used extensively in veterinary medicine as an antiseptic in drinking water for poultry for which it seems to have definite value. It is used as a wound dressing also. The stains produced by the chemical have been factors preventing its general use as an antiseptic. Hydrogen peroxide is not employed extensively as a disinfectant due to the ease with which it combines with organic matter; however, it does have some virtue as a cleansing agent for deep wounds, but its effervescing action belies its real value, and it should not be depended upon to any great extent. Metallic peroxides, CaO_2, MgO_2, ZnO_2, NaO_2, are claimed to be less reactive than H_2O_2. They are usually found in ointments and tooth pastes. Their antiseptic values are not great.

One of the most important factors influencing all disinfection is freedom from oily compounds and organic matter. The virtues of soap as a cleansing agent, serving to remove many bacteria from surfaces of the skin, are common knowledge. Numerous investigators have shown that most soaps also have a certain amount of antiseptic value. In general it has been found that the activity of soaps depends upon the fatty acid radicals present, the state of saturation of the fatty acids, the concentration of the soapy solutions, the temperature, and the amount of foreign material present. Various compounds of known disinfecting value have been added to soap with the assumption that a more effective process of sterilization could be accomplished. Critical evaluation of such compounds has failed to reveal a greater effectiveness than with the disinfectant alone. In some instances the presence of soap interfered rather than enhanced the action of the disinfectant.

Investigations of the synthetic soaps or detergents have revealed that they have germicidal activity. Such compounds are classified as either *cationic* or *anionic* detergents. The cationic detergents have been found to have greater germicidal activity than the anionic compounds. Cationic detergents are more active in the alkaline range and anionic in the acid range. The great popularity of these compounds as detergents, wetting agents, and emulsifiers has resulted in the synthesis of over 1,000 different ones since Domagk showed the value of roccal in 1935. Most of these compounds are nontoxic to living tissues and are safe to use as skin disinfectants. Some have been given internally to experimental animals without showing toxic effects. Zephiran, an alkyl-dimethyl-benzyl-ammonium chloride similar to roccal, has been shown to be an active germicide. In a dilution of 1:80,000 it may be used as a perservative for biological products, such as antiserums. Triethanolamine lauryl sulfate, commonly known as Drene, is an anionic compound effective against Gram-positive bacteria. McCulloch demonstrated that this compound was effective against *Str. agalactiae* and *Erysipelothrix rhusiopathiae.*

The quarternary ammonium salts, cationic surface-active agents, are the most recent additions to the long list of germicidal agents. Numerous compounds known by various trade names are widely used in disinfection. As a group these agents are satisfactory against nonsporeforming bacteria. They have the distinct value of being active in the presence of organic matter. Acetyl-beta-methylcholine chloride (mecholyl), a compound belonging to this group, ionizes to a high degree in solution and resembles the alkali metals in stability.

REFERENCES FOR FURTHER STUDY

Buchanan, R. E., and Fulmer, I. E. The Physiology of Bacteria. Williams & Wilkins Co., Baltimore, 1928.

Buschbaum, R., and Bloom, W. Proc. Soc. Exp. Biol. and Med. 28:1060, 1931.

Chick, H., and Browning, C. H. The Theory of Disinfection. A System of Bacteriology in Relation to Medicine, Privy Council, Med. Res. Council. His Majesty's Stationery Office, London, Vol. 1, Chap. V, 1930.

Daily, L. E. The Nitrofurans—A New Group of Chemotherapeutic Agents. Printed by the Eaton Laboratories, Norwich, N. Y., 1947.

Fildes, Paul. A Rational Approach to Research in Chemotherapy. Lancet. 1(238):955–57, 1940.

Gay, Frederich P., and associates. Agents of Disease and Host Resistance, Chap. 12, pp. 217–47, Charles C. Thomas, Baltimore, 1935.

German, W. Jour. Arch. Surg. 18:1920, 1929.

Kaplan, A. D. Vet. Med. 43, 1948.

Klatz, I. M., and Mellody, M. Jour. Bact. 57:477, 1949.

Knowles, A. T., Knowles, J. O., and Knowles, R. P. No. Amer. Vet. 29:495–96, 1948.

Lambert, R. A. Jour. Exp. Med. 24:683, 1916.

———. Jour. Am. Med. Assn. 67:1300, 1916.

———, and Meyer, J. R. Proc. Soc. Exp. Biol. and Med. 23:429, 1926.

Luchiesch, Matthew. Applications of Germicidal, Erythermal and Infrared Energy. D. Van Nostrand Co., New York, 1946.

McCulloch, E. C. Disinfection and Sterilization. Lea & Febiger, Philadelphia, 2nd Ed., 1945.

McCutcheon, John W. Synthetic Detergents Main Types, Uses, Properties and Prospects. Chemical Industries, November, 1947.

Reddish, G. F. The Newer Knowledge of Bacteriology and Immunology. Jordan and Falk, Chap. XXII, pp. 301–9, The University of Chicago Press, Chicago, 1928.

Rosenau, M. J. Preventive Medicine and Hygiene. 6th Ed., Sec. XVI, Disinfection, pp. 1379–1429, D. Appleton-Century Co., New York, 1935.

Ruehle, G. L. A., and Brewer, C. M. United States Food and Drug Administration Methods of Testing Antiseptics and Disinfectants. U.S.D.A., Washington, D. C. Circ. No. 198, 1931.

Salle, A. J., and Lazarus, A. S. Proc. Soc. Exp. Biol. and Med. 32:665, 1935.

———, McOmie, W. A., and Shechmeister, I. L. Jour. Bact. 34:267, 1937.

———, ———, ———, and Ford, D. C. Proc. Soc. Exp. Biol. and Med. 37:694, 1938.

———, ———, ———, ———. Jour. Bact. 37:639, 1939.

Shechmeister, I. L., and Salle, A. J. Proc. Soc. Exp. Biol. and Med. 38:295, 1938.

Sollmann, T. A Manual of Pharmacology. W. B. Saunders Co., Philadelphia, 1936.

Topley, W. W. C., Wilson, G. S., and Miles, A. A. The Principles of Bacteriology and Immunity. 3rd Ed. Williams & Wilkins Co., Baltimore, 1946.

Underwood, W. B. Textbook of Sterilization. American Sterilizer Co. Printed by the Lakeside Press, Chicago, 1935.

Woods, D. D. Brit. Jour. Exp. Path. 21:74–90, 1940.

Wooley, D. W. Science. 100:579, 1944.

6. | Antibiotic Agents

The discovery of penicillin will be recorded as one of the most significant contributions to medicine. This discovery is of significance to the entire field of bacteriology as well as to medicine. It has increased the scope of bacteriology, opening a broad new avenue for scientific endeavor. In principle, the antibiotic or antagonistic association of bacteria, yeasts, and molds is not new. It has been an interesting phase in the study of bacteria since the early contributions of Pasteur. Generally, the association of microscopic forms with each other has been lost from view because of the stress placed upon the study of pure cultures. For that reason every bacteriologist has disregarded contaminants on a Petri plate culture which show inhibition of the organism under study. Plates of milk, water, and soil samples have shown the presence of colonies which inhibit the growth of neighboring colonies. Beneficial associations also have been observed. It must be remembered that bacteria in nature do not live in pure cultures and many have a beneficial association with each other. The symbiotic relationship of many of the types of soil bacteria are well known. Many infections in animals and man are caused by more than one bacterial species. Although the primary and greatest damage to tissue may be due to only one species, there are numerous instances where two or more different species of bacteria share the responsibility. In influenza of swine the primary infecting agent is a filtrable virus; however, the disease is characterized by the symptoms produced by the associating infection caused by a small bacterium, *Hemophilus suis*. In some cases the primary infection is followed by a secondary one, frequently of a different type; in fact, the previous infection may predispose to the subsequent one.

When bacteria are cultured artificially, numerous examples of beneficial relationships are encountered in mixed cultures. If an aerobic organism is grown in a medium with an anaerobic one, the former will benefit the latter. The hydrolysis of proteins may be carried to the amino acid stage by the action of certain bacteria, thereby making those essential food elements available to other species of bacteria unable to utilize the complete protein molecule. Some microorganisms, particularly yeasts, are able to synthesize different compounds of the Vitamin B group. These substances are definitely known to serve as accessory growth factors for most bacteria.

Numerous well-known examples of antagonistic or antibiotic action may be cited. It is evident that a strict aerobic organism cannot live in the presence of an anaerobe. The pH of the medium produced by the acid-producing organism becomes too high for many types of bacteria to continue growth. Likewise marked alkalinity of a medium due to the hydrolysis of proteins inhibits the growth of still other types. These are examples of antagonisms commonly used to explain inhibition of growth. It is understandable, then, that the advent of specific antibiotic agents has increased tremendously the significance of antagonistic association.

Historical Development. Although the field of antibiotic discovery was stimulated by the discovery and use of penicillin, this substance was not the first one to be recognized. In 1877 Pasteur observed that the growth of the anthrax bacillus was inhibited by air-borne contaminants. Bouchard noted in 1888 that *Pseudomonas aeruginosa* was antagonistic to *Bacillus anthracis* and at one time filtrates of that organism were advocated in the treatment of anthrax. The early work of Bouchard was substantiated by other workers who showed that the products of *Ps. aeruginosa* were inhibitory to many different species of bacteria; furthermore, Emmerich and Löw were able to prepare an extract from the filtrate of cultures of this organism. This material was called *pyocyanase* and was found to have a destructive bacteriolytic effect upon numerous species of bacteria. This lytic substance was thought to be a proteolytic enzyme by early workers; however, recently Shoental has found three antibacterial substances in chloroform extracts of *Ps. aeruginosa* filtrates: pyocyanin, a-oxyphenazine, and a colorless substance. The antibacterial action of pyocyanin and other extracts has been shown by many, but the toxicity of the material has prevented its therapeutic use.

Antibiotic substances similar in action to pyocyanin have been found to be produced by numerous species of bacteria. In his comprehensive survey of this subject, Waksman lists 16 different strains of sporeforming bacteria and approximately the same number of nonsporeforming strains which show antibiotic activity against different bacteria.

Antibiotic action was not observed in bacteria alone. In 1922 Alexander Fleming, in England, observed that egg white contained a material which dissolved bacteria. He called it lysozyme. Although this material attracted considerable attention at the time, it did not gain chemotherapeutic popularity; nevertheless this discovery did bear fruit, for it enabled Fleming to recognize the antibiotic effect of a contaminating mold in a culture of staphylococci in 1929. Fleming recorded this observation as follows: [1]

> While working with staphylococcus variants a number of culture-plates were set aside on the laboratory bench and examined from time to time. In the examinations these plates were necessarily exposed to the air and they became contaminated with various micro-organisms. It was noticed that around a large colony of a contaminating mould the staphylococcus colonies became transparent and were obviously undergoing lysis. Subcultures of this mould were made and experiments conducted with a view to ascertaining something of the properties of the bacteriolytic substance which had evidently been formed in the mould culture and which had diffused into the surrounding medium. It was found that the broth in which the mould had been grown at room temperature for one or two weeks had acquired marked inhibiting, bactericidal and bacteriolytic properties to many of the more common pathogenic bacteria.

Nutrient broth in which the mold was grown contained the inhibiting agent which Fleming called "penicillin" because the mold was a species of Penicillium. He suggested at the time that this agent had chemotherapeutic potentialities but, like so many discoveries of this type, the time was not right for acceptance. Fleming did find use for the agent in the isolation of influenza bacilli from cocci, for the former organisms were not sensitive to penicillin whereas the latter were inhibited.

The application of antibiotic agents in the treatment of disease was really crystallized by the discovery of gramicidin by Dubos in 1939. This substance, produced by the sporeforming organism *Bacillus brevis*, was found to inhibit the growth of streptococci and pneumococci.

Penicillin was not to be forgotten. Bacteriologists and chemists, particularly Florey and Chain at Oxford University, England, had continued research on this important antibiotic and in 1940 had purified enough penicillin to prove that it was highly effective against infections caused by streptococci, staphylococci, and gas-gangrene bacilli. By 1943 the value of penicillin was proven beyond any doubt and, due to the insistency by the army that it be made available for use, the therapeutical manufacturing industry in the United States centered upon the manufacture of it.

Penicillin has one shortcoming. It is not particularly active against the Gram-negative rods. In 1942 Waksman and Woodruff described an antibiotic agent *streptothricin*, which was produced by a soil organism *Actinomyces lavendulae*. This agent inhibited the growth of Gram-negative bacteria. In 1944 Schatz, Bugie, and Waks-

---

[1] A. Fleming. On the Antibacterial Action of Cultures of a Penicillium with Special Reference to their Use in the Isolation of B. *influenzae*. Brit. Jour. Exp. Path. 10:226, 1929.

man discovered that *Actinomyces griseus* produced an antibiotic agent which was more active against Gram-negative organisms than was streptothricin. This new substance was named *streptomycin*.

During the 1940 decade practically every microbiologist kept his eyes open for organisms with antibiotic properties. Bacteria as well as molds were studied. In 1945 Johnson, Anker, and Meleney isolated an organism *Bacillus licheniformis,* a species closely related to *Bacillus subtilis,* which produced an antibiotic agent which they called *bacitracin.*

During the process of examining soils from various parts of the world for fungi which have antibiotic properties, Burkholder isolated an actinomycete, which he called *Streptomyces venezuelae,* from soil from Venezuela. It has been revealed that this organism is present in American soils also. The antibiotic agent produced by this organism was first reported in 1947 by Ehrlich, Bartz, Smith, Joslyn, and Burkholder. It was originally called chloromycetin but is now known as *chloramphenicol.* Chemical studies of this antibiotic have shown that it is a derivative of dichloroacetic acid and has the following chemical structure:

Chloramphenicol has the distinction of being the first of the important antibiotics to be synthetically produced in large quantities. It has been shown to be active against a large number of bacteria, thus gaining the distinction of being a "broad spectrum" antibiotic. Although it has not been shown to inhibit the growth of viruses, it is effective against the rickettsiae and other infectious agents of similar characteristics.

The discovery of chlortetracycline by Duggar in 1948 revealed another antibiotic with a "broad spectrum" inasmuch as it, too, is effective against a large variety of both Gram-positive and Gram-negative bacteria, as well as other infectious agents. Chlortetracycline (produced under the trade-mark name of Aureomycin by the Lederle Laboratories) is produced by a soil actinomyces, *Streptomyces aureofaciens.* It is manufactured in large quantities and is widely used as a therapeutic agent. In addition to this important use, this antibiotic has been shown to increase the growth rate of swine and chickens when fed in small amounts. The exact manner by which this effect is produced is not known. It is theorized that bacteria of low toxicity which are present in the intestinal tract are inhibited in growth, or that the antibiotic may enter into the metabolism of cells as an additional nutrient subtsance, or that it produces an increased activity of enzymes essential for cell metabolism.

In 1950 Finlay and associates of the Charles Pfizer Company announced the discovery of an agent they called Terramycin. This name is now used as a trade-mark name for the antibiotic by the Pfizer Company but the scientific name is *oxytetracycline*. The antibiotic is produced by the soil actinomycete, *Streptomyces rimosus*. It, also, has a wide spectrum of activity and it too has been shown to promote more rapid growth in young animals.

The close similarity of chlortetracycline and oxytetracycline led to the detailed chemical study of both compounds. In 1952, Stephens and associates announced the discovery of tetracycline, an antibiotic agent common to, but different than, the two parent substances. This agent is produced by both *Streptomyces aureofaciens* and *Streptomyces rimosus*. In addition to the production of this antibiotic by fermentation it can be produced by the catalytic hydrogenation of chlortetracycline. This latter discovery has opened the door to the probable development of various agents with slightly different chemical structures and with very specific activities against specific organisms.

The similarity of the three tetracyclines is shown by the structural formula of each, given on the following page. It is apparent that tetracycline differs from oxytetracycline by an OH group at carbon 5 and from chlortetracycline by a chlorine atom at carbon 7.

The above historical sketch mentions only those antibiotics which are of practical importance as pharmaceutical agents. The search for microorganisms which produce antibiotic substances continues. Literally hundreds have been discovered, in fact, many are known which have not been thoroughly tested. There is a natural tendency to conclude that the antibiotic agents produced commercially today are the superior ones. While this may be true at present, one should always expect to learn of new superior agents which will be produced from time to time.

So the search for antibiotic agents active against specific types of bacteria, and especially for filtrable viruses, still goes on.

In this search it is well to keep the desirable properties of an antibiotic for medical use constantly in mind. Florey, who contributed so greatly to the early clinical application of penicillin, lists these desirable properties as follows:

1. It must have a powerful action against some bacteria. It is improbable that any of the weaker antibiotics, of which there are many, will find a place as chemotherapeutic agents.

2. It must have specificity of action. From a study of bacteria affected has emerged the fact that the antibiotics possess in many

OXYTETRACYCLINE

CHLORTETRACYCLINE

TETRACYCLINE

instances remarkable specificity of action. They may have no action whatever against certain species, and yet be powerfully active against others. At one time we had the idea that any substance which would act against both Gram-positive and Gram-negative organisms—that is, a substance without any great specificity of action as between one bacterial species and another—would in all probability be toxic to animal cells. This we now know is not a completely valid generalization. Nevertheless, all the antibiotics so far investigated which have any prospect of being used in medicine have specific action.

3. A substance must possess little toxicity to the intact animal body, and the less of this the better. Not only must it lack toxicity to the intact body but also to individual cells such as leucocytes. It must not damage the kidneys if it is excreted and possibly concentrated by them, and its toxicity must not only be low following a single dose but it must not cause any changes in the body when given in frequent doses for a considerable length of time.

4. A substance must be active in the presence of body fluids such as serum, pus, and cerebrospinal fluid; substances very active in the test tube may be completely inactive in the body because of the inhibitory effect of body fluids.

5. The chemotherapeutic agent must not be destroyed by tissue enzymes. An indication of likely behavior in this respect is obtained by the reaction to trypsin. It is improbable that any substance which is destroyed by tissue enzymes or by trypsin will survive for long after injection into the blood stream; it will probably be destroyed rapidly and with it any possibility of its exerting antibacterial action. Though it is not essential, it is highly desirable that the drug should be absorbed from the gastrointestinal tract, so that it can be taken by mouth.

6. It should be stable. Penicillin has caused a great deal of trouble through its instability. Many of the difficulties in the early days of penicillin would have been avoided but for its particular liability to destruction.

7. It is also desirable that it should not be too rapidly excreted by the kidneys. Penicillin has this great disadvantage; because it is excreted by the tubules it leaves the body with great rapidity.

8. Another property which we have come to recognize as being serious is the capacity to produce in infecting bacteria a resistance to the chemotherapeutic drug itself. This was first noted with the sulfonamide compounds, for bacteria can become resistant to the sulfonamide drugs both in vitro and in vivo. It was also shown that bacteria became resistant to penicillin in vitro, and this is especially true of the staphylococci. Fortunately it appears to be much more difficult to acquire resistance to penicillin in vivo than in vitro, but the induction of resistance, even in vivo, is a marked property of streptomycin and no doubt will seriously interfere with its therapeutic use. It would appear that bacteria can rapidly acquire resistance to many other of the antibiotics of which we know.

Complete books have been written about the antibiotics, so the student is referred to the list at the end of the chapter for more extensive study. All of the significant antibiotics in veterinary medicine will be listed and discussed below very briefly.

Antibiotic Agents From Bacteria. Previous mention has been made of the antibiotic action of the substances pyocyanase, pyocyanin, and hemipyocyanin produced by *Pseudomonas aeruginosa.* Likewise, gramicidin produced by *B. brevis* has been noted; in addition to this agent, inhibitory substances are known to be produced by other bacteria.

Bacillus subtilis (Jansen and Hirschman 1944) has been found to produce an agent called *subtilin,* which is inhibitory to Gram-positive bacteria.

Bacitracin (Johnson, Anker, and Meleney, 1945) is another agent produced by *Bacillus licheniformis,* a species closely related to *B. subtilis.* This antibiotic received its name because the culture was isolated from the dirt débrided from the fractured leg of a child named Tracy. Bacitracin is produced commercially and has been found to be effective against the Gram-positive cocci and not affected by bacteria which do produce penicillinase. It has value in the topical treatment of cellulitis, wounds, ulcers, and superficial abscesses. Initial investigations demonstrated that the nephrotoxic property of the drug decreased its usefulness; however, that undesirable characteristic can be overcome by regulated dosage. Bacitracin may be given by the oral route, and is retained in the intestine and not readily absorbed. It is lethal to *Entamoeba histolytica,* one of the first of the antibiotic agents shown to affect protozoa. It has been used in the treatment of bovine mastitis with some success. Further investigation will reveal the value of this agent in the treatment of the various animal diseases.

In 1946 Foster and Woodruff recovered an agent they called *bacillin* from a culture of B. *subtilis.* This material was a water-soluble, thermostable substance but was somewhat toxic. Johnson and Burdon (1946) reported the extraction from cultures of *B. subtilis* a hemolytic agent called *eumycin* which was too toxic for internal use.

The *polymyxins* (Stansly, Shepherd, and White, 1947) are related antibiotics which are derived from *Bacillus polymyxa,* a sporeforming organism isolated from the soil. These substances are simple, basic polypeptides which form water-soluble salts with mineral acids. Five distinct antibiotic agents, designated polymyxin A, B, C, D, and E, have been isolated. The polymyxins are particularly active against Gram-negative bacteria and almost totally inactive against Gram-positive species. One Gram-negative genus, Proteus, is peculiarly resistant to the action of these antibiotics but most of the other genera, including Aerobacter, Brucella, Eberthella, Escherichia, Hemophilus, Klebsiella, Pasteurella, Pseudomonas, Salmonella, Shigella, and Vibrio, are sensitive. Among the above genera an occasional resistant species is observed but the development of resistance by sensitive strains has not been observed.

The use of polymyxin has been limited because of toxicity. It has been found that polymyxin B is less nephrotoxic than the others; consequently, it is produced commercially. This antibiotic has especial value in being active against several species of bacteria, particularly *Pseudomonas aeruginosa,* which are resistant to many other antibiotics. Various preparations of the drug are available, the topical and oral types being the most desirable, inasmuch as no toxic effects have been noted following those methods of administration.

Bacteriolytic and bacteriacidal properties have been observed in filtrates of *Bacillus mesentericus*. Another one of the spore-forming aerobic species, *Bacillus mycoides*, produces a thermostable substance which inhibits the growth of many different species of bacteria, including *Myco. tuberculosis*.

Among the nonspore-producing bacteria, *Pseudomonas fluorescens* has been shown to produce a thermostable filtrable agent which is antagonistic to *Bacillus anthracis* and *Corynebacterium diphtheriae*. In the red pigment produced by *Serratia marcescens* an alcohol-soluble substance has been shown to inhibit the growth of various Gram-positive bacteria. Other species of bacteria have been shown to be antagonistic to different pathogenic species grown in contact with them.

Up to the present time the antibiotic agent produced by bacteria gaining most prominence as a chemotherapeutic substance has been tyrothricin. Tyrothricin is a polypeptide, insoluble in water but soluble in alcohol. When treated with acetone-ether, tyrothricin yields two substances: soluble fraction *gramicidin* and the insoluble substance *tyrocidine hydrochloride,* commonly referred to as *tyrocidine.* Tyrothricine is active mainly against Gram-positive bacteria and because of its hemolytic property is limited to topical applications. It has been used in the treatment of bovine mastitis, being administered by infusion into the mammary gland through the teat canal. Although minor inflammation is produced in the mucosa by this treatment, the agent has been proven effective in treating streptococcal mastitis. Gramicidin is active against Gram-positive bacteria, particularly the streptococci. It, too, is toxic, which limits its use in the treatment of generalized infections. Tyrocidine is active against both Gram-positive and Gram-negative bacteria and no doubt would have gained greater popularity as a therapeutic agent had it not been for the discovery of more effective agents.

Other antibiotic agents produced by bacteria are: *diplococcin* from streptococci (Whitehead, 1933); *iodinin* from *Chromobacterium iodinum* (McIlwain, 1943); *phthiocol* from *Mycobacterium tuberculosis* (Lichstein and Van de Sand, 1946); *prodigiosin* from *Serratia marcescens* (Wrede and Rothhaus, 1945); *simplexin* from *Bacillus simplex* (Cordon and Haenseler, 1939).

Antibiotic Agents From Actinomyces. From the research of Waksman and co-workers a number of different species of actinomyces have been found to produce antibiotic substances. The first organism in this group was *Actinomyces antibioticus,* which produced inhibiting agents designated as *actinomycin* A and *actinomycin* B.

The first of these agents has been studied in greater detail than the second. It is soluble in alcohol and ether but not in water. A large group of different bacteria are sensitive to it but it has not been useful as a therapeutic agent because of its marked toxicity for animal tissue.

Streptothrycin is produced by *Actinomyces lavendulae*. This material is a thermostable organic base. It is soluble in water and in acid alcohol, but not in ether. The growth of various Gram-negative bacteria is inhibited by it and it has specific action against a few of the Gram-positive forms. It is not toxic to animal tissues.

The antibiotic agent which parallels penicillin as an effective chemotherapeutic agent is *streptomycin*. It has been previously noted that this agent was found to be produced by *Actinomyces griseus* by Schatz, Bugie, and Waksman in 1944. Since then this agent has been subjected to considerable investigation and is now being prepared in large quantities.

Streptomycin is produced by growing the culture of *A. griseus* in a meat extract medium to which glucose is added. After five to twelve days incubation the medium is filtered and the active agent is extracted with acid and further purified by alcohol extraction. It is an organic base, soluble in dilute acids and in water, but insoluble in chloroform and ether. It is a thermostable compound so does not deteriorate as quickly as penicillin. Streptomycin produces in some patients dizziness and deafness, due to the action of the agent on the auditory nerve. Some nephrotoxic effects have been noted also. These toxic characteristics have been largely removed by the addition of two hydrogen atoms to streptomycin creating *dihydrostreptomycin*.

In order to regulate the dosage of streptomycin it is evident that a standard potency must be available. Since this agent is effective against Gram-negative bacteria, a standard strain of *E. coli* was chosen as the organism for the development of a standard.

The unit of streptomycin was originally defined as that quantity of dry material which would inhibit the growth of *E. coli* in 1 ml. of nutrient broth. This was found to approximate one microgram. Consequently, when amounts of streptomycin are specified in dosage or assay, they are expressed in micrograms or grams.

As prepared and dispensed commercially, streptomycin is a white powder contained in sterile vials in 1-gram quantities. A suitable diluent is placed in the vial and from this known dilution, dosages containing the desired amount per cubic centimeter may be obtained.

The early investigations of Waksman and co-workers revealed that streptomycin was active against *Mycobacterium tuberculosis,* in addition to such Gram-negative bacteria as *Brucella abortus, Proteus vulgaris, Pseudomonas aeruginosa,* and *Salmonella schottmulleri.* This discovery is acknowledged to be the motivating force behind the rapid development of this agent. In 1944 Feldman and Hinshaw demonstrated that streptomycin suppressed the effect of experimentally induced tuberculosis in guinea pigs and now almost three-fourths of all streptomycin produced is used in the treatment of tuberculosis. Stubbs has found streptomycin effective in preventing the death of guinea pigs used for experimental brucellosis. The sensitivity of the Pasteurella to streptomycin has been revealed by Heilman by in vitro studies with *Pasteurella tularensis* as well as with experimental tularemia in mice. Coles tested the sensitivity of a number of species of bacteria pathogenic for animals, finding that the Gram-negative species were most sensitive while the Gram-positive cocci were least so. *Pasteurella multocida* and *Brucella abortus* are two important species which are quite sensitive to streptomycin. Hinshaw and McNeil demonstrated the value of this agent in the treatment of fowl cholera in turkeys.

Mention has been made previously to chloramphenicol, chlortetracycline, oxytetracycline, and tetracycline, so they will not be discussed here.

In addition to the above-mentioned antibiotics produced by actinomyces, two others deserve discussion. *Neomycin* is produced by *Streptomyces fradiae,* and was first reported by Waksman and Lechevalier in 1949. Upon more complete study this antibiotic has been shown to consist of at least three closely related chemical substances, which are designated neomycin A, B, and C. This antibiotic is active against a wide range of bacteria but unfortunately it contains a nephrotoxic substance which limits its use as a pharmaceutical agent.

Viomycin is produced by *Streptomyces puniceus* and was reported by Bartz and associates in 1950. However, research workers of Pfizer Laboratories had previously reported this antibiotic and they are given credit for its discovery. Likewise it became apparent that an antibiotic agent called *Vinactin,* which was reported by Mayer *et al.* in 1951 was identical to viomycin. It is now recognized that vinactin is composed of three active substances A, B, and C. Viomycin is considered to be vinactin A, which is the trade-mark name used by Ciba Pharmaceutical Products, Inc. Viomycin is active against the Gram-negative types of bacteria and has shown promise in the treatment of tuberculosis in man.

In 1952 McGuire and associates reported an antibiotic agent, *Erythromycin,* produced by *Streptomyces erythreus.* This antibiotic is active against the Gram-positive bacteria, being similar to penicillin in that respect. It has the added advantage of being effective against those strains of bacteria which have developed resistance to penicillin. While the trade-mark name of Erythromycin is used by Upjohn Company, the name Ilotycin is used by the Eli Lilly Company, and Erythrocin by Abbott Laboratories.

Carbomycin was first reported by Tanner *et al.* in 1952. It is produced by *Streptomyces halstedii*. The Chas. Pfizer Company, manufacturers of this new drug, use the trade-mark name, Magnamycin. Carbomycin is a mixture of two antibiotics designated A and B, and differing in that B is more readily absorbed from the intestinal tract with resulting higher blood levels. Both are active against the Gram-positive types of bacteria.

Antibiotic Agents From Molds. Penicillin is the best known agent produced by molds. Probably no subject has accumulated such extensive literature in so short a period of time as has penicillin. In addition to the thousands of periodical articles, three books have been written on the subject, one by Waksman, one by Herrell, and one by Kolmer.

Numerous strains of *Penicillum notatum* have been found, many of them producing a more potent penicillin than the original strain studied by Fleming.

In the production of penicillin three general methods may be used. The mold may be grown as a surface culture on fluid medium; it may be grown as a submerged culture in a fluid medium which is aereated and agitated; or it may be grown in a moist bran medium. The composition of the fluid media used in the growth of the mold varies to some extent but it has been found that corn-steep liquor and zinc are two ingredients which are definitely of value in producing a greater yield of penicillin. The maximum yield of penicillin is obtained after approximately seven days of incubation between 22° C. and 25° C. The mold growth is removed from the medium by filtration, leaving a clear yellowish brown filtrate. Penicillin exists in the filtrate as an organic acid and can be extracted with numerous solvents such as ether, amyl acetate, and n-butyl alcohol. While in solution, penicillin may be combined with various salts, of which sodium, procaine, potassium, and calcium have been the most widely investigated.

During recent years research has centered upon the chemistry of penicillin with the hope that a synthetic compound may be prepared. Although this has not been accomplished, the chemical structure of penicillin has been determined. Six different antibiotics which may be called penicillins have been purified. These are listed in Table 6.1.

The potency of penicillin is determined by the inhibition of growth of selected strains of staphylococci. A variety of technics such as serial dilution, turbidimeteric, and agar-cup methods have been developed to demonstrate the inhibition which is expressed in units per cubic centimeter. The original unit of potency determined by the Oxford group was based upon the comparison of any sample of penicillin with a standard. This group devised the method known as the Oxford-cup method. This consists of inoculating an agar

TABLE 6.1

STRUCTURE OF THE PENCILLINS (CHARACTERISTIC "R") *

DESIGNATION		CHARACTERISTIC "R"		
American	English	Name	Structure	Produced By
F	I	3-Hexenoic	$CH_3.CH_2.CH=CHCH_2CO-$	*P. notatum*
Flavacidin	....	4-Hexenoic	$CH_3.CH=CH.CH_2.CH_2.CO-$	*A. flavus*
Dihydro F	....	Caproic	$C_5H_{11}CO-$	*A. giganteus*
G	II	Phenylacetic	$C_6H_5CH_2.CO-$	*P. notatum*
X	III	p-Hydroxy-phenylacetic	$HO.C_6H_4.CH_2.CO-$	*P. notatum*
K	IV	Caprylic	C_7H_{15} $CO-$	*P. notatum*

* After Kavanagh.

plate with a standard strain of *Micro. aureus.* Upon the surface of the medium, small cylinders of a standard diameter (9 mm.) are placed. One cylinder is filled with a standard penicillin containing 1 unit of penicillin per cubic centimeter. The other dilutions of the unknown are placed in other cylinders. After incubating the plate, the extent of the clear zones around the cylinders are determined and compared with that of the standard. A unit of penicillin is that amount which, when dissolved in 1 ml. of water, gives the same area of inhibition as the standard. In order to have a more exact method of measurement an International Unit for penicillin has been established. It is 0.6 microgram of the sodium salt of penicillin G, which is approximately equivalent to the Oxford unit.

It has been previously noted that penicillin is more active against Gram-positive than against Gram-negative bacteria. Many of the Gram-positive forms are more susceptible to penicillin than others. Occasionally a strain of a sensitive organism such as *Micro. aureus* is found which is very resistant to the drug. This appears to be an inherent characteristic of the organism in many instances; however, it has been shown that sensitive organisms may develop drug fastness upon prolonged contact with penicillin. The mechanism by which such strains become resistant is not clear. It was discovered in the early period of research on this agent that the Gram-negative bacteria were resistant because of their ability to secrete an enzyme, called penicillinase, which was able to destroy penicillin. Naturally resistant strains of staphylococci have been shown to produce a penicillinase-like substance.

Although the sensitivity to penicillin of the various bacteria producing infection in animals has not been accurately determined, the following list may be considered indicative of the relative sensitivity of the important species as tested in vitro. Organisms are placed into three groups: highly susceptible, those inhibited by 0.01 to 0.06 unit per ml; moderately susceptible, those inhibited by 0.06 to 1 unit per ml.; those resistant, grown in the presence of over 1 unit per ml. of medium.

Highly Sensitive

Clostridium septicum
Clostridium novyii
Clostridium sordellii
Clostridium tetani
Clostridium perfringens
Corynebacterium pyogenes
Micrococcus aureus

Streptococcus agalactiae
Streptococcus canis
Streptococcus dysgalactiae
Streptococcus equi
Streptococcus pyogenes
Streptococcus uberis
Streptococcus zooepidemicus

Moderately Susceptible

Actinobacillus lignieresi
Actinomyces bovis
Bacillus anthracis
Corynebacterium renalis
Clostridium chauvoei
Erysipelothrix rhusiopathiae

Leptospira icterohemorrhagiae
Leptospira canicola
Listeria monocytogenes
Pasteurella multocida
Ornithosis virus
Psittacosis virus

Resistant

Aerobacter aerogenes
Brucella abortus
Brucella bronchisepticum
Brucella melitensis
Brucella suis
Coccidioides immitis
Corynebacterium equi
Escherichia coli
Hemophilus influenzae
Klebsiella species

Malleomyces mallei
Mycobacterium tuberculosis
Proteus ammoniae
Pseudomonas aeruginosa
Salmonella species
Shigella species
Vibrio species
Fowl pox virus
Influenza virus
Vaccinia virus

The mechanism by which penicillin inhibits the growth of bacteria has not been elucidated. It is generally conceded that the action is bacteriostatic, but numerous investigators have shown that under certain conditions penicillin is bacteriocidal. The action of penicillin is not instantaneous as is the case of a chemical disinfectant. For this reason it has been postulated that this agent interferes with cell metabolism during the active growth phase of bacteria, probably by "neutralizing" the action of essential enzyme systems. The amount of penicillin in a medium is not decreased by its action on living bacteria; therefore, it does not enter into chemical reactions whereby its chemical nature may be altered.

A number of other antibiotic agents may be isolated from the medium in which various species of molds have been grown.

Aspergillic acid (White and Hill, 1943), is produced by *Aspergillus flavus.*

Penicillic acid (Alsberg and Black, 1913), is formed by *Penicillium puberulum.* This species of mold also produces *puberulic acid.* (Birkinshaw and Raistrick, 1932).

Clavacin is an agent produced by *Aspergillus clavatus* (Waksman, Horning, and Spencer, 1942).

Fumigacin produced by *Aspergillus fumigatus* was discovered by Waksman, Horning, and Spencer, 1942. This species of mold also produces *fumigatin* (Anslow and Raistrick, 1938), *helvolic acid* (Chain, Florey, et al., 1943) and *Aspergillin* (Soltys, 1944).

Citrinin is produced by *Penicillium citrinum* (Hetherington and Raistrick, 1931).

Spinulosin has been isolated from cultures of *Penicillium spinulosum* (Oxford and Raistrick, 1942).

Gliotoxin (Weindling and Emerson, 1936) is produced by *Aspergillus gliocladium.*

Claviformin (Chain, Florey, and Jennings, 1942) is produced by *Penicillium claviforme.*

Flavacidin was found to be formed by *Aspergillus flavus* by McKee *et al.,* 1943.

Flavacin, another distinct antibiotic, was isolated from the same mold by Bush and Goth, 1943.

Gigantic acid (Wilkins and Harris, 1942) is produced by *Aspergillus giganteus.*

Glutinosin is produced by *Metarrhizium glutinosum* (Brian and McGowan, 1946).

Javanicin (Arstein, Cook, and Lacey, 1946) is produced by *Fusarium javanicum.*

Notatin (Penicillin B) (Coulthard *et al.,* 1942) and *Penatin* (Kocholaty, 1942) are produced by *Penicillium notatum.*

Viridin (Brian and McGowan, 1945) is produced by the fungus *Trichoderma viride.*

Antibiotics Produced by Miscellaneous Plants. The production of the antibiotic agents is not limited to bacteria actinomyces and molds. Numerous higher plants have been shown to yield these agents.

Clitocybine was recovered from the mushroom by Hollande in 1945.

Ramalina crystals from the lichen *Ramalina reticulata* were shown to have antibiotic action by Marshak in 1947.

Allicin (Cavallito and Bailey, 1944) was recoverd from garlic. *Canavalin* from the jack bean was reported by Farley in 1944. *Onion phytoncide* has been shown to have antibiotic properties by Tonkin in 1944 and Kohman in 1947.

Tomatin (Irving, Fontaine, and Doolittle, 1945) has been isolated from the green leaves of tomato plants.

REFERENCES FOR FURTHER STUDY

Alsberg, C. L., and Black, O. F. U.S.D.A. Bull., No. 270, 1913.

Anslow, W. K., and Raistrick, H. Biochem. Jour. 32:687, 1938.

Arstein, H. R. V., Cook, A. H., and Lacey, M. S. Nature. 157:333, 1946.

Birkinshaw, J. H., and Raistrick, H. Biochem. Jour. 26:441, 1932.

Brian, P. W., and McGowan, J. C. Nature. 156:144, 1945.

Bush, M. T., and Goth, A. Jour. Pharm. Exp. Therap. 78:164, 1943.

Cavallito, C. L., and Bailey, J. H. Science. 100:390, 1944.

Chain, E., Florey, H. W., and Jennings, M. A. Brit. Jour. Exp. Path. 23:202, 1942.

——, and Williams, T. I. Brit. Jour. Exp. Path. 24:108, 1943.

Coles, E. H. Am. Jour. Vet. Res. 9:152–56, 1948.

Cordon, T. C., and Haenseler, C. M. Soil Science. 47:207, 1939.

Coulthard, G. E., *et al.* Nature. 150:134, 1942.

Dubos, R. Jour. Exper. Med. 49:575, 1929.

——. Proc. Soc. Exp. Biol. and Med. 40:311, 1939. Jour. Exp. Med. 70:1 and 11, 1939.

——. The Bacterial Cell. Harvard University Press, Cambridge, Mass., 1946.

Duggar, B. M., *et al.* Aureomycin — A New Antibiotic. Ann. New York Acad. Med. 51:175–342, 1948.

Ehrlich, J., *et al.* Science. 106:417, 1947.

Emmart, E. W. Report, Antibiotic Study Section, Wash., D. C., 1947.

Emmerich, R., and Löw, O. Ztschr. f. Hyg. u. Infectionskrankh. 31:1, 1889.

Farley, D. L. Surg. Gyn. and Obst. 79:83, 1944.

Finlay, A. C., Hobby, G. L., P'an, S. Y., Regna, P. P., Routien, J. B., Seeley, D. B., Shull, G. M., Sobin, B. A., Solomous, I. A., Vinson, J. W., and Kane, J. H. Science. 110:85, 1950.

Fleming, A. Proc. Roy. Soc. London. 93:306, 1922.

——. Brit. Jour. Exp. Path. 10:226, 1929.

Foster, J. W., and Woodruff, H. B. Jour. Bact. 51:363, 1946.

Gardner, A. D. and Chain, E. Brit. Jour. Exp. Path. 23:123, 1942.

Gosio, B., 1896, in Florey, H. W. Brit. Med. Jour. 2:635, 1945.

Gratia, A., and Dath, S. C. R. Soc. Biol. 91:1442, 1924.

Hegarty, C. P., and Scheidy, S. F. Univ. Penn. Bull. 49:60, 1949.

Herrell, W. E. Penicillin and Other Antibiotic Agents. W. B. Saunders Co., Philadelphia, 1945.

Hobby, G. L., Dougherty, N., Lenert, T. F., Hudders, E., and Kiseluk, M. Proc. Soc. Exp. Biol. and Med. 73:503, 1950.

Hollande, A. C. Compt. rend. Acad. Sci. 221:361, 1945.

Hotchkiss, R. D., and Dubos, R. J. Jour. Biol. Chem. 141:144, 1941.

Irving, G. W., *et al.* Science. 102:9, 1945.

Jansen, E. F., and Hirschmann, D. J. Arch. Biochem. 4:297, 1944.

Johnson, B. A., Anker, H., and Meleney, F. L. Science. 102:376–77, 1945.

Johnson, E. A., and Burdon, K. L. Jour. Bact. 51:591, 1946.

Karel, L., and Roach, E. S. A Dictionary of Antibiosis. Columbia Univ. Press, 1951.

Kavanagh, F. Advances in Enzymology. 7:461, 1947.

Keefer, C. S. and Hewitt, W. L. The Therapeutic Value of Streptomycin. J. W. Edwards, Ann Arbor, Mich., 1948.

Kocholaty, W. Jour. Bact. 44:469, 1942.

Kohman, E. F. Science. 106:625, 1947.

Kolmer, John A. Penicillin Therapy. D. Appleton-Century Co., New York, 1945.

Lichstein, H. C., and Van de Sand, V. F. Jour. Bact. 52:145, 1946.

Marshak, A. Public Health Reports. 62:1, 1947.

Mayer, R. L., Crane, C., DeBoer, C. J., Komopka, E. A., Marsh, J. S., and Eisman, P. C. Proc. XII Int. Congress, Pure and Allied Chemistry, New York, 1951.

McGuire, J. M., Bunch, R. L., Anderson, R. C., Boaz, H. E., Flynn, E. H., Powell, H. M., and Smith, J. W. Ilotycin, a new antibiotic. Antibiotics and Chemotherapy. 2:281, 1952.

McIlwain, H. Biochem. Jour. 37:265, 1943.

McKee, C. M., Rake, G., and Houck, C. L. Jour. Bact. 47:187, 1943.

McNeil, E. and Hinshaw, W. R. Corn. Vet. 38:239, 1948.

Meleney, F. L. and Johnson, B. A. Amer. Jour. Med. 7:794, 1949.

Oxford, A. E., and Raistrick, H. Chem. and Ind. 61:128, 1942.

Pratt, R., and Dufrenoy, Jean. Antibiotics. J. B. Lippincott Co., Philadelphia, 1949.

Raistrick, H., *et. al.* Lancet. 2:625, 1943.

Schatz, A., Bugie, E., and Waksman, S. A. Proc. Soc. Exp. Biol. and Med. 55:66, 1944.

Sokoloff, B. The Miracle Drugs. Ziff-Davis Co., Chicago, 1949.

Soltys, M. A. Nature. 154:550, 1944.

Stansly, P. G. Amer. Jour. Med. 7:807, 1949.

Tanner, F. W., Jr., English, A. R., Lees, T. M., and Routien, J. B. Some properties of magnamycin, a new antibiotic. Antibiotics and Chemotherapy. 2:441, 1952.

Tonkin, B. Am. Rev. Soviet Med. 1:237, 1944.

Townley, R. W., Mull, R. P., and Scholz, C. R. Proc. XII Int. Congress, Pure and Allied Chemistry, New York, 1951.

Transactions of the Ninth Streptomycin Conference, St. Louis, Mo., 1950.

Vaudremer, A. Compt. rend. Soc. Biol. 74:278–752, 1913.

Waksman, S. A. Microbial Antagonisms and Antibiotic Substances, 2nd Ed. Commonwealth Fund, New York, 1947.

————. Streptomycin, Nature and Practical Applications. Williams and Wilkins Co., Baltimore, 1949.

————. Horning, E. S., and Spencer, E. L. Science. 96:202, 1942.

————, and Lechevalier, H. A. Science. 109:305, 1949.

————, and Woodruff, H. B. Jour. Bact. 44:373, 1942.

Weindling, R., and Emerson, O. H. Phytopath. 26:1068, 1936.

Welch, Henry, *et al.* Antibiotic Therapy. Blakiston Co., New York, 1954.

Welch, H., Randall, W. A., and Price, C. W. Jour. Am. Pharm. Assoc. 39:486, 1950.

Whiffen, A. J. Jour. Bact. 54:41, 1947.

White, E. C., and Hill, J. H. Jour. Bact. 45:433, 1943.

Whitehead, H. R. Biochem. Jour. 27:1793, 1933.

Wilkins, W. H., and Harris, G. C. M. Brit. Jour. Exp. Path. 23:166, 1942.

Wrede, F., and Rothhaus, A. Ztschr, f. Physiol. Chem. 226:95, 1945.

————, and Strack, E. Ztschr. f. Physiol. Chem. 140:1, 1924.

PART II

Infection, Resistance, and Immunity

7. The Mechanism of Infection

Disease is any departure from a state of health. Health is a normal functioning of all body activity. Immediately one recognizes that a normal state of health is difficult to determine. To all outward appearances an animal may be healthy, yet may be diseased; consequently, in the detection of disease one must utilize certain diagnostic methods, such as chemical and biological tests. Inability to determine what is a normal animal, or the normal state of health, has had a profound bearing upon the explanation of the devious effects of disease on animals of the same species.

Diseases are generally recognized by a definite chain of symptoms, and when they are sufficiently severe they represent an alteration of body fluids and cells. The agents of disease produce different effects; consequently, the various diseases are recognized by the differences in symptoms and the differences in the changes produced in body fluids and cells.

Diseases are divided into two general types, infectious and noninfectious. An *infectious* disease is one which is caused by a microorganism. The mere presence of microorganisms in the body, however, does not constitute *infection*. General infection is not regarded as occurring unless the organisms multiply in the body and produce symptoms of disease and pathological changes in tissues. A *noninfectious* disease is one which is caused by injury, vegetable or mineral poison, heat or cold, faulty nutrition, abnormal physiology, or abnormal tissue growth. A *contagious* disease is one which is caused by an organism that is readily transferred from one individual to another by direct or indirect contact. The terms *infectious* and *contagious* are sometimes used interchangeably. It is best, however, to limit the terms. *Infectious defines the cause of a disease, and contagious defines the ease and method of transmission.* Contagious diseases are all infectious, but all infectious diseases are not contagious; for example, tetanus and botulism in man and animals cannot be regarded as contagious because they result from contact with infected soil and foods which never may have been in contact with infected animals. Every gradation between highly contagious and noncontagious disease is known; hence, it is customary to indicate the degree of contagiousness by the use of modifiers, such as, highly contagious and slightly contagious. There has been a decided tendency during recent years to refer to the infectious diseases as communicable diseases and to eliminate using "contagious."

Among the infectious, or communicable, diseases of animals are the following: abscesses and similar pyogenic infections, strangles, pneumonia, meningitis, Brucellosis, tuberculosis, paratuberculosis, pseudotuberculosis, swine erysipelas, glanders, dysentery, hemorrhagic septicemia, swine plague, fowl cholera, anthrax, blackleg, malignant edema, actinomycosis, aspergillosis, ringworm, pleuropneumonia, foot-and-mouth disease, rinderpest, hog cholera, equine encephalomyelitis, fowl plague, rabies and the poxes, such as fowl pox.

Examples of noninfectious, or noncommunicable, diseases are: diabetes, azoturia, vitamin deficiency diseases such as rickets, mineral deficiencies, sweet clover disease, and plant poisoning.

Kinds of Bacteria in Relationship to Disease. Reference has been made previously to the relationship of bacteria to their food supply. It is desirable at this point to discuss them in relationship to their ability to produce disease as a result of their presence on or in a living animal. Bacteria may be classified as saprophytic and parasitic.

Saprophytic bacteria are those which live on dead matter. Since pathogenic bacteriology is almost completely concerned with the effect of bacteria on the living animal, the saprophytes do not appear to be of great significance. While this is true generally, there are some instances where the growth of bacteria on dead tissue may be harmful. For example, the putrefaction of retained placental tissues by bacteria may result in the absorption of the end products. This may cause a condition commonly referred to as toxemia, which in this instance may be more specifically called *sapremia.*

Parasitic bacteria are those which live at the expense of the host to which they may produce severe injury. The ideal parasite is one which does not injure the host sufficiently to cause great debility or death. Unfortunately many parasites do not possess the power to control the desirable characteristics of parasitism for their own good. During the evolution of their parasitic existence they have acquired properties which injure the host. These bacteria are called *pathogenic* bacteria. The injury produced by the pathogenic microorganism to the host varies from minor tissue damage to death. The variables operating in infectious disease are those contributed by the infecting agent and those possessed by the host. The student can understand, therefore, the complexity of disease when he realizes the interrelationships of numerous species of bacteria, numerous types of body tissues and fluids, and numerous species of animals.

Virulence. The characteristics which make one organism a harmless saprophyte and another a deadly pathogen are not thoroughly understood. Infectious disease is, no doubt, primarily a result of the action of certain chemical components of the organism along with the reaction to this chemical on the part of the tissues of the host. Whether disease is a result, therefore, of the potency of the organism or the weakness of the host is difficult to determine. There is a tendency to refer to the causal microorganism as the inciter of disease and to the host merely as a susceptible recipient. Bacteria vary in their ability to cause disease. This ability is usually summed up in the use of the terms *virulence* or *pathogenicity;* hence an organism is referred to as avirulent, slightly virulent, very virulent, or extremely virulent. The use of such modifying terms for various species of bacteria is based upon factors emphasized in the following discussion.

Some species of bacteria are able to produce toxins which are more lethal than those of other bacteria. This is true also in some strains of the same species. A good example of a toxin-producing organism is the bacillus responsible for tetanus in man and animals. This organism may be classified as a saprophyte but the effects of its deadly toxin make it apparent that it should be called a pathogen. Washed spores of this organism may be given orally to animals without producing injury; in fact, they may be introduced into healthy tissue without causing symptoms of the disease. However, if such spores are introduced into tissues along with necrotic tissue or with chemicals which may kill tissue cells, they germinate and produce a toxin which is disseminated throughout the body causing the muscle contraction characteristic of the disease. If the organism is grown artificially, so that toxin is produced, minute amounts of it, entirely free of the bacilli, will cause the same typical symptoms. An example of an entirely different type of organism is *Bacillus anthracis*, the cause of anthrax. This is a sporeforming bacillus. When washed spores are placed in healthy tissues, they germinate, the resulting organisms multiply rapidly and spread throughout the body of the animal quickly producing death. When this organism is grown in artificial media, the cell-free filtrate will not produce symptoms of the disease. These two examples represent the two extremes of pathogenic activity, with many species of bacteria being both toxic and invasive.

In addition to toxin, mentioned above, there are other substances produced by bacteria which endow them with virulence. Some of these substances are toxins while others are extracellular enzymes.

The production of hemolysin by bacteria has long been associated with virulence. While this may be true of some species it is not true of others, because entirely nonpathogenic species produce hemolysin. Recent studies on hemolysin (Bernheimer, 1947) indicate that this material is enzymatic. The substrates in which these enzymes reside are not known. Quite likely the substrates act as antigens explaining why hemolysins have been classified as toxins. A single bacterial species may produce more than one hemolysin. The Group A hemolytic streptococci, for example, produce two hemolysins which differ in their chemical properties and the method by which they cause hemolysis of erythrocytes. These hemolysins have been designated streptolysin O and streptolysin S. Streptolysin O is a rather labile protein containing sulfur and is oxidized by atmospheric oxygen. It can be reactivated by such a reducing agent as sodium hydrosulfite. This type of hemolysin is produced by many different species of bacteria. It is neutralized by specific immune serum and by cholesterol. The antisera from an animal immunized by one of the O hemolysins will neutralize the others, hence, it appears that they are not specific.

Streptolysin S is a lipoprotein and is not neutralized by cholesterol and is not reversely oxidizable. Antiserum for this hemolysin is prepared with difficulty and it does not neutralize streptolysin O. It is extractable from the streptococcal cells by means of serum — the S means serum extractable. It is very unstable being preserved only by lyophilization. This hemolysin produces degenerative effects on heart muscle and other parenchymatous organs as well as hemolysis. There is little doubt that it is associated with virulence. Hemolysis noted on the blood agar plate is considered due to streptolysin S. However, this does not mean that O has not been produced. It may have been oxidized. Blood of horses has been shown to possess antistreptolysin O which prevents the elaboration of this substance. The blood of all animals has not been assayed for the presence of antihemolysin, but rabbit blood is known to be comparatively free of it, consequently is most reliable for the preparation of blood agar.

Many different species, particularly the staphylococci, produce *leucocidin* which is able to cause the destruction of leucocytes. It appears likely that this material is identical to hemolysin O, inasmuch as it is oxidized in the same reverse manner. The accumulation of leucocytes in suppurative processes and the destruction of those leucocytes which have phagocytized masses of bacteria, makes it evident that the substance leucocidin is a protective mechanism which enables bacteria to multiply more abundantly in infected tissue.

The description of "fibrinolysin" by Tillett and Garner in 1933 contributed another substance by which certain of the streptococci and staphylococci may be enhanced in virulence. This substance, now called *streptokinase*, causes the dissolution of fibrin clots in a few minutes. It is known to be a kinase which activates a proteolytic enzyme normally present in plasma in an inactive form. The absence of fibrin is one of the characteristics of certain acute types of streptococcal infections, so it is presumed that this is due to streptokinase. This is supported by the fact that when the specific antibody, antistreptokinase, appears in the blood stream, fibrin appears in the infected tissues.

Pathogenic strains of *Micrococcus aureus* produce an enzyme-like substance, called *coagulase*, which is able to cause the coagulation of blood plasma from rabbits and human beings. The role this substance plays in virulence is not known. However, since most staphylococcic infections are localized, it may be presumed that the formation of coagulated masses of plasma about colonies of the organism in tissue, prevents the penetration of leucocytes and lytic agents of the body defense mechanism.

Clost. perfringens, as well as other members of the gangrene group of Clostridia, produces toxins which have a marked effect upon the blood-vascular system. It has been shown that this toxin is a *lecithinase* which brings about the hydrolysis of lecithin when acted upon by calcium ions. Lecithinase causes marked hemolysis and necrosis of other cells, so it is apparent that it has a direct influence on disease produced by these organisms.

Culture filtrates of *Clost. perfringens* also contain another proteolytic enzyme which has been called *collagenase*. This substance causes the disintegration of muscle tissue of laboratory animals by decomposing the reticular scaffolding. It has been suggested by MacFarlane and MacLennon, 1945, that collagenase may be responsible for the pulpy condition of muscle found in cases of gas gangrene. Both lecithinase and collagenase are neutralized by the action of commercial antitoxin.

Hyaluronic acid is a viscous, polysaccharide acid of high molecular weight, present in the intercellular ground substance of many different tissues. Numerous bacteria produce the enzyme *hyaluronidase* which hydrolyzes hyaluronic acid. Duran-Reynals, 1942, found that the injection of this enzyme into tissues increased permeability and allowed the rapid spread of injected solutions, India ink, and bacteria. He referred to the substance as a spreading factor. Previous to 1945 this investigator has observed the presence of this material in aqueous extracts of rabbit, guinea pig, and rat testes. It has since been shown that numerous bacteria, staphylococci, streptococci, pneumococci, corynebacteria, and clostridia produce hyaluronidase. The invasive qualities of these bacteria are enhanced, no doubt, by this substance which enables the bacteria to penetrate through the barrier of endothelial and epithelial cells.

It must be kept in mind, when considering the relationship of the toxins and enzymes to virulence, that all of these substances are not produced by all bacteria. One substance may be of aid to one species and another substance to another species. In general the bacteria producing disease in animals have not been sufficiently investigated to know the virulence pattern of all of them. The specific significance of each substance will be discussed along with the particular organism in subsequent chapters.

Bacteria in general may lose their virulence when subjected to certain environmental conditions such as growth on ordinary artificial media, at high temperatures, and in contact with chemicals. This decrease in virulence is known as *attenuation*. The anthrax bacillus maintains its virulence when grown on ordinary media but loses it when grown at 42°C. The virulence of bacteria can be increased also. The less virulent strains of hemorrhagic septicemia bacteria can be increased by successive passages through mice and egg embryos. Certain avirulent strains of bacteria can be made fully virulent when grown on media containing blood or blood serum. The loss, as well as the acquisition, of virulence appears to be involved in the phenomenon of dissociation. Bacteria in the S stage are more fully virulent than those in the R. Capsulated bacteria are more virulent when the capsule is present than in the dissociative noncapsulated state. Organisms are more virulent when they contain as a part of their chemical structure a specific polysaccharide, a substance which also has an important role in immunity. The Gram-negative bacteria possess an endotoxic substance known as O, or somatic, antigen, which is composed of carbohydrate, protein, and phospholipid. This component is located at or near the cell surface and is liberated upon the lysis of the cell. It is known to be highly toxic, but not in the manner of the various toxins and enzymes produced by Gram-positive cocci and bacilli. Injections of small amounts of purified endotoxin will produce a sharp rise in temperature, increase in blood sugar, and decrease in organic blood phosphorus in experimental animals. The pyrogenic substances present in water are believed to be endotoxic material resulting from the autolysis of Gram-negative bacteria present in the water. For this reason solutions used 'for intravenous injections should be made of freshly distilled water.

The number of bacteria present in the initial invasion of a host undoubtedly is a factor in virulence. The apparent increase in the virulence of a microorganism causing an infection in a herd is partially due to the increase in the number of bacteria to which the susceptible animals have access. It is obvious that two infected animals would liberate more bacteria than one, four more than two, etc. The relationship of the number of bacteria to virulence is illustrated in Table 7.1, by Martos, which shows the effect of various numbers of anthrax bacilli on mice.

The specificity of one species of bacteria for certain tissue has a marked bearing upon the determination of the virulence of that species; that is, the degree of virulence can be determined somewhat by the type of tissue affected. It is obvious that a micro-

TABLE 7.1

Effect of Various Numbers of Anthrax Bacilli on Mice

Number Mice	Number Bacilli	Number Died	Percentage Died	Duration of Life
10	20	10	100	2.6 da.
11	10	8	73	4.3
20	5	13	65	4.0
20	2	10	50	5.2
50	1	14	28	5.6

organism which produces a rapid and fatal pneumonia is more virulent than one which attacks intestinal tissue. One organ, in this instance, is more vital than the other, and its destruction causes the death of the host more quickly. The extent to which bacteria are able to multiply in tissue, also has some bearing upon its virulence and is governed greatly by the response of the defense mechanism of the tissues of the host. Some types of bacteria have the ability to repel this defense and multiply rapidly; others are easily destroyed by it.

Lastly, the host itself plays an important role in determining the virulence of a microorganism. Cuts, abrasions, and other effects of traumatism upon skin and mucous membranes may permit the entrance and establishment of bacteria which otherwise would not occur. The age of the host has an important bearing upon the establishment of bacteria and production of disease. As a rule young animals are more susceptible to infection than old ones. This is illustrated best by numerous diseases to which adults are resistant and children highly susceptible. Baby chicks are especially susceptible to *Salmonella pullorum* which produces a fatal septicemia and enteritis, while in the mature hen the organism localizes in the ovary where it causes a chronic type of infection. The reverse is true in avian tuberculosis which is found most commonly in old birds. Malnutrition has a bearing upon the susceptibility of the host to infection. Vitamin D deficiency produces an increased susceptibility of respiratory mucous membranes to infection. Experimentally it has been possible to infect pigeons, which are resistant otherwise, with anthrax subsequent to a period of starvation. Sudden and extreme exposure to cold has a bearing upon host resistance. Influenza appears in swine herds following sudden drops of temperature and exposure to cold, sleet, and rain. Hens which are naturally resistant to the anthrax bacillus may be infected with that organism when submerged in cold water which lowers their normal temperature. The reverse effect of cold is noted in cold-blooded animals: frogs die quickly with "red leg" when kept in warm water, but deaths cease when the water is decreased in temperature by a block of ice. The effect of fatigue on susceptibility is illustrated by the classical experiment of placing white rats, which are normally resistant to anthrax, upon a tread mill, and then injecting them with anthrax bacilli. After they have become fatigued, they will succumb to the disease. The genetic constitution of the host is a factor in resistance. Strains of chickens which are resistant to *Sal. pullorum* infection have been produced by inbreeding; likewise, strains of mice which are resistant to mouse typhoid have been produced.

In summary, virulence depends upon, (1) the toxins and enzymes produced, (2) the number of invaders, (3) the specificity of bacterial products for certain types of tissue, (4) the inherent resistance of the host, and (5) the factors which alter that resistance.

Transmission of Infectious Agents. Pathogenic microorganisms are transmitted from infected to susceptible animals in a variety of ways. Many species of bacteria are not capable of existing for long periods of time away from the body of the live animal. Other species are able to exist for long periods when protected from the action of sunlight and putrefaction. Certain species, especially the spore-forming types, remain viable after indefinite periods away from the host.

The majority of infections are transmitted by direct or indirect contact with animals harboring the infection. The habit of licking, characteristic of some animals, is a ready means of transmission. This is illustrated by the spread of diarrhea among calves and brucellosis among cattle. Rabies is spread among animals and to man by the bite of animals infected with the virus of that disease. The spread of mastitis among dairy cattle is due to the transmission of the microorganisms on the hands of the milker and by contaminated mechanical milking equipment. The streptococci of scarlet fever and septic sore throat are occasionally transmitted from infected milkers to the udder of the cow and then to man through the raw milk supply. Animals do not need to show symptoms of disease to eliminate pathogenic organisms. Many harbor the infection for some time after apparent recovery. Such is the case in *Sal. pullorum* infection: an infected chick may recover and grow to be a normal hen, but the organism will be localized in the ovary, and be transmitted from there. As a result of infection, animals may become immune to further effects of the organism, and yet they may harbor and eliminate organisms in great numbers. Typhoid fever in man is a typical example. Some people who recover from typhoid fever remain immune carriers. Bacteria are eliminated in the feces, which may contaminate water and milk supplies. Beyond any doubt, such conditions prevail among animals, and the persistence of infection of various kinds in herds is explained by the presence of the immune carrier. Animals may harbor pathogenic bacteria without revealing symptoms of disease. Cows may harbor and transmit *Brucella abortus*, the organism of brucellosis, yet they may never have aborted nor shown any other marked evidence of infection. The role of the goat in the transmission of undulant fever to man by the milk supply is another example. Animals of one species may harbor infectious agents but may not be visibly affected, yet when these agents are transmitted to animals of another species serious infection results. This is commonly referred to as *inapparent infection*. Pseudorabies is a good example. This virus disease is most severe in the bovine yet is not easily transmitted from animal to animal of that species. Swine do harbor the virus yet are not severely affected; in fact, in many outbreaks they are not visibly abnormal. Such animals do transmit the virus to the skin of cattle by biting or rubbing the skin with the snout.

Ticks, fleas, lice, and mosquitoes are often involved in the transmission of infection. In some of the protozoan infections, such as malaria, the passage of the parasites through the mosquito is an essential step in the life cycle. Bacteria are passively transferred by the blood-sucking parts of various arthropods, with no evidence of the presence of a bacterial life cycle which is completed by passage through an intermediate host. Bacteria, classed as Rickettsia, live in the cells lining the intestine of certain lice and ticks, from which they are transmitted to man causing such diseases as typhus and Rocky Mountain spotted fever. The length of time which pathogenic bacteria may survive in the transmitting insect is not known; in some instances, they apparently remain viable for a considerable period of time. The following diseases are known to be transmitted in this manner: bubonic plague in man and rodents by the rat flea, tularemia in man and rodents by ticks and blood-sucking flies, typhus and trench fever in man by lice, Rocky Mountain spotted fever in man by ticks, yellow fever in man by the mosquito, equine encephalomyelitis by mosquitoes and probably other blood-sucking insects, and anthrax in animals by blood-sucking flies.

The house fly is of importance in the transfer of pathogenic bacteria. This is especially true of typhoid fever because flies feed upon human feces which may contain typhoid bacteria and then feed upon or light upon dairy equipment, or directly upon food intended for human consumption.

Bacteria are transported from place to place by the dust of the air. Pullorum disease among chicks is spread by the soft down from chicks and by dust in the brooder house. Spores of bacteria and some of the more resistant actinomyces are spread for considerable distances by dust; this contaminates soil to which animals have access.

The living habits of animals make possible the spread of disease by the medium of the soil. Such diseases are generally due to spore-forming bacteria which enter the deeper tissues of the body through wounds. Tetanus is an excellent example of this method of transmission. The foods of animals are easily contaminated by bacteria of all types—the intestinal bacteria, those that are spore-forming, and even those of the respiratory tract; in fact, most of the secretions and excretions of animals have ample opportunities of reaching the food and water which animals consume. The watering tank on the farm is often a source of infection to the whole herd. Flowing streams have been known to carry the spores of anthrax bacilli for considerable distances. Experiments have revealed that tuberculosis is sometimes spread by streams.

The transmission of disease among animals by coition is not of common occurrence; however, suppurative infections involving the genital organs of the bovine and equine are spread in this manner. Gonorrhea and syphilis are excellent examples of diseases of man which are commonly spread by sexual contact.

Atria of Infection. The avenue through which an organism gains entrance to the body is called its *portal of entry* or its infection atrium. An infection arising from contact with infective external objects is termed *exogenous;* one caused by organisms constantly or normally present in the body or on it is termed *endogenous.* Infection frequently occurs through a break in the continuity of the skin or mucous membranes caused by wounds, the bites of animals, and blood-sucking parasites. Ordinarily, the intact skin is an efficient barrier against infection, but microorganisms occasionally enter through the glands or hair follicles. Some bacteria, such as the diphtheria bacillus, injure the unbroken mucous surface. Some disease organisms are known to have passed unharmed through the intestinal walls and to have entered the lymph vessels and the thoracic duct.

The lungs constitute the infection atrium in some types of pneumonia, probably in many cases of tuberculosis and aspergillosis. Many other infectious agents, especially the viruses, may enter into the general circulation through this channel.

The genital tract is the common infection atrium in syphilis and gonorrhea of man. *Brucella abortus* infection in cows frequently involves the cotyledons arriving there via the blood stream. The entrance of this organism through the external genitalia rarely occurs.

Cryptogenic infections are those in which it is impossible to determine the infection atrium. In some cases of tetanus, for example, careful search fails to reveal the channel through which the organism reaches the deeper tissues where toxin is liberated.

The path by which the organism enters the body of the host usually determines the type of infection which results. As a general rule, microorganisms show a marked specificity, or affinity, for certain types of tissue; for example, the typhoid bacillus infects intestinal tissue and the pneumococcus infects pulmonary tissue. These organisms, therefore, cause the typical disease when they gain access directly to the susceptible tissue; neither is dangerous when entrance is made through scratches in the skin. The reverse is true of tetanus which most frequently results from the penetration of the skin by sharp objects which introduce the spores of the organism; however, the organism can be isolated from the intestines and feces of normal animals. A few species of bacteria produce disease when entering by any or all of the infection atria; for example, the tularemia organism causes infection when it enters scratches in the skin, wounds caused by insect bites, the conjunctiva of the eye, the lungs, on dust particles or hair, and when taken into the intestinal tract in infected food. Some bacteria produce no lesions at the site of entry but localize at distant points. *Brucella abortus* enters through the digestive tract but most frequently involves lymphoid, uterine, and mammary tissues.

The Normal Protective Mechanism of the Animal Body. A discussion of the relationship of microorganisms to disease would not be complete without a brief description of the normal mechanism by which all animals are protected against infection. That this mechanism is an efficient one is apparent when one considers all of the possibilities of infection which animals encounter in their daily life; in fact, it is only when this natural protection fails to function that infection results. The type of tissue, the nature of secretions and their drainage, acidity, and alkalinity all function in normal protection against the infection.

The Skin. The hair coat of mammals and the feathers of birds serve to protect the skin. The layer of epithelial cells of the normal skin constitutes an effective barrier against bacterial invasion. The skin of animals is constantly covered with bacteria which are potentially disease-producing when they invade the subcutaneous tissues. Many bacteria do penetrate into the crypts of sweat glands and into hair follicles from which they enter into deeper tissues. Even under such conditions they encounter an additional protective mechanism, the tissue phagocytes.

The Mucous Membranes. The epithelial covering of the mucous membranes also constitutes an effective barrier against bacteria. This tissue is constantly bathed in mucus which prevents bacteria from becoming established in crypts and folds. The mucous membranes of the eyes are continually washed by lacrimal secretion and those of the external genitalia and the urinary tract are periodically flushed with urine which prevents the lodgement of bacteria.

The Lungs. The mucous membranes, the mucus, and the tortuous characteristic of the nasal cavity protect the upper air passages against infection and also prevent the passage of dust particles into the lower part of the pulmonary system. The trachea is lined with mucous membrane, and in the bronchi ciliated epithelium tends to sweep foreign particles outward; however, when bacteria surmount these barriers and reach the bronchioles and alveoli, infection results if they are in sufficient numbers to overcome the humoral and cellular defense of those tissues. The act of coughing makes it possible for bacteria to be carried outward in the mucus in which they have been entrapped.

The Intestinal Tract. The epithelial and mucous cells are most valuable barriers against infection throughout the digestive canal. Various secretions, however, have a protective function in addition to being primarily concerned with the digestion of food. Saliva has a feeble germicidal power and, in addition, keeps the mouth and esophagus bathed. Gastric juice is definitely inhibitory to many kinds of bacteria and their toxins because of the high hydrogen-ion concentration. Arnold has shown that the pH of the upper part of the intestinal tract governs the bacterial flora found there and that alteration of the pH toward alkalinity causes the anterior movement of lower intestinal types of bacteria. The peristaltic movement of the intestinal tract prevents the lodgement of bacteria, and accumulated masses of bacteria are dispersed by the constant mixing of the intestinal contents.

The Genito-urinary Tract. Previous mention has been made of the protective value of epithelium, mucous secretion, and urine lavage to the urinary tract and external genitalia. These factors prevent the establishment of infection in such tissues unless there has been massive contamination. The function of the urinary bladder as a collecting reservoir for urine prevents, except in rare instances, the ascent of bacteria into the ureters. The vital reproductive glands, testes and ovaries, are protected from external contamination by tortuous tubes which connect them with external parts. In the female the ciliated epithelium of the fallopian tubes serves as a noteworthy obstacle to bacteria. In the pregnant animal the cervix is sealed with a tenacious substance which is a most effective protection for the developing embryo.

The Eyes and Ears. The eyelashes and eyelids protect the eyes against foreign objects which may be contaminated with bacteria. The voluntary response of lacrimal glands when foreign particles do reach the eye aids in diluting the invading substance, and if it is not too heavy or does not become lodged, it will wash it away. The delicate mechanism of hearing is protected by the shell of the ear, the ear hairs, and ear wax. The invasion of the ear by bacteria from the exterior is extremely rare.

The Proof of the Relationship of a Microorganism to a Disease—Koch's Rules. In order to prove the relationship of an organism to a disease Koch proposed rules which must be fulfilled. The finding of an organism in diseased tissue is not enough proof that the organism is the cause. Koch found that:

1. The organism must be found in each case of disease.
2. The organism must be isolated and grown in pure culture.
3. The organism must reproduce the disease in the susceptible animal or in suitable experimental animals.
4. The organism must be isolated from the tissues of the experimental animal in pure culture.

These rules or postulates have been of great value in the study of infectious diseases since the time of Koch, and the observance of them has formed a firm basis for medical bacteriology. These rules have been fulfilled in practically all of the infectious diseases. In some cases it has been found difficult to satisfy each of the requirements, and exceptions based on the following reasons have been acknowledged:

(a) Organisms which have grown on artificial media for some time may dissociate to such an extent that virulence is lost. They are no longer able to reproduce the disease. Some strains of bacteria may be isolated directly from the infected animal and not be able to reproduce the disease until they have been increased in virulence by serial passage through experimental animals.

(b) One organism may be most effective in the presence of another one. This synergistic action has been proven in the relationship of the virus of swine influenza and the organism *Hemophilus suis.*

(c) In some cases the filtrable viruses cannot be grown on artificial media, but when living tissues are used in which viruses will multiply, even this rule can be fulfilled.

The relationship of an organism to the disease also is obtained by the use of serological tests, such as agglutination, precipitation, and protein sensitization.

Inoculation of Animals. In addition to the proving of the relationship of a microorganism to a disease, animals are inoculated for the following purposes:

1. To maintain microorganisms that do not grow on artificial media.
    (a) Viruses.
    (b) Rickettsia.
    (c) Spirochetes.
2. To obtain a pure culture of an organism.
    (a) When mixed with other bacteria.
    (b) When present in small numbers.
    (c) When the organism grows poorly on artificial media.
3. To determine virulence or toxicity.
4. To produce vaccines and aggressins for immunizing purposes, e.g.:
    (a) Rabies vaccine.
    (b) Canine distemper vaccine.
5. To produce antisera which are used for therapeutic or diagnostic purposes.
6. To standardize toxins and antitoxins.
7. To increase the virulence of bacteria which have been grown on artificial media for some time.

Animals may be inoculated by numerous parenteral methods. *Parenteral* methods are those in which material is inoculated into body tissues by any route except the intestinal tract. The method which is used in the inoculation of animals is governed by the type of organism, the type of material which is to be injected, and the purpose of the inoculation. Any of the following methods may be used:

1. *Cutaneous.* The material is placed upon or rubbed into the skin.
2. *Intracutaneous, intradermal.* The material is injected into the skin. Proteins, such as tuberculin, are usually injected in this manner to determine hypersensitivity.
3. *Subcutaneous.* Inoculation just beneath the skin is the most common method used in the study of bacteria.

4. *Intramuscular.* The inoculum is injected into the body of large muscles, such as those in the neck and the gluteal region.
5. *Intravenous.* The material is injected directly into a vein. The vein which is chosen varies with the different animals. In the rabbit the posterior auricular vein is used. In the horse, cow, and sheep the jugular vein is used. If rapid action is desired, this method is most frequently employed.
6. *Intracardial.* In small animals, such as rabbit and guinea pig, the material is injected directly into the heart.
7. *Intrathoracic.* Injections into the thorax are not made commonly.
8. *Intraperitoneal.* In guinea pigs this method is used for the injection of pathogenic bacteria in the process of diagnosis.
9. *Intraneural.* This method is not used except in the study of certain neurotropic viruses.
10. *Intracranial.* Injections are made directly into the cranium usually through a trephine opening or by means of a sharp, heavy needle at thin parts of the skull. The material is injected into the brain substance or subdurally.
11. *Intraocular.* Substances which affect the eye are placed beneath the eyelids, injected into the cornea, or into the anterior chamber.
12. *Intraspinal.* In some cases it is necessary to inject material directly into the spinal canal.
13. *Inhalation.* Material in the form of vapor or dust is inhaled into the deeper air passages.
14. *Intrapulmonary.* Substances are injected into the lungs.
15. *Intratracheal.* Fluids are injected into the trachea.
16. *Oral.* Material is fed or injected through a stomach tube.
17. *Rectal.* Fluids are injected into the rectum by an enema.
18. *Intramammary.* Drugs are commonly injected into the mammary gland of the bovine for the treatment of mastitis.

General Types of Infectious Diseases. After the animal body has been invaded, the type of organism, its specificity for tissue, the resistance of the individual, and the infection atrium will determine the localization or distribution of the organism and the type of disease produced.

Most bacterial infections are due to one species of an organism, and are termed *primary infections.* Many infections, however, are due to the presence of more than one species of organism. Since it is difficult to determine which organism is responsible for the condition, the disease is called a *mixed infection.* If a primary infection is followed by the invasion of another species of organism, the condition is termed a *secondary infection*. Organisms causing secondary infections are capable of producing primary infections. In some cases, the way must be prepared for the infection of a secondary organism. This is the case in swine influenza, in which the primary invading agent is a filtrable virus which produces an inflammation in the respiratory mucous membrane which is then conducive to invasion by the bacterium *Hemophilus suis*. The occurrence of mixed and secondary infections complicates the diagnosis of disease.

After invading the body, many organisms remain localized, producing *focal infections*. The localized lesions may remain quiescent until healed or the organism may gain access to the lymph or blood stream and be carried to other parts of the body. If the organism is carried to other parts of the body where it again localizes and produces abscesses, the condition is called *pyemia*.

Bacteriemia is a general term which denotes the presence of bacteria in the blood-vascular system. If these bacteria are of a certain type, such as the hemolytic streptococci, acute disease may result. *Septicemia* is the term given to such an infectious disease which is accompanied by fever, rapid pulse rate, and marked prostration. Pathologically, such a condition is characterized by petechial hemorrhages, hyperemia and edema; also degenerative changes in parenchymatous tissues.

Certain species of bacteria, notably the diphtheria and tetanus bacilli, produce potent toxins which cause tissue changes by which the diseases are recognized. In tetanus, the organism gains entrance through skin wounds. It localizes in subcutaneous tissues where it produces the toxin which finds its way to the central nervous system by way of the motor nerves and the lymph and blood streams.

A disease produced by toxin liberated by an organism and being disseminated throughout the body by the blood stream is called a *toxemia*. The term toxemia is used quite generally in clinical medicine to mean a condition in which toxic materials of any kind are considered the cause of the symptoms. In a later chapter the criteria for the term toxin will be discussed in detail.

A condition which results from the absorption of the end-products of tissue disintegration is called *sapremia*. The absorption of the products of the decomposition of dead fetuses and retained placental membranes causes such a condition.

The diseases which are characterized by skin eruptions are known as *exanthematous* diseases. Scarlet fever, measles, cow pox, and swine erysipelas are typical examples.

REFERENCES FOR FURTHER STUDY

Barber, M. A. Jour. Exp. Med. 6:634, 1909.

Bernheimer, A. W., and Cantoni, G. L. Jour. Exp. Med. 81:295–306, 1945.

Burnett, F. M. Biological Aspects of Infectious Disease. Cambridge University Press, Cambridge, 1940.

Cantoni, G. L., and Bernheimer, A. W. Jour. Exp. Med. 81:307–13, 1945.

Christensen, L. R. Jour. Gen. Physiol. 28:363–83, 1945.

———, and MacLeod, C. M. Jour. Gen. Physiol. 28:559–83, 1945.

Crowley, N. Jour. Path. and Bact. 56:27–35, 1944.

Dubos, R. J. The Bacterial Cell. Harvard University Press, Cambridge, 1945.

Duran-Reynals, F. Jour. Exp. Med. 58:161–81, 1933.

———. Bact. Rev. 6:197–252, 1942.

Gay, F. P., *et al.* Agents of Disease and Host Resistance. Chaps. 2, 3, 4, 5, 14. Charles C. Thomas, Baltimore, 1935.

Gladstone, G. P. Brit. Jour. Exp. Path. 27:394–418, 1946.

Hale, J. H., and Smith, W. Brit. Jour. Exp. Path. 26:209–16, 1945.

Herbert, D., and Todd, E. W. Biochem. Jour. 35:1124–39, 1941.

———, ———. Brit. Jour. Exp. Path. 25:242–54, 1944.

Kass, E. H., and Seastone, C. V. Jour. Exp. Med. 79:319–30, 1944.

Lancefield, R. C. The Harvey Lectures. Pp. 251–90, 1940–41.

MacFarlane, M. G., and Knight, B. C. J. G. Biochem. Jour. 35:884–902, 1941.

MacFarlane, R. G., and MacLennon, J. D. Lancet. 2(249):328–31, 1945.

MacLeod, C. M., and Pappenheimer, A. M. Bacterial and Mycotic Infections of Man. Pp. 68–89, J. B. Lippincott Co., Philadelphia, 1948.

Pasteur, L. Compt. rend. Acad. Sci. 92:209–11, 1881.

Rogers, H. J. Biochem. Jour. 40:5883–88, 1946.

Smith, Theobald. Parasitism and Disease. Princeton University Press, Princeton, 1934.

Smith, D. T., and Martin, D. S. Zinsser's Textbook of Bacteriology. 9th Ed. Appleton-Century-Crofts, Inc., New York, 1948.

Tillett, W. S., and Garner, R. L. Jour. Exp. Med. 58:485–502, 1933.

Todd, E. W. Jour. Path. and Bact. 67:423–45, 1938.

———. Jour. Exp. Med. 85:591–606, 1947.

Topley, W. W. C., Wilson, G. S., and Miles, A. D. Principles of Bacteriology and Immunity. 3rd Ed. Williams & Wilkins Co., Baltimore, 1946.

Watson, D. W., Cromartie, W. J., Bloom, W. L., Kegeles, G., and Heckly, R. J. Jour. Inf. Dis. 80:28–40, 1947.

8. | The Principles of Immunity

The relationship of the host to infection has been discussed but it is well to emphasize that infectious disease is a result of the coming together of two factors, a virulent organism and a susceptible host. Variability in the susceptibility of the host to virulent microorganisms has been a fascinating study since the germ theory of disease was established. Different species of animals vary in resistance to a given microorganism, and individual animals within the species also show the same type of resistance. The term *immunity* is used to express relative resistance to disease. It is defined more exactly as follows: Immunity is a condition in which an individual, or a species of animal, exhibits unusual or complete resistance to an infection for which other individuals, or other species, show a greater degree of susceptibility.

Immunity, as disease, is a relative term, and depends upon the operation of many variable factors, such as, the kind of organism, the dissociative state of the organism, the channels by which the organism invades, the mechanical resistance of the animal body, and the normal action of the leucocytes and blood plasma.

TYPES OF IMMUNITY

Immunity is divided into two types, *natural* and *acquired*. Natural immunity is subdivided into *species* immunity and *individual* immunity. Acquired immunity is either *active* or *passive*.

Natural Immunity. Most species of animals are immune to diseases which are found in other species. Typical examples are: horses are immune to the virus of hog cholera; swine are immune to equine encephalomyelitis; man is immune to canine distemper. This resistance, or immunity, is congenital, and since it is a function of species, it is known as *species immunity*. In certain instances, individuals within the species appear to be more resistant to a particular disease than others. In an outbreak of hog cholera in a herd of pigs, some never show marked symptoms of the disease. This is known as *individual immunity*, and may be explained by the fact that light cases of the disease may have occurred without detection. This explanation is considered more valid when the presence of some degree of immunity is revealed by the inoculation of hog cholera virus.

Acquired Immunity. Animals which are susceptible to disease are immunized in a variety of ways. If a durable immunity is desired, the animal must be injected with the organism, or its products, which stimulates the body cells to produce substances which prevent the growth of invading organisms. Since the cells of the immunized animal are active in producing the immune substances, or antibodies, the phenomenon is called *active* immunity. In some cases antibodies are transferred from an immune animal to a susceptible one in the serum. The recipient of the serum is rendered immune, but its body cells have not produced the immunizing substances. This is called *passive* immunity.

Active Immunity. Immunization of an animal is brought about by the various methods listed in the following outline:

A. By once having a natural case of the disease.
B. By injection of living microorganisms (vaccines).
    1. Nonlethal doses.
    2. Attenuated
        (a) By growing upon artificial culture media.
        (b) By growing at temperatures higher than normal.
        (c) By heating to 56°–60°C.
        (d) By growing in the presence of weak antiseptics.
        (e) By animal passage.
C. By injection of dead organisms (bacterins).
D. By injection of the products of organisms (filtrates or aggressins).
E. By injection of unaltered toxins in nonlethal doses or toxins which have been subjected to various attenuating processes (anatoxins or toxoids).

Bacteria and filtrable viruses vary in ability to produce immunity while they are causing an active case of infection. Some produce a relatively permanent and durable immunity, as is true for smallpox in man and canine distemper. Bacteria affecting the intestinal tract often cause an immunity which persists for the season. Many diseases, glanders and tuberculosis for example, do not result in any immunity. There is some evidence that the streptococci, with the exception of toxin-producing strains, do not produce immunity; in fact, they may produce an increased susceptibility.

Sublethal doses of pathogenic bacteria are injected to produce immunity in some diseases. In the bovine, for example, a certain amount of resistance against Brucellosis is conferred by the injection of living organisms in small doses. The method is a dangerous one to follow in the large majority of diseases because the resistance of individual animals is variable. When an animal has once developed some immunity, however, large doses of fully virulent organisms can be given to increase the immunity.

An active acquired immunity is commonly produced by the injection of bacteria which have been *attenuated,* that is, reduced in virulence. The methods by which bacteria are attenuated must be carefully controlled, however, so the chemical fraction of the organism which is responsible for cell stimulation, with subsequent antibody formation, is not destroyed. Some strains of organisms are relatively avirulent; yet they are able to produce an immunity against fully virulent strains.

In some of his earliest experiments in the field of immunity, Pasteur found that the fowl cholera organism was reduced in virulence when grown on artificial media; yet, when it was injected it was able to produce a resistance in chickens against virulent strains. He also demonstrated that the anthrax bacillus was attenuated when grown at 42°C. Such cultures were used to produce immunity against anthrax. Both of these fundamental methods are still used to reduce bacterial virulence. Sporeforming organisms, such as those causing blackleg and anthrax, are reduced in virulence when the spores are subjected to high temperatures. Phenol, formalin, ether, chloroform, and certain dyes are all used for the attenuation of various bacteria and viruses. Some bacteria and viruses are reduced in virulence by animal passage. The virus of smallpox, for example, is so attenuated by growing on the abdominal wall of cattle that it is used in smallpox vaccination.

The injection of dead bacteria (bacterins) stimulates the body cells to produce antibodies. The method of killing bacteria for this purpose varies; some prefer heat at 60°C. while others prefer chemicals, such as phenol and formalin.

The chemical bacterial components which are responsible for stimulating body cells to produce antibodies are liberated upon the death and disintegration of the bacterial cells. These disintegration products are used in the preparation of substances known as *filtrates* and *aggressins.* When bouillon cultures of bacteria have grown for several days, the surviving bacteria are removed by passing the medium through a porcelain filter. The filtrate is used for injecting animals in producing immunity. Live animals are sometimes used to produce aggressins. The process is the same as in the manufacture of a culture filtrate, except that the animal is the medium instead of the bouillon in a culture flask. The animal succumbs, and the body tissues and fluids, which contain the disintegration products of bacteria, are collected and filtered.

Some species of bacteria are grown in an artificial medium where they produce specific poison called *toxin*. This is separated from the bacteria by the process of filtration and is used to inject animals to induce the development of an active immunity. Toxin may be subjected to attenuating processes which do not alter its ability to stimulate body cells but which do destroy its ability to produce symptoms and lesions of disease. This will be discussed in greater detail in the following chapter.

Passive Immunity. After an animal has been immunized by the injection of any of the materials listed under active immunity, antibodies are present in the blood plasma. Susceptible animals are rendered temporarily immune by receiving injections of serum from an animal previously immunized. The passive immunity is only temporary, not lasting longer than four weeks in most cases. This period may be long enough, however, to protect the animal or herd through periods of exposure. Immune serum is used in conjunction with living organisms and toxins in producing a more lasting immunity. In hog cholera immunization, virus is injected simultaneously with immune serum. The virus produces death if injected alone; the immune serum prevents this, yet it allows enough of a body reaction to produce immunity. Immune serum is used, also, in the treatment of animals sick with a disease. If administered soon enough and in doses sufficiently large, the life of the animal is saved.

ANTIGENS AND ANTIBODIES

Antigens are those substances which, when introduced into the animal body, stimulate certain body cells to produce modified globulins, commonly called antibodies.

Antibodies are modified globulins produced in the animal body in response to the injection of antigens and reacting specifically with the antigens which have been injected so that they may be phagocytized, agglutinated, precipitated, or lysed. These reactions may occur *in vivo* or they may be demonstrated *in vitro* by suitable procedures.

Nature of Antigen. The definition of an antigen may imply that a wide range of chemical substances would qualify. Such is not the case. The best antigens are those with large molecules of high molecular weight, 10,000 or higher. Antigenic substances cannot pass through collodion or cellophane membranes nor can they pass through the walls of veins in the animal body. They are colloidal in solution. Substances which are weakly antigenic may be adsorbed on charcoal, collodion particles, or kaolin, which makes them more antigenic.

First, it was believed that only proteins possessed antigenic properties. Subsequent investigations have revealed that certain lipides, especially lecithin and cholesterol, when mixed with antigenic proteins will stimulate the formation of antibodies. The presence of a polysaccharide in combination with protein in the capsules of pneumococci is responsible for the type specificity of those microorganisms. The nature of the linkage between cell protein and polysaccharide is not known. The carbohydrate substances in their pure isolated state do not function as antigens, hence they are referred to as *partial-antigens* or *haptenes*. The specificity of the pneumococci, therefore, seems to depend on the ability to synthesize type-specific polysaccharide. Although the best antigenic substances are protein or at least linked with protein, not all protein substances are good antigens. Simple proteins, such as protamines, are not antigenic. Gelatin is nonantigenic. Erythrocytes are excellent antigens but hemoglobin is poorly antigenic.

In general any large protein molecule from any source is antigenic. Plant and animal proteins are antigenic. An animal's own protein does not serve as an antigen when injected into itself. The only known exception to this rule is the lens of the eye. This substance will act as an antigen upon injection but the antibody produced is lens antibody, having no relationship with the type specific protein of the animal from which it originated.

All antigens are highly specific. The protein of the oak leaf is different than the walnut leaf; horse serum is different than cow serum; sheep erythrocytes are different than rabbit erythrocytes; the muscle protein of the chicken is different than that of the duck. This specificity obviously resides in the structural differences of protein molecules. It is assumed that only certain parts of the molecule determines specificity and it is probable that the arrangement of amino acids is most important.

The study of the antigenic structure of bacteria has shown that the proteins of which the cells are composed are not entirely the same. The exact location of these various proteins in the bacterial cell is not known; nor is it probable that they ever will be known. The presence of a specific flagellar antigen has been determined. Our present knowledge, therefore, permits the designation of three known types of bacterial antigen determined by location: (1) flagellar antigen (H antigen), (2) capsular antigen, or carbohydrate substance, and (3) somatic (body) antigen (O antigen) — the remainder of the bacterial cell. That somatic antigen is composed of a variety of combinations of proteins is demonstrated by the agglutination test which will be described in detail in a later chapter; however, it is well to describe the relationship of antigenic structure to the determination of bacterial species at this time. As early as 1901 Durham showed that a single species of bacteria was composed of a multiplicity, a mosaic, of antigens. Denoting the different antigenic components of the bacterial cell by small letters and the corresponding antibody in the antiserum by large letters, he explained this multiplicity as follows:

Antigen		*Antibody*	
Bacterium 1.	a,b,c,d,e.	Serum 1.	A,B,C,D,E.
Bacterium 2.	c,d,e,f,g,h.	Serum 2.	C,D,E,F,G,H.
Bacterium 3.	e,f,g,h,j,k.	Serum 3.	E,F,G,H,J,K.

The serum prepared by the injection of Bacterium 1 agglutinates that organism. It also agglutinates Bacterium 2 because it contains antibodies for antigens c,d,e which are in that organism. It partially agglutinates Bacterium 3 because antibody E specific for antigen is present.

Individual natural immunity is partially explained by the presence of proteins of like nature in a number of unrelated species of bacteria or animals. The linkage of a protein with a different kind of chemical substance creates *heterophile antigen,* commonly called Forssmann antigen; for example, the injection of an emulsion of guinea pig viscera into a rabbit produces an antibody which causes the hemolysis of the red blood cells of the sheep. It is evident that an antigenic material of some sort is common to the guinea pig and to sheep red blood cells. This common antigen is an alcohol-soluble lipoid linked with protein. The lipoid alone will not stimulate the formation of heterophile antibody. Antigens of a heterogenous nature have been found in other types of tissue as well as in bacteria, yeasts, and Rickettsia. Heterophile antigens are classified into four groups: (1) those common to different species of bacteria; (2) those common to different classes of microorganisms (bacteria and yeasts); (3) those common to various species of bacteria and animal tissue; and (4) those common to different species of animals.

The addition of substances called *adjuvants* to suspensions of bacteria enhance their antigenic qualities. Aluminum potassium phosphate (alum), aluminum hydroxide, calcium phosphate, mineral oil, and water-in-oil emulsions are all used as adjuvants. None of these substances is in itself antigenic. The increased production of antibody following their use is presumed to be due to a slower absorption of the antigen with a resulting longer period of stimulation of antibody-forming cells.

It must be noted that the term antigen is also used in connection with certain diagnostic tests. These antigens may be the same as those used to stimulate the formation of antibody, but some may be different. For example, a suspension of bacteria may be injected in order to stimulate the formation of antibody and some of the same suspension may be used in performing the agglutination test. But in many instances the antigen used in the diagnostic test may be different. In the precipitation test it may be an extract of the bacterial suspension. Complicated antigens, which may be used for diagnosis, are sometimes artificially prepared. A protein may be used to coat erythrocytes, a process known as *sensitization*. The protein suspension may have been injected into the body of an experimental animal to produce antibody. The serum from this animal, when added to the suspension of sensitized erythrocytes, will cause them to clump together or agglutinate. The application of antigens in diagnostic tests will be described more fully in subsequent chapters.

Nature of Antibody. Antibody is any substance which is present in blood plasma and is able to neutralize and sensitize the antigen which stimulated its production. Although the specific nature of antibody is implied, it is not definitely stated. Antibody is specific for the antigen which stimulated its production, and antibody is produced as the result of antigen stimulation. One exception to this statement must be emphasized, however, for in most animals *normal antibodies* are detected for many antigens. The relationship of normal antibody to immune antibody has been and still is relatively unknown. The obvious explanation is that the normal is only a slight manifestation of the immune. That normal antibody is responsible for natural immunity does not appear to be true because many naturally immune animals do not possess any normal antibody against the organism to which they are naturally immune; likewise, many susceptible animals may show the presence of normal antibody for the organism to which they are susceptible. Normal and immune antibodies are both highly specific and both cause the same type of reaction which characterizes immune phenomena; for example, normal antibody specific for *Brucella abortus* may be found in bovine serum which will cause the agglutination of a suspension of the organism in a low titer, 1:25. When found in an infected cow, this antibody does not appear to differ from the immune antibody which will cause agglutination of a suspension of *Br. abortus* in a titer of 1:200. The latter titer is diagnostic of the disease while the former is not. The presence of *normal antibodies* for different antigens in the body of a normal animal is not readily explained. In general, normal antibodies may be divided into *four groups*. The *first group* is composed of antibodies which have been formed as a result of an unknown contact of the animal with the specific antigen. The *second group* is composed of antibodies which are formed as a result of heterophile antigen. A *third group* is made up of isoantibodies which are inherited characteristics, of which the isoagglutinin in blood grouping is the best example. The *fourth group* is more indefinite than the other three and is made up of antibody which is formed as a result of physiological maturity (Jungeblut and Engle).

Normal as well as immune antibodies have never been separated from protein. When antiserum is subjected to fractional precipitation, the antibody property is always found in the globulin fraction. The use of the Tiselius apparatus has characterized proteins by their rate of migration in an electric field of a known strength. This process, known as *electrophoresis,* has made possible the separation of normal horse serum into four different components. These are, albumin and three globulins, designated α (alpha), β (beta), and γ (gamma). The determination of the electrophoretic pattern of different serums containing antibodies has revealed that the antibodies are found in γ globulin, however some antibodies may be a mixture of β and γ globulin. Cameron demonstrated that as little as 4 ml. of γ globulin obtained from pigs protected 35 lb. pigs against 2 ml. of hog cholera virus. The same material agglutinated *Brucella abortus* and *Brucella suis* at a titer of 1:160. The fraction from bovine plasma gave a titer of 1:1280. Tests with other fractions proved beyond doubt that the agglutinins for Brucella are contained in γ globulin. If the presence of antibodies modifies the chemical characteristics of serum globulin, no one up to the present has been able to detect it. It appears true, then, that antibody is γ globulin altered in some way so that it reacts specifically with antigen. The injection of large numbers of different antigens into an animal causes the formation of an equal number of specific antibodies. This fact has led to the assumption that antibody is composed partly of the antigen for which it is specific. The tremendous amount of antibody formed by a small amount of antigen injected tends to disprove this assumption; furthermore, the injection of an antigen, such as R-salt-azobenzidin azo-egg albumen, a red compound, does not produce an antibody containing any of the red color (Heidelberger and Kendall).

Formation of Antibody. The alteration of globulin, antibody formation, takes place in those cells which are responsible for the production of globulin. The detection of the cells which are responsible has been the subject of much investigation. The extirpation of the spleen, the blockage of the reticulo-endothelial system by the use of colloidal particles, and the injury to the hematopoietic tissues, such as bone marrow, by the use of benzene have all tended to show that antibody is produced by the cells of the spleen, lymph glands, bone marrow, and by reticulo-endothelial cells throughout the body.

The production of antibody by tissue cultures of spleen and bone marrow further substantiates the role of such cells and indicates that the mechanism is not under the control of nerve impulses.

Harris and Ehrich, also Murphy and Sturm, have shown that lymphocytes may be a significant source of antibodies. By using fluorescence microscopy Kaplan, Coons, and Deane have determined the localization of various antigens in tissue cells. Pneumococcal polysaccharides were found in greatest concentration in the cells of the reticulo-endothelial system, the ordinary epithelium, and in fibroblasts. The presence of antigens in cells, however, does not prove the antibody-producing function of those cells.

The mechanism by which antigen stimulates body cells to produce antibody is not entirely solved. Although untenable in light of present day knowledge, the explanation of antibody production by Ehrlich has served a very useful purpose, for in seeking to disprove it, investigators have contributed much to the knowledge of the subject. Since Ehrlich's *lateral-chain* or *side-chain theory* of immunity has been of such interest in the past and is of great historical value, a description of it is given here, not, however, with the assumption that it explains antibody production.

In 1885 Ehrlich discussed the fundamental principle of cell nutrition. He contended that nutritive material was used by a cell only when the cell possessed a structure to which the food material became attached. Cell protoplasm was composed of a large central atom group with numerous side-chains, to which the large variety of nutrient materials became fixed and which then entered into cell metabolism. His central atom group may be illustrated with the structural formula of benzene.

$$
\begin{array}{c}
H \\
| \\
C \\
\diagup\;\diagdown \\
H\!-\!C \quad\; C\!-\!H \\
\| \qquad\quad | \\
H\!-\!C \quad\; C\!-\!H \\
\diagdown\;\diagup \\
C \\
| \\
H
\end{array}
$$

Any of the hydrogens can be replaced by some other atomic group, such as, COOH, NH$_2$, CHO, and OH. It is conceivable, then, that a large number of different compounds could be formed by this procedure.

Ehrlich based his side-chain theory of antibody production upon his conception of cell nutrition. Antigenic substances, such as toxins, were injurious only when cells possessed side-chains to which they could be attached. Ehrlich called the points of attachment in the cell, *receptors.* He assumed that the cells which reacted to an antigen, or a large variety of antigens, possessed a specific receptor for each type of protein substance. If the antigenic

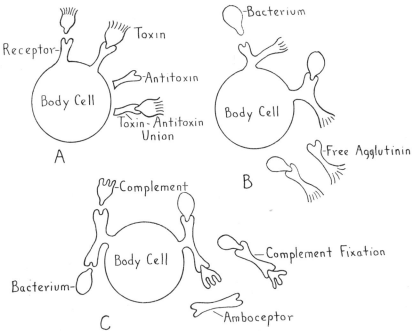

FIG. 8.1 — Diagram of Ehrlich's conception of antibodies. A, antibodies of the first order; B, antibodies of the second order; C, antibodies of the third order.

substance produced injury to the cell, the injured cell was stimulated to produce more receptors of the same type which were specific for the irritating substance. This explanation was based on the hypothesis of Weigert, that is, that an injury produced a hypercompensation on the part of tissues affected. The receptors were produced in such large numbers that they were liberated from the cell and became a part of the blood plasma. Here they became attached to the antigens and caused their neutralization. Cell receptors or antibodies of various kinds were produced, each having its definite function. Ehrlich referred to them as antibodies of the *first order, second order,* and *third order* (Fig. 8.1). Antibodies of the *first order* (antitoxin) were active in the *neutralization* of toxin. The phenomenon of *agglutination* was explained by the function of the antibodies of the *second order.* Ehrlich gave most of his attention to the *complement fixation* reaction which he explained so clearly by his descriptions of the functions of his antibodies of the *third order.*

Ehrlich's theory is no longer tenable because it is inconceivable that cells would have on hand the receptors necessary for the unlimited number of antigens which can be prepared. The cells which are irritated by the antigen have been shown to be those which, for the greatest part, are not responsible for antibody reproduction. Nerve cells, for example, do not produce antibody although they are vitally affected by tetanus toxin. It is difficult to visualize the detachment of receptors from cells and still assume that antibody production is similar to the normal physiologic functioning of cells as a nutritional process. Ehrlich's contention that antigen-antibody specificity is due to the configuration of atoms which may be represented by chemical formulae appears more true than ever. Work of recent years with synthetic antigens have shown that such may be the case.

Although Ehrlich's explanation of antibody formation is not altogether true, shadows of it are seen in the explanation of the process by Breinl and Haurowitz in 1930. They proposed that the presence of residual valencies give the globulin-forming amino acids a definite polar orientation. If foreign protein, antigen, comes in contact with such residual valencies, a reorientation of amino acids results, and as a consequence a new antibody-globulin is formed. Globulin-forming cells are unlimited in the new combinations which may be formed. Mudd, in 1932, also leaned toward the chemical explanation, basing his theory on the assumption that antibodies are modified serum globulins. He states:[1]

> . . . since antibodies are non-dialysable, it is altogether probable that at some stage they are synthesized from less complex units, such as, peptides and amino acids. As this synthesis proceeds in the presence of antigen, we may reasonably suppose some of the simpler structural units (e. g., peptides) will be combined, either stoichimetrically or by adsorption, with the antigen. Further synthesis, for instance, by the coupling of amino acids to the peptide, we suppose will now occur in an orienting environment, namely the antigen-protoplasm interface. (The terms antigen "surface" and antigen-protoplasm "interface" are used without intended implication as to whether the antigen is in molecular dispersion in micellae, or forms part of a cell surface.) Any "building stone," it is assumed, can be added to the growing antibody molecule only if it conforms to the spatial and chemical requirements of the interface in which synthesis is proceeding. In brief, the chemical groupings coupled to the molecule undergoing synthesis at the antigen surface must be adapted spatially and in their chemical affinities to the antigen surface at the region in which coupling occurs. The completed antibody molecule will possess to some degree a stereochemical correspondence with the antigen since each structural unit has been selected and oriented, at the moment of synthesis into the antibody molecule, to fit the local configuration and affinities of the antigen surface. Thus we suppose an antibody "specific" for the antigen, i. e., possessing specific stereochemical correspondence with it, to have been formed.

---

[1] Stewart Mudd. Jour. Immunol. 23:423, 1952.

Pauling has proposed a somewhat similar theory. He contends that both ends of the polypeptide chain making up the globulin molecule are altered by contact with antigen, giving the molecule its antigen-specificity.

Shades of the old Ehrlich theory are observed in the explanation of antibody formation proposed by Burnett. He believes that "adaptive" enzymes contained in antibody-forming cells are permanently modified in the process of utilizing antigens which enter such cells. These enzymes continue to produce globulins conforming to the pattern of the most persistent and recent stimulation.

Obviously the exact method by which antibody is formed is not known. That it is a result of an alteration of serum globulin either by a chemical or physical action on the globulin-secreting cells by antigen appears fundamental. Satisfactory explanations of this phenomenon by the scientists of the future will be welcome additions to scientific literature.

The variations in antibody production which are observed in natural disease, by differences in the resistance of individuals to infection, have not been explained. It has been presumed that these differences are manifestations of normal body function. Apparently, there are many factors which may influence the production of antibody in the animal body. Wissler and co-workers have noted a definite relationship of protein-reserves to antibody production. The administration of high-quality protein to protein-depleted rats led to an increased production of hemolysin. Chase, White, and Dougherty have reported that the rate of antibody production to sheep erythrocytes was increased in mice, rats, and rabbits by the subcutaneous injection of aqueous adrenal cortical extract. They suggest that the enhancement of antibody titer is due to the increased rate of release of antibody from lymphocytes affected by augmented amounts of pituitary-adrenal cortical hormones.

There is no doubt that the union of antigen with antibody is most significant in immunity. However, it must be emphasized that natural resistance to disease does not involve antigen-antibody union. For example, the resistance of the horse to the virus of hog cholera is not explained by the neutralization of the hog cholera virus by hog cholera virus-antibody in the plasma of the horse. This type of resistance was referred to earlier in this chapter under the heading *species immunity*. At this place it is logical to note a difference between natural or inheritable resistance, and immunity involving antigen-antibody union. In the example just given, hog cholera-virus-neutralizing antibody does not exist in the plasma of the horse, yet that animal is completely resistant. Numerous other examples of natural resistance could be cited as accepted facts, although not easily explained. It is well to repeat that it takes a combination of *pathogenic agent* and *susceptible host* to produce disease.

In practically every infectious disease of man and animals anti-body is formed during the infectious process. However, antibody does not appear immediately, nor does the animal become at once immune. The same generalization can be made concerning the injection of antigens into the animal in the immunizing process. The rate of production of antibody depends upon the amount of antigen injected. In general, measurable antibody does not appear until five days have elapsed. In very acute disease, the animal may die before antibody is produced. In chronic disease more antigen is released from infected tissue, furthermore, there is prolonged release of antigen, so a greater antibody titer results. As the animal recovers, antibody diminishes. A parallel condition exists when an animal is injected with antigen. Antibody production can be markedly increased by continued injections. The production of hyperimmune serum in swine for use in hog cholera vaccination is a good example. The pig in which anti-hog cholera serum is produced may be immune, but in order to produce a more potent antiserum a large quantity of hog cholera virus is injected.

In general, antibody disappears from the circulation when the animal completely recovers from the disease or when no more injections are given. Exceptions to this generality are to be noted in those diseases where the infecting agent has become localized. An excellent example of this condition is observed in *Salmonella pullorum* infection. The disease caused by this organism is most apparent as an acute infection in the newly-hatched chick. Many die during the first few days after hatching. Unfortunately many recover, the organism becoming localized in the ovary of the female. When such a hen reaches egg laying maturity, each egg she lays may contain the organism; hence the cycle of infection is completed. Such an infected hen may be detected by the agglutination test; meaning that this chronic disease results in the production of agglutinating antibody.

Although detectable antibody may disappear from an animal after the stimulation of antigen ceases, there is no reason to doubt that production ever completely ceases during the lifetime of the animal. After antibody has disappeared, an injection of antigen will cause it to reappear much sooner than it did originally. This is called an *anamnestic reaction*. Furthermore, the injection of unrelated antigens may cause antibody to form which are specific for those antigens to which the animal has been previously exposed.

Action of Antibody. The action of antibody upon its homologous antigen is more familiar because most of the available information concerning immunology is based upon how the antibody affects the antigen and the function of various accessory factors which result in the various phenomena related to the immune state.

Ehrlich attempted to explain these phenomena by his side-chain theory of immunity when he divided antibodies into three orders and concluded that the neutralization of antigens by antibodies was similar to the neutralization of a strong acid by a strong base. The fact that some uncombined antigen and antibody remains following immunity reactions makes Ehrlich's explanation doubtful. Arrhenius and Madsen explained the reaction as being similar to that of a weak acid and a weak base where some of each of the reacting substances remains unaltered. Immunity reactions show many of the characteristics of adsorption reactions between two colloids of opposite charge. This view, initiated by Bordet and supported by many, is best illustrated by the action of iodine on starch. A dilute solution produces a light blue color; a strong solution produces a deeper blue color. The union of antigen-antibody, however, does not explain all the phenomena associated with immune reactions although it is fundamental to all of them. Whether the reaction is chemical or physical is not known. Recent conceptions by Marrack lead to the belief that it is chemical.

The union of antibody with antigen sensitizes the latter so that it may be acted upon by various forces, accessory factors, which bring about the completion of the various reactions associated with immunity. *One of the most outstanding characteristics of immunity is the fact that the sensitization of antigen by antibody is highly specific.* That is, antibody will unite with and sensitize only that antigen which has been responsible for its formation. Another important characteristic of antigen-antibody union is that it is fundamental to those reactions which occur later; consequently, every immunity reaction appears to be a two-phase phenomenon, (1) combination and (2) reaction.

The first phase may occur without any physical change in the reacting ingredients. It usually is rapid, being complete in a few minutes. Unless the mixture is subjected to certain conditions characteristic of the second phase it would not be possible to detect that combination of antigen and antibody has occurred.

The second phase of antigen-antibody union is characterized by reactions which are known as neutralization, precipitation, agglutination, complement fixation, and phagocytosis.

Early workers in the field of immunology, following the lead of Ehrlich, conceived that different types of antigens were responsible for the formation of different antibodies and that these antibodies all acted in their own unique way. There was developed, then, a nomenclature, much of which is still in general use, for the different antigens and antibodies. Table 8.1 gives the name of the antigen, the antibody, the accessory factors necessary for the complete reaction, and the results of the reaction.

The Unitarian Theory. The early conception that the antibodies, *agglutinin, precipitin, opsonin,* and *amboceptor,* had separate and individual functions has been responsible for much confusion. The similarities between the agglutination and precipitation reactions tended to make this assumption doubtful, and Zinsser clarified the problem by his "unitarian hypothesis."

This theory contends that the fundamental process in all immunologic reactions is the *union of antibody with antigen.* This process, as previously indicated, is a *sensitizing action* which prepares the antigen for the function of various accessory factors; hence, after a given *antigen* has been *sensitized* by contact with its *homologous antibody,* any of the reactions may occur. If the antigen is toxin, neutralization occurs. If the antigen is a suspension of bacterial cells and if an electrolyte is present, agglutination is the result. Precipitation of protein substances follows in the presence of an electrolyte. Lysis of bacterial cells takes place in the presence of normal serum and phagocytosis of bacteria is brought about if phagocytic body cells are placed in contact with the sensitized bac-

TABLE 8.1

ANTIGEN–ANTIBODY REACTIONS

ANTIGEN	ANTIBODY	ACCESSORY FACTORS	RESULTS OF REACTION
Toxin	Antitoxin	Action of an electrolyte	Precipitation with neutralization of toxic principle
Entire cells: Bacteria, blood cells, *Agglutinogen*	*Agglutinin*	Action of an electrolyte	Clumping of cells — *agglutination*
Proteins: *Precipitinogen*	*Precipitin*	Action of an electrolyte	Flocculation of protein molecules — *precipitation*
Entire cells: Bacteria, etc.	*Opsonin*	Micro- and Macrophages	Ingestion and lysis of the antigenic cell
Entire cells or extracts	*Amboceptor sensitizer*	*Complement alexin*	Fixation of complement with resulting lysis of antigenic cell
Any protein: *Anaphylactinogen*	*Anaphylactin Allergin*	Unknown	Endothelial damage and muscle contraction

teria; therefore, it is quite probable, under natural conditions of disease, recovery, and resulting immunity, that all of the reactions mentioned above do take place because all of the accessory factors are present in the body of the animal.

Each of the antigen-antibody reactions will be discussed in greater detail in following chapters.

REFERENCES FOR FURTHER STUDY

Anson, M. L. In Advances in Protein Chemistry. Academic Press, New York, 1947.

Bordet, J., and Gay, F. P. Studies in Immunity. John Wiley & Sons, London, 1909.

Boyd, W. C. Fundamentals of Immunology. 2nd Ed. Interscience Publishers Inc., New York, 1947.

Breinl, F., and Haurowitz, F. Zeit. f. Phys. Chem. 192:45, 1930.

Burnett, F. M. The Production of Antibodies. Macmillan, Melbourne, 1941.

Cameron, H. S. Am. Jour. Vet. Res. 8:153–56, 1947.

Chace, J. H., White, A., and Dougherty, T. F. Jour. Immunol. 52:267–78, 1946.

Dubos, R. J. The Bacterial Cell. Harvard University Press, Cambridge, 1945.

Ehrlich, Paul. Studies in Immunity. John Wiley & Sons, New York, 1910.

Felix, A. A System of Bacteriology. Med. Res. Council. 7:412. His Majesty's Stationery Office, London, 1930.

Gay, F. P., and associates, Agents of Disease and Host Resistance. Chap. 18. Charles C. Thomas, Baltimore, 1935.

Harris, T. N. and Ehrich, W. E. Science. 101:28, 1945.

———, ———. Jour. Exp. Med. 84:157–65, 1946.

Haurowitz, F. Lancet. 252:149–51, 1947.

Kabat, E. A., and Mayer, M. M. Experimental Immunochemistry. Charles C. Thomas, Springfield, 1948.

Kaplan, M. H., Coons, A. H., and Deane, H. W. Jour. Exp. Med. 91: 15–30, 1950.

Kolmer, J. A. Infection, Immunity and Biological Therapy. W. B. Saunders Co., Philadelphia, 1925.

Marrack, J. R. Chemistry of Antigens and Antibodies. Special Report Series No. 230. Med. Res. Council. His Majesty's Stationery Office, London, 1938.

Mudd, Stewart. Jour. Immunol. 23:423, 1932.

Murphy, J. B., and Sturm, E. Proc. Soc. Exp. Biol. and Med. 66:303–7, 1947.

Park, W. H., and Williams, A. W. Pathogenic Microorganisms. 11th Ed. Lea & Febiger, Philadelphia, 1939.

Pauling, L. Jour. Am. Chem. Soc. 62:2643, 1940.

Raffel, Sidney; Immunity, Hypersensitivity, and Serology. Appleton-Century-Crofts, Inc., New York, 1953.

Topley, W. W. C., Wilson, G. S., and Miles, A. A. The Principles of Bacteriology and Immunity. 3rd Ed. Williams & Wilkins Co., Baltimore, 1946.

Wissler, R. W., Woolridge, R. L., Steffee, C. H., and Cannon, P. R. Jour. Immunol. 52:267–78, 1946.

Zinsser, Hans. Resistance to Infectious Diseases. 4th Ed. The Macmillan Co., New York, 1931.

9. | Toxin and Antitoxin

TOXINS

Various types of antigens which are used to produce immunity have been discussed previously. Of these, toxins are of great importance. The word toxin is often used to cover a wide variety of substances, but generally is used to denote a bacterial poison which is capable of producing disease in a susceptible animal. Bacteriologically speaking, toxins are divided into two types: *exotoxins* and *endotoxins*. Each type has certain characteristics by which it may be recognized.

EXOTOXINS

1. Excreted by bacteria in the medium in which they are grown.

2. Highly specific for certain tissues and cells such as nerve, muscle, erythrocytes, producing typical symptoms of disease of which tetanus is a good example.

3. Very toxic. Amounts small as 0.001 ml. of some toxins lethal to guinea pigs.

4. Unstable, quickly losing toxicity when exposed to 60° C., when exposed to various chemicals, and when stored at room temperature.

5. Highly antigenic, stimulating the formation of specific neutralizing antitoxins in animals which have been injected.

6. Converted into toxoids by treatment with formalin and other chemicals. Retain specific antigenicity but lose toxicity.

ENDOTOXINS

1. Intracellular substances liberated by bacterial disintegration into the medium in which the bacteria are grown.

2. Not specific for tissue, but do produce general effects such as fever. Do not produce specific symptoms of disease.

3. Weakly toxic in general, but certain Gram-negative bacteria produce endotoxin lethal in 0.5 ml. amounts in mice.

4. Stable, remaining toxic after exposure to 60° C., unchanged by chemicals, and by storage at room temperature.

5. Not highly antigenic, not stimulating the formation of specific neutralizing antitoxins, but do stimulate formation of antibodies which can be demonstrated by agglutination, precipitation, and complement fixation.

6. Not converted into toxoids by action of chemicals; antigenicity remains unaltered.

Ordinarily the term *toxin* is used to mean *exotoxin* and will be used in this manner in the following discussion.

Sources of Toxins. Toxins are produced by a number of bacteria, plants, and animals. The bacteria which produce toxins are relatively few, but the list is being increased as the poisonous products of more of the bacteria are discovered. The toxins vary in ability to cause disease; this makes it difficult to form a definite list of toxin-producing bacteria. The best criterion of toxicity is the ability of the toxin to stimulate the formation of an antitoxin which possesses definite neutralizing properties. The following species of bacteria are known to produce true toxin:

Streptococcus pyogenes—erythrogenic toxin in scarlet fever.

Micrococcus aureus—hemolysis, necrosis in man and animals.

Clostridium tetani—tetanus or lockjaw in man and animals.

Clostridium chauvoei—blackleg in cattle and sheep.

Clostridium septicum—malignant edema in man and animals.

Clostridium perfringens—wound infection in man, dysentery and enterotoxemia in animals.

Clostridium novyi—infectious necrotic hepatitis in sheep.

Clostridium botulinum—food poisoning in man and animals.

Shigella dysenteriae—dysentery in man.

Corynebacterium diphtheriae—diphtheria in man.

Corynebacterium pseudotuberculosis—ulcerative lymphangitis in the horse and caseous lymphadenitis in sheep.

Pseudomonas aeruginosa—suppurative processes in man and animals.

Hemolysin, leucocidin, and fibrinolysin which are produced by a number of different species of bacteria are classed as toxins.

Some of the plants are able to produce powerful toxins. *Ricin* from the castor-oil bean and *abrin* from the jequirity bean are typical examples. *Robin* is a toxin from the bark of the locust. Certain of the mushrooms or "toadstools" produce potent toxins.

The poisons of certain snakes, scorpions, and spiders are the oldest toxins known.

The Nature of Toxins. Although each of the above toxins has characteristics peculiar to itself, there are characteristics common to all. Toxins are water-soluble products which respond to all of the reactions characteristic of protein substances. This does not imply that toxins are proteins, and in the future improved methods of separation and purification may reveal their true chemical nature. Toxins are precipitated with albumose and peptone fractions of proteins by the action of ammonium sulphate, aluminum sulphate, zinc chloride, alcohol, or nucleic acid. Although these chemicals are used to concentrate toxins, they are not of value in separating them from the fractions of proteins. Toxins are noncrystalline, and they cannot be dialyzed except through very thin membranes. Toxins are labile, particularly with respect to heat and chemicals. A temperature of 60°C. is destructive to toxins, and at least 95 per cent of the toxin molecules are destroyed by 56°C.; however, an exception is the streptococcus toxin which is not totally destroyed by boiling for 20 minutes. Light and oxygen are detrimental to toxins. Proteolytic ferments, such as trypsin and erepsin, destroy toxins. Toxins are destroyed by an acid reaction of pH 5.5.

The action of toxins upon tissues can be studied only by their injection into susceptible animals; in fact, the presence of toxin in a bacterial filtrate can be detected only by such a procedure. There are no chemical tests which reveal the presence of toxin. The potency of many of the toxins is an important characteristic. Tetanus toxin is so powerful that 1 ml. will cause the death of 50,000 to 75,000 guinea pigs. Botulism toxin is considered to be the most powerful poison known. Toxins exert their action, however, only after a "period of incubation," or a sufficient lapse of time following injection to allow the toxin to become fixed to the susceptible tissue.

A very small dose of toxin will stimulate body cells to produce specific antibodies or antitoxins, which will neutralize the toxins in definite proportions. Antitoxic sera are used for the protection of individuals who are immunized by a simultaneous injection of toxin and in the treatment of individuals who are suffering with an infection caused by a toxin-producing organism. In tetanus, for example, the life of the animal is saved by the prompt injection of tetanus antitoxin. After the toxin has become fixed to nerve tissue, however, the effectiveness of tetanus antitoxin is considerably reduced.

Animals are immunized against infections caused by toxin-producing bacteria, by the injection of toxin in nonlethal doses, or by the injection of attenuated toxin. Ehrlich demonstrated that the toxin molecule is composed of two parts which he termed *toxophore* and *haptophore*. The action of a toxin in producing disease is due to the toxophore part of the molecule. This is the thermolabile and chemolabile fraction of the molecule. Toxin is combined or united with tissue by the haptophore fraction, and it is this part which functions as the antigen. Ehrlich observed that the toxophore fraction was destroyed upon standing, but that the haptophore fraction was not altered. This same decrease in toxicity is produced by the action of a chemical such as formalin and iodine. Ehrlich called the haptophore portion *toxoid*. These fundamental discoveries of Ehrlich have been of great value in developing methods of producing immunity against toxins. They have facilitated the production of antitoxin without undue losses of producing animals. In the production of tetanus antitoxin, horses are given injections of tetanus toxoid in order to form a basal immunity against subsequent injections of toxin. Toxoids are used without the simultaneous use of antitoxin in producing an immunity against many diseases. Diphtheria and tetanus toxoids are universally used in medicine.

Tissue Specificity of Toxins. One of the most important characteristics of a toxin is its specificity for a certain tissue. The toxin liberated by *Clostridium tetani* is specific for two types of tissue—nerve tissue and erythrocytes. Toxin which combines with nerve tissue is called *neurotoxin* and in the case of tetanus, *tetanospasmin*. Toxin which acts on erythrocytes is called *hemotoxin* or *hemolysin* because it causes a lysis of the red blood cell with liberation of hemoglobin.

The toxins of *Streptococcus pyogenes* are able to cause hemolysis of erythrocytes and the formation of an erythema. Diphtheria toxin effects the nerve centers of the vascular system and produces degenerative changes in heart muscles, kidneys, and liver. The toxin of botulism causes a paralysis of the muscles supplied by the cranial nerves.

Determination of the Potency of Toxins. With the more powerful toxins, the death of a susceptible experimental animal is used as a criterion of potency. In order to compare a toxin produced by one strain of an organism with that produced by another, standard doses, methods of injection, time of action, size of animal, and species of animal are considered. The smallest dose of a certain toxin which will kill an animal in a definite time is called the *minimum lethal dose*, designated M.L.D. The exact definition of an M.L.D. varies with the toxin. An M.L.D. of tetanus toxin is defined as the least amount that will kill a *350 gram* guinea pig in 96 hours. An M.L.D. of diphtheria toxin is the least amount that will kill a *250 gram* guinea pig in 96 hours.

Toxins which cause the hemolysis of red blood cells also are tested for potency; for example, the minimum hemolytic dose, M.H.D., of staphylococcus toxin is the amount which will hemolyze 1.0 ml. of a 2 per cent suspension of rabbit erythrocytes in one hour at 37°C.

The toxin of the scarlet fever streptococcus produces an erythema. Susceptible children are used in order to test the potency of this toxin. The toxin is injected into the skin of the arm and the unit of measurement is called the skin test dose, S.T.D. The smallest amount which gives a reaction 1.5 cm. in size in 24 hours is designated the S.T.D. of scarlet fever toxin.

ANTITOXIN

Antitoxin shows all the characteristics generally attributed to antibodies.

An antitoxin is produced by body cells in response to a stimulus by a toxin and is specific for the toxin which has stimulated its production. Antitoxins combine with toxins in the body of the immune animal and in test tubes in the laboratory. In a great many respects the combination of toxin with antitoxin *in vitro* is of the same type as the combination of chemicals. Since toxin-antitoxin union follows the law of constant proportions, Ehrlich believed the reaction to be a chemical one, similar to the neutralization of a strong acid by a strong base. Toxins and antitoxins combine slowly, however, and until a certain stability has been reached, the two substances may show a reversible reaction. In most instances a certain amount of each of the reacting substances remains free. This led Arrenhius and Madsen to explain toxin-antitoxin reactions as similar to the action of a weak acid with a weak base. Bordet believed that the reaction is an adsorption phenomenon, similar to the adsorption of ink by a blotter. The toxin is neutralized in proportion to the amount of antitoxin which is adsorbed by it. Ramon has demonstrated that toxin is precipitated by antitoxin and that the reaction is so definite that it may be used as a standarization procedure. This indicates that the union of toxin-antitoxin is similar to any precipitation reaction involving antigen and antibody and the action of an electrolyte.

Antitoxins are relatively stable but are destroyed by a temperature of 62°C. Refrigeration at 3° to 5°C. maintains antitoxin satisfactorily, and when dried *in vacuo* there is little deterioration over long periods of time. The addition of 0.5 per cent chloroform preserves antitoxin.

Production of Antitoxin. The production of antitoxins for the immunization of animals and man against the various toxins follows the same general procedure. The toxin is prepared and standardized; a suitable animal, usually the horse, is injected to produce antitoxin; the serum is collected, filtered, and concentrated; the antitoxin is standardized or tested for potency. Tetanus antitoxin is used more than any other antitoxin in veterinary medicine; therefore, a brief description of its manufacture will be given to illustrate the general procedure of antitoxin production.

Tetanus Toxin. A culture of *Clostridium tetani* which produces a highly potent toxin is chosen for toxin production. The organism is grown in veal-infusion broth containing 0.5 per cent sodium chloride and 7 per cent peptone. Dextrose can be added to the medium to enhance the growth of the organism, but apparently it does not increase the potency of the toxin. The medium is covered with a layer of petrolatum and is then sterilized to drive out oxygen previous to inoculation. The medium is incubated at 34° to 35°C. for 10 to 14 days for maximum toxin production. The potency of the toxin decreases after 14 days. The soluble toxin is separated from the living bacteria by passing through a Berkefeld N filter. The filtrate can be preserved by the addition of 0.5 per cent phenol, or the toxin may be precipitated with ammonium sulphate and preserved in the dry state. The toxin in the dry state is easily dissolved in sterile salt solution and may be placed in various dilutions for the purpose of standardization.

The toxin is then tested for potency. This is done by making a series of dilutions of 1:1,000, 1:5,000, 1:10,000, 1:15,000, 1:20,000, 1:25,000, and injecting 1 ml. of each dilution into a series of 350-gram guinea pigs. The weakest dilution which causes the death of the guinea pig in 96 hours is chosen as the M.L.D.

Tetanus Antitoxin. The horse used for production of antitoxin must be in good condition and absolutely free from disease of any kind. The animal is given a foundation immunity by the injection of tetanus toxoid or by the injection of toxin and antitoxin. The animals are then given 10–20 guinea pig M.L.D.'s at three-day intervals; the doses are gradually increased until the animal receives as much as 1,000 ml. of culture filtrate. Toward the end of the fifth or sixth month after immunization is started, samples of serum are taken and tested for the potency of the antitoxin. When the antitoxin has reached a satisfactory potency, the animal is bled (Fig. 9.1), and the clear serum, antitoxin, is removed after the blood has clotted. It is preserved as whole serum by the addition of 0.5 per cent phenol or 0.4 per cent tricresol. The whole serum may be used therapeutically or it may be concentrated.

The concentration of antitoxin is based upon the fact that blood serum is a mixture of various proteins, pigments, and inorganic salts and that antitoxin is one of the protein fractions. Concentration is desirable for two reasons; first, to eliminate those serum fractions which may cause anaphylactic reactions, and second, because there is little reason for injecting inert substances in therapeutic treatment. All of the methods which have been devised for the concentration of antitoxin are based upon the differences in solubility or coagulability of the various serum constituents. The original methods of Gibson and Banzhaf have formed the basis for most of the methods which are in use at present.

Many methods are used throughout the world for standardizing tetanus antitoxin. The method used in the United States follows the one originally described by Rosenau and Anderson in 1908. The standard of measurement of antitoxin is called the immunity unit. The *immunity unit* for tetanus antitoxin is *ten times the least amount of serum necessary to save the life of a 350-gram guinea pig for 96 hours against the official test dose of standard toxin.* The official test dose of toxin consists of a precipitated toxin preserved under special conditions at the laboratories of the National Institute of Health in Washington, D. C. This toxin is sent to laboratories to be used in standardizing antitoxin. In order to find the immunity unit (I.U.), various dilutions are made of the antitoxin which are then mixed with a standard dose of toxin. After the toxin and antitoxin are placed together, the mixtures are kept at room temperature and then injected subcutaneously into a series of guinea pigs weighing approximately 350 grams.

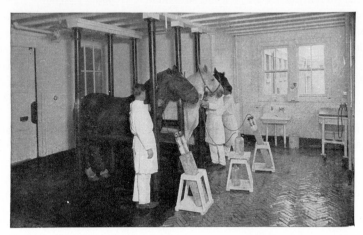

FIG. 9.1 — Bleeding horses in antiserum production.

After the potency of the antitoxin in terms of immunity units is determined, the antitoxin is placed in vials containing varying amounts and is ready for therapeutic use.

Other Methods of Standardizing Antitoxins. Ramon demonstrated as early as 1922 that a precipitate results when toxin and antitoxin are mixed in definite proportions. This method has been developed during recent years and is a valuable adjunct to the biological method of standardization. The unit of toxin which is used in the standardization of antitoxin is called the Lf dose. An Lf unit is the volume of toxin flocculating with one unit of antitoxin and is determined by flocculation tests with antitoxin of known potency. The results which are obtained with this method agree with the guinea-pig method although it has not replaced the older technic. Since the toxoids react in the same general proportions with antitoxin as does toxin, the test is of greater value in the standardization of toxoids.

Römer and his co-workers demonstrated that the injection of small amounts of diphtheria toxin into the skin of guinea pigs produces small areas of necrosis at the point of injection. Mixtures of toxin-antitoxin do not result in necrosis unless a small amount of unneutralized toxin is present in the mixture. These investigators were able to determine the amount necessary to produce necrosis;

hence they arrived at a method of testing the potency of antitoxin. The rabbit has been substituted for the guinea pig in the test by some investigators. It has been observed that the rabbit skin is more sensitive to the toxin than is that of the guinea pig, and a larger number of tests can be made on one animal. The method has not come into use in the standardization of diphtheria antitoxin in commercial establishments, but it has been found to be of value in detecting the presence of minute amounts of antitoxin in blood serum. The Schick test in man is a practical application of the principle of the test for determining susceptibility to diphtheria.

REFERENCES FOR FURTHER STUDY

Arrhenius, S. Immuno-chemistry. The Macmillan Co., New York, 1907.

Banzhaf, E. J. The Preparation and Purification of Toxins, Toxoids and Antitoxins. The Newer Knowledge of Bacteriology and Immunology. Pp. 745–58. University of Chicago Press, Chicago, 1928.

Bayne-Jones, Stanhope. The Titration of Toxins and Antitoxins by the Flocculation Method. The Newer Knowledge of Bacteriology and Immunology. Pp. 759–71. University of Chicago Press, Chicago, 1928.

Boyd, W. C. Fundamentals of Immunology. 2nd Ed. Interscience Publishers, New York, 1947.

Bordet, Jules. On the Mode of Action of Antitoxins on Toxins. Studies in Immunity. Trans. by F. P. Gay. Pp. 259–79. John Wiley & Sons, London, 1909.

Ehrlich, Paul. Collected Studies on Immunity. Trans. by C. Bolduan. Pp. 481–560. John Wiley & Sons, London, 1906.

Gay, F. P., and associates. Agents of Disease and Host Resistance. Charles C. Thomas, Baltimore, 1935.

Glenny, A. T. Active Immunization with Toxin. A System of Bacteriology. Pp. 107–93. Med. Res. Council. His Majesty's Stationery Office, London, 1931.

Kolmer, J. A. Infection, Immunity and Biologic Therapy. Pp. 203–26. W. B. Saunders Co., Philadelphia, 1923.

Maver, Mary E. The Physical Chemistry of Toxin and Antitoxin. The Newer Knowledge of Bacteriology and Immunology. Pp. 739–44. University of Chicago Press, Chicago, 1928.

Park, W. H., and Williams, A. W. Pathogenic Microorganisms. 11th Ed. Lea and Febiger, Philadelphia, 1939.

Sherwood, N. P. Immunology. Pp. 205–69. The C. V. Mosby Co., St. Louis, 1935.

Simonds, J. D. Sublethal Intoxications with Bacterial Products. The Newer Knowledge of Bacteriology and Immunology. Pp. 772–81. University of Chicago Press, Chicago, 1928.

Wadsworth, A. G. Standard Methods. 3rd Ed. Williams & Wilkins Co., Baltimore, 1947.

Wells, H. G. The Chemical Aspects of Immunity. Pp. 132–46. The Chemical Catalog Co., New York, 1929.

Zinsser, Hans, Enders, John F., and Fothergill, L. D. Immunity. The Macmillan Co., New York, 1939.

10. Agglutination and Precipitation

When a small amount of homologous immune serum is added to a *suspension of bacteria* in salt solution, the bacteria form in small clumps which cause them to settle to the bottom of the test tube. This phenomenon is known as *agglutination*. When a small amount of homologous immune serum is added to *any protein in a salt solution*, the protein molecules are brought together forming aggregates with the immune serum which are large enough to produce a distinct turbid layer at the junction of the reacting substances. This phenomenon is known as *precipitation*.

The distinction between agglutination and precipitation is as follows: Agglutination occurs when the antigen is in suspension in the form of individual cells or finely divided particles. Precipitation occurs when the antigen is a colloid in solution. Otherwise the two reactions are fundamentally the same.

AGGLUTINATION

The clumping of bacterial cells in the presence of an immune serum was observed by Charrin and Roger in 1889, Metchnikoff in 1892, Isaeff and Ivanoff in 1894, Bordet in 1895, and Washburn in 1896. Of these, Bordet attached much significance to the reaction and sought to explain the mechanism which caused it. Gruber and Durham, in 1896, called attention to the specificity of the reaction and to the possibilities of group agglutination. It was these investigators who first used the term *agglutinin* for the antibody responsible for the reaction. In 1896, when Widal and Grünbaum independently found that the blood serum of typhoid fever patients would agglutinate typhoid bacilli, the true value of the reaction as a means of diagnosing disease was established. Since then, numerous diseases of man and animals have been diagnosed by the agglutination test. The value of the reaction has not been limited to the diagnosis of disease, for it is also of use in the differentiation of closely related types of bacteria. Erythrocytes are also agglutinated; this reaction is universally used in the typing of blood.

The Antigen. There is no reason to assume that the antigen which stimulates body cells to produce the antibody functional in agglutination is different than any antigen. The fundamental criteria which separate agglutination from other antigen-antibody reactions are those conditions or accessory factors essential for the clumping of particles in suspension. These will be given presently.

A more satisfactory agglutination reaction results when the entire bacterial cell is used as an antigen, inasmuch as the entire body cell is used in preparing the bacterial suspension used in the test. *It is appropriate to state here in our discussion that this bacterial suspension is also called the antigen.* Prior mention has been made of the mosaic nature of bacterial cells in respect to their protein composition. It is well to emphasize that each protein molecule acts as an antigen, consequently large numbers of specific antibodies are formed as a result of the injection of a bacterial suspension into an animal. In general terms the body of the bacterial cell is composed of somatic or O antigen. The flagella surrounding the bacterial cell are antigenic and are known as flagellar or H antigen. It is obvious that if one wishes to prepare antibody which will cause the specific agglutination of a flagellated bacterium, the antigen used to stimulate the formation of this antibody must be composed of flagellated bacteria.

Other cells, particularly erythrocytes, are satisfactory antigens. Most significant use is made of the agglutination of red blood cells in the typing of blood prior to blood transfusion in man. The details of this technic are given later in the chapter. Previous mention has been made of another use of erythrocytes in agglutination. A suspension of such cells may be placed in contact with a bacterial extract for the adsorption of the extract to the erythrocytes. If a positive antiserum is then added to the suspension, the erythrocytes will agglutinate, due to the presence of the adsorbed bacterial extract.

Other substances may be used as antigens in agglutination. Collodion may be divided into extremely small particles by physical manipulation. These particles may be coated with a desired protein, usually the endotoxin of an organism which cannot be placed in a suitable suspension, such as an actinomyces. Antibody is then prepared by injecting the protein or endotoxin into an experimental animal. This antibody can then be used to cause the agglutination of the protein-coated particles of collodion.

The Antibody. The agglutination reaction is due to the sensitizing action of antibody on cells in suspension. This antibody is commonly called *agglutinin,* but it must not be inferred that it is different from antibody. The terms *normal agglutinin* and *nor-*

mal agglutination are often used when discussing this reaction. These are expressions meaning that the agglutination of bacteria may be brought about by normal serum. In the use of the agglutination reaction for testing cattle for Brucellosis, agglutination of the bacterial suspension is often observed in the 1:25 titer. This is considered due to normal agglutinin and not of diagnostic significance. The explanations for the presence of normal agglutinin in serum are the same, obviously, as those given in the last chapter for normal antibody.

Method of Agglutinin Action. Numerous explanations of the mechanism of agglutination have been advanced since the discovery of the reaction. Of all of these, the one advanced by Bordet in 1899 has been the most accurate. At that time he called attention to the need of salt in the reaction and stated that the entire phenomenon of agglutination may be divided into two phases, of which the first is experimentally produced without the second; the first is a period during which the isolated particles are affected by the agglutinin, and the second is a period of agglutination. The individuality of the particles affected is of significance only in the first phase. During the second phase, particles or cells in obedience to molecular attraction show, in their agglutination, only such characteristics as occur in the clumping of mineral particles.

The most helpful conception of the agglutination reaction is found in comparing it with the phenomenon termed "salting out" of proteins. A study of the effect produced by passing an electric current through a bacterial suspension generally shows the bacteria moving toward the positive electrode. This proves that the bacterial cells carry a negative charge and tend to repel each other, thus keeping them in suspension. If high concentrations of many salts are added to the bacterial suspension, the bacterial cells flocculate. Saturated ammonium sulphate, for example, will flocculate, or agglutinate, bacteria. The electric charge on the bacteria has been changed; they no longer repel each other; they cling together and settle out.

The specificity of the reaction makes it apparent that it is not one totally dependent upon the action of salts. As pointed out by Bordet, it consists of a two-phase reaction. The *first phase* represents the union of antibody with the antigen, that is, agglutinin with bacterial cell. The mechanism of this union is not known at the present time. Two explanations have been advanced: One is that the bacteria are coated over by a film of antibody, globulin, which changes the nature of the surface so coated to that of globulin; the second is that antibody molecules are attached in compact groups to the different antigenic portions of the organism, thereby changing the nature of the surface of the organism. Whatever the method of attachment may be, it is known that a specific union exists and the physical characteristics of the surfaces of bacterial cells are changed. The *second phase* of the reaction, the flocculation of particles in suspension by the reduction in potential by an electrolyte, is more understandable. Northrop and DeKruif have shown that bacteria have cohesive force, as well as surface potential, and that a dialyzed immune serum added to a bacterial suspension slightly decreases both forces. A salt solution decreases the potential still lower, and when it reaches a value of 15 millivolts, the cohesive force, unaltered by salt, causes the bacteria to adhere to one another, to form larger aggregates to produce agglutination.

Although it takes only a minute amount of agglutinating serum to sensitize bacteria, a positive reaction is not obtained when the serum is diluted too much. This is often referred to as the post zone in a series of dilutions. Occasionally, the first few dilutions of a series do not agglutinate but the next few tubes give a positive reaction. This prezone or prozone reaction has not been completely explained but is presumed to be due to globulin which coats the bacteria so that cohesiveness is reduced to such an extent that agglutination does not occur.

Autoagglutination. Spontaneous agglutination of suspensions of bacteria often occurs; for example, difficulty is sometimes experienced with bacteria used for agglutination tests because they flocculate spontaneously; that is, they agglutinate in the absence of specific antiserum. Autoagglutination, which makes bacteria unsuitable for agglutination studies, is observed in many bacterial groups, particularly in the streptococci, the bacilli, and most of the actinomyces. It has been found that autoagglutination may be overcome by growing the organisms at lower temperatures, and in some cases in a serum medium. Autoagglutination is a characteristic intimately connected with the action of salt and a method which helps to prevent it, and to obtain suitable suspensions for study is to reduce the concentration of salt in the suspending fluid.

Acid Agglutination. Most bacteria in suspension may be agglutinated by the addition of acid; this is due to the increased concentration of hydrogen ions in the medium. Some species of bacteria are agglutinated at a lower hydrogen-ion concentration than others; this fact has been suggested as a basis for the identification and classification of bacteria, but it has not been generally adopted. Acid agglutination is of great practical significance in laboratories where routine agglutination testing is done. The use of acid in cleaning test tubes and pipettes should be limited and they should be thoroughly rinsed.

Group Agglutination. The statement that agglutinins are specific must be elaborated upon. It has been shown that the serum homologous for a certain organism may clump, to a lesser degree, some other species or closely related forms, and in rare instances, species quite unrelated. This is because all of the agglutinogen released by a particular organism is not of one type; the agglutinins produced, therefore, are likewise of different types. It is entirely probable that closely related organisms possess some identical agglutinogens; consequently, they have some common agglutinins. Agglutination of an organism by a heterologous serum is termed *group agglutination.* The agglutinins which are specific for the organism are called its *chief agglutinins,* and those common to two or more organisms are termed *coagglutinins.* It has been demonstrated that differences exist between the agglutinins produced by various strains of the same organism. It is important, therefore, in testing the agglutinating power of any serum, to dilute it to such an extent that the action of the coagglutinins is negligible so the action of the specific or chief agglutinins will be recognized.

The agglutinin absorption test is based upon the existence of coagglutinins. In the agglutinin absorption test suspensions of the different strains or species of organisms are added, one at a time, to the serum. To each individual strain, or species, is absorbed the agglutinin for that strain, or species. The test is used in the differentiation of closely related bacteria. Figure 10.1 illustrates group agglutination. If antiserum 1 is added to a suspension of organism 1, all of the agglutinin will be absorbed. If, however, antiserum 2 is added to suspension 1, agglutinins A and F will be absorbed. If all of organisms 1 are removed from the suspension by centrifuging, and if the supernatant fluid is added to suspension 2, agglutination will result because of the presence of agglutinin B which had not been absorbed by suspension 1. The same procedure may be applied to organism 3.

Agglutination in Bacterial Differentiation. The above discussion of agglutinin absorption illustrates an important application of the agglutination reaction. Certain groups of bacteria, especially the Salmonella, are quite similar in morphology and in their biochemical characteristics. By determining the antigenic structure of each, the members of this genus can be identified. As a result of this procedure numerous O antigens and H antigens have been listed for each strain. Naturally a large number of strains have been described on this basis. A more detailed description of the technic used and a list of the different antigenic types will be found in the chapter devoted to the Salmonella.

Significance of Agglutinins in Immunity. Since agglutinins are formed in the animal as a result of infection and artificial immunization, it is natural to speculate concerning the function of the phenomenon in the immunizing process. The agglutination of bacteria in the animal body has been demonstrated by numerous investigators. It it assumed that as a result of this agglutination more organisms are engulfed by phagocytes than would be true otherwise; therefore, it is evident that the reaction is of value as an aid in ridding the body of invading organisms. It has been definitely demonstrated that agglutination itself does not kill the organism. Pfaundler has called attention to the fact that a mixture of serum containing typhoid agglutinin with typhoid bacteria will cause the latter organisms, when incubated, to grow into threads. This is known as the *Pfaundler thread reaction.*

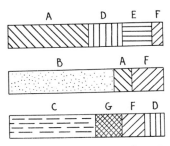

FIG. 10.1 — Diagram of antigenic structure of bacteria functioning in group agglutination.

Agglutination Tests in Disease Diagnosis. The fact that an organism developing in the body generally incites the production of a specific agglutinin has led to the wide use of that substance in the diagnosis of certain infectious diseases; that is, all diseases do not result in an appreciable production of agglutinin. The test is carried out by mixing the serum from a suspect with a suspension of the organism responsible for the disease. If agglutination occurs in proper dilutions, it is evident that the specific organism is or has been present in the patient. The principal disease organisms which cause the production of appreciable amounts of agglutinin are: *Salmonella typhosa* (typhoid fever), *Salmonella paratyphi* (paratyphoid), *Brucella* species (brucellosis in animals and man), *Salmonella pullorum* (pullorum disease), *Escherichia coli* (colibacillosis in animals and man), *Salmonella* species which cause food infections in man and enteritis in animals, *Pseudomonas aeruginosa* (suppuration in animals and man), *Malleomyces mallei* (glanders), *Pasteurella pestis* (bubonic plague), *Pasteurella tularensis* (tularemia in animals and man), and *Erysipelothrix rhusiopathiae* (swine erysipelas). Many other organisms stimulate the production of agglutinins, so the test is used in an experimental way for differentiating bacteria.

In the diagnosis of disease by agglutination, three different types of tests are used: The microscopic test, the macroscopic tube test, and the macroscopic plate, or rapid test.

The Microscopic Test. The microscopic test was first used by Widal and by Grüber for the diagnosis of typhoid fever, and for that reason it is often referred to as the Grüber-Widal test, or simply the Widal test. The technic of this test may be used in the diagnosis of diseases other than typhoid fever and may be used in the laboratory in the differentiation of closely related types of bacteria.

The technic consists of several dilutions, 1:10, 1:20, 1:40, etc. of the serum of the suspect. A loopful of each serum dilution is placed upon a clean cover glass and a loopful of the bacterial suspension is added and mixed carefully. A control is prepared by adding a loopful of the bacterial suspension to a loopful of physiological salt solution on a cover glass. Both cover glasses are then inverted on a hollow-ground glass slide and examined under the high-dry lens of the microscope. If the organism is motile, the control should show the organisms uniformly distributed over the field moving about actively. The organisms in the test may show no change, but if the serum has come from a patient infected with the organism, the bacteria will soon begin to clump together, and in the course of a few minutes to an hour, practically all of the organisms will be clumped with very few, if any, remaining in the field. Motility is lost in motile forms. The test is a very delicate one; agglutination may be secured in dilutions as great as 1:100,000. The higher the dilution at which agglutination occurs, the greater is the specificity of the reaction. As has been observed, the dilution must be great enough in every case to escape the activity of the normal and the common group agglutinins. Serum from an animal that has been immunized against a specific organism may be used in the recognition of that organism. Typhoid serum, in this way, can be used in the detection of the typhoid bacillus. Such a test also enables one to differentiate between closely related forms, such as the varieties of the Salmonella group.

The Macroscopic Tube Test. In the macroscopic tube test a series of small test tubes is prepared, each tube containing a definite amount of a physiological-salt-solution-suspension of the organism. To each tube is added varying quantities of serum, making dilutions of 1:25, 1:50, 1:100, 1:200, and higher if desired. A positive reaction is indicated by the appearance of small flocculi of bacteria, which soon settle to the bottom of the test tube, leaving the supernatant fluid clear. The reaction may not be complete for several hours of incubation at 37°C. and should stand for 48 hours before final observations are made. Check tubes, in which the liquid should remain uniformly turbid, should always be kept as controls. Dead bacteria are agglutinated as readily as are live ones; so most of the antigen used in the agglutination test is treated with phenol to reduce the hazard of handling it, particularly in pipetting.

The Macroscopic Plate Test. A heavy suspension of bacteria is used for the macroscopic plate test. Approximately 0.03 ml. of this suspension is placed in each of four squares on a heavy plate glass. To each square is then added .04, .02, and .01 of the serum from the suspect. The two materials are thoroughly mixed, and if the plate and reacting substances are warm, flocculation will occur immediately if the serum is positive.

Many technical procedures connected with the three tests described above have been omitted in this discussion. The student should consult manuals of laboratory technic for the details of each test.

HEMAGGLUTINATION — ISOANTIBODIES

Certain bacteria and toxic substances from some plants and from a few animals contain substances which agglutinate red blood cells. Such agglutinins are termed *hemagglutinins*. The extract from the navy bean is used in the agglutination of red blood cells in the clarification of anti hog cholera serum. The red blood cells are agglutinated by the extract, and when the blood is centrifuged, the cells form in a compact mass in the bottom of the centrifuge cup. Hemagglutinin, like any antibody, is formed by the injection of the red blood cells of one species into another.

One of the most significant reactions involving agglutination of red blood cells is the clumping of the cells of one individual by the serum of another individual of the same species. When agglutination occurs in the blood stream, it results in the formation of emboli of the red blood cells and if they become lodged in capillaries of the brain, this may cause fatal cerebral hemorrhage. The antibody responsible for this reaction is known as *isoantibody,* and in this particular case is called *isohemagglutinin.* The phenomenon is of great significance in man because the blood of human beings may be classified into four main groups, or types.

The typing of blood prior to blood transfusions is now a matter of routine to prevent fatalities due to agglutination of the red blood cells of the donor by the agglutinin in the serum of the recipient. In man the four blood types are designated, according to the nomenclature of Landsteiner, O, A, B, and AB. It is apparent that an agglutinin must be present in the serum of the recipient when the blood cells of the donor are agglutinated. Landsteiner has designated these agglutinins by Greek letters; hence, the agglutinins found in the four groups of individuals are as follows:

Group O has alpha (α) and beta (β) agglutinins
Group A has beta (β) agglutinin
Group B has alpha (α) agglutinin
Group AB has no agglutinins.

It is obvious, therefore, that sera from A and B individuals are required for typing. These sera are obtained from commercial laboratories. A number of methods are used in blood typing, and the slide method serves as a good example. A drop of known A and B serum is added to an equal amount of a 5 per cent suspension of the blood to be typed. The two drops are mixed thoroughly, covered with a glass cover slip and are then observed under the microscope. The reactions to be expected are as follows:

A and B sera do not agglutinate the red blood cells of O individuals because these individuals already possess α and β agglutinins.

A serum agglutinates the red blood cells of B individuals because it contains β agglutinin. It will also agglutinate the cells of an AB individual for the same reason.

B serum agglutinates the red blood cells of A individuals because it contains α agglutinin. It will also agglutinate the red blood cells of AB individuals for the same reason.

Since Group O blood is affected by neither α nor β agglutinin, such individuals are referred to as universal donors. *Although agglutinin may be present in the serum of the donor which is incompatible for the red corpuscles of the recipient, the factor of dilution makes it ineffective.* The blood of a Group AB individual does not contain agglutinin so the persons in that group are referred to as universal recipients. The four blood types are inherited according to the Mendelian formula; consequently, a certain amount of value is attributed to blood typing as an aid in establishing parenthood. The distribution of the blood groups among the various races of the world has served as an aid in tracing the origin and development of the different races.

The presence of blood groups in the various species of lower animals has been observed. Although the groups in many cases are ill-defined, and not of great practical importance, their presence has been found in goats, horses, cattle, rabbits, cats, dogs, chickens, pigs, and monkeys. Neither guinea pigs nor mice appear to be divided into blood groups. The agglutinins of anthropoid apes have been found to correspond closely to the grouping in man; this is of great biological significance.

In 1941 Landsteiner and Wiener demonstrated that the serum of rabbits which had been injected with erythrocytes of the rhesus monkey, agglutinated erythrocytes of a large per cent of the white population in New York City. The antigen has been designated Rh factor because it was first discovered in the blood of the rhesus monkey. Subsequent investigations of this factor have revealed its widespread prevalence in the blood of people of all nationalities. The significance of Rh factor in unexplained anemia of the newborn was a most noteworthy discovery. It is now known that an Rh negative mother will develop Rh antibody if her fetus possesses Rh positive blood as a result of genes inherited from an Rh positive father. Such antibody will be transmitted back to the fetus through the maternal circulation producing the condition called erythroblastosis fetalis. Rh antibodies are also produced by the transfusion of Rh positive blood to a person who is normally Rh negative. This reaction is considered to be responsible for some of the transfusion accidents which formerly were difficult to explain. The typing of blood is complicated by the antigenic complexity of Rh factor.

The function of a similar phenomenon in foals was discovered by Bruner, Hull, Edwards, and Doll in 1948, and has been reported upon in greater detail by Bruner and associates in 1950 and by Doll in 1952 and 1953. These investigators have shown that hemolytic icterus in foals is due to the presence of erythrocyte antibody in the colostrum of the mare. This antibody is produced by erythrocyte-antigen liberated in utero by the fetus from certain stallions possessing a certain type of erythrocyte. Mares bred to stallions having the same type blood do not produce antibody. Foals sired by stallions whose erythrocytes did not match those of the mare did not develop icterus when given colostrum from another mare immediately after birth. The condition in the foal was corrected by removal from its dam and withdrawing 1,500 ml. of antibody-laden blood and administering 2,000 ml. of compatible blood. This antigen-antibody reaction has nothing in common with the Rh factor other than being due to a somewhat similar mechanism. An analogous reaction occurs in rabbits and dogs.

A similar process was found to exist in swine by Bruner, Brown, Hull, and Kinkaid in 1949. They demonstrated that anemia and death occurred in baby pigs when the gestating sow was injected with erythrocytes of the boar to which she was bred. The condition was found in newborn pigs following the feeding of colostrum from the sow. In 1953 Buxton and Brooksband, in England, reproduced the same condition. They called attention to the probability that many cases of icterus found in newly born pigs are due to maternal iso-immunization.

PRECIPITATION

Kraus was the first one to observe precipitation in 1897. While working with broth filtrates of *Pasteurella pestis* and the cholera vibrio, he found that upon mixing the clear filtrates with their respective immune sera, a cloudy precipitate was formed. He named the antibodies responsible for the reaction *precipitins*. He, furthermore, found that the reaction was specific, for the immune sera of each of the two organisms which he studied did not produce precipitation in the filtrate of the opposite organism, nor would they precipitate the filtrates of other types of bacteria. These observations of Kraus opened the path for numerous applications of the precipitin reaction, and today it is used in the study of any protein, as well as linkages of protein to other materials.

As was previously stated, the precipitation reaction is similar to agglutination, the only difference being the size of the antigen. The antigen which induces the development of precipitin, doubtlessly, is the protein molecule itself. The precipitins are quite specific but *group precipitation* takes place when related proteins are treated with a serum homologous to one of them. The blood sera of various ruminants, for example, exhibit group precipitation. An antiserum homologous to human serum will precipitate the serum of anthropoid apes. The work of Nuttall has shown quite definitely the limits of group precipitation. He tested 900 kinds of blood, using in all 30 antisera, and made a total of 16,000 combinations. He showed that, on the whole, the closer the relationship the greater was the amount of common or group precipitation. For example, he determined that the blood of apes of the old world yields a heavier precipitate with human antiserum than does that of apes of the new world. Another exception to specificity has been found in the protein of the crystalline lens; an antiserum for lens protein of man or the ox will produce a precipitate in solutions containing the lens protein from other animals that are not at all closely related. It has been suggested that cataract of the eye may be due to the formation of an autoprecipitin for the protein of the lens and its consequent partial coagulation or precipitation *in situ.*

The mechanism of precipitation is analogous to agglutination. In the precipitation of protein molecules the size of the antigen is a great deal smaller than in the agglutination of bacteria; consequently, a great deal more antibody is needed to produce sensitization. In agglutination the antigen is standard and stationary as to the relative number of suspended particles, and the amount of antiserum used varies in different dilutions. In precipitation the antigen is diluted, and the different titers are obtained by this dilution. The amount of antiserum used in the different dilutions remains stationary. For example, in a precipitation test for bovine serum, the following dilutions are made of normal bovine serum; 1:10, 1:100, 1:500, 1:1,000, 1:5,000, and 1:10,000. To 0.5 ml. of each dilution is added 0.5 ml. of anti-cow serum from the rabbit. The dilution of the agglutinin in the agglutination reaction tends to make it more specific, whereas the dilution of the precipitinogen in the precipitation reaction tends toward specificity. These facts are readily understood when the relative sizes of a protein molecule and an entire bacterium are considered.

Uses Made of the Precipitation Phenomenon. Several practical applications have been made of precipitation in the differentiation of proteins. These are: (1) the recognition of blood stains and stains of other body fluids such as semen, and the differentiation of meats from different species of animals, such as horse from beef and venison from calf; (2) the classification of bacterial strains as is done with the streptococci; (3) the diagnosis of bacterial infections such as anthrax (Ascoli test) and syphilis (Kahn test); (4) the standardization of toxins and antitoxins such as diphtheria and tetanus discussed in the last chapter; (5) the diagnosis of parasitic infestations, for example, trichinosis; (6) the identification of closely related plants. Some of these reactions, particularly the differentiation of bacteria and diagnosis of disease, will be discussed in the chapters devoted to those organisms.

Recognition of Blood Stains. It is sometimes necessary in murder trials to determine with certainty the origin of a blood stain. The fact that the stain has been produced by blood may be easily demonstrated by a chemist, but he has no ready means of telling with certainty whether the blood is of animal or human origin. Uhlenhuth was the first to call attention to the value of the precipitation test in legal medicine. The test, when properly carried out, enables the determination to be made with a high degree of certainty. An antiserum specific for human blood first must be secured by injections of human serum into a rabbit, at intervals of a few days, for a period of two weeks. A piece of the material with the blood stain on it is placed in a watch-glass and 5 ml. of sterile physiological salt solution is added. This is allowed to stand until the blood proteins have been dissolved. If any dirt or sediment appears in the solution, it is removed by filtration. An effort is made to secure a dilution of the suspected blood serum of about 1:1,000. The diluted serum is placed in a series of test tubes and the specific antiserum is added. If the blood stain is human blood, a precipitate will be apparent in the course of a few minutes. The reliability of the test has been recognized by many courts, and the results have been accepted as evidence. By varying the procedure, the same method may be used in differentiating animal blood proteins.

Differentiation of Meats. Meat inspection, particularly in certain European countries, includes the differentiation of meats. In some localities large quantities of horse flesh are used for food, but the law forbids the sale of horse flesh as beef. There are certain chemical differences between the two, differences in the composition of the fat and in the abundance of glycogen, but these differences require chemical analysis and examination for their recognition. The precipitation test furnishes an easier and more reliable method for differentiation; furthermore, the testing may be extended to an examination of mixed meats, such as sausages, and the various kinds of meats present are determined. Specific antisera are prepared for each type of meat which is to be recognized, by mincing the meat and soaking it in physiological salt solution. This extract is then used in the immunization of a rabbit by repeated injections during several weeks. The flesh to be tested is likewise extracted with physiological salt solution; the solution is filtered and tested with the various specific antisera. A prominent precipitate is given with its homologous antiserum, and the differentiation is made.

In many cases the meat which is suspected of adulteration is cooked or smoked; these processes change the nature of the precipitinogen. In such cases, it is necessary to use as the antigen, which is injected to produce immune serum, serum or other tissue extracts which have been heated to about 70°C. The precipitins which result from the injections of such antigens are called *coctoprecipitins*.

REFERENCES FOR FURTHER STUDY

Arkwright, J. A. Agglutination. A System of Bacteriology. Pp. 380–423. Med. Res. Council of Great Britain. His Majesty's Stationery Office, London, 1931.

Arrhenius, S. Immuno-Chemistry. Chap. IX, The Precipitins and Their Antibodies. The Macmillan Co., New York, 1907.

Bailey, G. H. The Functional Role of Agglutinins. The Newer Knowledge of Bacteriology and Immunology. Pp. 802–10. University of Chicago Press, Chicago, 1928.

Bordet, Jules. The Mechanism of Agglutination. Studies in Immunity. Trans. by F. P. Gay. John Wiley & Sons, London, 1909.

Bruner, D. W. Cornell Vet. 40:11–16, 1950.

————. Brown, R. G., Hull, F. E., and Kinkaid, Alice. Blood Factors and Baby Pig Anemia. Jour. Am. Vet. Med. Assn. 115:94–96, 1949.

————; Doll, E. R., Hull, F. E., and Kinkaid, Alice. Further Studies on Hemolytic Icterus in Foals. Am. Jour. Vet. Res. 11:22, 1950.

————. Hull, F. E., and Doll, E. R. The Relation of Blood Factors to Icterus in Foals. Am. Jour. Vet. Res. 9:237–42, 1948.

————, ————, Edwards, P. R., and Doll, E. R. Icteric Foals. Jour. Am. Vet. Med. Assn. 112:440–41, 1948.

Buxton, J. C., and Brooksband, N. H. Haemolytic Disease of New-Born Pigs by Iso-Immunization of Pregnancy. Vet. Record, 65, 1953.

Cavelti, P. A. The Technic of Collodion Particle Agglutination. Jour. Immunol. 57:141–54, 1947.

Dean, H. R. The Precipitation Reaction. A System of Bacteriology. Pp. 424-51. Med. Res. Council of Great Britain. His Majesty's Stationery Office, London, 1931.

Doll, E. R. Observations on the Clinical Features and Pathology of Hemolytic Icterus of Newborn Foals. Am. Jour. Vet. Res. 13:504, 1952.

————. Evidence of the Production of an Anti-isoantibody by Foals Affected with Hemolytic Icterus. Cornell Vet. 43:44, 1953.

————, Richards, M. G., Wallace, M. E., and Bryans, J. T. The Influence of an Equine Fetal Tissue Vaccine upon Hemagglutination Activity of Mare Serums: Its Relation to Hemolytic Icterus of Newborn Foals. Cornell Vet. 42:496, 1952.

Fitzgerald, J. G., and Fraser, D. T. Bacterial Agglutinins and Their Applications. The Newer Knowledge of Bacteriology and Immunology. Pp. 811-23. University of Chicago Press, Chicago, 1928.

Gay, F. P., and associates. Agents of Disease and Host Resistance. Chap. 20. The Phenomenon of Agglutination; Chap. 21, The Precipitin Phenomenon. Charles C. Thomas, Baltimore, 1935.

Kolmer, J. A. Infection, Immunity and Biologic Therapy. Pp. 254-335. W. B. Saunders Co., Philadelphia, 1923.

Landsteiner, K. The Specificity of Serological Reactions. Charles C. Thomas, Baltimore, 1936.

Northrop, J. H. The Mechanism of Agglutination. The Newer Knowledge of Bacteriology and Immunology. Pp. 782-801. University of Chicago Press, Chicago, 1928.

Powell, H. M. Precipitins and Their Applications. The Newer Knowledge of Bacteriology and Immunology. Pp. 824-30. University of Chicago Press, Chicago, 1928.

Park, W. H., and Williams, A. W. Pathogenic Microorganisms. 11th Ed. Lea and Febiger, Philadelphia, 1939.

Raffel, Sidney. Immunity, Hypersensitivity, and Serology. Appleton-Century-Crofts, Inc., 1953.

Sherwood, H. D. Immunology. The C. V. Mosby Co., St. Louis, 1935.

Topley, W. W. C., Wilson, G. S., and Miles, A. A. The Principles of Bacteriology and Immunity. 3rd Ed. Williams & Wilkins Co., Baltimore, 1946.

Wells, H. G. The Chemical Aspects of Immunity. Chap. VI. Agglutination and Precipitation. The Chemical Catalogue Co., New York, 1929.

Zinsser, H., Enders, J. F., and Fothergill, L. D. Immunity. 5th Ed. The Macmillan Co., New York. 1939.

11. | Cytolysis and Complement Fixation

The functions of antibodies present in immune serum were discussed in the two preceding chapters. That antitoxin has the ability to neutralize toxin and that antibodies, called agglutinins and precipitins, are able to sensitize particles in suspension, causing flocculation when an electrolyte is present, have been observed. Another important property of sensitizing antibody is the sensitization of bacteria and erythrocytes so that they are acted upon by a normal substance in blood plasma which produces lysis, or cytolysis. As a result of this action, the protoplasm of the cells diffuses into the surrounding medium; this, in the case of erythrocytes, is apparent by the liberation of hemoglobin.

Bacteria which invade the deep tissues of the body and into the blood and lymph streams are destroyed by the lytic action of normal blood plasma. As early as 1792, John Hunter demonstrated that blood did not putrefy readily. Nearly a century later Lister, 1881, von Fodor, 1887, Nuttall, 1888, and Buchner, 1889, revealed the destructive action of normal blood for pathogenic bacteria. Nuttall demonstrated the lytic power of the blood of various species of animals for anthrax bacilli, but he found that this power was lost when the blood stood for a few days or was heated to 60°C. Buchner found that the plasma from clotted blood was able to lyse bacteria and confirmed the action of 60°C. He conceived that the lytic property was due to a ferment, or enzyme, to which he gave the name *alexins,* from a Greek word meaning *to ward off* or *protect.* In 1891, Daremburg discovered that the erythrocytes of one species of animal are lysed by the serum of another species and that this lytic property is also destroyed by 55°C.

The Pfeiffer Phenomenon. In an attempt to find a suitable immunizing material to check an extensive epidemic of cholera caused by the cholera vibrio, Pfeiffer and his co-worker Isaeff made some fundamental discoveries. They found that normal guinea pigs died when they received injections of the cholera vibrio and that large numbers of the organisms were present in the body. The injection of the organism into the peritoneal cavity of a guinea pig which had survived an experimental injection resulted in the rapid destruction of the bacteria. This protective function was transferred from an immune guinea pig to a normal one, and the vibrios were destroyed when mixed with immune serum and injected into the peritoneal cavity of a normal guinea pig. The reaction was specific, and Pfeiffer used it as a method of identifying the true cholera vibrio.

Metchnikoff demonstrated that the reaction would take place in a test tube when a small quantity of peritoneal exudate was added to the immune serum and suspension of the organism; in this way he proved that the peritoneal endothelium was not essential in the reaction as Pfeiffer believed.

Bordet's Contributions to the Phenomenon. Bordet found that the addition of fresh immune serum produced the lysis of the cholera vibrio, but the aging of the serum or heating to 55°C. for one-half hour destroyed the lytic property. The addition of *normal* serum to heated immune serum, however, restored the lytic property. Accordingly, Bordet concluded that the action of the immune serum was due to two substances:

1. A thermostable substance, *sensitizer*, which sensitized the cholera vibrio to the action of the second substance, was present in immune serum but not in normal serum.

2. A thermolabile material, *alexin*, which was able to cause the lysis of cells previously sensitized by the immune serum, was present in normal serum as well as in fresh immune serum.

Subsequently, Bordet demonstrated that the lysis of red blood cells was brought about by the same essential phenomenon. The injection of erythrocytes of one species into another species produced immune bodies, *sensitizers*, for the erythrocytes which were injected. The serum of the immunized animal, therefore, was capable of causing the sensitization of erythrocytes in the presence of the *alexin* in normal serum.

Both phenomena, bacteriolysis and hemolysis, Bordet explained, were due to the modification of the bacterial cells and the erythrocytes by the sensitizer and the subsequent adsorption of the *alexin;* he further demonstrated that the action of the sensitizer was similar to the action of fixing agents or mordants on tissues, which increased the adsorption of dyes that otherwise would not be adsorbed.

Ehrlich's Explanation of the Phenomenon. The fundamental principles of the phenomenon of the lysis of bacteria and erythrocytes, as shown by Bordet, were accepted by Ehrlich and his pupils. The explanation of the phenomenon, however, was not. In conformity with the receptor conception of antibodies in general, Ehrlich explained that lysis was due to an antibody equipped with two haptophore or combining groups. He called this antibody *amboceptor*. This antibody had the property of combining on the one hand with the antigen, bacteria, or erythrocytes, and on the other with the normal lytic substance which he named *complement*. The term *complement fixation* originated with Ehrlich. He believed that the complement was united to the antigen by the amboceptor, thereby he differed considerably with Bordet who thought the union was due to the action of amboceptor, or sensitizer, upon the antigen. In light of present-day knowledge the explanation of Bordet is more acceptable.

Definition of Terms. In the foregoing discussion numerous terms have been used for the antibody and for the lytic substance which are fundamental for this phenomenon. Although the terms used by Bordet and by Ehrlich are still found in current literature, it is well to confine the forthcoming discussion to those terms which are most commonly used, some of which are different than those previously mentioned.

The antibody which is developed as the result of infection or by the injection of bacterial antigens fundamentally acts on antigens as a sensitizing substance. In previously discussed reactions it has been called antitoxin, agglutinin and precipitin. It must be repeated that it is one substance, antibody. In the description of the reaction which is to follow, the antibody which unites with the infectious agent or with products of the infectious agent will be called *sensitizer*. The antibody operating in the reaction which causes the lysis of erythrocytes, called sensitizer by Bordet and amboceptor by Ehrlich, is now commonly called *hemolysin*. It must be constantly kept in mind that this is likewise a sensitizing antibody, and that a different term is used for the purpose of clarity. There must not be any confusion of the term hemolysin used as an antibody with the term hemolysin used as a toxin. These substances are entirely different although the end result of their action is the liberation of hemoglobin from the erythrocyte.

The lytic substance which is present in normal plasma, called alexin by Bordet and complement by Ehrlich is now called *complement*. This latter term has become well fixed in our contemporary literature. The reaction, as inferred by the chapter heading, which will be explained in the forthcoming discussion is called *complement fixation*.

The Antigens in Complement Fixation. All of the original conceptions of lysis were based upon the effect which was produced upon the intact cell; for example, cholera vibrios were observed to undergo disintegration, and red blood cells were known to lose their hemoglobin. It was assumed, then, that intact cells must be used as the antigen which is to be injected to stimulate the formation of the antibody. In general this theory is still accepted, although the knowledge of complete and partial antigens does reveal that proteins of cells may serve as antigens. In this respect, an antigen which is injected to stimulate antibody formation must be differentiated from the antigen which is used in a complement-fixation test for the diagnosis of disease. In such diseases as brucellosis and glanders the fixation test may be used for diagnosis. One might presume that since whole organisms are present in the body producing the disease, that whole organisms must be used as the antigen in the test. This is not true, for complement is just as readily fixed when extracts of the organism are used as when whole organisms are used for the test antigen. It has been observed, furthermore, that complement is fixed in the precipitation test. This is of great importance in the complement-fixation test, for in the preparation of an hemolytic antigen, the red blood cells may not be completely washed free of blood serum. A subsequent test, then, may remove complement by virtue of the precipitation of the serum by the specific antibody.

Nonspecific antigens may be used in complement fixation. In the Wassermann test for syphilis, lipid extracts of normal organs, such as beef heart, are used. To such lipid substances cholesterol is added which makes the antigen more suitable. This antigen, obviously, has nothing in common with the spirochete which is the cause of syphilis, yet the serum of a person affected with that disease causes the fixation of complement to the antigen. This nonspecific reaction is thought to be due to a serological similarity between certain normal tissue lipids and the antigens of the spirochete.

In the fixation of complement by erythrocytes, with the subsequent liberation of hemoglobin, the entire cell must be used. The stroma of the cell appears to function as an antigen in the production of hemolysin as well as serving as the antigen in the fixation of complement. It is obvious that, when the hemolysis of erythrocytes is used as the indicator of complement fixation, entire normal cells must be used. The blood of each species is distinctive in composition and serves as a specific antigen.

Certain antigens are unsuitable for use in complement fixation because of their anticomplementary action. It is apparent that hemolytic toxin cannot be used because of the specific hemolytic action of this substance.

Antigens prepared from tissues of animals affected by various viruses are used as antigens in complement fixation. These will be discussed in greater detail in the section devoted to virology.

The production of lytic antibodies for various types of cells has been investigated; for example, the destruction of cancer cells of rats and mice by the action of a specific lytic antiserum has been shown by Lumsden. The function of blood platelets in controlling hemorrhage has been demonstrated by Ledingham and Bedson by the production of experimental hemorrhagic purpura by the injection of a blood platelet antiserum.

Antibody in Complement Fixation. The complement fixation test which may be used for the diagnosis of a disease requires two antibodies. One of these antibodies may be called the bacterial antibody, if the disease to be diagnosed is a bacterial disease. It could be termed the "diagnostic" antibody. It is the antibody sought for in the test and its presence would determine the cause of the disease in question. The other antibody used in complement fixation is hemolysin. This is produced artificially by the injection of the erythrocytes of one animal, sheep, into another animal, rabbit. After a series of injections hemolytic antibody, hemolysin, for sheep erythrocytes is present in the serum of the rabbit.

That both antibodies are sensitizing antibodies can be shown by the fact that the bacterial antibody will agglutinate its homologous antigen, if it is particulate enough, or will cause precipitation, if it is a protein suspension. The hemolytic antibody will agglutinate a suspension of sheep erythrocytes. The union of antibody with antigen in complement fixation is the same as in other antigen-antibody reactions. Both the bacterial antibody and hemolytic antibody show the properties ascribed to antibody in general, but in complement fixation, complement is fixed by the antigen-antibody complex. One characteristic of antibody which is significant in complement fixation is its thermostable nature. It is not destroyed by 56°C. Furthermore, it is not injured by contact with a preservative, such as 0.5 per cent phenol, nor is it altered by standing in the refrigerator for a considerable period of time.

Nature and Action of Complement. The perishable nature of complement has prevented, until recent years, significant contributions concerning its chemical composition. Since the original conception of its enzyme nature by Büchner, complement has been considered to be a lipase, a protease, a peptidase, an intracellular catalyst, a simple chemical like oleic acid, and a combination of lipids, soaps, and proteins. By some, complement has been considered to be only a colloidal attribute of fresh serum; its action dependent on the physico-chemical state of serum.

Certain physical properties and chemical agents which affect complement are recognized as being significant. Complement is inactivated by exposure to 56°C. for 30 minutes, although most serum proteins are not injured by this temperature. Complement is most stable within the pH ranges of 6.0 to 6.5; consequently, strong concentrations of acids and alkalies are detrimental to it. Other agents, such as chloroform, ether, alcohols, soaps, and certain alkaloids are destructive. Complement is inactivated in a few hours if allowed to stand at room temperature and will disappear in three or four days when kept at refrigeration temperatures. Filtration of serum through a Berkefeld filter removes complement. Other materials such as kaolin, shellac, cholesterol, and casein adsorb complement.

Reviews of complement by Pillemer and by Heidelberger reveal that complement is an integral chemical part of serum and that it has numerous functions. Complement is now known to consist of four components. Dialysis of fresh serum against distilled water or treatment with carbon dioxide water or dilute hydrochloric acid will separate complement into two thermolabile fractions. The water-insoluble, carbon-dioxide-insoluble, acid-insoluble component, commonly called "mid-piece," is now called $C'1$. The water-soluble, carbon-dioxide-soluble component, commonly called "end-piece," is referred to as $C'2$. Following the above discoveries, subsequent studies of complement revealed that it could be inactivated by treatment with washed yeast cells, hence a third component labeled $C'3$ was discovered. It was then shown that the exposure of complement to ammonia rendered it inactive, so the fourth component $C'4$ was revealed. The heating of complement to 56°C. destroys $C'1$ and $C'2$ but does not alter the heat-stable components $C'3$ and $C'4$. Other detailed chemical properties of these components have been discovered which may be found in the reviews mentioned above.

The origin of complement in the body has been a subject of considerable investigation. Early workers, such as Büchner, believed that it was produced by leucocytes. Metchnikoff was of the opinion that complement was present in blood serum only after leucocyte injury. Extracts of leucocytes, however, have never yielded complement, so it is now believed that the substance does not originate in those cells. Since complement is a mixture of globulins and a mucoprotein it is presumed that it arises from the same source as globulin. This is conceded to be the cells of the reticulo-endothelial system and the lymphocytes.

It is significant that the various components of complement are not all found in the serums of all animals. Normal guinea pig serum contains a greater concentration of all components than other serums. This accounts for the universal choice of guinea pig serum as a source of complement. Cow, horse, sheep, and squirrel serums do not hemolyze sheep erythrocytes because of the absence of $C'2$ component. These serums consist almost entirely of $C'1$ component.

The outstanding property of complement is its ability to cause the lysis of sensitized bacterial cells, particularly the Gram-negative types. The ability of complement to cause the hemolysis of erythrocytes is fundamental in the complement-fixation test. It combines with numerous antigen-antibody complexes to which it becomes fixed. This substance stimulates the activity of the leucocytes thereby aiding the animal in the destruction of invading bacteria. It aids immune serum in the destruction of certain viruses. It apparently has a role in tissue sensitization. It is considered to play a part in the neutralization of toxin *in vivo* subsequent to toxin-antitoxin union. Complement appears to influence the sedimentation rate of erythrocytes.

The Fixation of Complement. The fixation of complement to antigen-antibody has not been satisfactorily explained. It cannot be attached until antigen unites with antibody. The conception of Ehrlich that antibody acted as a "between-body" for antigen and complement has been discarded. Likewise, the explanations of Bordet are not tenable in light of present knowledge about complement.

Heidelberger has studied the combining action of the various components of complement on red blood cells and hemolysin. When the hemolysin combines with the red blood cell, the surface patterns of the anti-serum molecules or the anti-serum, red-blood-cell aggregate changes and different groups are in contact with the complement components. C′4 combines first or simultaneously with C′1 to the red-blood-cell aggregates. The fixation of C′4 is accompanied by the fixation of C′2. The absorption of these components in this order renders the red blood cell susceptible to the action of unattached C′3 and hemolysis results. C′3 is not taken up by the fixed complex and is not used up in the process of hemolysis, indicating that it has enzymatic properties. It has been rather clearly demonstrated that erythrocytes are not entirely coated with hemolysin and then with complement. The union of hemolysin with erythrocyte apparently occurs in certain places on the cell and it is on such sensitized areas that complement becomes fixed, producing the effect which is recognized as hemolysis.

The fact that the components of complement are variable in different species has been mentioned above. This would have a bearing on the application of the complement-fixation test in the diagnosis of disease. Other factors influence the value of the complement-fixation test as a diagnostic agent. All antigen-antibody complexes do not fix even guinea pig complement. For example, horse antiserum for the type-specific pneumococcus polysaccharides do not. Anti-complementary factors have been found to be of significance in the reaction. The bacterial antigen or tissue extracts or suspensions used as antigen may have anticomplementary effect, thus reducing the amount of complement in a test to prevent a satisfactory result. The size of the antigen-antibody aggregate apparently has an effect on complement fixation. The maximal power of fixation is possessed by particles large enough to cause opalescence but not visible to the eye. Complement is fixed to antigen-antibody mixtures rapidly at first but becomes slower as the particles become larger. Most complete fixation occurs when antigen-antibody and complement are mixed simultaneously.

Early investigators found that definite proportions of antigen-antibody and complement combined. This discovery was and still is a fundamental factor in complement fixation. The amount of each reacting substance is not necessarily equal. It has been shown that complement and hemolysin can supplement each other in hemolysis. Within certain limits, hemolysis will result if hemolysin is decreased and complement increased, or if complement is decreased and hemolysin increased. In general, the amount of hemolysin and complement are carefully determined by titration previous to their use in any diagnostic procedure. The reason for this will be made apparent in the discussion which follows.

Applications of Complement Fixation. Complement fixation has been used to the greatest extent for the diagnosis of disease. At one time this reaction was the only test used for the diagnosis of brucellosis. It was replaced by the agglutination test which is now used. The diagnosis of glanders was considered at one time to be most reliably made by complement fixation, but it has been largely replaced by the mallein test and allergic skin test. At present the complement-fixation test is not used as a routine diagnostic procedure for many of the animal diseases.

The complement-fixation reaction is used as a research tool in immunology. Many antigen-antibody combinations can be proven only by complement fixation. The reaction has had increased use for this purpose in recent years.

A great deal of the understanding of complement fixation has been made possible by the value of the Wassermann test in the diagnosis of syphilis. This test is still used in public health laboratories for the diagnosis of this disease.

Description of the Complement-Fixation Test. The understanding of complement fixation will be more complete if the fundamentals of a diagnostic test are given. Brucellosis is chosen as the disease to be diagnosed because most everyone is familiar with it and experimentally all of the essential ingredients needed for the test are available in most laboratories.

A. Reacting Agents Required.

1. Dilute suspension of *Brucella abortus*, the bacteriolytic antigen.

2. The serum of the cow suspected of being infected with brucellosis. The normal complement in this serum is inactivated

by exposure to 56°C. for one-half hour. The bacterial antibody, sensitizer, may or may not be present in this serum. The objective of the test is to detect its presence.

3. Pooled serum from a number of normal guinea pigs. This is the complement. The potency of complement is determined by preliminary titration.

4. A 2 per cent suspension of sheep erythrocytes. These cells have been washed in physiological saline so as to be free of normal complement. This is the hemolytic antigen.

5. Serum from a rabbit which has been given a series of injections of sheep erythrocytes. This is the hemolytic antibody, hemolysin. The potency of hemolysin is determined by preliminary titration.

6. Physiological, 0.85 per cent, sodium chloride solution.

B. Titration of Hemolysin.

The potency of hemolysin varies with the individual and with the number of injections of sheep erythrocytes which the rabbit has received. A satisfactory hemolysin is produced by five injections of 5 ml. of a 10 per cent suspension of sheep cells four days apart. The rabbit is then bled and the serum collected and preserved by adding an equal part of neutral glycerin. A 1:100 stock dilution is prepared as follows:

Saline solution...94.0 ml.
Glycerinized hemolysin (50 per cent)............... 2.0 ml.
Phenol (5 per cent in phy-saline)...................... 4.0 ml.

For titration, a series of 10 higher dilutions are then prepared.

```
No.  1   0.5 ml. hemolysin (1:100  ) + 4.5 ml. saline solution = 1:1,000
No.  2   0.5 ml. hemolysin (1:1,000) + 0.5 ml. saline solution = 1:2,000
No.  3   0.5 ml. hemolysin (1:1,000) + 1.0 ml. saline solution = 1:3,000
No.  4   0.5 ml. hemolysin (1:1,000) + 1.5 ml. saline solution = 1:4,000
No.  5   0.5 ml. hemolysin (1:1,000) + 2.0 ml. saline solution = 1:5,000
No.  6   0.5 ml. hemolysin (1:3,000) + 0.5 ml. saline solution = 1:6,000
No.  7   0.5 ml. hemolysin (1:4,000) + 0.5 ml. saline solution = 1:8,000
No.  8   0.5 ml. hemolysin (1:5,000) + 0.5 ml. saline solution = 1:10,000
No.  9   0.5 ml. hemolysin (1:6,000) + 0.5 ml. saline solution = 1:12,000
No. 10   0.5 ml. hemolysin (1:8,000) + 0.5 ml. saline solution = 1:16,000
```

The titer of hemolysin is obtained by using each of the above dilutions with complement and sheep red blood cells. The amounts of each of these ingredients are given in Table 11.1.

The contents of each tube are thoroughly mixed and the tubes are placed in a water bath at 37°C. for one hour. The tubes are then examined to determine the titer of the hemolysin. *The unit of hemolysin is the highest dilution that shows complete hemolysis.*

TABLE 11.1

TITRATION OF HEMOLYSIN

Tube Number	Hemolysin 0.5 ml.	Complement ml. (1:30 dil.)	Sheep R.B.C. ml. (2% susp.)	Saline Solution ml.
1	1:1,000	0.3	0.5	1.7
2	1:2,000	0.3	0.5	1.7
3	1:3,000	0.3	0.5	1.7
4	1:4,000	0.3	0.5	1.7
5	1:5,000	0.3	0.5	1.7
6	1:6,000	0.3	0.5	1.7
7	1:8,000	0.3	0.5	1.7
8	1:10,000	0.3	0.5	1.7
9	1:12,000	0.3	0.5	1.7
10	1:16,000	0.3	0.5	1.7

C. Titration of Complement.

In the titration of complement varying amounts of the 1:30 dilution are set up in a series of test tubes. Two units of the previously titrated hemolysin are used. Inasmuch as this amount varies, the volume of fluid in each tube is regulated by adding the amount of saline which brings the volume to 3 ml. The various amounts are given in Table 11.2.

TABLE 11.2

TITRATION OF COMPLEMENT

Tube Number	Complement ml. (1:30 dil.)	Hemolysin 2 units (units)	Sheep R.B.C. ml. (2% susp.)	Saline Solution q.s. 3 ml.
1.........	0.1	2	0.5	....
2	0.15	2	0.5	....
3	0.2	2	0.5	....
4	0.25	2	0.5	....
5	0.3	2	0.5	....
6	0.35	2	0.5	....
7	0.4	2	0.5	....
8	0.45	2	0.5	....
9	0.5	None	0.5	....
10	None	2	0.5	....

The complement unit is the highest dilution which shows complete hemolysis.

D. The Complement-Fixation Test.

The titration of hemolysin and complement has emphasized that when definite amounts of these substances are mixed with a suspension of sheep erythrocytes, hemolysis will result. Hemolysis will not result if complement is not present. It is clear, therefore, that a controlled and standardized hemolytic system can be used as an indicator of complement fixation. This is its function in a complement-fixation test for the diagnosis of disease.

It has been stated repeatedly that complement is fixed by most antigen-antibody combinations. In the example, brucellosis, complement would be fixed if the serum of the cow suspected of having brucellosis is mixed with a suspension of the causal organism, *Brucella abortus*, in the presence of complement. It is equally obvious that if the suspect serum is from a noninfected animal, there will

TABLE 11.3
THE COMPLEMENT-FIXATION TEST

Tube	Br. abortus antigen	Suspect s serum	Complement 1:30	Sheep R.B.C.	Hemolysin	Saline Sol.	Results
	(*ml.*)	(*ml.*)	(*units*)	(*ml.*)	(*units*)		
1......	0.2	0.1	2	0.5	2	q.s. 3 ml.	No hemolysis if animal infected
2......	....	0.1	2	0.5	2	q.s. 3 ml.	Hemolysis, serum control
3......	0.4	0.2	2	0.5	2	q.s. 3 ml.	No hemolysis if animal infected
4......	....	0.2	2	0.5	2	q.s. 3 ml.	Hemolysis, serum control
5......	0.2	....	2	0.5	2	q.s. 3 ml.	Hemolysis, antigen control
6......	0.4	....	2	0.5	2	q.s. 3 ml.	Hemolysis, antigen control
7......	....	....	2	0.5	2	q.s. 3 ml.	Hemolysis, hemolytic system control
8......	....	....	2	0.5	....	q.s. 3 ml.	No hemolysis, complement control
9......	....	....	....	0.5	2	q.s. 3 ml.	No hemolysis, hemolysin control
10......	....	....	....	0.5	....	q.s. 3 ml.	No hemolysis, saline sol. control

be no sensitizer for *Brucella abortus* present; hence, fixation of complement will not result.

The complement-fixation test is a combination of two systems, bacterolytic and hemolytic, with complement the deviating substance between them. By studying Table 11.3, it is noted that the bacterial antigen, suspect serum, and complement are mixed. This is followed by a period of one hour incubation, which allows the fixation of complement *if antibody for Br. abortus is present in the suspect serum*. This is followed by the addition of the hemolytic system, sheep R.B.C., and hemolysin. After a period of incubation the test is read. If the complement has been fixed by the bacterial system — in other words, if the test is positive — the erythrocytes will not be hemolized. If the complement has not been fixed in the bacterial system, the erythrocytes will be hemolized in all the tubes where the hemolytic agents are present. It is now apparent why it is essential to titrate the sheep-cell hemolysin and the complement. In conducting routine diagnostic complement-fixation tests it is not

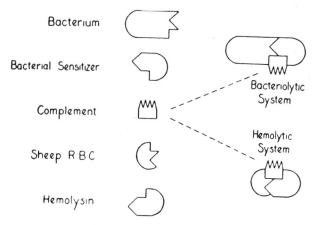

FIG. 11.1 — Diagrammatic scheme of the complement-fixation reaction.

necessary to use as many controls as given in Table 11.3; they are inserted in this example to emphasize the need of controlling a mechanism as sensitive as the hemolysis of such delicate cells. Figure 11.1 illustrates the reaction in a diagrammatic way.

Applications of Hemolysis. In 1898 Bordet reported the specific antigenic natures of the erythrocytes of the different species of animals. Ferguson, in 1941, demonstrated that a specific hemolysin was produced in rabbits by the injection of bovine erythrocytes. Furthermore, erythrocytes from various genetically different bovines produced specific antibody in the rabbit. Upon pursuing this procedure, Ferguson, Stormont, and Irwin detected thirty antigens in the erythrocytes of cattle by transfusing the blood from one individual to another or by immunizing rabbits with bovine cells. Subsequently Owen, Stormont, and Irwin noted the frequency of the various antigens in various dairy breeds. They found the test reliable enough to be used in determining the parentage of an unknown individual calf.

The Phenomenon of Conglutination. Ehrlich and Sachs observed that the addition of fresh, unheated horse serum to a suspension of red blood cells of the guinea pig produced slight hemolysis. They further observed that the addition of heated cow serum to a suspension of the red corpuscles caused no hemolysis. The addition of both heated cow serum and fresh horse serum produced an active hemolysis.

In checking the above experiments Bordet and Gay observed that the inactivated cow serum had but slight agglutinating power for the corpuscles of the guinea pig, and that fresh horse serum likewise agglutinated them slowly and slightly, whereas a mixture of the two sera caused rapid and complete agglutination. The cow serum increased the hemolysin and agglutinin of the horse serum; Bordet and Gay, therefore, concluded that this property was due to a thermostabile substance peculiar to the ox serum. This they called *conglutinin*, and classed it with the colloids. Their explanation is that guinea pig corpuscles are affected by sensitizers in a combination of both the horse and cow serum and are then able to fix the complement of the horse serum. The complement possesses but slight hemolytic power, but when the corpuscles have become sensitized and laden with the complement, their properties of molecular affinity are modified to the extent that they become capable of attracting the conglutinin of the cow serum which combines with them. The result is twofold: Agglutination occurs, and the corpuscles are more readily destroyed by complement.

Pfeiler, Strenge, and others have made use of the conglutination test for the diagnosis of dourine, glanders, syphilis, and various other diseases. The technic for the glanders conglutination test is much the same as that for complement fixation. A definite quantity, established by previous titration, of normal unheated horse serum is added to a tube containing inactivated blood serum of the horse suspected of having glanders, and an extract of the glanders bacillus, previously titrated. This mixture is incubated 1 hour at 37°C. The inactivated cow serum, also previously titrated, and a suspension of washed red blood cells of the sheep or some other animal, are then added. A second incubation for 1 or 2 hours is then made.

If the serum which is being tested is from an animal infected with glanders, the red blood cells settle to the bottom, leaving the fluid clear; if the serum is from a noninfected animal, the corpuscles gather in clumps at first, and later they slowly hemolyze.

The conglutination test is applicable in asses and mules which possess anticomplementary substances in their blood serum; furthermore, the ingredients of the test are more easily obtained than are those for complement fixation. The test is considered even more delicate than the complement-fixation test and requires more careful titration of the reagents. Pfeiler believed that it has a greater degree of accuracy, and cited cases in which it was positive where both agglutination and complement fixation were negative; subsequent postmortem verified the accuracy of the test.

This reaction is somewhat of a laboratory curiosity at this time and is not used in disease diagnosis. It should be of value, however, in studying antigen-antibody relationships and for that reason deserves more thorough study in light of modern concepts.

REFERENCES FOR FURTHER STUDY

Bordet, J. Ann. de l'Inst. Past. 12:668–95, 1898.

Bordet, Jules. Studies on Immunity. Pp. 186–258, 280–311, 333–38. Translated by F. P. Gay. John Wiley & Sons, London, 1909.

Boyd, W. C. Fundamentals of Immunology, 2nd Ed. Interscience Publishers, New York, 1947.

Browning, C. H. Complement, pp. 332–52, Vol. 6, System of Bacteriology. Med. Res. Council. His Majesty's Stationery Office, London, 1931.

Dubos, J. Bacterial and Mycotic Infections of Man. J. B. Lippincott Co., Philadelphia, 1948.

Ehrlich, Paul. Collected Studies on Immunity. Pp. 1–35, 56–142, 181–282, 390–403, 561–76. Translated by Charles Bolduan. John Wiley & Sons, London, 1906.

Ferguson, L. C. Jour. Immunol. 40:213–42, 1941.

———, Stormont, C., Irwin, M. R. Jour. Immunol. 44:147–64, 1942.

Gay, F. P., and associates. Agents of Disease and Host Resistance. Pp. 370–89. Charles C. Thomas, Baltimore, 1935.

Heidelberger, M. Am. Scientist, 34:597–610, 1946.

Kabat, E. A., and Mayer, M. M. Experimental Immunochemistry. Charles C. Thomas, Springfield, 1948.

Muir, R. Bactericidal Action, pp. 267–94 and Hemolytic Action, pp. 295–331, Vol. 6, System of Bacteriology. Med. Res. Council. His Majesty's Stationery Office, London, 1931.

Owen, R. D., Stormont, C. J., and Irwin, M. R. Jour. Anim. Sci. 3:315–21, 1944.

Pillemer, L. Chem. Rev. 33:1–26, 1943.

Raffel, Sidney. Immunity, Hypersensitivity, and Serology. Appleton-Century-Crofts, Inc., New York, 1953.

Sherwood, N. P. Immunology. Pp. 370–437. C. V. Mosby Co., St. Louis, 1935.

Topley, W. W. C., Wilson, G. S. and Miles, A. A. The Principles of Bacteriology. 3rd Ed. Pp. 158–66. Williams & Wilkins Co., Baltimore, 1946.

Wadsworth, Augustus. The Complement Fixation Reaction with Bacterial Antigens. The Newer Knowledge of Bacteriology and Immunology. Pp. 831–37. University of Chicago Press, Chicago, 1928.

Zinsser, H., Enders, J. F., and Fothergill, L. D. Immunity. Pp. 194–232. The Macmillan Co., New York, 1939.

12. Phagocytosis

Phagocytosis is the process by which foreign particles, including bacteria, are ingested by leucocytes and by certain endothelial
cells of the body. In many respects the phenomenon is similar to
the ingestion of food particles by single-celled animals, such as the
amoeba. Phagocytosis is a normal function of body cells, but is
definitely stimulated by the invasion of pathogenic bacteria.

The discovery of phagocytosis is credited to Eli Metchnikoff.
In his study of the origin of the intestine and the process of
intracellular digestion, Metchnikoff observed that mobile cells of
the mesoderm accumulated about grains of carmine introduced
into the body of the jellyfish. He then demonstrated that when
sharp thorns were introduced under the skin of starfish larvae,
mobile cells clustered about the thorns. From these facts, Metchnikoff concluded that inflammation is a reaction of mesodermic cells
against an invading agent, and the function of leucocytes is a
protective and curative one. The term *phagocytes,* meaning devour-
ing cells, was coined for these cells. The real function of phagocytes in the disease process was shown by Metchnikoff by his
work with small, transparent crustaceans, the *daphniae,* which he
found to be infected with a fungus producing sharp, needle-like
spores. These spores penetrated the intestinal wall and were attacked by the mobile phagocytes which digested them. Carrying
his researches into the field of the diseases of larger animals he
demonstrated that virulent anthrax bacilli were not phagocytyzed,
but attenuated anthrax bacilli were readily engulfed, and further,
that active phagocytosis was apparent in immune animals. Metchnikoff believed that immunity was due entirely to phagocytosis and
that the ability of phagocytes to engulf invading microorganisms
was caused by the stimulation, or training, of the phagocytes during
the immunizing process. He published his first work on the theory
in 1884.

Metchnikoff divided the phagocytic cells into two groups: the
wandering cells, and the fixed cells. He called the polymorpho-

nuclear leucocytes *microphages,* and the mononuclear leucocytes, *macrophages;* all of which were classed as wandering cells. These cells were the most active phagocytes, and Metchnikoff assigned different functions in disease to them. The fixed phagocytes, he concluded, were prevalent in the lymph nodes and spleen and are the cells which are now recognized as part of the reticulo-endothelial system.

The rise of the alexin, or humoral, theory of Buchner and its subsequent development by Pfeiffer, Bordet, Ehrlich, and others caused Metchnikoff a great deal of concern. He fitted the phagocytic theory into the humoral theory, however, by showing, to his satisfaction, that alexin was liberated only after the leucocytes were damaged by the inflammatory process. He called the liberated material *cytase.* His conception of the relationship of the two phenomena has been proven erroneous, but his theory of phagocytosis was not severely shaken and at present is accepted as the most fundamental process in immunity.

The Antibody in Phagocytosis, Opsonin. The phagocytosis of virulent bacteria is due to the action of the antibody, *opsonin,* which sensitizes the bacteria so that they are approached and engulfed by phagocytic cells. Denys and Leclef, in 1895, were the first to show that the antibodies in immune serum affected the microorganism and made it more easily phagocytized. This was contrary to the belief of Metchnikoff and his pupils who had believed that immune serum stimulated the leucocytes to greater activity.

Wright and Douglas, in 1904, showed that a substance in immune serum increased the number of bacteria which were phagocytized by leucocytes. They also demonstrated that this substance acted upon the microorganisms and not upon the phagocytes. Because this action prepared bacteria as food for the phagocytes, they named the antibody *opsonin,* meaning *to prepare food.*

The role of opsonin in the phagocytic process is demonstrated by the following procedure: The blood from a suitable animal is drawn into physiological salt solution, defibrinated, and centrifuged. The cells are thrown to the bottom, and the leucocytes form in a layer between the red cells and the plasma. The leucocytes are removed, washed, and are again centrifuged until free of blood serum and erythrocytes. The leucocytes are mixed with a dilute suspension of bacteria, and the mixture is incubated for 15 minutes. A smear is made of the mixture and is stained by a suitable dye. When the smear is viewed under the microscope, it is observed that the bacteria are not engulfed by the leucocytes. A similar preparation is made with the addition of an homologous immune serum. In this smear a large number of bacteria are found within the leucocytes.

Phagocytosis, as has been stated, is a normal function in the body and is a process by which most of the saprophytic and relatively avirulent bacteria are destroyed. In fact, the virulence of microorganisms is due, in part at least, to their ability to repel phagocytes. Normal serum stimulates the phagocytic process; consequently, there has been considerable speculation concerning the difference between the function of normal serum, as represented presumably by normal opsonin, and immune opsonin. Whether the normal and the immune opsonins are identical has been a controversial subject for many years. Normal opsonin is similar to components C′1 or C′2 of the serum complement for it is thermolabile, that is, 58° to 60°C. destroys it. The immune or specific opsonin, on the other hand, is relatively thermostable. It is generally admitted that normal opsonin is not identical with complement; however, it is known that the presence of complement, or a thermolabile substance similar to complement, does augment the action of immune opsonin. This substance also has been shown to increase the action of immune opsonin in sensitizing cells for phagocytosis. The substance apparently cannot sensitize cells alone, and its action has been described as that of a catalyst which hastens the union of opsonin with bacteria, thereby promoting phagocytosis. The specificity and action of opsonin seems to be an extension of the properties of normal serum, not differing from other types of antibody relationships and supporting still more the unitarian conception of antibodies.

The Opsonic Index. *The opsonic index* is the ratio of the sensitizing power of the serum of an infected animal as compared with that of a healthy individual. The ratio between the two sera is determined by the relative effect they have on phagocytic action. Although it is not always necessary, it is customary to use leucocytes of the species of animal under investigation. The technic is as follows:

Preparation of Leucocytes. Leucocytes are secured by collecting blood in physiological salt solution, and defibrinating and centrifuging it. (The use of sodium citrate is contraindicated in this work because of the depressing effect of the citrate ion on phagocytosis.) The cells are washed repeatedly in salt solution until all the serum is removed. The upper layer of corpuscles, rich in leucocytes, is carefully pipetted and placed in a small test tube. Leucocytes can be collected in large quantities from small experimental animals within a few hours after an intraperitoneal injection of peptone or aleurone, which causes the concentration of leucocytes in the peritoneal cavity.

Preparation of Bacterial Emulsion. The organisms are prepared in a perfectly homogenous suspension. A 24-hour slant agar culture is used; the growth is washed off with sterile physiological salt solution, and is then shaken and diluted to a faint opalescence. Filtration may be necessary in order to remove unbroken clumps.

Preparation of Serum. Normal serum and serum from the animal to be tested are secured by bleeding, allowing the blood to clot, centrifuging and taking off the serum with a pipette, and transferring it to a small test tube. Before they are ready for use, both of the sera are diluted 1:10.

Technic of the Test. A capillary pipette is prepared from glass tubing, and a mark is made about 2 cm. from the end. The suspension of leucocytes is then drawn up to the mark, an air bubble is similarly drawn, and then the serum to be tested is drawn to the same mark, followed by a second air bubble, and finally an equal amount of the bacterial suspension. The contents are blown out on a watch glass and thoroughly mixed by drawing up and down in the pipette a few times. The mixture is then drawn into the capillary pipette, the end of which is sealed in the flame. It is then placed in an opsonic incubator at 37°C. for 15 minutes, where it is rotated frequently to assure thorough mixing during the incubating period. The procedure is repeated with the use of the normal serum. At the completion of incubation, the end of the pipette is broken, and smears are made of the contents which are stained with Wright's stain.

Computation of the Opsonic Index. The total number of bacteria ingested by 100 polymorphonuclear leucocytes is tabulated, and the average number per leucocyte calculated. This is termed the *phagocytic index.* This number is determined for normal serum and the serum to be tested. The *opsonic index* is now more exactly defined as the *ratio* between the phagocytic index of the test serum and the phagocytic index of the normal serum.

Phagocytic Cells. The division of phagocytic cells into two groups, motile and fixed, which was made by Metchnikoff, has been found to be entirely valid as has his division of the wandering leucocytes into microphages and macrophages. The cellular elements of the blood have been extensively investigated since the original work of Metchnikoff, and the origin of the cells has been a subject of great interest. While the origin of the majority of them, their relationships with one another, and their function in the animal body have been generally agreed upon, there still are some phases of the subject open to investigation.

The microphages of Metchnikoff embrace the polymorphonuclear leucocytes or neutrophiles, the eosinophiles, and basophiles. These cells have their origin from the myeloblasts in bone marrow. The neutrophiles comprise 72 to 75 per cent of the white blood cells and to them has been ascribed the most important task of phagocytosis. The eosinophiles do not appear to have a great deal of phagocytic value although they have been shown to have some ability to engulf bacteria. These cells become more numerous in certain bacterial infections, in animal parasite infestations, and in foreign body invasion; however, their exact function in such disturbances is not well known. The basophiles apparently are not phagocytic, in the true sense of the term, although bacteria have been observed in their cytoplasm.

The macrophages of Metchnikoff, which include the mononuclear leucocytes, the fixed tissue cells, and the wandering tissue cells, have been of increasing interest in immunity. Reference has been made to these cells in the discussion of the origin of antibody in Chapter 7, where it was emphasized that they have an important role in the production of antibody. Their dual purpose makes them even more interesting. These cells have been termed by Aschoff, "The Reticulo-endothelial System." They include: *the reticular cells* of the splenic pulp and of cortical nodules, and the pulp cords in the lymph nodes; the *endothelial cells* of the sinuses of the lymph nodes, the blood sinuses of the spleen, the liver sinusoids, the capillaries of the bone marrow, adrenals, and hypophysis; the *histiocytes,* or the clasmatocytes, of Ranvier; the *splenic pulp cells;* and the *septal cells* of the lung.

The Phagocytic Process. The act of phagocytosis is divided into three distinct parts: the approach of the phagocyte to the particle, or cell, to be phagocytized; the ingestion of the particle, or cell; and the disintegration, or digestion, within the phagocyte.

The Approach. Phagocytes are drawn to foreign particles, including bacteria which are present in the body tissues, by the force known as *positive chemotaxis.* In this particular phenomenon this force is thought to be a result of surface tension effects. The surface tension on the side of the phagocyte nearest the bacteria is lowered, and as a consequence, the phagocyte migrates toward the particle and engulfs it. That the attraction of leucocytes to bacteria and other particles is positive chemotaxis, has been repeatedly demonstrated. It is, in all practical respects, the same phenomenon as that of ingestion of food particles by amoeba and other protozoa. The phagocytosis of foreign particles, dead tissue, and nonpathogenic bacteria is doubtless a function of normal phagocytosis; that is, there is no need for the intervention of an additional amount of the antibody material, opsonin.

One of the important characteristics of pathogenic bacteria is their ability to resist phagocytosis; in fact, they exert such a marked negative chemotaxis that the phagocytes are actually repelled. This property is noted in the action of anthrax bacilli which is due to the capsular substance of the organism. The neutralization of this material is considered the function of opsonin, thereby permitting the phagocytosis of the anthrax bacilli during the process of immunization. This material, which is present within the capsules of capsulated bacteria and is no doubt a part of the ectoplasm of noncapsulated bacteria, has been termed "aggressin" by Bail. Its function as an antigen which is used in the stimulation of antibody, or antiaggressin, was discussed in the chapter relating to antigens and antibodies. The neutralization of the negative chemotactic force of pathogenic bacteria by opsonin is referred to as a sensitization process. There is no reason why this procedure should be considered different from the sensitization of bacteria to the action of an electrolyte or complement, and if the unitarian view of antibody is accepted, one realizes that the procedure is the same, that is, the denaturization, or "coating over," of bacterial protoplasm by globulin.

The approach of phagocytes toward bacteria is usually characterized, at least in the case of less pathogenic species, by a mass movement of phagocytes toward the invader. Because of their great number and definite mobility, the polymorphonuclear leucocytes predominate in this movement. They possess a greater amount of cytoplasm than other leucocytes and may pass between (diapedesis) the endothelial cells of capillaries and lymph vessels toward the positive chemotactic influence. This influence can become generalized throughout the body in a relatively short time and may cause a condition called *leucocytosis*, which is characterized by a marked increase in the number of leucocytes in the blood stream. This phenomenon is observed in many pyogenic infections as well as other inflammatory reactions and is used as a factor in the diagnosis of disease, an example of which is appendicitis in man.

The Ingestion. The second phase of the act of phagocytosis, the *ingestion* of the bacteria, is the continuation of the first phase. As the phagocyte comes in contact with the bacteria, it flows around them and incorporates them within its cytoplasm. This process is a simple one for the mobile phagocytes. The fixed phagocytes, however, are held in place by their contact with adjacent cells. In this instance the bacteria must be brought to them; this is done by the blood and lymph streams, and considerable phagocytosis occurs at points where the flow of these streams is slow and in tissues where it becomes static. The act of ingestion does not mean destruction. In many instances the ingested material is not destroyed by the phagocyte. The best example of this is in tuberculosis. Tubercle bacilli are readily engulfed by leucocytes as they wander about in glandular crypts of the mucous membrane and in lymph vessels. In many cases this "accidental phagocytosis" of tubercle bacilli is harmful to the animal. The polymorphonuclear leucocytes do not appear to have the ability to digest tubercle bacilli; hence, they carry such organisms to the deeper tissues, the regional lymph nodes, or in many cases into the blood stream, and on to the lungs. This forms a focus of the infection because the tubercle bacilli are able to multiply within the leucocyte and ultimately destroy it; consequently, in tuberculosis, it is necessary for other cells, such as the mononuclear leucocytes, to intervene and to defend the body against the assisted invasion. The act of ingestion is responsible for the concentration of bacteria in certain tissues where body defenses, such as the action of various types of phagocytes, encapsulation of the process, and in many cases calcification, rid the body of the invading organisms.

The ingestion of bacteria by leucocytes results in the death of many of the leucocytes. A substance known as *leucocidin* is produced by many species of bacteria, notably the staphylococci and streptococci. It is by virtue of this substance, in addition to the action of aggressin noted previously, that these bacteria are considered to be virulent. Leucocidin is usually a toxin-like substance produced by bacteria. It is produced in broth cultures, and its effect upon leucocytes is demonstrated by the action of the filtrate. It is able to resist 56°C. and has been shown to be an antigen, in that its injection produces antileucocidin.

The Digestion. Metchnikoff assumed that the destruction of bacteria was brought about by phagocytes and was due to two substances formed by them. The microphages produced *microcytase* which he considered identical with complement, or alexin, and which was active in the normal destruction of bacteria. The macrophages produced *macrocytase* which was active in the destruction of dead tissue and other debris. In the assumption that phagocytes are able to produce a substance which has a disintegrating action upon bacteria, Metchnikoff was right. His division of the function of the phagocytes was wrong as, also, was his contention that the substance was similar to complement. One of the most substantial proofs for the distinction between "cytase" and complement is the fact that the latter is thermolabile (56°C.) and the former is heat resistant.

The nature of the bactericidal substance present in phagocytes is not entirely known. It does not seem to be identical with various enzymes produced by leucocytes such as leucoprotease which can be purified by precipitation and still show proteolytic activity without bactericidal property. The proteolytic enzymes of the polymorphonuclear cells act in a weakly alkaline medium while those of the mononuclear cells are more effective in a weakly acid medium. Lipase is produced by cells of the macrophage group. This is clearly demonstrated in tuberculosis and leprosy, where it has been shown that the lipoid constituents of the bacilli are removed by mononuclear cells, whereas this is not true of polymorphonuclear leucocytes.

Unfortunately, certain types of bacteria may not be destroyed by the phagocyte after they have been ingested. This is apparent in tuberculosis, where the tubercle bacilli are ingested by polymorphonuclear leucocytes and transported to regional lymph nodes where the primary lesion of tuberculosis, the tubercle, develops. In other diseases, such as brucellosis, the causal bacteria are ingested, but apparently not quickly digested. Their presence in the phagocyte protects them against antibody and the lytic process. This is thought to explain the chronic nature of that disease as well as the recurring acute attacks of the infection.

The Significance of Phagocytosis in Immunity. The role of phagocytosis in immunity has been acknowledged as an important phenomenon since its description by Metchnikoff. That it is the only means by which the animal body is protected against pathogenic bacteria, as contended by Metchnikoff, has been doubted by many. The demonstration of the bactericidal action of blood plasma followed by the advent of the humoral theory of immunity, made it evident that lysis, too, had a part to play in the destruction of microorganisms. The neutralization of toxin by antitoxin has demonstrated that a direct neutralizing process is active in destroying certain poisons of bacteria. The division of immunity into the three parts—neutralization, humoral, and cellular—is logical, but how much of immunity may be ascribed to each is rather difficult to ascertain. We may dispose of the part toxin-antitoxin plays by admitting that this is a function which is operative in all diseases produced by toxins of any marked potency. The division of the resulting immunity into humoral and cellular is a more difficult task. That the lysis of bacteria takes place when the necessary reacting substances are placed in a test tube is well established. It may be assumed that the same thing occurs in the animal body. Furthermore, it has been proven that when leucocytes, bacteria, and antibody are placed together in a test tube, the bacteria are destroyed. This occurs within the body as has been demonstrated. The division of immunity into *temporary* and *permanent* is helpful in showing a difference between the humoral and cellular effects.

It is assumed that humoral immunity is active when antibody is noted in the blood plasma. Antibody is detected by the agglutination, precipitation, or complement-fixation tests. As long as this substance is present in great amounts, high titers, it is supposed that humoral immunity is still an effective means of destroying bacteria. In those conditions where antibody is demonstrated and yet the animal is in the acute stage of the disease, the mere presence of antibody does not assure the animal protection against death, nor does it mean that the animal will be protected against chronic infection. In most cases, however, the presence of antibody is conducive to recovery. During this recovery process, lysis and phagocytosis are no doubt the active forces in bacterial destruction. Ultimately, however, in many conditions it is not possible to demonstrate the presence of antibody in blood plasma, and yet the animal is entirely immune. By what means is the animal protected? Lysis and phagocytosis both are enhanced by the action of antibody, and it seems logical to assume that the absence of antibody affects each equally.

Metchnikoff was of the opinion in his very early work on phagocytosis that the phenomenon was due to the stimulation of the phagocyte. The discovery of opsonin negated that assumption. Wassermann and Citron in 1905 were of the opinion that cells could be conditioned to the effects of foreign substances without the action of antibody. This first suggestion of the existence of a "local immunity" has been considerably advanced by the work of Besredka, Gay, and his co-workers, and by many others. Definite evidence has accumulated which appears to demonstrate that phagocytic cells can be trained to be effective against a specific type of antigenic substance. This training appears to be an inheritable phenomenon which is possessed by the cells for long periods of time. In a sense, then, the original conception of Metchnikoff, that phagocytosis is due to the stimulation of the phagocyte, seems to be partly true. The action of the antibody, opsonin, speeds up the union of phagocyte and the invading microorganism. The presence of a marked immunity in the absence of demonstrable antibody is explained by the presence of a property in phagocytes which is passed on to the newly formed cells. It is assumed, then, that cellular immunity is more durable than humoral and plays an exceedingly important role in temporary infections. It is generally conceded, also, that natural immunity is due largely to the action of phagocytes.

Phagocytosis in Disease Diagnosis. At one time the determination of the opsonic index of a patient was considered a practical method of diagnosing disease. Experimental error and the availability of more adequate diagnostic tests discouraged its use. A modification of the opsonic index determination under the name of the *opsonocytophagic test* has been suggested during recent years as an aid in the diagnosis of brucellosis of man.

Gould and Huddleson describe the test as follows: [1]

> . . . the Brucella opsonic test is performed by incubating a mixture of a live, forty-eight hour culture of *Brucella abortus* and the patient's ci-

[1] S. E. Gould and I. F. Huddleson. *Diagnostic Methods in Undulant Fever (Brucellosis).* Jour. Amer. Med. Assn. 109:1971, 1937.

trated blood in a water bath at 37°C. for thirty minutes. The mixture consists of 0.1 cc. of a saline suspension of organisms having a turbidity of 6 mm., as measured by the Gates apparatus, and 0.1 cc. of the patient's citrated blood having a dilution of 0.8 per cent citrate (5 cc. of blood added to 0.2 cc. of 20 per cent sodium citrate in saline solution). A smear of the mixture is then made on a glass slide, dried rapidly with an electric fan and treated with 0.5 cc. of Hasting's stain for thirty seconds, after which, 1 cc. of distilled water having a pH of 6.4 is added for ten minutes. Twenty-five polymorphonuclear leukocytes are examined and their opsonic power classified according to the number of Brucella organisms counted within each cell, as follows: negative, no phagocytized bacteria; slight, from 1 to 20; moderate, from 21 to 40, and marked, over 40. The Brucella opsonic (opsonocytophagic) test in a subject reacting negatively to the intradermal test will almost always show little or no phagocytosis. A subject reacting positively to the intradermal test is classified as infected when less than 40 per cent of his polymorphonuclear leukocytes show marked phagocytosis and as infected but with questionable immunity if from 40 to 60 per cent of his polymorphonuclears show a marked phagocytosis. A subject reacting to the intradermal test is classified as immune when 60 per cent or more of his polymorphonuclear leukocytes show marked phagocytosis of Brucella organisms.

REFERENCES FOR FURTHER STUDY

Besredka, A. Local Immunization. Williams & Wilkins Co., Baltimore, 1927.

Fenn, W. O. The Mechanism of Phagocytosis. The Newer Knowledge of Bacteriology and Immunology. Pp. 861–69. University of Chicago Press, Chicago, 1928.

Gay, F. P. Local and Tissue Immunity. The Newer Knowledge of Bacteriology and Immunology. Pp. 881–91. University of Chicago Press, Chicago, 1928.

———, and associates. Agents of Disease and Host Resistance. Pp. 296–309, 444–54. Charles C. Thomas, Baltimore, 1935.

Gould, S. E., and Huddleson, I. F. Diagnostic Methods in Undulant Fever (Brucellosis). Jour. Amer. Med. Assn. 109:1971–74, 1937.

Kolmer, J. A. Infection, Immunity and Biologic Therapy. Pp. 171–202. W. B. Saunders Co., Philadelphia, 1923.

Metchnikoff, Elie. Immunity in Infective Diseases. English translation by F. G. Binnie. Cambridge University Press, Cambridge, 1907.

Metchnikoff, Olga. The Life of Elie Metchnikoff. Houghton Mifflin Co., Boston, 1921.

Mudd, S., McCutcheon, M., and Lucke, B. Phagocytosis. Physiological Reviews. 14:210–370, 1934.

Raffel, Sidney. Immunity, Hypersensitivity, and Serology. Appleton-Century-Crofts, Inc., New York, 1953.

Sherwood, N. P. Immunology. Pp. 69–99. The C. V. Mosby Co., St. Louis, 1935.

Wells, H. G. The Chemical Aspects of Immunity. Pp. 254–68. The Chemical Catalog Co., New York, 1929.

Wherry, W. B. The Mechanism of Phagocytosis. The Newer Knowledge of Bacteriology and Immunology. Pp. 870–80. University of Chicago Press, Chicago, 1928.

Zinsser, H., Enders, J. F., and Fothergill, L. D. Immunity. Pp. 284–339. The Macmillan Co., New York, 1939.

13. | Anaphylaxis and Allergy

Injection of bacteria and other protein substances stimulate body cells to produce antibodies. These antibodies neutralize and sensitize antigens; consequently, various phenomena which are associated with the state of immunity result. By these processes the susceptible tissue are protected against further attacks of the invading agent, a condition which is called *prophylaxis,* meaning "with protection." Another type of reaction exists which is directly opposite to immunity. When a protein substance is injected into an animal parenterally, that is, subcutaneously or intravenously, and is followed in two weeks by another injection, a reaction is noted which varies from a minor respiratory disturbance to death. The animal obviously becomes more sensitive to the protein instead of becoming immune; it possesses a hypersensitive condition which is called *anaphylaxis,* meaning "without protection." Immunity and anaphylaxis, however, do have many characteristics in common: Both are induced by protein substances; both are specific in action; both involve the action of body cells; and both are brought about by antigen-antibody union. Marked differences existing between immunity and anaphylaxis are: Immunity protects, anaphylaxis does not; immune reactions can be demonstrated in vitro, anaphylaxis can be demonstrated only on living cells. The mechanisms of the two reactions appear similar, but the results differ.

In 1798, Jenner was probably the first to observe hypersensitiveness when he noted that smallpox or cowpox patients appeared to be more sensitive to smallpox or cowpox substances than if they had not had the disease. Some time later, 1839, Magendie found that the injection of egg albumen into rabbits produced a hypersensitive state, and subsequent injections of the same substances produced death. The most significant early contribution to the subject was made by Richet and his co-workers, Hericourt and Portier, in 1898. They first observed that the injection of eel serum produced an increased susceptibility in the dog, and later that the injection of an extract of the tenacles of sea anemones also produced the same type of sensitivity. They coined the word *anaphylaxis*.

In 1903 Arthus described an unusual phenomenon which has since been named for him. He injected rabbits subcutaneously with a horse serum at six-day intervals. The first three injections were readily absorbed by the tissues; the fourth was followed by some edema at the site of injection; and after the sixth or seventh injection, the skin at the site of injection became gangrenous, and a deep abscess scar was finally formed. If the sensitized animal was injected intravenously with the serum, it appeared restless, lay on its abdomen, and respiration frequently increased; it defecated frequently, finally fell on its side, and commonly died, all within the span of 2 or 3 minutes.

In 1903, several observers noted that a reaction often followed the injection of diphtheria antitoxin which was, in some cases, so severe that it caused death. Von Pirquet independently, and later with Schick, explained the reaction as one due to an *allergy* (*allos* = altered, *ergeia* = reactivity) caused by horse serum. They named the disease *serum sickness*. Theobald Smith had been concerned with deaths in guinea pigs which were being used in the technic of diphtheria toxin-antitoxin standardization. He observed that when a guinea pig was injected with horse serum and a second injection was given after a period of ten days or more, the pig would show signs of hypersensitiveness, and if sufficient quantity, 5 or 6 ml., were injected intraperitoneally, death would result in a few minutes. The first injection served to sensitize the animal to the second injection. This phenomenon in the guinea pig is so striking that it has been used by many investigators in the study of the anaphylaxis reaction. Almost simultaneously Otto in Germany and Rosenau and Anderson in the United States studied the Theobald Smith reaction, and the American investigators developed important fundamental criteria for it, and determined that the reaction was due to horse protein alone.

These fundamental observations were followed by attempts by many to explain the mechanism of the reaction. Wolff-Eisner believed it was due to an endotoxin which was liberated by a lysin formed as a result of the first injection. Vaughn and Wheeler demonstrated that proteins, in general, are split by chemical means into two portions: one which, when injected into an animal, gives rise to symptoms resembling those of anaphylaxis, and another which is inert. The protein which is to be split is boiled in absolute alcohol containing 2 per cent sodium hydroxide. The toxic fraction is soluble in alcohol; the nontoxic fraction is insoluble in alcohol. Each of these fractions gives the protein reactions and is classified as a protein, or as a complex polypeptid or peptone. When injected into guinea pigs, these fractions behave quite differently. The alcohol-insoluble portion cannot produce anaphylactic symptoms, but can be used in sensitizing animals against the protein from which it was derived. The alcohol-soluble portion produces anaphylactic symptoms when injected, but does not sensitize against the proteins; consequently, Vaughn and Wheeler believed that foreign proteins were split by substances formed by a first injection, and as a result the toxic portion produced a reaction.

Classification. Since these early contributions were made, numerous examples of hypersensitivity have been described. The reactions to the hypersensitive state have been found to vary in intensity. Different types of material have been found to induce the condition, and different tissues have been found to respond to the reaction. For these reasons a classification of the reactions is desirable. Coca considered the whole condition as hypersensitiveness and divided it into anaphylaxis and allergy. Kolmer proposed the name allergy for a general term and suggested two subdivisions, hypersensitiveness and anaphylaxis. At present, the classification suggested by Coca is widely used. The hypersensitive condition is conceded to be of two types: One which is usually more acute, is induced by a definite sensitization, often experimental, and produces definite symptoms, is known as *anaphylaxis;* the other type of reaction is, in general, less severe, does not have definite sensitizations, has variable symptoms, and is known as *allergy.* There is some tendency to classify anaphylaxis as those conditions which are induced in the lower animals by a definite sensitization and to use the term allergy for those hypersensitive conditions which are observed in man. Active sensitization with different proteins has not been carried out with man as the experimental animal to the extent of finding out how he may react to anaphylaxis. Allergic reactions have been observed in animals, although not to any great extent, and it is doubtful if animals will soon reach the state of heredity when they will become as hypersensitive as man to so many different chemical and physical agents. Bacterial allergies, however, appear to be identical in man and the lower animals. Unless allergy in man is primarily hereditary, there appears to be no reason why he should be more easily sensitized to bacterial proteins as a result of infection than are lower animals.

Although anaphylaxis and allergy are both expressions of hypersensitive conditions, and, therefore, appear to have a fundamental mechanism in common, they are different in many respects. These differences have been summarized by Tuft and are given in Table 13.1.

ANAPHYLAXIS

Terminology. *Anaphylaxis* is a reaction which results from the parenteral injection of a nontoxic dose of a foreign protein which is followed by the injection of an increased dose of the same protein in ten to fourteen days. The protein which serves as the antigen in this reaction is called *anaphylactogen.* The antibody which is a necessary part of the reaction is termed *anaphylactin.* The first dose of

TABLE 13.1

DIFFFERENCES BETWEEN ANAPHYLAXIS AND ALLERGY*

	ANAPHYLAXIS	ALLERGY
Occurrence	Artificially Induced	Spontaneous
Hereditary factor	Absent. May be congenital—if so, sensitization exists to same substance as in sensitized mother. Sensitization lasts short time.	Frequently present — inherited through both mother a n d father. Rarely congenital—sensitization against substances other than those of parent, and of long duration.
Nature of antigen	Anaphylactogen must be soluble protein.	Many nonprotein substances, e.g., drugs, capable of acting as allergens.
Characteristic antibodies	Anaphylactic antibodies and precipitins.	Reagins
Pathology and symptomatology	Shock organ variable in different species but constant in individual members—bronchial muscle in guinea pig, liver in dog, and pulmonary artery in rabbit. Symptoms due to contraction of nonstriated muscle and are the same irrespective of the type of antigen injected.	Shock organ different not only in different individuals but even in same individual in response to single antigen, e.g., nose, bronchial mucosa, skin, etc. Symptoms more often due to edema and rarely or never to contraction of smooth muscle; extremely variable in response to different antigens.
Desensitization	Relatively easy, at least in guinea pig.	Difficult to produce or to prove.

* From Tuft's Clinical Allergy, Copyright W. B. Saunders Co.

the antigen which is given to the animal is known as the *sensitizing dose.* The period which elapses between injections is often termed the *incubation period,* but it could be called, more appropriately, the *sensitizing period.* The second injection of the antigen is termed the *shocking dose,* or *toxic dose,* because it induces the condition called *anaphylactic shock.*

Fundamental Criteria. During years of experimentation a number of fundamental criteria which characterize anaphylaxis have been developed and are summarized as follows:

1. It is possible to sensitize a suitable animal by means of a great variety of proteins, such as blood serum of various animals, egg-white, milk, plant proteins, bacterial proteins, animal parasite proteins, yeast proteins, and mold proteins. Sensitization can be affected in many cases by the injection of minute quantities of the proteins; in some cases only a fraction of a milligram is required. The protein can be heated without destroying its sensitizing power.

2. It is possible to secure an anaphylactic shock in an animal that has been previously injected with a sensitizing dose of a protein only after the lapse of a definite period has followed the first injection; the length of this period depends greatly upon the size of the sensitizing dose.

3. The sensitization of an animal, in general, can be accomplished best by the parenteral introduction of the protein; however, some cases have been recorded showing sensitization as the result of ingestion or rectal injections.

4. The type of anaphylactic reaction secured differs with the species of animal, and to a lesser degree, with the site, the amount of protein used, and the method followed in making the second injection. Different proteins produce the same type of reaction in the same species of animal.

In the guinea pig the first sign of reaction is usually evident within a few seconds to a few minutes after injection. The animal then appears restless and scratches its nose with its front feet. Usually urine and feces are passed. There is a decided drop in temperature in animals showing anaphylactic shock, even though the reaction is a slight one. The breathing becomes more rapid, and the animal falls on its side. There is evidence of dyspnea. Generally the animal dies in convulsions; however, an occasional quiet death has been observed. Usually the heart beats for a time after breathing ceases. If very small quantities of protein are injected, the animal often shows the first symptoms, but gradually recovers. In acute anaphylaxis, death occurs in 2 to 5 minutes.

Rabbits are not easily sensitized. A number of preliminary injections are required before a marked reaction results. Generally reactions are: defecation, urination, decided weakness, drooping head, body resting on the ground, breathing irregular and labored, and convulsions followed by death promptly or within several hours.

In dogs the anaphylactic symptoms are: a decided fall in blood pressure, evidence of cerebral anemia, vomiting, urination, defecation, gradual weakness, and finally death. The reaction has been shown to center about the liver and portal circulation.

Cats, mice, and rats are difficult to sensitize. Cats possess a marked susceptibility to foreign protein, but the reasons why mice and rats do not respond readily are not understood.

Anaphylactic shock has been observed in cattle, horses, and goats. In general, the reactions are characterized by dyspnea and muscular weakness.

In all species of animals the reaction appears to be characterized by the action upon nonstriated muscle; therefore, it has been generally concluded that the differences in the reaction in the different species of animals are due to the comparative amounts of nonstriated muscle in various parts of the body, that is, the bronchioles and bronchii of the guinea pig, the pulmonary arteries of the rabbit, and the hepatic veins of the dog.

5. The reaction is highly specific. An animal sensitized against a particular protein will react only when that protein is injected.

6. A condition of passive anaphylaxis may be induced by the injection of blood serum from a sensitized animal into a normal animal. Such an animal reacts to the injection of the protein in the same manner as an actively sensitized individual.

7. The injection to produce the anaphylactic reaction gives the most rapid results when made intravenously or into the heart; intraperitoneal injection is somewhat less rapid in its action; and subcutaneous injections produce still slower reactions.

8. An animal which has just recovered from an anaphylactic shock does not show the same symptoms when a second injection is made immediately, but the animal becomes hypersensitive again after a lapse of a few days. If a small dose of protein is injected into the animal, a large dose injected later may not cause a reaction. Probably this *desensitization* is due to the exhaustion of all of the specific antibody which is present in susceptible cells.

Explanation of Anaphylaxis. The theories which have been advanced to explain anaphylaxis are grouped into two different types, the proteolytic and antigen-antibody reaction. The proteolytic theory is based largely upon the work of Vaughn and Wheeler who assume that the cleavage of protein molecules by a lytic substance occurs forming toxic and nontoxic parts, and that the reaction is due to the toxic parts. The toxicity of peptone and other protein cleavage products is given as added proof. The fact that the materials concerned in the complement-fixation reaction were found to be highly toxic and that complement was decreased by the anaphylactic reaction led to the assumption that complement is the lytic substance responsible for the reaction. This explanation of the reaction on the basis of a toxic substance has led to the use of the term anaphylatoxin for the toxic substance. The lytic theory is considered untenable in light of numerous observations. Normal complement has never been shown to be a proteolytic enzyme, and its decrease during anaphylactic reactions may be explained by the effect of the reaction upon numerous body processes. A poison has never been demonstrated in the blood following antigen-sensitizer-complement action. The anaphylactic reaction occurs too rapidly to permit the formation of a toxic substance by a lytic process. Isolated muscle strips, completely devoid of serum complement, show the reaction typical of anaphylaxis; for these reasons and many others, the action of an anaphylatoxin in anaphylaxis is discounted at the present time, even though anaphylactoid reactions are produced by protein cleavage products such as peptone and histamin.

The antigen-antibody theory of anaphylaxis was primarily suggested by the fact that the hypersensitive condition of one animal can be transferred to a normal animal by the transfer of blood serum. It was considerably augmented by the discovery of Doerr and Russ that the ability of a serum to confer passive sensitization was in direct proportion to its precipitin titer. The relationship of precipitation of proteins to the anaphylactic reaction has been shown by many investigators. The reaction is considered to take place upon sensitized cells or within them, and as a consequence their colloidal characteristics are altered. How this alteration causes the anaphylactic reaction is not known. *Histamin,* which is a derivative of the amino acid histidine, is a substance which is found in many body cells. Histamin is definitely toxic; in fact, injection of it produces symptoms similar to anaphylactic shock. It is of speculative interest to assume that the antibody-antigen reaction in sensitized cells liberates histamin, or as Zinsser states, "As a result of the union of antigen with cellular antibody, a chemical change is initiated as a result of which a histamin-like substance is liberated which has powerful effects and gives rise to the vascular and smooth muscle changes underlying the physiological mechanism of anaphylactic symptoms."

The toxicity of histamin has been classed with the anaphylactoid reactions by some investigators. Wells is of the opinion that true anaphylaxis and histamin shock are similar. He states:[1]

The chief respects in which histamin fails to account for all the phenomena of anaphylaxis are:

1. Histamin fails to desensitize animals or tissues, yet produces strong reactions in the uterus strip that has been thoroughly desensitized.

2. Histamin does not produce the temperature reactions usual in anaphylaxis.

3. Histamin does not produce the changes in coagulability of the blood usual in anaphylaxis.

---

[1] Harry Gideon Wells. *The Chemical Aspects of Immunity.* The Chemical Catalog Co., Inc., New York, 1929, pp. 240–41.

4. Quinine augments the susceptibility of sensitized animals to the foreign protein but does not affect the intoxication produced by histamin.

In respect to item one in the previous list, cne should not expect histamin to desensitize if it is the active product of an antigen-antibody reaction since it is this reaction alone that is prevented by desensitizaticn. As to items two and three, it is probable that these phenomena result from other products of the antigen-antibody reaction, since presumably many different substances are produced. The effect of quinine, item four, might be found to be an influence on the antigen-antibody reaction if this possibility were investigated. At least histamin seems to have a synergetic relation to anaphylactic shock, probably because the points of attack of histamin and anaphylactic reactions are identical.

In his review of anaphylaxis Dragstedt is of the opinion that histamin plays a significant role in producing symptoms in the rabbit, guinea pig, and dog. This author also believes that heparin and choline may be of significance in producing some of the reactions found in anaphylaxis.

Significance of Anaphylaxis. Anaphylaxis, as a whole, appears to have three definite uses: It may be used to study the nature of the specificity among proteins; it may explain the mechanism of serum sickness and related hypersensitive conditions; it may facilitate the study of various diseases which result because of bacterial invasion.

In the practice of veterinary medicine, animals often die of "shock" during the immunizing process. Many of these instances are difficult to explain, but many, no doubt, are due to previous sensitization. Taylor and Casserly reported the occurrence of anaphylaxis in cattle which had been treated with anthrax anti-serum when antiserum was again injected. Hadwen, and Bruce and Strockbine have reported anaphylaxis in cattle following the removal of Hypoderma larvae from the back, that is, if the larvae were crushed during the process. The injections of extracts of the parasite were found to produce typical reactions. Sheep are hypersensitive to extracts of *Oestrus ovis* upon the injection of extracts of the larvae of that parasite. Schlotthauer has described anaphylaxis in calves during immunization with calf scours vaccine. Williams and Hagan observed a hypersensitive condition in calves which followed the use of calf scours antiserum.

It is obvious, therefore, that cases of anaphylaxis may result in the practice of veterinary medicine. Caution should be used in giving injections of foreign proteins to animals without obtaining a history of previous treatment.

ALLERGY

In man the incidence of hypersensitive conditions which are generally called *allergic* has been determined in some communities, and it is believed that the average is about 10 per cent. Much attention has been given to the study of allergy. The information gathered from such investigation has been collected in numerous textbooks completely devoted to the subject. The excellent treatise on the subject by Cooke and associates is highly recommended to the student for detailed study.

Allergy in animals has not been studied to any great extent although some reports are found in literature. Schnelle, Burns, and Pomeroy each have reported instances of food allergy in the dog. It is believed by many that "heaves" in the horse is a typical example of a condition, resulting from a respiratory hypersensitivity. Respiratory difficulty, which is relieved by the first frost in the fall, has been noted in cows during summer months. Close observation will probably reveal other allergic conditions in animals.

Terminology. The antigen which is active in producing the allergic condition is known as *allergen,* and the antibody which is thought to react with it is called *allergin.* Coca proposed a subdivision of allergy which embraced those conditions which were known to be subject to hereditary influence, which he called *atopy.* The antigen in this reaction is known as *atopen* and the antibody *reagin.*

Allergy is divided into the following numerous types depending upon the tissue involved in some cases, and in others upon the type of antigen: *serum sickness, hay fever, asthma, alimentary allergy, skin allergy, drug allergy, physical allergy,* and *bacterial allergy.*

Bacterial Allergy. Bacterial allergy is of importance in veterinary medicine. There are numerous diseases in animals in which a hypersensitive state is produced and which is used as a means of diagnosis. The mechanism by which body cells become hypersensitive to extracts of bacteria is not known. It does not appear to be a function which is common to immune-antibody formation. In some conditions, an allergic state is manifest before immune-antibodies can be detected in the blood stream. In many diseases, the allergic state persists long after circulating immune-antibody has disappeared. As in other types of allergic conditions, the reaction in bacterial allergy takes place in the hypersensitive cells. In some cases, notably in tuberculosis, the sensitization is produced only after the organism has invaded tissue which responds to the invasion by forming the tubercle. Whether a combined tissue-organism product is responsible for the sensitization, or whether the organism extracts which are released after phagocytic action are responsible is unknown. The injection of protein extracts of the tubercle bacillus into tissue does not produce the same type of sensitivity to tuberculin as does the actual infection.

There are a number of characteristics which distinguish bacterial allergy from anaphylaxis. It is not possible to transfer the hypersensitive state passively from a hypersensitive animal to a normal one. A number of hours must elapse following the injection of antigen before the hypersensitive reaction is obtained. A number of animal species, notably the rat, are difficult to sensitize for anaphylaxis. Most animal species, if they are susceptible to the microorganism in question, develop bacterial hypersensitivity and react in the same way to test antigens. There are no specific shock tissues or shock organs in animals as observed in anaphylaxis.

The significance of bacterial hypersensitivity to the disease process has been a subject of considerable conjecture. The chief argument has centered upon the harmfulness of the reaction. The extensive areas of inflammation with resulting necrosis which develop in tissue following the injection of test antigens indicate that the development of a hypersensitive state is harmful to the animal. However, it has been suggested that the formation of edema in the injection site is a defense reaction by which the antigen is immobilized and ultimately destroyed. There are those who contend that all disease is a hypersensitive reaction and is manifested only in those animals which have an inherited hypersensitivity. Cases where an increased hypersensitivity is developed as a result of infection merely prove that the animal possesses a normal basic hypersensitivity which is augmented by the development of lesions.

It is possible to desensitize an animal which is hypersensitive to bacterial protein. However, this must be done with small doses, or necrosis of tissue will result. After a period of time elapses, the hypersensitive condition returns.

The methods used in detecting hypersensitive conditions resulting from bacterial infections will be discussed in the chapters devoted to the different groups of organisms. In the diagnosis of certain diseases in which an allergic state is produced, bacterial extracts may be used: tuberculin for tuberculosis, Johnin for Johnin's disease, mallein for glanders, and brucellin for brucellosis.

In addition to bacteria there are a few animal parasites which produce hypersensitivity. It is possible to diagnose trichinosis by the intradermal injection of extracts of *Trichinella spiralis*. The presence of nematodes of various species, particularly Ascarids, can be detected by an allergic test.

The Shwartzman Phenomenon. In 1928, Shwartzman described a phenomenon of local tissue reaction which is of interest and significance. The action of the bacterial exotoxins on specific tissues has been known for some time. It has been presumed that other types of tissue reactions, inflammation in general, are produced by the so-called endotoxins which are liberated upon bacterial disintegration. In studying the latter type of reaction Shwartzman gave rabbits a single intradermal injection of *B. typho-*

sus culture filtrate followed 24 hours later by an intravenous injection of the same filtrate. Four hours after the intravenous injection, severe hemorrhagic necrosis appeared at the prepared site. Grossly it was dark blue, swollen, with an angry red periphery, and histologically it showed disruption of the venules, extensive hemorrhage, thrombosis, and necrobiosis of all the cells. The reaction extended from the superficial layers of the skin through the entire thicknes of the abdominal wall to the peritoneum.

He found that a 24-hour period of incubation was necessary between the skin dose and the second dose which in all cases must be given intravenously. The reaction is produced when filtrates of types of bacteria other than the original type are given in the second injection. The phenomenon is significant because it aids in the explanation of certain types of bacterial allergy such as the Arthus reaction as well as certain inflammatory reactions which result in hemorrhage and necrosis.

REFERENCES FOR FURTHER STUDY

Balyeat, Roy M. Allergic Diseases: Their Diagnosis and Treatment. 4th Ed. F. A. Davis Co., 1936.

Bray, G. W. Recent Advances in Allergy. 3rd Ed. P. Blakiston's Son & Co.. Inc., 1937.

Burns, P. W. Allergic Reactions in Dogs. Jour. Amer. Vet. Med. Assn. 83:627–37, 1933.

Cooke, R. A. and associates. Allergy in Theory and Practice. W. B. Saunders Co., Philadelphia, 1947.

Davies, G. O. Hypersensitiveness in Animals. The Vet. Rec. 58:285–87, 1946.

Dragstedt, C. A. Anaphylaxis. Physiol. Rev. 21:563, 1941.

Gay, F. P. Agents of Disease and Host Resistance. Pp. 36–119. Charles C. Thomas, Baltimore, 1935.

Hadwen, S. Jour. Amer. Vet. Assn. 60:724–28, 1922.

——, and Bruce, E. A. Jour. Amer. Vet. Med. Assn. 51:15–44, 1917.

Kolmer, John A. Infection, Immunity and Biologic Therapy. W. B Saunders Co., 1923.

Pomeroy, B. S. Cornell Vet. 24:335, 1934.

Raffel, Sidney. Immunity, Hypersensitivity, and Serology. Appleton-Century-Crofts, Inc., New York, 1953.

Ratner, Bret. Allergy, Anaphylaxis and Immunotherapy. Williams and Wilkins Co., Baltimore, 1943.

Schlotthauer, C. F. No. Amer. Vet. 14:24–27, 1933.

Schnelle, G. B. No. Amer. Vet. 14:37, 1933.

Schroeder, C. R. Jour. Am. Vet. Med. Assn. 106:351, 1945.

Shwartzman, Gregory. Phenomenon of Local Tissue Reactivity. Paul B Hoeber, Inc., 1937.

Scott, W. M. Anaphylaxis and Related Phenomena. A System of Bacteriology. Pp. 457–89. Med. Res. Council, 1931.

Sherwood, N. P. Immunology. Pp. 464–570. The C. V. Mosby Co., 1935.

Symposium on Allergy. Amer. Jour. Med. Vol. 3, 1947.

Taylor, W. J., and Casserly, T. L. Jour. Amer. Vet. Med. Assn. 59: 704–10, 1921.

Topley, W. W. C., Wilson, G. S., and Miles, A. A. The Principles of Bacteriology and Immunity. 3rd Ed. Williams & Wilkins Co., Baltimore, 1946.

Tuft, Louis. Clinical Allergy. W. B. Saunders Co., Philadelphia, 1938.

Vaughan, W. T. Allergy and Applied Immunology. C. V. Mosby Co., 1934.

Wells, H. G. The Chemical Aspects of Immunity. Pp. 225–53, The Chemical Catalog Co., Inc., 1929.

Zeissig, Alexander. Jour. Amer. Vet. Med. Assn., 88:139–53, 1936.

Zinsser, H., Enders, J. F., and Fothergill, L. D. Immunity. The Macmillan Co.. 1939.

PART III

Classification and Characteristics of Pathogenic Bacteria, Yeasts, and Molds

14. The Classification and Nomenclature of Bacteria

One of the cardinal characteristics of nature is the orderliness of living things. All animals and plants are divided into distinct species. These species of animals and plants are able to reproduce only with their kind. Since this is a genetic truth, similar individuals are reproduced, and the orderliness of all nature is continued. Such simple forms as bacteria follow the same genetic rules as animals and plants. The bacteria, therefore, are classified and named in the same manner as animals and plants, and, as a result, definite information concerning the various groups is available. Furthermore, it is possible to learn the names and to correlate the activities and characteristics of one group with those of another.

Since the bacteria are classified as plants, the system of botanical nomenclature proposed by the Swedish biologist, Carl von Linné (Linnaeus), during the years 1750 and 1760, is taken as the starting point for bacterial nomenclature. In 1773–74 the Danish naturalist, Otto Frederich Müller, arranged the bacteria then known into a system which was subsequently enlarged in 1786. C. G. Ehrenberg extended this classification in 1838 and added the descriptions of numerous types of protozoa and bacteria. During the period between 1872–76, the most fundamental early contributions to the subject of classification were made by Ferdinand Cohn who differentiated between the bacteria and protozoa; his classification has been used as the basis of those which have followed.

The rapid discovery of all the various species of bacteria, as well as characteristics so significant to health and comfort of man, has made the subject of the classification of bacteria a most complex one. The systems of classification now in use have developed about the work of Buchanan, the various committees on classification and nomenclature of the Society of American Bacteriologists, of the International Society of Microbiologists, and of the National Botanical Congress, as well as the various contributors throughout numerous editions of Bergey's Manual of Determinative Bacteriology. It is obvious that there should be an international system of classification and nomenclature, and as knowledge of the bacteria increases, changes in existing systems will be made. This is an inevitable mark of progress. It must be recognized that bacteriology, as a science, is still quite young and that it takes time to reach the period of organization so characteristic of middle and old age. The student, therefore, must expect to replace new names for old from time to time and to look for a well-known organism in a group different from the one of which he has learned that it is a member.

Rules of Bacteriological Nomenclature. Since the time of Linnaeus, botanists and zoologists have followed the binominal system of nomenclature. Numerous other rules have been adopted from time to time until the lists of rules of Zoological Nomenclature and of Botanical Nomenclature are quite extensive. A committee is preparing a list of Rules for Bacteriological Nomenclature to be adopted by the International Congress of Microbiology.

It is not within the scope and purpose of this text to list the rules for naming bacteria. It is desirable, however, that students become familiar with a few of the general principles which are followed.

1. The scientific name of a microorganism is composed of two words, both Latin.

2. The name does not need to be a descriptive one; in fact, descriptive names are apt to be misleading. The name *Micrococcus aureus* is descriptive of the golden micrococcus; however, it is now recognized that this organism may become nonpigmented, or white; yet, it retains all of its other characteristics. Descriptive names given to bacteria years ago often lose their significance in light of new discoveries. When descriptive names are used, there is a marked tendency to use more than the one species name: this leads to such absurd names as *Bacillus saccharobutyricus fluorescens liquefaciens.*

3. The first name of the organism is a proper noun and always begins with a capital letter. It is the *genus* name of the group to which the organism belongs. The name *Micrococcus* is a generic name.

4. The second name begins with a small letter and designates the species of the organism. If it is an adjective it must agree grammatically with the generic name and if it is a noun modifying the generic name, it must be in the possessive case.

5. Bacteria are classified into the various taxonomic groups as are animals and plants, hence:

every individual belongs to a species,
every species belongs to a genus,

every genus belongs to a family,
every family belongs to an order,
every order belongs to a class,
every class belongs to a phylum,
and every phylum belongs to a kingdom.

The names of the different groups take different endings. These are illustrated by listing the various taxonomic groups of *Micrococcus aureus*.

Species—aureus
Genus—Micrococcus
Family—Micrococcaceae—ending *aceae*
Order—Eubacteriales—ending *ales*
Class—Schizomycetes—ending *cetes*
Phylum—Thallophyta—ending *a*
Kingdom—Plant

If a greater number of intermediate categories are required for lucid classification, subclasses, suborders, subfamilies, tribes and subtribes, subgenera and subspecies, or varieties may be designated.

Bases for Bacteriological Classification. Bacteria are classified by using any of the characteristics which fall under the following general heads:

1. *Morphology.* Morphology is used for differentiation whenever practical. For example, the bacteria are placed in the plant kingdom, the class schizomycetes, into the various orders, and into families largely on this basis.

2. *Physiology.* When considering the more closely related groups, such as the genera, physiological characteristics must be used. For example, the sporeforming, rod-shaped bacteria are placed into the family *Bacillaceae* on the basis of morphology. The two genera *Bacillus* and *Clostridium* are formed, however, on the basis of physiological function, oxygen relationship.

3. *Antigenicity.* Within the genus and in some cases the formation of subspecies, the antigenic structure of bacteria forms the basis for differentiation. The antigenic relationships of bacteria are detected by the serological tests, such as agglutination and precipitation. The value of the use of antigenic structure is noted in the differentiation of the pneumococci into thirty-two different strains. The species of the genus Salmonella are classified largely upon the basis of antigenic differences.

4. *Pathology.* Bacteria are not grouped into species or genera on the basis of the different types of diseases which are produced; yet the specific pathology of disease is acknowledged as one of the important characteristics of pathogenic bacteria, and from the point of view of medical bacteriology, is not given the prominence it deserves. The type of infection which the organism causes enters

into the coining of names such as *Streptococcus pyogenes* and *Salmonella choleraesuis.*

All of the different characteristics considered pertinent to the complete description of bacteria are included in a chart which has been compiled by the Committee on Bacteriological Technic of the Society of American Bacteriologists.

The Relationship of Bacterial Variation to Classification. Early workers in bacteriology described cultures which are recognized today as being composed of a number of different species of bacteria. For example, Hallier described as pure cultures what were actually numerous types of bacteria; he pictured them as varying in morphology from short rods to forms as complex as molds. Obviously, such cultures were not pure, but were contaminated with Aspergillus and Penicillium molds. As methods of obtaining pure cultures of bacteria became available, it was concluded that a pure culture was composed of only one definite type of an organism and that the daughter cell always produced a type of cell, a type of colony, and a type of physiology exactly like that of the mother cell. This conception, aptly called monomorphism, held sway for many years.

As the study of bacteria progressed, it became increasingly apparent that bacteria do vary from the accepted normal forms under certain conditions. This variation, or dissociation as it is also called, may be morphological or physiological. Some variations appear spontaneously in a culture while others develop slowly usually augmented by the environment of the culture.

Numerous examples of morphological dissociation may be cited. Changes in the shape of the individual cells of a culture are often observed. A particular organism may be ovoid on solid media but an elongated bacillus in a fluid medium. *E. coli* is normally a flagellated organism when grown in fluid media, yet may not develop flagella when grown for some time on solid media. *Bacillus anthracis,* when grown on a common nutrient medium, is noncapsulated; yet, when it is grown on a medium containing a carbohydrate and serum, it will produce a capsule. This same bacillus normally produces spores, but one of the classical experiments performed by Pasteur was to develop a nonsporeproducing culture by cultivation at 42°C.

Greatest emphasis has been given to the different types of colony variations which appear in cultures. These variations often explain the differences in virulence of a bacterial culture. The cocci and Gram-negative bacteria normally grow in a type of colony which is smooth (S). However, colonies of this type of microorganism are often encountered which are mucoid (M), and sometimes, when grown on a less nutritive medium, may form rough (R) colonies. In some instances these variations are reversible, but many of the variants are permanent. The R form appears to represent the last stage in reproductive maturity. An organism in its S form has an antigenic structure more complete than in the R form. An organism in the M form is often more virulent when in the S form; however, the S form is more virulent than the R form. Under conditions of artificial cultivation the variation is from S to R, presumably because the individual cells of the R colony are more able to subsist on the food available in artificial media. When such a culture is injected into a susceptible animal and disease results, the S form of the organism is usually isolated. In this instance, the fluids and cells of the animal body apparently provide the nutrient substances essential for the growth of S type organisms. Since they are more virulent that R, they resist body defenses, such as phagocytosis, reproduce at a greater rate, consequently predominate in the culture.

In certain types of bacteria the R type of colony represents the normal virulent phase. For example, *Bacillus anthracis* is normally R and when variant S type colonies appear they are less virulent. Colonies of virulent *Myco. tuberculosis* are of the R type.

The change from S to R may occur suddenly or slowly. In the latter instance intermediate variants are observed. These colonies are designated as SR, Sr, or sR depending upon which type the new colony most nearly resembles. These intermediate types are not as stable as the S and R types, showing a tendency to revert to either permanent S or R types of colonies.

Numerous examples of physiological variation could be cited. Some of these are examples of a rather specific mutation, while others appear to be merely adaptive processes of the organism. As long ago as 1907 Massini observed that a non-lactose-fermenting strain of *E. coli* would develop the ability to ferment lactose when grown in the presence of that carbohydrate. This property was reflected in the type of colony which developed in the mother non-lactose-fermenting colony. The loss or acquisition of the ability to ferment a certain carbohydrate appears to be a variant property of many bacteria. Upon this criterion, strains of a given species of a bacterium are recognized. *Sal. pullorum,* for example, is not recognized usually as a maltose fermenting organism. However, well-defined strains of this bacterium are isolated which do produce acid in maltose. These are referred to as maltose fermenting strains. Other examples of other physiological reactions of bacteria could be cited, such as variation in H_2S production and nitrate reduction. Many of these variations are due apparently to the adaptive nature of the enzyme system of bacteria. The enzymes are formed under the influence of the presence of the substrate, calling into action, as it were, certain enzymes which have become dormant but which awaken and become active when a certain type of food is present. This same adaptable property of bacteria is observed when a culture grows not at all or at least poorly upon primary isolation from animal tissue, but grows abundantly after it has been cultivated on artificial medium for some time. This fact often explains the different results obtained in the study of one species of an organism by different investigators. One has studied recently isolated strains while the other has studied old laboratory strains. Their results may agree, in the main, but differences in detailed reactions are common.

Previous mention has been made of the loss of virulence when an organism dissociates from an S colony to an R. Variations in virulence are encountered when there are no visible changes in the type of colony. Loss of virulence, commonly called attenuation, often occurs when cultures are grown artificially for some time. When the various factors which make up the composite picture of virulence are reviewed, it is obvious that certain properties would be lost under artificial conditions, and promptly regained when under natural conditions. The loss of toxin production may mean a great deal in terms of disease, but may mean very little in the life of a microorganism. There is a tendency on the part of many investigators to overemphasize the significance of many physiological processes. There are instances when variable reactions should be considered the rule rather than the exception.

Since the advent of antibiotic agents, another variable characteristic, drug fastness of bacteria, has been introduced. Among the staphylococci, for example, it is not unusual to find strains which are extremely resistant to penicillin. The same is true of many other species which normally are considered to be sensitive to a certain antibiotic agent. In some instances this resistance is an inheritable characteristic of the strain and in other instances drug fastness is developed as a result of contact of the organism with the drug. This becomes a serious matter when it becomes apparent that a penicillin-resistant strain of organism is developed and may become widespread throughout a herd. In the treatment of tuberculosis of man with streptomycin, it is found that certain cases of that disease are caused by streptomycin-resistant strains of tubercle bacilli. Such instances are quite unfortunate and other means of treatment must be provided. The explanation of the acquisition of drug fastness by bacteria will not be available until the reason for drug sensitivity becomes known.

The relationships of bacterial variation or dissociation to bacterial phylogeny present an interesting phase of bacteriology. Upon first thought, the viruses may be considered to represent the most primitive forms of life, because of their size. However, when the specific cell-parasite nature of viruses is recognized, it is apparent that these forms probably represent the very advanced forms of living agents. The autotrophic bacteria, those which derive their energy from the oxidation of simple inorganic compounds, more nearly represent the most primitive type of life—probably the beginning of life on our planet. It is apparent that as the tremendous numbers of different types of bacteria have developed a parasitic existence on man, plants, and animals, a process of variation or dissociation still was in operation. It is entirely conceivable and probable that this process continues and such examples given in the foregoing discussion are only expressions of evolution.

The Systematic Arrangement of Bacteria. Reference to the position of the bacteria in the plant kingdom was made in Chapter 2: Consequently, it is not necessary to repeat that classification here. The phylum Thallophyta is divided into different classes among which is the class Schizomycetes. This class is divided into eight different orders on the basis of morphology. These are listed as follows: I. Eubacteriales, II. Actinomycetales, III. Spirochaetales, IV. Rickettsiales, V. Thiobacteriales, VI. Chlamydobacteriales, VII. Caulobacteriales, and VIII. Myxobacteriales. Of these, the first four contain species of bacteria which produce diseases in animals and man. The orders are divided into numerous families, which in turn are divided into tribes; the tribes are divided into genera and the genera into species.

In most of the systematic bacterial classifications which have been published, the organisms are arranged in what is known as a key. There are a number of types of keys, but the dichotomous key is the type used most often, and it is most satisfactory. In a dichotomous key the organisms are divided into two groups on the basis of a differentiating characteristic; these two groups are in turn divided into two others and so on until only one group remains; for example:

   a. Cells spherical
      b. Cells Gram-positive
         c. cells aerobic
         cc. cells anaerobic
      bb. Cells Gram-negative
  aa. Cells not spherical

Any of the different characteristics of bacteria may be used in forming a key. The orders, families, tribes, genera, and species are usually divided by means of a key. Such a key is found in Bergey's *Manual of Determinative Bacteriology.* The student will become familiar with the use of these keys in his laboratory work.

A list of the orders, families, and genera which contain species of bacteria producing diseases in man and animals is given below.

The species which make up each generic group will be discussed in detail in chapters devoted entirely to them.

Order	Family	Genus
Eubacteriales	Pseudomonadaceae	Pseudomonas
		Vibrio
	Micrococcaceae	Micrococcus
	Neisseriaceae	Neisseria
	Lactobacteriaceae	Diplococcus
		Streptococcus
	Corynebacteriaceae	Corynebacterium
		Listeria
		Erysipelothrix
	Achromobacteriaceae	Alcaligenes
	Enterobacteriaceae	Escherichia
		Aerobacter
		Klebsiella
		Proteus
		Salmonella
		Shigella
	Parvobacteriaceae	Pasteurella
		Malleomyces
		Actinobacillus
		Brucella
		Bacterioides
		Spherophorus
		Fusobacterium
		Hemophilus
	Bacillaceae	Bacillus
		Clostridium
Actinomycetales	Mycobacteriaceae	Mycobacterium
	Actinomycetaceae	Nocardia
		Actinomyces
Spirochaetales	Spirochaetaceae	Spirochaeta
	Treponemataceae	Borrelia
		Treponema
		Leptospira
Rickettsiales	Rickettsiaceae	Rickettsia
		Coxiella
		Cowdria
	Bartonellaceae	Bartonella
		Haemobartonella
		Grahamella
		Eperythrozoon
	Chlamydozoaceae	Miyagawanella
		Colesiota

REFERENCES FOR FURTHER STUDY

Bergey, D. H., Breed, R. S., Murray, E. G. D., and Hitchins, A. P. Manual of Determinative Bacteriology. 6th Ed. Williams & Wilkins Co., Baltimore, 1948.

Buchanan, R. E. General Systematic Bacteriology. Williams & Wilkins Co., Baltimore, 1925.

————, and Buchanan, Estelle D. Bacteriology. 5th Ed. The Macmillan Co., New York, 1951.

————, St. John-Brooks, R., and Breed, R. S. International Bacteriological Code of Nomenclature. Jour. of Bact. 55:287–306, 1948.

Burrows, Wm. Textbook of Microbiology. 16th Ed. W. B. Saunders, Philadelphia, 1954.

Dubos, R. J. The Bacterial Cell. Harvard University Press, Cambridge, 1945.

Luria, S. E. Recent Advances in Bacterial Genetics. Bact. Rev. 11:1–40, 1947.

Smith, D. T., and Martin, D. S. Zinsser's Textbook of Bacteriology. 9th Ed. Chap. 9. Appleton-Century-Crofts, Inc., New York, 1948.

15. The Genus Streptococcus

The streptococcus group includes all of those bacteria which are spherical and usually occur in chains of variable lengths of two to forty cells. All of the species described are Gram-positive. Spores are never produced. The various species show differences in their ability to produce acid from carbohydrates. In general, they produce scant, dewdrop-like growth on the surface of culture media, preferring enriched media and microaerophilic conditions. They are widely distributed, but are most common upon the skin, mucous membranes, and in the intestines of man and animals, as well as in milk. They are not common as saprophytes in nature apart from animals or their excretions.

Classification. An acceptable classification of the streptococci appears to be developing out of the mass of research on the group; at least a tendency to place the numerous species into definite categories is being followed.

In the early observations of micrococci by Pasteur, Koch, and other investigators, no attempt was made to separate them according to cell arrangement. Rivolta described chain-forming cocci in pus from cases of strangles in the horse in 1873. Ogston (1881) was apparently the first to show that the micrococci were associated with various types of infections in man and that they could be separated into two groups, those growing in chains and those in grape-like clusters. In 1883, Fehleisen described a chain-forming coccus as the cause of erysipelas in man. The following year Rosenbach isolated from an abscess in man a coccus to which he gave the name *Streptococcus pyogenes,* thus establishing the genus name *Streptococcus.* The relationship of a streptococcus to scarlet fever was first demonstrated by Klein in 1886 when he isolated *Micrococcus scarlatinae* from the throats of scarlet fever patients and traced the source of the infection to milk. Nocard and Mollereau, in 1887, isolated a streptococcus from a cow with which they produced experimental mastitis in a cow and in a goat. As a result of the isolation of streptococci from specific diseases there was a tendency to consider each a separate species and to give it a name similar to the disease produced.

Lingelsheim in 1891 suggested that two types, to be known as *Streptococcus longus* and *Streptococcus brevis,* be recognized; he believed the more virulent forms produce long chains, usually of more than six cells, and the less virulent forms short chains with fewer than six cells. A strict adoption of this classification proved impractical because variations occurred in different media and under different environments.

Schottmüller's classification in 1903 proposed the use of blood agar in differentiation. The more virulent types he termed *Str. longus* or *Str. erysipelatos.* These formed long chains and hemolyzed blood cells. His *Str. mitis* or *Str. viridans* were found to be less virulent, to produce shorter chains, and to be devoid of the power of hemolysis. His *Str. mucosus* proved to be an encapsulated form and more closely related to the pneumococci.

The classification proposed by Andrewes and Horder in 1906, and adopted by Winslow and Winslow in 1908, was the first to use a combination of pathogenicity and fermentation as a basis of differentiation. This classification considered only one pathogenic species, *Str. pyogenes;* the remaining five were saprophytic.

Smith and Brown, in 1915, separated pathogenic streptococci which were obtained from milk-borne tonsillitis patients into two groups on the basis of hemolysis. One group, *alpha* hemolytic, produced a greenish discoloration and partial hemolysis of the blood corpuscles surrounding the colony; the other, *beta* group, produced a zone of complete hemolysis around the colony on blood agar.

In 1916, Holman published a classification of the streptococci in which he divided them into two groups on the basis of hemolysis, and subsequently divided each subgroup by means of carbohydrate fermentation. This classification has served as the basis of most of the systematic treatises on the streptococci since that time.

Brown set forth in 1919, in a most comprehensive report, the criteria for studying the hemolytic streptococci and strengthened the position of the different types which he and Smith had described previously. He recognized and described four types which could be distinguished by their action or lack of action on blood agar: alpha type; beta type; α' type, a type intermediate to α and β; and gamma type, a type which did not alter blood corpuscles, i.e., nonhemolytic.

In a series of reports beginning in 1928, Rebecca Lancefield has reported that the hemolytic streptococci may be divided into groups on the basis of the precipitation reaction using specific carbohydrate substance, designated as "C substance," as the antigen. By using the Lancefield typing technics the streptococci have been studied by various investigators with the formation of the following groups: Group A, which is composed of the more virulent human strains typified by *Str. pyogenes;* Group B, which includes the bovine mastitis streptococci typified by *Str. agalactiae;* Group C, which is made up of hemolytic animal and human strains which are now called *Str. equisimilis,* certain strains *Str. canis* from the dog, and a distinct species, *Str. equi;* Group D, in which is placed the enterococci and strains isolated from dairy products; Group E, which includes a few strains isolated from milk and not associated with infection in man or animals; Group F, a minute colony type isolated from the respiratory tract of man; Group G, comprised of both a minute colony type and a large colony type, the former of which has been isolated from the respiratory tract of man and the latter from dogs; Group H, isolated from the respiratory tract of man but of doubtful virulence; Group K, comprised of strains isolated from the respiratory tract of man, likewise of doubtful virulence; Group L, includes strains isolated from the genital tract of the dog; Group M, strains which have been isolated from respiratory tissues of the dog; Group N, which includes streptococci found in milk, typified by *Str. lactis* and *Str. cremoris.*

Several of the above groups may be divided into serologic types. The antigen which may be used for type differentiation varies with the group. In Group A the various serologic types are determined by protein antigens, in Group B by polysaccharides, in Group C by proteins, and it is believed that the antigens are polysaccharide in nature in Groups D, E, F, and G.

Additional tests for differentiating bacteria in general have been used for the streptococci. It is not feasible to discuss them in detail here, but the following deserve mentioning: optimum growth temperature, survival temperature, optimum hydrogen-ion range, maximum hydrogen-ion production in glucose broth, growth in presence of 6.5 per cent NaCl, growth in and reduction of methylene blue milk, growth in 40 per cent bile-blood agar, reaction to bacteriophage, and fibrinolytic activity. With this formidable array of differential methods it would seem that the streptococci should be adequately classified.

In 1937, Sherman compiled the information then available concerning the streptococci. This review has been of great value to those studying and working with this group of microorganisms. It lists all of the important species of streptococci causing infection in man and animals and the significant nonpathogenic species which frequently are found in fluids and tissues.

The differentiation of the strains of streptococci occurring in man from those found in animals has been one of the problems of bacteriologists. Present-day methods have aided in accomplishing this problem. It has been conceded for many years that two animal species, *Streptococcus agalactiae* (*mastitidis* of Sherman) and *Streptococcus equi* are distinct species and may be recognized by their cultural and physiological characteristics. Furthermore these species occur in the cow and horse respectively, neither being transmitted to man.

It was demonstrated by Davis in 1912, and since then by other investigators that *Str. pyogenes* may be transmitted from infected human tissues by the milker to the bovine udder where it may localize and may produce a typical mastitis. The growth of organisms in such tissue serves as a potential hazard to human health in the form of milk-borne epidemics of scarlet fever and septic sore throat. Acute bovine mastitis also may be caused by a hemolytic streptococcus of animal origin. This organism was named *Str. zooepidemicus* by Frost and Engelbrecht in 1936. In the process of detecting the infected cow in milk-borne epidemics, it is obvious that methods should be available for the differentiation of *Str. pyogenes* and *Str. zooepidemicus*. These differences are clearly established by Lancefield's grouping and by the use of sorbitol (see Table 15.1).

When the technic of serological typing by Lancefield became widely used, it became evident that numerous unrelated strains, in fact species, of streptococci were placed in Group C. The recognition of *Str. equi* as a definite species was accepted but the classification of other strains presented more of a problem. In the absence of better terminology these strains were referred to as "*human* C" or "*animal* C," depending on their source. In their 1940 review of the streptococci, Frost and Engelbrecht described and used the name *Streptococcus equisimilis* for strains of streptococci fitting the characteristics of "*animal* C" strains. The studies of the hemolytic streptococci by Evans in 1944 reveals that *Str. equisimilis* may be found in a wide variety of human and animal tissues where they produce infection. While these studies do not differentiate the strains isolated from man from those isolated from animals, it has been demonstrated by Hansen that they may be distinguished by the fibrinolysis test of Tillett and Garner. Hansen found that twenty-nine of the animal strains failed to cause the lysis of human fibrin, whereas the strains isolated from man were able to do so.

The species of the genus *Streptococcus* which will be discussed in detail are *Streptococcus pyogenes*, *Streptococcus zooepidemicus*, *Streptococcus agalactiae*, *Streptococcus uberis*, *Streptococcus dysgalactiae*, *Streptococcus equi*, *Streptococcus equisimilis*, and *Streptococcus canis*.

Steptococcus pyogenes

Synonyms. *Str. erysipelatos, Str. puerperalis, Str. septicus, Str. articulorum, Str. anginosus, Str. scarlatinae, Str. epidemicus, Str. hemolyticus.*

Distribution and Transmission. The organism is found universally where man has lived for some time. It is present on skin and

TABLE 15.1

DIFFERENTIAL CHARACTERISTICS OF STREPTOCOCCI AFFECTING ANIMALS

Name	Hemolysis	Salicin	Mannite	Inulin	Lactose	Raffinose	Trehalose	Sorbitol	Sodium hippurate	Litmus Milk — Acid	Litmus Milk — Coagulation	Litmus Milk — Reduction	Lancefield Group
Str. pyogenes ..	Beta	+*	±	—	+	—	+	—	—	+	—	±	A
Str. zooepidemicus	Beta	+	—	—	+	—	—	+	—	+	—	—	C
Str. equi	Beta	+	—	—	—	—	—	—	—	+	—	—	C
Str. equisimilis..	Beta	+*	—	—	±	—	+	—	—	+	—	±	C
Str. agalactiae..	Gamma, Alpha or narrow Beta	+*	—	—	+	—	+	—	+	+	+	±	B
Str. dysgalactiae.	Gamma, Alpha or narrow Beta	—	—	—	+	—	+	—	—	+	—	+	C
Str. uberis......	Gamma, Alpha or narrow Beta	+	+	+	+	—	+	+	+	+	±	++	?
Str. canis........	Beta	+	—	—	+	—	—	—	—	+	—	+	C
Group L.........	Beta	—	—	—	±	—	—	—	—	+	+	+	L
Group E.........	Beta	+	+	—	—	—	+	±	—	—	—	—	E

* Occasional strains are negative.

mucous membranes, apparently waiting an opportunity to invade into deeper tissues. Immune carriers, subinfected cases, or severely infected cases serve to spread the organism.

Morphology and Staining. *Streptococcus pyogenes* is a coccus 0.5 to 1μ in size arranged in chains of various lengths (Fig. 15.1). The length and character of the chains are variable in different media and under varying conditions of growth, and likewise in strains isolated from different sources; for example, chains are apt to be shorter in artificial than in natural media. Sometimes there is a tendency toward diplococcus formation, and the chains may be made up of many such diplococci. The organism is nonmotile and does not produce spores. It is Gram-positive, although in older cultures a few decolorized cells may be observed. Capsules are not produced by the majority of strains when grown under ordinary conditions. Certain variant strains have been described which do produce capsules. These strains have been known under the name of *Str. epidemicus.* Other strains produce capsules early in the growth period upon enriched media.

Growth Requirements and Characteristics. The organism may be isolated upon common media from infected tissue, although media to which blood, serum, or ascitic fluid is added obtains and maintains more satisfactory growth. It is aerobic and microaerophilic and has an optimum growth temperature of 37°C.

On solid media the colonies are small, smooth, glistening, dewdrop-like, finely granular, and with age become opaque with a raised central portion. See Figure

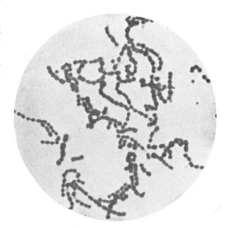

FIG. 15.1 — **Streptococcus pyogenes** bouillon culture, ×2,500. (From Nowak: Documenta Microbiologica, courtesy Gustav Fischer.)

15.2. No pigment is produced. On blood agar, beta type of hemolysis is distinct after 24 hours incubation. Bouillon is uniformly clouded in early stages of growth, forming a finely granular sediment as the culture ages, which settles on the sides and bottom of the culture tube. No pellicle is formed.

Resistance. A temperature of 60°C. for 30 minutes kills the organism, and boiling is effective immediately. The commonly used disinfectants at standard concentrations are effective. The organism perishes rather quickly on laboratory media, and for that reason must be subcultured at least once each month. Cultures may be maintained longer in blood bouillon, sealed tightly or in a semisolid agar.

This streptococcus, in common with all of the pathogenic species of streptococci, is sensitive to sulfanilamide, penicillin, and Aureomycin.

Biochemical Properties. *Str. pyogenes* produces acid but no gas from glucose, lactose, salicin, sucrose, trehalose, and some strains from mannitol, and does not ferment sorbitol, inulin, arabinose, or raffinose. It produces a final pH of 6.0–4.8 in glucose broth. Gelatin is not liquefied. Milk is acidified but rarely coagulated. Indol is not formed. Nitrates are not reduced. Sodium hippurate or starch is not hydrolyzed. Esculin is split by some strains. The organism is not soluble in bile but will not grow on 40 per cent bile-blood agar.

On the basis of group-specific carbohydrate substance C, *Str. pyogenes* belongs in Group A. At least 40 serologic types in the Group A streptococci have been determined by the use of two antigenic protein substances. These antigens are called type-specific protein M and T substance. They have been rather thoroughly studied but space does not permit their description here. The reader is referred to the work of Lancefield and Dole for a detailed discussion.

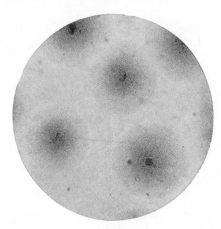

FIG. 15.2 — **Streptococcus pyogenes** colonies on agar, × 50. (From Nowak: Documenta Microbiologica, courtesy Gustav Fischer.)

Griffith has found 27 serological types on the basis of agglutination. By using Griffith's agglutination technic Evans studied 444 strains of Group A streptococci obtained from various parts of the world. She concluded that agglutinative types shift from place to place and that certain types are associated with definite diseases. For example, types 3, 8, and 10 were found to be scarlatinal types, with more or less limited ability to produce other diseases. Type 19 is a predominant scarlatinal type which commonly causes all kinds of streptococcal ailments. Types 5, 13, 14, and 18 do not commonly produce rash, but they have a tendency to produce suppurative and miscellaneous diseases. Type 6, which also has a tendency to produce suppurative diseases, may be found more commonly than the others in scarlet fever.

Str. pyogenes produces two soluble hemolysins which cause the hemolysis of erythrocytes. Study of these substances has revealed that one is oxygen labile and for that reason is called *streptolysin* O. Under ordinary aerobic conditions of growth the production of this hemolysin by a streptococcus culture is not detected. This substance is not lethal to mice in large doses. It is neutralized by streptolysin O antiserum, and the serum of patients suffering with a *Str. pyogenes* infection contains a specific neutralizing antibody. The other type of hemolysin produced by *Str. pyogenes* is called *streptolysin* S because it is extracted from the streptococcal cells by serum. This substance is not oxygen labile; consequently it is the hemolysin responsible for the hemolysis of erythrocytes observed on the blood agar plate. Antibodies against this hemolysin can be induced only by the injection of intact streptococcal cells. This substance is quite toxic to animal tissues, producing degenerative changes in parenchymatous cells and hemolysis of erythrocytes. The animal usually dies within 24 to 48 hours.

Str. pyogenes produces a leucocyte-destroying substance known as *leucocidin*. It has been shown that this substance is similar, if not identical, to streptolysin O.

Numerous strains of this streptococcus produce *erythrogenic* toxin responsible for the characteristic skin lesions of scarlet fever. Persons who have had a typical case of scarlet fever develop immunity to this toxin. In order to detect susceptibility to scarlet fever, diluted toxin (Dick test) may be injected intradermally into the arm. Those susceptible to the disease will have a reaction characterized by swelling and erythema surrounding the point of inoculation. No reaction results if the person has had scarlet fever and has become skin immune to the toxin.

The production of a fibrinolysin by streptococci was first shown by Tillett and Garner in 1933. The detection of this substance in filtrates of streptococcal cultures constitutes a test for the differentiation of certain strains of streptococci. It is assumed that fibrinolysin is functional in the infectious process by preventing the formation of fibrin clots which ordinarily control hemorrhage. Christensen has demonstrated that the lysis of fibrin depends on the action of two substances. One is a proenzyme called *plasminogen* which is an inactive proteolytic factor in all human sera. The other substance called *streptokinase* is liberated by the streptococcal cell. The streptokinase acts with the plasminogen to form the active proteolytic enzyme called *plasmin,* which digests fibrin and other proteins. This digestive process may be inhibited by one of the following factors: (a) the presence of the antibody antistreptokinase induced by a natural streptococcal infection; (b) the presence of antiprotease in the blood; (c) a deficiency of the proenzyme, plasminogen, in the blood.

Certain strains of *Str. pyogenes* have been found to produce another proteolytic enzyme called *proteinase.* This substance is distinct from streptokinase; in fact, its presence in a streptococcus culture prevents the formation of streptokinase or destroys it as it is formed. When active, this enzyme digests milk, gelatin, casein, human and rabbit fibrin. Its role in the infectious process is not known.

Those strains of Group A streptococci which form capsules are known to produce *hyaluronic acid.* This substance is the main component in the capsule of *Str. pyogenes* as well as other species of streptococci of Group C. It is found also as a natural component of many tissues of the animal body where it appears to serve as a "continuity substance" between cells and tissue spaces. It is not antigenic and its role in the infectious process is unknown unless it acts as a phagocytosis inhibiting material. It has been shown that when capsulated streptococci are treated with hyaluronidase, they become susceptible to phagocytosis.

Certain other strains of streptococci produce *hyaluronidase* that is recognized as the important enzyme in the substance referred to as "spreading factor." The most significant property of this material is its ability to attack hyaluronic acid thereby permitting the spread of streptococci and their products. For this reason hyaluronidase is considered a factor in bacterial virulence, although critical experiments to prove this relationship have not been too successful.

Pathogenicity. *Streptococcus pyogenes* causes a number of diseases in man. It is associated with scarlet fever, septic sore throat, tonsillitis, various suppurative inflammatory conditions, septicemia, focal infections, ulcerative endocarditis, rheumatic fever, puerperal sepsis, and erysipelas. It may be a secondary invader in such diseases as diphtheria, measles, smallpox, tuberculosis, pleurisy, and pneumonia. The organism invades the bovine mammary gland, producing mastitis. In such instances it is transmitted from an infected person during the milking process. When such occasions occur, a milk-borne epidemic of scarlet fever or septic sore throat may result. Evans studied in some detail the data concerning 29 milk-borne outbreaks of streptococcal infection in man in order to determine the agglutinative type of the organism. The ability of certain strains of *Str. pyogenes* to produce scarlet fever and for other strains to produce only sore throat is emphasized in her report. It has been noted by other investigators that it is difficult to distinguish between septic sore throat and the sore throat present in scarlet fever. The characterization of a milk-borne outbreak as septic sore throat or as scarlet fever, often depends on whether the population involved has experienced a recent natural epidemic of scarlet fever. If such is the case, they have become skin immune to erythrogenic toxin but not throat immune to the streptococcus. Alford, Gunter, and Edwards reported the isolation of Group A streptococci from the genital tract of 12 cows in a herd of dairy cows. Six of these cows were considered to be difficult breeders but the infection disappeared from the genital tract before conception occurred.

Some strains of *Str. pyogenes* are highly virulent for the mouse and rabbit. The guinea pig is more resistant.

Immunity. Immunity is not produced by one's having had an infection. The toxin of the scarlet fever streptococcus will produce a skin immunity in persons having that disease. The resistance of throat tissues, however, which are the usual seat of the infection, does not appear to be increased; in fact, recovered patients may remain carriers of the organism for considerable periods of time. Bacterin and vaccine therapy in *Streptococcus pyogenes* infection have been found to be of value in some cases. Immune serum, especially scarlet fever antitoxin, has been shown to be of great value in treating cases of scarlet fever.

Diagnosis of Str. pyogenes Infections. Direct smears of the exudate from the lesions of the disease usually reveal long-chained streptococci which may be considered sufficient for the usual diagnosis. Hemolysis may be detected only by the use of blood media. To satisfactorily place the organism in its correct group, the Lancefield technic must be used in conjunction with other biochemical tests.

Streptococcus zooepidemicus

Synonyms and History. *Str. pyogenes,* "*animal pyogenes,*" *Str. genitalium.*

The organism has been isolated from numerous types of tissue and from a variety of species of animals. In most cases it has been considered similar to *Str. pyogenes*. In 1929 Ogura demonstrated the distinction between the human and animal strains, and in 1933 Edwards definitely revealed that two distinct species exist. The antigenic classification of Lancefield shows that the strains of streptococci usually affecting man belong in Group A; whereas, the strains found in animals are placed in Group C.

Distribution and Transmission. *Str. zooepidemicus* is universally found where domesticated animals are kept. The organism commonly produces sporadic infection in animals; however, some cases of bovine mastitis have been reported.

In Kentucky the organism has been encoutered as a cause of genital infection in mares and is, no doubt, transmitted by coitus. Whether the presence of the organism in the genital tract of normal mares indicates an immune carrier state, or whether the organism is normally present and infection indicates a decrease in resistance is not known. In a study of the hemolytic streptococci isolated from swine, Collier reported two strains of the organism from suppurative arthritis, one strain from a cervical abscess, and one strain from vegetative carditis.

The presence of the organism in so many species of animals suggests that cross-infection among animal species may occur; for example, it is possible for this streptococcus to be transmitted from the genital tract of a mare to the udder of a cow if both animals are kept in the same barn lot or to both or either cows and horses from an infected pig or to pigs from an infected horse or cow.

Morphology and Staining. *Str. zooepidemicus* is not significantly different from *Str. pyogenes* to warrant repetition; however, the fact may be emphasized that recently isolated strains of the organism produce capsules especially when grown upon blood or serum media. It is Gram-positive although some strains are easily decolorized, and in most stained preparations an occasional Gram-negative cell may be found.

Growth Requirements and Characteristics. This streptococcus is grown readily on meat infusion agar upon first isolation from infected tissues but needs serum or blood in the medium in successive subcultures. The addition of tryptose to the medium definitely increases growth. The organism is aerobic and microaerophilic. Optimum growth temperature is 37°C.

A flocculent growth is formed on the bottom of tubes of bouillon with a clear supernatant liquid. Some strains are found to produce a faint cloudiness in bouillon. On serum agar, colonies of this organism are larger and more moist than other species of streptococci. The colonies show a tendency to become dry and slightly wrinkled as they age.

Str. zooepidemicus is decidedly beta hemolytic. Wide zones of hemolysis are present around colonies. On pour plates of blood agar the organism forms relatively large spreading colonies between the medium and the bottom of the Petri dish. In the medium itself colonies are large and flatly lenticular.

Resistance. The organism is not resistant to desiccation or sunlight. Laboratory cultures perish unless they are transferred regularly once a month. The thermal death point is 68°C. in 10 minutes. It is easily killed by the ordinary chemicals used in disinfection.

Biochemical Properties. *Streptococcus zooepidemicus* forms acid in lactose, salicin, sorbitol, glucose, and sucrose. Some strains produce acid in maltose. Arabinose, trehalose, raffinose, inulin, adonitol, populin, glycerol, rhamnose, dulcitol, sorbose, erythritol, and inositol are not fermented. Sodium hippurate is not hydrolyzed; starch is hydrolyzed; esculin is not split; gelatin is not liquefied. Milk is rendered slightly acid but is not curdled. It produces a final pH of 5.0–4.6 in glucose broth. Indol is not formed. Nitrates are not reduced.

Antigenic Structure and Toxins. *Str. zooepidemicus* belongs to Group C of Lancefield.

Beta hemolysin is formed as is evident by the marked hemolysis of blood agar. The organism differs from *Str. pyogenes* since it does not produce fibrinolysin as was demonstrated by Tillett and Garner.

Pathogenicity. This streptococcus may be called the beta hemolytic streptococcus of animals and bears a pathogenic relationship to those species as does *Str. pyogenes* to man. The organism produces severe infection, often ending in septicemia and death.

Among the animal hosts the horse appears to be the most susceptible. In the mare the organism has been isolated from cases of cervicitis and metritis, and it has been considered to be the cause of abortion and sterility. It is the principal infecting agent in navel infection, joint infection, peritonitis, and septicemia in very young foals. The organism has been recovered from the semen of infected stallions. Infection in the horse is not confined to the genitalia, for cultures have been obtained from the respiratory tract following influenza as well as from subcutaneous wounds in various parts of the body.

In the bovine this streptococcus may cause cervicitis and metritis. It is often associated with mastitis in the cow, and some investigators consider it the cause of acute septicemic conditions which follow some cases of mastitis. Fortunately it is not as frequently involved in bovine mastitis as are other udder streptococci. Because of the presence of this organism in the udder of cattle and its resemblance on blood agar to *Str. pyogenes,* it was once thought to be pathogenic to man. At the present time it is not considered capable of producing infection in man, although Frost and Engelbrecht report the isolation of cultures from the throats of dairy employees not in contact with infected cows. It must be remembered that *Str. pyogenes* can cause infection in the bovine udder, hence, it may be transmitted to man through the milk supply. Since this is true, it is imperative that marked beta hemolytic strains of udder streptococci be subjected to further laboratory diagnosis.

This streptococcus has been isolated from cases of arthritis, adenitis, abortion, wound infection, and septicemia in swine.

Cultures of the organism have been recovered from foxes which have died of pneumonia as well as from the lymph gland of a sheep. The organism is capable of killing rabbits by intraperitoneal injection, but guinea pigs and rats are resistant. Mice are susceptible and succumb quickly.

Immunity. An animal is not rendered immune by an infection produced by this organism. An increased phagocytic activity probably exists during and following an infection, but it does not persist. It is commonly incorporated in mixed bacterins which are used for domestic animals.

Diagnosis. It is apparent that an infection produced by *Str. zooepidemicus* can be diagnosed correctly only by the isolation and identification of the culture. This organism is beta hemolytic, ferments sorbitol, but does not ferment trehalose nor hydrolyze sodium hippurate. These criteria in addition to the identification of it as belonging to Group C by the Lancefield technic are sufficient for diagnosis.

Streptococcus agalactiae
Streptococcus dysgalactiae
Streptococcus uberis

These three species of streptococci are biochemically and serologically different; however, they are associated with bovine mastitis and are usually referred to as the "mastitis streptococci." Since these species of streptococci are similar and are encountered in the same tissue, it is deemed advisable to discuss them as a group.

Synonyms and History. *Str. agalactiae* was first isolated from cases of mastitis in cows and described by Nocard and Mollereau in 1884 and in subsequent publications in 1885 and 1887. Although numerous udder streptococci were described by various investigators during the following years, the next most significant description was by Kitt in 1893. Lehmann and Neumann used the name *Streptococcus agalactiae* in 1890 and Migula *Str. mastitidis* in 1900. The former name has been generally adopted for the organism.

Up to 1929 nearly all cases of streptococcic mastitis were thought to be caused by *Str. agalactiae*. Minett, Stableforth, and Edwards in that year pointed out that some cases of mastitis were caused by streptococci with characteristics different from those of *Str. agalactiae*. These organisms were designated by them as "non-hemolytic group II." Further work by Edwards revealed a third type of streptococcus which he designated as "non-hemolytic group III." In 1930 Diernhofer described streptococci from mastitis cases which were the same as those of groups II and III of Minett, Stableforth, and Edwards. Later, 1932, Diernhofer suggested the names *Str. dysgalactiae* and *Str. uberis* for the streptococci which corresponded to groups II and III, respectively. These species names have now been adopted for these two organisms.

Distribution and Transmission. These three species of streptococci are widely distributed and are found wherever dairy cows are kept. Incidence of streptococcus mastitis is often high. As high as 80 per cent infection is reported in large dairy herds. Few herds are entirely free from the disease. There are a number of factors concerning transmission of mastitis which are not clearly understood at present; however, it is generally agreed that the most common manner of spreading it is by the hands of the milker or the teat cups of the milking machine. It has been proven that flies are capable of transmitting the disease.

Ingalls and Johnson recovered *Str. agalactiae* nine times in 28 attempts from the external surface of the teats of infected quarters.

In all cases, a minimum of eight hours had elapsed from the time of milking and the organisms were recovered as late as the fifth day following the last milking.

Morphology and Staining. The morphology and staining of *Str. agalactiae* and *Str. dysgalactiae* are not significantly different from *Str. pyogenes*. *Str. uberis* shows less tendency to form long chains, usually occurring in pairs or short chains.

Growth Requirements and Characteristics. These organisms may be isolated directly from milk taken from an infected udder. The incubation of the milk sample for 12 to 24 hours insures greater success. They may be readily grown upon nutrient media to which serum or blood has been added. The use of sodium azide, crystal violet blood agar facilitates the isolation of these organisms from milk samples which may have become contaminated with other bacteria. It is aerobic and microaerophilic and grows best at 37°C. There are no significant differences in colony characteristics among these three organisms. They appear upon solid media as discrete, transparent, dewdrop-like colonies which are characteristic of the streptococci. Growth in liquid media is somewhat variable. *Str. agalactiae* and *Str. dysgalactiae* usually produce a flocculent growth in the bottom of the tube with a clear supernatant liquid above, while *Str. uberis* produces a uniform turbidity in broth medium. *Str. agalactiae* produces a narrow zone of beta or alpha hemolysis or no hemolysis at all upon blood agar. Hemolysis never extends as far from the colony as with *Str. pyogenes*. Brown has described characteristic "double-zone" hemolysis by beta hemolytic strains of *Str. agalactiae* if the blood agar cultures are refrigerated after 24 hours incubation at 37°C.

Str. dysgalactiae and *Str. uberis* are described as non-hemolytic; however, some strains produce beta hemolysis when they are grown on sodium azide blood agar.

Resistance. Resistance of these species in general is similar to that of *Str. pyogenes;* however, *Str. agalactiae* has been found in pasteurized milk. This would suggest that this organism is able to resist pasteurization temperatures occasionally while *Str. pyogenes* has never been shown to survive proper pasteurization.

Watts has shown that *Str. agalactiae* remained viable for three years after a milk culture had been thoroughly desiccated over pure sulphuric acid. In a relative humidity greater than 60 per cent the organism perished in eleven weeks but in a relative humidity of 10–25 per cent it remained viable for three years.

Spencer, McCarter, and Beach concluded that *Str. agalactiae* died out rapidly in barn bedding; most of the organisms were dead after 24 hours but a few lived as long as six to nine days. These investigators found the organism on the hands of dairy attendants who hand-milked infected cows.

Biochemical Properties. The biochemical properties of these three organisms are alike in that they do not produce indol, liquefy gelatin, or reduce nitrates. Table 15.1 shows the reactions on the various test media which may be used in differentiating these streptococci.

Antigenic Structure and Toxins. *Str. agalactiae* is placed in Lancefield's Group B and appears to be the only definite species in this group. Four subgroups, namely Ia, Ib, II, and III, have been described under Group B. *Str. dysgalactiae* has been placed in Lancefield's Group C. The antigenic structure of *Str. uberis* is very heterogeneous. Most strains show no serological relationship to established Lancefield groups or to each other, although they appear to be identical biochemically. It has been suggested that the antigenic structure of this organism is lacking in type-specific substances.

The production of hemolysin by this group of streptococci is not marked. Some strains of *Str. agalactiae* produce a soluble hemolysin, while the other two species do not. An erythrogenic toxin is not formed. Fibrinolysin has not been demonstrated.

Pathogenicity. It is generally conceded that a large per cent of the cases of mastitis in badly infected herds is caused by *Str. agalactiae*. It causes a parenchymatous mastitis which is characterized by acute onset followed by a progressively chronic condition resulting in fibrosis of the infected gland. Infection is usually permanent carrying over from one lactation to another and with occasional "acute attacks" of the disease.

Mastitis caused by *Str. dysgalactiae* is less frequent; usually less than 10 per cent of the cases of streptococcic mastitis are due to this organism. The disease is usually more acute with less tendency toward chronic, permanent infection than in the case of *Str. agalactiae*. *Str. uberis* may be associated with an acute mastitis which later becomes chronic. Its course is more transient with less tendency to permanent infection. This organism also has been found in the udder of some cows without producing any disturbance. Less than 10 per cent of the cases of streptococcic mastitis are found to be caused by this organism.

The character of the milk in mastitis is quite variable depending largely upon the severity and stage of infection. In acute stages it may appear as a curdled mass composed of purulent exudate, dead tissue cells, coagulated milk proteins, and bacteria. In chronic cases it may appear normal macroscopically, but there usually is a slight increase in the number of leucocytes and a large number of streptococci.

These organisms are not pathogenic for farm animals other than the bovine nor have they been found to be pathogenic for any other organ except the mammary gland of the cow. Although *Str. aga-*

lactiae has been isolated from various tissues of man, it is considered to have only an opportunist role in human disease processes.

Experimental animals have been considered resistant to *Str. agalactiae.* Kaplan *et al.* have shown, however, that when a strain of the organism is passed through a series of four mice, increase of virulence results.

Immunity. Immunity is not produced by an attack of mastitis due to *Str. agalactiae.* Cows may be continuously infected for years. Bacterins have been used in treatment with little success. Autogenous bacterins have been used also and have appeared to be more valuable. Spontaneous recoveries of cases of mastitis due to *Str. dysgalactiae* suggest a possible immunity; however, little work has been done on this subject.

Diagnosis. The cultivation of streptococci from the milk is indicative of mastitis. This may be done by incubating a sample of milk from an infected udder using the milk as the culture medium, or the organism may be grown on any other suitable medium. Blood agar is preferred as it not only grows the organism, but also shows its action upon blood. Sodium azide, crystal violet blood agar is a more valuable medium for the routine isolation of streptococci since it inhibits the growth of contaminants which may be confusing. The demonstration of streptococci in milk should be followed by identification of the organism for accurate diagnosis. Inoculation of the organism into the test media shown in Table 15.1 will accurately diagnose the disease and differentiate the organism from the saprophytic streptococci which are occasionally present.

Hotis and Miller have devised a test for the detection of *Str. agalactiae* infection, but it is much less accurate in detecting other streptococci such as *Str. dysgalactiae.* The test is performed by adding 0.5 ml. of sterile 0.5 per cent aqueous solution bromcresol-purple to 9.5 ml. of milk. The milk is incubated 24 hours at 37°C., and the test is read. The appearance of canary-yellow colonies of bacterial growth along the walls and in the bottom of the test tube is diagnostic of *Str. agalactiae* infection. The yellow color formed around the colonies is due to the fermentation of lactose to acid which changes the bromcresol-purple to the yellow range of the indicator. Although *Str. dysgalactiae* and *Str. uberis* are capable of fermenting lactose, they never grow in clumps as does *Str. agalactiae.* The growth of *Str. agalactiae* in clumps in this test appears to be associated with agglutination.

In 1944 Christie, Atkins, and Munch-Peterson reported a reaction which since has become known as the CAMP Test. They observed that around colonies of staphylococci cultured on bovine blood agar a double zone of hemolysis occurred. In this type of hemolysis, called alpha-beta hemolysis, a clear zone of beta hemolysis is surrounded by a darker zone of incompletely hemolyzed erythrocytes. When milk containing mastitis streptococci was cultured on bovine blood agar plates containing colonies of alpha-beta staphylococci, the colonies of streptococci growing in the alpha zone were surrounded by a wider zone of beta hemolysis than was observed in colonies growing elsewhere on the plate. Murphy, Stuart, and Reed, in 1952 observed that 96.6% of the cultures of *Str. agalactiae* were positive to the CAMP Test, 85.1% of the cultures of *Str. uberis* were positive, and none of the cultures of *Str. dysgalactiae* were positive. They have considered the test of value in typing the mastitis streptococci.

Various indirect methods have been devised for the diagnosis of mastitis, but do not identify the causal agent. These tests include the chloride, catalase, strip cup, and bromthymol blue tests.

Streptococcus equi

Synonyms and History. The disease, strangles, in horses has a long recorded history. It was described by Solleysel in 1664, and its contagious nature was determined by Lafosse in 1790. Apparently a streptococcus was first considered to be responsible for the disease by Rivolta in 1873 when he described cocci found in exudate from typical cases of strangles. In 1886 Perroncito observed the same type of cells in exudate and considered them to be the cause of the disease. Baruchello is credited with being the first to isolate the organism in 1886 and to reproduce the disease. Sand and Jensen described the organism in 1887 and are credited with being the first to use the name *Streptococcus equi* in 1888. Schütz isolated and distinguished it from other streptococci in 1888. In his classification of 1901, Chester used the name *Streptococcus capelletti*. Matzuschita referred to it as *Streptococcus contagiosae equorum* in 1902. In 1913 Bongert used the name *Streptococcus Schütz*.

Distribution and Transmission. *Str. equi* appears wherever there are horses. Epizootics of strangles constantly occur in horse populations. The organism is spread by close contact and by contaminated water and feeds. There is evidence that infected horses remain resistant carriers of the organism and are sources of the infection for considerable periods of time.

Morphology and Staining. In its general appearance *Str. equi* does not differ from the other species of the group. Long chains of cocci are usually found in fluids and in pus from infected animals; however, short chains have been observed, and it is believed that they are even more virulent. Capsules may be demonstrated on many of the cocci in smears made from lesions of the disease and from media containing serum. The organism is Gram-positive, but it may be decolorized more easily than other members of the group. It is easily stained by the aniline dyes.

Growth Requirements and Characteristics. In most cases, the organism is isolated in pure culture from the deeper portion of the characteristic abscesses. More abundant growth is obtained upon primary isolation by the use of slightly alkaline, serumized media under microaerophilic conditions. The organism is the most difficult to cultivate of any of the streptococci. Colonies are small, convex, and transparent. In water of the agar slant it produces a whitish, flocculent precipitate. In agar stabs, nodular outgrowths from the line of puncture develop. In broth, the majority of strains form a flocculent deposit with a clear supernatant fluid. Some strains produce uniform turbidity. Colonies on blood agar are moist, mucoid-like, even though they are small. A wide zone of beta hemolysis is produced on blood agar.

Resistance. *Str. equi* is more resistant to heat than some of the other species although it is not as resistant as some previous investigators believed. It is killed promptly by boiling, in 10 minutes at 65°C. to 70°C., and in 50 minutes at 60°C. The cresol compounds destroy the organism readily. Gentian violet also exerts a marked action. Mercury salts appear to be less effective. It is more resistant to disinfectants and to desiccation when it is present in purulent exudate.

Biochemical Properties. Acid is formed from glucose, salicin, sucrose, mannose, galactose, and maltose. It fails to ferment lactose and sorbitol, which serves to differentiate it from *Str. pyogenes* and *Str. zooepidemicus*. It also fails to ferment mannitol, trehalose, arabinose, raffinose, inulin, and glycerol. Litmus milk is not changed. Sodium hippurate is not hydrolyzed. Nitrates are not reduced. It does not grow in 40 per cent bile-blood agar. It is not bile-soluble. Gelatin is not liquefied.

Antigenic Structure and Toxins. The organism belongs to Group C of Lancefield's classification. Antigenic subtypes have not been reported. Bazeley studied 32 strains of the organism collected from 26 distinct outbreaks of strangles in Australia. By cross-protection tests in mice he found definite cross protection by the univalent serum against all strains. It forms hemolysin and leucocidin, but does not produce erythrogenic toxin. Some strains are reported to lyse human fibrin although the majority fail to do so.

Pathogenicity. *Streptococcus equi* is considered one of the main causes of strangles, which is most prevalent in young horses. It is often a secondary invader in respiratory diseases such as influenza and contagious pleuropneumonia of horses. It may be found in the genital tract of the mare. Strangles is first characterized by a catarrhal discharge, with inflammation of the nasal mucous membranes, followed quickly by a swelling of the adjacent lymphatic glands and of the submaxillary and pharyngeal lymph nodes in which abscesses generally develop. The infection spreads through the lymph channels, but generally remains localized in the tissues adjacent to the original point of infection. Metastatic infections may occur in any of the organs of the body; and in the chronic types of the disease, great variations in localization are found. Fatal termination is rare, but sometimes occurs, due to septicemia, pyemia, or pneumonia.

Subcutaneous inoculation of the organism into the horse will usually provoke abscess formation at the point of injection. The introduction of pure cultures into the nasal cavity of young, susceptible horses gives rise to the characteristic purulent catarrh with secondary abscess formation in the lymph nodes. It is obvious that, in addition to age, other predisposing factors, such as exposure to cold and fatigue, lower the resistance of animals to the disease. Variations in the virulence of the organism may account for the epizootic character of the disease. Bazeley has shown that cultures of *Str. equi* four and one-half hours old are much more virulent than cultures twenty-four hours of age. He attributes this to the high surface electric charge of the young cultures as compared to the old. He believes that this explains why young, actively multiplying streptococci are not readily phagocytized.

Pus from abscesses in strangles kills white mice, with evidence of acute septicemia in two to four days, or after a longer period as a result of pyemia. An abscess generally develops at the point of inoculation. Rabbits and guinea pigs succumb to the injection of large quantities of the organism, but are not readily infected. Cattle, sheep, swine, dogs, and birds are very resistant. Man is not susceptible to the organism.

Immunity. Immunity is conferred by an attack of *Str. equi* infection. Some animals appear to suffer second attacks of the disease, but this is often due to mistaken diagnosis of the first attack. Animals five years old are usually resistant to the disease. These facts have led to the assumption that artificial immunization is of value.

Immunization with bacterins and vaccines have not given completely satisfactory results. The use of a herd-autogenous bacterin is more successful than the use of polyvalent bacterins. Allen has reported favorable results following the use of a pyovaccine which he prepared by placing the contents of an abscess in contact with ether for 12 hours, followed by subsequent dilution with sterile salt solution. Richters has recommended the use of a polyvalent immune serum simultaneously with a methylene blue treated vaccine.

Bazeley in Australia has produced an effective vaccine by exposing very young cultures of *Str. equi* to moderate heat for a short time. The use of this vaccine reduced the incidence of strangles in horses to a significant degree.

Immune serum used at once after the appearance of symptoms is of value in reducing the severity of the disease and preventing sequelae. Convalescent serum has been used with evident success.

Diagnosis. Presumptive bacteriologic diagnosis may be made by identification of a Gram-positive streptococcus from the lesions characteristic of the disease. Since *Str. zooepidemicus* also may be found in upper-respiratory diseases of horses, it is necessary to distinguish between it and *Str. equi* by the use of appropriate media. Serological reactions have not been used in the diagnosis of the disease.

Streptococcus equisimilis

Synonyms and History. This streptococcus has been described under various names, such as *Str. equi*, "animal pyogenes," *Str. pyogenes*. However, most workers have called attention to the characteristics which have indicated that a separate species really exists.

The name *Str. equisimilis* was proposed by Frost and Engelbrecht in 1936 to designate strains of streptococci which belonged in Lancefield Group C but which were biochemically different from *Str. zooepidemicus* and *Str. equi*.

In her detailed studies of the hemolytic streptococci in 1944 Alice Evans has described this species more thoroughly and has called atttention to the different species of animals from which it may be isolated as well as from man.

Distribution and Transmission. This organism, apparently, is one of the species of streptococci which may be found among people and various species of animals throughout the world. In common with other members of the genus it is transmitted directly from animal to animal by close contact and by water and feed to which animals have common access.

Inasmuch as *Str. equisimilis* is found in both animals and man, there is every reason to assume that animals may serve as a source of human infection. Instances have been reported where infection caused by the organism in man has followed contact with exudate from a case of strangles in the horse, which likewise was caused by this streptococcus. No doubt there is freer exchange of it between animals and man than is generally recognized.

Morphology and Staining. There is nothing peculiar nor different about *Str. equisimilis* which can be used to differentiate it from other streptococci. It does not produce capsules.

Growth Requirements and Characteristics. *Str. equisimilis* is not as fastidious as *Str. pyogenes* or *Str. equi* in its growth requirements. It will grow rather abundantly on meat infusion agar. Blood agar, which should be used routinely for the primary isolation of all streptococci, is the most suitable medium. On this medium the organism grows abundantly and produces marked beta hemolysis. The zones of hemolysis average 4.0 mm. The colonies are discrete and opaque.

In fluid media this streptococcus forms a fairly heavy sediment in the bottom of the tube. Some strains show initial clouding of the medium which clears as the culture ages.

Resistance. The action of chemicals on *Str. equisimilis* is similar to other members of the genus.

Biochemical Properties. *Str. equisimilis* produces acid in glucose, maltose, sucrose, trehalose, and glycerol. Animal strains uniformly produce acid in salicin but some strains isolated from man may fail to ferment that carbohydrate. Most strains from either animal or human sources do not ferment lactose, but occasional strains may be isolated which will produce acid. No acid is produced from sorbitol, mannitol, arabinose, inulin, or raffinose. Slight acid may be produced in milk by certain strains, otherwise no change is observed in that medium. It does not hydrolyze starch and esculin. Ammonia is produced in peptone media. Gelatin is not liquefied.

Antigenic Structure and Toxins. It has been noted previously that *Str. equisimilis* belongs in Lancefield Group C. On the basis of agglutination, Evans has found that the strains she studied fell into at least three different types.

Antigenic relationships, on the basis of cross-protection tests, between *Str. equisimilis* and *Str. pyogenes* have been recorded. Likewise, on the basis of cross-protection tests antigenic relationships have been observed between *Str. equisimilis* and *Str. equi.*

Although the hemolysins of this streptococcus have not been studied, the marked beta hemolysis produced by it indicates that these toxins probably are similar to those produced by *Str. pyogenes*. It is probable that other toxins are likewise similar.

Evans noted that the animal and human strains of *Str. equisimilis* were not distinguishable by biochemical reactions. Hansen found that human strains of this organism were able to lyse human fibrin whereas the animal strains were unable to do so. Evans has reported the same results.

Pathogenicity. *Str. equisimilis* has been isolated from various conditions in many animal species and man.

In her studies, Evans reported cultures from strangles and metritis of the equine. In our laboratory, Packer has isolated this streptococcus from strangles, cervicitis, and wound infection in the equine.

This microorganism has been encountered by many workers in exudates and tissues from the bovine. Hadley and Frost demonstrated artificial infection of the udder and isolated it from milk samples from ten cows. Evans reported it in bovine metritis and mastitis. Packer has isolated it from mastitis in the cow and Ruebke from the prepuce of the bull. It is not considered to be a common streptococcus in the bovine, comparing with *Str. zooepidemicus* in this respect.

The distribution of the various species of streptococci in swine has not received detailed study. In his study of the streptococci in this animal, Collier has isolated *Str. equisimilis* from suppurative adenitis, suppurative arthritis, vegetative endocarditis, suppurative periostitis, suppurative dermatitis, pneumonia, septicemia, and aborted fetus. Of 67 strains isolated from swine, 39 were identified as *Str. equisimilis*.

The presence of this streptococcus in pyometria, purulent rhinitis, and purulent conjunctivitis in the canine has also been observed by Packer. In this regard, attention must be called to another streptococcus, *Str. canis,* of the dog. By referring to Table 15.1 it will be noted that *Str. equisimilis* ferments trehalose but *Str. canis* does not, thus permitting the differentiation of these two streptococci.

Evans has reported avian strains of *Str. equisimilis* which were isolated from bronchitis. In the discussion of *Str. gallinarum* which follows it will be noted that numerous reports of streptococcal infections in chickens have been made. It is quite difficult to determine the species of organism studied in many of the early reports because many of the important differential carbohydrates were not used. Those investigators who study avian diseases should take particular care in the identification of the streptococci. From such reports it will be possible to distinguish the most important streptococcus in the avian family.

The presence of strains which have been designated as "human C" in various diseases of man has been known for many years. In her report Evans has reported cultures from scarlet fever, pneumonia, hemorrhagic small pox, erysipelas, lymphadenitis, nasal discharge, abscessation, septicemia, puerperal fever, and empyema. It is apparent that the organism is widely distributed.

Immunity. No information is available concerning the immunity produced by an infection with *Str. equisimilis,* but it would be rather safe to presume that there is no deviation from the general rule in all streptococcal infection.

Diagnosis. The incrimination of *Str. equisimilis* as the infectious agent in animal and human disease is possible only after the isolation and definite identification of the organism.

Streptococcus gallinarum

Synonyms and History. Norgaard and Mohler isolated and described a streptococcus in 1902 which produced a highly fatal septicemia in chickens. Dammann and Mangold described an encapsulated streptococcus in 1905 to which they gave the name, *Streptococcus capsulatus gallinarum*. The organism was associated with an epizootic of "sleeping sickness" in chickens. Moore and Mack, 1905, described the organism and the disease. In 1908, Grave described a capsulated streptococcus of the chicken. Magnusson in 1910 investigated a highly acute septicemia of fowls caused by a streptococcus. Kernkamp, 1927, isolated a streptococcus from chickens which had died with an idiopathic peritonitis. Hudson found a streptococcus associated with fowl septicemia in 1933.

Lack of complete descriptive data does not permit the conclusion that all the above mentioned streptococci are of the same species, but until more definite results have been established, they will be classified as *Str. gallinarum*. Many of the descriptions suggest that some of the strains should be classified as *Streptococcus zooepidemicus*. The failure to ferment sorbitol has been mentioned in some reports. This suggests that these cultures may have been *Str. equisimilis*.

Distribution and Transmission. The organism has been found in the United States, Germany, and Sweden. The method of transmission among birds in the flock is not known, but the nature of the severe type of septicemia indicates that it is spread through water or contaminated feed.

Morphology and Staining. Short chains of six to eight cells predominate. Long chains are found in fluid media. Cells are diplococcoid on solid media. Uneven sizes are common. Some strains are capsulated. The organism is Gram-positive.

Growth Requirements and Characteristics. *Str. gallinarum* can be isolated from the blood and tissues of infected birds. If blood is added to the surface of agar, growth is stimulated. Young colonies on agar are white and gelatinous, and as they become older, brownish centers and bluish borders are evident. A maximum size is reached in 72 hours. A flocculent sediment is formed in bouillon. Beta hemolysis is formed on blood agar.

Resistance. Resistance is typical of the group.

Biochemical Properties. The organism ferments glucose, fructose, lactose, maltose, sucrose, dextrin, starch, galactose, and salicin; does not ferment arabinose, adonitol, dulcitol, erythritol, inositol, mannitol, and sorbitol; does not ferment lactose in milk sufficiently to produce coagulation.

Antigenic Structure and Toxins. Hemolysin and leucocidin are produced. Nothing is known about antigenic types.

Pathogenicity. The organism is most pathogenic for chickens in which it produces a typical acute septicemia. It produces a peritonitis which accompanies the septicemia. Rabbits, pigeons, ducks, and white mice succumb to injection of the organism. Guinea pigs are resistant.

Immunity. Little is known of the immunity produced naturally by the infection in surviving birds. It has been observed that active immunity can be conferred by the injection of bouillon culture filtrates and by vaccination with killed cultures, and that passive immunity can be established by the injection of the blood serum of an immunized animal. The latter is of doubtful value due to the apoplectiform nature of the disease.

Diagnosis. The organism is identified as a Gram-positive streptococcus in smears from the blood and internal organs as well as by culture.

Streptococcus canis

A study of the streptococcic infections of dogs by Stafseth, Thompson, and Neu in 1937 revealed a new species, *Streptococcus canis*. This organism and the conditions which it produces in the canine were again discussed by Stafseth in 1940. This organism was the one most commonly found in infected dogs although two other types were isolated.

Streptococcus canis is 0.9 to 1μ in size, occurs singly and in pairs but often in chains of varying lengths. The shape and size of the individual cells in a single chain vary from well-rounded forms to elliptical or rod-shaped elements. It is Gram-positive. It is definitely beta hemolytic, forming a zone on blood agar up to 5 mm. in diameter. Colonies of the organism vary from 0.5 to 1 mm. in size and are convex, smooth, glistening, faintly yellowish white, opaque with entire margins. This streptococcus grows best on blood agar, but it will grow on neopeptone chicken infusion agar. It forms a fine to coarse granular sediment with a clear supernatant fluid when grown on neopeptone chicken infusion broth. *Streptococcus canis* produces acid but no gas in glucose, lactose, maltose, salicin, and sucrose. It does not ferment mannite, sorbitol, or trehalose. It belongs to Group C of Lancefield.

The female genital tract appears to be the natural habitat of this streptococcus, and Stafseth, Thompson, and Neu were able to isolate it from the prepuce of a male four days after mating to an infected female. The organism has been isolated from abscesses which have followed antirabies inoculation, emphasizing the fact that care must be taken in cleaning and disinfecting the skin of dogs prior to biological therapy. *Str. canis* has been isolated from the umbilicus, intestines, heart, lungs, kidneys, vagina, blood, peritoneal cavity, and femorotibial articulation of pups; hence, it is considered to be of considerable significance to very young dogs. It is considered to be the cause of "acid milk" in puppies and is thought to be the chief etiological agent in canine tonsillitis.

The female appears to be a persistent carrier of the organism; consequently, it is doubtful that immunity follows an active infection. Stafseth, Thompson, and Neu treated two cases of articular and muscular rheumatism successfully with an autogenous vaccine.

Since other species of streptococci, not as yet sufficiently studied to warrant description here, are found in the dog, accurate diagnosis of the presence of *Str. canis* can be obtained only by the isolation and identification of the organism.

Miscellaneous Streptococci

In 1922, Bayne-Jones described a hemolytic streptococcus which causes a respiratory infection and septicemia of cats, to which the name *Streptococcus feline* was given. The organism was culturally and biochemically identical with *Str. pyogenes* but serologically distinct. It is possible that this organism belongs to the *"animal pyogenes"* group.

The presence of beta hemolytic streptococci in the lymph nodes of the cervical region of swine was reported by Newsom in Colorado in 1937 and by Stafseth and Clinton in Michigan in 1941. The organisms described by these investigators did not appear to be identical. Stafseth and Clinton reported that their streptococcus belonged in Lancefield's Group E, which was the first time such a source of this organism had been reported. In his study of streptococci isolated from swine, Collier found 13 out of 67 strains studied were classified as Group L and 5 strains were Group E.

The presence of alpha hemolytic varieties of streptococci in animal disease is not well established. This type is found in animals with mastitis and in some cases of wound infection. Thorp has found viridans type of streptococci associated with pneumonia in the pig. It is probable that these organisms may be of some importance in chronic infections in animals, as well as in man. Organisms of this type are found in the mouth and intestinal tract of both man and animals. *Str. equinus* appears to be a rather well-defined species of the viridans type which is found as a saprophyte in the intestine of the horse.

An unusual motile streptococcus has been reported by Bruner, Edwards, Doll, and Moran. This organism was isolated from an aborted equine fetus and was belived to have produced the abortion. It grew readily on meat infusion agar; was Gram-positive; individual cells were oblong rather than spherical and arranged in short chains or small groups. The organism was found to be monotrichous and cultures grown in semisolid agar showed slight growth from the needle track, indicating slight motility. This streptococcus produced acid but not gas in glucose, lactose, sucrose, mannitol, sorbitol, trehalose, and salicin. It hydrolyzed sodium hippurate; reduced methylene blue milk; grew on 40 per cent bile blood agar. Narrow zones of beta hemolysis were observed around deep colonies in blood agar. It was found to belong to Group D.

Nonhemolytic streptococci are often found in animal tissues. Most gamma types are considered saprophytic, and for that reason have not been completely studied except from the point of view of systematic relationships. Many species are of use in dairy manufacturing. They grow well in milk and in milk products, and for that reason are of significance in milk sanitation. *Str. lactis* is one of the most common organisms of this type; however, it is not a normal inhabitant of the bovine udder; in fact, it is rarely found there. It gains access to milk from contaminated utensils. Recent work indicates that its normal habitat is plants; this explains its prevalence in raw milk. For the detailed description of this and other streptococci of significance in milk processing, the student is advised to consult Hammer's text on Dairy Bacteriology.

REFERENCES FOR FURTHER STUDY

Alford, J. A., Gunter, J. J., and Edwards, C. D. Cornell Vet. 45:357, 1955.

Avery, C. T., and Cullen, G. E. Jour. Exp. Med. 29:215–34, 1919.

Ayers, S. H. Jour. Inf. Dis. 33:155–60, 1923.

———, and Mudge, C. S. Jour. Inf. Dis. 31:40–50, 1922.

———, and Rupp, P. Jour. Inf. Dis. 30:388–99, 1922.

Bazeley, P. L. Aust. Vet. Jour. 18:189–94, 1940.

———. Aust. Vet. Jour. 19:62–85, 1941.

———. Studies with Equine Streptococci. III Vaccination Against Strangles. Aust. Vet. Jour. 18:141–55, 1942.

Bergey, D. H., *et al.* Manual of Determinative Bacteriology. 6th Ed. Williams & Wilkins Co., Baltimore, 1948.

Brocq-Rousseu, Forgeot, and Urbain. Le Streptocoque Gourmeux. Five parts. Revue de Pathologie Comparée et d'Hygiène Générale 25, 1925.

Brown, J. H. The Use of Blood Agar for the Study of Streptococci. Rockefeller Inst. Med. Res., Monograph No. 9, 1919.

Bruner, D. W., Edwards, P. R., Doll, E. R., and Moran, A. B. Cornell Vet. 38:313–14, 1948.

Christensen, L. R. Jour. Gen. Physiol. 28:363–83, 1945.

Christie, R., Atkins, N. E., and Munch-Peterson, E. Aust. Jour. Exp. Biol. and Med. Sci. 22:197, 1944.

Collier, J. R. Unpublished data.

———. Proc. Book 88th Ann. Conv. Amer. Vet. Med. Assn. P. 169, 1951.

Czarnetzky, E. J., Morgan, I. M., and Mudd, S. Jour. Exp. Med. 67:643–57, 1938.

Davis, D. J. Jour. Amer. Med. Assn. 58:1852–54, 1912.

———, and Capps, J. A. Jour. Inf. Dis. 15:135–40, 1914.

Dick, G. F., and Dick, G. H. Jour. Amer. Med. Assn. 82:301–2, 1924.

Dimock, W. W., and Edwards, P. R. Ky. Agr. Exp. Sta., Bull. 338, 1933.

———, and Snyder, Ethel. Jour. Amer. Vet. Med. Assn. 64:288–99, 1923.

Edwards, P. R. Jour. Bact. 23:259–66, 1932.

———. Jour. Bact. 35:527–36, 1933.

———. Jour. Bact. 27:527–34, 1934.

———. Ky. Agr. Exp. Sta., Bull. 536, 1935.

Edwards, S. J. Jour. Comp. Path. Ther. 45:43–57, 1932.

Evans, Alice C. Streptococcus Bacteriophage: A Study of Four Serological Types. Public Health Repts. 49:1386–1401, 1934.

———. Studies on Hemolytic Streptococci. Four parts. Jour. Bact. 31 and 32, 1936; 34, 1937.

———. Studies on Hemolytic Streptococci. VIII. *Streptococcus equisimilis.* Jour. Bact. 48:267–84, 1944.

———. Jour. Inf. Dis. 78:1–17 and 18–24, 1946.

Frost, W. D., and Engelbrecht, M. A. The Streptococci. Willdof Book Co., Madison, 1940.

Garner, R. L., and Tillett, W. S. Jour. Exp. Med. 60:239–67, 1934.

Griffith, F. The Serological Classification of *Streptococcus pyogenes.* Jour. Hyg. 34:542–84, 1934.

Hammer, B. W. Dairy Bacteriology. 3rd Ed. John Wiley & Sons, Inc., New York, 1948.

Hansen, P. A. A Bibliography on Mastitis. N. Y. (Geneva) Agr. Exp. Sta., Mimeo. Bull. 1, 1934.

———. Mastitis. III. The Identity of *Streptococcus agalactiae.* N. Y. (Geneva) Agr. Exp. Sta., Tech. Bull. 232, 1935.

Hansen, P. L. Skand. VetTidskr. 33:257–80, 1943.

Holman, W. L. The Classification of Streptococci. Jour. Med. Res. 34:377–443, 1916.

Hotis, R. P., and Miller, W. T. A Simple Method for Detecting Mastitis Streptococci in Milk. U. S. D. A., Cir. No. 400, 1936.

Hucker, G. J. Mastitis. V. The Presence of Mastitis Streptococci in Bovine Mammary Tissue. N. Y. (Geneva) Agr. Exp. Sta., Tech. Bull. 241, 1937.

Ingalls, W. L., and Johnson, E. P. Amer. Jour. Vet. Res. 8:321–24, 1947.

Jones, F. S. The Streptococci of Equines. Jour. Exp. Med. 30:159–78, 1919.

Kaplan, M. M., Raiziss, G. W., and Moetsch, J. C. Amer. Jour. Vet. Res. 3:392–94, 1942.

Lancefield, Rebecca C. The Antigenic Complex of *Streptococcus haemolyticus*. Five parts. Jour. Exp. Med. 47, 1928.

————. A Serological Differentiation of Human and Other Groups of Hemolytic Streptococci. Jour. Exp. Med. 57:571–95, 1933.

————. Two Serological Types of Group B Hemolytic Streptococci with Related, but Not Identical, Type-specific Substances. Jour. Exp. Med. 67:25–40, 1938.

————. Jour. Exp. Med. 78:465–76, 1943.

————, and Dole, V. P. Jour. Exp. Med. 84:449–71, 1946.

————, and Stewart, W. A. Jour. Exp. Med. 79:79–88, 1944.

Minett, F. C. Jour. Path. Bact. 40:357–64, 1935.

————, and Stableforth, A. W. Jour. Dairy Res. 5:223–32, 1934.

Murphy, J. M., Stuart, O. M., and Reed, F. I. Cornell Vet. 42:133, 1952.

Newsom, I. E. Vet. Med. 37:137–38, 1937.

Ogston, A. Brit. Med. Jour. 1:369–75, 1881.

Ogura, K. Jour. Jap. Soc. Vet. Sci. 8:174–203, 1929.

Packer, R. A. Personal communication. April, 1950.

Plastridge, W. N., and Hartsell, S. E. Jour. Inf. Dis. 61:110–21, 1937.

Rosell, J. M. Cornell Vet. 21:317–33, 1931.

Ruebke, H. J. Personal communication. April, 1950.

Sand, G., and Jensen, C. O. Deutsche Zeitschr. Thiermed. 13:437–64, 1888.

Schütz. Archiv Thierheilkunde. 14:172–218, 1888.

Sherman, James M. The Streptococci. Bact. Rev. 1:1–97, 1937.

Spencer, G. R., McCarter, J., and Beach, B. A. Amer. Jour. Vet. Res. 7:32–36, 1946.

Stableforth, A. W. Jour. Path. Bact. 45:263–77, 1937.

Stafseth, H. J. Jour. Amer. Vet. Med. Assn. 96:230–35, 1940.

————, and Clinton, I. Jour. Amer. Vet. Med. Assn. 99:468–70, 1941.

————, Thompson, W. W., and Neu, L. Jour. Amer. Vet. Med. Assn. 90:769–81, 1937.

Stewart, W. A., Lancefield, R. C., Wilson, A. T., and Swift, H. F. Jour. Exp. Med. 79:99–114, 1944.

Swift, H. A. Chap. 11, The Streptococci, in Dubos' Bacterial and Mycotic Infections of Man. Lippincott Co., Philadelphia, 1948.

Thomson, D., and Thomson, R. The Pathogenic Streptococci. Annals Pickett-Thomson Research Lab. 4, 1928.

Topley, W. W. C., Wilson, G. S., and Miles, A. A. The Principles of Bacteriology and Immunity. 3rd Ed. Williams and Wilkins Co., Baltimore, 1946.

Winslow, C.–E.A., and Palmer, G. T. Jour. Inf. Dis. 7:1–16, 1910.

————, and Winslow, Anne R. The Systematic Relationships of the Coccaceae. New York, 1908.

Watson, R. F., and Lancefield, Rebecca C. Jour. Exp. Med. 79:89–98, 1944.

Watts, P. S. Jour. Path. Bact. 57:191–97, 1945.

16.

The Genera
Diplococcus and Neisseria

The organisms in the group of diplococci are spherical or oval in shape, and the cells are usually in pairs. All the organisms are nonmotile and are nonspore-producing. One genus, Diplococcus, produces capsules. Species of both genera grow sparsely on solid media in dewdrop-like colonies and ferment carbohydrates with acid formation only. They are strictly parasitic for man and cause specific diseases.

The species of this group are placed in two genera, Diplococcus and Neisseria; the separation is made upon the basis of the reaction to the Gram stain and on morphology. *Diplococcus pneumoniae* is Gram-positive; the cells are elongated, pointed, and capsulated. *Neisseria intracellularis* and *Neisseria gonorrhoeae* are Gram-negative; the cells are spherical and noncapsulated.

None of the above species produces disease in animals, but all are sufficiently important to the student in animal bacteriology to warrant brief discussion. Additional references are given at the end of the chapter for the convenience of the student.

Diplococcus pneumoniae

Synonyms and History. *Pneumococcus, Streptococcus pneumoniae, Diplococcus lanceolatus, Fränkel's pneumococcus.*

The presence of cocci in the exudate from cases of pneumonia was noted by Klebs (1875), Eberth (1881), Koch (1881), Leyden (1882), and Friedländer (1882). Pasteur, Chamberland, and Roux (1881), and Sternberg (1881) isolated an organism from the blood of rabbits which had died of a septicemia following the injection of human sputum. In cases of pneumonia, Telamon (1883) observed lancet-shaped organisms with which he infected rabbits. Fränkel (1884) is accredited with being the first to isolate the organism and to give a clear description of it and its relationship to pneumonia. Weichselbaum (1886) found it to be the most common organism in pneumonia. In 1900, Neufeld concluded that the organism is bile-soluble. Neufeld and Haendel (1910) observed that the pneumococci are of more than one serological type. This finding was confirmed by Avery, Chickering, Cole, and Dochez in 1917. Since that time, Avery and his pupils and many others have contributed to the subject. At present thirty-two serological types of pneumococci are known.

Distribution and Transmission. The pneumococci are found all over the civilized world exempting no class of people from infection. Some of the types of the organism seem to be normal inhabitants of the human mouth. It is believed, however, that immune carriers are responsible for pneumonia which is caused by the more virulent strains. The disease appears as a sporadic one. Epidemics are rarely observed, and for this reason predisposing factors, such as fatigue, exposure, faulty nutrition, and alcoholism, are considered important. The organism is transmitted by hand-to-mouth contact.

Morphology and Staining. The organism is 0.5 to 1.25 microns in size. It usually occurs in pairs with occasional chains of four or six cells. It is ovoid or lanceolate with adjacent cells bluntly rounded at the point of contact (Fig. 16.1). Capsules are present in tissue or exudates but absent on artificial media, unless serum is present. The organism is nonmotile, does not form spores, and is Gram-positive.

Growth Requirements and Characteristics. The organism may be isolated in pure cultures from the blood in some cases. The preliminary injection of sputum into white mice aids in the isolation of pure cultures. It grows best at 37°C., but some strains grow at 25°C. in the presence of carbon dioxide. It is a facultative aerobe.

On serum agar the colonies are flat, moist, discrete, and transparent, with a slight elevation of the edges. Some strains form mucoid colonies. Dissociation has been found to occur under certain conditions. Typical S (smooth) colonies produce R (rough colonies). The R types are usually noncapsulated and avirulent. Since the R type is often found in convalescent cases, it is thought that recovery may be aided by the dissociation of virulent S to avirulent R types due to the action of immune serum.

Alpha hemolysis with the typical green zone around the colony is formed in blood agar. Broth is clouded initially with subsequent settling of the cells as the culture ages.

Resistance. The thermal death point for *Dip. pneumoniae* is 60°C. for 30 minutes. It readily perishes in cultures but has been known to live for considerable periods of time in pulmonary exudate. It is readily killed by the common disinfectants. The R forms are more resistant than the S.

Biochemical Properties. *Dip. pneumoniae* produces acid from lactose, sucrose, inulin, usually from raffinose, frequently from salicin; does not ferment mannitol; does not liquefy gelatin; does not reduce nitrates; does not form indol. The organism is soluble in bile (1:10), which is an important distinguishing characteristic. Milk serves as a good medium and is acidified and coagulated although slowly by some strains.

Antigenic Structure and Toxins. The antigenic structure of the pneumococci is better known than that of any other group of microorganisms. The basic antigen is composed of nucleoprotein which is contained in the body of the cell. Covering this is a protein-lipoid substance which determines the species. The capsular material is composed of complex polysaccharides by which the different types are recognized.

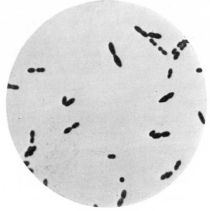

FIG. 16.1 — **Diplococcus pneumoniae** from an agar culture, $\times$ 2,000. (From Nowak: Documenta Microbiologica, courtesy Gustav Fischer.)

The agglutination of organisms, the precipitation of extracts, or the swelling of the capsule, "Quellung reaction" of Neufeld, by type-specific antisera may be used as the basis of type determinations. For rapid typing the capsule-swelling reaction is used most often.

Four original types of pneumococci, designated I, II, III, IV, have been considered of greatest importance. At the present time, thirty-two different types have been found. Types I and II appear to be most prevalent in the United States.

The organism produces a soluble hemolysin and leucocidin. It does not produce fibrinolysin for human fibrin, but does produce a substance which prevents the clotting of rabbit serum.

Pathogenicity. *Diplococcus pneumoniae* is the cause of lobar pneumonia in man. It may cause other types of infection, such as sinusitis, otitis media and meningitis, pleurisy, peritonitis, endocarditis, and arthritis. Mice are highly susceptible, and virulent strains kill rabbits quickly. Guinea pigs are resistant, although organisms resembling the pneumococci have been observed in spontaneous outbreaks of pneumonia in that animal. Lobar pneumonia has been produced experimentally in the monkey. Spontaneous pneumonia due to the organism has been reported in monkeys held in captivity. Horses, swine, sheep, dogs, cats, fowls, and pigeons are resistant.

Immunity. Type-specific immune serum gives favorable results in both preventive and curative treatment. Antisera concentrated and purified by the technic of Felton show great promise. The determination of the type of pneumococcus causing the disease is imperative for successful treatment. Vaccines and bacterins are not widely used in immunization, although numerous investigators report that such materials are of value in decreasing the incidence of the disease in susceptible populations.

One attack of the disease does not confer an immunity. When recovery takes place, increased activity of phagocytes is considered responsible.

Diagnosis. The laboratory diagnosis of pneumonia is concerned chiefly with the determination of the type to which the invading pneumococcus belongs.

Neisseria intracellularis

Synonyms and History. *Diplococcus intracellularis meningitidis, Diplococcus meningitidis, Micrococcus weichselbaumii, Streptococcus meningitidis, Neisseria meningitidis.*

Marchiofava and Celli were the first to observe the organism in meningeal exudate from man in 1884. It was first cultured and identified as a separate species by Weichselbaum in 1887. The causal relationship of the organism to epidemic cerebrospinal meningitis has been demonstrated since that time by numerous investigators.

Distribution and Transmission. The disease caused by this diplococcus occurs in epidemic form in most heavily populated areas. It is a disease of some concern in army life. Numerous epidemics of the disease have occurred in the eastern part of the United States and on the Pacific coast. The Middlewest and South have escaped serious epidemics. The resistant carrier seems to constitute the chief source of the infection. The organism is spread by nasal and oral discharges. It gains entrance to the nasopharynx where it may cause slight inflammatory disturbances. Whether the organism enters the meninges by way of the lymph vessels or the blood stream is not known, but the large percentage of blood cultures which are positive favor the latter route.

Morphology and Staining. The organism is spherical, and when in diplococcic form the adjacent sides of the cells are flattened. It varies in size from 0.6 to 1μ. It is nonmotile, nonsporeforming, and noncapsulated. Granules of a metachromatic nature are shown by the Neisser stain. It is Gram-negative. Masses of cells are found in polymorphonuclear leucocytes from spinal fluid (Fig. 16.2).

Growth Requirements and Characteristics. The meningococcus is isolated in pure culture from material obtained from the spinal canal by lumbar puncture. It grows best on media to which serum or blood has been added and the pH has been adjusted to 7.4–7.6. The colonies on serum agar are transparent, circular, and hemispherical with a bluish-grey tinge. The colonies are larger than those of the streptococci but not as large and opaque as the staphylococci. No hemolysis is produced in blood agar. Growth in broth occurs near the surface and produces a faint clouding; a granular sediment forms on the bottom of the tube. The optimum temperature for growth is 37°C. Oxygen is essential for maximum growth.

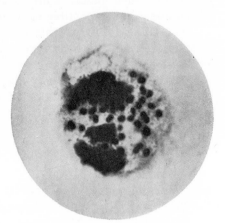

FIG. 16.2 — **Neisseria intracellularis** in polymorphonuclear leucocyte of cerebrospinal fluid, × 2,000. (From Nowak: Documenta Microbiologica, courtesy Gustav Fischer.)

Resistance. The organism is easily killed by 55°C. in a few minutes. Desiccation kills cultures quickly, and they must be transplanted often or kept tightly sealed in order to maintain them. Ordinary disinfectants destroy the organisms quickly.

Biochemical Properties. *Neisseria intracellularis* forms acid from glucose and maltose; does not ferment fructose, sucrose, and mannitol; does not change litmus milk; reduces methylene blue; does not form indol or H_2S.

Antigenic Structure and Toxins. The meningococci are not composed of one homogenous antigenic group. According to Gordon, four different groups are recognized by agglutinin-absorption tests. Some investigators maintain that there is considerable overlapping in several of the groups, and it is practical to recognize only two types.

The organism produces a powerful toxin by which typical symptoms and lesions are produced experimentally in rabbits. Whether this toxin is an endotoxin or exotoxin is not known, but evidence points strongly toward the latter. A weak hemolysin and leucocidin are produced.

Pathogenicity. *Neisseria intracellularis* infection is observed most commonly in children and young adults. The disease is an acute inflammation of the meninges, accompanied by a purulent exudate. The mortality in the disease is usually high, but not 100 per cent as is often the case in meningitis caused by other bacteria. Death is thought by many to be due to a toxemia.

Injection of pure cultures of the organism into the spinal canal of the goat has been found to produce meningitis, and inoculation into the monkey has resulted in a duplication of the disease as it occurs in man. Rabbits, guinea pigs, and mice are susceptible to intravenous and intraperitoneal injections but are killed more quickly by subdural inoculations.

Immunity. It is probable that an attack of the disease results in immunity, although data to this effect are not conclusive. Polyvalent immune serum is used in treating cases of the disease. The serum must be injected directly into the spinal canal in order to be effective. This necessitates the removal of fluid to keep the pressure on the cord equalized. Vaccines have been used on a large scale in armies, but the results are not available. The value of vaccine prophylaxis is still in the doubtful stage.

Diagnosis. Lumbar puncture, with the demonstration in smears of a Gram-negative diplococcus, occurring principally within the leucocytes, constitutes a satisfactory diagnosis. The agglutination test may be applied but is not used in practice. Some investigators believe that the test is of value in detecting resistant carriers of the organism.

Neisseria gonorrhoeae

Synonyms and History. *Micrococcus gonorrhoeae, Diplococcus gonorrhoeae,* diplococcus of Neisser, gonococcus.

Neisser, in 1879, noted the occurrence of a characteristic coccus in gonorrheal pus. Bumm, in 1885, succeeded in obtaining the organism in pure cultures and determined the causal relationship of the organism to the disease by inoculations into human subjects.

Distribution and Transmission. Gonorrhea is found throughout the civilized world. No class or race is exempt from infection. Transmission occurs in the greatest percentage of cases by direct sexual contact. Infection of the conjunctiva may result from the use of recently infected towels or from infected hands. Infection from toilet seats and toilet accessories is possible but occurs rarely; this is equally true of bed linen and clothing.

Morphology and Staining. *Neisseria gonorrhoeae* is a typical diplococcus. The cells are spherical with adjacent edges flattened and slightly indented, giving the appearance of a kidney bean. It is nonmotile, nonsporeforming, and noncapsulated. It stains Gram-negative, which is important, as this renders possible differential diagnosis between the common staphylococci and the gonococcus. Microorganisms are abundant in the purulent secretion of a typical infection; many are present in polymorphonuclear leucocytes (Fig.

16.3). Methylene blue and Wright's stain are especially suited for the direct staining of such smears.

Growth Requirements and Characteristics. Growth is best obtained on media to which serum or ascitic fluid has been added. It is a strict aerobe, and the optimum temperature for growth is 36°C. Surface colonies on serum agar are thin, greyish, opalescent, amorphous, and glistening with entire edges and with a slimy consistency. In fluid media, growth is more abundant toward the surface, and a fine, granular sediment forms as the culture ages.

Resistance. *Neisseria gonorrhoeae* is easily killed by 55°C. in 5 minutes. Drying kills it in a few minutes, although cells may remain viable in undried pus for 18 to 20 hours. The organism quickly succumbs to ordinary surface disinfectants and is especially sensitive to silver nitrate and other silver salts. It is killed by diathermy, 41.5° to 43°C. in 2 to 7 hours.

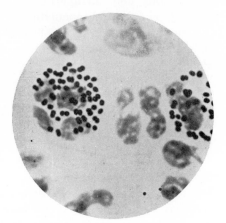

FIG. 16.3 — **Neisseria gonorrhoeae** undergoing phagocytosis, × 2,000. (From Nowak: Documenta Microbiologica, courtesy Gustav Fischer.)

Biochemical Properties. The saccharolytic powers of the organisms are negligible; dextrose is fermented with acid formation. Litmus milk is unaltered. Methylene blue reduction is negative. Indol and H_2S formation are negative.

Antigenic Structure and Toxins. The group is not antigenically homogenous. Two types have been described; one type is composed of recently isolated strains, and the other type of old laboratory strains. Some antigenic relationships with *N. intracellularis* apparently exist. Culture filtrates are toxic, but the exact nature of the toxic substance is not known; however, it is probable that it is not an exotoxin.

Pathogenicity. Man is the only natural host for the microorganism. It produces acute suppurative infection in the male and female genital tracts and may produce cystitis, proctitis, stomatitis, and conjunctivitis. Sterility in the male and female is a common sequela of the infection. Prior to the discovery of the sulfa drugs and antibiotics it was considered to be the cause of 60 to 75 per cent of the surgical operations on female genitalia, 60 per cent of the blindness in the newborn, and 10 per cent of all blindness. Duration of the infection is indefinite in some cases. Mice, rabbits, and guinea pigs are killed by subcutaneous, intraperitoneal, and intravenous injections. The genital tracts of all animals are reistant to the infection.

Immunity. One infection does not confer an immunity. The individual may harbor the infection for years even though the acute stage does not reappear. Agglutinating, precipitating, and alexin-fixing antibodies are demonstrated during infections. Vaccines are used, but are of doubtful value. Autogenous bacterins have shown some promise. Immune serum has been used, but beneficial results have not been proven.

Diagnosis. The demonstration of Gram-negative diplococci in pus from typical cases is sufficient for the diagnosis of acute cases. Internal infection is diagnosed by agglutination, precipitation, or, in some cases, by alexin-fixation.

REFERENCES FOR FURTHER STUDY

Avery, C. T., Chickering, N. T., Cole, R., and Dochez, A. R. Acute Lobar Pneumonia. Prevention and Serum Treatment. The Rockefeller Inst. Med. Res., Monograph No. 7, 1917.

Branham, S. E. The Meningococcus (Neisseria intracellularis) Bact. Rev. 4:59–96, 1940.

Gay, F. P., *et al.* Agents of Disease and Host Resistance. Pp. 509–88. Charles C. Thomas, Baltimore, 1935.

Jordan, E. O., and Burrows, W. A Textbook of General Bacteriology. 12th Ed. Pp. 235–68. W. B. Saunders Co., Philadelphia, 1938.

Mahoney, J. F., and Thayer, J. D. The Gonococci. In Bacterial and Mycotic Infections of Man, R. J. Dubos, ed. Chap. 26. Lippincott Co., Philadelphia, 1948.

McLeod, J. W., *et al.* The Pneumococcus. A System of Bacteriology in Relation to Medicine. Vol. II, p. 164. His Majesty's Stationery Office, London, 1929.

Murray, E. G. D. The Meningococcus. A System of Bacteriology. Vol. II, 291–325, His Majesty's Stationery Office, London, 1929.

Neufeld, F., and Haendel, L. Mitteilungen über Vorkommen und Bedeutung atypischer Varietaten des Pneumokokkus. Arb. Kais. Ges. Amt. 34:293, 1910.

Pelouze, P. S. Gonorrhea in the Male and Female. 2nd Ed. W. B. Saunders Co., Philadelphia, 1931.

Schoenboch, E. B. The Meningococci. In Bacterial and Mycotic Infections of Man, R. J. Dubos, ed. Chap. 25. Lippincott Co., Philadelphia, 1948.

Thomson, D. Gonorrhea. Oxford Medical Publications. Frowde and Hodder and Stroughton, London, 1923.

Topley, W. W. C., Wilson, G. S., and Miles, A. A. The Principles of Bacteriology and Immunity. 3rd Ed. Williams and Wilkins Co., Baltimore, 1946.

Tulloch, W. J. The Gonococcus. A System of Bacteriology. Vol. II, 239. His Majesty's Stationery Office, London, 1929.

White, B. The Biology of the Pneumococcus. The Commonwealth Fund, New York, 1938.

17. The Genus Micrococcus

In the 1948 edition of Bergey's Manual, the staphylococci have been combined with the micrococci under the genus name Micrococcus. This change is based upon the priority of the name Microsphaera used by Cohn in 1872. Throughout this chapter the genus name Micrococcus will be adopted but the general descriptive term staphylococcus will be used serving as a transition to the general use of the term micrococcus in the literature.

The staphylococci are spherical or ovoid cells usually arranged in grapelike clusters, although pairs and short chains are seen frequently in fluid media. They are nonsporeforming, nonmotile, noncapsule-producing, and Gram-positive. White, yellow, or orange, water-insoluble pigments are formed. They are aerobic and facultative, liquefy gelatin, and ferment a number of carbohydrates to acid. The organisms are found in suppurative processes in man and animals.

Micrococci were found present in pus by Ogston in 1881, and in 1883 he divided them into two groups, *Staphylococci* and *Streptococci*. In 1884, Rosenbach cultivated them upon artificial media and differentiated between two species, which he named *Staphylococcus pyogenes aureus* and *Staphylococcus pyogenes albus*. Passet, 1885, isolated a third species, *Staphylococcus pyogenes citreus*. The investigations of Garre, 1885, Bumm, 1885, and Bockhart, 1887, in which they subjected themselves to inoculations, proved the relationship of these cocci to human infections.

Migula, 1895, assigned the genus name *Micrococcus* to the group. In 1900, in his System der Bacterien, he referred to the species as *Micrococcus aureus, Micrococcus albus,* and *Micrococcus citreus.* Andrewes and Gordon, 1905-06, reported a study of 300 cultures of staphylococci and concluded "that *Staphylococcus pyogenes albus* is merely a nonpigmented variety of the golden form, and that *Staphylococcus pyogenes citreus* is an intermediate variety. The chromogenesis is a physiological function which is readily lost. Our experiments have not yielded any instance of the gain of a chromogenic function in a primitively white variety. The species may conveniently be termed *Staphylococcus pyogenes,* the suffixes 'aureus,' 'albus,' and 'citreus' being employed when desired. Its cardinal reactions are the formation of acid in mannite media, and the rapid liquefaction of gelatin, usually manifested in 48 hours. This is clearly the most important and virulent of the pathogenic staphylococci as well as the commonest." Andrewes and Gordon also recognized four different types of staphylococci in man—*Staphylococcus pyogenes, Staphylococcus epidermidis albus, Staphylococcus salivarius,* and the scurf staphylococcus. In 1909, Winslow and Rogers formed the genus names *Aurococcus* and *Albococcus* for the golden- and white-pigmented strains. Buchanan, 1911, used the genus name *Micrococcus* for the group. In 1917, Buchanan placed these cocci in the genus *Staphylococcus.* This genus name had been used by most systematic treatises since that time and had seemed to be definitely established.

Much of the investigation of this group of bacteria has centered around the methods of differentiating between the species. It has been noted that the first separation was made upon the basis of pigmentation. Winslow, Rothberg, and Parsons, 1920, concluded that the staphylococci form a single group and that there is no sharp set of characteristics separating the orange and white strains. Dudgeon and Simpson, 1928, supported this view, contending that strains of *Staph. aureus* and *Staph. albus* merge into one another, and that they are represented on one extreme by the heavily golden-pigmented *Staph. aureus* and on the other by the white *Staph. albus.* Hucker, 1924, concluded after a study of the *Staphylococcus-Micrococcus* groups, that there is no marked difference between the various species, but that characteristics such as chromogenesis, nitrate reduction, ability to utilize ammonium salts as the source of nitrogen, gelatin liquefaction, and action on milk can be used to classify the various species.

The distinction between the pathogenic and nonpathogenic strains of staphylococci has been a problem of increasing interest during recent years. This interest has been augmented considerably by the recognition of the various effects which staphylococcus exotoxins produce upon body tissues, for it is apparent that pathogenicity and toxin production are closely related.

STAPHYLOCOCCUS TOXINS

The pathogenic staphylococci produce potent culture filtrates for which the following terms are employed: lethal toxin, dermonecrotoxin, hemotoxin, leucocidin, enterotoxin, coagulase, fibrinolysin, and hyaluronidase. It is generally agreed that the lethal, dermonecrotic, and hemolytic action of broth filtrates of staphylococci are due to a single toxin. The status of leucocidin as a true toxin, is doubtful although it has been shown to be antigenic and to possess other properties which characterize a toxin. Enterotoxin, coagulase, and fibrinolysin appear to be by-products of metabolism, the action of which is specific but is not classed as toxin.

Production of toxins by the staphylococci requires the use of special media. Numerous formulae are available for this purpose; none of them differ significantly. Important requirements for such a medium are: a reaction of pH 7.4–7.6, the presence of buffer salts or buffering agents which control pH, the absence of fermentable carbohydrates, the growth in the presence of at least 20 per cent CO_2, and the presence of semisolid agar.

Staphylococcus toxin is rendered inactive at a temperature between 55° and 60°C. Light and methylene blue cause a destruction of the toxic principle but do not harm the antigenicity. Mineral acids destroy the toxin, while the action of organic acids is variable. Colloidal iron and manganese inhibit lethal toxin. No effects have been observed for colloidal gold, silver, or platinum. It has been reported that glycerol, ethylene glycol, sucrose, and glucose cause a partial destruction of the dermonecrotic action of toxin. Hypertonic solutions of sodium chloride and other salts of sodium, potassium, and magnesium inhibit the action of hemotoxin and dermonecrotoxin. The toxin can be concentrated and purified by precipitation with acetic acid and with trichloracetic acid. It has been found that toxin, leucocidin, and coagulase are retained by filtration through Seitz filter-discs. Berkefeld "N" filter candles, however, do not retain an appreciable amount of these substances.

The action of each of the active principles of staphylococcus filtrate is described briefly.

Lethal Toxin. The injection of a potent staphylococcal toxin into a susceptible rabbit is followed in 5 to 15 minutes, or in some cases longer (2 to 24 hours) by a fatal reaction. The animal becomes unsteady, and paralysis of the hind legs develops; the respiration becomes irregular and gasping; incoordination of movements occurs; pupils of the eyes are contracted followed by wide dilatation; violent convulsions are often followed by death. On autopsy, serosanguinous exudates are found in the body cavities; hyperemia and hemorrhage with intravascular hemolysis are noted. Tissue destruction ranges from cloudy swelling to intense necrosis. Dolman has reported that the guinea pig, horse, cat, and mouse are also susceptible to this lethal effect.

Dermonecrotoxin. As the name implies, this toxin causes a necrosis of skin. It has been demonstrated experimentally in the rabbit and occurs in natural infections in the pustular dermatitis of the dog.

Hemotoxin. The staphylococci have been noted for their ability to produce hemolysis on the blood agar plate or in a test tube containing erythrocytes in suspension. This characteristic is one of the definite properties of the pathogenic staphylococci.

Three antigenically distinct hemolysins have been described. These have been designated α-hemolysin, β-hemolysin, and γ-hemolysin. The α- and β-hemolysins may be produced by the same strain of staphylococcus forming a double-zone effect on the agar plate. The α-hemolysin produces the clear zone immediately surrounding the colony while the presence of β-hemolysin is noted by a wider, less hemolytic zone. This hemolysin is augmented by incubation of cultures at 10°–20°C. after sufficient incubation at 37°C. to produce satisfactory growth; consequently, the term "hot-cold" hemolysis may be used. It is not essential to resort to hot-cold incubation to develop the double-zone. The α-hemolysin is particularly active against rabbit erythrocytes, but less active against sheep cells and not active against human erythrocytes. Both α- and β-hemolysins may be detected by the use of bovine or sheep blood agar. The production of β-hemolysin is a significant characteristic of the animal strains of staphylococci. Minnett found that only five out of ninety-seven animal strains failed to produce β-hemolysin. The γ-hemolysin is active on rabbit erythrocytes but is antigenically distinct from α-hemolysin.

Christie and North have observed that β-hemolysin is able to denature globulin and to some extent albumen of human serum and suggest that this function may be a means of detecting β-toxin-producing strains. These authors suggest that the effect produced upon globulin and albumen may limit the spread of the staphylococcal lesion.

Williams and Harper have observed that strains of staphylococci grown on 2 per cent sheep blood agar and incubated in air containing 30 per cent carbon dioxide, would produce both α- and β-hemolysin. It was not possible to distinguish, on the plates, those strains that produced β-hemolysin alone, from those which produced both α- and β-hemolysins. These authors observed another hemolysin distinct from α and β which was active on a variety of mammalian erythrocytes, including human. They suggest that this hemolysin should be called δ-hemolysin.

Leucocidin. This toxin principle was described by Van de Velde in 1874 and has the distinction of being the first bacterial leucocidin to be observed. The importance of leucocidin in staphylococcal infections has been recognized for some time, but it has not been studied experimentally to any great extent. In 1901 Neisser and

Wechsberg devised a method by which the effect of leucocidin could be determined by noting that live leucocytes consume oxygen whereas dead ones fail to do so. The utilization of oxygen is detected by the use of methylene blue. Valentine, 1936, outlined a method of studying leucocidin by demonstrating the effect it produces on leucocytes in a series of smears stained with the Leishman stain. He demonstrated that leucocidin is distinct from α-hemotoxin by showing that it destroys rabbit and human leucocytes but has little or no effect upon the erythrocytes of either species. The rabbit leucocyte, however, is susceptible to α-hemotoxin toward which the human leucocyte is relatively immune.

Leucocidin is antigenic, and numerous workers have demonstrated the production and neutralizing qualities of antileucocidin. Although some methods have been suggested for measuring this antibody, no standard unit has been formulated.

Enterotoxin. It was reported by Barber, in 1914, that an acute gastroenteritis in humans was produced by milk that contained large numbers of white staphylococci. The organism was isolated in almost pure culture from the udder of a cow. The ability of certain strains of staphylococci to produce an enterotoxin has been shown by numerous investigators. The most common type of food involved has been bakery products, particularly those filled with custards. Raw milk, cream, and ice cream have been incriminated in some instances. Other foods which have been found to cause staphylococcic food poisoning have been meat, gravy, cheese, oysters, and fish cakes. The natural conditions under which enterotoxin is produced are not well understood; however, a protein medium, warm temperatures, and microaerophilic conditions seem to suffice. The toxin produces nausea accompanied by dizziness and prostration, severe abdominal pain, and diarrhea usually within 4 hours after the food has been eaten.

This period of "incubation" is significant because it differentiates this type of food poisoning from Salmonella infection which usually appears 24 to 48 hours after consuming the contaminated food. Fatal cases of staphylococcal food poisoning have not been reported.

Surgalla has demonstrated that enterotoxin may be produced in a medium containing from 2 to 16 amino acids as a source of nitrogen. Growth did not occur in a medium containing only three amino acids unless glucose was also present. The amount of enterotoxin formed was reduced in the simple synthetic media as compared to the medium customarily used.

Enterotoxin is not destroyed by 100°C. for 30 minutes. By virtue of this characteristic it is shown to be clearly distinct from the other toxic products of staphylococci. It has been reported that N/100

NaOH and N/100 HCl destroys enterotoxin, and that ethyl ether or chloroform removes it from acid aqueous solution. The material is nonvolatile and nondialyzable; it is less readily adsorbed on filters than hemotoxin. The antigenic properties of enterotoxin have been questioned by many. Reoccurring attacks of food poisoning presumably due to enterotoxin have not indicated substantial resistance. However, Surgalla, Bergdoll, and Dack have demonstrated by the use of the gel-diffusion precipitation test, the presence of antitoxin in the serum of rabbits immunized with enterotoxin.

The incidence of enterotoxin-producing strains of staphylococci in man and the various species of animals is not known. Outbreaks of food poisoning caused by this toxin have followed the preparation of such food by people later proven to be carriers of the organism. Likewise, outbreaks have followed the use of animal foods, particularly milk, ham, and chicken. The presence of staphylococci on the skin and mucous membranes of cattle, swine, and chickens has been repeatedly demonstrated.

The detection of enterotoxin-producing strains of staphylococci presents a most difficult problem. One certain proof is the vomit reaction produced in the human being, but the use of the "human volunteer" method is not practical for large-scale studies, for obvious reasons. Monkeys are susceptible to enterotoxin but they become resistant after a period of use; furthermore they are expensive. The "kitten test" has been useful in experimental studies of this substance, but young kittens are not always available, due to seasonal breeding characteristics of that animal. Suckling pigs have been used, but this animal is seasonal although somewhat elastic in respect to the time of breeding. The frog has been used by Robinton. Dack has observed a seasonal relationship in this animal inasmuch as no reaction to enterotoxin was observed during the winter season.

All enterotoxin-producing strains of staphylococci are hemolytic and coagulase-positive; however, it must be emphasized that all hemolytic and coagulase-positive strains are not capable of producing enterotoxin.

In a critical assay of the kitten test, Fulton found that three of the four strains of staphylococci isolated from a food poisoning epidemic did not produce reaction in kittens. These three strains produced α-hemolysin whereas the kitten-positive strain produced β-hemolysin. Purified α- and β-lysins produced vomiting in kittens, but α-lysin was nontoxic to human volunteers.

Coagulase. In 1903, Loeb demonstrated the coagulation of goose plasma by broth cultures of *Micrococcus* var. *aureus*. Since that time, the substance has been studied by several investigators who have shown a close relationship between it and pathogenicity. Rabbit and human plasma are most readily clotted, although dog plasma has been coagulated by some strains. In the routine detection of coagulase-producing strains of staphylococci an equal volume of broth culture or a loopful of agar plate culture is added to fresh, citrated rabbit plasma, diluted 1:5 in broth. The ingredients are thoroughly mixed and placed in the 37°C. incubation or in a water bath held at that temperature. The tube is examined for clotting at intervals over a period of three hours. Practically all of the pathogenic strains will show clotting within one hour. Some strains are slow, however, so incubation is usually continued overnight. The clot which is formed is usually quite solid and compact, but occasional strains are observed which produce a "thready" accumulation of fibrin. No one has shown a relationship between the type of clot and pathogenicity.

Coagulase is resistant to heat; some strains produce a more heat-resistant substance than others. Variations of 50°C. to 100°C. for 30 minutes have been reported. Its antigenicity is doubtful. Staphylococcus antihemotoxin has no effect upon it. The active principle in coagulase is precipitated by alcohol, acetic acid, or half-saturation with ammonium sulphate. The active principle may be dialyzed through cellophane after precipitation with alcohol but not before.

In a study of 32 coagulase-positive strains of staphylococci, Spink and Vivino observed that all but one of these strains were able to resist the bactericidal action of blood. Eleven coagulase-negative strains were all killed by normal defibrinated blood. Four coagulase-positive strains which had been cultured artificially for four years lost the ability to coagulate plasma and also their resistance to the killing action of normal blood. These results substantiate the correlation between the property to coagulate plasma and pathogenicity.

In 1945 Hale and Smith demonstrated that phagocytosis of coagulase-positive staphylococci was reduced by the presence of coagulable plasmas. They suggested that this inhibitory mechanism is due to the production of a fibrin film on the surface of the organisms. As further proof of the relationship of coagulase to pathogenicity, W. Smith, Hale, and M. M. Smith demonstrated that the presence of a coagulable plasma increased the virulence of staphylococci to mice and guinea pigs.

Fibrinolysin. Like many other types of bacteria, particularly the streptococci, the staphylococci produce a substance which is able to liquefy fibrin. Although Tillett and Garner found that only a few strains of staphylococci possess the property of fibrinolysis, other workers, Fisher, Aci, Madison and Madison, and Dart have found that many strains are so endowed. The power of lysing fibrin appears to be confined to human strains which are isolated from internal lesions. Madison and Dart found that 80 per cent of all strains isolated from human internal processes are capable of liquefying fibrin. They observed that 90 per cent of all strains isolated from superficial human infections were unable to liquefy fibrin and that none of the 24 strains isolated from animals was lytic, excepting two horse strains which were able to lyse horse fibrin only.

Fibrinolysin is not known to be antigenic, although it has been precipitated from culture filtrates by alcohol and acetone. It is possible that this property is an expression of the proteolytic ability of certain strains of staphylococci. Christie and Wilson studied the fibrinolytic properties of human and animal strains of staphylococci and concluded that the factor responsible for this property is associated with coagulase and α-hemolysin. Fibrinolysis is inhibited or masked by β-hemolysin; hence, clearing of fibrinogen agar is a good indication of pathogenicity of human strains, which do not produce β-hemolysin under usual conditions of artificial growth. This medium would not be applicable for the identification of animal strains which do produce β-hemolysin.

Hyaluronidase. The production of "spreading factor" or hyaluronidase by the staphylococci has been shown by numerous investigators. The properties and action of this substance, as produced by staphylococci, is not different than hyaluronidase produced by other bacteria.

Antigenic Relationship of the Staphylococci. Numerous attempts have been made to classify the staphylococci on the basis of antigenic relationship. Most of the work has been directed toward the differentiation of pathogenic from nonpathogenic strains. Agglutination and agglutinin absorption have been used. Some success with these methods has been reported, but these tests have given way to the precipitation reaction during recent years. A correlation between antigenicity and pathogenicity has been reported. Julianelle and Wieghard designated the pathogenic strains of staphylococci Group A on the basis of the precipitation of polysaccharide antigens. They placed the nonpathogenic types in Group B. They noted that Group A is composed largely of orange-pigmented, hemolytic, mannitol-fermenting, and gelatin-liquefying strains of staphylococci.

Cowan, 1938, classified the staphylococci on the basis of biological and serological characteristics. He included pigmentation, mannitol fermentation, hemolysis, plasma coagulation, the Voges-Proskauer reaction, and gelatin liquefaction in his biological tests. On the basis of these tests he divided the staphylococci according to the following scheme:

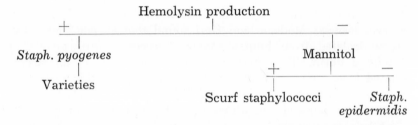

Cowan revived the name *Staph. pyogenes* of Andrewes and Gordon for the hemolytic group. The varieties are represented by strains which produce a hemotoxin, those which produce both α- and β-hemotoxin, and those which produce only β-hemotoxin. The precipitation reactions show that the majority of α and αβ strains belong in one serological group. He found an absolute correlation between hemolysin and coagulase production, and suggested it as the most valuable criterion for pathogenicity.

The susceptibility of cultures of staphylococci to various strains of bacteriophage has been used as an aid in identification. Although the application of this technic apparently does not differentiate species of the organism, it does serve to distinguish strain differences which are of value in epidemiological studies (Fisk and Mordvin).

The Species of Staphylococci. With limited present knowledge it is difficult to assign specific names to any of the pathogenic staphylococci, and for that reason Cowan's use of *Staph. pyogenes* appears justifiable. Much confusion is liable to result, however, between it and *Strep. pyogenes*.

As stated at the beginning of the chapter, Bergey's Manual lists the staphylococci in the genus Micrococcus and assigns to the pathogenic species the names *Micrococcus pyogenes* var. *aureus* and *Micrococcus pyogenes* var. *albus*. The distinguishing feature between these two species is the ability of the former to produce a golden pigment while the latter forms white colonies. The names of other species, which in the past classifications have been listed under the genus Staphylococcus, are changed to *Micrococcus citreus, Micrococcus epidermidis*, etc.

Those species which are considered important in animal infections will be discussed.

Micrococcus pyogenes var. aureus

Synonyms and History. *Staphylococcus aureus, Staphylococcus pyogenes aureus, Micrococcus aureus, Staphylococcus pyogenes*. The organism was first described as present in pus by Ogston, 1881, and cultivated by Rosenbach in 1884.

Distribution and Transmission. This staphylococcus is distributed widely throughout the world and makes up the normal bacterial flora of the skin and mucous membranes of man and animals. It occurs chiefly in the upper respiratory tract of man. It is present in many animal products, such as milk and meat. When it is found in those foods, its origin is usually from infected persons who have prepared or handled the food or from an infected animal. The organism has been called, very appropriately, an "opportunist type" because it is commonly present on tissues and waits for suitable conditions for invasion.

Morphology and Staining. The organism is spherical, and sometimes slightly flattened where two cells are appressed. In pus and blood it is usually found in grapelike clusters, justifying the name staphylococcus. In culture media the cells are grouped irregularly, and pairs and short chains are not uncommon (Figure 17.1). The diameter of the cells varies from 0.8 to 1μ. The organism does not produce spores, capsules, or flagella. It stains well with ordinary aniline dyes and is Gram-positive.

Growth Requirements and Characteristics. *Micro. pyogenes* var. *aureus* is secured frequently in pure culture by making inoculations directly from a suppurating process, first cleaning the outer portion and securing material on a sterile platinum needle. In general, it is best to plate out the drop of pus obtained in this way. The organism grows well in all common laboratory media, and abundant growth is produced on blood or serum media. Selective media are of value in the isolation of staphylococci. This is particularly true of those media containing a high concentration of sodium chloride, such as mannitol salt agar and staphylococcus medium No. 110. In these media the growth of other bacteria is inhibited and colonies of staphylococci which ferment mannitol and produce golden pigment are easily detected.

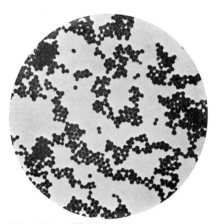

FIG. 17.1 — **Micrococcus pyogenes** var. **aureus** agar culture, × 2,000. (From Nowak: Documenta Microbiologica, courtesy Gustav Fischer.)

It is an aerobe and facultative anaerobe. The optimum temperature for growth is 37°C. It has a wide pH range for growth, but the optimum is 7.2.

Agar-plate colonies are round, smooth, glistening, opaque, low, convex, amorphous, edge entire, and of a golden color. The growth is butyrous in consistency. In broth a uniform turbidity is present with a powdery sediment. A faint ring forms on the test tube at the surface of the medium. Gelatin liquefaction is infundibuliform or saccate in type. Growth is luxuriant upon potato, and the orange pigment is produced in great abundance. The aureus pigmentation is lost by continued growth upon artificial media.

Resistance. Staphylococci are the most resistant of the cocci. Varying reports are given concerning its resistance to heat which, no doubt, is due to the different conditions under which the tests are made. Usually a temperature of 60°C. for half an hour destroys all the cells, but some individual cells require 80°C. for the same length of time. Staphylococci are more resistant to chemicals than many of the nonsporeforming organisms. Death is accomplished in: 1 per cent phenol in 35 minutes; 2 per cent phenol in 15 minutes; 0.5 per cent $HgCl_2$ in 1 hour; 10 per cent formaldehyde in 10 minutes. The organism is surprisingly resistant to drying, remaining alive in dried pus for months. Gentian violet kills the organism in 5 to 10 minutes in dilutions as high as 1:25,000. This dye in 2 per cent aqueous solution is used often in treating staphylococcus skin infections in man and animals.

The pathogenic staphylococci are generally inhibited by sulfathiazole, penicillin, and Aureomycin. Penicillin-resistant strains may be encountered which have never been grown in the presence of that substance. Dissociation of penicillin-sensitive strains into insensitive strains may be artificially produced by contact with penicillin.

Biochemical Properties. *Micro. pyogenes* var. *aureus* produces acid from glucose, maltose, mannitol, lactose, sucrose, and glycerol but not from salicin, raffinose, or inulin; acidifies and coagulates litmus milk which is slowly peptonized by some strains; produces hemolysis on blood agar. The organism is indol negative, NH_3 positive, M.R. positive, and V.P. positive; reduces methylene blue; reduces nitrates to nitrites; forms slight H_2S; hydrolyzes gelatin and coagulated serum.

Antigenic Structure. This staphylococcus is represented by only one antigenic group, designated Group A by Julianelle and Weighard. According to Cowan it may be divided into three varieties, α, αβ, and β, on the basis of the type of hemolysin which is produced.

The organism produces an exotoxin characterized by its lethal, dermonecrotic, and hemolytic properties. It produces leucocidin, enterotoxin, coagulase, and fibrinolysin.

Pathogenicity. *Micro. pyogenes* var. *aureus* is associated with most of the cases of suppurative wound infection in man and animals. It may localize in any tissue of the body; consequently, it is the most common cause of pyemia. The organism is found in man and is considered one of the etiologic agents in the following: osteomyelitis, sinusitis, tonsillitis, boils, mastoiditis, endocarditis, and ulcerative keratitis. It is found as a secondary invader in smallpox, diphtheria, septic sore throat, scarlet fever, tuberculosis, and pneumonia. In animals the organism has been found associated with the following diseases: mastitis in the cow and ewe, pustular dermatitis in the dog, abscess formation in all species including fowls. The presence of the organism in arthritis in geese was noted by Rowlands and Smith. The prevalence of this organism in bovine mastitis is becoming increasingly apparent. Packer found it in 76 per cent of 2,296 bacteria-positive samples of milk examined for the presence of bacteria causing mastitis. MacDonald found staphylococci in more than half of 280 samples of milk examined in Norfolk, England. This author observed that bovine strains were affected by one type of bacteriophage which he suggested as a useful clue to the source of certain staphylococcal infections in man. Schalm and Woods reported that variation from test to test is common in dairy herds infected by this organism. However, the average incidence may be over 50 per cent of the cows. Older cows are more prone to be infected although some show the development of resistance.

In a series of studies McDiarmid reported that staphylococci produced pyemia in lambs following infection of tick-bite wounds. It is associated with other bacteria in numerous diseases.

The severity of the infections in man and animals is probably influenced by the toxins which are produced; for example, wound infections and boils are produced by dermonecrotoxin and leucocidin. Aranow and Wood have reported a case which showed all the cutaneous reactions characteristic of scarlet fever and from which an erythrogenic toxin-producing strain of *Micro. pyogenes* var. *aureus* was isolated from the blood stream. Toxin produced by this organism was neutralized by commercial scarlet fever antitoxin. Gastroenteritis in man, and possibly in dogs, is caused by enterotoxin.

The rabbit is the most susceptible of the laboratory animals and is chosen universally for the experimental animal in staphylococcus research. Julianelle observed that staphylococci are not highly infective to the rabbit or mouse in the absence of traumatism or lowered resistance. Generalized infection is obtained in the chick embryo. Rats and pigeons are susceptible. Mice and guinea pigs are comparatively resistant. Kittens are sensitive to enterotoxin.

Immunity. An infection with *Micro. pyogenes* var. *aureus* does not produce a noticeable immunity to subsequent attacks. Probably there is a temporary rise in the phagocytic power due to opsonin, but this is soon lost. This organism is incorporated in most of the mixed bacterins which are used for animal immunization.

In view of the toxin-producing ability of the organism, it appears that the most satisfactory immunity would be produced by toxoids and antitoxins for the various toxic substances. It has been found that the use of formalinized toxin, toxoid, is of value in chronic skin infections in man and produces favorable results in pustular dermatitis of dogs. A beneficial effect of antitoxin upon conditions produced experimentally in animals has been demonstrated, but the use of this immunizing material in natural infections is of doubtful value. It may be used with success in cases of septicemia and pyemia caused by the organism. Antitoxin may be found in the blood of apparently normal animals. Miller and Heishman found antitoxin in the blood of 57 of 220 cows and heifers. Furthermore, they observed that there was four to six times more antitoxin in the colostrum than in the blood. Richou and Holstein found that the treatment of staphylococcal mastitis of the bovine with toxoid reduced the incidence of infection in the herd to a significant extent.

The Health Organization of the League of Nations, 1935, outlined a method of standardizing staphylococcus toxin and antitoxin by using hemolysis as the indicator. International standard units for titration purposes were proposed. A minimal hemolytic dose, M.H.D., of the toxin is that amount of toxin which will hemolyze 1.0 ml. of a 2 per cent suspension of rabbit erythrocytes in 1 hour at 37°C. The unit of antitoxin is that amount which will neutralize 200 M.H.D. of toxin. Standard antitoxin may be secured from the National Institute of Health of the U. S. Public Health Service to be used for standardization.

Diagnosis. Demonstration of a staphylococcus on direct smears from a lesion is diagnostic if it is present in great numbers and is the only organism to be found. The identification of *Micro. aureus* is accomplished by the use of specific media and tests. The production of toxins, particularly enterotoxin, is essential in the diagnosis of cases of food poisoning. Pathogenic strains of the organism are identified by the production of beta hemolysis and coagulase.

Schalm, 1948, has observed that toxicogenic coagulase-positive staphylococci produce typical reactions in the Hotis test of milk samples. These organisms produce adherent green, greenish-brown, brown, or russet-colored colonies with white centers after the milk sample has been incubated 16 to 20 hours. Upon further incubation, 40 hours, digestion of the milk is produced. However, Schalm and Woods, 1953, have concluded that the presence of beta hemolysis surrounding colonies of the organism cultured from milk samples is ample for the identification of the organism.

Micrococcus pyogenes var. albus

It was noted previously that pigmentation is used as the criterion to distinguish this organism from *Micro. pyogenes* var. *aureus*. It has been considered by many to be only a nonpigmented variant of the aureus strains. It is readily apparent to those who study the staphylococci that numerous nonpigmented strains can be isolated. In fact, unless isolation is made upon special media, such as No. 110, colonies of staphylococci are sometimes white.

The designation of strains of any organism, one variety or another, on the basis of colony color without specifications of growth is most confusing, not only to the student but to anyone interested in taxonomy. It likewise is confusing to those investigators who report the isolation of bacteria from unusual cases. For example, Pounden and Krauss in 1947 reported 2 cases of abortion in dairy cows caused by a coccus resembling *Staphylococcus albus*. Subsequently, Pounden, Ferguson, Knoop, and Krauss reported additional cases of abortion which were caused by an organism resembling *Staphylococcus albus*.

It is quite apparent that additional research must be done on the genus Micrococcus in order to clarify many of the interrelationships of the members of this genus.

Micrococcus ascoformans

It is doubtful whether this organism is sufficiently different from *Micrococcus pyogenes* var. *aureus* to warrant specific designation. As a matter of fact, it is not listed in Bergey's Manual. The following discussion is continued in this edition, with the hope that someone will study the bacteriology of botryomycosis and clarify its etiology.

This staphylococcus has been isolated from cases of botryomycosis in horses and more rarely from cattle and swine. Superficially this condition resembles fibromas and other neoplasms. The infection usually takes place where the surface of the skin has been abraded, as by harness, and through wounds at castration. The tissues involved become greyish and eventually form a fibrous mass of considerable size (Fig. 17.2). Metastatic infection through the lymph channels often results in the involvement of considerable areas and infection of the internal organs, particularly the lungs. Throughout the infected tissues gelatinous masses, zoogela, are found and are composed of a thick capsular material surrounding

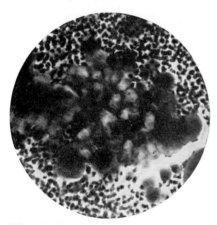

FIG. 17.2 — **Micrococcus ascoformans** colony in pus, × 220. (From Nowak: Documenta Microbiologica, courtesy Gustav Fischer.)

the organisms. These masses of cocci are frequently large enough to be visible to the naked eye and appear as collections of granules the size of tiny sand grains. Under the microscope they resemble mulberries. The capsular material forms a saclike membrane around the entire colony, and other colonies or masses arise as though by a process of budding. It appears likely that the formation of this mass, which is coagulated plasma, is the result of coagulase produced by pathogenic strains of *Micrococcus pyogenes* var. *aureus*.

Miscellaneous Micrococci

In the genus Micrococcus are placed twenty other species in addition to the two previously mentioned. All of these have been found on the skin and mucous membranes of man and animals and many have been isolated from milk of the bovine. The pathogenic role of these species is quite questionable; at least no serious infection is attributable to any of them. Their chief importance is the confusion they may cause in the isolation of pathogenic micrococci. The routine use of blood agar, however, eliminates the confusion caused by the nonpathogenic species of micrococci for none of them is hemolytic.

The genera Gaffkya and Sarcina, likewise contain species which may be found on the skin and mucous membranes of man and animals. None of them is pathogenic to any marked extent, although some have been considered to be the causes of the lesions from which they were isolated.

REFERENCES FOR FURTHER STUDY

Andrewes, F. W., and Gordon, M. Biological Characters of Staphylococci Pathogenic to Man. Suppl. to 35th Ann. Rept. Loc. Govt. Board, Rept. Med. Officer. App. B., No. 7, 543, 1907.

Aranow, H., and Wood, W. B. Jour. Amer. Med. Assn. 119:1491–95, 1942.

Barber, M. A. Philippine Jour. Sci. Sect. B., 9:515–19, 1914.

Bergey, D. H., et al. Manual of Determinative Bacteriology. 6th Ed. Williams and Wilkins, Baltimore, 1948.

Blair, J. E. The Pathogenic Staphylococci. Bact. Reviews. 3:97–146, 1939.

———. The Staphylococci. In Bacterial and Mycotic Infections of Man, R. J. Dubos, ed. Chap. 13. Lippincott, Philadelphia, 1948.

Burkey, E. L. Jour. Immun. Four parts. 24 and 25, 1933.

Christie, R., and North, E. A. Aust. Jour. Exp. Biol. Med. Sci. 19:323–27, 1941.

———, and Wilson, H. Aust. Jour. Exp. Biol. Med. Sci. 19:329–32, 1941.

Cowan, S. T. Jour. Path. Bact. 46:31–45, 1938.

Crabtree, J. A., and Litterer, W. Amer. Jour. Pub. Health. 24:1116–22, 1934.

Denison, G. A. Amer. Jour. Pub. Health. 26:1168–75, 1936.

Dolman, C. W. Can. Pub. Health Jour. 23:125–32, 1932.

———. Can. Med. Assn. Jour. 30:601–10, 1934.

Dudgeon, L. S., and Simpson, J. W. H. Jour. Hyg. 27:160–73, 1928.

Fisher, A. M. Bul. Johns Hopkins Hosp., 59:393–414, 1936.

———. Bul. Johns Hopkins Hosp. 59:415–26, 1936.

Fulton, F. Brit. Jour. Exp. Path. 24:65–72, 1943.

Gay, F. P., and associates. Agents of Disease and Host Resistance. Pp. 500–508. Charles C. Thomas, Baltimore, 1935.

Glenny, A. T., and Stevens, M. F. Jour. Path. Bact. 40:201–10, 1935.

Grubb, T. C. Jour. Lab. Clin. Med. 23:1150–53, 1938.

Gwatkin, R. Can. Pub. Health Jour. 28:185–91, 1937.

Hale, J. H., and Smith, W. Brit. Jour. Exp. Path. 26:209–16, 1945.

Julianelle, L. A. Proc. Soc. Exp. Biol. Med. 36:117–19, 1937.

———. Jour. Immunol. 48:155–61, 1944.

———, and Wieghard, C. W. Proc. Soc. Exp. Biol. Med. 31:947–49, 1933–34.

———, ———. Jour. Exp. Med. 62, 11, 1935.

Loeb, L. Jour. Med. Res. 10:407–19, 1903–04.

Madison, R. R. Proc. Soc. Exp. Biol. Med. 33:209–11, 1935–36.

———, and Dart, E. E. Proc. Soc. Exp. Biol. Med. 34:299–300, 1936.

MacDonald, A. Mon. Bull. Min. Hlth. Emerg. Publ. Hlth. 5:230–23, 1946.

McDiarmid, A. Vet. Rec. 58:103–5; 243–44, 1946.

———. Vet. Rec. 60:1–3, 1948.

Miller, W. T., and Heishman, J. O. Amer. Jour. Vet. Res. 4:265–69, 1943.

Minett, F. C. Jour. Path. Bact. 42:247–63, 1936.

Neisser, M., and Wechsberg, F. Z. Hyg. Infektionskrankh. 36:299–349, 1901.

Packer, R. A. No. Amer. Vet. 28:591–92, 1947.

Parker, J. T. Jour. Exp. Med. 40:761–72, 1942.

———, and Banzhaf, E. J. Jour. Immun. 13:25–29, 1927.

Pike, R. M. Jour. Immun. 26:69–80, 1934.

Pounden, W. D., and Krauss, W. E. Jour. Amer. Vet. Med. Assn. 111:35–36, 1947.

———, Ferguson, L. C., Knoop, C. E., and Krauss, W. E. Jour. Amer. Vet. Med. Assn. 111:376–77, 1947.

Richou, R., and Holstein, G. Rec. Med. Vet. 117:329–38, 1941.

Rowlands, W. T., and Smith, H. W. Jour. Comp. Path. 55:125–31, 1945.

Schalm, O. W. Amer. Jour. Vet. Res. 9:11–19, 1948.

———, and Woods, G. M. Amer. Jour. Vet. Res. 14:530, 1953.

———, ———. Amer. Jour. Vet. Res. 14:534, 1953.

Shaughnessy, H. J., and Grubb, T. C. Can. Pub. Health Jour. 28:229–34, 1937.

Smith, W., Hale, J. H., and Smith, M. M. Brit. Jour. Exp. Path. 28:57–67, 1947.

Spink, W. W., and Vivino, J. J. Jour. Clin. Invest. 21:353–56, 1942.

Stone, R. V. Proc. Soc. Exp. Biol. Med. 33:185–87, 1935–36.

Surgalla, M. J. Jour. Inf. Dis. 81:97–111, 1947.

———, Bergdoll, M. S., and Dack, G. M. Jour. Immunol. 72:398, 1954.

Topley, W. W. C., Wilson, G. S., and Miles, A. A. The Principles of Bacteriology and Immunity. 3rd Ed. Pp. 473–92. Williams & Wilkins Co., Baltimore, 1946.

Valentine, F. C. O. Lancet 1:526–31, 1936.

Williams, R. E. O., and Harper, G. J. Jour. Path. Bact. 59:69–78, 1947.

Winslow, C.-E. A., Rothberg, W., and Parsons, E. I. Jour. Bact. 5:145–67, 1920.

Zinsser, Hans, Enders, J. F., and Fothergill, L. D. Immunity. 5th Ed. Chap. 23. Pp. 638–50. The Macmillan Co., New York, 1939.

18. | The Genus Pseudomonas

Bacteria which belong to the genus Pseudomonas are found principally in water and in the soil. They produce a water-soluble, green, blue, or yellowish-green pigment which diffuses through the medium. Some of the members of the group are motile; others are nonmotile; all are Gram-negative. Over thirty species of the group have been described, but only one, *Pseudomonas aeruginosa*, is pathogenic for man and animals.

Pseudomonas aeruginosa

Synonyms and History. *Bacterium aeruginosum, Bacillus pyocyaneus, Pseudomonas pyocyaneous, Pseudomonas pyocyanea, Bacterium pyocyaneum.*

Years ago a blue-green exudate on surgical dressings was common, and in 1850 Sedillot, a French surgeon, showed that the discoloration was transferable. In 1860, Fordas isolated a crystalline substance which he called *pyocyanine* from stained linen removed from suppurating wounds. These results were confirmed in 1862 by Lücke, who showed that the condition was infective and was always associated with the presence of small vibrios. Much of our knowledge concerning these organisms is due to the work of Gessard who isolated the organism in 1882 and continued his studies until 1925.

Distribution and Transmission. *Pseudomonas aeruginosa* is world-wide in distribution and is found in water and soil. Judging from the ease with which it causes skin infection, it is logically concluded that the organism is a common contaminant of the skin of man and animals. It is inserted into deeper tissues by punctures and lacerations. Sinuses are infected often by contaminated water which contains the organism.

Morphology and Staining. This organism is a slender rod, 0.5μ by 1-3μ, with rounded ends. It is motile by means of one to three polar flagella (Fig. 18.1). It does not produce capsules or spores. The organism is Gram-negative and is easily stained by the usual aniline dyes.

Growth Requirements and Characteristics. The organism is cultured readily on the ordinary nutrient media of the laboratory under aerobic conditions; however, it can be grown anaerobically. The colonies produced on agar are large, irregular, translucent, spreading, and greyish with a dark center, and entire or undulate edge (Fig. 18.2). A bluish-green, water-soluble pigment diffuses throughout the medium, although all strains of the organism do not produce pigment. An abundant growth occurs in broth with the formation of a thick pellicle, dense turbidity, and a heavy sediment. The medium usually becomes green, which changes to brown as the culture ages.

Resistance. The ordinary disinfectants easily kill *Ps. aeruginosa*. Heat at 55°C. is destructive in 1 hour.

Biochemical Properties. The carbohydrate-fermenting ability of *Ps. aeruginosa* is variable. This is due to the composition of the medium in which the carbohydrate is tested. Various investigators have reported that glucose is the only carbohydrate which is fermented by this organism; however, others have demonstrated that when

FIG. 18.1 — **Pseudomonas aeruginosa** showing polar flagellum, × 2,000. (From Nowak: Documenta Microbiologica, courtesy Gustav Fischer.)

the source of nitrogen in the medium is decreased, the detection of acid formation in many different carbohydrates is possible. The organism is able to produce ammonia from peptone, thereby producing an alkalinity which neutralizes acids which are formed when the usual amounts of beef extract and peptone are used. By the use of a medium containing final concentrations of 0.3 per cent beef extract, 0.5 per cent peptone, and 1.0 per cent carbohydrate, Cone detected decided or slight acid reactions in arabinose, xylose, glucose, fructose, galactose, glycerol, and mannitol. Acid was not produced in media containing sucrose, maltose, lactose, raffinose, inulin, dextrin, and dulcitol. In a study of a variety of Pseudomonas species Bender found that the fermenting ability of this group was clearly revealed when a synthetic medium composed of ammonium chloride 0.2 per cent, magnesium sulfate 0.05 per cent, potassium hypophosphate 0.08 per cent, and carbohydrate 0.3 per cent was used.

Kopper has described a strain of the organism which was cultivated in a phosphate-buffered solution containing creatinine as the only source of carbon and nitrogen. This strain produced the enzyme creatinase by which it was able to utilize creatinine.

Ps. aeruginosa varies in its ability to form indol; however, the majority of strains fail to do so. Nitrates are reduced to nitrites; H_2S is produced by some strains; catalase is produced. The organism is negative to the methyl red and Voges-Proskauer tests. It hydrolyzes gelatin, with the formation of a slow crateriform liquefaction. The organism coagulates milk by a rennet-like enzyme, and increases the alkalinity of the medium as the culture ages. It slowly hydrolyzes casein and coagulated blood serum.

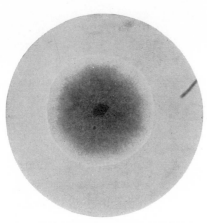

FIG. 18.2 — **Pseudomonas aeruginosa** colony on agar plate, × 40. (From Nowak: Documenta Microbiologica, courtesy Gustav Fischer.)

The production of water-soluble pigments is one of the most outstanding characteristics of most strains of *Ps. aeruginosa.* Cultures which have been isolated recently from the animal body are able to produce two pigments: One is a green pigment called *pyocyanin,* soluble in water and in chloroform; the other is a yellowish-green pigment called *fluorescin,* soluble in water but not in chloroform. Both phosphate and sulphate are required in the medium for the production of fluorescin, but neither is required for pyocyanin. Both pigments are oxidation products of colorless substances and are not produced when the organism is grown under anaerobic conditions. Some cultures lose their ability to produce pigments and never regain this characteristic. Young has demonstrated that *Ps. aeruginosa* does not produce pigment or antibiotic substances if sufficient glucose is present in the medium to be fermented and produce an acid reaction.

In addition to the active proteolytic enzymes produced by this organism, an enzyme-like substance, called *pyocyanase* by Emmerich and Low, is produced. This substance is able to hemolyze red blood cells and to cause the inhibition of growth of anthrax bacilli. For that reason it has been advocated as a therapeutic agent for anthrax and other diseases. Fukuhara showed in 1909 that pyocyanase is lipoidal in nature. In 1934 Hettche demonstrated that the bacteriolytic and hemolytic properties of the alcohol and acetone extracts of the organism are due to fatty acids. In the same year Kramer found the chloroform- and ether-soluble pyocyanase to be active against a number of organisms, including the anthrax bacillus, diphtheria bacillus, *Bact. coli, Bact. typhi,* hemolytic streptococci, and *Staphylococcus albus.*

In 1941 Shoental noted that *Ps. aeruginosa* may produce three compounds that are antibacterial in action: pyocyanin, α-hydroxyphenazine. and an oil that forms an insoluble salt with calcium, barium, and the heavy metals.

In a study of the bactericidal activities of the α-oxyphenazine and the lipoidal substance produced by *Ps. aeruginosa,* Zweig tested these substances against a number of different species of bacteria pathogenic to animals. The concentrations necessary to kill the organisms varied with the organism and time of exposure and ranged from 1:1,000 to 1:1,000,000 for α-oxyphenazine. The lipoidal product was about one-half as active.

Antigenic Structure and Toxins. The detailed antigenic structure of this organism is not known.

A thermostable exotoxin is produced by the organism which, if given 40- to 60-ml. doses, is able to cause the death of rabbits. An antitoxin which will neutralize the toxin can be produced.

Pathogenicity. *Pseudomonas aeruginosa* is found in wound infections in a number of the domestic animals, particularly the pig. It is the most prevalent organism in "bull nose" in the pig. The pigment produced by the organism imparts a blue-green color to purulent exudate. The organism has been recovered from septicemia in chickens by Essex, McKenney, and Mann. An acute disease of turkeys in Michigan caused by the organism has been reported by Stafseth, Mack, and Ryff. Many infections in man have been attributed to this organism. These include: inner ear infection, pericarditis, meningitis, septicemia, bronchopneumonia, infant diarrhea, and wound infection.

This organism has been isolated from clinical cases of bovine mastitis and although it is not a common cause of this infection, it must be listed with other bacteria as one of the etiological agents. A severe outbreak of mastitis may be caused by the organism, as illustrated by Cone and by Tucker.

The presence of *Ps. aeruginosa* in a disease of equines had not been reported until 1949 when Doll, Bruner, and Kinkaid isolated it from an aborted equine fetus. In this report they stated that the organism had been previously isolated from an aborted equine fetus at the Kentucky Station in 1944. The organism is frequently encountered in the genital tract of both equine and bovine species. As a consequence, it may be found with regularity in bull semen used for artificial insemination. Its marked proteolytic propensities indicate that caution should be used to eliminate it from semen intended for artificial insemination. The above report of the organism in the equine emphasizes that in this animal caution likewise should be used in protecting semen intended for use in artificial insemination. Farrag and Mahmoud report from Cairo, Egypt, that a high percentage of cases of otorrhea in dogs is caused by this organism.

The organism produces death in guinea pigs, pigeons, rats, and rabbits within 24 to 36 hours following intraperitoneal or subcutaneous injection. Extensive edema and suppuration are caused by the subcutaneous injection of the organism or of exudates containing the organism. A serofibrinous and purulent peritonitis is produced by intraperitoneal inoculation.

Pseudomonas aeruginosa has been identified as indistinguishable from *Phytomonas polycolor* by Elrod and Braun. These authors have found the organism as a pathogen on tobacco and able to cause soft-rot in vegetables. The ability of this organism to thrive and produce disease in both plants and animals makes it quite unique in bacteriology and likewise introduces an interesting transmission relationship among the wide variety of hosts.

Immunity. The infections caused by this organism are not frequent enough in animals to warrant immunizing procedures. Experimentally, antitoxins and bacterins have been proven of immunizing value, and the use of small doses of the organism produces localized abscesses with resulting immunity. The organism is often incorporated into mixed bacterins, particularly for swine.

Diagnosis. The organism is recognized by isolation in pure culture. It is often a secondary invader with streptococci and staphylococci and for that reason it is essential to plate the material which is to be examined. Deubler and Cole claim that milk serum titers are high enough to warrant the use of the agglutination test in the diagnosis of mastitis caused by *Ps. aeruginosa*.

REFERENCES FOR FURTHER STUDY

Bender, R. C.   A Study of Some Microorganisms Surviving Water Chlorination. Master of Science Degree Thesis. Iowa State College Library, Ames, 1942.

Cone, J. F.   Jour. Agr. Res. 58:141–47, 1939.

Deubler, M. J., and Cole, E. J.   Amer. Jour. Vet. Res. 16:511, 1955.

Doll, E. R., Bruner, D. W., and Kinkaid, A. S.   Jour. Amer. Vet. Med. Assn. 114:292, 1949.

Elrod, R. P., and Braun, A. C.   Jour. Bact. 4:633–44, 1942.

Essex, H. E., McKenney, F. D., and Mann, F. C.   Jour. Amer. Vet. Med. Assn. 77:177, 1930.

Farrag, H., and Mahmoud, A. H. Jour. Amer. Vet. Med. Assn. 122:35, 1953.

Gay, F. P., and associates. Agents of Disease and Host Resistance. Pp. 703–7. Charles C. Thomas, Baltimore, 1935.

Hettche, H. O. Zeitschr. f. Immunitätsf. 83:499–505, 1934.

Kopper, P. H. Jour. Bact. 54:359–63, 1947.

Kramer, Hans. Zeitschr. f. Immunitätsf. 84:505–34, 1935.

Shoental, R. Brit. Jour. Exp. Path. 22:137–47, 1941.

Stafseth, H. J. Poultry Science. 19:126–30, 1940.

Topley, W. W. C., Wilson, G. S. and Miles, A. A. The Principles of Bacteriology and Immunity. 3rd Ed. Williams & Wilkins Co., Baltimore, 1946.

Tucker, E. W. Cornell Vet. 44:110, 1954.

Wilson, W. J., and Bulloch, W. The Colon Group and Similar Bacteria. A System of Bacteriology. Vol. 4, pp. 326–37. Med. Res. Council. His Majesty's Stationery Office, London, 1929.

Young, G. Jour. Bact. 54:109–17, 1947.

Zweig, J. Vet. Jour. 102:55–70, 1946.

19. The Genus Vibrio

Twenty-one species of the genus Vibrio, most of which occur in water, are recognized. Characteristics of this genus are as follows: short cells, bent rods single or united into spirals; motile by means of single, or occasionally two or three, polar flagella. Many species liquefy gelatin and are active ammonifiers; they are aerobic and facultative anaerobic; no endospores are formed; they are usually Gram-negative; a few species are pathogenic.

The pathogenic species include: *Vibrio comma,* which produces Asiatic cholera in man; *Vibrio metchnikovii,* the cause of an acute enteritis in chickens; *Vibrio fetus,* the etiologic agent in vibrionic abortion of ewes and cows; and *Vibrio jejuni,* the cause of an acute enteritis in mature cattle and calves. In addition to the specific diseases which they cause, these species differ in other respects. *Vibrio comma* does not coagulate milk, whereas *Vibrio metchnikovii* does; both of these species liquefy gelatin, which is not true of *Vibrio fetus* and *Vibrio jejuni.* Jones, Orcutt, and Little have shown that *Vibrio fetus* and *Vibrio jejuni* can be differentiated by the agglutination test.

Vibrio comma

Synonyms and History. *Spirillum cholerae asiaticae, Pacinia cholerae asiaticae, Microspira comma, Vibrio cholerae, Vibrio cholerae asiaticae.*

The organism was discovered in 1883 by Koch while he was working as head of a commission to study the disease in Alexandria during an Egyptian epidemic. The toxicity of cultures of the organism was noted by Pfeiffer in 1891. The early development of knowledge concerning the natural lysis of bacteria was done with *Vibrio comma;* Gruber and Durham used the organism in much of their early work on agglutination.

Distribution and Transmission. The organism has caused numerous widespread epidemics of cholera some of which have extended to America. The organism has its true home in the dells of the Ganges from which most epidemics have originated. At present the organism causes endemic cholera in various parts of Asia but is not prevalent in any other continent.

Three types of individuals, the infected case, the convalescent case, and the healthy carrier serve as centers from which the organism is spread. The organism is eliminated in fecal matter and gains access to susceptible individuals by contact, by fomites, and by water and food. Flies are also a means by which the organism is spread.

Morphology and Staining. *Vibrio comma* is a short, curved rod, 0.4μ by 1.5μ in size. It is commonly called the "comma bacillus" because of its comma shape. Spiral filaments develop in old cultures but are rarely seen in intestinal discharges. In old cultures, thickened and irregularly clubbed and granular shapes are frequent (Fig. 19.1). The organism is actively motile by means of one polar flagellum (Fig. 19.2). It is noncapsulated and nonsporeforming.

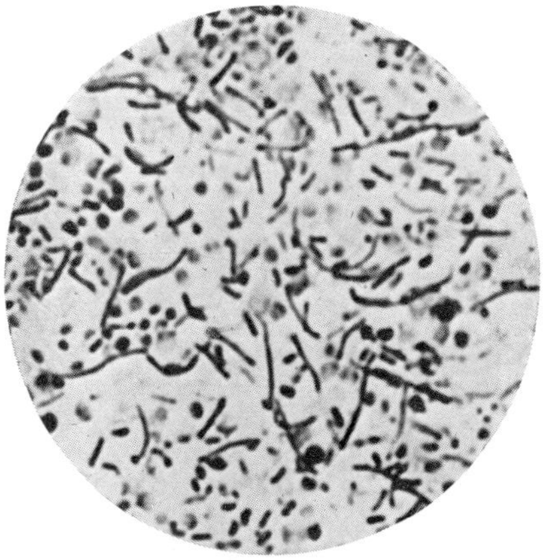

The organism is not stained as readily as many other bacteria. It is Gram-negative.

FIG. 19.1 — **Vibrio comma** from an old culture showing numerous coccoid forms, × 2,000. (From Nowak: Documenta Microbiologica, courtesy Gustav Fischer.)

Growth Requirements and Characteristics. This species of Vibrio is aerobic and is easily isolated from the stools of cholera patients. It grows at room temperature but more abundantly at 37°C. It grows best in an alkaline medium.

Gelatin plate colonies of the organism are round, small, opaque, with smooth or slightly granular surface, and are yellowish-white. A thin transparent extension grows from the central heavier colony (Fig. 19.3). The growth is similar on agar. An abundant growth occurs in broth, producing moderate turbidity, and a powdery sediment and a thick pellicle are formed.

Resistance. The cholera vibrio is destroyed by 56°C. in half an hour. It is easily destroyed by desiccation, sunlight, and the common disinfectants.

Biochemical Properties. *Vibrio comma* produces acid but no gas from dextrose, maltose, mannitol, galactose, sucrose, and levulose; does not ferment lactose, inulin, or dulcitol; forms hydrogen sulphide; reduces nitrates; liquefies coagulated serum and gelatin; forms indol; produces ammonia and catalase. It causes an increased alkalinity in litmus milk, which is generally not coagulated or peptonized in 14 days.

Antigenic Structure and Toxins. An O antigen is common to all strains of the organism, but three subtypes have been described. Bacteriolytic serum causes the liberation of toxic substances which produce death in guinea pigs. Such substances are not classed as true toxins, inasmuch as antitoxins are not produced. Hemolysins are produced by some strains.

Pathogenicity. The cholera vibrio is not pathogenic for lower animals. The guinea pig may be infected by the alkalinization of the intestinal tract prior to the feeding of virulent cultures. Intraperitoneal inoculation with a young culture kills the guinea pig within 48 hours. Man is variable in resistance; predisposing factors, such as gastric disorders produced by overeating and drinking, are significant.

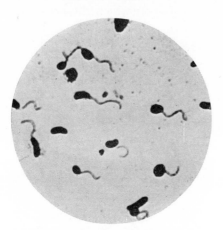

FIG. 19.2 — **Vibrio comma** showing young flagellated cells, Van Erssenghem stain, × 2,000. (From Nowak: Documenta Microbiologica, courtesy Gustav Fischer.)

The organism produces such a severe diarrhea in man that the intestinal epithelium is desquamated, giving rise to "rice water" stools. Most of the conditions associated with the disease in man are attributed to the loss of water during the initial stage of purgation.

Immunity. Recovered cases are definitely immune to the disease. Bacterins and vaccines are used in prophylactic treatment but without marked success. Antiserum is not of value. Sensitizing antibodies which are active in agglutination and alexin fixation are observed in the serum of recovered patients. The natural disease is too acute, however, for these tests to be of value in diagnosis.

Diagnosis. The isolation of the organism is the only sure method of diagnosis.

Vibrio metchnikovii

Synonyms and History. *Vibrio nordhafen, Microspora metchnikovii, Spirillum metchnikovii.*

In Odessa, Russia, Gamaléia isolated *Vibrio metchnikovii* in 1888 from chickens which had died of an acute intestinal infection.

He observed the similarity of the diseases produced by this organism and the vibrio of human cholera and noted the differences between the disease this vibrio produced and the septicemic cholera of chickens. Metchnikoff, in 1891, described an immunity which was produced in the guinea pig by the injection of *Vibrio metchnikovii*.

Distribution and Transmission. The original work of Gamaléia appears to be the only record made of the isolation of the organisms from the natural disease. The distribution and transmission of the organism, therefore, are not known.

In 1946, Kaschula and Canham observed outbreaks of disease in chickens in Natal, So. Africa, from which this organism was isolated. This is the first report of the organism in So. Africa. Much of the data on the morphology and physiology of the organism are based upon studies made of strains in culture collections.

Morphology and Staining. *Vibrio metchnikovii* is a curved rod, 0.5μ by 2μ in size, with

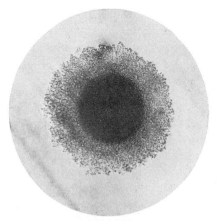

FIG. 19.3 — **Vibrio comma** on gelatin plate, × 45. (From Nowak: Documenta Microbiologica, courtesy Gustav Fischer.)

round ends. Variable shapes, such as coccoid and spiral, have been observed in old cultures. It is motile by means of a single polar flagellum. It does not produce spores or capsules.

The organism is stained readily by the common dyes and is Gram-negative.

Growth Requirements and Characteristics. This vibrio is aerobic and grows at room temperature. It is cultivated easily upon most of the common media, such as nutrient agar, upon which it produces small, yellowish, round, glistening colonies. It clouds bouillon and produces a delicate white pellicle.

Resistance. A temperature of 50°C. kills the organisms in 5 minutes.

Biochemical Properties. *Vibrio metchnikovii* produces acid but no gas from dextrose and lactose; produces indol; reduces nitrates to nitrites; liquefies gelatin and solidifies egg medium; coagulates milk with the formation of acid.

Antigenic Structure and Toxins. The organism does not produce true toxins. It is antigenically distinct from *V. comma*.

Pathogenicity. The organism produces an acute, fatal gastro-enteritis in chickens and is especially pathogenic for young ones. It produces a marked inflammation of the intestinal mucous membrane, causing the formation of a sanguinous, yellowish-grey fluid. It does not affect other tissues; this is noteworthy in regard to the heart, since it differentiates this disease from septicemia.

The temperature of the animal does not increase.

The pigeon and guinea pig are susceptible to the organism; this fact provides a method used to differentiate it from *Vibrio comma*. Large doses cause death in rabbits and mice.

Diagnosis. Isolation and identification of the organism are the only positive methods of diagnosis.

Vibrio fetus

Synonyms and History. *Spirillum fetus.* In 1913, McFadyean and Stockman isolated a vibrio from cases of abortion in ewes and cows in England. Theobald Smith, in the United States, described an organism in 1918 which he isolated from cows with abortion. He considered it identical with the organism of McFadyean and Stockman, and the following year, 1919, Smith and Taylor named it *Vibrio fetus.*

Distribution and Transmission. In addition to the original discovery of the organism in England and in New Jersey, the isolation of the organism from sheep and cattle has been reported from Connecticut, Wyoming, New York, Iowa, Illinois, Montana, and California. Cases of abortion in ewes and cows which are known not to be caused by *Brucella abortus* should be investigated with respect to *Vibrio fetus.*

The organism is eliminated from the infected animal before and after abortion. Grass pastures and other feeds are thereby contaminated and transmit the organism to susceptible animals. Marsh and associates have shown that infection is not carried over by infected ewes from one breeding season to the next.

The increased use of artificial insemination in the bovine has been shown by Easterbrooks and Plastridge to be a method of transmitting the organism.

Morphology and Staining. In young cultures *Vibrio fetus* is comma-shaped and S-shaped, measuring 0.2 to 0.5μ in breadth by 1.5 to 5μ in length (Fig. 19.4). In old cultures a number of the short cells cling together, forming long spirals which may extend entirely across the field of the oil-immersion objective. Granules, which are stained by 1 per cent toluidin blue and by Wright's or Giemsa's stain, are observed in both young and old cultures, and are often located in one end of a cell (Fig. 19.5). Stockman reports that these granules are filtrable but no growth is obtained from the filtrate. The organism is motile by means of a single polar flagellum. Rhoades has observed by electron microscopy that the comma-shaped organism usually has a polar flagellum, whereas many of the S-forms have bipolar flagella. It is not capsulated and does not form spores. Ryff and Lee have described "ribbon" forms of the organism which they suggest may be resistant dissociative phases that serve to perpetuate the infection.

Vibrio fetus is stained densely by alkaline methylene blue, crystal violet, and carbol fuchsin. It is Gram-negative.

Growth Requirements and Characteristics. The organism is obtained from the placenta of an aborting animal and from the stomach, liver, lungs, and kidneys of the aborted fetus. It grows best in microaero-philic conditions and in an atmosphere of 10 per cent carbon dioxide, but is not strictly anaerobic. The optimum temperature for growth is 37.5°C.

A medium containing blood serum, whole blood, bits of fresh tissue, or stomach contents is best suited for primary isolation. Huddleson has found that a semisolid agar medium

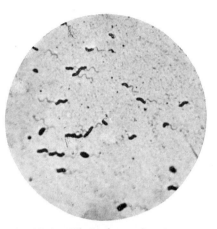

FIG. 19.4 — **Vibrio fetus** showing normal, curved, flagellated cells, × 1,000. (From Smith, courtesy Journal Experimental Medicine.)

known as "thiol" is superior to other media for the cultivation of *Vibrio fetus*. In this medium the organism grows profusely at or within 0.5 mm. of the surface of the medium, reaching maximum growth in 4 days. He observed that the vibrios will remain alive for at least 150 days without intervening transfer in tubes of this medium.

An agar slant, enriched by any of the above tissues and sealed after inoculation, yields growth after three or four days of incubation. It appears as two narrow, greyish-white, opaque lines, less than 1 mm. broad, extending upward from beneath the surface of the condensation water where the agar slant comes in contact with the glass. The growth extends around and between the agar butt and the test tube, producing a thin, veil-like layer. The condensation water is slightly clouded by the organisms in it.

On blood agar, the organism forms fine, pin-point, bluish areas from 1 to 3 mm. in diameter visibly raised above the surface of the medium.

The organism produces a faint clouding in fluid media after it has become adapted to growth under artificial conditions.

Resistance. *Vibrio fetus* is killed in 5 minutes at 58°C. and is readily killed by drying, direct sunlight, and chemical disinfectants. Laboratory cultures must be transferred weekly in order to maintain them, and they must be stored in a dark chamber because they are sensitive to light. Cultures of the organism survive in room temperatures longer than at refrigerator temperatures of 5°–6°C.

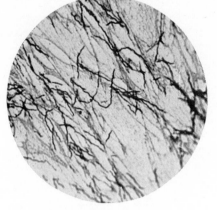

FIG. 19.5 — **Vibrio fetus** showing long spirals in old cultures, × 1,000. (From Smith, courtesy Journal Experimental Medicine.)

Vibrio cultures covered with heavy mineral oil were found to be viable at the end of 33 days by Ward and Lee.

Linderstruth and Ward studied the survival of three strains of this vibrio mixed in hay, soil, and manure. These materials were kept at 6°C., 20°C., and 37°C. and examined for viability of the organism at 10, 20, and 30 days. Survival was noted in all materials at the end of 10 days, survival at 6°C. in 20 days, and no survival at the end of 30 days.

Plastridge and Easterbrooks have found that 500 micrograms of streptomycin per milliliter of diluted bull semen will prevent infection of cows by the process of artificial insemination. The organism is not sensitive to Aureomycin, Terramycin, bacitracin, gramicidin, and tyrothricin.

Biochemical Properties. *Vibrio fetus* does not ferment arabinose, dextrose, dextrin, dulcitol, galactose, inulin, lactose, levulose, maltose, mannitol, raffinose, salicin, sucrose, sorbitol, and trehalose. It does not form indol but is nitrate-positive. Most investigators report no change in litmus milk, but Price, Poelma, and Faber reported some reduction. The organism does not alter gelatin.

The production of catalase is considered by Bryner and Frank to be a method of differentiating *Vibrio fetus* from nonpathogenic strains of Vibrio which are also found in the genital tract of the bovine and which do not produce catalase. The latter strains produce H_2S while *Vibrio fetus* does not.

Antigenic Structure and Toxins. Both H and O antigens have been observed for *V. fetus*. Various strains of the organism studied with the agglutination test have appeared to be antigenically homogenous, although certain strains have been found to be more agglutinable than others.

Variable results obtained with the agglutination test in the diagnosis of vibriosis in cattle and sheep indicate that there are a number of different antigenic strains of the organism. Marsh and Firehammer found that the majority of ovine strains they studied were of one type but that there were three other types. The bovine strains were of a fifth type. There was some relationship between the bovine type and two of the less common ovine types.

Price, Poelma, and Faber have shown that cross-agglutination and reciprocal absorption tests, using heat-treated cell suspensions, indicate that the somatic antigens of the bovine strains were of four different types which were designated as types I, II, II, and IV. An ovine strain, not antigenically related to the bovine strains, was designated type V.

It has been shown that antigenic components are shared by *V. fetus* and *Brucella abortus,* thus leading to confusion in the diagnosis of abortion in cattle. For example, Kiggins and associates demonstrated, by using agglutinin absorption tests, that brucella antigen removed both *V. fetus* and brucella agglutinins from *Br. abortus* antiserum, whereas the vibrio antigens absorbed all of the *V. fetus* antibodies from *Br. abortus* antiserum but did not reduce the titer for *Br. abortus* appreciably. They concluded that *V. fetus* infection does not interfere with the agglutination test for brucellosis, and that *Br. abortus* infection may interfere with the agglutination test for vibriosis if the *V. fetus* antigen is made from strains which possess antigenic components similar to those of *Br. abortus.*

Specific toxins have not been demonstrated for *V. fetus.*

Pathogenicity. *Vibrio fetus* causes abortion in the pregnant guinea pig, producing lesions characterized by epithelial sloughing, hyperemia, hemorrhage, myometrial and subendometrial edema, and cystic uterine glands, according to Ristic and associates. The above investigators have also shown that abortion is caused in pregnant hamsters and that the infection may be transmitted by coitus from the infected male to the female.

The organism has not been shown to be pathogenic to rabbits, swine, rats, and mice.

Plastridge and Williams have observed that the chick embryo is killed within five days by *Vibrio fetus* and that the organism grows in the allantoic fluid. According to Webster and Thorp, the organism grows in the chorioallantoic membranes of infected embryos and, in addition, lesions are found in cutaneous tissues, liver, kidney, spleen, gizzard, and brain.

It localizes in the uterine mucous membrane producing premature parturition in the ewe and cow. Ryff and Lee have found that ewes were not uniformly susceptible to experimental infection and that various strains of the organism were not uniform in pathogenicity. Lee and Scrivner evaluated various methods of producing abortion in pregnant ewes. Some were given a drench containing the fetal fluids, vaginal fluids, and cultures of the organism; some were injected intravenously with the culture; some were given combinations of the above. In general those animals in which the cultures were injected intravenously aborted while those receiving the organisms in a drench did not. The organism may be present in the uterine discharge days before abortion occurs. Specific lesions are not found in organs other than the uterus.

Rhoades and Hardenbrook, in 1947, reported *Vibrio fetus* as the cause of abortion in dairy cows in Illinois. This was the first report of the disease from that state in the cow. They did not produce abortion in pregnant cows by injecting cultures of the organism intravenously. The presence of vibrionic abortion in cattle herds of Connecticut was reported by Plastridge, Williams, and Petrie in 1947 and by Plastridge and Williams in 1948. They were able to demonstrate the presence of the infection in cows by the use of the agglutination test. The above investigators observed that the infection is most prevalent during the first year after its introduction into the herd and that animals over two years of age are all susceptible if they have never been previously exposed. In addition to abortion in the bovine, the organism is considered to produce a low-grade infection in the uterus which causes infertility.

In Sweden, Olson observed that abortion in cattle was a sporadic disease even in a herd where the disease was present. Over a period of 20 years, 1924–1943, 2,105 cases of vibrionic abortion occurred, being 10 per cent of the total number of aborted placentas examined during that time.

The ability of *Vibrio fetus* to produce infection in the human being was not reported until 1947 when Verge in France described abortion in a woman at the sixth month of pregnancy after an acute illness. During the course of her illness a mixed infection with a staphylococcus was revealed on culture of the peripheral blood. The vibrio which was isolated was identified as *V. fetus* and Verge claims that this is the first time it has been isolated in France from either animals or man. Infection is believed to have originated from a cow which had recently aborted. Ward, in 1948, isolated *Vibrio fetus* from a skin wound of a laboratory worker who had handled cultures of the organism. Although a larger Gram-positive rod was also present in the lesion, it is considered significant that the vibrio was able to multiply in the human body.

Other reports of human infection have been made, but the organism is not considered to be an important pathogen for man.

Immunity. Little is known concerning the active immunity to the infection produced by this organism. Agglutinating antibodies are produced during an active infection and are easily developed in the rabbit by the subcutaneous injection of the organism. Agglutinating antibodies usually do not persist in the cow or ewe until the next season and such animals may then conceive.

Bacterin therapy has been reported of no value in producing immunity by Plastridge and associates.

Diagnosis. The diagnosis of vibriosis in cattle and sheep is essential to determine the cause of abortion and the cause of infertility. The latter problem is considered to be the most important.

It is essential to isolate *V. fetus* from an aborted fetus in order to differentiate the abortion caused by it from that produced by *Brucella abortus* or any other cause.

The agglutination test is recognized as a valuable method of detecting infected animals which may be spreading the infection. Blood serum and vaginal mucus are used in the agglutination test. Antigens used for the test must be so prepared that H antigen is preserved, hence the use of hot formalinized saline as the diluent.

A positive reaction in 1:200 is considered suspicious and 1:400 is positive evidence of infection. Blood serum is usually positive before the vaginal mucus in an infected cow, although the reaction persists in the mucus longer than in blood serum. The tampon method is a valuable technical aid in collecting vaginal mucus for the test.

Vibrio jejuni

Synonyms and History. In 1927, Smith and Orcutt isolated a vibrio from the spleen of a calf suffering with a severe diarrhea. This vibrio was similar to *Vibrio fetus* in morphology and physiology, but was different antigenically. In a series of papers published in 1931, Jones and Little, and Jones, Orcutt, and Little described an organism which proved to be the etiologic agent of a condition referred to as "winter dysentery" in cows and calves. The morphology and physiology of the organism plus the fact that it was commonly isolated from the jejunum of infected animals led them to name it *Vibrio jejuni*.

Distribution and Transmission. The natural cases of the disease from which the organism was isolated were found in cattle herds in New Jersey. The experimental production of the disease by oral inoculation of infective fecal matter and of pure cultures suggests that the organism is naturally transmitted by the medium of contaminated water and feed.

Morphology and Staining. *Vibrio jejuni* is notably pleomorphic, presenting three different forms in the same preparation; the first is active, short, and slightly convoluted with a flagellum at one or both poles; the second is less active, with two or more complete coils; the third is comparatively nonmotile and is long and convoluted (Fig. 19.6). As the cultures of the organism age, the cells form into clumps and then disintegrate into fragments and granules.

The organism is stained well by the ordinary dyes after prolonged exposure. It is Gram-negative.

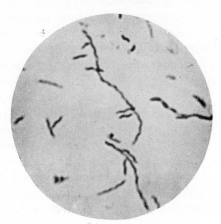

Growth Requirements and Characteristics. This organism can be isolated from the material in the lumen of the intestine, but it is more successfully isolated when bits of intestinal mucosa are washed, then ground, and inoculated into the condensation fluid of blood agar. Contamination with colon types of bacteria is prevented by the

FIG. 19.6 — **Vibrio jejuni,** × 2,000. (From Jones, Little, and Orcutt, courtesy Journal Experimental Medicine.)

preliminary washing and by the inoculation of secondary cultures from the primary ones. The organism is microaerophilic; hence, all cultures are sealed.

The optimum pH for growth is 7.6; the organisms fail to grow in slightly acid or in definitely alkaline media. The optimum temperature for growth is 37.5°C.

The growth of the organism is maintained in the laboratory by adding pieces of fresh kidney to veal-infusion agar.

On blood agar the condensation fluid becomes cloudy in four or five days, and later delicate lines become visible at the border of the agar. After several transfers these border lines become well defined, and a delicate film spreads over the lower part of the slant. Many strains grow well on the surface of blood agar after they have been cultured for some time.

In bouillon, old laboratory strains produce a slimy tenacious mass in the bottom of the tube.

Resistance. This organism is killed within 5 minutes by a temperature of 55°C. It remains alive for six days when inoculated into moist, autoclaved cow feces but perishes when the feces become thoroughly dry. It survives for 24 hours in distilled water. It is not soluble in bile.

Biochemical Properties. *Vibrio jejuni* does not ferment carbohydrate media and does not liquefy gelatin or blood serum.

Antigenic Structure and Toxins. The strains of the organism studied by Jones, Orcutt, and Little fall into two groups on the basis of agglutination. One group is composed of two strains isolated from diarrhea in cows, and the other is composed of all the strains isolated from the intestinal tracts and livers of calves. The calf group, in turn, is divided by agglutinin absorption into a group which possesses a complete antigen and another which has a partial antigen.

No one of the vibrios classified as *Vibrio jejuni* is antigenically similar to *Vibrio fetus.*

Toxin production has not been reported.

Pathogenicity. The organism is not pathogenic to laboratory animals under usual conditions. Guinea pigs and white rats resist intraperitoneal injections. Some recently isolated strains produce an increase in temperature and diarrhea in rabbits. The administration of 0.5 gm. of sodium bicarbonate to the rabbit increases the pathogenicity of the organism resembling *Vibrio cholerae* in this respect. When it is injected intraperitoneally, the organism produces necrotic foci in the liver of white mice.

Jones and Little found that the disease could be produced experimentally in calves, was less severe but was of the same type of enteritis observed in naturally infected cases. Pure cultures isolated from the infected intestinal tract of such cases were able to reproduce the disease in other susceptible calves. It was observed that the feeding of sodium bicarbonate to calves was not necessary in order to produce infection as was observed in the experimental infection of rabbits by oral administration.

In the bovine, the organism causes a severe diarrhea characterized by dark brown or black feces, often containing mucus and blood. The principle lesions are catarrhal inflammation of the jejunum and upper ileum and degenerative changes in the liver. The disease is rarely fatal.

In 1946, Levy described the isolation of an organism which resembled *V. jejuni* by blood culture and from the feces of people suffering with severe gastroenteritis. Milk was suspected as being the vehicle for the organism. Attempts to trace the source of the suspected milk supply failed.

Immunity. Agglutinating antibodies are produced by the injection of living cultures into rabbits. Facts are not available concerning the immunity or antibodies produced in the bovine during and following an attack of the disease.

Diagnosis. The organism is identified by isolation and differentiated from other vibrios, such as *Vibrio fetus,* by agglutination test.

Miscellaneous Vibrios

In 1944 Doyle described a vibrio which he isolated in pure culture from the mucosa of the colon of swine which had died of dysentery. This organism has not as yet been given a name. It forms irregular translucent colonies on blood agar plates incubated in a 10 to 15 per cent carbon dioxide atmosphere for 48 hours. Inoculation of cultures of the organism into pigs produces typical cases of dysentery.

REFERENCES FOR FURTHER STUDY

Barger, E. H. Report of a Case of Abortion Induced by *Vibrio fetus*. Jour. Amer. Vet. Med. Assn. 72:468–74, 1928.

Binns, W., and Fincher, M. G. Cornell Vet. 44:512, 1954.

Brocklehurst, I. W. Vet. Jour. 102:279–82, 1946.

Bryner, J. H., and Frank, A. H. Amer. Jour. Vet Res. 16:76, 1955.

———, ———. Amer. Jour. Vet. Res. 16:634, 1955.

Doyle, L. P. A Vibrio Associated with Swine Dysentery. Amer. Jour. Vet. Res., 5:3–5, 1944.

Easterbrooks, H. L., and Plastridge, W. N. Jour. Amer. Vet. Med. Assn. 120:199, 1952.

Firehammer, B. D., and Marsh, H. Amer. Jour. Vet. Res. 14:392, 1953.

Gamaléia, M. N. *Vibrio metchnikovi* (n. sp.). Ann. de l'Inst. Past. 2:482–88 and 552–57, 1888.

Gay, F. P., and associates. The Vibrios and Asiatic Cholera. Agents of Disease and Host Resistance. Charles C. Thomas, Baltimore, 1935.

Graham, Robt., and Thorp, Frank, Jr. Vibrionic Abortion in Sheep. Jour. Amer. Vet. Med. Assn. 76:568–73, 1930.

Huddleson, F. Jour. Bact. 56:508, 1948.

Hughes, D. E., and Gilman, H. L. Cornell Vet. 43:463, 1953.

Jones, F. S., Orcutt, Marion, and Little, F. S. Vibrios (*Vibrio jejuni*, n. sp.) Associated with Intestinal Disorders of Cows and Calves. Jour. Exp. Med. 53:853, 1931.

Kaschula, V. R., and Canham, A. S. Jour. So. Afr. Vet. Med. Assn. 17:150–57, 1946.

Kiggins, E. M., Plastridge, W. N., Williams, L. F., and Easterbrooks, H. L. Amer. Jour. Vet. Res. 16:291, 1955.

Kolle, W., and Hetch, H. Revised by John Eyre. Asiatic Cholera. Chap. XIV, Experimental Bacteriology. George Allen & Unwin, Ltd., London, 1934.

Lee, A. M., and Scrivner, L. H. Amer. Jour. Vet Res. 11:50–54, 1941.

Levy, A. J. Yale Jour. Biol. Med. 18:243–58, 1946.

Lindenstruth, R. W., and Ward, B. Q. Jour. Amer. Vet. Med. Assn. 113:163, 1948.

McEntee, K., Hughes, D. E., and Gilman, H. L. Cornell Vet. 44:376, 1954.

McFadyean, Sir John, and Stockman, Sir S. Abortion in Sheep. Part III. Dept. Comm. Rept. for Board of Agr. and Fisheries of Great Britain into Epizootic Abortion. 1913.

Mackie, T. J., Greig, E.D.W., Harvey, W.F., and Bulloch, W. The Cholera Vibrio and Related Organisms. A System of Bacteriology. 4:338–445. Med. Res. Council, His Majesty's Stationery Office, London, 1929.

Marsh, H., and Firehammer, B. D. Amer. Jour. Vet. Res. 14:396, 1953.

———, ———, and Scrivner, L. H. Amer. Jour. Vet. Res. 15:352, 1954.

———, and Tunnicliff, E. A. Jour. Amer. Vet. Med. Assn. 126:100, 1955.

Morse, E. V., and Ristic, M. Amer. Jour. Vet. Res. 15:599, 1954.

Moynihan, I. W., and Stovell, P. L. Can. Jour. Comp. Med. 19:105, 1955.

Olson, A. Skand. VetTidskr. 36:1–36. 1946.

Plastridge, W. N., and Easterbrooks, H. L. Amer. Jour. Vet. Res. 13:145, 1952.

———, ———, and Williams, L. F. Jour. Amer. Vet. Med. Assn. 123:516, 1953.

———, ———, ———, Kiggins, M. S., and Walker, E. Amer. Jour. Vet. Res. 16:493, 1955.

———, and Williams, L. F. Cornell Vet. 38:165–80, 1948.

———, ———, Chernak, C., and Easterbrooks, H. L. Jour. Amer. Vet. Med. Assn. 118:367, 1951.

———, ———, Easterbrooks, H. L., Walker, E. C., and Beccia, R. N. Vibriosis in Cattle. Bull. 281, Storrs Agr. Exp. Sta., U. of Conn., Storrs, Conn., 1951.

———, ———, and Petrie, D. Amer. Jour. Vet. Res. 8:178–83, 1947.

Price, K. E., Poelma, L. J., and Faber, J. E. Amer. Jour. Vet. Res. 16:164, 1955.

Rhoades, Harry E. Amer. Jour. Vet. Res. 15:630, 1954.

———, and Hardenbrook, Harry, Jr. Cornell Vet. 38:8–13, 1947.

Ristic, M., and Morse, E. V. Amer. Jour. Vet. Res. 14:399, 1953.

———, ———, Wipf, L., and McNutt, S. H. Amer. Jour. Vet. Res. 15:309, 1954.

———, Sanders, D. A., and Tyler, M. E. Amer. Jour. Vet. Res. 16:246, 1955.

———, Wipf, L., Morse, E. V., and McNutt, S. H. Amer. Jour. Vet. Res. 15:137, 1954.

Ryff, J. F., and Lee, A. H. *Vibrio fetus* in Sheep. Amer. Jour. Vet. Res. 6:149–58, 1945.

Smith, Theobald. Spirilla Associated with Disease of the Fetal Membranes in Cattle (infectious abortion). Jour. Exp. Med. 28:701–20, 1918.

———. Further Studies on the Etiological Significance of *Vibrio fetus*. Jour. Exp. Med. 37:341, 1923.

———, and Orcutt, M. L. Vibrios from Calves and Their Serological Relation to *Vibrio fetus*. Jour. Exp. Med. 45:391–98, 1927.

———, and Taylor, M. S. Some Morphological and Biological Characters of the Spirilla (*Vibrio fetus* n. sp.) Associated with Disease of the Fetal Membranes of Cattle. Jour. Exp. Med. 30:299–312, 1919.

Stockman, Sir S. Vibrionic Abortion. Jour. Amer. Vet. Assn. 60:499–504, 1919.

Verge, J. Rev. Path. Comp. 47:309–12, 1947.

Ward, B. Q. Jour. Bact. 55:113–14, 1948.

———, and Lee, A. M. Jour. Amer. Vet. Assn. 112:227–28, 1948.

Webster, H. D., and Thorp, Frank, Jr. Amer. Jour. Vet. Res. 14:118, 1953.

Welch, Howard, and Marsh, H. Vibrionic Abortion in Sheep. Jour. Amer. Vet. Med. Assn. 65:203–11, 1924.

20.

The Genera Escherichia, Aerobacter, Klebsiella, and Proteus

THE ENTEROBACTERIA

Intestinal infections which occur in animals and in man are commonly caused by Gram-negative, plump rods which do not form spores. These organisms are known under the collective name enterobacteria and are classified in the family Enterobacteriaceae.

This family is characterized as follows: Many are parasitic upon animals and some upon plants; they are Gram-negative rods widely distributed in nature; they grow well on artificial media; all species attack carbohydrates, forming acid, or acid and visible gas; all produce nitrites from nitrates; the flagella are peritrichous when present.

The family is divided into tribes which in turn are divided into numerous genera and species. There are six genera—Escherichia, Aerobacter, Klebsiella, Proteus, Salmonella, and Shigella—which contain species of special interest to students in veterinary bacteriology. Reactions produced in various media by representative strains of these genera are given in Table 20.1.

THE GENUS ESCHERICHIA

Organisms which are placed in the genus Escherichia are widely distributed in nature and are commonly found in normal intestinal tracts of man and animals. Due to the widespread nature of the group, a large number of species have been isolated, described, and named.

The 1948 Edition of Bergey's Manual recognized three species of Escherichia which are differentiated by the following key:

I. Citric acid and salts of citric acid not utilzed as sole source of carbon
   A. Hydrogen sulfide not produced
      1. *Escherichia coli*

II. Citric acid and salts of citric acid utilized as sole source of carbon

TABLE 20.1
DIFFERENTIATION OF ENTEROBACTERIA *

		E. coli	*E. freundii*	Arizona type	Klebsiella	Aerobacter	Proteus	Salmonella	Shigella
S S agar............		R	R	C	R	R	C	C	C
Br. green agar.........		Gr	Gr	R	Gr	Gr	R	R	R
Motility..............		+	+	+	−	+	+	+	−
Kliglers	Slant	y	y	R	y	y	R	R	R
iron	Butt	yg	yg	yg	yg	yg	yg	yg	y
agar	H₂S	−	+	+	−	−	+	+	−
Urea................		−	−s	−	+s	−	+	−	−
Glucose.............		ag	ag	ag	ag	ag	ag	ag	a
Lactose.............		ag	ag	ags	ag	ags	−	−	−
Adonitol.............		−	−	−	ag	v	v	−	−
Dulcitol.............		v	v	−	v	v	−	ag	v
Salicin.............		v	v	−	ag	ags	v	−	−
Sucrose.............		v	v	−	ag	ag	v	−	−
Indol...............		+	−	−	−	v	v	−	v
Methyl red...........		+	+	+	−	−	+	+	+
Voges-Proskauer.......		−	−	−	+	+	v	−	−
Gelatin..............		−	−	+	−	+	+	−	−
Simmons' citrate.......		−	+	+	+	+	v	+	−

*R = red; C = colorless; Gr = green; y = yellow; yg = yellow with gas; − = no change; + = positive; +s = positive slow; a = acid; ag = acid and gas; ags = acid gas slow; v = variable.

A. Hydrogen sulfide produced
  2. *Escherichia freundii*
B. Hydrogen sulfide not produced
  3. *Escherichia intermedium*

The name *Escherichia coli* embraces a number of strains of bacteria which have been isolated from the intestinal tract of man and animals where it is frequently associated with disease. In addition to the main species of *E. coli*, three varieties are identified by their ability to ferment sucrose and salicin:

(1) *Escherichia coli* var. *acidilactici* does not ferment sucrose or salicin.

(2) *Escherichia coli* var. *neapolitana* ferments sucrose and salicin.

(3) *Escherichia coli* var. *communior* ferments sucrose but not salicin.

Escherichia freundii is an organism most commonly found in soil and water and to some extent in the intestinal tract of man and animals. It is not considered to be pathogenic so will not be described. Its importance in veterinary bacteriology is confined to the confusion it may create in the identification of cultures belonging to the genus Escherichia originating in animals or man.

Escherichia intermedium, likewise, is found in soil and water and infrequently in the intestinal tract of man and animals. It will not be described. The reader is referred to Bergey's Manual for a complete description of the two organisms mentioned above.

Escherichia coli

Synonyms and History. *Bacillus coli, Bacterium coli,* the colon bacillus—these and a host of other synonyms are given in Bergey's Manual, but it is not essential to list them here.

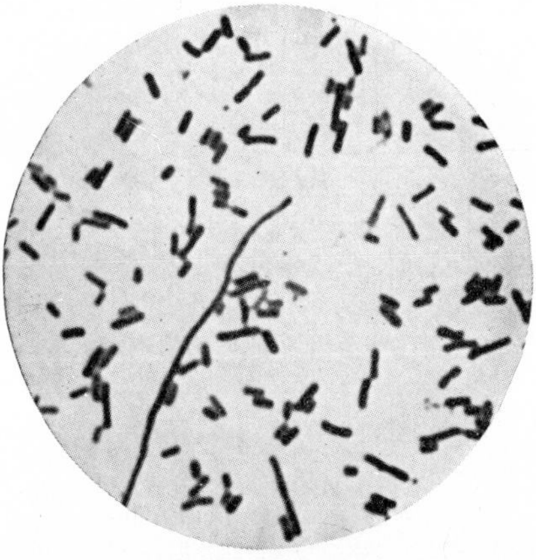

Escherichia coli was first isolated by Escherich in 1885 from the feces of infants but was more completely described in 1886. Since that time the organism has been found in the intestinal tract of practically all vertebrates.

Distribution and Transmission. The organism is world-wide in distribution. It is transmitted by water and feed which are contaminated with fecal matter.

FIG. 20.1 — **Escherichia coli** 24-hour agar culture, × 2,000. (From Nowak: Documenta Microbiologica, courtesy Gustav Fischer.)

Morphology and Staining. *E. coli* is a short rod, 0.5μ by 1.0μ to 3.0μ, varying from coccoid bipolar shapes to long filamentous forms (Fig. 20.1). It usually occurs singly but short chains are not uncommon. It does not produce spores. It is usually motile with peritrichous flagella, but some strains do not possess flagella.

The organism is readily stained with aniline dyes and is Gram-negative.

Growth Requirements and Characteristics. The organism is aerobic and facultatively anaerobic in the presence of a fermentable carbohydrate. The optimum temperature for growth is 37.5°C. but growth occurs over a range of 15° to 45°C. It grows best at a pH of 7 but grows within a wide pH range. It grows readily upon common laboratory media.

On the agar plate the colonies formed are white to yellowish-white, turning to brown or golden-brown with age; they are moist, glistening, opaque, and circular with an entire edge (Fig. 20.2). Young colonies are finely granular; as they grow older, they become coarsely granular.

In broth the organism produces a diffuse cloudiness and a heavy sediment but no pellicle.

The characteristic appearance of the colonies of *E. coli* on eosin-methylene blue agar is of value for identification. On this medium the colonies formed have blackish centers and a metallic sheen very much like that of indelible ink. On litmus-lactose agar the colonies are red in color and produce a red zone in the medium around the colonies.

Resistance. The organism is usually destroyed by 60°C. in 30 minutes, but heat-resistant strains may survive. Some individual cells are able to survive freezing in ice for six months; 95 per cent of the cells are destroyed in 2 hours by freezing in liquid air. Death is readily accomplished by drying and by the action of the common disinfectants.

Biochemical Properties. *Escherichia coli* produces acid and gas from glucose, lactose, fructose, galactose, maltose, arabinose, xylose, rhamnose,

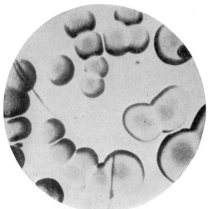

FIG. 20.2 — **Escherichia coli** colonies on agar plate, × 10. (From Nowak: Documenta Microbiologica, courtesy Gustav Fischer.)

and mannitol; may or may not ferment sucrose, raffinose, salicin, esculin, dulcitol, and glycerol; is variable in the fermentation of sucrose and salicin; rarely ferments pectin and adonitol; never ferments dextrin, starch, glycogen, and inositol. It is methyl red-positive and Voges-Proskauer-negative; produces catalase; does not liquefy gelatin; forms indol; reduces nitrates; coagulates and acidifies milk with no peptonization; oxidizes potato to a dark brown color; does not produce H_2S.

Antigenic Structure and Toxins. Following the technic which was used for the antigenic typing of the salmonellae, Kauffmann of Denmark, in 1942–43, published his first results on the typing of *Escherichia coli.* He revealed that certain strains of *E. coli* which were believed to be inagglutinable were bearers of an antigen, L antigen, which prevented O agglutination. Knipschildt, 1945, showed that these bacteria possessed two other antigens A and B in addition to the L antigen. All three antigens A, B, and L were located in the capsule of the organism and all inhibited O agglutination. After recognizing the presence of such antigens, it became possible to recognize antigenic strains, and upon this basis Kauffmann demonstrated 55 different antigenic strains and Knipschildt increased the number to 110. Later in 1945 Vahlne showed that the A, B, L antigens were really only a quantitative relationship rather than qualitative antigens so the term K antigen was adopted for the capsular antigens. The presence of flagella upon *E. coli* indicated that H antigen should be in the antigenic picture. The maintenance of flagella was solved by Vahlne by the passage of *E. coli* organisms through semisolid agar in a U-tube. Consequently, he was able to add 19 different H antigens to the 3 discovered by Kauffman.

The Kauffman–Knipschildt–Vahlne *E. coli* antigenic scheme is based upon the three antigens O, K, and H. The source of the cultures typed by the above-mentioned investigators was the human being and for that reason may have limited application in veterinary bacteriology, although strains common to animals and man have been revealed.

In a most comprehensive treatise Wramby of Sweden in 1948 classified the antigenic strains isolated from calves and a few from chickens by using the scheme mentioned above. Many calf strains could be placed with the homo strains but it was clear that a considerable number were confined to calves. In their publication *Identification of Enterobacteriaceae*, Edwards and Ewing have summarized the antigenic structure of the various strains of this organism, to which the student is referred for details.

The organism does not produce exotoxin.

Pathogenicity. Strains of the organism which have been isolated recently from a disease process will produce death in guinea pigs, mice, rats, and rabbits within 48 hours. The animals die with a fibrino-purulent peritonitis and in some cases a septicemia.

In the larger animals the organism has been isolated from numerous tissues affected with disease. In some cases it appears to be the only organism present, but in many it occurs as a secondary invader. The ease with which the organism grows on culture media is thought to explain its frequent isolation from a wide variety of sources.

Most of the cases of calf dysentery, "white scours," or coli-bacillosis, are produced by *E. coli;* in fact, all young animals appear to be more susceptible to the organism than old ones. It is also associated with pyelonephritis, navel infection, joint infection, cervicitis, cystitis, mastitis, and metritis of the bovine.

E. coli is recognized as an inciter of suppurative exudates and has been isolated from wound infections and abscesses of various animals. It invades the blood stream during the agonal stages of many diseases and for that reason septicemia is commonly attributed to it. In some cases, however, septicemia is caused by particularly virulent strains.

Hjärre and Wramby (1945) in Sweden described a specific granuloma-like condition which was found along the intestinal tract. The lesion was considered to be an atypical form of avian tuberculosis, but a capsulated culture of *E. coli* was the only organism isolated. These investigators subsequently have found that such an organism is the etiological agent. The disease in chickens is referred to as Hjärre's disease although the original discoverers prefer the term, coligranuloma.

In man, the organism produces fatal intestinal infection in infants and in mature people is associated with peritonitis following intestinal perforations, gall bladder infections, inflammation of the pancreas, infections involving the uro-genital tract, pneumonia, and meningitis. It is found in the majority of the abscesses and fistulae involving the perineal region of man.

Immunity. Natural infection results in the formation of antibodies, but little is known concerning the immunity which is produced.

Bacterins prepared from the organism have been found of value in chronic cases. The organism is commonly incorporated in the mixed bacterins which are to be used in the various species of animals to protect against intestinal infections. Mixed bacterins containing numerous strains of the organism which have been isolated from cases of calf diarrhea are used for immunization against the disease. The calf is immunized the first day of life. Autogenous bacterins prepared from a single strain of the organism isolated from a herd have been found valuable in the herd.

It is apparent that the use of strains of *E. coli* in mixed bacterins as prophylactic agents for animal diseases should be based upon antigenic types, but, as yet, no one has typed the strains of *E. coli* found in the United States.

Immune serum has been proven effective in treating calves which are infected with *E. coli.*

Diagnosis. This organism is identified by isolation in pure culture and growth on various differential media. In the diagnosis of disease, media which are used for preliminary isolation must be sufficiently nutrient to support the growth of other organisms suspected. If this is not done, one is able to isolate *E. coli* from numerous tissues, because it grows on most any type of medium.

THE PARACOLON GROUP

The isolation and study of the enterobacteria has revealed the existence of a group of bacteria, similar to *E. coli* in many respects but differing sufficiently to warrant discussion. These bacteria are commonly called the paracolon bacteria or the paracolon group.

The fermentation of lactose has been the basis of classifying the enteric bacteria since the early days of bacteriology, so it is understandable that an organism should be placed in a separate category if it did not ferment lactose as rapidly as a typical Escherichia. In this instance, however, it is not a question of whether lactose is fermented or not but how slowly lactose is fermented. Consequently, there has appeared in the literature numerous descriptions of organisms of this group which are characterized by the slow fermentation of lactose.

In classifying these bacteria, Borman, Wheeler, and Stuart in 1944 formed the genus Paracolobactrum. Bergey's Manual (1948) recognizes three species: *P. aerogenoides, P. intermedium,* and *P. coliforme.* All of the above species were obtained from cases of human gastroenteritis.

In the course of routine serological typing of the Salmonella cultures which were submitted to them, Edwards and his associates encountered cultures which could not be classified as Salmonella and which resembled the Escherichia. Although this group was, as a rule, somewhat slow in fermenting lactose, this characteristic could not be used entirely as a basis of group selection. Inasmuch as the description of a culture by Caldwell and Ryerson, in 1939, isolated from a horned lizard in Arizona, indicated the existance of a separate group, the name Arizona group was coined. Subsequent descriptions of this group by numerous workers were summarized by Edwards, West, and Bruner in 1947. In this summary the above authors describe the Arizona group of paracolon bacteria as motile coliform bacteria which produce abundant H_2S, but fail to form indol; are methyl red-positive and Voges-Proskauer-negative; produce acid and gas from glucose; do not utilize *d*-tartrate or ferment sucrose, dulcitol or salicin; ferment lactose with varying avidity and liquefy gelatin. In this study of 373 cultures it was found they could be divided into 19 groups and 55 types by antigenic analysis. All of the types were serologically related to Salmonella and the various types were found to be related to infections in animals. The cultures which were studied were isolated from reptiles, fowls, rodents, swine, man, and egg powder.

In their study of the paracolon bacteria Hinshaw and McNeil revealed their presence in gopher snakes, lizards, turkey poults, and rattlesnakes. The significance of these bacteria in reptiles was emphasized and the incrimination of such animals as sources of infection to avian species as well as domestic animals and man, was a most worthwhile contribution.

Upon continued study of the characteristics of paracolon bacteria of human origin, Edwards, West, and Bruner described cultures which they designated the Bethesda group, because most of the cultures originated from Bethesda, Md. They describe this group as follows: slow lactose-fermenting cultures that are methyl red-positive, Voges-Proskauer-negative, indol-negative, H₂S-positive, d-tartrate-positive and Simmons' citrate-positive. Urea utilization is negative when tested by the method of Rustigian and Stuart (1941), but most cultures give positive tests by the method of Christensen (1946). Dulcitol usually is fermented promptly, although dulcitol-negative strains occur. Sucrose generally is not fermented, although occasional cultures may ferment sucrose.

A third group of paracolon bacteria called the Ballerup group was described by Bruner, Edwards, and Hopson in 1949. This group is so named because the original culture which was considered to be the type species of the group was named *Salmonella ballerup*. This group is characterized as follows: motile or nonmotile coliform bacteria which produce abundant H₂S but fail to form indol; usually are methyl red-positive and Voges-Proskauer-negative; promptly produce acid and gas from glucose, arabinose, maltose, rhamnose, xylose, trehalose, mannitol, and sorbitol; attack lactose, sucrose, dulcitol, and salicin with varying avidity, but fail to ferment inositol; utilize d-tartrate, usually utilize sodium citrate, and rarely liquefy gelatin. Practically all of the 45 cultures which were originally placed in this group by the above investigators originated from cases of gastroenteritis in man, but cultures from a hog, a hen, a duck, oysters, and sewage were included.

The latter two groups are now classified together under the term Bethesda-Ballerup Group.

THE KLEBSIELLA-AEROBACTER GROUP

It has become apparent that the microorganisms which are methyl red-negative, Voges-Proskauer-positive, and citrate-positive belong in one group. They have been divided into two genera: Klebsiella, which are nonmotile, and Aerobacter, which may be both motile or nonmotile. The nonmotile forms are indistinguishable from

Klebsiella, but in the past these have been classified as *Aerobacter aerogenes*. Edwards and Ewing state that these should be classified as Klebsiella and that the motile forms can be classified as *Aerobacter cloacae;* therefore, *Aerobacter aerogenes* should be discarded as a species. No doubt, a future edition of Bergey's Manual will contain the above changes, but until that occurs, it is best to adhere to the nomenclature which is official. For that reason the name *Aerobacter aerogenes* will be used.

Aerobacter aerogenes is found frequently in the same environment as *E. coli*. Its natural habitat is considered to be water and soil; this explains its frequency in water, as well as its presence in the intestinal tract of man and animals. It is rarely pathogenic but has been isolated from cases of cystitis in man and in the dog. This organism is encountered in bovine mastitis, where it persists and causes clinically apparent cases of the disease.

The Coli-Aerogenes Test in Water Analysis. In the bacteriological examination of water supplies, the presence of *Escherichia coli* and *Aerobacter aerogenes* is used as an indication of fecal contamination; and thus indicates that the typhoid fever organism, also, may be present in the water. Routine methods which are designed to detect coli-aerogenes organisms are followed in public health laboratories. A general outline of the test follows:

The test is based upon the assumption that the coli-aerogenes group includes all Gram-negative, nonsporeforming bacteria which ferment lactose with the formation of acid and gas and grow aerobically on standard solid media.

The test is divided into three parts: the Presumptive, the Partially Confirmed, and the Completed.

1. The Presumptive test is positive for the coli-aerogenes group if 10 per cent or more gas forms in a standard lactose broth fermentation tube within 24 hours at 37°C.
2. The appearance of aerobic, lactose-splitting colonies on Endo agar or on eosin-methylene blue plates made from a positive lactose fermentation tube constitutes the Partially Confirmed test for the presence of coli-aerogenes organisms.
3. The Completed test requires the inoculation of lactose broth from a typical colony of nonsporeforming, Gram-negative bacteria taken from a plate in the Partially Confirmed test. The lactose must be fermented to acid and gas for a positive test.

In the genus Klebsiella one species, *Klebsiella genitalium,* is pathogenic for animals. Bruner considers this organism as a variety of *Klebsiella pneumoniae,* but it would seem that host specificity would be adequate to classify it as a separate species.

Two species, *Klebsiella genitalium* and *Klebsiella pneumoniae*, will be discussed below.

Klebsiella genitalium

Synonyms and History. The name *Encapsulatus genitalium* was given to an organism which was isolated from the genital tract of mares. It was discussed in the annual report of the director of the Agricultural Experiment Station of Kentucky in 1924. Dimock and Edwards of Kentucky described the organism and the disease it produces more completely in 1926.

Distribution and Transmission. *Klebsiella genitalium* has been found in mares in Kentucky and Virginia, but little is known of its general distribution.

It is readily transmitted through breeding, generally by the infected stallion. Lack of asepsis in artificial insemination and in the examination of a number of mares for genital abnormalities is a factor in the spread of the infection.

Morphology and Staining. The organism is a nonmotile, encapsulated rod which varies in morphology from coccoid shapes to long forms. It varies from 0.9 to 1.7μ in breadth by 1.8 to 3.7μ in length. The coccoid form is most prevalent in old cultures.

It is stained readily with the ordinary aniline dyes and is Gram-negative. The capsule surrounding the organism is easily demonstrated by any of the capsule stains.

Growth Requirements and Characteristics. *Klebsiella genitalium* is aerobic and facultatively anaerobic, grows abundantly on the common media incubated at 37°C. The optimum pH for growth is 6.8 to 7.2.

Colonies of the organism on the agar plate are large, raised, and round with an entire edge. On the agar slant, the growth is yellowish in color, moist, glistening, and so viscid that the culture flows to the bottom of the test tube. The organism produces a marked turbidity and a heavy, ropy sediment in broth. A typical nail-head type growth occurs on gelatin.

Resistance. The bacterium is easily killed by a temperature of 60°C. for 20 minutes and by the common disinfectants.

Biochemical Properties. *Klebsiella genitalium* produces acid and gas from glucose, lactose, sucrose, raffinose, xylose, salicin, glycerol, and adonitol; does not ferment inulin; does not form indol; is methyl red-negative and Voges-Proskauer-positive; reduces nitrates to nitrites; does not liquefy gelatin. It is able to utilize citrate as a source of carbon. It grows abundantly in milk, producing an initial slimy ropiness followed by acidification, coagulation, and gas formation.

Antigenic Structure and Toxins. The equine strains of the organism belong to the same antigenic group according to agglutination and precipitation reactions. Cross agglutination has been noted with strains of *Klebsiella pneumoniae*.

The organism does not produce exotoxin.

Pathogenicity. *Klebsiella genitalium* produces septicemia in guinea pigs and rabbits, causing death in 12 to 24 hours. Rabbits injected intravenously with large doses of the organism may die within 24 hours.

Intra-uterine injection of saline suspensions of living cultures of the organism into a mare reproduces a marked cervicitis and metritis accompanied by a copious, slimy, purulent exudate in a few days. The organism can be isolated from the cervix, uterus, fallopian tubes, and inguinal lymph glands of mares suffering with a natural infection. Interference with the oestrus cycle and the production of permanent sterility are common sequelae of the infection.

Immunity. Data are not available concerning the immunity produced by the organism.

Diagnosis. *Klebsiella genitalium* infection is diagnosed by the isolation and identification of the organism. Agglutinins are formed, no doubt, during the disease, but the agglutination test is not routinely used in diagnosis.

Klebsiella pneumoniae

In 1882, Friedländer described a "micrococcus" which he had isolated from a case of lobar pneumonia in man. Subsequent investigations of the organism by Fränkel and by Weichselbaum in 1886 revealed that the organism was a short rod which occasionally presented coccoid forms.

Klebsiella pneumoniae is the type species of the genus Klebsiella, and strains of the organism are commonly used in studying organisms of the same group which have been isolated from other sources. Edwards included strains of the organism and related encapsulated bacteria in his studies of *Klebsiella genitalium*.

The organism is normally a short, plump rod with rounded ends. It is extremely pleomorphic, varying in length from 1.5 to 5μ. It is surrounded by a heavy capsule two or three times as large as the organism itself (Fig. 20.3). The organism is easily cultured on ordinary agar media on the surface of which it forms white, mucus-like colonies which are slimy and semifluid in consistency. It ferments a number of carbohydrates, forming both acid and gas, and gives the reactions common to the group on other types of media.

Klebsiella pneumoniae is composed of a number of different strains which are not agglutinated by the same antisera. Julianelle has shown that the antigenic structure of the organism is changed by dissociation. The S forms are mucoid, encapsulated, virulent, and possess a group-specific antigen in the cell bodies and type-specific polysaccharide partial antigens in the capsules. The non-capsulated, avirulent R forms contain only the group antigen of the cell bodies. Julianelle divided the strains of the Friedländer group into 4 types, called A, B, C, and X, by using anti-S serum in the agglutination and precipitation tests.

In his comparison of the strains of *Klebsiella genitalium* with *Klebsiella pneumoniae* and other similar encapsulated bacteria, Edwards recognized only two antigenic types, I and II, by precipitin reactions. The strains of *Klebsiella genitalium* were placed in type I. *Klebsiella pneumoniae* is considered to be one of the causes of pneumonia in man.

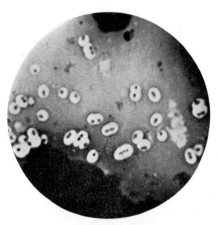

FIG. 20.3 — **Klebsiella pneumoniae** in mouse blood showing thick capsules, × 2,000. (From Nowak: Documenta Microbiologica, courtesy Gustav Fischer.)

The isolation of an organism, indistinguishable from it antigenically, has been reported by Barnes from cases of bovine mastitis.

THE GENUS PROTEUS

The bacteria in the genus Proteus are Gram-negative, pleomorphic rods (Fig. 20.4) which are actively motile by means of peritrichous flagella. They ferment dextrose and sucrose, forming both acid and gas, but do not ferment lactose. They liquefy gelatin and do not give a positive reaction to the Voges-Proskauer test. On moist media the motile types produce typical ameboid colonies which rapidly spread across the surface of the plate (Fig. 20.5); nonmotile forms produce dense, nonspreading colonies.

Strains of one of the species, *Proteus vulgaris,* have been extensively investigated because of their diagnostic importance in typhus fever of man. Weil and Felix, in 1917, demonstrated that certain strains, which they designated X2 and X19, were agglutinated by the sera of typhus fever patients. In the course of this investigation, Weil and Felix introduced the term H

(Hauch = film) for the motile forms and the term O (ohne Hauch = without film) for the nonmotile forms of the organism. Immune sera of rabbits prepared by injecting H and O cultures revealed that two types of agglutinin developed. The O agglutinin caused the agglutination of O organisms, forming fine clumps, and the H agglutinin agglutinated H organisms, forming coarse clumps.

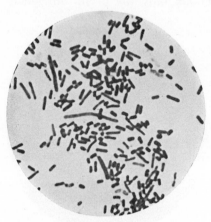

The O immune serum contained only O agglutinins, but the H serum contained both H and O agglutinins. Since then the terms O and H have been adopted as the designations of types of agglutination, that is, O pertains to fine clumps and H to coarse clumps.

Proteus vulgaris is not significant as a pathogenic organism. It is not the cause of typhus fever or any other of the Rickettsia diseases. The real explanation of the positive agglutination tests with X2 and X19 strains of the organism is not known. The organism has been associated as a secondary invader with other organisms in wound infections and diseases of mucous membranes. It has been isolated from cases of cystitis and pyelitis in man following the obstruction of the urinary tract by calculi.

FIG. 20.4 — **Proteus vulgaris** from agar culture, × 2,000. (From Nowak: Documenta Microbiologica, courtesy Gustav Fischer.)

Proteus hydrophilus

Workers in experimental laboratories are often troubled, usually during autumn months, with epidemics among frogs of a disease which is due to *Proteus hydrophilus*. The disease produced by the organism is a typical septicemia, and the hemorrhages which occur in the skin have led to the use of the term "red leg." Frogs which are kept in warm, stagnant water are more susceptible to the infection; consequently, the best preventive for the disease is cold, clean, running water.

Proteus hydrophilus is a short, plump, aerobic rod, 0.6µ by 1.3µ in size; is motile by means of peritrichous flagella; stains Gram-negative. It produces greyish-white, stippled, translucent, moist colonies on the agar slant, and forms a heavy turbidity in broth and a thick pellicle. The organism ferments glucose, maltose, sucrose, and mannitol, forming acid and gas, but does not ferment lactose; reduces nitrates; produces indol; liquefies gelatin; coagulates and peptonizes litmus milk.

In addition to the frog, this organism is pathogenic for salamanders, fish, mice, guinea pigs, and rabbits, in which it produces a septicemia. Pure cultures of the organisms produce a tetanic condition in frogs. An alcohol-precipitated toxin produces effects similar to those caused by caffein, digitalis, and veratrin on muscles. Toxins soluble in alcohol produce paralysis.

There are at least two definite serological types of *P. hydrophilus.* When used as bacterins, each type produces immunity in experimental animals against both types; however, passive immunization can be demonstrated only against the homologous type.

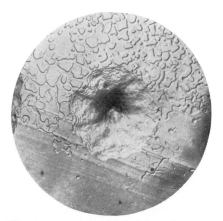

FIG. 20.5 — **Proteus vulgaris** colony on agar plate showing thin, filmy growth around the main colony, × 70. (From Nowak: Documenta Microbiologica, courtesy Gustav Fischer.)

Proteus ammoniae

Synonyms and History. In 1925 Hager and Magath described an organism which they found to be associated with incrusted cystitis in man. They called this organism *Salmonella ammoniae*. In a subsequent study in 1928 Magath gave a detailed description of the organism and suggested that it belonged to the genus Proteus, although some minor characteristics did not conform to a typical Proteus organism. In a study of 32 strains of the organism, isolated from various sources, Fulton and Harrison emphasized that the organism was sufficiently characteristic to be considered a member of the Proteus group.

The relationship of *P. ammoniae* to animal infections has been emphasized during recent years by Packer by the isolation of the organism from a variety of animals.

Distribution and Transmission. The distribution of *P. ammoniae* is not known. The presence of the organism in so many different animal species and different tissues indicates that it is rather ubiquitous, and infections caused by it are sporadic due to predisposing factors.

Morphology and Staining. *Proteus ammoniae* is a plump rod 0.5μ by 1.4μ in size; is motile with peritrichous flagella; is nonsporeforming and noncapsulated. The organism is easily stained by the commonly used bacteriological stains and is Gram-negative.

Growth Requirements and Characteristics. Colonies formed by the organism on solid media are thin and transparent, typical of the veil-like growth characteristic of the genus Proteus.

In fluid media *P. ammoniae* produces a marked turbidity due to abundant growth.

Resistance. This organism is not resistant to the common disinfectants. It is not susceptible to penicillin, but its growth is inhibited by streptomycin.

Biochemical Properties. *P. ammoniae* produces acid and gas from glucose, galactose, glycerol, trehalose, and xylose. The ability of the organism to ferment sucrose has been of concern to numerous investigators. This led Hager and Magath to question the inclusion of the organism in the genus Proteus. Fulton and Harrison have shown that the organism produces acid and gas in 5 per cent but not in 0.5 per cent sucrose. The rapid growth of actively proteolytic bacteria often causes such a marked alkalinity that acids produced from carbohydrates are neutralized. This has been proven true of *Pseudomonas aeruginosa*. The use of a protein-free medium in which the carbohydrate is placed reveals fermentation which has been considered negative. By using this medium, the composition of which is given in Chapter 18, Packer has demonstrated that *P. ammoniae* produces acid and gas in 0.3 per cent sucrose and salicin in 10 days. The organism does not ferment lactose, mannite, maltose, dulcitol, arabinose, inositol, inulin, raffinose, rhamnose, sorbitol, adonitol, dextrin, fructose, and soluble starch. It liquefies gelatin, reduces and peptonizes litmus milk. The decomposition of urea is an outstanding characteristic of this organism. Colonies of the organism on S-S medium have black centers and the sulfurous odor characteristic of H_2S production.

Antigenic Structure and Toxins. Various species of this organism have not been subjected to detailed antigenic study. On the basis of limited agglutination tests the species is serologically heterogenous. Specific toxins have not been described.

Pathogenicity. Previous mention has been made of the relationship of this organism to incrusted cystitis in man. Fulton and Harrison studied cultures isolated from stool specimens and from a mastoidectomy in man. Packer has isolated the organism from nine cases of hematuria and cystitis in the dog, two cases of urinary tract infection in cows, two cases of omphalophlebitis in the turkey; one case of each of the following: prostatitis in the dog, endocartitis in the pig, bacteriemia in the turkey, pneumonia in the dog, skin wound in the dog, and skin wound in the cow.

Craige isolated Proteus organisms from 101 dogs showing a variety of symptoms including peritonitis and omphalitis in newborn puppies, acute bloody diarrhea, chronic dysentery, and nervous disorders. Autogenous bacterins used in 49 cases gave rather satisfactory results.

White mice usually are killed within 24 hours by intraperitoneal injections of *P. ammoniae*. Some strains are pathogenic for the guinea pig whereas others are not able to produce death. In their study of the organism Hager and Magath were able to produce the lesion of incrusted cystitis in guinea pigs and in rabbits when a primary inflammation was produced in the bladder mucosa by the injection of 0.5 to 1 cc. of a 0.1 per cent alcoholic solution of salicylic acid.

Immunity. No information is available concerning the immunity produced by the organism.

Diagnosis. The close similarity of this organism with *E. coli* makes it imperative that urine cultures be subjected to close examination. The usual presence of the swarming, ameboid colony of the organism is sufficient to identify it as a Proteus. Carbohydrate fermentation must be used for definite identification.

REFERENCES FOR FURTHER STUDY

Barnes, L. E. Jour. Amer. Vet. Med. Assn., 125:50, 1954.

Craige, J. E. Jour. Amer. Vet. Med. Assn., 113:154, 1948.

Dimock, W. W., and Edwards, P. R. Jour. Amer. Vet. Med. Assn., 70:469–80, 1927.

———, and Snyder, Ethel M. Sterility in Mares. 37th Ann. Rept. of the Ky. Agr. Exp. Sta., p. 18, 1924.

Edwards, P. R. Relationships of the Encapsulated Bacilli with Special Reference to *Bact. aerogenes*. Jour. Bact., 17:339–53, 1929.

———. The Relationship of Encapsulated Bacilli Found in Metritis in Mares to Encapsulated Bacilli from Other Sources. Jour. Bact., 15:245–66, 1928.

———, and Ewing, W. H. Identification of Enterobacteriaceae. Burgess Publishing Co., Minneapolis, 1955.

———, West, M. G., and Bruner, D. W. Antigenic Studies of a Group of Paracolon Bacteria (Bethesda Group). Jour. Bact., 55:711, 1948.

———, ———, ———. Arizona Group of Paracolon Bacteria. Ky. Agr. Exp. Sta. Bull. 499, Univ. Ky., Lexington, Ky., 1947.

Emerson, H., and Norris, C. Jour. Exp. Med., 7:32, 1905.

Fulton, M., and Harrison, P. E. Jour. Bact., 46:365–67, 1943.

Gay, F. P., and associates. Agents of Disease and Host Resistance. Chaps. 30, 31, and 32. Charles C. Thomas, Baltimore, 1935.

Hager, B. H., and Magath, T. B. Jour. Amer. Med. Assn., 85:1352, 1925.

Hinshaw, W. R., and McNeil, E. Jour. Bact., 53:715, 1947.

Hjärre, A., and Wramby, G. Skandinavisk Veterinärtidskrift, 35:449, 1945.

Julianelle, L. A. Jour. Exp. Med., 44:683–96, 735–51, 1926.

Kauffmann, F. Jour. Immunol., 57:71, 1947.

Knipschildt, H. E. Undersgelser over coligruppens serologi med saerligt henblik poa kapsedformerne. Diss. Copenhagen, 1945.

Kulp, W. L., and Borden, D. G. Jour. Bact., 44:673–85, 1942.

Magath, T. B. *Proteus ammoniae.* Jour. Inf. Dis., 43:181–83, 1928.

Packer, R. A. *Proteus ammoniae* in Animals. Personal communication.

Thomas, L. J., and Cahn, A. R. Jour. Parasit., 18:219–31, 1932.

Topley, W. W. C., and Wilson, G. S. Principles of Bacteriology. Chap. XXVII. Williams & Wilkins Co., Baltimore, 1936.

Vahlne, G. Serological typing of the colon bacteria, with special reference to occurrence of *B. coli* in man under normal and pathological conditions particularly in appendicitis. Diss. Lund, 1945. Acta Path. et Microbiol. Scandinav. Suppl. 62, 1945.

Wallace, G. I., Thomas, L. J., and Cahn, A. R. Proc. Soc. Exp. Biol. Med., 29:1098, 1932.

West, M. G., and Edwards, P. R. The Bethesda-Ballerup Group of Paracolon Bacteria. Pub. Health Serv. Publ. No. 362. U. S. Govt. Printing Office, Washington, 1954.

Wilson, W. J. The Colon Group and Similar Bacteria. A System of Bacteriology. Vol. 4, Chap. IV. Med. Res. Council. His Majesty's Stationery Office, London, 1929.

Wramby, G. Investigations into the antigenic structure of *Bact. coli* isolated from calves. Appelbergs Boktryckeriaktiebolag, Uppsala, 1948.

21. | The Genus Salmonella

Salmonellae are nonsporeforming, Gram-negative rods closely related morphologically and physiologically to the other genera of the family Enterobacteriaceae. They are usually motile, although nonmotile forms occur; produce acid and gas from glucose, maltose, mannitol, and sorbitol; do not ferment lactose, sucrose, or salicin; do not form indol, coagulate milk, or liquefy gelatin. They are parasitic upon man and animals and usually produce inflammatory reactions in the intestinal tract.

The first organism representative of the group was isolated in 1885 by Smith and Salmon from pigs which had died of hog cholera. They believed the organism to be the cause of the disease; consequently, the name *Bacillus cholerae suis* was given to it. This organism was considered to be the cause of hog cholera until 1904 when de Schweinitz and Dorset discovered that the real cause was a filtrable virus. Subsequently this organism has been found to be a secondary invader to the virus disease and to be one of the causes of infectious enteritis in the pig. The second organism of the group was isolated by Gärtner in 1888 from a fatal case of gastroenteritis in a young man who had eaten raw meat taken from a diseased cow. The organism was named *Bacillus enteritidis*. The name Salmonella was proposed for the genus by Lignières in 1900 in honor of D. E. Salmon, the first Chief of the United States Bureau of Animal Industry.

During the intervening years numerous species of bacteria fulfilling the description for this genus have been described. Four of the group, *Salmonella paratyphi*, *Salmonella schottmuelleri*, *Salmonella herschfeldii*, and *Salmonella typhosa* are well known as species which are pathogenic for man. These species are not known to produce infection in animals, and their occasional isolation from animals is considered to be as a result of contamination. The rest of the species in the genus which are to be discussed are pathogenic for a wide variety of animals in which they produce enteric infection. The only exceptions are *Sal. abortivoequina* and *Sal. abortusovis,* which cause abortion in the equine and ovine species, respectively.

The selection of the most common species of Salmonella which infect animals from the large number of antigenic types has been difficult. In 1946 Bruner and Edwards tabulated the occurrence of the 12 most common Salmonella. The prevalence of various types of Salmonella in domestic animals has also been tabulated (Table 21.1) by Bruner and Edwards. This emphasizes the widespread

TABLE 21.1

TOTAL OUTBREAKS OF SALMONELLOSIS AND NUMBER OF SALMONELLA TYPES ENCOUNTERED IN ANIMALS (FOWLS AND MAN NOT INCLUDED)

Source	Types	Outbreaks
Horses	3	42
Cattle	11	60
Sheep	6	33
Other ruminants	2	2
Swine	38	958
Dogs	4	18
Foxes	7	74
Other carnivora	5	6
Rats	5	18
Mice	4	23
Guinea-pigs	4	29
Other rodents	2	13
Reptiles	10	8
Lower primates	5	5

Total animal species, 23; total Salmonella types, 46; total outbreaks, 1,289. Edwards, P. R., and Bruner, D. W. Proc. 50th Annual Meeting U.S.L.S.A., 1946.

incidence of organisms of this group and the large number of different species of animals involved.

In 1948 Edwards, Bruner, and Moran reported the occurrence and distribution of the Salmonella in animals, reptiles, and man in the United States. This report was based upon the antigenic study of 12,331 cultures during the period 1934 to 1947. Part of their data are given in Table 21.2. Only 20 species out of 111 were selected by taking the five most common Salmonella species in each species of animals. The reader is referred to Bulletin 525 for complete details. It is significant to note that these organisms are exceedingly widespread among various animal hosts and in many cases animals other than the primary hosts are involved. The prevalence of *Sal. typhimurium* must be emphasized. It appears difficult to select a primary host for this organism. The presence of all but two of the

TABLE 21.2
OUTBREAKS OF SALMONELLA INFECTIONS IN VARIOUS ANIMAL SPECIES AND IN MAN

																		Totals	
	Turkeys	Chickens	Pigeons	Ducks	Game Birds	Canaries	Horses	Cows	Sheep	Pigs	Dogs	Foxes	Rats	Mice	Guinea Pigs	Reptiles	Man	Animal Species	Outbreaks
1. *Sal. paratyphi*																	28	1	28
2. *Sal. abortivoequina*	2						29											1	29
3. *Sal. schottmuelleri*		5						3	4	6			6	1			109	6	130
4. *Sal. derby*	121	9	106	1	3			3		16							49	7	202
5. *Sal. typhimurium*	976	145		32	13	26	18	16	22	76	29	18		7	44	1	357	17	1,892
6. *Sal. bredeny*	74	15		2	10			1	1	21	1						16	9	141
7. *Sal. choleraesuis*	1	3				1				785	7	28			1		141	10	982
8. *Sal. oranienburg*	87	125	1	1	4			10	5	2							127	6	346
9. *Sal. bareilly*	92	102			1					4		2					43	7	245
10. *Sal. muenchen* (Oreg.)	15	3									4					4	34	5	67
11. *Sal. newport*	69	24		2				2		11			10	1	1	2	151	10	268
12. *Sal. typhosa*																	40	1	40
13. *Sal. enteritidis*	18	4										22		17	13		28	8	101
14. *Sal. dublin*	1					1		5		6							1	5	44
15. *Sal. pullorum*	93	926			1	1		19				1						7	1,025
16. *Sal. gallinarum*	47	82			1	1		1		2	1	1					16	8	151
17. *Sal. anatis*	160	34	53	8	2	1		1	2	2		2	1			1	64	13	344
18. *Sal. meleagris*	99	6	1		2					15							16	6	125
19. *Sal. give*	81	9		2	1			1		1							36	7	140
20. *Sal. worthington*	25	18		1				1		10	1						14	7	81

Adapted from: The Genus Salmonella, Its Occurrence and Distribution in the United States. P. R. Edwards, D. W. Bruner, and Alice B. Moran. Ky. Agr. Exp. Sta., Bull. 525. Lexington, 1948.

species in man indicates that most animal species should be considered as a source of Salmonella infection for man.

Classification. The classification of the Salmonella has undergone significant changes during the time such organisms have been recognized as significant agents of disease. In common with other groups of bacteria, carbohydrate fermentation has been recognized as a fundamental basis for classification. The fermentation of the carbohydrates, xylose, arabinose, inositol, maltose, and trehalose as well as the production of hydrogen sulphide are used in differentiating the group selected for discussion (Table 21.3).

TABLE 21.3
DIFFERENTIAL METABOLIC CHARACTERISTICS OF REPRESENTATIVE SALMONELLA

Species	Xylose	Arabinose	Trehalose	Inositol	Maltose	H₂S Produced
Sal. paratyphi	—	AG	AG	—	AG	—
Sal. schottmuelleri ...	AG	AG	AG	AG	AG	+
Sal. hirschfeldii	AG	AG	AG	—	AG	+
Sal. typhosa	V	V	A	—	A	+
Sal. typhimurium	AG	AG	AG	AG	AG	+
Sal. abortivoequina ...	AG	AG		—	AG	V
Sal. abortusovis	AG	AG	—	—	AG	+
Sal. choleraesuis	AG	—	—	—	AG	V
Sal. typhisuis	AG	AG	AG	—	AG	—
Sal. enteritidis	AG	AG	AG	—	AG	+
Sal. pullorum	AG	AG	AG	—	V	+
Sal. gallinarum	A	A	A	—	A	V
Sal. anatis	AG	AG	AG	—	AG	+

A = acid; G = gas; — = negative; + = positive; V = variable.

According to Table 21.3, the common species of the Salmonella associated with animal diseases can be differentiated. One exception must be noted; that is, the reactions of *Sal. schottmuelleri* and *Sal. typhimurium*. The similarity in the reactions between these two species appears to indicate that they should be placed in one species. It must be emphasized, however, that physiological reactions are only one set of criteria by which bacteria are classified. In this instance, these two species can be separated on the basis of differences in antigenic structure (Table 21.4). Moreover, they are different in respect to pathogenicity. *Sal. schottmuelleri* is pathogenic for man, whereas *Sal. typhimurium* is associated with animal diseases.

In addition to the carbohydrate fermentations and other tests which are commonly employed in the laboratory for the differentiation of bacteria, a few other specific tests have been designed for the Salmonella group. Stern described a fuchsin-sulphite-glycerol meat-extract medium in which "Stern positive" organisms formed a deep lilac color due to the formation of an aldehyde by the fermentation of the carbohydrate. A second test, known as the Bitter test, specifies a medium containing 0.5 per cent rhamnose in milk; incubation is required for 15 hours and then methyl red is added to determine acid formation. The medium used in the test has been modified by the use of various salts, 0.5 per cent peptone, and a fermentable carbohydrate, such as rhamnose, xylose, and maltose. A third reaction depends on the ability of the organisms to ferment *d*-tartrate which is added to a nutrient medium.

TABLE 21.4

ANTIGENIC STRUCTURE OF REPRESENTATIVE SALMONELLA

Type	Species	Somatic O-Antigen	Flagellar H-Antigen	
			Phase 1	Phase 2
A........	*Sal. paratyphi*	1,2,12	a	....
B........	*Sal. schottmuelleri*	1,4,5,12	b	1,2
	Sal. typhimurium	1,4,5,12	i	1,2
	Sal. abortivoequina	4,12	....	e,n,x
	Sal. abortusovis	4,12	c	1,6
	Sal. bredeny	1,4,12,27	l,v	1,7
C₁........	*Sal. choleraesuis*	6,7	c	1,5
	Sal. typhisuis	6,7	c	1,5
D........	*Sal. typhosa*	9,12,Vi	d	....
	Sal. enteritidis	1,9,12	g,m	....
	Sal. dublin	1,9,12	g,p	....
	Sal. gallinarum	1,9,12	....	....
	Sal. pullorum	9,12	....	....
E₁........	*Sal. anatum*	3,10	e,h	1,6
	Sal. meleagridis	3,10	e,h	l,w
F........	*Sal. rubislaw*	11	r	e,n,x
G........	*Sal. worthington*	1,13,23	l,w	z
H........	*Sal. horsham*	1,6,14,25	l,v	e,n,x
	Sal. brazil	16	a	1,5
	Sal. hull	16	b	1,2

Serological Classification of the Salmonella. The classification of bacteria by the use of serological reactions, such as agglutinin absorption, has been used for the Salmonella more than for any other group of bacteria.

This was due to the initial contribution of White and of Kauff-mann. In the United States the typing of Salmonella cultures has been centered at the Agricultural Experiment Station, University of Kentucky, at Lexington under the guidance of P. R. Edwards and at the Beth Israel Hospital in New York City under the supervision of F. Schiff. Inasmuch as Edwards studied, mainly, the Salmonella isolated from animals, his reports are of most significance to veterinary bacteriology. In 1949 Edwards moved to the laboratories of the Communicable Disease Center of the United States Public Health Service at Atlanta, Ga., where he continues his study of the Salmonella and related microorganisms.

It is not considered necessary to list the 151 antigenic types of Salmonella, given in Bergey's Manual, but the antigenic formula of the important species will be given.

The serological classification is based upon the antigenic structure of the various species of organisms. The terminology used by Weil and Felix for the Proteus strains has been adopted for the Salmonella; accordingly, the antigens of the organisms are divided into two groups, O antigen and H antigen.

The O antigen, or somatic antigen, is composed of the bacterial cell body and is prepared by heating the bacterial suspension for an hour at 80°–100°C. or by extraction with hot alcohol. These procedures remove the H flagellar antigens. The various O antigens are designated by numerals, 2, 3, 4, etc.; and upon the basis of close relationships the species of the Salmonella are placed into groups designated Types A, B, C, etc. (see Table 21.4). A single species may have more than one O antigen; that is, it has a group antigen which may be common to many of the members of its group.

The H antigen, or flagellar antigen, is composed of cell flagella and is prepared by subjecting the bacterial suspension to formalin which, supposedly, fixes the flagella over the surface of the bacterium thereby covering the O antigens of the cell body. This antigen is heat labile. The H antigens of the Salmonella are *diphasic*; that is, they are of more than one type. The two phases are designated *specific phase* and *nonspecific phase*. The specific phase is composed of only those antigenic components which are specific for the species, or strain, of the organism. These antigens are designated a, b, c, etc. The nonspecific phase is represented by the antigens shared by other species, in other group types. These antigens are designated 1, 2, 3, 4, etc. The antigenic formulae of all the Salmonella species which are to be discussed in this chapter are listed in Table 21.4, along with other representative antigenic types.

The antisera which are used for typing the Salmonella must be prepared from known strains of organisms in known stages of biology. The production of flagella antiserum presupposes that the organism which is injected possesses flagella. *Sal. pullorum* is nonflagellated; therefore, it does not have H antigen. An S→R dissociation results in the loss of certain components of the cell essential for complete O antigen. Since various environmental conditions produce dissociative changes in the Salmonella, the phase of the organism, S or R, must be known in the recognition of species. It is needless to emphasize that the recognition of a number of strains of Salmonella requires the use of numerous antisera and scores of agglutinin-absorption tests.

Salmonella paratyphi

Synonyms and History. *Bacterium paratyphi* Type A, *Bacillus paratyphosus* Type A, *Salmonella paratyphi* A.

This organism was first isolated by Gwyn in 1898 from a case which was clinically like typhoid fever, but the serum of the patient did not agglutinate the typhoid organism. In 1900, Schottmüller isolated two different organisms from cases similar to typhoid fever. He termed these organisms paratyphoid A and paratyphoid B; this terminology has become firmly established in medical literature. Extensive study of various strains of these organisms has revealed that they are separate species; consequently, the A and B designations have been dropped, and the names *Salmonella paratyphi* for the type A, and *Salmonella schottmuelleri* for the type B, are becoming established.

Distribution and Transmission. *Sal. paratyphi* is widely distributed throughout the world. It is transmitted through the agencies of meat, milk, and water which have been contaminated with fecal matter from infected people.

Morphology and Staining. The organism is a short, plump rod, 0.6μ by 3.0 to 4.0μ in size; is motile with peritrichous flagella; is noncapsulated; is nonsporeforming; is stained readily by the common laboratory staining methods; and is Gram-negative.

Growth Requirements and Characteristics. *Sal. paratyphi* is easily grown on laboratory media enriched with meat extracts. It is aerobic and facultatively anaerobic. It grows best at a pH of 7.2.

On agar surface, colonies of the organism are greyish, homogeneous, smooth, glistening, with an entire or slightly undulate edge.

In broth the organism produces a light, uniform turbidity and forms a light, powdery sediment.

The growth on potato is not abundant, being limited to a greyish-white streak.

Resistance. This organism, in common with all of the Gram-negative, nonsporeforming, rod-shaped bacteria, is easily killed by 60°C. in 20 minutes and is quickly destroyed by the common chemical disinfectants. All such organisms, however, survive in fecal material where they are protected from the action of sunlight and desiccation. They survive freezing and, consequently, live through winter periods.

Biochemical Properties. *Sal. paratyphi* produces acid and gas from glucose, fructose, galactose, mannose, arabinose, maltose, trehalose, dextrin, glycerol, mannitol, dulcitol, isodulcitol, and sorbitol; does not ferment lactose, sucrose, raffinose, xylose, salicin, inulin, adonitol, or inositol; reduces nitrates to nitrites; does not produce indol; does not form H_2S; acidifies litmus milk slightly; is negative to the Bitter test; is Stern negative; does not ferment *d*-tartrate; does not liquefy gelatin.

Antigenic Structure and Toxins. The antigenic structure of the organism is given in Table 21.4. No exotoxins are produced.

Pathogenicity. The organism is pathogenic for man, producing paratyphoid fever. It is not of significance in the lower animals, although the isolation of the organism from the pig has been reported.

This organism is typical of all of the species of Salmonella which are pathogenic to mice, guinea pigs, and rabbits when suitable doses are inoculated intravenously and intraperitoneally. Variability in pathogenicity of the different species is observed when cultures are given orally or are injected subcutaneously.

Immunity. Recovery from the disease produces an immunity. This organism is commonly incorporated with *Salmonella schottmuelleri* and *Salmonella typhosa*, forming the triple vaccine usually employed in routine immunization. Antibodies are produced during an infection.

Diagnosis. The organism is identified by culture reactions. The agglutination test is valuable as a diagnostic method.

Salmonella schottmuelleri

Synonyms and History. *Bacillus paratyphi alcaligenes, Bacterium paratyphi* Type B, *Bacillus schottmuelleri, Salmonella paratyphi B, Bacterium schottmuelleri.*

This organism was described first by Schottmüller in 1900 in relationship to an intestinal infection in man.

Distribution and Transmission. The organism is widely distributed, and cases of the disease produced by it are more numerous than those produced by *Sal. paratyphi.* Infections often occur as epidemics resulting from the contamination of food and water with human fecal material from an infected case or an immune carrier.

Morphology and Staining. This organism is typical of the group.

Resistance. *Salmonella schottmuelleri* is typical of the group.

Biochemical Properties. The organism produces acid and gas from glucose, fructose, galactose, mannose, arabinose, xylose, maltose, dextrin, trehalose, glycerol, mannitol, dulcitol, sorbitol, isodulcitol, and inositol; does not ferment lactose, sucrose, inulin, salicin, adonitol, or usually raffinose; produces H_2S; does not reduce nitrates; does not form indol; does not liquefy gelatin; produces an increased alkalinity in litmus milk; is variable in its reaction to the Bitter test and the Stern test. The fermentation of *d*-tartrate is negative in strains isolated in this country.

Antigenic Structure and Toxins. (See Table 21.4.) Exotoxins are not produced.

Pathogenicity. *Salmonella schottmuelleri* causes paratyphoid fever in man similar to that produced by *Salmonella paratyphi*. Its role in acute gastroenteritis of the food-poisoning type is controversial; although it is not a frequent cause of this type of disease, it has been isolated from typical cases. It is not considered a natural pathogen of animals, but strains of the organism have been isolated from enteritis in chickens and other birds and from bovine milk. The close relationship between this organism and *Sal. typhimurium* emphasizes the need of careful identification of it when it is suspected as the cause of animal infections.

Immunity. Recovery from an infection produced by the organism results in immunity. This organism is also incorporated into the triple vaccine used for enteric fevers. Agglutinating antibodies are produced by an infection.

Diagnosis. The organism is identified by cultural methods. The disease is diagnosed by the use of a specific antigen of the organism in the agglutination test.

Salmonella typhosa

Synonyms and History. *Bacillus typhosus, Bacillus typhi abdominalis, Bacterium typhi, Eberthella typhi, Salmonella typhosus, Bacterium typhosum, Eberthella typhosa.*

Typhoid fever is one of the diseases which led to the belief that living agents were the cause of certain types of disease and that such agents could be transmitted from one person to another. Budd believed this to be true of typhoid fever as early as 1856. The organism was first observed in infected human tissues by Eberth in 1880, but it was isolated and described by Gaffky in 1884.

Distribution and Transmission. *Salmonella typhosa* is distributed quite generally over the entire world, but is most prevalent in those countries and areas where little is done to prevent the contamination of water and food supplies.

The organism is transmitted from an infected person to a susceptible one by means of any medium which can be contaminated with fecal matter. At one time the infected case was the usual source of the infective material, but the resistant carrier has now become of greater significance. Petruschky reported in 1898 that typhoid organisms remain in urine of typhoid convalescents for months. Subsequently it was shown that the organisms are also present in feces and that 2 to 3 per cent of infected persons remain typhoid carriers for the rest of their lives. The story of Mary Malone, commonly known as "Typhoid Mary," is one of the classical illustrations of the damage which may result from an immune carrier.

The organism can be transmitted to food by means of contaminated water which comes in contact with the food directly or with utensils which are used in handling food. The fingers of a carrier may transmit the organism to food or to utensils. Flies may carry the organism from fecal matter to food or to utensils. Although water is the most common vehicle in the transmission of the

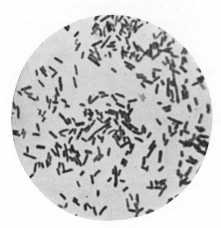

FIG. 21.1 — **Salmonella typhosa** from 24-hour agar culture, × 2,000. (From Nowak: Documenta Microbiologica, courtesy Gustav Fischer.)

organism, milk is one of the important foods which can be contaminated. A number of milk-borne epidemics of typhoid fever occur in the United States each year. Practically all of them are caused by the consumption of raw milk which has been contaminated by immune carriers or by contaminated water used in washing milk utensils. Whether the typhoid bacillus may invade the bovine mammary gland, become established there and produce infection has been a question in the minds of many. Scott and Minett, 1947, contributed to the solution of the problem by their unsuccessful attempt to produce infection in the cow with *Sal. typhosa*. It is obvious that a great many of the methods which are used in milk sanitation should be directed toward the prevention of the spread of this organism.

Morphology and Staining. *Salmonella typhosa* is a plump, short rod, 0.5 to 0.8μ in diameter by 1 to 3μ in length (Fig. 21.1). Some individual cells and some cultures are long and threadlike. It is actively motile by means of peritrichous flagella. It is noncapsulated and nonsporeforming.

The organism is stained readily by the usual staining methods and is Gram-negative.

Growth Requirements and Characteristics. This organism is aerobic and facultatively anaerobic, grows well on meat infusion media at a pH of 7.2, and grows best at 37.5°C.

On the agar surface the organism forms small, greyish, transparent colonies which become opaque as the culture ages.

In broth, the typhoid organism produces a uniform turbidity, rarely a pellicle.

The growth on potato is thin and glistening and is limited to a narrow streak.

Resistance. The organism is easily destroyed by ordinary surface disinfectants such as chlorine 200 p.p.m. Heating at 143°F. for 30 minutes or 160°F. for 15 seconds kills the organism; consequently, the temperatures used in milk pasteurization are important safeguards to health.

Biochemical Properties. *Salmonella typhosa* produces acid but not gas from glucose, levulose, galactose, xylose, maltose, raffinose, dextrin, glycerol, mannitol, and sorbitol; does not ferment lactose, sucrose, inulin, rhamnose, inositol, salicin, or usually arabinose or dulcitol. It produces H_2S; reduces nitrates to nitrites; does not form indol; does not liquefy gelatin; produces a slight initial acidity in litmus milk and an increased alkalinity as the culture ages.

Antigenic Structure and Toxins. The organism is closly related antigenically with other salmonellae, and on the basis of antigenic structure is placed in Group D with *Sal. enteritidis, Sal. pullorum,* and *Sal. gallinarum.* An antigen, Vi, which is related to virulence has been described for the organism. The typhoid bacillus does not produce a true toxin; however, a heat-resistant substance, presumably endotoxin, is liberated by the organism. This substance is thought to be the cause of the marked toxicity in persons suffering with typhoid fever.

Pathogenicity. *Salmonella typhosa* is primarily pathogenic only to man. The organism produces symptoms in seven to fourteen days following infection. In the early stages of the disease the organism is present in the blood stream, and the destruction of intestinal tissue, which is so characteristic of the disease, is considered due to the excretion of bacterial products or the localization of bacteria subsequent to the bacteremia.

Septicemia may be produced in guinea pigs and rabbits by the intravenous injection of large doses of the organism which is found in the gall bladder of some of the surviving animals.

A disease typical of typhoid fever in man can be produced in chimpanzees by feeding cultures of the organism.

Immunity. Persons who recover from an attack of typhoid fever are immune to the general effects of the organism; however, the persistence of the organism in the gall bladder of some individuals belies a total immunity. Antibody is formed by the infection, thereby producing a certain degree of humoral immunity.

Typhoid fever vaccines are widely used in prophylactic treatment, especially in the army and navy. While it is difficult to evaluate such treatment exactly, it is believed by most authorities that the incidence of cases is reduced. Vaccines which have been prepared in such a manner as to preserve the heat-labile Vi factor are considered to be of greater value than those which have not been so treated.

Salmonella typhimurium

Synonyms and History. *Bacillus typhi murium, Bacterium aertrycke, Salmonella pestis caviae, Salmonella psittacosis.*

In 1892, Loeffler isolated from a natural outbreak of a typhoid-like disease in mice an organism which he called *Bacillus typhi murium.* This animal has been the only one with which the name has been associated until recent years. Biochemical and serological reactions reveal that it is identical with many other heretofore recognized species of Salmonella; consequently, on the basis of priority, it has been chosen as the species name which embraces many others.

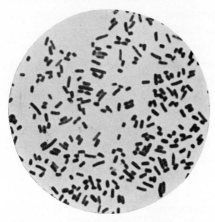

Sal. aertrycke of de Nobele, 1898, is one of the species of the genus which had become well established in animal bacteriology, but it now becomes a synonym of *Sal. typhimurium.* This constitutes an important change which the student must remember in the study of past literature.

Sal. pestis caviae, which was isolated from an intestinal infection in guinea pigs by Wherry in 1908, is now a synonym of *Sal. typhimurium.*

FIG. 21.2 — **Salmonella typhimurium** from an agar culture, × 2,000. (From Nowak: Documenta Microbiologica, courtesy Gustav Fischer.)

Sal. psittacosis, isolated from parrots by Nocard in 1893 and considered to be the cause of psittacosis until the revelation of a filtrable virus as the etiologic agent, is now placed under *Sal. typhimurium.*

Distribution and Transmission. The organism is widely distributed geographically, and among numerous species of animals and birds; in fact, it occurs in all warm-blooded vertebrates. (See Table 21.2.) It produces a typical paratyphoid, intestinal inflammation; consequently, it is transmitted by the medium of food and water contaminated by fecal matter. Normal animals are known to harbor the organism. In birds this organism, in common with many of the other salmonellae, is transmitted through the ovary of the mature bird to the embryo.

In a study of the Salmonella isolated from snakes in California, Hinshaw and McNeil found that 11 out of 41 (26.8 per cent) snakes yielded cultures of Salmonella. Five different types were isolated, *Sal. meleagridis, Sal. typhimurium, Sal. newport, Sal. rubislaw,* and *Sal. panama.* The isolation of these cultures from snakes is considered significant since infection in turkey poults yielded the same types of Salmonella in many instances. It is apparent that such reptiles may serve as reservoirs of infection.

Morphology and Staining. This bacterium is typical of the group. See Figures 21.2 and 21.3.

Resistance. It is typical of the group.

Growth Requirements and Characteristics. It is typical of the group.

Biochemical Properties. *Salmonella typhimurium* produces acid and gas from glucose, fructose, galactose, arabinose, maltose, xylose, dextrin, mannitol, sorbitol, trehalose, and inositol; does not ferment lactose, sucrose, raffinose, inulin, salicin, or adonitol. It produces H_2S; does not form indol; reduces nitrates; produces an increasingly alkaline reaction in litmus milk; does not liquefy gelatin. Strains of the organism vary in reaction to the Bitter test, the Stern test, and in the fermentation of d-tartrate. Edwards has shown that the Bitter test, employing maltose and xylose as the fermentable carbohydrate, can be used for the epizootic relationships of strains of *Sal. typhimurium*.

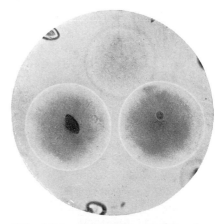

FIG. 21.3 — **Salmonella typhimurium** colony on agar plate, × 45. (From Nowak: Documenta Microbiologica, courtesy Gustav Fischer.)

Antigenic Structure. The antigenic structure of the organism is given in Table 21.4. Edwards has found that the pigeon strains have somatic antigen 4 and are classified as 4 variants, but they do not possess antigen 5 with regularity.

Although old-culture filtrates produce symptoms similar to anaphylactic shock in experimental animals, the organism does not produce specific exotoxins.

Pathogenicity. *Salmonella typhimurium* is the cause of acute and fatal intestinal infections of mice, rats, guinea pigs, sheep, calves, horses, chickens, turkeys, parrots, and pigeons. The symptoms of the disease are characterized by increased temperature, severe diarrhea, and marked weakness. Upon post-mortem examination the intestinal mucous membrane shows marked hyperemia, and in acute cases, hemorrhage. Schofield (1946) recorded an outbreak of fatal enteritis in cattle due to this organism.

Lukas and Bradford have emphasized the importance of the organism as a cause of paratyphoid in turkeys by finding that 32.7 per cent of Salmonella cultures were of this species and that it was responsible for 46.5 per cent of the uncomplicated paratyphoid outbreaks.

Chinchillas *(Chinchilla laniger)* have been found susceptible to *Sal. typhimurium,* and in instances of herd infection show a high mortality. Chronic, acute, and peracute cases are observed in a herd of mixed ages and sexes.

The prevalence of *Sal. typhimurium* in so many animal species (Table 21.2) forecasts the occurrence of outbreaks in man. It must be emphasized that this organism was responsible, during the period 1934–47, for more outbreaks in the human family than any other Salmonella species.

Immunity. Artificial immunity has been practiced for mice which have been used for experimentation purposes for *Sal. typhimurium.* The majority of reports reveal that solid immunity is not obtainable without incurring high death losses during treatment.

Infections produced by the organism are so sporadic in nature that widespread immunization of susceptible birds and flocks is not practical. Strains of the organism are commonly incorporated in mixed bacterins which are used for intestinal infections in the various domesticated animals.

Coburn, Armstrong, and Psyche observed that it is advantageous to immunize chinchillas with an autogenous bacterin, and it is especially desirable to immunize the dam and sire early in the period of pregnancy, for it enhances the production of living litters and the survival of the young.

Diagnosis. The extensive distribution of *Sal. typhimurium* among animals necessitates the use of specific antisera for correct identification, although the organism is identified in a general way by biochemical reactions. Agglutinins are formed during the progress of the natural disease and may be used for diagnosis.

Salmonella abortivoequina

Synonyms and History. *Bacillus abortivus equinus, Bacillus abortus equi, Bacterium abortum-equi, Salmonella abortus-equi.*

In 1893, Smith and Kilborne isolated a Gram-negative rod from mares which had aborted. Lignières, in 1905, reported finding a bacillus belonging to this group in aborting mares and in cows in France and Argentina. In 1912, Good, in Kentucky, described an organism which was associated with equine abortion; subsequently, in 1913, he proposed the name *Bacillus abortivus equinus.* Good and Smith, in 1916, published a complete literature summary and a description of the disease and of the organism.

Distribution and Transmission. This organism was introduced, apparently, into the United States in 1886, and first made its appearance in states of the Mississippi Valley from which it has spread to numerous other states. Abortion in mares, caused by this organism, is not considered to be prevalent, although sporadic cases do appear. Unfortunately, many of the cases are not studied bacteriologically; consequently, the exact distribution of the organism is not known.

The organism is thought by some to be transmitted by an infected stallion; however, the short incubation period of the disease and experimental infection of pregnant mares by feeding cultures of the organism, have emphasized the fact that the organism is obtained by the ingestion of infected feed, such as grass, from contaminated pastures.

Morphology and Staining. It is typical of the group.

Growth Requirements and Characteristics. The organism is aerobic and facultatively anaerobic and grows abundantly on common laboratory media.

Colonies of the organism on an agar plate are small, round, slightly elevated, glistening colonies which become finely granular in structure as they age. Older colonies are dry and membranous, and entire colonies can be pushed along the surface of the agar or lifted from it with the inoculating needle. These colonies are irregular and appear like rosettes with a wrinkled surface.

On the agar slant, growth is dull and parchment-like, developing thin wrinkles close to the water in the bottom of the tube as well as a thin pellicle on the water itself.

In broth a uniform turbidity develops in 24 hours. Cultures which have dissociated to the R develop a heavy pellicle which sinks en masse to the bottom of the tube. Smooth strains do not form a pellicle.

Resistance. The organism does not differ from other members of the group in resistance to surface disinfectants. The need of an antiseptic douche for infected mares led Good and Smith to test various chemicals which may be used for that purpose. They found that a one-tenth per cent solution of potassium permanganate kills the organism in 1 minute, 1 per cent carbolic acid in 1 minute, 1:1,000 methylene blue in 5 minutes, and a saturated solution of boric acid in 3 hours.

Biochemical Properties. *Salmonella abortivoequina* produces acid and gas from xylose, raffinose, arabinose, dulcitol, glucose, mannitol, maltose, dextrin, and trehalose; does not ferment lactose, adonitol, and inositol; varies in the fermentation of sorbitol and rhamnose. It does not liquefy gelatin; does not produce indol; varies in the production of H_2S; varies in reaction to the Bitter rhamnose test; is negative to Stern glycerol; varies in the fermentation of d-tartrate; produces an increased alkalinity in litmus milk.

Antigenic Structure and Toxins. The organism belongs to Group B on the basis of somatic antigen. H antigen is shared with other strains of Salmonella not related to equine abortion.

It does not produce an exotoxin, but a comparatively potent endotoxin is released by the organism. Large doses of killed suspensions of the organism injected subcutaneously into horses produce symptoms characterized by inappetence, chills, fever, and stiffness.

Pathogenicity. *Salmonella abortivoequina* causes abortion in mares and jennets following natural infection. Parenteral injection of the organism produces abortion in guinea pigs, rabbits. sows, ewes, mares, and jennets. The recovery of the organism from aborted bovine fetuses has been reported. It is not pathogenic for man.

Immunity. In 1916, Good and Smith demonstrated that pregnant mares were protected from the infection by the injection of a number of doses of bacterin. Since that time, bacterins have been reported to give highly satisfactory results in preventing abortion. Kelser (1921) reported that bacterins injected during the fourth and ninth months of pregnancy were used widely in United States Army Remount Depots with highly satisfactory results.

Diagnosis. Infectious abortion in mares is diagnosed by the isolation and identification of the organism from the aborted fetus and vaginal exudate from the mare. The agglutination test is also of value in detecting infected mares.

Salmonella abortusovis

In 1921, Schermer and Ehrlich isolated an organism from ewes which had aborted. They found the organism belonged in the paratyphoid group; consequently, they named it *Bacillus paratyphi abortus ovis*. In 1925, Bosworth and Glover discovered the organism was the cause of abortion in ewes in England. The organism has not been reported from the United States.

Salmonella abortusovis is similar to the other members of the group in morphology and culture characteristics. It produces acid and gas from glucose, maltose, mannitol, xylose, and sorbitol; does not ferment lactose, sucrose, salicin, inositol, or rhamnose; is variable in fermenting arabinose, dulcitol, and dextrin. It produces H_2S slowly and does not change litmus milk.

Lovell found the English and German strains to be antigenically identical. The organism shares somatic antigen with other members of Group B. Apparently it is pathogenic only for sheep, for it has not been reported from other animals or from man.

Salmonella choleraesuis

Synonyms and History. *Bacillus cholerae suis, Bacterium cholerae suis, Bacillus suipestifer, Salmonella choleraesuis, Salmonella suipestifer.*

This organism was first isolated and described in 1885 by Salmon and Smith, and was named *Bacillus cholerae suis*. It was considered to be the cause of hog cholera until the real cause, a filtrable virus, was discovered in hog cholera, and it was found to be one of the infecting agents in infectious enteritis in Iowa pigs by Murray, Biester, Purwin, and McNutt in 1927 and 1928.

Distribution and Transmission. The organism is widely distributed throughout the world where large numbers of pigs are raised. It is transmitted by the ingestion of feed and water contaminated by feces from infected animals. The repetition of the infection on certain farms year after year indicates that the organism lives through the winter season in fecal material or is present in animals which have become immune carriers.

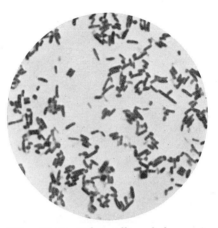

FIG. 21.4 — **Salmonella choleraesuis** smear from agar culture, × 2,000. (From Nowak: Documenta Microbiologica, courtesy Gustav Fischer.)

Morphology and Staining. It is typical of the group. See Figures 21.4 and 21.5.

Resistance. The organism is typical of the group.

Growth Requirements and Characteristics. It is typical of the group.

Biochemical Properties. *Sal. choleraesuis* produces acid and gas from glucose, fructose, galactose, mannose, xylose, maltose, glycerol, mannitol, dulcitol, isodulcitol, sorbitol, and dextrin; does not ferment arabinose, inositol, lactose, sucrose, salicin, inulin, raffinose, and trehalose. It reduces nitrates; does not form indol; does not liquefy gelatin; produces a slight initial acidity in milk followed by alkalinity and clearing of the medium; ferments *d*-tartrate. It is negative to the Bitter rhamnose test and to the Stern test. *Sal. choleraesuis* does not produce H_2S; however, it must be emphasized that *Sal. choleraesuis* var. *kunzendorf* does produce H_2S and the two species may be identified on that basis.

Antigenic Structure and Toxins. See Table 21.4. The antigens of this organism are similar to *Sal. paratyphosum* C, and organism producing a certain type of enteric fever in man. It is also closely related in antigenic structure to *Sal. choleraesuis* var. *kunzendorf* which lacks a type specific H antigen.

Pathogenicity. *Sal. choleraesuis* is the cause of acute infectious enteritis found in pigs of all ages throughout the United States. Freshly isolated cultures of the organism reproduce the typical disease when they are fed or injected parenterally. The organism has also been recovered from cattle, dogs, and fowls and occurs more frequently than any other Salmonella in foxes.

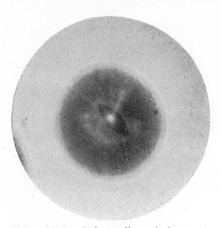

FIG. 21.5 — **Salmonella choleraesuis** colony on agar plate, × 30. (From Nowak: Documenta Microbiologica, courtesy Gustav Fischer.)

Mice are more susceptible than any of the other laboratory animals; they die of a septicemia within a few days after inoculation. Guinea pigs are susceptible when cultures are fed or injected. The rabbit is especially susceptible to this organism, succumbing to very small does given parenterally.

The organism has been recovered from cases of food poisoning in man. The Kunzendorf variety has been isolated most frequently from such cases. Henderson isolated the organism from a urinary tract infection in a farmer 49 years of age.

Three cases of pneumonia in man caused by *Sal. choleraesuis* were reported by Levine and Plattner in 1944. These authors suggest that blood cultures and the agglutination test with *Sal. choleraesuis* antigen should be used in cases of atypical pneumonia in man.

Immunity. Mature animals which recover from an attack of this organism are presumably immune. It was the first organism to be used in the preparation of a bacterin for immunizing purposes by Salmon and Smith; bacterin-therapy was used for hog cholera until the discovery of the virus and virus antiserum. The function of bacterins in producing immunity in pigs is of doubtful value due to the massive doses of the organism which enter the susceptible intestinal tract of pigs on contaminated feeds. Infectious enteritis due to this organism can be prevented best by observing well-established rules of swine sanitation and nutrition.

Diagnosis. Infection due to *Sal. choleraesuis* is detected by the isolation and identification of the organism. This includes the determination of the antigenic structure.

Salmonella typhisuis

Salmonella typhisuis was isolated by Glässer in 1909 from young pigs with a typhoid-like infection known as ferkeltyphus. This organism has been reported from Germany, but as far as is known it is not present in the United States. It has been considered a strain of *Salmonella choleraesuis* since the two are antigenically alike. It varies from *Sal. choleraesuis,* however, since it produces acid and gas from arabinose and trehalose but does not form hydrogen sulphide. The organism forms a more delicate growth on solid media and produces gas more slowly in fermentable media than *Sal. choleraesuis.*

It is pathogenic only for young pigs and has not been involved in human infection.

Salmonella enteritidis

Synonyms and History. *Bacillus enteritidis, Bacterium enteritidis.* This organism was first isolated by Gärtner, in 1888, from a fatal case of meat poisoning in man and from beef that had produced the disease. Since then the organism and its different varieties have been isolated from numerous animals and from man.

Antigenic classification and other special tests have revealed that there are a number of varieties of *Salmonella enteritidis.*

All of the strains are similar in morphology, colony characteristics, and resistance to the other members of the Salmonella group.

Biochemical Properties. *Salmonella enteritidis* produces acid and gas from glucose, fructose, galactose, mannose, arabinose, xylose, maltose, trehalose, dextrin, glycerol, mannitol, dulcitol, and sorbitol; does not ferment lactose, sucrose, inulin, salicin, raffinose, adonitol, and inositol. The organism does not form indol; forms H_2S; reduces nitrates to nitrites; does not liquefy gelatin.

Pathogenicity. *Salmonella enteritidis* produces enteritis in rodents and in man. It has been isolated from cattle but is not of any consequence as the cause of disease in that animal in this country.

Salmonella enteritidis var. *danysz* was originally isolated from an epidemic of enteritis in field mice, but is now thought to be more pathogenic for rats.

Salmonella enteritidis var. *essen* has been isolated from ducks' eggs and from ducks. It also has been known to produce gastroenteritis in man.

Salmonella enteritidis var. *dublin* is considered one of the primary causes of calf diarrhea. It has been found also in pigs and foals. This strain is one of the important causes of food poisoning in man.

Salmonella enteritidis var. *rostock* has been isolated from cattle but has not been known to produce disease in man.

Higgens, Christiansen, and Schroeder report an infection in a flock of 900 turkeys caused by *Sal. enteritidis*. The disease involved 100 birds and was characterized by purulent exudate in the tendon sheaths of the hock joint.

The different varieties of *Salmonella enteritidis* are able to produce a severe gastroenteritis in mice and guinea pigs. The inflammatory reaction is produced by a potent endotoxin which is liberated by the organism. The endotoxin is resistant to heat and is not antigenic, resembling the enterotoxin of the staphylococci.

Immunity. Infections which are caused by *Salmonella enteritidis* and its different varieties are so sporadic that little is known about the immunity which may result following the active disease. It is presumed that these infections, in common with those which are produced by other salmonellae, produce an immunity. Calf enteritis produced by the organism seems to support this presumption, for this animal is resistant to infection as it passes out of the age of calfhood.

Salmonella enteritidis is commonly incorporated in mixed bacterins which are used to immunize calves. The antiserum which is used in the treatment of cases of calf enteritis should be polyvalent; that is, it should include antibodies against this organism along with those of other organisms which are known to be the cause of the disease.

Diagnosis. The presence of this organism is detected by isolating and identifying it by the use of biochemical reactions.

Salmonella pullorum

Synonyms and History. *Bacterium pullorum, Bacillus pullorum.*

Salmonella pullorum was first isolated from chicks suffering with severe diarrhea and was described by Rettger in 1899, and more completely described by Rettger and Stoneburn in 1909. At this time considerable confusion existed concerning this organism and the one responsible for typhoid in chickens, now called *Salmonella gallinarum*. Smith and Ten Broeck, in 1915, were the first to show the differences between the two organisms. It is possible to distinguish *Sal. pullorum* and *Sal. gallinarum* on the basis of carbohydrate fermentation; however, the antigenic structure of the two is identical, and on this basis they both are placed in the genus Salmonella by the Salmonella subcommittee.

Distribution and Transmission. The organism is widely distributed over the world where chickens are present in large numbers.

The transmission of *Sal. pullorum* from an infected chick to a susceptible one is commonly through feed and water. An unusual mode of transmission exists in this disease. Many of the infected chicks which survive an infection remain carriers of the organism. The organism shows a definite affinity for the developing ovary of the pullet in which it localizes and produces a condition typified by shrunken, distorted, and undeveloped ova; however, many ova do develop into eggs. These eggs contain the organism, and when they are incubated and hatched, an infected chick results. This chick will then infect others; hence, the cycle of the infection is continued.

Sal. pullorum may be transmitted from an infected adult member of a flock to other adults. Gwatkin has shown that adult turkeys also may be infected by contact with infected adult chickens. Although turkeys do not maintain the infection as do adult hens during the period of infection, they lay eggs which contain the organism.

The role of the infected rooster in the transmission of *Sal. pullorum* has been investigated by many. In general it is believed that this manner of transmission is not too frequent but may happen. The hazard is great enough to warrant the removal of infected males of all species of domestic fowl from the flock.

Morphology and Staining. The organism is similar to the other Gram-negative rods in size and shape. It does not possess flagella which is an important characteristic in respect to antigenic structure. The normal shape of the organism is short and plump, but Van Roekel has described variants which are extremely long and filamentous (Fig. 21.6).

Growth Requirements and Characteristics. The organism is isolated in pure culture by opening the infected chick with aseptic precautions and streaking blood or liver and spleen pulp upon the surface of meat infusion agar. The organism is aerobic and facultatively anaerobic; grows best at 37°C. and a pH of 7.2.

The normal organism produces smooth, glistening, opalescent, entire colonies on nutrient agar (Fig. 21.7). Van Roekel has described variants which form rough, dry, and opaque colonies with markedly irregular edges (Fig. 21.8). Mucoid colonies also have been described. Variation is induced more easily by growing the organism on liver infusion agar.

Resistance. It is typical of the group.

Biochemical Properties. *Sal. pullorum* produces acid and gas from glucose, fructose, galactose, mannose, arabinose, xylose, mannitol, and isodulcitol; does not attack lactose, sucrose, dextrin, salicin, raffinose, sorbitol, adonitol, dulcitol, or inositol. The organism has been considered unable to ferment maltose. Hinshaw reports the finding of an occasional strain which produces acid from this carbohydrate. In a study of 300 strains of the organism, Hinshaw, Browne, and Taylor found 40 strains which did not ferment maltose, 27 anaerobic strains which did ferment maltose, and 260 aerobic strains which were able to produce acid in this carbohydrate. They were able to isolate non-maltose-fermenting strains as variants from stock cultures of maltose-fermenting strains. It produces H_2S; reduces nitrates to nitrites; does not form indol; does not liquefy gelatin; produces initial slight acidity in milk with increasing alkalinity; is negative to the Bitter rhamnose test, and the Stern glycerol test; does not ferment d-tartrate.

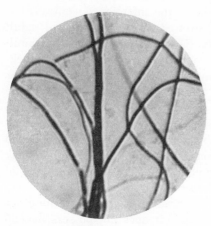

FIG. 21.6 — **Salmonella pullorum** showing long filamentous variant types, × 1,200. (Courtesy Van Roekel.)

Antigenic Structure and Toxins. *Sal. pullorum* posseses only somatic antigen since it is nonmotile. The complete antigenic formula of the organism is considered to be 9, 12. However, antigenic variants 12_1, 12_2, and 12_3 have been observed. Strains of the organism are classified as standard, variant, or intermediate types. Williams has found that the three antigenic types may be differentiated by a macroscopic ammonium sulfate sedimentation test. The significance of antigenic variability of *Sal. pullorum* is emphasized in agglutination testing of adult hens for the detection of reactors (Wright). It is apparent that a testing antigen should contain both regular and variant forms if the variant is known to exist in the territory to be tested.

Pathogenicity. *Salmonella pullorum* produces an acute disease in chicks during their first few days of life and is characterized by a severe enteritis and bacteremia. The fecal material is white in color and pasty in consistency. This color led to the name bacillary white diarrhea, but one of the terms salmonellosis, paratyphoid, or pullorum disease is considered more appropriate. In mature hens the organism produces a chronic infection characterized by a shrunken and misshapen ovary. Acute septicemia has been reported in mature chickens.

In an outbreak of *Sal. pullorum* infection in canaries in which 50 birds of a flock of 75 died, Edwards was able to isolate the organism from 13 of the birds autopsied.

This organism infects turkeys in the same manner as chickens, but as previously noted it does not appear to be as chronic a disease in the turkey hen as in the chicken.

Sal. pullorum has been isolated from other species of animals including the cow, pig, and fox. The importance of it as an agent of disease in mammals is not considered very great. It is significant to observe that no serious outbreaks of infection in man have been caused by this organism.

Of special interest is the isolation of *Sal. pullorum* from a dog by Brown, Bruner, and Moran in 1948. The animal had been in poor condition and received a diet of raw eggs before it was destroyed. Upon autopsy an intense icterus was found along with an enlarged liver and petechial hemorrhages in the lungs. The organism was isolated from many different tissues.

Immunity. An absolute immunity to the organism does not appear to develop. A local tissue immunity, particularly in the intestinal tract, appears

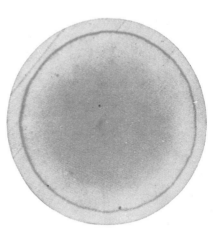

FIG. 21.7 — **Salmonella pullorum**, normal smooth S colony, × 125. (Courtesy Van Roekel.)

to develop in chicks which survive an infection. The localization of *Salmonella pullorum* in the ovary makes it evident that a generalized immune condition does not exist. Agglutinins are present in the blood stream of the hen which harbors the organism in the ovary.

Diagnosis. The presence of the organism in the chick is determined by the isolation and identification of it.

The agglutination test is used to diagnose the condition in mature hens. Two types of tests are commonly used, the macroscope tube test and the macroscopic plate test, or rapid test. The rapid plate test can be done in the field, employing whole blood instead of the clear serum which is used in the laboratory. The dissociation or variation of the organism from the normal S to the abnormal R necessitates care in the selection of strains of the organism for the production of suitable bacterial suspensions for the agglutination test. It is also essential to include all antigenic types in the antigen.

Rice has described an indirect complement-fixation test which has been found to be of value as a supplementary serologic method in experimental studies where the agglutination reaction may give indeterminate results.

Salmonella anatum

In 1919, Rettger reported a disease which he observed in duck-lings from which he isolated an organism typical of the Salmonella group. The following year Rettger and Scoville described the organism in detail and named it *Bacterium anatis*.

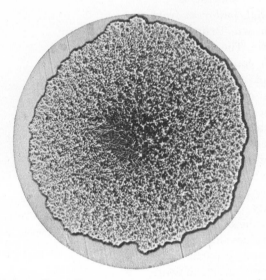

FIG. 21.8 — **Salmonella pullorum,** variant rough R colony, $\times$ 25. (Courtesy Van Roekel.)

The disease is extremely acute and fatal. Rettger and Scoville describe the symptoms as follows: [1]

> The affected individuals appeared weak and sluggish, and remained close to the heating pipes. They were not easily aroused, and did not go in search of food, as did the others. They ate at times, however, and their crops were distended. One of the marked symptoms was intense thirst. After drinking, some of the ducklings drew themselves to full height, staggered a few seconds, keeled over and after one or two gasps died—hence the name "keel" for the disease. Few of the ducklings died after they were from three to four weeks of age; the greatest mortality occurring within the first week or ten days. Examination of the dead ducklings revealed no lesions of any pathologic condition except, perhaps, paleness of the tissues as a whole and light body weight.

The organism is obtained from ovarian and abdominal cysts of breeding ducks which appear to be carriers of the infection; consequently, it resembles the infection cycle of the disease in chickens caused by *Sal. pullorum*.

Craige isolated *Sal. anatum* from the feces of a dog showing symptoms of diarrhea and encephalitis.

The prevalence of *Sal. anatum* in many different species of animals has become evident since the antigenic typing of the Salmon-

[1] L. F. Rettger, and M. M. Scoville, Jour. Inf. Dis., 26: 215, 1920.

ella became the customary method of identification. Reference to Table 21.2 emphasizes that the organism has been recovered from 13 different animal species including the turkey, chicken, pigeon, duck, game birds, canary, sheep, pig, dog, fox, rat, reptiles, and man. The presence of *Sal. anatum* in dogs is emphasized by the report of Galton, McElrath, Stucker, and Hardy in 1950, in which 297 cultures of this organism were identified out of 937 of all salmonellae. Likewise, the presence of the organism in swine was noted in 547 of 1,476 total fecal isolations of salmonellae by Galton and associates.

Sal. anatum is similar to *Sal. pullorum* in morphology, but cultures of the organism on solid media are heavier than *Sal. pullorum*.

The organism produces acid and gas from glucose, fructose, galactose, maltose, dextrin, arabinose, xylose, mannitol, dulcitol, trehalose, and rhamnose; does not ferment lactose, sucrose, inulin, raffinose, salicin, or inositol. It is positive to the Bitter rhamnose test and the Stern glycerol test; ferments *d*-tartrate; produces an alkaline reaction in litmus milk; does not liquefy gelatin; reduces nitrates to nitrites; does not form indol.

The antigenic structure of *Sal. anatum* is sufficiently different from the other species in the genus to place it in Group E_1. See Table 21.4.

Agglutinating antibody is produced in breeding ducks which are infected with the organism; consequently, it is possible to detect such cases by the agglutination reaction.

Salmonella gallinarum

Synonyms and History. This organism was first isolated in 1889 by Klein in England from chickens suffering with a disease referred to as fowl typhoid. He named the organism *Bacillus gallinarum*. In 1895 Moore, in the United States, isolated an organism which he called *Bacterium sanguinarum* from cases of "infectious leukemia" in fowls.

The isolation of a similar organism, *Salmonella pullorum*, from chicks in 1900 by Rettger opened the way for extensive investigation of the two organisms, and various conclusions have been reached by different individuals. In Germany it has been concluded that the two organisms are identical or that *Salmonella pullorum* is just a variety of *Salmonella gallinarum*. This opinion has not been accepted by all. The Salmonella subcommittee places the organism in the genus Salmonella because its O antigen is identical with *Salmonella pullorum*.

An organism isolated by Hadley, Elkins, and Caldwell in 1918, and named *Bacterium jeffersonii,* has been found to be antigenically identical with *Salmonella gallinarum;* consequently, it is now considered to be a synonym of the organism under discussion.

Morphology and Staining. *Salmonella gallinarum* is a short, plump rod, 0.4 to 0.6μ by 0.8 to 1.6μ in size. It usually occurs singly, but short chains are sometimes observed in blood smears. It is non-flagellated, nonsporeforming, and noncapsulated.

The organism is stained with the common dyes and is Gram-negative. If blood smears are stained with methylene blue or dilute carbol fuchsin, the organism appears distinctly bipolar, not unlike the typical *Pasteurella avicida* of fowl cholera.

Growth Requirements and Characteristics. The organism is easily isolated from the blood and liver of typical cases of fowl typhoid. It grows well on meat infusion media adjusted to a pH 7.2. It is aerobic, facultatively anaerobic, and grows best at 37°C.

On the agar plate the colony of the organism is small, blue-grey, moist, circular, and entire.

The organism produces a uniform turbidity in broth and the formation of a granular sediment. A thin, filmy pellicle is observed in some strains.

Resistance. The organism is easily killed by any of the disinfectants. Its thermal death point is 60°C. in 10 minutes. It is not resistant to desiccation but does live for some time in fecal material from infected chickens.

Biochemical Properties. *Salmonella gallinarum* produces acid but no gas from glucose, fructose, galactose, mannose, xylose, arabinose, maltose, dextrin, mannitol, dulcitol, and isodulcitol; does not ferment lactose, sucrose, glycerol, salicin, or sorbitol. It reduces nitrates in the presence of Difco peptone; does not liquefy gelatin; does not form indol. The organism does not acidify or coagulate litmus milk. Some strains produce hydrogen sulphide.

Antigenic Structure and Toxins. *Salmonella gallinarum* possesses the O antigen 1, 9, and 12, which is similar to *Salmonella pullorum* and many other species in Group D of the Salmonella antigenic classification. Numerous reports are found which emphasize the close antigenic relationship of *Salmonella pullorum* and *Salmonella gallinarum*. For the most part, these reports have resulted from studies of the problems related to the testing of flocks of laying hens in order to detect fowls infected with *Sal. pullorum*. The blood from a chicken infected with either organism will cause the agglutination of a suspension of either organism.

Salmonella gallinarum does not produce a true toxin, although an effective endotoxin has been demonstrated.

Pathogenicity. *Salmonella gallinarum* is the cause of an acute intestinal and generalized infection of fowls usually past the first few weeks of life. Artificial infection of young chicks produces a disease typical of the infection caused by *Sal. pullorum*. Leucocytic infiltration of the liver and other parenchymatous tissue is characteristic of fowl typhoid; however, this disease differs from the leucosis which is caused by a filtrable virus. Boney, 1947, reported the isolation of this organism from turkeys.

When fed or injected parenterally, the organism is capable of producing disease in rabbits and all poultry as well as in wild birds and canaries.

Immunity. Fowl typhoid bacterins have been used in flocks which are periodically affected with the disease, but are not considered a substantial method of controlling the disease; furthermore, Runnells and Thorp have demonstrated that the sera of such birds give a positive agglutination test with *Sal. pullorum* antigen.

Diagnosis. Fowl typhoid is diagnosed by the isolation and identification of *Salmonella gallinarum*. Since *Salmonella pullorum, Salmonella typhimurium, Pasteurella avicida,* and other species of closely related organisms also may produce a disease in the fowls and birds similar to fowl typhoid, suitable culture media must be chosen for differentiation. Hinshaw has found that a gelatin medium containing 0.15 per cent cysteine hydrochloride is valuable for identification. *Salmonella gallinarum* produces a characteristic yellowish-white or grayish turbidity in this medium when incubated at 37°C. for 72 hours, whereas *Sal. pullorum* does not produce turbidity.

The cross reaction of this organism with *Sal. pullorum* limits the value of the agglutination test as a method of diagnosing fowl typhoid. However, Moore has shown that polyvalent *Sal. gallinarum* antigen is more sensitive than standard *Sal. pullorum* antigen.

REFERENCES FOR FURTHER STUDY

Bergey, D. H., *et al.* Manual of Determinative Bacteriology. 6th Ed. The Williams & Wilkins Co., Baltimore, 1948.

Boney, W. A. Amer. Jour. Vet. Res., 8:133, 1947.

Bosworth, T. J., and Glover, R. E. Contagious Abortion in Ewes. Vet. Jour., 81:319–34, 1925.

Brown, R. G., Bruner, D. W., Moran, A. B. Jour. Amer. Vet. Med. Assn., 114:29, 1949.

Bruner, D. W., and Edwards, P. R. Biochemical and Serological Studies of Microorganisms of the *Salmonella cholerae-suis* Group. Ky. Agr. Exp. Sta. Bull. 404. Lexington, 1940.

———, and Moran, A. B. Cornell Vet., 39:53, 1949.

Coburn, D. R., Armstrong, W. H., and Psyche, W. W. Amer. Jour. Vet. Res., 3:96–99, 1942.

Craige, J. E. Jour. Amer. Vet. Med. Assn., 105:33, 1944.

Dimock, W. W., and Good, E. S. Jour. Amer. Vet. Med. Assn., 71:25–31, 1927.

Edwards, P. R. Standard Strains of Salmonella. Ky. Agr. Exp. Sta., Cir. No. 50, 1939.

Edwards, P. R. Jour. Amer. Vet. Med. Assn., 107:545, 1945.

———, and Bruner, D. W. The Significance of Biological Types of *Salmonella typhimurium*. Ky. Agr. Exp. Sta. Bull. 400. Lexington, 1940.

———, ———, Cornell Vet., 36:318, 1946.

———, ———, and Moran, A. B. The Genus Salmonella: Its Occurrence and Distribution in the United States. Ky. Agr. Exp. Sta. Bull. 525, U. of Kentucky, Lexington, 1948.

———, ———, ———. Further Studies on the Occurrence and Distribution of Salmonella Types in the United States. Jour. Inf. Dis., 83:220, 1948.

———, and Ewing, W. H. Identification of Enterobacteriaceae. Burgess Publishing Co., Minneapolis, 1955.

———, and Hull, F. E. Bacillary White Diarrhea and Related Diseases of Chickens. Ky. Agr. Exp. Sta., Res. Bull. 296, 1929.

Galton, M. M., Lowery, W. D., and Hardy, A. V. Jour. Inf. Dis., 95:232, 1954.

———, McElrath, H. B., Stucker, C. L., and Hardy, A. V. Proc. Book, 87th Ann. Conv. Amer. Vet. Med. Assn., 1950.

———, Smith, W. V., McElrath, H. B., and Hardy, A. V. Jour. Inf. Dis., 95:236, 1954.

Gauger, H. C., Greaves, R. E., and Cook, F. W. Paratyphoid of Pigeons. Tech. No. Carolina State Agr. Exp. Sta. Bull. 62. Raleigh, 1940.

Good, E. S., and Smith, W. V. Further Investigations of the Etiology and Control of Infectious Abortion in Mares. Ky. Agr. Exp. Sta. Bull. 204, 1916.

Gwatkin, R. Efficiency of Homologous and Heterologous Antigens in Detecting Reacting Birds in a Variant-Infected Flock. Can. Jour. Comp. Med., 9:183, 1945.

———. Comparison of Whole Blood and Tube Tests with Regular and Variant Antigen and a Combination of the Two Antigens. Can. Jour. Comp. Med., 9:216, 1945.

———. Serological Reactions of Regular and Variant Types of *Salmonella pullorum*. Can. Jour. Comp. Med., 10:254, 1946.

———. Antigenic Differences in Strains of *Salmonella pullorum*. Amer. Jour. Vet. Res., 8:204, 1947.

———. Infection in the Male and Experiments on Transmission to the Female. Can. Jour. Comp. Med., 10:377, 1946.

———. Response to Oral Infection with *Salmonella pullorum* in Comparable Groups of Turkeys and Chickens. Can. Jour. Comp. Med., 12:47, 1948.

———. Infection of Adult Turkeys by Mouth and by Contact with Infected Hens. Can. Jour. Comp. Med., 13:103, 1949.

———, and Bond, E. W. Examination of Colonies from Regular and Variant Form Subcultures of *Salmonella pullorum*. Can. Jour. Comp. Med., 11:289, 1947.

Higgens, W. A., Christiansen, J. B., and Schroeder, C. H. Poult. Sci., 23:340–41, 1944.

Hinshaw, W. R. Cysteine and Related Compounds for Differentiating Members of the Genus Salmonella. Hilgardia, 13:583–621, 1941.

———. Salmonellosis of Turkeys. Vet. Med., 42:179, 1947.

———, Browne, A. S., and Taylor, T. J. Jour. Inf. Dis., 72:197–201, 1943.

————, and McNeil, E. The Use of the Agglutination Test in Detecting *Salmonella typhimurium* Carriers in Turkey Flocks. Prof. 47 Ann. Meet. U. S. Livestock Sanit. Assn., p. 106, 1943.

————, ————. Amer. Jour. Vet. Res., 6:264–66, 1945.

————, ————. Avian Salmonellosis. Its Economic and Public Health Significance. Off. Rpt. Eighth World's Poultry Congress. 1948.

Karsten and Ehrlich. Das seuchenhafte, durch Paratyphusbazillen hervorgerufene Verwerfen bei Schafen. Deutsche Tier. Woch. 31: 307, 1923.

Kauffmann, Fritz. Der heutige Stand der Paratyphusforschung. Zentrlb. für gs. Hyg., 25:273–311, 1931.

Kelser, R. A. Jour. Amer. Vet. Med. Assn., 59: 284–94, 1921.

Levine, M. G., and Plattner, E. B. Amer. Jour. Clin. Path., 14: 342–43, 1944.

Lovell, R. Jour. Path. Bact., 34: 13–22, 1931.

Lukas, G. N., and Bradford, D. R. Jour. Amer. Vet. Med. Assn., 125:215, 1954.

Mallmann, W. L. Bacterium Pullorum Studies. Mich. Agr. Exp. Sta., Tech. Bull. 68, 1925.

Moore, E. N. Cornell Vet., 37:21, 1947.

Murray, Chas., Biester, H. E., Purwin, D., and McNutt, S. H. Studies in Infectious Enteritis of Swine. Jour. Amer. Vet. Med. Assn., 72, First paper, pp. 34–90, 1927. Second paper, pp. 1003–22, 1928.

Rettger, L. F., and Scoville, M. M. *Bacterium anatum.* (n. sp.) Jour. Inf. Dis., 26: 215–29, 1920.

Rice, C. E. Technique of the Indirect Complement-fixation Test for Activity with *Salmonella pullorum* Antigens. Can. Jour. Comp. Med., 12: 69, 1948.

———— and Gwatkin, R. A. Comparison of Titers Obtained by Indirect Complement Fixation and Agglutination Methods for Chicken Sera. Can. Jour. Comp. Med., 13: 165, 1949.

Salmonella Subcommittee (Nom. Comm. Internat. Soc. Microbiol.) The Genus Salmonella Lignières, 1900. Jour. Hyg., Camb., 34:333–50, 1934.

————. Proc. 3rd Internat. Cong. Microbiol. The Williams & Wilkins Co., Baltimore, 1940.

Schermer and Ehrlich. Weitere Beiträge über die Paratyphuserkrankungen der Haustiere. Ber. Tier. Wchn. 37: 469–73, 1921.

Schofield, F. W. Can. Jour. Comp. Med., 10: 271, 1946.

Scott, W. M., and Minett, F. C. Jour. Hyg., Camb., 45:159, 1947.

Topley, W. W. C., Wilson, G. S., and Miles, A. A. Principles of Bacteriology and Immunology. 3rd Ed. Williams & Wilkins Co., Baltimore, 1946.

Van Roekel, H. A Study of Variation of *Salmonella pullorum.* Mass. Agr. Exp. Sta. Bull. 319, 1935.

White, P. B. The Salmonella Group. A System of Bacteriology 4: 86–158. Med. Res. Council. His Majesty's Stationery Office, London, 1929.

Williams, J. E. Amer. Jour. Vet. Res., 14:465, 1953.

Wright, M. L. Jour. Amer. Vet. Med. Assn., 112: 241, 1948.

————, and Edwards, P. R. Amer. Jour. Vet. Res., 9:386, 1948.

Younie, A. R. Can. Jour. Comp. Med., 5: 64, 1941.

22. | The Genus Shigella

There are a number of species of nonmotile, Gram-negative rods which are placed in the genus Shigella. One of them, *Shigella dysenteriae*, causes dysentery in man. *Shigella equirulis* is associated with purulent nephritis, septicemia, and joint infection in foals. A few species have been isolated from chickens which have shown symptoms of a severe intestinal infection.

Shigella dysenteriae

Synonyms and History. *Bacillus dysenteriae, Bacillus shigae,* Shiga bacillus, Flexner bacillus, Sonne bacillus, *Bacterium dysenteriae.*

The dysentery bacilli are composed of a number of varieties which have many characteristics in common, especially pathogenicity; yet they vary in carbohydrate fermentation much more than many of the other types of bacteria which are placed in separate species on that basis. The first and most typical organism of the group was isolated by Shiga in Japan in 1898. A second type was isolated by Flexner in the Philippines in 1900, although at that time he considered it to be the same organism discovered by Shiga. Kruse demonstrated that the two types were serologically distinct. In 1902 Martini and Lentz showed that the Shiga and Flexner strains were easily distinguishable by fermentation reactions.

In 1904 Duval described a lactose-fermenting organism in cases of typical dysentery. This type is included with the dysentery bacilli and is commonly designated the Sonne type. A fourth organism, first described by Schmitz in 1917 as the cause of an epidemic dysentery in a Rumanian war prison camp, is included in the dysentery group. This organism is known as the Schmitz dysentery bacillus but has been assigned the species name *Shigella ambigua.* It produces indol and is serologically independent of the other dysentery organisms.

Distribution and Transmission. The dysentery organisms are widely distributed throughout the world and are frequently associated with epidemic disease where a large number of persons congregate together and live under insanitary conditions.

The organism is commonly transmitted by water and food which have been contaminated by human excreta. Hand contamination of food and cooking utensils is not as common as in typhoid fever. Flies are considered to be a more significant transmitting factor in dysentery than in typhoid. The immune carrier is known to exist in dysentery but is not as great a factor as in typhoid.

Morphology and Staining. *Shigella dysenteriae* is a short, plump rod, 0.4 to 0.6μ by 1.0 to 3.0μ. It occurs singly. It is nonmotile.

The organism is Gram-negative.

Growth Requirements and Characteristics. This group of organisms is typical of the other Gram-negative rods of the genera Salmonella and Eberthella. Smooth S to rough R colony dissociation is frequently observed among the Shigella organisms.

Biochemical Properties. The strains or types of dysentery bacilli differ in respect to many of the biochemical reactions.

The Shiga type produces acid from glucose but does not ferment mannitol, lactose, rhamnose, salicin, or xylose; does not produce indol; produces an alkaline reaction in milk.

The Flexner type is not homogenous in respect to biochemical reactions. None of the strains ferments mannitol. Three subgroups are recognized by the use of maltose and sucrose: (a) The Hiss-Russell, or Y organism, does not ferment maltose or sucrose; (b) the Strong strain ferments sucrose but not maltose; (c) the Flexner strain ferments maltose but not sucrose consistently.

The Sonne type is the only one of the group which produces acid in lactose and causes the coagulation of milk. It agrees with the Flexner type in fermenting mannitol. It forms acid in arabinose, salicin, rhamnose, and raffinose and varies in the fermentation of maltose and sucrose. Subtypes have been formed by the fermentation of xylose and maltose.

The Schmitz type, or *Shigella ambigua*, is the only one of the dysentery bacilli to produce indol. It agrees with the Shiga variety in that it is unable to ferment many of the carbohydrates but differs from that organism inasmuch as it produces acid in rhamnose.

Antigenic Structure and Toxins. The different strains of dysentery bacilli appear to be antigenically homogenous for each type with the exception of the Flexner type which is composed of a number of heterogenous strains. The group lacks the flagellar specific antigen which is so significant in the Salmonella group; consequently, comparatively little is known concerning the antigenic structure of the group.

The Shiga type is characterized by the soluble exotoxin which it produces. This toxin is fatal to the rabbit, producing diarrhea and paralysis of the limbs; but is less active in guinea pigs, producing diarrhea with no paralysis. The other types do not produce true toxin although the endotoxins of all are fatal to rabbits when given in large doses intravenously.

Pathogenicity. The dysentery bacilli are pathogenic to man and resemble the typhoid bacillus in this respect. They produce a type of intestinal infection in man which is distinguished from typhoid fever by a shorter incubation period, two to three days, by a more persistent diarrhea, by a lower temperature, and by the localization of the infection in the colon instead of in the small intestine. The condition is prone to become chronic, producing a persistent diarrhea over a period of several weeks. The Shiga variety produces the most severe type of case and is more fatal than the others.

When cultures of dysentery bacilli are injected intravenously or intraperitoneally into rabbits and guinea pigs, they produce lesions in the intestines which are similar to those produced by the natural disease in man. The same type of infection is not produced by feeding virulent cultures or toxins. These results suggest that the seat of the infection is in the submucous cells due to the elimination of the organism or its toxins.

Immunity. Vaccines have been proven to be of value in prophylactic procedures; however, they must be of a polyvalent nature to be effective. Antiserum has been used in the treatment of cases of the disease, and in the case of Shiga antiserum, the results have been satisfactory.

Diagnosis. The blood serum of a dysentery patient agglutinates dysentery bacilli. The various types must be identified by culture reactions.

Shigella equirulis

Synonyms and History. This organism was first observed in 1908 by Theiler in South Africa in cases of purulent nephritis of horses. In a report covering the years 1908-09, Meyer in South Africa called the organism *Bacillus nephritidis equi*. Van Straaten referred to the organism as *Bacillus equuli* in 1916-17. Magnusson called the organism *Bacterium viscosum equi* in 1917. In the United States it was first isolated and described by Snyder in 1925. She used the name *Eberthella viscosa*.

Much of the information concerning this organism and the disease it produces has been contributed by Dimock and Edwards of Kentucky. In 1931, Edwards published a detailed study of the organism in which he advanced reasons for using the name *Shigella equirulis*.

Distribution and Transmission. The reports of the organism rom various parts of the world indicate that it is widely distributed. n the United States it has been reported from Kentucky, New York, ɪnd Indiana. Britton has observed this organism as the cause of he death of foals in California.

The methods by which foals are infected with the organism are ʌot known. Dimock, Edwards, and Bullard reported the average age ɪt death as 2.9 days; the appearance of the disease so soon after ɔirth indicates that infection occurs *in utero*. The organism has ɔeen isolated from verminous aneurysms in old horses, and it has ɔeen claimed that the organism is carried by the larvae of intestinal ʌematode parasites.

Morphology and Staining. *Shigella equirulis* is a small, non-motile rod, 0.3 to 0.4μ by 0.4 to 0.8μ in size. It is notably pleomorphic, ɪnd single cells, streptococcus-like chains, and long filaments occur n the same smear. The organism is considered noncapsule-pro-ducing, although some investigators report the presence of capsular ʌaterial.

Young cultures of the organism are stained easily by the ɪsual stains and are Gram-negative.

Growth Requirements and Characteristics. The organism is an ʌerobe and facultative anaerobe, and grows readily in media con-ɪaining fresh meat infusion.

When the organism is isolated from infected tissue and grown ɔn the surface of agar media, it forms a characteristically rough, ɪry, irregular mucoid colony. Well-isolated colonies frequently ʌttain 3 to 5 mm. in size. The colonies are raised, are sometimes ʌemispherical, and are opaque. The surface is definitely lobulated which makes the colony appear radially striated in transmitted light. As the culture ages, a clear, smooth border develops from the edge ɔf the colony.

Many of the cultures dissociate from the normal rough type ɪo a smooth nonmucoid colony. Edwards found that incubation above 37°C. combined with an acid reaction in the medium tends to accelerate the change from rough to smooth. Dwarf colonies are also found in cultures of *Shigella equirulis*.

In broth, the growth of the rough form of the organism is first apparent as a collection of small masses of bacteria along the side ɔf the tube and floating in the medium near the surface. A thin pellicle then develops, and the sides of the tube become covered with bacteria. A thick viscid sediment forms as the culture ages, and the medium becomes decidedly turbid. The smooth form of the organism produces a uniform turbidity in broth and does not form a pellicle or much sediment.

Resistance. The organism is readily destroyed by chemical disinfectants and by 60°C. in 15 minutes. It does not remain viable on laboratory media unless it is subcultured every week.

Biochemical Properties. *Shigella equirulis* produces acid from glucose, fructose, xylose, lactose, galactose, maltose, sucrose, mannitol, dextrin, raffinose, and glycerol; does not ferment rhamnose, dulcitol, isodulcitol, sorbitol, or inositol; varies in fermenting salicin, inulin, starch, adonitol, and arabinose. It does not produce indol; reduces nitrates to nitrites; is negative to the Voges-Proskauer test; does not liquefy gelatin; acidifies, and some strains coagulate litmus milk; is negative to the methyl red test.

Antigenic Structure and Toxins. The organism is composed of a number of heterogenous strains which give positive agglutination and precipitation reactions only with their homologous antisera.

Toxin production has not been reported for the organism.

Pathogenicity. *Shigella equirulis* has been isolated from equines only. In foals it produces arthritis which usually involves the back, hip, and knee joints; glomerulonephritis followed by suppuration and necrosis; and septicemia. The condition is frequently called pyosepticemia and "joint ill." The organism produces the same typical lesions when it is injected subcutaneously into a young foal. Older colts and adult horses are more resistant although abscesses develop at the point of inoculation.

In an examination of 2,025 specimens, of which 1,150 were aborted fetuses and 875 were dead foals, Dimock, Edwards, and Bruner (1947) reported that *Shig. equirulis* was responsible for the death of a larger number of foals than any other microorganism.

It is generally conceded that the organism is not pathogenic for rabbits, guinea pigs, and rats, although enormous doses do produce death within 24 hours.

Immunity. The sudden and acute nature of the disease in the newborn foal eliminates the opportunity for any very definite immunizing treatment. The dam's blood has been used, but the value of it in accurately diagnosed cases of the disease is doubtful.

Diagnosis. *Shigella equirulis* infection in foals is diagnosed by the isolation and identification of the organism.

Shigella pfaffii

In 1905, Franz Pfaff reported the isolation of an organism from canary birds which had died of an acute infectious disease characterized by a severe enteritis and necrotic foci in the liver and spleen. In 1918, in the course of the study of the colon-typhoid organisms in birds, Hadley, Elkins, and Caldwell reported the characteristics of the Pfaff culture which they obtained from the

Kral collection. These investigators assigned the name *Bacterium pfaffi* to the organism.

Shigella pfaffii, as it is now known, is a short, Gram-negative, nonmotile rod averaging 1.4μ in length. It is stained readily by ordinary dyes, but peripheral or bipolar staining characteristics are not prominent. There are no colony characteristics formed by the organism by which it is distinguished from *Salmonella gallinarum*. The organism does not alter litmus milk, produce indol, form H_2S or reduce nitrates. It produces acid but no gas from dextrose, levulose, xylose, arabinose, maltose, dextrin, mannite, and salicin; does not ferment sucrose, raffinose, lactose, inulin, adonitol, or dulcitol. Its distribution and pathogenicity for birds other than the canary are not known. It does not produce infection in the rabbit.

No antigenic relationship exists with any known member of the paratyphoid-enteritidis group.

Shigella rettgeri

This organism was first isolated in Connecticut by Rettger in 1909 from chickens which were infected with a disease resembling fowl cholera. This original culture was studied by Hadley, Elkins, and Caldwell in 1918 and designated *Bacterium rettgerei*. *Shigella rettgeri* is a short, Gram-negative, nonmotile rod, 0.5 to 0.8μ in length. It is stained readily with ordinary dyes, but the bipolar characteristics are not apparent. The growth of the organism on the surfaces of solid media is similar to other members of the group. It grows luxuriantly on potato. It changes litmus milk to an alkaline reaction in eight days but does not alter its consistency. The organism produces acid but not gas from dextrose, levulose, galactose, mannose, xylose, adonitol, mannite, and salicin; does not ferment arabinose, raffinose, sucrose, lactose, maltose, dextrin, inulin, dulcitol, and erythritol. It does not form indol or H_2S, nor reduce nitrates.

The organism does not exhibit an antigenic relationship with any other member of the paratyphoid-enteritidis group. Its distribution and pathogenicity for other fowls are not known.

REFERENCES FOR FURTHER STUDY

Britton, J. W. Cornell Vet., 35:375, 1945.

Dimock, W. W., Edwards, P. R., and Bruner, D. W. Cornell Vet., 37:89, 1947.

———, ———, and Bullard, I. F. *Bacterium viscosum equi*. A Factor in Joint-ill and Septicemia in Young Foals. Jour. Amer. Vet. Med. Assn., 73: 163, 1928.

Edwards, P. R. Studies on *Shigella equirulis (Bact. viscosum equi)*. Ky. Agr. Exp. Sta. Bull. 320, 1931.

Edwards, P. R., and Ewing, W. H. Identification of Enterobacteriaceae. Burgess Publishing Co., Minneapolis, 1955.

Gardner, A. D., and O'Brien, R. A. The Dysentery Group of Bacilli, A System of Bacteriology. 4:161-253. Med. Res. Council. His Majesty's Stationery Office, London, 1929.

Gay, F. P., and associates. Agents of Disease and Host Resistance. Chaps. 28 and 31. Charles C. Thomas, Baltimore, 1935.

Hadley, P., Elkins, M. W., and Caldwell, D. W. The Colon-Typhoid Intermediates as Causative Agents of Disease in Birds. R. I. Agr. Exp. Sta. Bull. 174, May, 1918.

Park, W. H., and Williams, A. W. Pathogenic Microorganisms. Pp. 493-524. Lea and Febiger, Philadelphia, 1939.

Pfaff, F. Eine infektiöse Erkrankung der Kanarienvögel. Centbl. Bakt., etc., Abt. 1 Orig., 38:281, 1905.

Zinsser, H., and Bayne-Jones, S. A Textbook of Bacteriology. D. Appleton-Century Co., New York, 1939.

23. | The Genus Brucella*

The microorganisms of the genus Brucella are minute, coccoid rods which are Gram-negative. On initial culture, one of the group, *Brucella abortus,* requires an atmosphere containing an increased amount of carbon dioxide but when adjusted to aerobic conditions it grows readily. The organisms produce an increased alkalinity in milk but are almost inactive in the fermentation of carbohydrates, except for limited utilization of some of the simple sugars such as glucose. There are four species in the genus, *Brucella melitensis, Brucella abortus, Brucella suis,* and *Brucella bronchiseptica.*

The position of *Brucella melitensis, Brucella abortus,* and *Brucella suis* in the genus Brucella has never been questioned to any extent, although at one time they were classified in the genus Alcaligenes. *Brucella bronchiseptica* is the only motile species and its classification in the genus has been seriously questioned by many. The only basis for placing this organism along with the other three species is the increased alkalinity it produces in protein media, especially milk. It was on this basis that the Brucella were once classified as Alcaligenes. In 1936 Topley and Wilson called the canine distemper organism *Brucella bronchiseptica.* In the 1939 edition of Bergey's Manual this classification was followed and repeated again in 1948.

Inasmuch as the three closely related species of Brucella are usually discussed as a group and the disease which they produce is known as brucellosis, they will be discussed as a group.

Brucella melitensis
Brucella abortus
Brucella suis

Synonyms and History. In 1887 Bruce described the first member of the genus Brucella from cases of Malta fever in the Island

---

*The author is indebted to Dr. S. H. McNutt for the preparation of this chapter.

of Malta. He later named it *Micrococcus melitensis*. In 1905 it was shown that goats were usually infected and that people contracted the disease mainly from infective goat milk. In 1897 Bang, in Denmark, discovered *Br. abortus* in cases of abortion in cows and showed that it was the cause of the disease now known as Bang's disease, or brucellosis, an infectious abortion of cattle. In 1914, Traum found *Br. suis* in cases of abortion in swine. It was not until the work of Evans in 1918 that the close relationship of *Br. melitensis* and *Br. abortus* was established. She found them to be closely related morphologically, physiologically, and serologically, but showed by agglutinin absorption tests that they could be distinguished to a considerable extent.

It has been proved that even though agglutination tests and agglutination absorption tests are very useful, differentiation by this means alone often is impossible. For example, it is difficult to classify rough types by this means because they elicit a different type of agglutinin than when they were smooth. Smooth strains will not absorb the agglutinin produced by the rough type and rough strains will not absorb the agglutinin produced by the smooth. Absorption furnishes valuable additional information where other tests prove inconclusive.

Meyer in 1920 suggested the name Brucella for the genus. Evans concluded that the organisms were so much alike that they might produce similar disease conditions in different species of animals. In general, this has been proven to be true. The first recognized case of undulant fever caused by *Brucella abortus* in man is credited to Keefer in 1924. These findings stimulated research and resulted in the discovery of many cases, not only in this country, but in many parts of the world. It was found that all three species affect man. In this country the early cases of undulant fever were found in the east and southwest. Woodward recognized the first case in Iowa; this led to the extensive and meritorious work of Hardy and his associates. It has been generally concluded that *Br. melitensis* is most pathogenic for man, *Br. abortus* the least so, and *Br. suis* intermediate. In their study of cases of undulant fever in Iowa, Borts and Jordan find that *Br. suis* produces the most severe type of the disease and that *Br. melitensis* is intermediate. Each species has its natural host. The goat is the natural or true host for *Br. melitensis*, cattle for *Br. abortus*, and swine for *Br. suis*. Each species spreads readily among members of its natural host, tending to persist indefinitely in large groups. Other species of animals, including man, are accidentally infected and are considered foreign hosts; thus cattle may be infected with *Br. suis* but are quite resistant. Epidemics of milk-borne brucellosis due to *Br. suis* have been reported. In a study of the pathogenicity of

Br. suis for cattle Washko, Hutchings, and Donham found that the organism became established in the bovine udder following inoculation into the open teat orifice. *Br. abortus* is of no importance as a disease-producing agent in swine. Subcutaneous injection of *Br. abortus* into hogs produces a low agglutination titer for Brucella in such animals and it is possible that natural exposure occasionally might result in a like reaction, but no significant disease is produced and evidence that hogs act as spreaders of *Br. abortus* has not been obtained. Artificial exposure of hogs to *Br. melitensis* results in a disease much like that caused by *Br. suis*. An epidemiological study of *Br. melitensis* infection in man has led to the discovery of herds of Iowa hogs naturally infected with *Br. melitensis*. This study also indicates that infection with *Br. melitensis* may persist for long periods of time in herds of hogs and that the organism spreads from hog to hog. Damon and Scruggs have reported the isolation of this organism from hogs in Indiana. The isolation of *Br. melitensis* from human patients whose only known source of infection has been cow's milk has indicated that the bovine may harbor that species of organism. As support of this probability, Damon and Fagan (1947) reported the isolation of *Br. melitensis* from a guinea pig which had been injected with milk from cows that had aborted.

Distribution and Transmission. Brucella infections are worldwide. Infection by *Br. melitensis* is largely confined to those regions where goats are raised, especially Europe and North Africa. *Brucella suis* is confined to hog-raising regions. Cattle are raised in most parts of the world, and Bang's disease is nearly universal. In the United States, *Br. melitensis* is confined largely to the southwest, and perhaps to the hog-growing areas; *Br. suis* is especially prevalent where there are large hog populations, and *Br. abortus* is found among cattle everywhere. The incidence of infection, especially in cattle, is proportional to the amount of traffic; in certain parts of the southern states and range country, there has been little traffic in cattle, and the incidence of infection is low. This is also true of hogs. It is interesting to note that there are no reports of infection in sheep in this country although it is common in Europe. This indicates that sheep are resistant to American strains of *Br. abortus* and *Br. suis* and possibly more susceptible to *Br. melitensis*.

Brucellosis is most commonly contracted through ingestion of infective material. The organisms can pass through any mucous membrane. A few drops of a suspension of *Br. abortus* placed in the conjunctival sac of a cow quickly results in infection. The organisms are known to pass through the broken skin, and it is also thought that they can pass the unbroken skin. Tovar has shown that ticks, bed bugs, and fleas can be infected with all three species of Brucella. Only ticks are able to infect by biting and they are able to transmit the bacteria to the eggs and larvae. The Brucella are obligate parasites but can live for a considerable time outside the animal body. For this reason infected animals are the main source of danger in transmission. Food and water contaminated by diseased animals are always dangerous. It is apparent that direct or indirect association of clean animals with infected animals, or the eating of infective materials, will lead to infection. For man, the handling of diseased animals and their products, eating of infective meat, and drinking of infective milk are especially dangerous. Laboratory workers who handle Brucella organisms often become infected.

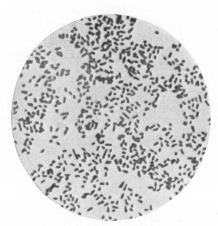

FIG. 23.1 — **Brucella abortus,** × 2,000. (From Nowak: Documenta Microbiologica, courtesy Gustav Fischer.)

Morphology and Staining. *Brucella abortus, Brucella suis,* and *Brucella melitensis* are almost identical in size and shape. As has been mentioned, *Br. melitensis* was considered to be a micrococcus for many years. All species are distinctly coccoid in shape (Fig. 23.1). They are best described as coccobacillary organisms about 0.5μ in diameter by 0.5 to 2μ in length. They are nonmotile and do not form endospores. Capsules have been demonstrated by a special staining technic. Brucella are readily stained with the aniline dyes, are not acid-fast, and are Gram-negative.

Growth Requirements and Characteristics. Brucella grow on most ordinary laboratory media but thrive especially well if the pH is 6.6 to 6.8; however, when very few are transplanted, initial growth is delayed. They grow best in the presence of many of their kind. For this reason, in primary isolation many of the usual contaminating organisms outgrow them; hence, if many contaminators are present, it is best to attempt isolation by guinea pig inoculation. This is also true when only a few Brucella are present in relatively large amounts of material such as milk. Where contamination with other organisms is scant or absent, inoculations are made on solid or in liquid medium. Solid medium, such as liver infusion agar or potato agar, is preferred. On prolonged incubation the surface of such solid medium is apt to become too dry. This can be corrected if the cultures are placed in tight containers.

In common with most other bacteria the Brucella have rather specific nutritional requirements. In a study of *Br. suis* McCullough *et al.* found that thiamine, niacin, cystine, histidine, tyrosine, phenylalanine, tryptophane, and magnesium salts were essential for growth, whereas glycine, lysine, arginine, methronine, glutamic acid, isoleucine, aspartic acid, serine, biotin, calcium pantothenate, manganese and iron salts were stimulating, and 1 per cent glucose essential, for maximum growth.

Gerhardt and Wilson have also found that a nitrogen source such as asparagine, glutamic acid, or histidine was essential for maximum growth.

The organisms are aerobic and facultatively anaerobic. In a semisolid agar medium, colonies form at varying distances from the surface (Fig. 23.2).

All Brucella require carbon dioxide for growth; although *Br. suis* and *Br. melitensis* need no more than is naturally found in the air, it is often desirable to place initial cultures of Brucella in con-

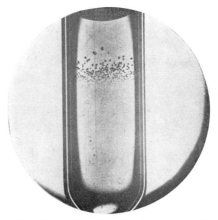

FIG. 23.2 — **Brucella abortus** deep colonies in agar shake culture, natural size. (From Nowak: Documenta Microbiologica, courtesy Gustav Fischer.)

tainers that can be sealed and to which may be added 5–10 per cent CO_2. It is absolutely necessary to do this with initial cultures of *Br. abortus* or to increase the CO_2 tension by some other method. It has been shown that *Br. abortus* obtained directly from infected animals will not grow in the air. Bang first isolated the organism in deep solid medium. Later it was grown in sealed containers in which a part of the oxygen had been exhausted by the reaction of hydroxides on pyrogallic acid. Smith grew *Br. abortus* in test tubes sealed with sealing wax. Later, Huddleson used 10 per cent CO_2 in closed containers. The last method is most satisfactory. Visible colonies should develop in 72 hours on liver infusion agar, but are often delayed; consequently, it is best to allow negative cultures to incubate 15–20 days or even longer, especially if the CO_2 requirements are not optimum. Borts found some cultures that required more than 30 days incubation for growth in initial isolations.

On liver agar the colonies appear small and delicate, but in one or two days reach a diameter of 1–2 mm., and after continued incubation may be 8–9 mm. (Fig. 23.3). At first the colonies are semitransparent with a light bluish tinge by transmitted light, and in older colonies this coloring is retained about the margins. This character is in no way distinctive since it is a common characteristic with many of the enterobacteria; however, most of the tissues cultured for Brucella are not contaminated with other organisms that have this characteristic. Colonies, especially old ones, are in the shape of a very low cone. They are distinctly pointed in the centers with a smooth circular margin and a smooth, shining, glistening surface; thus it is easy to differentiate them from other colonies which are flat, have irregular margins and dry or granular surfaces. Brucella colonies are not opaque as are those of many organisms, but are translucent and semitransparent. Old colonies show a distinct, small, dark area in their centers when viewed by transmitted light. Pigmentation on liver agar is not marked. Growth appears light brown or yellowish-brown. Pigmentation is most apparent on potato; here the colors are dull yellows, browns, or even bordering on slate. Color may vary with the same strain at different times.

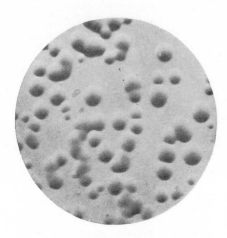

FIG. 23.3 — **Brucella abortus** colonies on agar plate, × 25. (From Nowak: Documenta Microbiologica, courtesy Gustav Fischer.)

Huddleson and associates have shown that all three species of Brucella undergo colony dissociation and they have described the dissociation pattern for each species. Assuming that the normal colony is smooth (S), other types may be described as smooth intermediate (SI), sector smooth intermediate (Sec.SI), mucoid (M), sector smooth mucoid (Sec.SM), sector mucoid (Sec.M), rough (R), and pseudosmooth (PS). By using the above terminology and by designating subtypes as R_1, R_2, etc., eighteen dissociation types have been described for *Br. abortus*, thirty-four for *Br. suis*, and nineteen for *Br. melitensis*. The student is referred to Memoir 6, 1952, by Huddleson *et al.* for the detailed description of each of the dissociation types.

Tetrazolium salts have been shown by Huddleson to be of value in differentiating the three species of Brucella and also the different colony dissociation types.

Huddleson recommends gentian violet 1:200,000 in liver agar for isolation on solid medium. This concentration does not inhibit any of the Brucella but does delay or prevent growth of many Gram-positive organisms. Brucella colonies on this medium have the same general characters as those on liver agar but are stained bluish-violet.

Blood cultures are commonly employed for isolation in cases of undulant fever. For one satisfactory method, 60 cc. of blood are withdrawn from the patient during the height of the fever; 10 cc. of this are placed in a small flask containing 40–50 cc. of liver infusion broth or other suitable liquid medium, and the remainder of the blood is placed in a second flask containing the same amount of broth. Incubation is continued for about 14 days or longer if growth is not obtained before. If contamination is found, injections of the blood-broth culture are made into guinea pigs from time to time during the incubating period.

Resistance. The three species exhibit no differences in their ability to resist adverse conditions. All are killed in the pasteurization of milk in 10–15 minutes. In salt solution and broth cultures they are killed more quickly and at a lower temperature. Dry heat at 70°C. for one hour does not kill. In agar cultures they may live a year or more; on the other hand, they may die in six to eight weeks. The determining factor seems to be the amount and concentration of end products in such cultures. Masses of organisms dried at 55–60°C., stoppered, and kept in the ice box may live a year or more. They have been found to survive for about seventy days in soil and for about thirty-five days in water. They are readily killed by the common disinfectants. In this respect they are similar to most members of the colon-typhoid group.

According to Elberg and Glassman, aerated broth cultures of *Brucella suis,* stabilized by the presence of dextrin and ascorbic acid, retain their original, viable cell count after storage for two months at 20 to 25°C. An aerated broth culture of *Br. suis* stabilized by the presence of dextrin and stored at 20 to 25°C. for 175 days retained 25 per cent of its original viable cell count and 100 per cent of its virulence.

The Brucella are not sufficiently sensitive to penicillin to warrant the use of that drug in treatment. Kraft has observed that virulent strains of *Br. abortus* are more resistant to the action of penicillin than is Strain 19 (see under Immunity, below). In fact, she believes that penicillin resistance can be used as a method of differentiating Strain 19 from other strains of *Br. abortus.* Streptomycin, Aureomycin, chloramphenicol, and para-aminobenzoic acid, however, do inhibit the growth of these organisms and these drugs have been found to be of value in treating cases of brucellosis in man. The use of these drugs in animals has been limited to experimental procedures.

Biochemical Properties. The Brucella organisms do not produce indol; do not liquefy gelatin; are Voges-Proskauer and methyl red negative; reduce nitrates to nitrites. Urease and catalase are produced, but Sanders and Warner have shown that *Br. melitensis* varies according to geographic area in the number of strains which are urease and catalase positive. Biochemical differences are found, however, that help to divide the group. *Br. suis* always produces hydrogen sulphide in considerable quantities for as long as ten to fourteen days. *Br. abortus* usually produces H_2S but, ordinarily, not to the extent or for the length of time found for swine strains. Bovine strains may produce no H_2S, little H_2S, or as much as do swine strains. *Br. melitensis* produces little or no H_2S. The bacteriostatic action of dyes is shown in Table 23.1, prepared from results obtained by following the method of Meyer. Huddleson, who first employed the bacteriostatic action of dyes for the differentiation of Brucella, uses a dilution of 1:100,000 of dyes. He finds that basic fuchsin and thionin give the most consistent results. *Br. abortus* grows only on the medium containing the basic fushsin, *Br. suis* on that containing the thionin, and *Br. melitensis* on both. Pyronin is often in an impure form, and for that reason is unsatisfactory. If desirable dye is used, growth of *Br. suis* is inhibited in suitable dilutions whereas *Br. melitensis* and *Br. abortus* are not. *Br. melitensis* neither grows as luxuriantly in thionin as does *Br. suis,* nor in basic fuchsin as does *Br. abortus*. All strains utilize glucose, but the bovine strains are apt to use the least. Other test substances, such as alcohols and sugars, may be attacked slightly after prolonged incubation. Chemical analysis by Huddleson shows that there are distinct differences in the composition of the three species.

Antigenic Structure and Toxins. All of the species of Brucella have major antigens in common, but agglutinin-absorption tests reveal minor antigenic differences. Dissociation or variation from smooth to rough affects the antigenic structure. Exotoxins have not been demonstrated. The bacteria are capable of producing an allergic condition in infected individuals which may persist indefinitely. Ottosen and Plum have prepared a purified extract of *Brucella abortus* which did not elicit the formation of agglutinin or complement-fixing antibodies in rabbits but did produce marked allergic sensitivity in guinea pigs.

The presence of an antigen common to the Brucella and *Vibrio comma* has been shown by Eisele and co-workers. Human beings who have been vaccinated for cholera will give a positive agglutination reaction with Brucella antigen.

The relationship of capsular material to virulence has been shown by Gonzalez, who was able to increase virulence of *Br. melitensis* and *Br. abortus* for mice by serial passage and the injection of starch or mucin along with the bacteria. The highly virulent cultures produced in this manner were capsulated. The sera of animals which had been immunized with capsulated strains produced agglutination for capsulated strains. The agglutinins appear o be different than those produced by smooth noncapsulated strains. The serum of patients suffering with *Br. melitensis* infec-,ion agglutinated the capsulated strains. It was shown in 1950 by Dlitzki and Oren that the virulence of *Brucella abortus* for mice :an be enhanced by injecting 0.5 cc. of a 10 per cent suspension of nucin along with 0.5 cc. of a 4-fold concentration of a 48-hour :ulture.

Pathogenicity. The Brucella produce infection which is most ιcute in laboratory animals, less so in man, and still less in cattle. [n hogs the disease resembles that of both man and cattle in varying

TABLE 23.1

BACTERIOSTATIC ACTION OF DYES

	BASIC FUCHSIN	THIONIN			CRYSTAL VIOLET	
	1:50,000	1:30,000	1:50,000	1:75,000	1:50,000	1:100,000
Brucella abortus	+	−	−	−	−	±
Brucella suis	−	+	+	+	−	−
Brucella melitensis	+	−	+	+	+	+

+ = growth.   − = no growth.

:rom symptoms which are pronounced, general, and local to those which are difficult to detect. Brucellosis in sows can result in ιbortion as it can in cattle. The symptom of abortion has been greatly overemphasized, not only in hogs, but in cattle also. In Iowa t is roughly estimated that brucellosis accounts for approximately 40 per cent of all abortions in sows. It has been proven that inocula-:ion of pregnant sows may cause infection, but abortion does not ιlways result; that is, abortion is not the disease but rather a symptom :hat is sometimes observed. This is also true for cattle but to a .esser degree. About 60 per cent of all abortions are caused by Bang's disease in Iowa. In certain herds, free of Bang's disease, it ιas been observed that about 3 per cent of all pregnant cows abort. A report from New York State shows that 5 per cent of such animals n that region abort. Consideration of these facts shows that total ιumbers of abortions are enormous, even where Bang's disease is ιot a factor. Abortions are encountered in diseased goats; they are rare in mares and in human beings. In cases of abortion, a placentitis s produced; with Bang's disease, this is a serious matter, not only because it endangers the life of the fetus, but also because it results in injury to the uterus that may affect future pregnancies. Such inflammation results in a lowered tone of the uterus and renders it susceptible to secondary infections following abortion or parturition. After secondary invaders are once established, they often do more damage than Brucella. The retention of the placenta is also considered a symptom of Bang's disease, but retained membranes may be, and often are, as common in Bang's disease free herds as they are in infected herds. The only difference lies in the ease with which the retained membranes may be removed. In Bang's disease such membranes are removed with difficulty; those retained from other causes are more easily removed. *Brucella abortus* is not found in the nongravid uterus of cows and disappears from that organ soon after parturition or abortion. Its most favored site is the udder, where it causes an interstitial mastitis; it is also considered a predisposing factor to other infections of the udder. The Brucella have a predilection for the male sex glands. Manthei, DeTray, and Goode have demonstrated the organism in the semen of a naturally infected bull on 80 consecutive collections. It is evident that bulls used for natural service or for artificial breeding should be free of infection. The organisms are easily isolated from the internal organs of infected hogs, especially the lymph nodes, spleen, liver, uterus, and kidneys as well as from the blood stream. Isolation from cattle is usually difficult when the organism is not present in the udder, pregnant uterus, or associated lymph nodes. The Brucella are often associated with bursitis and nontraumatic fistulae of horses; are found in lesions in and about articulations of many animals; and are sometimes associated with pneumonia and enteritis of newborn calves.

Immunity. It is emphasized again that cattle are the true hosts for *Br. abortus,* swine for *Br. suis,* and goats for *Br. melitensis,* but each natural host may be infected with the other two species. It has been shown by Hoerlein, for example, that *Br. melitensis* is as pathogenic as *Br. suis* for swine. With the possible exception of man and some laboratory animals, other animals are quite resistant to the Brucella. The guinea pig, rabbit, mouse, rat, sheep, horse, and dog can be infected. The guinea pig is easily infected while the dog, although having much chance of exposure, rarely shows symptoms and is thought to be relatively resistant. Abortion in the canine, due to brucellosis, has been observed, and Morse and co-workers have isolated the organisms from the aborted feti as well as from surviving puppies. The infection is usually associated with fistula of the poll and withers in the horse. The sheep appears to be most susceptible to *Br. melitensis.* White rats inoculated with small amounts of any of the Brucella are thereafter immune, but if they are injected with initial large amounts, they die in a day or so. Chickens are considered to be naturally resistant to Brucella, al-

although experimental infections may be produced. For example, Felsenfeld and associates produced bacteriemia in chickens by intramuscular and intraperitoneal injection and by feeding live cultures. They considered *Br. melitensis* more pathogenic to chickens than the other two species.

There is also an age resistance that can be easily demonstrated; in general, the usual infectious disease attacks the young more often and more severely than older animals. In brucellosis the order is reversed in man and cattle. Young calves can be infected but throw off the disease readily. The sexually mature cattle are as easily infected, if not more so, and the infection is more lasting. In calves there is more antagonism between the host and the parasite; therefore, soon after infective feed is eliminated, the calf rids itself of Brucella, unless, as is true in some rare instances, the infection becomes dormant, and the agglutination test becomes negative. Such rare dormant infections become active when the animal reaches sexual maturity.

Some infected cattle remain diseased throughout their lives; others recover in a few months. Between these extremes all the other possibilities occur. It is generally believed that many recovered animals are highly resistant to subsequent reinfection; it is further believed that some animals that recover can be reinfected. Again, between these two extremes, many possibilities exist. It is thought that the character of the particular strain with which the animal is infected has much to do with the duration of disease and the amount of immunity acquired.

The use of an avirulent strain of *Br. abortus* by Buck in 1930 for the vaccination during calfhood indicated a superior method of immunization. This strain, known as Strain 19, was used on an extensive experimental scale by the Federal Bureau of Animal Industry and in 1940 permission was given for its use as an aid in controlling brucellosis in the various states. This strain of *Br. abortus* is quite stable, not varying in virulence or antigenicity. Cameron and Meyer have shown that the consecutive passage of it through 26 swine did not alter its characteristics.

Strain 19 vaccine is a living culture which must be prepared according to procedures outlined by the Division of Virus-Serum Control of the B.A.I. The relative avirulence of this strain has been mentioned, but because it is a living culture, the inoculation of it into calves produces a positive agglutination reaction. This reaction is lost in the majority of vaccinates by the time they reach breeding maturity. Unfortunately, a small per cent do not become negative and this is one objection to its use.

Calves are vaccinated with Strain 19 vaccine when 4 to 8 months old with 5 ml. subcutaneously. It has been shown by Rabstein and Cotton that 0.2 ml. of vaccine given intradermally produces just as high an agglutinin titer as 5 ml. given subcutaneously and that the titer tends to disappear sooner. McDiarmid in England found that the immunity produced in guinea pigs by 0.04 ml. of Strain 19 vaccine given intradermally compared favorably with 1 ml. given subcutaneously. Campbell and Rodwell in Australia introduced the intracaudal (tip of the tail) method of vaccination for brucellosis, giving a 0.2 ml. dose. Neither the intradermal nor the intracaudal method of vaccination is practiced much in the United States. Berman, Beach, and Irwin could find no significant difference in the immunity produced by vaccinating sexually mature cattle with 5 ml. of Strain 19 subcutaneously or 0.25 ml. intracaudally.

In 1946 Verwey and Scheidy found that desiccation of *Brucella abortus* Strain 19 vaccine by lyophilization affords a satisfactory method of preserving and maintaining the culture in a viable state. This method reduces the hazard of having a nonviable vaccine for use in the field and allows a longer use-date after its manufacture. Most of the vaccine used is prepared by this procedure.

Live, Sperling, and Stubbs have observed that guinea pigs were protected against artificial exposure to virulent *Br. abortus* four to six weeks after immunization with ether-killed injections of that organism. Subsequently, Live and Danks reported that ether-killed *Br. abortus* adsorbed on alum or combined with Falba[1] and mineral oil gave promise as an immunizing agent.

In 1947 Huddleson reported that when live cell suspensions of mucoid phases of *Br. suis* and *Br. melitensis* were prepared in a suitable concentration and injected into normal guinea pigs, they were capable of producing a high degree of active immunity against experimental infection with all three species of Brucella. The vaccine-treated guinea pigs that were found to be free from infection after exposure did not show specific agglutinins in the blood serum in dilutions of 1:25 or above. The use of mucoid variants as a vaccine (M vaccine) for the production of immunity against brucellosis in cattle is in the experimental stage.

Brucellosis in hogs may be self-limiting. In small droves of swine the disease can run through the entire lot and recovery may take place in a few months. In larger herds the infection is apt to persist. The amount of immunity afforded by one attack of Brucella infection in swine is not known. The use of Strain 19 for producing immunity in swine has been of little value.

In general, it is believed that, in most animals, recovery from one attack of brucellosis affords sufficient immunity to protect against subsequent exposures to natural infection. This is especially

---

[1] Trade name of a lanolin-like substance prepared by Pfaltz and Bauer, Inc., New York.

true of infection in man, but is difficult to determine because an initial infection may become dormant only to resume activity at a later date. When symptoms again develop in a supposedly recovered individual, the question arises as to whether or not a new infection is present.

Anti-Brucella serum contains agglutinins and complement-binding antibodies. Immune serum, so far produced, has little or no influence on the course of the disease.

Diagnosis. The organism is found in large numbers on stained smears made of uterine exudate which has been obtained from a cow that has recently aborted (Fig. 23.4). The isolation of Brucella from the tissues or excretions of the animal body also establishes a diagnosis; however, a diagnosis is usually made by serological methods that have proven reliable. A combination guinea pig inoculation and the agglutination test of its blood at a later date is also reliable. In this case it is not absolutely necessary to isolate the organism. Many guinea pigs will recover from inoculations with Brucella, and it is obviously impossible to obtain cultures from them, but even these animals, if bled at the proper time, will show agglutinins in their

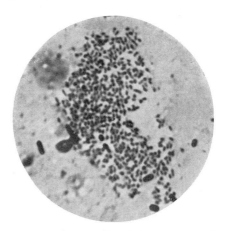

FIG. 23.4 — **Brucella abortus,** smear of uterine exudate, × 2,000. (From Nowak: Documenta Microbiologica, courtesy Gustav Fischer.)

blood; hence, the agglutination test of the guinea pig's blood should be employed in conjunction with an attempt to isolate the organism from the animal's tissues. The blood of normal guinea pigs does not contain agglutinins for Brucella. Some laboratories allow the inoculated guinea pigs to go thirty-six days before they are bled and examined. Others allow only twenty-four days. A period of approximately twenty-four days has some advantages because it allows ample time for agglutinins to develop and for the infection to develop, and at the same time is sufficiently short to test many guinea pigs before they recover. Lesions which will heal in thirty-six days are often present at the end of the twenty-four-day period.

Complement-fixation is a reliable diagnostic test. It is believed that complement-fixing antibody is formed in the blood of infected animals a short time before agglutinins appear; otherwise it holds no advantage over the agglutinin test; in fact, the latter has supplanted it because it can be conducted more easily, more quickly, and with less chance of error on the part of the operator. Selection of proper strains of the Brucella is one of the important factors in the agglutination test. Rough or variant strains must be avoided. The smooth type is disease-producing, stays in uniform suspension exceedingly well, and in all ways is an ideal type for the test. Different variants often show different characters; for instance, some are auto- or thermo-agglutinating; some are only slightly so; others agglutinate in any serum; still others do not. It appears that there are different types of variants, all of which should be avoided.

Br. *melitensis* is most apt to become variant in culture media and for this reason is little used. *Br. suis* strains are satisfactory, but they too are apt to become rough. *Br. abortus* strains are the best, and although some become rough, others have been kept for years on laboratory media without producing variants. Such strains are nearly fixed in type if kept on solid medium. All laboratories employ only strains that have not shown variants. If it should become necessary to rid a strain of its variants, this can be done by guinea pig inoculation. In about 14 days after inoculation the variants will disappear in the animal's body, leaving only the smooth type. This is not true of at least some of the mucoid variants mentioned above which may persist in the body of the guinea pig for more than 50 days. Isolation of desirable agglutinating types can be obtained from mixed cultures by plating and examination of likely colonies. It is necessary to test the growth from several colonies because, with the usual variant on the common laboratory medium, there is little or no difference between the colonies of variants and those of smooth types.

In routine diagnosis two kinds of agglutination tests are employed. One is usually referred to as the tube test and the other the plate or rapid test. Both have their advantages, and both give about the same final results; in fact, the plate test is standardized to conform to the tube test. If one prepares the materials and conducts the test himself, the tube test is more simple. It is necessary to understand the tube test in order to prepare sera and standardize plate-test antigen. For the tube test, the suspension of the organism is made in physiological salt solution containing 0.5 of 1 per cent phenol. The density of the suspension is made to compare with tube No. 1 of the McFarland nephelometer. Donham and Fitch estimate that this should be 0.04 per cent suspension of bacteria. The serum from the suspect is added to the bacterial suspension making dilutions 1:25, 1:50, 1:100, 1:200, and higher if desired. Readings are made after 48 hours' incubation at about 37°C.

In brucellosis of cattle a reaction of 1:25 is without significance. A reaction of 1:50 is considered suspicious, and one of 1:100 is generally regarded as indicating infection. An exception is noted when an animal has been calf-vaccinated with Strain 19. In this case 1:50 is considered negative, 1:100 suspicious, and 1:200 positive. The organism can usually be isolated from cattle showing reactions of 1:500 or higher. In hogs it is easy to isolate Brucella from animals having reactions of 1:50 and sometimes in animals with reactions of 1:25; however, the disease in hogs is one of shorter duration than in cattle, and one may obtain cultures before the agglutination titer has reached a high level. A reaction of 1:50 in the hog should be considered significant although Kernkamp and Roepke have shown that herds of swine apparently free of brucellosis may have some individuals whose sera will give a titer of 1:25 to 1:50. The application of the agglutination test to swine should be considered on a herd basis, and if any individuals in the herd show a titer of 1:100, the herd should be considered to be in an infected one. Tests on individual sows or boars from a herd are of little value in determining the brucellosis status of the herd. In man a reaction of 1:80 or 1:100 indicates infection present or past. Some people with titers of 1:300 show no symptoms, even though, in a few such cases, the organism can be isolated from their blood stream. It should be remembered that all lesions and symptoms of disease cannot be attributed to Brucella merely because the organism is present; for example, it is known that cows affected with Bang's disease may abort from other causes. It is often difficult to determine just which symptoms and lesions are due to Brucella infection and which are due to other causes.

The development of the ABR Test (Abortus Bang Ring) or the *Brucella abortus* Ring Test by Fleischhauer of Germany, in 1937, has provided another method of diagnosing brucellosis in cattle. This test consists of the use of an hemotoxylin-stained *Brucella abortus* antigen which is added to 2 ml. of whole milk. Upon standing, the stained bacterial cells will rise with the cream forming a purple layer if the animal is infected with brucellosis. In this positive reaction the bacteria have been agglutinated by the agglutinin in the milk serum forming clumps of bacteria large enough to be carried to the surface along with the fat globules. If the animal is not infected, the cream layer is white and the milk remains a light purple because the bacteria remain in suspension. This test can be applied to a composite sample of milk from the herd, thereby serving as an effective method of detecting herds of cattle in which one or more individual reactors exist. It is an effective screening test allowing control officials to concentrate on certain herds during the interim between annual or semiannual routine serological tests. Furthermore, if the test is applied to milk samples monthly, the newly infected herds can be detected.

A combination of the ABR test and the plate test, whereby ring-test antigen and milk are placed on a glass plate, has been shown by Blake, Manthei, and Goode to be a satisfactory test.

Brucella bronchiseptica

Synonyms and History. Although numerous types of organisms have been isolated from typical cases of canine distemper, the first organism which compares favorably with the one under discussion was isolated by Galli-Vallerio in 1896 and described again in 1908. He named his organism *B. caniculae,* considered that it represented a position between the typhoid and hemorrhagic septicemia groups, and that it resembled *B. pestis* in morphology. In 1901 Lignières considered an organism which he called *Pasteurella canina* as the cause of canine distemper. His organism did not ferment carbohydrates but exhibited many other characteristics similar to the organism of Galli-Vallerio.

The organism now recognized as *Brucella bronchiseptica* was isolated and described in the United States by Ferry in 1911 and was called *Bacillus bronchicanis* but was changed in 1912 to *Bacillus bronchisepticus.* Quite independently, in 1911, M'Gowan in England described the same type of organism as Ferry, but he did not propose a name. In 1912, Torrey and Rahe published an extensive study of canine distemper and of the organism, *Bacillus bronchisepticus,* which they considered to be the cause of the disease.

In 1918 Evans included *Bacillus bronchisepticus* among cultures of the Malta fever-contagious abortion group in a comparative study. She found morphological, physiological, and serological relationships among the different organisms; consequently, she assigned the canine organism to the genus Bacterium with *Bacterium melitensis* and *Bacterium abortus.*

The shakeup of the genus Bacterium and the formation of new generic names found the organism under the name *Alcaligenes bronchisepticus* in Bergey's Manual in 1923. This appeared to be a reasonable classification because many investigators, particularly Torrey and Rahe, noted a marked relationship to *B. fecalis alkaligenes.*

In 1905 Carré announced that the cause of canine distemper was a filtrable virus. This discovery did not become established, however, because of the extensive research of Ferry, M'Gowan, and Torrey and Rahe. Largely because of the failure of the bacteriological agents to produce a durable immunity in young dogs against the disease, the question of etiology was reopened by Hardenbergh in 1925. The question was promptly and securely closed in 1926 when Laidlaw and Dunkin published the results of their research in which they found that the primary cause of canine distemper was a filtrable virus.

The results of Laidlaw and Dunkin have been universally accepted; consequently, the organism *Brucella bronchiseptica* has been relegated to the role of an important secondary invader to the virus along with other microorganisms. Due to the absence of any etiological relationship to the disease, the organism has not been subjected to present-day comparative study with other organisms such as the Brucella.

Distribution and Transmission. If pulmonary involvement in canine distemper is taken as an indication of the presence of *Brucella bronchiseptica,* the organism is widely distributed. It is transmitted by contact.

Morphology and Staining. The organism is a short, slender rod, 0.4 to 0.5μ in diameter by 1.5 to 2μ in length. It usually occurs singly, but pairs are found, and in fluid media chains may be observed. It is motile by means of peritrichous flagella, is nonspore-forming, and noncapsule-producing.

The organism is stained by the usual dyes, but many cells show decided bipolar staining. It is Gram-negative.

Growth Requirements and Characteristics. *Brucella bronchiseptica* grows best under aerobic conditions, at a temperature of 37°C. and in a medium adjusted to a pH of 7.0 or 7.2. It requires a medium which is enriched with animal tissues or plasma.

The organism grows slowly upon primary isolation from the lung of an infected dog. No visible growth is present on the agar surface after 24 hours of incubation, but at the end of 48 hours, tiny, circular, dewdrop-like colonies appear scattered over the plate. As the culture ages, the colonies increase in size up to 6 to 8 mm., becoming flat, glistening, and opalescent by reflected light and translucent with a smoky tinge by transmitted light.

In broth, the organism produces a uniform turbidity with a finely granular sediment but no pellicle. Growth forms on the surface of the medium at the sides of the tube within 72 hours. The sediment in old cultures rises in a twisted cone when the tube is shaken. Old cultures of the organism liberate a stale odor similar to that of musty bread.

The growth of this organism is very characteristic on potato. In 24 hours the culture is abundant, moist, raised, glistening, and yellowish-brown in color accompanied by a greenish or greyish darkening of the potato. Upon aging, the growth becomes darker brown, and the potato also becomes darker.

Resistance. The organism is killed by 55°C. in 20 minutes, thereby showing less resistance to heat than other Gram-negative, nonsporeforming rods. It is not resistant to light, desiccation, or the common disinfectants, and is not destroyed by freezing.

Biochemical Properties. An outstanding property of this organism is its inability to ferment any of the carbohydrates. Another distinctive characteristic is its action on litmus milk. After 24 hours' incubation a deep blue ring appears extending about one-half inch from the surface of the medium. In 72 hours the ring is a deeper blue, and the rest of the medium is a deeper blue than the control. In five to ten days the entire medium is blue-black in color. As the culture stands, the lower third of the medium bleaches to a faded-blue color. The organism does not form indol or hydrogen sulphide. Torrey and Rahe divide the strains of the organism into two groups on the basis of nitrate reduction. Strains in Group A do not reduce nitrates and those in Group B reduce nitrates to nitrites.

Antigenic Structure and Toxins. The organism is homogenous antigenically according to the agglutination test. It shows some affinity to *Brucella abortus,* but relatively little is known about its antigenic fractions.

True toxins are not produced, but the organism produces hemolysin for dog, rabbit, and guinea pig erythrocytes.

Pathogenicity. The original work on this organism indicated that it was the cause of canine distemper. Experimental inoculation of young dogs with the organism produced typical cases of distemper. Although the primary cause of the disease is a filtrable virus, it is evident that *Brucella bronchiseptica* is an important secondary agent and that the fatality of the infection is largely attributed to the pneumonia which it causes.

M'Gowan reported finding the organism in the ferret, monkey, goat, guinea pig, rabbit, cat, and dog. He also reported the isolation of the organism from the nasal exudate of an attendant who had been handling rabbits and guinea pigs.

In 1943 Phillips recorded the isolation of *Brucella bronchiseptica* in pure culture from bronchial exudate of pigs in Ontario, Canada. These animals had exhibited unthriftiness and chronic coughing.

Immunity. Bacterins and immune serum were commonly used for the immunization of dogs until the work of Laidlaw and Dunkin. It was acknowledged before that time, however, that such immunizing agents were not satisfactory.

The organism is recognized as important in canine distemper, and for that reason animals in which canine distemper immune serum is produced are also immunized with *Brucella bronchiseptica* and other organisms which have been incriminated as secondary invaders.

Diagnosis. The isolation of the organism from the nasal secretion of the infected dog is indicative of invasion by this organism but not necessarily by the virus of canine distemper. Agglutinins for the organism are produced during a typical infection, but the agglutination test is not used as a diagnostic agent. The symptoms of the infection are so characteristic that laboratory confirmation is rarely needed.

REFERENCES FOR FURTHER STUDY

Andrews, F. N., and Hutchings, L. M. Amer. Jour. Vet. Res., 7:385, 1946.

Bang, B. Zeitschrift für Tiermedizin, 1:241, 1897.

Bass, C. C., and Watkins, J. A. Arch. of Internat. Med., 6:717, Dec., 1910.

Bergey, D. H., *et al.* Bergey's Manual of Determinative Bacteriology. 6th Ed. The Williams & Wilkins Co., 1948.

Berman, D. T., Beach, B. A., and Irwin, M. R. Amer. Jour. Vet. Res., 15:406, 1954.

Blake, G. E., Manthei, C. A., and Goode, E. R. Jour. Amer. Vet. Med. Assn., 120:1, 1952.

Borts, I. H., McNutt, S. H., and Jordan, Carl F. Jour. Amer. Med. Assn., 130 (Apr. 6, 1946) No. 14, p. 966.

Bruce, D. Practitioner, London, 39:161, 1887.

Bruhn, P. A. Amer. Jour. Vet. Res., 9:360, 1948.

Bunnell, D. E., Hutchings, L. M., and Donham, C. R. Amer. Jour. Vet. Res., 8:367, 1947.

Cameron, H. S. Amer. Jour. Vet. Res., 7:21, 1946.

————, and Meyer, M. E. Cornell Vet. 42:42, 1952.

Campbell, A. D., and Rodwell, A. W. Jour. Comp. Path. and Therap., 55, 1945.

Cotton, Cornelia M. An Intense Study of Post-Vaccination Responses in Groups of Calves Vaccinated Intracutaneously With Strain 19 Brucella. Amer. Jour. Vet. Res., 14:337, 1953.

————, and Swope, R. E. Amer. Jour. Vet. Res., 9:164, 169, 1948.

Cotton, W. E. Jour. Amer. Vet. Med. Assn., 62 (1922), p. 179.

————, and Buck, J. M. Jour. Amer. Vet. Med. Assn., 80:342, 1932.

Damon, S. R., and Fagan, R. Pub. Hlth. Rep. Wash., 62:1097, 1947

————, and Scruggs, J. H. Pub. Hlth. Rep. Wash., 65:374, 1950.

Delez, A. L., Hutchings, L. M., and Donham, C. R. Amer. Jour. Vet. Res., 8:225, 1947.

Elberg, S. S., and Glassman, H. N. Amer. Jour. Vet. Res., 8:314, 1947.

Eisele, C. W., McCullough, N. B., and Beal, G. A. Ann. Int. Med., 28:833, 1948.

————, ————, ————, and Burrows, W. Proc. Soc. Exp. Biol. Med., 61:89, 1946.

————, ————, ————, and Rottschaefer, W. Jour. Amer. Med. Assn., 135:983, 1947.

Evans, A. C. Jour. Inf. Dis., 22:580, 1918.

————. Pub. Health Repts., 38:1948, 1923.

————. Pub. Health Repts., 39:501, 1924.

Felsenfeld, O., Young, V. M., Loeffler, E., Ishihara, S. J., and Schroeder, W. F. Amer. Jour. Vet. Res., 12:48, 1951.

Ferry, N. S. Amer. Vet. Rev., 37:499–504, 1910.

————. Etiology of Canine Distemper. Jour. Inf. Dis., 8:399–420, 1911.

Fitch, C. P., Donham, C. R., Bishop, Lucille, and Boyd, W. L. Univ. of Minn. Tech. Bull. 73, 1930.

Fleischhauer, G. Berl. Tierärztl. Wschr., 53:527, 1937.

Galli-Valerio, B. Der Mikroörganismus der Hundestaupe. Central. f. Bakt., 19:694, 1896.

Gerhardt, P., and Wilson, J. B. Jour. Bact., 56:17, 1948.

Gilman, H. L., and Legrow, W. R. Amer. Jour. Vet. Res., 8:192, 1947.

Giltner, Ward. Brucellosis: A Public Health Problem. Mich. Agr. Exp. Sta.. Mem. No. 1, 1934.

Good, C. S., and Smith, W. V. Jour. Bact., 1:415, 1916.

Hallman, E. T., Sholl, L. B., and Delez, A. L. Mich. Agr. Exp. Sta., Tech. Bull. 93, 1928.

Hardenbergh, J. G. Jour. Amer. Vet. Med. Assn., 69:478–84, 1926.

Hardy, A. V. Pub. Health Repts., 43:2459, 1928.

———, Jordan, C. F., Borts, I. H., and Hardy, G. C. Nat. Inst. of Pub. Health, Bull. 158, 1930.

Henricsson, Erik. Epizootic Abortion and Undulant Fever. Isaac Marcus Boktryckeri-Aktiebolag, Stockholm, 1932.

Henry, B. S., Traum, J., and Haring, C. M. Hilgardia, 6:356, 1932.

Hillaert, E. L., Hutchings, L. M., and Andrews, F. N. Amer. Jour. Vet. Res., 9:84, 1950.

Hoerlein, A. B. Amer. Jour. Vet. Res., 13:67, 1952.

Huddleson, I. F. Brucellosis in Man and Animals. New York, The Commonwealth Fund. Oxford University Press, London, 1943.

———. Amer. Jour. Vet. Res., 7:5–10, 1946.

———. Amer. Jour. Vet. Res., 8:374, 1947.

———, Richardson, M. A., Warner, J., and Baltzer, B. Studies in Brucellosis, III. Memoir 6, Mich. St. Agr. Exp. Sta., East Lansing, 1952.

Hutchings, L. M., Delez, A. L., Andrews, F. N., and Donham, C. R. Amer. Jour. Vet. Res., 7:11, 379, 388, 1946.

Keefer, C. S. Bulletin of the Johns Hopkins Hospital, Baltimore, 35:6, 1924.

Kernkamp, H. C. H., and Roepke, M. H. Amer. Jour. Vet. Res., 9:46, 1948.

Kraft, Mary E. Amer. Jour. Vet. Res., 16:295, 1955.

Laidlaw, P. P., and Dunkin, G. W. Jour. Comp. Path. and Ther., 39:201–30, 1926.

Live, I. Amer. Jour. Vet. Res., 10:347, 1949.

———, and Danks, A. G. Amer. Jour. Vet. Res., 12:175, 1951.

McCullough, N. B., Eisele, W., and Pavelchek, E. Pub. Hlth. Rep. Wash., 64:537, 1949.

———, ———, and Beal, G. A. Jour. Inf. Dis., 83:55, 1948.

———, Herbst, E. J., Roessler, W. G., and Brewer, C. R. Jour. Bact., 53:5, 1947.

McDiarmid, A. Vet. Rec., 60:227, 1948.

M'Gowan, J. P. Jour. Path. Bact., 15:372–426, 1911.

Manthei, C. A. Amer. Jour. Vet. Res., 9:40, 1948.

———, DeTray, D. E., and Goode, E. R. Proc. Book 87th Ann. Conv. Amer. Vet. Med. Assn., 1950.

Meyer, K. F., and Shaw, E. B. Jour. Inf. Dis., 27:173, 1920.

———, and Zobell, C. E. Jour. Inf. Dis., 51:72, 1932.

Morse, E. V., Ristic, M., Witt, L. E., and Wipf, L. Jour. Amer. Vet. Med. Assn., 122:18, 1953.

Murray, C., McNutt, S. H., and Purwin, P. Jour. Amer. Vet. Med. Assn., 80:336, 1932.

Ottosen, H. E., and Plum, H. Amer. Jour. Vet. Res., 10:5, 1949.

Phillips, C. E. Can. Jour. Comp. Med., 7:58–59, 1943.

Plastridge, W. N. Bovine Brucellosis: A Review of the Literature on Diagnosis and Control. Proc. U. S. Livestock San. Assn., 58th Ann. Meeting, 1954.

———, and McAlpine, J. G. Jour. Inf. Dis., 49:127, 1931.

Rabstein, M. M., and Cotton, Cornelia M. Proc. 46th Ann. Meet. U. S. Livestock San. Assn., p. 129, 1942.

Rinjard, P., and Hilger, A. Bull. Acad. Vet. France, No. 7, 1:272, 1928.

Roepke, M. H., *et al.* The Milk and Cream Ring Test for Brucellosis. Proc. 52nd Ann. Meet. U. S. Livestock San. Assn., 1948.

Runnells, R. A., and Huddleson, I. F. Cornell Vet., 15:376, 1925.

Sanders, E., and Huddleson, I. F. Amer. Jour. Vet. Res., 9:75, 1950.

———, and Warner, J. Amer. Jour. Vet. Res., 14:388, 1953.

Schroeder, E. C., and Cotton, W. E. U. S. D. A. Ann. Rept. of the Bur. of Ani. Ind., p. 139, 1911.

Smith, T. Jour. Med. Res., 29:291, 1913.

Symposium on Brucellosis. Amer. Assn. Adv. Sci., Washington, 1950.

Thomsen, A. Brucella Infection in Swine. Levin and Munkgaard, Copenhagen, 1934.

Topley, W. W. C., and Wilson, G. S. The Principles of Bacteriology and Immunity. pp. 631–51. William Wood & Co., Baltimore, 1936.

Torrey, J. C., and Rahe, A. H. Jour. Med. Res., 27:291–364, 1912–13.

Tovar, R. M. Amer. Jour. Vet. Res., 8:138, 1947.

Traum, J. U. S. D. A., Ann. Rept. of the Bur. of Ani. Ind., p. 30, 1914.

Van der Hoeden, J. Tijdschrift voor Diergeneeskunde, 59:612, 1932.

Verwey, W. F., and Scheidy, S. F. Jour. Amer. Vet. Med. Assn., 109:362, 1946.

Washko, F. V., Hutchings, L. M., and Donham, C. R. Amer. Jour. Vet. Res., 9:342, 1948.

Watkins, W. W., and Lake, G. C. Jour. Amer. Med. Assn., 89:1581, 1927.

24. | The Genus Pasteurella*

Microorganisms belonging to the genus Pasteurella are usually coccoid, short, plump rods; however, elongated cells are sometimes observed. They are generally capsulated, but noncapsulated forms have been reported. The majority of the species are nonmotile, and all are nonsporeforming. They are Gram-negative and are stained more distinctly at either pole, giving rise to the term, bipolar, which is frequently used to characterize the group. The ability of these organisms to ferment carbohydrates is limited; although acid is produced in a number of sugar media, gas is never produced. The various species are parasitic and frequently pathogenic for animals and man.

The species of the Pasteurella group are conveniently divided into three subgroups on the basis of host relationship and type of disease.

A. The members of the hemorrhagic septicemia group are found in lower animals. There are two species in this group:
   Pasteurella multocida
   Pasteurella hemolytica
B. The members of the second group cause acute, subacute to chronic infections in rodents and are transmissible to man. There are two species in the group:
   Pasteurella pestis
   Pasteurella tularense
C. The one species in the third category causes a chronic, focalized caseation necrosis in rodents. It is:
   Pasteurella pseudotuberculosis

In addition to the variable hosts and the types of disease, the above species can be distinguished on the basis of the characteristics given in Table 24.1.

---

* The author is indebted to Dr. C. T. Rosenbusch for the preparation of this chapter and to Dr. G. R. Carter for aid in its revision.

Pasteurella multocida

Synonyms and History. The organisms which produce a septicemia in the lower animals have been recognized as belonging to several genera, such as Escherichia, Salmonella, Shigella, Streptococcus, and Bacillus. The term *hemorrhagic septicemia* designates a particular type of septicemia which is characterized by hemorrhage of the capillaries in the submucous and subserous membranes.

TABLE 24.1

DIFFERENTIAL CHARACTERISTICS OF THE PASTEURELLA

	Past. multocida	Past. hemolytica	Past. pestis	Past. tularensis	Past. pseudo-tuber-culosis
Motility	—	—	—	—	+
Hemolysis	—	+	—	—	—
Growth in bile	—	—	+	—	+
Indol formation	+	—	—	—	—
Litmus milk	neutral	acid	neutral	no growth	alkaline
Glucose	+	+	+	+	+
Saccharose	+	+	—	—	±
Lactose	—	+	—	—	—
Raffinose	—	+	—	—	—
Rhamnose	—	—	+	—	+

The name was first used by Hueppe in 1886 to describe the disease produced by the bipolar organisms. The name *Pasteurellosis*, first proposed by Lignières in 1900, is finding its way back into the literature, and is a more appropriate term.

The isolation of different strains of *Pasteurella multocida* by different individuals from different hosts and at different times has introduced into the literature a number of names for the hemorrhagic septicemia group. They are scattered throughout the various systematic classifications of bacteria, but most of them are given in Bergey's Manual.

The first significant report of an organism of this group was made by Bollinger in 1878 following an investigation of a fatal disease among wild animals and cattle. The fowl cholera organism was described by Rivolta in 1877, by Perrincito in 1879, and also by Toussaint in the same year. The most complete description of fowl cholera and the organism was made by Pasteur in 1880. In the United States, Salmon and Smith observed the organism in 1880. In 1880, Davaine, and in 1881, Gaffky, described the rabbit septicemia organism. Loeffler and Schütz studied and described the organism of swine septicemia in 1882. In 1885, Kitt made a comparative study of the organisms producing fowl cholera, rabbit septicemia, swine septicemia, and the septicemia of wild animals and cattle. He concluded that they were similar in many respects and referred to them as *Bacterium bipolare multocidum.* In 1886, Hueppe noted the similarity of the diseases which were produced by these ovoid, bipolar organisms and suggested the name *septicemia hemorrhagica* for the disease. Poels described the organism of calf pleuropneumonia in 1886. Oreste and Armanni reported the buffalo strain in 1887, Galtier the sheep strain in 1887, and Lignières the equine strain in 1897. Much later, 1926, Meyer and Batchelder isolated a strain from rat septicemia.

In 1887, Trevisan used the name *Pasteurella* for the bipolar organisms and listed three species, *Pasteurella cholerae-gallinarum, Pasteurella davainei,* and *Pasteurella suilla.* In 1896 Flügge called the various hemorrhagic septicemia organisms *Bacillus boviseptica, Bacillus suisepticus,* etc. These classifications represent the early tendency to form a species name on the basis of the host affected. In following this procedure in detail, Lignières listed the organisms causing Pasteurellosis as follows:

> *Pasteurella aviaire* producing natural infection in all the birds.
> *Pasteurella bovine,* producing hemorrhagic septicemia in wild animals and bovines, barbone of buffalo, and pleuropneumonia of calves.
> *Pasteurella ovine,* producing hemorrhagic septicemia, pneumoenteritis, and enzootic pneumonia in sheep.
> *Pasteurella porcine,* producing swine plague.
> *Pasteurella equine,* producing contagious pleuropneumonia in the horse.
> *Pasteurella canine,* producing all forms of disease in dogs.

This list of Lignières' was too inclusive and obviously embraced organisms not belonging to the Pasteurella group. His system of nomenclature, however, was quite acceptable and has been adopted by most bacteriologists since that time. The genus Pasteurella became established, and the species names were based upon the nomenclature of Flügge; hence, *Pasteurella aviseptica, -boviseptica, -oviseptica, -suiseptica, -equiseptica, -lepiseptica,* and *-muriseptica.*

During recent years comparative studies of strains of the organism isolated from the different animals have failed to support the zoological classification. All of the strains are morphologically, biochemically, serologically, and pathologically similar. As a consequence, there has been a tendency to use one name for the variety of strains. Lehmann and Neumann adhered to this method of classification throughout all of their early classifications and called the organism *Bacillus hemorrhagicae septicemiae.* In 1935 Gay and his associates suggested the use of *Pasteurella pluriseptica* or *septica,* and in 1936 Topley and Wilson suggested the name *Pasteurella septica* and that the animal origin be indicated where necessary. As a result of comparative studies, Rosenbusch in 1937, and Rosenbusch and Merchant in 1938 used the name *Pasteurella multocida* for the typical hemorrhagic septicemia organisms because the first inclusive name, *Bacterium bipolare multocidum,* was used by Kitt in 1885.

Distribution and Transmission. The organism is encountered throughout the world and is frequently the cause of great economic loss. Since typical organisms have been isolated from respiratory and digestive tracts of normal animals, the primary relationship of the organism to the disease has been

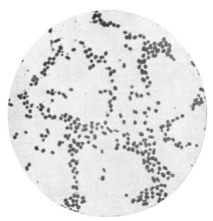

FIG. 24.1 — **Pasteurella multocida** smear from agar culture, × 2,000. (From Nowak: Documenta Microbiologica, courtesy Gustav Fischer.)

doubted frequently. These organisms may act as secondary invaders to other diseases or to debilitative predisposing factors. The occurrence of epizootics and sporadic outbreaks, especially of fowl cholera, may indicate that these organisms can acquire virulence while being harbored in the animal, since the nature of these organisms requires continual parasitism for existence.

The organism is transmitted by contact and by the consumption of contaminated food and water. In some cases droplet infection is of significance.

Morphology and Staining. *Pasteurella multocida* is a small coccoid rod 0.25 to 0.4µ by 0.6 to 2.6µ in size (Fig. 24.1). After repeated culture on agar, the organism tends to form longer rods and to become more pleomorphic, forming chains, filaments, and rods of various sizes. When grown in bouillon or carbohydrate media for prolonged periods, marked pleomorphicity is noted. The organism usually possesses a capsule when recently isolated, especially from the acute type of hemorrhagic septicemia. The bacterial covering is carbohydrate in nature, varies in size, and can be demonstrated with an India ink preparation but not with the usual capsule stains. Virulent strains may lose their capsular material after continued subculture on artificial media.

When smears of blood or other tissue are stained with methylene blue or carbol fuchsin, the organism is distinctly bipolar (Fig. 24.2). It is Gram-negative.

Growth Requirements and Characteristics. The organism is an aerobe and facultative anaerobe. Its optimum temperature for growth is 37°C. The pH growth range is from 6 to 8.5 with an optimum of 7.2 to 7.4.

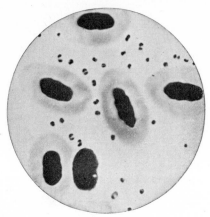

FIG. 24.2 — **Pasteurella m u l t o c i d a,** blood smear, fowl cholera, X 2,000. (From Nowak: Documenta Microbiologica, courtesy Gustav Fischer.)

The use of digested protein media or proteose peptone stimulates the growth of the organism. The organism can be grown in beef infusion media, but better growth is obtained when blood or blood serum is added to the media. Some strains fail to grow in media not containing blood serum.

Webster and Hughes described three types of colonies on solid media: fluorescent, intermediate, and blue. The fluorescent, or iridescent, colonies are moderate in size, whitish, opaque, generally unstable and pathogenic. The intermediate colonies vary in appearance between fluorescent and the blue forms. The blue colonies, although not necessarily rough in appearance, correspond in many ways to the R forms of other species. They are smaller, dewdrop-like (Fig. 24.3), and of a relatively low virulence. Strains giving rise to blue colonies are most frequently recovered from chronic infections, while acute infections usually yield strains giving rise to fluorescent colonies. Many strains of *Past. multocida* recovered from carrier states and chronic processes are composed of predominantly mucoid variants. The mucoid colonies are large and slimy in appearance and range in virulence between the fluorescent and blue variants.

In broth the organism recently isolated produces a diffuse clouding. Some strains form a flocculent precipitate which is characteristic of the rough phase of the organism. In old cultures a pellicle is often formed in broth, and a sticky sediment collects in the bottom of the tube.

The organism is not soluble in bile. There is usually no growth on potato.

Resistance. The organism is easily destroyed by 60°C. for 10 minutes or by 0.5 per cent phenol for 15 minutes. The organism remains infective in manure for a month and in decomposing carcasses for three months. A 1:5,000 solution of bichloride mercury and a 3.5 per cent solution of cresol are effective in a few minutes.

Past. multocida is notoriously difficult to keep alive upon artificial media when kept like other stock cultures of bacteria, sealed and in a refrigerator. Cultures will remain viable for years, however, if the culture tube is well-stoppered with a rubber stopper and kept at room temperature. Most cultures will lose their virulence on artificial media; however, it can usually be restored by animal passage.

This organism is sensitive to all of the commonly used antibiotics. The sulfa compounds, especially sulfathiazole, sulfamethazine, and sulfamerazine are effective against it *in vivo*.

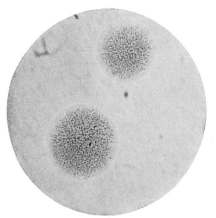

FIG. 24.3 — **Pasteurella multocida** colony on agar plate, × 70. (From Nowak: Documenta Microbiologica, courtesy Gustav Fischer.)

Biochemical Properties. *Pasteurella multocida* ferments glucose, mannose, galactose, saccharose, and mannitol but does not ferment, lactose, maltose, raffinose, trehalose, rhamnose, inositol, adonitol, inulin, salicin, dextrin, and starch. Some strains produce a slight amount of acid in sorbitol, glycerol, and fructose. The organism produces indol, catalase, and NH_3; reduces nitrates to nitrites; reduces methylene blue; does not produce methyl acetyl carbinol, and is negative to the methyl red test. It does not alter litmus milk or liquefy gelatin. It does not produce H_2S.

Antigenic Structure and Toxins. Carter has shown that the organism possesses two major antigenic fractions: a somatic or group antigen, which is probably a glycolipid; and a soluble-specific immunogenic polysaccharide associated with the capsule. On the basis of this capsular substance, strains of *Past. multocida* have been divided into four principal serological groups: Types A, B, C, and D. A number of different techniques have been employed for the typing of *Past. multocida*, but the method which has given the most satisfactory results has been a hemagglutination test. In this test the capsular polysaccharide is adsorbed to erythrocytes. These treated cells are agglutinated in the presence of the specific immune serum.

Much of the difficulty which has attended the typing of *Past. multocida* has been due to the complex dissociation pattern of the organism.

The mucoid strains have not been typable because their capsules are composed of nonantigenic hyaluronic acid.

Type A strains predominate in outbreaks of fowl cholera. Type B cultures have been most frequently recovered from cases of hemorrhagic septicemia in buffalo and cattle particularly in tropical and subtropical countries. Type C is generally the most frequently isolated from dogs and cats. Type D cultures do not appear to have a very definite host affinity. Many of the non-typable mucoid strains have been found complicating virus pneumonia of swine.

Both serological and immunological methods have been employed for typing *Past. multocida*. Rosenbusch and Merchant, and Little and Lyon have utilized the agglutination test with limited success. Roberts has divided his strains into four principal groups by means of mouse protection tests.

The organism does not produce exotoxin, but autolysed cultures contain endotoxin. Weil has demonstrated nontoxic aggressins or "infection-favoring" substances in the inflammatory exudates of Pasteurella-infected animals.

Pathogenicity. *Pasteurella multocida* is pathogenic for a large number of different animals; however, the organism varies in virulence from the highly virulent to the comparatively avirulent types. The virulence of the organism can be increased by animal passage, chicken embryo passage, and growth upon blood or blood serum media. Spontaneous dissociative changes which occur in cultures also contribute to the loss of virulence in some strains. Probably the most important role that *Past. multocida* plays in disease is that of a secondary invader when the resistance of the animal has been reduced by various stresses.

The more susceptible of the experimental animals are the mouse, rabbit, and pigeon. Guinea pigs are more resistant. Chickens are more susceptible to fowl strains, although highly virulent ovine and bovine strains are able to produce death.

The acute infections caused by *Pasteurella multocida* are characterized by a septicemia frequently accompanied by blood-vascular congestion, submucous and subserous hemorrhages, and an enteritis. The less acute form of the disease is accompanied by serofibrinous or hemorrhagic lesions in the mucosa and in tendon sheaths. The chronic type is characterized by necrotic areas, abscesses, and the accompanying debilitative conditions, such as anemia, diarrhea, and cachexia.

In the fowl, the most common form of the disease is the peracute fowl cholera which is characterized by petechial hemorrhages of the mucous membranes of various organs and by enlargement of the liver and spleen. Areas of focal necrosis are found in the liver of the chicken in the chronic forms.

In addition to chickens, serious losses are produced by this organism in domestic ducks, geese, and turkeys. Outbreaks of pasteurellosis may be encountered in wild fowl. Hudson has reported the disease in pheasants, and Quortrup, Queen, and Merovka observed an extensive epizootic in wild duck in Texas.

In cattle, hemorrhagic septicemia occurs in either the pectoral or edematous forms. The pectoral form involves the lungs and the pleural cavity and is accompanied by petechial hemorrhages in those tissues. The edematous type appears as an extensive edema of the subcutaneous tissues and the organs and tissues of the peritoneal cavity. It appears that hemorrhagic septicemia seldom appears in the United States or Canada as an important epizootic. Recent observations have disclosed that shipping fever in Canada, once believed to have been a hemorrhagic septicemia, is nonsepticemic but is a bronchopneumonia. However, sporadic cases of hemorrhagic septicemia are still seen occasionally in the bovine. The disease in calves is characterized by a typical pleuropneumonia. *Past. multocida* may localize in various tissues, including the brain. Isolation of the organism from a heifer showing symptoms of encephalitis has been recorded by Kingman. Numerous investigators have found the organism to be present in bovine mastitis.

In sheep, the organism produces an acute form characterized by typical hemorrhagic septicemia, a subacute form typified by a bronchopneumonia, and a chronic form characterized by a chronic pleuropneumonia. Biester, Schwarte, and Packer demonstrated that the organism may localize in the brain of sheep, producing symptoms characteristic of encephalitis.

In swine, acute epizootic pasteurellosis is an infrequent disease on this continent. However, *Past. multocida* is an important secondary invader of the widespread virus pneumonia of pigs.

In horses, the organism is not common although it has been found as a secondary invader in contagious pleuropneumonia.

In dogs and cats, the organism is not considered as a common agent of disease, although it has been isolated from these animals. The possibility must be noted that such animals may have fed upon a bird or mammal which had died of an infection caused by *Past. multocida*, thereby becoming infected in that manner. Outbreaks of pasteurellosis in mink raised in captivity have been reported as initiated by feeding meat from another species of animal which had died of this disease. Smith has reported the isolation of the organism from a monkey which had died enroute from Chicago, Illinois, to Sioux City, Iowa.

In rabbits, the disease is manifested by a hemorrhagic septicemia with pleuropneumonia or "snuffles." Subcutaneous abscesses are considered typical of the chronic form of the disease.

In rats, *Pasteurella multocida* produces the usual hemorrhagic septicemia picture.

In view of the broad range of animal species subject to *Past. multocida* infections, it is not surprising that an occasional infection has been encountered in man. Such infections are usually localized in nature, causing pneumonia, pleurisy, pericarditis, empyema, and meningitis. Most of the conditions reported were chronic, indicating that man possesses considerable natural resistance to the organism. Dog and cat bites have been reported as initiating local *Past. multocida* infections.

Immunity. The first method of bacterial prophylaxis was developed by Pasteur in 1880 with an avian strain of the organism. He used an organism which had been attenuated by prolonged cultivation upon unsealed media. This vaccine produced a mild reaction in susceptible chickens, but the animals were immune to subsequent inoculations of virulent cultures. This type of the vaccine has not come into general use because it has been reported that it may produce fowl cholera in some birds.

Tissue aggressin prepared by Weil's technic has been used as an immunizing agent for the prevention of pasteurellosis in cattle, sheep, and swine. Artificial aggressins or culture filtrates are also used for prophylaxis. Chemically killed broth bacterins prepared from a variety of *Past. multocida* strains are widely used.

Passive immunity has been produced in many instances by the use of hyperimmune serum.

The value of immunizing agents for the prevention of pasteurellosis has been questionable. Recent contributions to our knowledge of the immunology, serology, and dissociation pattern should make it possible for conscientious laboratories to prepare their bacterins and antisera along rational lines. The chick embryo vaccine developed by Carter has been used effectively for the prevention of fowl cholera. Bain has evolved a bacterin in which virulent organisms are incorporated in lanolin and mineral oil. It has been successful in the prevention of bovine hemorrhagic septicemia in Asia.

Diagnosis. A tentative diagnosis of pasteurellosis can be made by demonstrating typical bipolar rods in smears made from heart blood and liver tissue. The organism can be isolated upon agar slant cultures, and inoculations can be made into mice, young rabbits, or into pigeons. The presence of bipolar staining rods is not a dependable criterion for accurate diagnosis since many of the Gram-negative rods appear bipolar in tissue smears.

The most dependable diagnosis of *Pasteurella multocida* infection must employ the fermentation reactions on saccharose, lactose, rhamnose, xylose, and arabinose, along with the other biochemical reactions given in Table 24.1.

Pasteurella hemolytica

Synonyms and History. The first report of an organism typical of this species was made by Jones in 1921 when he reported a separate group of Pasteurella organisms which fermented lactose, did not produce indol, but did hemolize blood. In 1932 Newsom and Cross isolated the organism from cattle and sheep and suggested the name *Pasteurella hemolytica*.

Several other reports of an organism which apparently belongs to this species, have been made by a number of investigators. These include: Magnusson (1914) with an atypical hemorrhagic septicemia culture from a reindeer, Besemer (1917) with a calf strain, Spray (1923) with a group of *Pasteurella oviseptica* cultures, Jorgensen (1925) with organisms originating from the normal bacterial flora of cattle, Tanake (1926) with his buffalo cultures, Eddington (1930) with nine cattle cultures, Ochi (1931 and 1933) with six avirulent sheep strains, and Hellesnes (1935) with a virulent cattle strain. Rosenbusch and Merchant (1938) confirmed the results of Newsom and Cross with nine cultures.

Distribution and Transmission. This organism has been reported from the United States although other reports indicate it is present in Sweden, Norway, England, and Japan.

It is probably transmitted by contact.

Morphology and Staining. The organism is a short, nonmotile, encapsulated Gram-negative rod which is indistinguishable from *Pasteurella multocida* when recently isolated. It becomes increasingly pleomorphic after it is grown in artificial media for some time.

Growth Requirements and Characteristics. The growth requirements of this organism are similar to those of *Pasteurella multocida*.

On solid media, the colonies of *Pasteurella hemolytica* are round, flat, fluorescent, smooth, and moist; however, fluorescence is a variable characteristic.

Beta hemolysis may be present on initial isolation, but this hemolytic faculty diminishes as a result of repeated subculture on laboratory media. It returns, however, upon passage of the culture through mice or the chicken egg embryo. Hemolysis can sometimes be discerned only under the colony when the latter is scraped off the agar.

In broth the organism produces a diffuse cloudiness, and there is a marked sediment in cultures which have been maintained for a long time in culture media. A heavy viscid precipitate forms in old broth cultures.

Resistance. This organism is similar to *Past. multocida* in resistance.

Biochemical Properties. *Pasteurella hemolytica* forms acid but not gas from lactose, maltose, saccharose, mannitol, glucose, dextrin, galactose, glycerol, inositol, fructose, raffinose, sorbitol, and xylose. It does not ferment adonitol, salicin, rhamnose, or inulin. Some strains are able to produce a slight acid reaction in mannose, dulcitol, and arabinose. This organism does not form indol; reduces nitrates to nitrites; does not produce methyl acetyl carbinol. All of the strains of the organism produce beta hemolysis. Litmus milk is acidified and coagulated in 48 hours.

Antigenic Structure and Toxins. The organism is antigenically homogenous.

Exotoxins have not been reported.

Pathogenicity. *Pasteurella hemolytica* is relatively nonpathogenic for mice and rabbits, and virulence is entirely lost after the cultures have grown on artificial media for some time.

This organism has been found to be present in pneumonia of cattle and sheep, and Carter has found it to be the predominant bacterium in shipping fever in Canada. The importance of the organism in circumstances where resistance has been lowered has been emphasized by workers in Great Britain and Europe.

Tunnicliff has recovered cultures of an organism closely resembling *Past. hemolytica* from cases of mastitis in ewes.

Immunity. Information concerning the immunity produced by this organism is not available. The disease produced by it is not frequent enough to be of great economic significance.

Diagnosis. The causal relationship of this organism to pneumonia in cattle and in sheep can be proven only by the isolation and identification of the organism. For this purpose the nonproduction of indol, the fermentation of lactose, and the hemolysis of blood are outstanding reactions.

Pasteurella pestis

Synonyms and History. *Bacterium pestis, Bacterium pestis bubonicae, Bacillus pestis.*

This organism has been the cause of numerous pandemics of bubonic plague or "black death" throughout periods in the history of man. It has been estimated that 10,000,000 persons died of this disease in India during the period 1896 to 1917. It was during this epidemic that the organism was first isolated and described by Kitasato and by Yersin, working independently, but reporting their work in 1894.

Distribution and Transmission. Widespread epidemics of bubonic plague have not occurred any place in the world since the turn of the present century. The organism has become established in the rodent population of various continents where a chronic type of the disease has become endemic in man. These areas include parts of China, India, Siberia, southern Russia, the Uganda district of east central Africa, western Africa, south Africa, and in Argentina.

In California, Meyer and his co-workers have reported the organism from squirrels, and other rodents, in which it has caused sporadic cases of the disease known as sylvatic plague.

The transmission of plague to man governs the type of disease produced. The rat was recognized as being related to the disease in 1903, and in 1908 the rat fleas *Xenopsylla cheopsis* and *Ceratophyllus fasciatus* were found to be carriers of the organism. The bubonic form of the disease in man results from the bite of the flea. The pneumonic type of plague may result from the generalization of the disease due to flea bites but is more common during cold seasons when there is direct transmission of the organism from person to person in close contact. The infection among rodents is transmitted by fleas, by contact, by food infection, and by cannibalistic practices.

Morphology and Staining. *Pasteurella pestis* is a short, non-motile rod measuring 0.5 to 0.7μ in width and 1.25 to 1.75μ in length. In body fluids it appears singly, in pairs, or in short chains. The organism is extremely pleomorphic in bubonic lesions and on salt agar, forming filaments, club-like forms, and yeastlike cells (Fig. 24.4). In the animal body the organism produces a thin layer of mucoid capsular material. It is nonmotile and nonsporeforming.

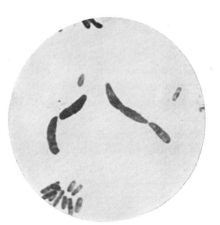

The organism is stained easily by ordinary dyes and is distinctly bipolar. It is Gram-negative.

Growth Requirements and Characteristics. This organism grows best at a temperature varying from 25° to 30°C. It is aerobic and facultatively anaerobic. A pH range of 6.2 to 7 is best suited for growth. It

FIG. 24.4 — **Pasteurella pestis,** involution forms on salt agar, × 2,000. (From Nowak: Documenta Microbiologica, courtesy Gustav Fischer.)

grows on all ordinary culture media, although growth is favored by the presence of serum.

On solid media, colonies of the organisms are flat, grey to greyish-white, translucent, iridescent, undulate with a notched margin and a raised center (Fig. 24.5). Variant colonies, considered rough and avirulent, are larger, more opaque, and have a crateriform center.

In broth the organism grows moderately, producing a floccular deposit which does not disintegrate upon shaking. As the culture ages, the sediment increases and tends to form on the sides of the tube. In some cultures a thin pellicle is formed.

The organism is not soluble in bile and grows on MacConkey's bile salt medium. A thin layer of growth is usually formed on potato.

Resistance. *Pasteurella pestis* is killed by 55°C. in 5 minutes and immediately by 5 per cent phenol. It is not resistant to drying or to direct sunlight. Cultures of the organism kept in an ice box will survive for months if the culture tubes are sealed. Organisms in infected spleens from mice have remained viable for seven years when preserved in glycerine.

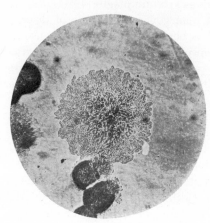

FIG. 24.5 — **Pasteurella pestis** colony on gelatin plate, × 110. (From Nowak: Documenta Microbiologica, courtesy Gustav Fischer.)

Biochemical Properties. The organism produces acid but no gas from glucose, maltose, mannitol, salicin, arabinose, and some strains from dextrin, glycerol, and xylose. It does not ferment lactose, saccharose, inulin, dulcitol, raffinose, adonitol, or sorbitol; does not produce indol; does not reduce nitrates; produces a small amount of H_2S. The organism is catalase positive, methyl red positive, and Voges-Proskauer negative. It produces NH_3; does not reduce methylene blue; does not change litmus milk; does not liquefy gelatin.

Antigenic Structure and Toxins. There appears to be only one type of *Pasteurella pestis*. A heat-labile capsular antigen and a heat-stable somatic antigen have been described. The somatic antigen possesses some relationship to *Pasteurella pseudotuberculosis*.

True toxins have not been described.

Pathogenicity. *Pasteurella pestis* is pathogenic to man and various species of rodents including the rat, mouse, squirrel, wild guinea pig, rabbit, and hare. Experimentally, the organism produces infection readily in mice, rats, guinea pigs, rabbits, and monkeys, but cats, dogs, pigs, cattle, sheep, goats, and horses are difficult to infect. With the exception of the sparrow, birds are difficult to infect.

The disease in man is of primary importance. The septicemic and pneumonic forms of the disease are fatal in 60 to 95 per cent of the cases. The bubonic form of the disease is most common but is not as fatal.

Different forms of the disease are found in rats during natural infections. The acute type is characterized by blood-vascular congestion over the entire body. The subacute type causes enlargement of superficial lymph nodes accompanied by edema and hemorrhage. The spleen is enlarged, and the liver is covered with small hemorrhages and areas of focal necrosis. In the chonic form the organism localizes in the lymph nodes, liver, and spleen, where areas of caseation necrosis and abscess formation are produced.

Experimental animals, particularly guinea pigs, show typical buboes following subcutaneous inoculation, and the liver and spleen are studded with necrotic foci.

Immunity. One attack of the disease produces an immunity to further infections. In 1895 Yersin, Calmette, and Borrel produced an immunity in rabbits and horses by the injection of killed cultures. The serum taken from immune horses protected rabbits against inoculations of virulent organisms. Haffkine, in 1897, produced the first successful human vaccine consisting of heat-killed broth cultures prepared by repeated reinoculation of the medium over a period of six weeks. Avirulent and attenuated vaccines which are thought to produce a better immunity than heat-killed products have been used also.

Passive immunity by the use of hyperimmune horse serum has been reported by several investigators to be of value during the early stages of the disease.

Diagnosis. Direct smears which are made from material obtained by puncturing an enlarged lymph node often reveal the presence of this typical bipolar organism. Cultures and guinea pig inoculation are often essential for definite diagnosis.

Great care must be followed in the collection of suspected fluid and tissue from human cases and from dead rats for the purpose of laboratory examination. Such materials must be placed in tight containers which are distinctly labeled.

Pasteurella tularense

Synonyms and History. *Bacillus tularense, Bacterium tularense, Brucella tularense.*

Pasteurella tularense was first observed by McCoy in 1911 in a plaguelike disease of the ground squirrel, *Citellus beechyi,* in Tulare county California. In 1912 McCoy and Chapin succeeded in isolating the organism on egg-yolk medium. They named the organism *Bacterium tularense* and were able to reproduce the disease with cultures.

The greatest part of the literature concerning this organism and the disease which it produces has been contributed by Francis and his co-workers since 1919.

The position of this organism in the genus Pasteurella is open to serious question. Francis has shown that it has a definite antigenic relationship to the Brucella group and upon that basis Topley and Wilson refer to the organism as *Brucella tularensis*. Other investigators are reticent to follow this classification. Bergey's Manual listed the organism as *Pasteurella tularensis* in 1939; Zinsser and Bayne-Jones, 1939, prefer to take a course between the Brucella and Pasteurella and call it *Bacterium tularense*.

In 1932 Reimann published a comparative study of *Pasteurella pseudotuberculosis, Pasteurella tularensis,* and *Pasteurella pestis* in which he concludes that all three of the organisms are closely related and should be classified in the same group. He found that a 1:800 dilution of sodium ricinoleate caused the clearing of suspensions of all three species in 2 hours. This was not true of the Brucella.

Distribution and Transmission. The organism is widely distributed throughout the world, having been reported from Japan, Russia, Norway, Sweden, and Austria. On this continent, it has been reported from Canada and from forty-six of the states and the District of Columbia.

Pasteurella tularense is transmitted in a variety of ways. It can be carried by blood-sucking flies, ticks, lice, and fleas. Cases result from contact with infected animals. The hair or fur from infected animals may carry the organism to the eyes or into the respiratory tract of man. The organism is not transmitted by contact from person to person.

Among wild animals the organism is usually transmitted by insect vectors and by cannibalism. It has been demonstrated that the organism passes from the parent tick with the eggs, thence to the larvae and the nymph stages, but not to the adult. The presence of the organism in insects results in the appearance of the greatest number of cases of the disease among wild animals during the late summer months. Cases of tularemia in man also occur during summer months, but the disease is most prevalent in the colder months during the hunting season for rabbits and squirrels. It is obvious that the infection remains endemic in rabbit and squirrel populations during the winter season or that resistant carriers of the organism exist.

An outbreak of tularemia in a human population in Russia was described by Tsareva as a water-borne infection. Presumably the water had been contaminated by water rats infected with the disease. The isolation of the organism from cold-water streams in western United States also indicates that the infection may be spread by water. Pahm found that the disease may be transmitted from an infected hog to man during the process of butchering.

Morphology and Staining. *Pasteurella tularense* is a small, pleomorphic, nonmotile rod, 0.2 by 0.3μ to 0.7 by 3μ in size. In young cultures ovoid and bacillary forms are found, but in old cultures the organism is coccoid. It is nonmotile and nonsporeforming. Clear zones around the organism considered capsules are observed in smears of animal tissue.

The organism is stained unevenly with most of the common dyes revealing forms which appear swollen on one end and pointed on the other. Smears from animal tissues show the presence of many bipolar forms when methylene blue or carbol fuchsin is used. It is Gram-negative.

Growth Requirements and Characteristics. The organism is strictly aerobic and grows best at a temperature of 37°C. The optimum pH for growth ranges from 6.8 to 7.3.

Pasteurella tularense cannot be cultured on ordinary media. McCoy and Chapin found that egg yolk contained some essential growth substance. Francis subsequently demonstrated that when cystine or cysteine hydrochloride was added to the medium that growth resulted; consequently, either of those substances is incorporated in media which are used in the study of the organism. Traub and co-workers have listed 13 essential amino acids in a medium they recommend. Growth is also stimulated by the presence of a small piece of rabbit spleen in the medium. Larson has observed that the organism grows readily in the chicken embryo when introduced in the yolk sac.

On a solid medium the organism forms minute, dewdrop-like, translucent colonies which vary from a viscid to a buttery consistency.

Resistance. The organism is killed in 10 minutes at 58°C. and is destroyed in 1 per cent tricresol in 2 minutes. Saline suspensions of the organism containing 0.1 per cent formalin are not virulent after 24 hours' exposure. The organism remains viable for years when present in spleen tissue preserved in glycerine and kept at −14°C. It has been found viable in the feces of bedbugs after drying for 26 days.

Past. tularense is susceptible to the action of streptomycin, Aureomycin, and various of the sulfonamide compounds.

Biochemical Properties. *Pasteurella tularense* is not as saccharolytic as the other members of the genus. It produces only a slight amount of acid from glucose, glycerol, maltose, mannose, fructose, and dextrin. Hydrogen sulfide is produced in a cystine medium. Catalase is produced, being greatest after 12 hours in incubation and then reaching a stable level at 48 hours, according to Avi-dor and Yaniv. The organism is soluble in sodium ricinoleate.

Antigenic Structure and Toxins. The different strains of

Pasteurella tularense are antigenically homogenous. An antigenic relationship exists with *Brucella abortus* and *Brucella melitensis,* but neither organism is able to absorb the homologous agglutinin from *Past. tularense* antiserum.

Exotoxin is not produced.

Pathogenicity. The organism has been found to produce natural infection in the following animals: ground squirrels in California and Utah; wild rabbits and hares throughout the United States; wild rats and wild mice in California; sheep in Idaho; quail and grouse in Minnesota; wild rabbits in Japan, Norway, and Canada; water rats in Russia; beaver in Montana; beaver and muskrats in Canada; chipmunk in Idaho. The organism is known to infect carnivora, foxes and dogs, which have eaten infected rabbits. Tularemia is a fatal septicemia in rodents, particularly in rabbits. The lesions of the disease are most predominant in the liver where numerous areas of focal necrosis are observed. Similar lesions are also found in the spleen, lungs, and bone marrow in some cases.

In a study of the comparative susceptibility of various laboratory animals, Downs and associates have found that white mice, rabbits, guinea pigs, hamsters, and cotton rats are all susceptible. Chicks and dogs are less susceptible than the above animals. In dogs the infection remains localized. Young monkeys succumb to an injection of as few as 20 bacteria but do localize the bacteria more effectively than any other experimental animal except the dog.

According to Lillie and Larson, the golden hamster is markedly susceptible to *Past. tularense,* showing extensive lesions following experimental inoculation by a variety of routes.

In man, the disease has been divided into as many as five clinical types.

1. The *ulceroglandular type* is characterized by the formation of a papule in the skin which develops into an ulcer and is accompanied by enlargement of the regional lymph nodes.
2. The *oculoglandular type* is typified by a conjunctivitis accompanied by the enlargement of the regional lymph glands.
3. The *glandular type* is not accompanied by skin or eye lesions but presents enlargement of skeletal lymph glands.
4. The *typhoid type* is characterized by a high temperature and evidently represents the septicemic or bacteremic stage of the disease.
5. The *pneumonic type* is often an extension of any of the above types and represents the localization of the organism in the lungs. This type is the most fatal.

Lide has described a case of congenital tularemia which occurred in the mother during the eighth month of pregnancy causing the death of the fetus. Necrotic granulomatous lesions were found in various organs of the fetus and organisms morphologically similar to *Past. tularense* were found in chorionic villi.

Immunity. Recovery from tularemia results in a permanent immunity. This is true of wild animals, experimental animals, and man. Specific agglutinins remain in the circulation for years after recovery from the disease; this has resulted in the diagnosis of infections years after recovery has taken place.

An acetone-extracted vaccine prepared from peptone broth has been shown, by Downs and his associates, to be effective in producing immunity in the white rat against experimental infection. The essential antigenic substance was found to be protein in nature and the vaccine resisted heating to 100°C. and remained effective after storage in a refrigerator for eight months. Coriell, Downs, and Clapp noted that Swiss mice could be protected by vaccination, but a high percentage of the animals which survived the challenge inoculation continued to harbor virulent organisms for several weeks. Larson prepared an ether-extracted vaccine from yolk sacs of infected chicken embryos which was effective in immunizing white rats.

Hyperimmune serum prepared in either horses, goats, rabbits, or sheep has been found effective experimentally and according to Foshay is valuable in clinical cases of the disease in man. Larson has observed that if immune serum is withheld for 24 hours after the injection of *Past. tularense* white rats are not protected against infection.

Diagnosis. The disease in rodents is more accurately diagnosed by the isolation of the organism. For this purpose it is necessary to inject the tissue emulsion from a suspected lesion into the guinea pig or white rat. This animal usually dies within a week, and cultures are made from the heart blood, spleen, and liver on blood-glucose, cystine agar, or coagulated egg-yolk medium.

In human cases showing generalized symptoms, the blood may be injected into guinea pigs from which the organism can be isolated in case of death.

If the disease has passed the first week, the agglutination test can be used as a means of diagnosis in any animal or in man. Infected animals and man show allergic reactions to intradermal injections of oxidized bacillary suspensions of *Past. tularense;* however, the value of such a test is limited by the fact that skin allergy persists for some time following recovery from the disease.

Pasteurella pseudotuberculosis

Synonyms and History. In 1883 Malassez and Vignal observed an organism which was isolated from guinea pigs after they had been injected with material taken from lesions of human tuberculosis. Whether this organism was the one under discussion is doubted. The first authentic report of the organism was made by Pfeiffer in 1889 when he referred to it as *Bacterium pseudotuberculosis rodentium*.

Since the organism is motile, some question its inclusion in the Pasteurella group. Reimann and Rose, however, have shown that it is quite similar to *Pasteurella pestis* and *Pasteurella tularense* in many respects which offset the fact that flagella are present.

Distribution and Transmission. The organism is widely distributed throughout the world and it produces spontaneous epidemics of disease in guinea pigs and other rodents.

The organism is probably transmitted by the ingestion of infected food. It is not known to be transmitted by insects.

Morphology and Staining. *Pasteurella pseudotuberculosis* is a small, pleomorphic cocco-bacillus which is similar to *Past. pestis*. The organism is motile in broth cultures incubated at 22°C. It is noncapsulated.

The organism is stained bipolar and is Gram-negative.

Growth Requirements and Characteristics. The organism is aerobic and facultatively anaerobic. Its optimum temperature for growth is 30°C. It grows well on all ordinary culture media and is uninfluenced by serum or dextrose.

The colonies of the organism on an agar surface are round, umbonate, finely granular, translucent, greyish-yellow, even-bordered with an opaque center and a flat, clearer periphery showing striations. The colonies are buttery in consistency. A rough variant with an irregular surface and a crenated edge has been described.

Broth cultures show a moderate turbid growth and a viscid precipitate. A slight ring of surface growth forms in old cultures. On potato the organism produces a thin, yellowish membranous growth which later turns brown.

Resistance. *Pasteurella pseudotuberculosis* is not resistant to ordinary disinfectants. It is killed by a temperature of 60°C. in 10 minutes.

Biochemical Properties. The organism produces acid, but no gas, from glucose, maltose, mannitol, salicin, arabinose, fructose, galactose, rhamnose, and glycerol; some strains ferment saccharose. It does not ferment lactose, dulcitol, sorbitol, or raffinose; does not produce indol; reduces nitrates; produces H_2S and NH_3. The organism is positive to the catalase test and the methyl red test but is negative to the Voges-Proskauer test. It reduces methylene blue; turns litmus milk slightly alkaline; does not liquefy gelatin.

Antigenic Structure and Toxins. The organism possesses two types of antigens, one a heat-labile H or flagellar antigen, and the other a heat-stable O or somatic antigen. The flagellar antigen is formed only at temperatures below 25°C. The somatic antigen consists of three to five different types, one of which is related to the O antigen of *Salmonella schottmuelleri.* In addition to these antigens there is a different heat-stable somatic antigen of the rough form which is similar to the somatic antigen of *Pasteurella pestis.*

An endotoxin was prepared by lysis of two different strains of *Past. pseudotuberculosis* with bacteriophage by Lazarus and Nozawa. The endotoxin produces marked circulatory changes and death in less than 12 hours in rabbits, guinea pigs, and white mice. In addition to death in experimental animals, the endotoxin in small doses produces skin necrosis of guinea pigs. After detoxification wtih formalin, this toxin is not able to stimulate the production of antitoxin.

Pathogenicity. *Pasteurella pseudotuberculosis* causes a condition called pseudotuberculosis in rodents, especially guinea pigs. The disease may be an acute septicemia or may follow a chronic course. In the chronic type of the disease the organism localizes in the mesenteric lymph nodes, the liver, the spleen, and the lungs, where it produces small necrotic nodules. A severe diarrhea usually accompanies the infection. Leader and Baker have reported a fatal disease in the chinchilla from which the organism was isolated.

Rosenwald and Dickinson isolated the organism from sick and dead turkeys in ten different flocks in Oregon. This organism has been isolated, likewise, from turkeys by Blaxland in England.

Other species of animals, in addition to those mentioned, are susceptible to this organism. Jamieson and Saltys have isolated it from cases of epididymo-orchitis in rams in Scotland. Eieland, of Norway, has observed it in silver foxes and in swine.

Experimentally, the organism has produced infection in the guinea pig, mouse, rabbit, wild rat, dog, cat, and the horse. Obscure cases of human infection are reported in the literature. Guinea pigs which are inoculated with the organism usually die in two to three weeks.

Immunity. Nothing is known concerning the immunity produced by the organism.

Diagnosis. The differentiation of this organism from *Pasteurella pestis* is most important. This can be done only after the organism is isolated in pure culture. The presence of flagella and the alkaline reaction produced in litmus milk serve to distinguish this organism from the one of bubonic plague.

REFERENCES FOR FURTHER STUDY

Avi-dor, Y., and Yaniv, N., Jour. Bact., 63:751, 1952.

Bain, R. V. S. Nature, 173:584, 1954.

Bell, J. F., Owen, C. R., and Larson, C. L. Jour. Inf. Dis., 97:162, 1955.

Bergey, D. H., *et al.* Bergey's Manual of Determinative Bacteriology. The Williams & Wilkins Co., Baltimore, 1948.

Biester, H. E., Schwarte, L. H., and Packer, R. A. Amer. Jour. Vet. Res., 3:268–73, 1942.

Blaxland, J. D. Vet. Rec., 59:317, 1947.

Carter, G. R. Amer. Jour. Vet. Res., 11:252, 1950.

——. Can. Jour. Med. Sci., 30:48, 1952.

——. Can. Jour. Comp. Med., 18:359, 1954.

——. Amer. Jour. Vet. Res., 16:481, 1955.

——, and Annau, E. Amer. Jour. Vet. Res., 14:475, 1953.

——, and McSherry, B. J. Can. Jour. Comp. Med., 19:177, 1955.

Coriell, L. L., Downs, C. M., and Clapp, M. P. J. Immunol., 56:245, 1947.

Downs, C. M., *et al.* J. Immunol., 56:217, 229, 1947.

Eieland, E. Saertrykk av Norsk Veterinaer-Tidsskrift Nr. 1 and Nr. 3, 1947.

Eveleth, D. F., Goldsby, A. I., and Nelson, C. I. Vet. Med., 64:73, 1949.

Francis, E., Lillie, R. D., and Parker, R. R. The Pathology of Tularemia. Nat. Inst. of Health, Washington, D. C. Bull. 167, 1937.

Gay, F. P., and associates. Agents of Disease and Host Resistance. Chap. 34. Charles C. Thomas, Baltimore, 1935.

Hudson, C. B. Jour. Amer. Vet. Med. Assn., 104:211, 1944.

Jamieson, S., and Saltys, M. A. Vet. Rec., 59:351, 1947.

Kingman, H. E. Jour. Amer. Vet. Assn., 106:109, 1945.

Kitt, T. Ueber eine experimentelle, der Rinderseuche ähnliche Infectionskrankheit. Sitz. d. Gesell. f. Morph. u. Phy., I, 1885, Munchen.

Kolle, W., and Hetch, O. Edited by John Eyre. Experimental Bacteriology. Chapt. 19 and 20. George Allen and Unwin, Ltd., London, 1934.

Langford, E. V. Can. Jour. Comp. Med., 18:28, 1954.

Larson, C. L. The Growth of *Past. tularensis* in the Yolk Sac of Developing Chick Embryo. Publ. Hlth. Rep. Wash., 60:587, 1945.

——. Immunization of White Rats against Infections with *Past. tularensis.* Publ. Hlth. Rep. Wash., 60:725, 1945.

——. A Serum Protection Test in Tularemia Infections in White Rats. Publ. Hlth. Rep. Wash., 62:1793, 1947.

Lazarus, A. S., and Nozawa, M. M. Jour. Bact., 56:187, 1948.

Leader, R. W., and Baker, G. A. Paper No. 1275, Wash. Agr. Exp. Sta., Wash. St. Coll., Pullman, Wash., 1953.

Lide, T. N. Arch. Path., 43:165, 1947.

Lillie, R. D., and Larson, C. L. Publ. Hlth. Rep. Wash., 60:1243, 1945.

Little, P. A., and Lyon, B. M. Amer. Jour. Vet. Res., 4:110–12, 1943.

Mitchell, A. J., Pirie, J. H. H., and Ingram, A. The Plague Problem in South Africa. So. African Inst. Med. Res., 3:85–256, 1926.

Morgan, B. B. Tularemia in Wisconsin. Trans. Wisc. Acad. Sc. Arts and Let., 39:1, 1949.

Owen, C. R., Bell, J. F., Larson, C. L., and Ormsbee, R. A. Jour. Inf. Dis., 97: 167, 1955.

Pahm, J. M. Ind. State Med. Assn. Jour., 40:1154, 1947.

Parker, R. R. Publ. Hlth. Rep. Wash., 60:17, 1945.

Pestana, B. R., Arantes, M., and Rugai, E. Pasteurelose Humana. Revista do Inst. Adolfo Lutz, 1:357–60, 1941.

Priestley, F. W. Jour. Comp. Path. Therap., 49:348, 1936.

Pullen, R. L., and Stuart, B. M. Jour. Amer. Med. Assn., 129:495–500, 1945.

Quortrup, E. R., Queen, F. B., and Merovka, L. J. Jour. Amer. Vet. Med. Assn., 108:94–100, 1946.

Rosenbusch, C. T., and Merchant, I. A. Jour. Bact., 37:69, 1939.

Rosenwald, A. S., and Dickinson, E. M. Amer. Jour. Vet. Res., 5:246–49, 1944.

Schutze, H. Pasteurella Trevisan. A System of Bacteriology. 4:446–82. Med. Res. Council. His Majesty's Stationery Office, London, 1929.

Smith, H. C. Jour. Amer. Vet. Med. Assn., 124:147, 1954.

Traub, A., Mager, J., and Grossowicz, N. Jour. Bact., 70:68, 1955.

Trevisan, V. Batteriologica Applicata alla Medicina Reale Institute Lombardo di Scienze e Lettere, Rendiconti 20:94–95, 1887.

Tsareva, M. I. Zh. Mikrobiol, Moscow. No. 7–8, 48, 1945.

Tunnicliff, E. A. Pasteurella Mastitis in Ewes. Vet. Med., 44:498, 1949.

25. The Genera Hemophilus and Moraxella

In classifying bacteria, it is often difficult to determine the appropriate place for all of them. Such is the case of the genera Hemophilus and Moraxella. The former genus has become well established because it has certain distinguishing characteristics. The latter, however, has not become well established, especially in its relationship to the genus Hemophilus, yet both are classified in the tribe Hemophileae. Representative species of both genera are coccobacilli but the similarity appears to end with this characteristic. In their study of this problem of proper classification, Murray and Truant have concluded that the genus Moraxella does not belong in the tribe Hemophileae but there is no other suitable niche in which to place it.

THE GENUS HEMOPHILUS

This group of bacteria requires certain growth-promoting substances known as X-factor and V-factor. These substances are present in the hemoglobin of animals and in the fresh juice of certain plants. It was because of the stimulating effect of hemoglobin on these organisms that the name Hemophilus was created. The organisms are small, coccoid, nonmotile, nonsporeforming, noncapsulated bacilli that are found, for the most part, in the respiratory tracts of animals and man. These bacteria are frequently associated with the disease, influenza; consequently, they are often referred to as the influenza group.

Many of the species which are placed in this group are not significant as inciters of disease in animals and man. Some of them have been described by only a few investigators and are not considered of great importance; however, there are a few species which are important factors in human and animal infections.

The species which are of particular interest to students in veterinary bacteriology are:

Hemophilus influenzae is associated with human influenza.

Hemophilus suis is associated with swine influenza.

Hemophilus canis is found in prepucial secretions of dogs.

Hemophilus gallinarum is associated with infectious coryza of fowls.

Hemophilus ovis is isolated from a respiratory infection of sheep.

Hemophilus cuniculi is found in subcutaneous abscesses of rabbits.

Relationship of Hemophilus influenzae to Hemophilus suis. A most unusual and interesting relationship exists between human influenza and swine influenza. The diseases in the two animals are symptomatically and pathologically alike, so definite interest is attached to the two organisms which have been isolated from typical cases of the disease in man and in swine.

Hemophilus influenzae was first described by Pfeiffer in 1892 and was conceded to be the cause of human influenza. This conclusion was accepted as true until the pandemic of influenza in 1918 when many investigators failed to find the typical organism in many cases of the disease. Filtrates of nasal exudate were found to reproduce the disease, and it was concluded that the primary cause was a filtrable virus. The etiological role of *Hemophilus influenzae* in the infection has not been discarded by many; consequently, there is yet no unanimity of opinion in respect to the true cause of the disease. The most acceptable theory is that a virus is the primary inciting agent in the disease and that other organisms, such as, *Hemophilus influenzae,* streptococci, and pneumococci are important secondary invaders.

In 1918, Koen, working in the Federal Bureau of Animal Industry as a field investigator of swine diseases in Iowa, observed a swine disease which was similar to human influenza, so prevalent at that time. He called the condition "flu" because of the similarity. In 1920 Murray isolated a small Gram-negative coccus which he considered the cause of the disease. McBryde, Niles, and Mosky in 1928 isolated a pleomorphic, Gram-positive bacillus and *Bacillus suisepticus* from the lungs of influenza swine. In 1930 Fulton also isolated a Gram-positive organism from cases of swine influenza. A significant report was made in 1931 by Lewis and Shope concerning the etiologic factors responsible for swine influenza. They found that the disease was caused by the synergistic action of a filtrable virus and an organism which they considered so similar to certain strains of *Hemophilus influenzae* that they called it *Hemophilus influenzae* (variety suis). In 1932 Köbe of Germany observed a similar organism in a chronic disease of pigs called "ferkelgrippe," and the following year Köbe and Kirchenbauer, independently, further emphasized the resemblance of this organism to *B. influenzae.* The first evidence to show that the two organisms were different antigenically was introduced by Schlüter in 1936 when he demonstrated antigenic differences by the use of complement-fixation and complement-fixation-absorption tests.

In 1938 Rosenbusch found that *Hemophilus influenzae suis* was distinguishable from *Hemophilus influenzae* on the basis of carbohydrate fermentation. The swine organism fermented maltose and sucrose but not xylose or dextrose, while the human strains fermented xylose and dextrose but not maltose or sucrose.

Hauduroy classified the swine influenza organism as *Hemophilus suis*, a name which Bergey's Manual also uses in the 1948 edition.

Hemophilus suis

Synonyms and History. *Hemophilus influenzae* variety *suis, Hemophilus influenzae-suis, Bacterium influenzae suis.*

This organism was first isolated and described by Lewis and Shope in 1931.

Distribution and Transmission. Reports indicate that the organism is present in Germany and in the United States. Swine influenza was prevalent in the middle-western part of the United States following the epidemic of human influenza in 1918, but the disease has decreased among swine herds until only sporadic cases are reported at the present time.

The virus, which is the inciting factor in the disease, is transmitted by direct contact. The organism is considered a normal inhabitant of the upper respiratory tract of some animals, but it, too, is transmitted by contact during the active stage of an epizootic.

Morphology and Staining. *Hemophilus suis* is a small, slender rod, 0.2μ in thickness and varying from 0.5 to 2μ in length. A few long, curved threadlike shapes are often observed. As the culture of the organism ages, coccoidal forms begin to appear, and when the culture is 48 hours old most of the organisms are coccoid in shape. Extremely large, coccoidal, and club-shaped forms are found in some cultures. The organism resembles the morphology of *Hemophilus influenzae* (Fig. 25.1).

The staining capacity of this organism is not as great as other similar types of bacteria. The ordinary alkaline methylene blue imparts only a faint blue color. A heavier stain is obtained by the use of phenolized methylene blue which is steamed during the staining process. The organism is Gram-negative.

Growth Requirements and Characteristics. The swine influenza bacillus is a strict aerobe and grows best at 37°C. The reaction of the medium for maximum growth is pH 7.2.

The outstanding characteristic of this group is the requirement of X and V growth factors and should be re-emphasized. These two factors have received considerable attention from the investigators who have studied the human organism. The substance known as X-factor is present in the hemoglobin of any animal and is intimately related to the iron-containing fraction of this pigment. This factor is heat-resistant; consequently, media containing heated blood, such as chocolate agar, is frequently used for artificial cultivation. The X-factor is also present in vegetable tissue, especially potato. Certain organisms can activate iron compounds in culture media to function as X-factor. The substance called V-factor is present in the juices of the following vegetables and fruits: potatoes, tomatoes, lemons, apples, bananas, coconuts, and green peas. Red blood cells recently removed from an animal also contain this substance; however, fresh serum has a destructive effect on it. V-factor always must be added to the medium after sterilization because it is easily destroyed by a temperature of 100°C. The characteristics of this factor are similar to vitamin C, but are not identical with those of that vitamin.

On the surface of solid media *Hemophilus suis* produces small, circular, grayish, semitranslucent, flattened colonies that have a sharply contoured edge. They are similar to those produced by the human influenza organism (Fig. 25.2).

Hemophilus suis produces a faint turbidity in broth due to the feeble growth of the organism.

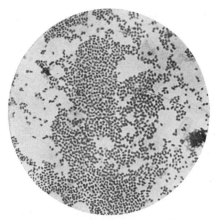

FIG. 25.1 — **Hemophilus influenzae** from agar culture, × 2,000. (From Nowak: Documenta Microbiologica, courtesy Gustav Fischer.)

Resistance. This organism is similar to all of the Gram-negative, nonsporeforming rods in resistance to heat, light, desiccation, and chemical disinfectants.

Biochemical Properties. In the study of any of the biochemical activities of this organism, it is emphasized that both X- and V-factors must be added to the media; failure to do so undoubtedly will yield variable results.

Hemophilus suis is not an actively saccharolytic microorganism. Shope and Lewis report no demonstrable action on glucose, lactose, saccharose, dulcitol, mannitol, glycerol, inulin, or arabinose. Rosenbusch reports the fermentation of maltose and traces of acidity in saccharose and a few strains in mannitol. The organism reduces nitrates to nitrites; does not produce hydrogen sulphide; does not liquefy gelatin. This organism does not produce indol; this is a characteristic similar to that of some of the strains of *Hemophilus influenzae*. Growth is scanty in litmus milk, and the medium remains unchanged.

Antigenic Structure and Toxins. The antigenic relationship of *Hemophilus suis* to *Hemophilus influenzae* has been subjected to careful study by a number of investigators. In their original work Lewis and Shope noted the antigenic heterogeneity of *Hemophilus suis;* this is also a characteristic of *Hemophilus influenzae* according to numerous reports. Rosenbusch observed that on the basis of agglutinin-absorption tests, the strains of *Hemophilus suis* were more homogenous than the strains of *Hemophilus influenzae;* however, he noted a definite cross-agglutination between the two species.

The different antigenic fractions of *Hemophilus suis* have not been determined.

This organism does not produce a soluble toxin. It is not hemolytic.

Pathogenicity. The pathogenicity of *Hemophilus suis* depends upon the previous action of the filtrable virus upon the mucous membranes of the respiratory tract. Shope demonstrated that the clinical and pathological pictures of swine influenza depend upon these two etiologic agents operating in synergistic action, and that neither the virus nor the organism can produce the disease when injected alone.

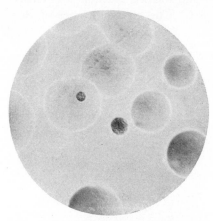

FIG. 25.2 — **Hemophilus influenzae** colonies on agar plate, × 40. (From Nowak: Documenta Microbiologica, courtesy Gustav Fischer.)

Hemophilus suis is variable in virulence to rabbits and guinea pigs. Some strains produce death in 24 hours while the majority do not produce any observable symptoms. The organism is pathogenic to white mice, producing a 50 per cent mortality, according to Shope. White rats are resistant.

Further discussion of the relationship of the virus to swine influenza will be found in the section of the book devoted to the filtrable virus diseases.

Immunity. Swine which have recovered from attacks of influenza are immune. The presence of virus-neutralizing antibodies in the blood serum of these swine indicates that the immunity is a virus immunity and is not related to *Hemophilus suis*.

Diagnosis. The presence of *Hemophilus suis* can be detected only by demonstrating the organism by the inoculation of suitable culture media. For this purpose, chocolate agar or chocolate agar plus sterile potato infusion is recommended.

Hemophilus canis

Synonyms and History. While working as an assistant to Pfeiffer in the period during which the human influenza bacillus was discovered, Friedberger in 1903 isolated an organism, which he termed *Bacillus haemoglobinophilus canis* from the prepucial exudate of the dog. In 1922 Rivers described the organism in more detail, called attention to its growth requirements, and suggested the name *Hemophilus canis*.

Distribution and Transmission. If the prevalence of prepucial exudate is the determining criterion of its presence, this organism is widely distributed throughout the dog world. Presumably, it is transmitted by contact due to habits of male animals of the canine family.

Morphology and Staining. *Hemophilus canis* is a small, nonmotile rod which is very similar to *Hemophilus suis* and *Hemophilus influenzae*. The organism is Gram-negative.

Growth Requirements and Characteristics. *Hemophilus canis* is aerobic and grows best at 37°C. and at a pH 7.0 to 7.2.

Rivers was the first to note that this organism differs from *Hemophilus influenzae* in its relationship to X and V growth factors. *Hemophilus canis* requires the presence of X-factor but, apparently, is able to synthesize V-factor or does not need it for growth.

On chocolate agar the organism produces small, round, grayish-white colonies which tend to become larger and more opaque as the culture ages.

A diffuse growth occurs in the proper fluid medium.

Resistance. The organism is typical of the other members in the group.

Biochemical Properties. *Hemophilus canis* forms acid without gas from glucose, fructose, galactose, mannitol, sucrose, and xylose; does not ferment maltose, lactose, dextrin, arabinose, or glycerol; forms indol and reduces nitrates.

Antigenic Structure and Toxins. Information concerning the antigenic relationship of this organism to others of the Hemophilus group is not available. It does not produce exotoxin.

Pathogenicity. *Hemophilus canis* is not considered pathogenic. Its presence in purulent prepucial exudate may indicate that it has a low-grade type of virulence. It has never been incriminated in the acute respiratory infections of the dog; however, this problem has not been completely explored. Even though Rivers speculated concerning the possibility of the organism becoming established in the respiratory tracts of people who handle dogs, it is not considered pathogenic to man.

The white mouse, the guinea pig, and the rabbit are not susceptible to *Hemophilus canis*.

Immunity. Nothing is known about the immunity produced by this organism.

Diagnosis. The isolation of the organism from the prepucial exudate is possible only by the use of a nutrient medium containing hematin. It is differentiated from the other species in the genus by means of carbohydrate fermentation.

Hemophilus gallinarum

In 1932 DeBlieck reported finding an organism in the respiratory tract of chickens which showed a typical type of fowl pox. The organism was Gram-negative and hemophilic so it was named *B. haemoglobinophilus coryza gallinarum*. Nelson, in 1932, observed the same type of an organism in an uncomplicated epizootic of coryza in the domestic fowl. In 1933 Delaplane and Stuart reported the organism from Rhode Island, and in the same year Pistor, Hoffman, Beach, and Schalm found it in California.

Hemophilus gallinarum shows the morphology which is typical of the group—small, coccoid, pleomorphic, Gram-negative rods. Nelson reported the growth of the organism in blood at the base of agar slants which had been inoculated with a filtrate of nasal exudate. This may indicate that extremely small forms of the organism exist. Gregory has found that a medium containing filtered yeast extract and 1 per cent sodium chloride was more satisfactory for obtaining growth of the organism. This author observed that X-factor (hemin) was not essential for growth. On this medium the organism forms a fine confluent growth barely visible to the unaided eye. More abundant growth is obtained when the medium is incubated in a moist chamber to prevent desiccation.

Intranasal inoculation of cultures of the organism produces the typical disease in a susceptible chicken. Subcutaneous inoculation produces edema with subsequent suppuration at the point of injection. Turkeys, pigeons, sparrows, and crows are resistant. Rabbits and guinea pigs are also resistant.

The rhinitis produced by *Hemophilus gallinarum* is distinct from laryngotracheitis, produced by a filtrable virus, as shown in cross-immunity tests by Delaplane, Erwin, and Stuart.

Hemophilus ovis

In 1925 Mitchell isolated from the respiratory tract of sheep an organism which he called *Hemophilus ovis*. Apparently this is the only report of the organism in the literature.

Hemophilus ovis is a short, coccoid, pleomorphic rod, quite typical of the influenza group. It is Gram-negative and stains poorly with aniline dyes.

On chocolate agar, colonies are distinct, viscid, moist, and glistening, and about the size of a pin head. After continued growth the colonies become flatter with an elevated center and lose their viscidity. In broth the organism produces a slight turbidity and forms in floating, ropy strands which settle to the bottom of the culture tube and form a slimy precipitate.

Hemophilus ovis produces acid but not gas from sorbitol, raffinose, fructose, galactose, glucose, maltose, mannitol, mannose, and sucrose; produces slight acidity in lactose and xylose; does not ferment inositol, salicin, inulin, arabinose, or rhamnose. It does not form indol; reduces nitrates to nitrites; does not liquefy gelatin; does not alter litmus milk to which blood is added.

The organism produces an acute bronchopneumonia in adult sheep. In addition to the lung lesions, degenerative changes are found in the liver, kidneys, and heart muscle. Intravenous inoculation of the organism into a sheep produces the typical form of the disease. The guinea pig and rabbit are susceptible. The chicken is resistant.

Intranasal instillation of the organism into the guinea pig produces death in four days, indicating that the organism gains entrance through the respiratory tract of sheep affected with the disease.

Hemophilus cuniculi

In 1929 Gibbons isolated a hemophilic organism from subcutaneous abscesses in the domestic rabbit. Hauduroy lists the organism as *Hemophilus cuniculi*.

The organism is a short bacillus, 0.3 to 0.4µ by 1.0 to 1.2µ in size. It usually occurs singly, but chains are found. It is capsulated and nonmotile. The organism is Gram-negative.

Blood agar is most suitable for artificial cultivation, and on this medium the organism forms round, smooth, watery, transparent colonies which are the size of a pin point. The growth is similar, although not as luxuriant, upon serum agar. After prolonged artificial cultivation upon blood agar the organism can be grown on ordinary beef-extract agar. A marked turbidity is produced in infusion broth.

Hemophilus cuniculi is aerobic and facultatively anaerobic. It produces acid but no gas from glucose, fructose, mannitol, maltose, lactose, sucrose, galactose, salicin, dextrin, and xylose; does not ferment dulcitol or inulin. It does not form indol; does not alter milk; does not liquefy gelatin.

Experimental subcutaneous inoculation of the organism into rabbits produces the typical, circumscribed hard abscesses which persist for about a month. It causes death in mice within five days by producing a septicemia. Guinea pigs are relatively resistant.

THE GENUS MORAXELLA

Representative species of the genus Moraxella are coccobacilli commonly found in a diploid arrangement. They vary in size especially in old cultures, many cells contain large vacuoles, peripheral chromatin granules, fat, and glycogen. Some strains are capsulated. They are Gram-negative to Gram-variable. Hematin or other growth factors considered essential to the various species of the genus Hemophilus are not required for the Moraxella.

Two species, *M. bovis* and *M. anatipestifer* have been shown to be pathogenic to animals.

Moraxella bovis

In 1919 Allen isolated a small bacterium from bovine infectious keratitis. The organism was similar to the Morax-Axenfeld bacillus which is considered to be the cause of infectious conjunctivitis in man. Jones and Little found the same type of organism associated with the disease in 1923. Hauduroy classified the organism as *Hemophilus bovis* in 1927. As a result of his bacteriological study of bovine infectious keratitis in 1945, Baldwin demonstrated the etiological relationship of the organism to the disease, which was confirmed by Reid and Anigstein the same year.

The role of this organism as the primary infecting agent in infectious keratitis could not be confirmed by Farley *et al.* (1950). It is their belief that the organism is an important secondary invader in the disease but there are other factors of primary importance.

In the 1948 edition of Bergey's Manual this organism was placed in a new genus, Moraxella, because of its diplococcoid shape.

Moraxella bovis is a short rod 0.5 to 1.0μ in width and 1.5 to 2.0μ in length. It is found usually in pairs, but short chains are observed. Pleomorphism is noted in old cultures. A definite capsule is present in young cultures. Neither flagella nor spores are produced. The organism is Gram-negative.

Horse blood agar, pH 7.2 to 7.5, is the most satisfactory medium for isolation. On this medium small, round, translucent, grayish-white colonies develop in 24 hours. These colonies are surrounded by a narrow zone of beta hemolysis. As the culture ages, the colonies enlarge and develop a small raised area in the center. Growth is more scant on plain and serum agar media. On coagulated serum medium, the organism forms small colonies which sink into the medium, due to the liquefaction. As the culture ages, liquefaction is extended throughout the medium. The organism grows slowly in nutrient broth, forming a light turbidity and a coarse sediment.

M. bovis does not produce acid in any of the carbohydrates; in fact, the medium tends to become more alkaline. Litmus milk becomes alkaline with the development of three zones: the upper zone composed of deep blue fluid; the medium zone containing soft curd lighter in color; and the third zone white, coagulated casein. Nitrates are not reduced to nitrite; indol is not formed; gelatin is liquefied slowly.

The lesions typical of infectious keratitis have been reproduced in bovines by the use of cultures of the organism by Jones and Little, by Baldwin, by Reid and Anigstein, by Barner, and by Jackson. Farley and co-workers were unable to reproduce the disease in cattle by using 24-hour cultures of the organism which were inoculated under the eyelids of normal cattle. Rabbits and guinea pigs were refractory, likewise, to numerous intraocular exposures. These investigators found that *M. bovis* caused the death of 10- and 12-day-old chicken embryos when cultures were injected beneath the inner shell membrane. Sheep are not infected.

Baldwin noted that animals were resistant to the organism after recovery from infection. However, some remain carriers of the organism, thus serving as reservoirs until the next season. Jones and Little observed that flies are agents of transmission.

In their study of calf pneumonia, Thorp, Shigley, and Farrell found an Hemophilus-like organism associated with the disease. This organism is similar to *H. suis* in morphology and gives positive cross-agglutination results in titers of 1:300 and 1:640. As far as is known, no comparison has been made between this organism and cultures of *M. bovis* isolated from infectious keratitis.

Moraxella anatipestifer

In 1932 Hendrickson and Hilbert described an organism which had been isolated from ducklings. They named it *Pfeifferella anatipestifer*. Bruner and Fabricant, in 1954, studied cultures of an organism, isolated from ducklings, which fitted the description of the above and concluded it should be classified as *Moraxella anatipestifer*. These investigators do not consider that the organism has a primary role in producing disease in ducklings; in fact, they consider it to be nonpathogenic.

M. anatipestifer is a short Gram-negative rod occurring singly, in pairs, and in short chains. It is nonmotile and does not form spores. Growth is best obtained in a medium containing horse serum and in 5 to 10 per cent carbon dioxide. Colonies on solid media are small and dewdrop-like. In thioglycollate medium a ring of growth is noted 1 cm. below the surface. It does not ferment carbohydrates but does liquefy gelatin, coagulated blood serum, and coagulated egg medium.

REFERENCES FOR FURTHER STUDY

Allen, J. A. A Preliminary Note on Infectious Keratitis. Jour. Amer. Vet. Med. Assn., 54:307–13, 1919.

Baldwin, E. M. A Study of Bovine Infectious Keratitis. Amer. Jour. Vet. Res., 6:180–87, 1945.

Barner, R. D. Amer. Jour. Vet. Res., 13:132, 1952.

Bruner, D. W., and Fabricant, I. Cornell Vet., 44:461, 1954.

DeBlieck, L. A Haemoglobinophilic Bacterium as the Cause of Contagious Catarrh in the Fowl. Vet. Jour., 88:9–13, 1932.

Delaplane, J. P., Erwin, L. E., and Stuart, H. O. A Hemophilic Bacillus as the Cause of An Infectious Rhinitis (Coryza) of Fowls. R. I. Agr. Exp. Sta., Bull. 244, 1934.

Farley, H., Kliewer, I. O., Pearson, C. C., and Foote, L. E. Amer. Jour. Vet. Res., 11:22, 1950.

Friedberger, E. Ueber ein Neues zur Gruppe des Influenzabacillus Gehöriges hämoglobinophiles Bakterium *(Bacillus haemoglobinophilus canis)*. Centralbl. f. Bakt., etc., 1 Abt. Orig., 33:401, 1903.

Gay, F. P., and associates. Agents of Disease and Host Resistance, Chap. 37. Charles C. Thomas, Baltimore, 1935.

Gibbons, N. E. Hemophilus sp. and Neisseria sp. in Skin Abscesses in Rabbits and Guinea Pigs. Jour. Inf. Dis., 45:288–92, 1929.

Gregory, D. W. Nutrient Requirements of *H. gallinarum*. Amer. Jour. Vet. Res., 5:72–77, 1944.

Hendrickson, J. M., and Hilbert, K. F. Cornell Vet., 22:239, 1932.

Jackson, F. C. Amer. Jour. Vet. Res., 14:19, 1953.

Jones, F. S. and Little, R. B. An Infectious Ophthalmia of Cattle. Jour. Exp. Med., 38:139–48, 1923.

——, ——. The Transmission and Treatment of Infectious Ophthalmia of Cattle. Jour. Exp. Med., 39:803–10, 1924.

Lewis, P. A., and Shope, R. Swine Influenza. Jour. Exp. Med., 54:361–72, 1931.

Mitchell, Chas. A. *Hemophilus ovis* (nov. spec.) as the Cause of a Specific Disease in Sheep. Jour. Amer. Vet. Med. Assn., 68:8–18, 1925.

Murray, R. G. E., and Truant, J. P. Jour. Bact., 67:13, 1954.

Nelson, J. B. Etiology of Uncomplicated Coryza in the Domestic Fowl. Soc. Exp. Bio. Med., 30:306–07, 1932.

Rivers, T. M. *Bacillus hemoglobinophilus canis* (Friedberger). Jour. Bact., 7:579, 1922.

Rosenbusch, C. T. Some Studies on Swine Influenza, I. Comparative Study of *Hemophilus influenzae suis* and *Hemophilus influenzae*. Doctoral Thesis, Iowa State College Library, Ames, Iowa, 1938.

Scott, W. M. The Influenza Group of Bacteria. A System of Bacteriology, 2:326–94. Med. Res. Council, His Majesty's Stationery Office, London, 1929.

Shope, R. Swine Influenza. Jour. Exp. Med., 54:349–60, 373–85, 1931.

Thorp, W. T. S., Shigley, J. J., and Farrell, M. A. Studies on the Etiology and Pathology of Calf Pneumonia. Amer. Jour. Vet. Res., 3:342–49, 1942.

26. The Genus Malleomyces

Classifications of bacteria are subjected to frequent changes. The glanders bacillus is an excellent example of how an organism may be shifted from one genus to another, from one family to another, and from one order to another. At the present time the organism is called *Malleomyces mallei*.

The genus Malleomyces includes the short rods, which sometimes form threads and show a tendency toward branching. They may be either motile or nonmotile; stain Gram-negative; show a tendency toward bipolar staining; coagulate milk slowly; may liquefy gelatin; grow best on blood-serum media. These organisms are specialized for a parasitic existence on hosts in which they are capable of producing disease.

Two species are classified in this genus: *Malleomyces mallei* causes glanders in the horse and is infectious for man; *Malleomyces pseudomallei* produces a glanders-like disease in rats, guinea pigs, rabbits, and man, and has been reported only from India and Indo-China.

Malleomyces mallei

History and Synonyms. Loeffler and Shütz, in 1882, were the first to show that equine glanders was caused by an organism which they termed the glanders bacillus (rotzbacillus). Flügge called the organism *Bacillus mallei* in 1886. It was called *Corynebacterium mallei* by Lehmann and Neumann in 1899, *Bacterium mallei* by Migula in 1900, and *Mycobacterium mallei* by Chester in 1901. In 1918, the name *Pfeifferella mallei* was listed by Buchanan, although it was his intention to call the organism *Loefflerella mallei* in commemoration of the contributions of Loeffler to bacteriology. *Pfeifferella mallei* was becoming well established in the literature when Pacheco, in 1933, concluded that the organism should be called *Brucella mallei*. In the same year, Thompson studied cultures of the glanders organism, of pseudoglanders, and of actinobacillosis and concluded that the three were similar enough to be placed in the same genus, Actinobacillus. This name was adopted by Bergey's Manual in 1934 and was becoming established in the literature.

In 1933 Pribram revived the name Malleomyces for the genus in which the glanders organism was placed. This was done because of the name *Malleomyces equestris* which was used by Hallier in 1870 as a result of his work on what he considered to be an organism causing glanders, but according to his descriptions was obviously not an organism but was a contaminated culture.

The inclusion of the glanders organism in the genus Actinobacillus, as proposed by Thompson, has been questioned by Topley and Wilson who still preferred the name *Pfeifferella mallei* in 1936. Holden, in association with Gay, in 1935, sought to settle the controversy by proposing the name *Loefflerella mallei*. This appeared to be a happy solution, and many hoped that the name would be adopted. The 1948 edition of Bergey's Manual, however, used the name *Malleomyces mallei*.

Distribution and Transmission. The disease glanders, which is caused by this organism, has been widely distributed throughout the world. In many countries where a concerted effort has been made to eradicate the disease, cases are extremely rare. In the United States the disease has ceased to be a major problem.

Glanders is a disease involving the respiratory tract and subcutaneous tissues. The organism is transmitted chiefly through the common watering trough, feed, and by direct contact. The isolation of the equine population on the farm has contributed a great deal to the disappearance of glanders. The perfection and use of adequate diagnostic methods with the subsequent destruction of the infected animals have also served as effective control measures. The practice of approved sanitary methods in places where large numbers of horses are kept together has proven an effective means of controlling the disease.

Human infection is usually obtained through skin cuts and abrasions during contact with glanders exudate.

The disease has been reported in dogs, cats, and other carnivora following the eating of meat from a glandered horse.

Morphology and Staining. *Malleomyces mallei* is a slender rod with rounded ends, and normally is 0.3 to 0.5μ in breadth and 1.5 to 5μ in length. Old cultures are pleomorphic; they are composed of forms which range from coccoid cells to extremely long filaments some of which are slightly branched. Many of the cells, especially the filaments, present a beaded appearance, and numerous cells of normal size appear to have one or more minute vacuoles in the protoplasm (Fig. 26.1). Miller and co-workers have found, with the aid of the electron microscope, that the refractile bodies resemble lipoid globules. In smears which are made from a glanders lesion in a mouse, the organism is definitely bipolar but the polar granules are more distinct than in other bipolar staining cells. This organism is noncapsule-producing, nonmotile, and nonspore-producing. It is not stained easily by the common dyes and is Gram-negative.

Growth Requirements and Characteristics. The glanders bacillus is aerobic and facultatively anaerobic. The most favorable temperature for artificial cultivation is 37°C. although some growth occurs between temperatures of 25° to 40°C. A slightly acid reaction, pH 6.6, is most conducive to satisfactory growth.

The organism grows well on most of the common laboratory media, but the addition of serum and glycerin yields a more rapid and abundant culture. After two days' incubation upon glycerin agar the organism produces a small, round, amorphous, translucent colony (Fig. 26.2). Growth on solid media has a tendency to be slimy and tenacious in consistency. Surface colonies become yellowish-brown as the culture ages.

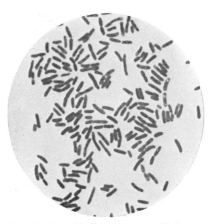

FIG. 26.1 — **Malleomyces mallei,** 24-hour agar culture, × 2,000. (From Nowak: Documenta Microbiologica, courtesy Gustav Fischer.)

In glycerin bouillon the bacillus produces a light turbidity and forms a thin, slimy pellicle; the medium becomes darker brown as the culture stands.

The organism is distinctly characterized by the growth which forms on potato. After 48 hours incubation, a yellowish, viscid, semitransparent growth appears and gradually turns yellowish-brown and eventually to a rich mahogany. The potato medium is oxidized to a brownish-green color. *M. mallei* grows readily on the media used for the cultivation of tubercle bacilli; glycerol is definitely stimulating.

Resistance. This organism is not resistant to adverse conditions. It is killed by 55°C. in 10 minutes. Natural desiccation and sunlight do not permit the organism to live long outside of the body. According to Miller *et al.* "roccal," hypochlorite, iodine, and mercuric chloride are highly effective as disinfectants, whereas phenol is less effective and lysol is ineffective. The organism remains viable in tap water for at least four weeks.

Streptomycin has been found of value in treating cases of glanders in man.

Biochemical Properties. An outstanding feature of *Malleomyces mallei* is its inability to ferment carbohydrate media, although some strains do produce a slight acid reaction in glucose and salicin after prolonged incubation. It does not produce indol; does not reduce nitrates; is negative to the M.R. and V.P. tests. The organism produces a slight amount of H_2S, NH_3, and catalase. A slight acidity is formed in litmus milk, and in two to three weeks a soft curd is developed. The organism does not liquefy gelatin.

Antigenic Structure and Toxins. For practical diagnostic purposes the organism is antigenically homogenous when mallein or the complement-fixation test is used. The study of numerous strains of the organism by agglutination, precipitation, and complement-fixation has revealed at least two antigenic types.

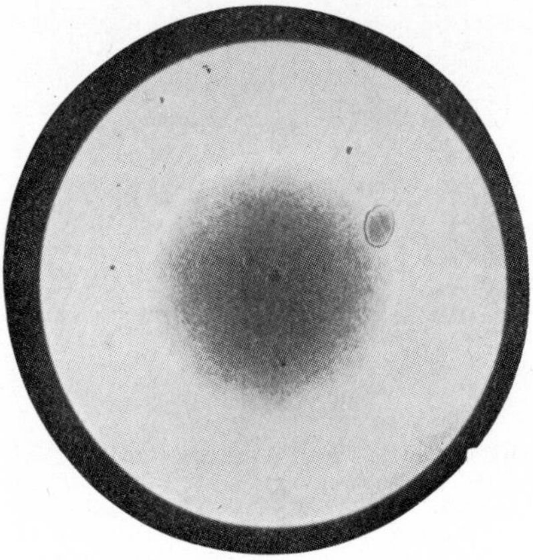

The glanders bacillus does not produce a true toxin, although an endotoxin is thought to be the cause of the emaciation and pyrexia which accompany the disease. This endotoxin, known as mallein, is better known as a diagnostic agent.

Pathogenicity. *Malleomyces mallei* is primarily pathogenic to horses and mules in which it produces a typical chronic infection. The disease is commonly classified into three types — pulmonary glanders,

FIG. 26.2 — **Malleomyces mallei** on agar plate, × 45. (From Nowak: Documenta Microbiologica, courtesy Gustav Fischer.)

nasal glanders, and cutaneous glanders, or farcy.

Pulmonary glanders, which is observed in practically all cases of the disease, is characterized by the formation of round, grayish, firm, encapsulated nodules embedded throughout the lung tissue. These nodules are similar to the tubercles found in tuberculosis. Many of the nodules contain a yellowish, cheesy pus and are surrounded by a zone of inflammation, while others are firm and composed of fibrous connective tissue. In some cases, entire areas of the lungs may be replaced by this fibrous type of tissue.

Nasal glanders is typified by the formation of nodules in the mucous membrane of the nasal cavity, particularly of the septum. Many of these nodules rupture and liberate a mucopurulent exudate which becomes mixed with the serous or mucopurulent exudate already discharging from the nostrils. The ruptured nodules form ulcers with irregular, raised, and hyperemic borders. These ulcers heal slowly, but when they heal, a stellate scar is formed in the mucous membrane. The regional lymph nodes are commonly swollen in nasal glanders.

In farcy, or cutaneous glanders, the typical glanders nodules, or "farcy buds," form along the lymph vessels between affected lymph nodes. These often rupture through the skin and discharge a yellowish pus, and form into deep ulcers which heal slowly.

Malleomyces mallei is very pathogenic for the guinea pig and the field mouse, but is less so for the rabbit, cat, and dog.

In the male guinea pig the organism localizes in the testes, following intraperitoneal inoculation, and produces an orchitis characterized by swelling which is followed by ulceration in approximately two weeks. This reaction was first described by Loeffler, but its diagnostic value was recognized by Strauss after whom it is named. In their study of the virulence of *M. mallei* and *M. pseudomallei* Miller et al. observed that strains of these organisms varied in virulence and that the hamster was the most susceptible animal. Ferrets were also quite susceptible, but guinea pigs were only moderately so, by comparison. Rabbits, mice, rats, and monkeys were least susceptible. Lesions remain localized at the point of injection in dogs and cats.

Glanders in man is commonly confined to the formation of cutaneous ulcers at the point of invasion with subsequent enlargement of the regional lymph nodes. More acute and fatal cases have been described in which pulmonary lesions, similar to those in the horse, have been found.

Immunity. An immunity is not produced by the active disease. Many different types of immunizing agents have been used in glanders, but none of them has proven to be of value.

Antibodies are produced by the natural infection, but their presence in blood plasma does not halt the progress of the disease to any significant degree.

Diagnosis. From the viewpoint of prevention and eradication, the diagnosis of glanders is important due to the chronicity of the disease. The presence of the infection in the horse must be detected during the early stages so that the animal may be removed from the herd. A variety of diagnostic methods are available for glanders.

The method most commonly used is known as the *mallein test.* This test is an allergic reaction due to the sensitization of the cells of the animal by the end-products of bacteria during the natural infection. It is similar to the tuberculin test. Although the reactions are fundamentally the same, being due to an allergic condition, there are four different mallein tests. In the *subcutaneous test* mallein is injected beneath the skin, and a positive reaction is obtained by swelling at the point of injection and an increase in the temperature of the animal. The *ophthalmic test* involves the introduction of mallein, either in fluid or tablet form, under the eyelids. A positive reaction results in an intense reddening of the mucous membrane accompanied by a purulent, yellow exudate, usually within 6 to 8 hours after the introduction of the mallein. In the *cutaneous test,* mallein is injected into the skin or is rubbed into an abraded area on the skin along the side of the neck. An edematous swelling at the point of injection indicates a positive reaction. A modification of the cutaneous test is known as the *palprebral test.* In this test the mallein is injected into the skin close to the edge of the lower eyelid. A positive reaction, usually within 36 hours, is characterized by an extensive edema of the eyelid, accompanied by congestion of the conjunctiva and a mucopurulent secretion. The last test is the method used in routine testing of animals for glanders.

The *agglutination, precipitation, complement fixation,* and *conglutination tests* have all been used for the diagnosis of glanders. These tests are technically the same as other similar tests; consequently, they need not be discussed here.

The Strauss reaction may be used for the diagnosis of glanders, but other organisms, such as *Brucella abortus,* can produce an orchitis in the guinea pig, and for that reason the test has lost much of its value.

The diagnosis of glanders by the use of culturing methods has never gained prominence. This has been due to the presence of so many other types of bacteria in the nasal exudate of infected animals. However, Toyoshima and Shibuya have devised a medium containing thionine which they claim is of value for the isolation of *Malleomyces mallei* from the nasal discharge of infected horses.

Malleomyces pseudomallei

In 1913 Whitmore described a glanders-like disease in man at Rangoon and called it melioidosis. He proposed that the organism be called *Bacillus pseudomallei.* In 1925 Stanton and Fletcher observed the same organism in epizootics among laboratory animals in the Federated Malay States and considered that the most appropriate name was *Bacillus whitmori.* Since then the organism has been found in laboratory animals and in man in various localities in Indo-China and Ceylon.

The classification of this organism has been subjected to much of the same treatment as *Malleomyces mallei.* Its morphology and biochemical activity, however, have led some to doubt its close relationship with the glanders organism. In 1930 it was classified as *Flavobacterium pseudomallei* in Bergey's Manual. The comparative study of Thompson detected a relationship with the actinobacillus which led to the inclusion of the Whitmore bacillus in the genus

Actinobacillus. Gay and Holden call it *Loefflerella whitmori;* Topley and Wilson use the name *Pfeifferella whitmori.*

Malleomyces pseudomallei is a short, motile, Gram-negative, aerobic rod. It forms thick, opaque, cream-colored colonies on solid media. On glycerin the growth tends to become wrinkled. In broth the organism produces a uniform turbidity and forms a pellicle. A heavy, cream-colored growth forms on potato.

This organism is able to produce acid from glucose, maltose, lactose, sucrose, and mannitol, but much of the saccharolytic power is lost by continued artificial growth. It does not produce indol, but does form H_2S; liquefies gelatin; acidifies litmus milk.

Malleomyces pseudomallei produces in rabbits and guinea pigs a natural infection which is similar to glanders in the horse but is more acute. In the septicemic form of the disease the animals live only a few days. In the more chronic form yellowish nodules are found in the nasal mucous membrane and in the lungs. The disease is nearly always fatal.

The occurrence of the organism in other animals has been reported. Stanton, Fletcher, and Symonds reported finding the organism in the nasal discharge of a horse, and Nicholls isolated it from an abscess in the spleen of a cow.

In man, *Malleomyces pseudomallei* produces a fatal infection characterized by a generalized distribution of nodules throughout the entire body, with the greatest number in the lungs.

The only certain method of diagnosis is the isolation of the organism. The rapidity of the disease does not allow the formation of antibody which may be used in the diagnosis of acute cases. The more chronic cases of the disease can be diagnosed by serological tests if the antigenic relationship of this organism and *Malleomyces mallei* is considered.

REFERENCES FOR FURTHER STUDY

Bergey, D. H., *et al.* A Manual of Determinative Bacteriology. 6th Ed. The Williams & Wilkins Co., Baltimore, 1948.

Fletcher, W. Melioidosis. A System of Bacteriology, 5:56–66. Med. Res. Council, His Majesty's Stationery Office, London, 1929.

Holden, M., in Gay, F. P., and associates. Agents of Disease and Host Resistance, Chap. 36. Charles C. Thomas, Baltimore, 1935.

Kolle, W., and Hetsch, O. Edited by John Eyre. Experimental Bacteriology. Chap. 39. George Allen and Unwin, Ltd., London, 1934.

Miller, W. R., Pannell, L., Cravitz, L., Tanner, W. A., and Ingalls, M. S. Studies on Certain Biological Characteristics of *Malleomyces mallei* and *Malleomyces pseudomallei.* I. Morphology, Cultivation, Viability, and Isolation from Contaminated Specimen. Jour. Bact., 55:115, 1948.

——, ——, ——, ——, and Rosebury, T. II. Virulence and infectivity for Animals. Jour. Bact., 55:127, 1948.

Minnett, F. C., and Bullock, W. Glanders. A System of Bacteriology, 5:13–55. Med. Res. Council. His Majesty's Stationery Office, London, 1929.

Thompson, L. Systematic Relationships of Actinobacillus. Jour. Bact., 26:221–27, 1933.

Topley, W. W. C., and Wilson, G. S. Principles of Bacteriology and Immunity. 3rd Ed. The Williams & Wilkins Co., Baltimore, 1946.

Toyoshima, T., and Shibuya, U. A Simple Cultivation Method for the Isolation of *Bac. mallei.* Jour. Jap. Soc. Vet. Sci., 16:136–53. English Summary, p. 19. Part 1, 1937.

27. The Genus Actinobacillus

Microorganisms placed in the genus Actinobacillus must show the following characteristics: that they are medium-sized rods which vary in form from coccoid to long, filamentous cells; are aerobic; are stained Gram-negative; ferment a number of carbohydrates forming acid but no gas; grow best in CO_2 on primary isolation; and are pathogenic for animals.

Only one species, *Actinobacillus lignieresi*, is of significance to animal health, although another, *Actinobacillus actinoides*, has been isolated from calves with pneumonia.

Actinobacillus lignieresi

Synonyms and History. In 1902 Ligniéres and Spitz described an actinomycosis-like disease in cattle of Argentina. They referred to the organism as the Actinobacillus and called the disease actinobacillosis. Nocard confirmed their findings in 1902. Since then the organism has been isolated and described by numerous workers, and the disease is recognized as a rather prevalent one.

Distribution and Transmission. The particular type of infection due to *Actinobacillus lignieresi* is characterized by caseous abscesses in cervical lymph nodes, especially the submaxillary. This disease, widely spread throughout the cattle population of all countries, is more prevalent in some sections than others.

The invasive quality of the organism is low, and its method of transmission is not known.

Morphology and Staining. *Actinobacillus lignieresi* is extremely pleomorphic under natural circumstances. It varies in size from coccoid forms 0.4μ in diameter to elongated filaments up to 15μ. It is nonmotile, noncapsulated, and nonsporeforming. An outstanding morphological characteristic of the organism is the tendency to form in aggregates, or clumps, in the infected tissue. When the caseous material from a typical abscess is carefully examined, these clumps are recognized as small, brownish-white granules. Examination of these granules under the microscope reveals that they are composed of a stellate arrangement of clublike processes. It is this morphology which is so confusing with similar granules formed by *Actinomyces bovis*. When these granules are broken and smears are made, *Actinobacillus lignieresi* is found to be a uniform, Gram-negative rod as compared to the filamentous, branched, Gram-positive cells of *Actinomyces bovis*.

Growth Requirements and Characteristics. *Actinobacillus lignieresi* is aerobic, but growth is increased by the presence of CO_2. It is not anaerobic. The organism grows most abundantly at 37°C. and in a slightly alkaline serum medium.

On agar surfaces the growth is scant, bluish in color, transparent, and flat. In nutrient broth the organism grows abundantly and forms a distinct pellicle. It does not grow well on potato.

Resistance. The organism is killed by a temperature of 60°C. within 15 minutes. It is not resistant to disinfectants, sunlight, or desiccation. Laboratory cultures must be transferred to fresh medium each week, or they perish.

Biochemical Properties. *Actinobacillus lignieresi* produces acid from glucose, maltose, mannitol, fructose, galactose and sucrose; does not ferment dulcitol, inulin, or salicin. After prolonged incubation acid is produced in lactose, raffinose, and glycerol. Most strains produce no change in litmus milk, but some strains produce slight acid but no coagulation. Indol is not usually produced but some strains may produce a faint reaction following prolonged incubation.

Antigenic Structure and Toxins. Agglutinins are formed in the infected animal. Strains of the organism appear to be antigenically homogenous. It does not form toxin.

Pathogenicity. The Actinobacillus causes the formation of abscesses in the cervical region, particularly in the submaxillary lymph nodes. It also causes some of the cases of "wooden-tongue" in cattle. It may metastasize to other parts of the body and become localized. When experimentally inoculated into the udder, it has been reported as having produced chronic mastitis.

Marsh and Wilkins report that the organism has been isolated in Montana from sheep which have an infection around the lips, with subsequent localization in the cervical lymph nodes. A similar condition is reported from South Africa by Thomas and in England by Taylor. Davis and Stiles isolated the organism from a typical outbreak of actinobacillosis in rams in New Mexico.

The organism has been found responsible for a considerable percentage of the cases of mammary abscesses in the sow.

When inoculated into the male guinea pig, *Actinobacillus lignieresi* produces an orchitis very similar to that caused by the glanders bacillus. Rabbits, cats, and dogs are more resistant to the organism than guinea pigs, but they succumb to intravenous inoculation.

Immunity. Immunity is not produced by the infection. Bacterins and immune serum are not used for this disease. The cases which occur are too sporadic to make general immunization worthwhile.

Diagnosis. It is emphasized again that the presence of the "sulphur granule" is not diagnostic of actinobacillosis. In order to distinguish the organism from *Actinomyces bovis,* it is necessary to break the granules and stain the smear with Gram stain. The presence of small, coccoid, Gram-negative rods is indicative of *Actinobacillus lignieresi.*

The agglutination test has been used successfully for the diagnosis of the disease by some workers.

Actinobacillus actinoides

In 1918 Theobald Smith described an organism which he isolated from a peculiar type of pneumonia in the calf. The organism was similar in many respects to the Actinobacillus, so Smith called it *Bacillus actinoides.*

The bacillus forms typical ray-fungus colonies when grown in the condensation water of serum agar. The individual organism is 0.4 to 0.5µ in diameter and is Gram-negative. It can be grown only in a CO_2 atmosphere and in serum media which are kept sealed. Colonies on solid media are variable in size; some are minute and dewdrop-like; others are large and opaque. In the cultures the organism appears in three forms: as a bacillus; as a coccus-like endospore or arthrospore; and as a conglomerate Actinomyces-like flake, or colony, with peripheral clubs.

Actinobacillus actinoides has been reported by Smith as occurring in more than one herd of calves, but the extent of the infection is not known. The pneumonia is characterized by a suppurative bronchopneumonia with some encapsulation of older lesions. It is not pathogenic for laboratory animals.

Gunning found an organism typical of *Actino. lignieresi* in an outbreak of bronchopneumonia in heifer calves. The lungs of the infected animals also contained lungworms (*Dictyocaulus* sp.) which this author considered as primary to the infection and suggested that the bacteria were secondary invaders.

In 1922 Jones described a similar organism which he isolated from an epidemic of rat pneumonia. In 1930 this organism was studied by Nelson who referred to it as *B. actinoides* var. *muris.*

REFERENCES FOR FURTHER STUDY

Davis, C. L., and Stiles, G. W. Actinobacillosis in Rams. Jour. Amer. Vet. Med. Assn., 95:754, 1939.

Gunning, O. V. Vet. Rec., 58:447, 1946.

Jones, F. S. An Organism Resembling *Bacillus actinoides* Isolated from Pneumonic Lungs of White Rats. Jour. Exp. Med., 35:361, 1922.

Lignières, J., and Spitz, G. Actinobacillos. Revista de la Soc. Med. Argentina, No. 53, 1902.

――――, ――――. Nouvelle Contribution a l'Étude des Champignons Produisant des Actinomycosis. Ann. de Parasit. 2:1, 1924.

Marsh, H., and Wilkins, H. W. Actinobacillosis in Sheep. Jour. Amer. Vet. Med. Assn., 94:363–64, 1939.

Nelson, J. B. The Bacteria of the Infected Middle Ear in Adult and Young Albino Rats. Jour. Inf. Dis., 46:64–75, 1930.

――――. The Biological Characters of *B. actinoides* var. *muris*. Jour. Bact., 21: 183–95, 1931.

Radtke, G. Ueber die Erreger der Aktinomykose, Ber. Tierärz. Woch., 51:797, 1935.

Shahan, M. S., and Davis, C. L. The Diagnosis of Actinomycosis and Actinobacillosis. Amer. Jour. Vet. Res., 3:321–28, 1942.

Smith, H. W. Penicillin Iodides and Sulfas for *Act. lignieresi*. Vet. Rec., 63: 674, 1951.

Smith, T. A Pleomorphic Bacillus from Pneumonic Lungs of Calves Simulating Actinomycosis. Jour. Exp. Med., 28:333, 1918.

――――. The Capsules or Sheaths of *Bacillus actinoides*. Jour. Exp. Med., 34:593, 1921.

Taylor, A. W. Vet. Bull., 16:259, 1946.

Thomas, A. D. Actinobacillosis and Other Complications in Sheep Which May Arise from the Feeding of Prickly Pear (*Opuntia* sp.). 17th Rept. Dir. Vet. Ser. and Ani. Ind., Union South Africa, Part 1, 215–29, 1931.

Thompson, L. Systematic Relationships of Actinobacillus. Jour. Bact., 26:221–27, 1933.

Topley, W. W. C., Wilson, G. S. Principles of Bacteriology and Immunity, 3rd Ed. The Williams & Wilkins Co., Baltimore, 1946.

28. The Genus Spherophorus

In this genus are placed those very pleomorphic rods, which are anaerobic, nonmotile, nonsporeforming, and Gram-negative. In elongated cells metachromatic granules may be observed.

The genus name Spherophorus is newly created, being used for the first time in the 1948 edition of Bergey's Manual. The classification of the type species, *Spher. necrophorus,* of the genus has presented a problem for systematic bacteriologists for some time. This organism appeared to have a rather firm place in the genus Actinomyces for many years. It has been classified in the genus Fusiformis but that name was not used to any extent.

There are a number of species listed under this genus but the only one of significance to animal disease is *Spherophorus necrophorus.*

Spherophorus necrophorus

Synonyms and History. *Bacillus necrophorus, Bacillus diphtheriae vitulorum, Streptothrix cuniculi, Bacillus filiformis, Streptothrix necrophora, Fusiformis necrophorus.*

In 1884 Loeffler observed this organism in material taken from cases of calf diphtheria. He was able to obtain primary growth of the organism upon calf serum inoculated with necrotic tissue from mice in which he had succeeded in producing typical lesions. In 1891 Schmorl isolated an organism which he called *Streptothrix cuniculi* from necrotic lesions around the lips of the rabbit. Since that time the organism has been isolated from a large number of animals showing typical necrotic lesions which have given rise to the term necrobacillosis for the disease.

Distribution and Transmission. *Spherophorus necrophorus* is widely distributed throughout the world. It has been isolated from the intestinal tract of man and animals; thus it appears to be a normal inhabitant of animal tissues. Infections associated with this organism are also associated with filthy, insanitary conditions. These infections may reach epizootic proportions in certain animals, particularly in calves and horses. The organism is a frequent secondary invader in other diseases in which primary necrosis or destruction of tissue exists.

Morphology and Staining. *Spherophorus necrophorus* is a slender, pleomorphic organism varying from coccoid cells 0.5 to 1.5µ in size to filaments 100µ in length. In young cultures the filamentous forms are most prevalent, but as the culture ages these filaments appear to segment and to break up into numerous coccoid and bacillary forms (Fig. 28.1). This process of segmentation gives the organism a typical beaded appearance when stained with carbol fuchsin (Fig. 28.2). Numerous of the short rods contain granules in each end which gives them a typical bipolar appearance. The organism is easily but not heavily stained by the aniline dyes and is Gram-negative. It is nonmotile, nonsporeforming, and does not show branching.

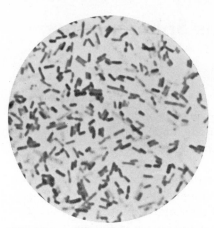

FIG. 28.1 — **Spherophorus necrophorus** from an old bouillon culture, × 2,000. (From Nowak: Documenta Microbiologica, courtesy Gustav Fischer.)

Growth Requirements and Characteristics. This organism is a strict anaerobe and grows at a temperature between 30° and 40°C. Hagan found that the organism produces enough hydrogen peroxide in the presence of air to cause inhibition of growth. Beveridge believes, however, that the oxygen intolerance of the organism is due partly to the oxidation-reduction potential and partly to the slight catalase formation by the organism. Catalase causes the neutralization of the peroxide. The organism grows most abundantly in a medium which is slightly alkaline, but growth occurs between pH 6.0 to 8.4.

It is difficult to obtain a pure culture of *Spherophorus necrophorus,* especially from skin and mucous membrane lesions, on account of bacterial contamination. Pure cultures are more easily obtained from contaminated material by inoculating a rabbit subcutaneously with the necrotic material. Subcutaneous abscesses develop within a week, and in many cases isolated abscesses are formed in the liver. The organism can be isolated from these abscesses usually in pure culture. Feldman, Hester, and Wherry found that bovine liver abscesses were quite satisfactory sources of pure cultures. Necrotic material is transferred from the abscess to a number of tubes of Rosenow's dextrose-brain broth. These tubes are incubated at 37°C. for several days, and from them shake-agar cultures are made. Isolated colonies in the shake culture are then transferred to tubes of dextrose-brain broth for cultivation. On serum agar, incubated under anaerobic conditions, the organism forms small, round, opaque, circular colonies quite similar to those of the streptococci (Fig. 28.3). In broth the organism produces a uniform turbidity and the formation of a slight, fine, dirty-white sediment. As the culture ages, the medium clears, and the sediment increases in quantity and becomes darker in color.

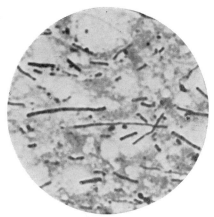

FIG. 28.2 — **Spherophorus necrophorus** in smear of infected tissue, × 2,000. (From Nowak: Documenta Microbiologica, courtesy Gustav Fischer.)

Resistance. The necrophorus bacillus is killed in 15 minutes by a temperature of 55°C. It is not resistant to chemical disinfectants. Kelser reports that 4 per cent acetic acid is a satisfactory germicide and is of value in treating necrotic dermatitis in the horse, which is caused by the organism.

It is difficult to maintain cultures of this organism on artificial media, and for that reason subcultures must be made at weekly intervals. The viability of this organism appears to be more pronounced in nature, for it persists in contaminated soil, and some believe that growth occurs under certain conditions. Beveridge sought to reveal the symbiotic action of aerobic organisms on the growth of *Spherophorus necrophorus* in air. He found that the necrophorus bacillus survived longer in the air when mixed with cultures of *Staph. aureus* and *E. coli* than when alone. This indicates that the organism is protected, at least from the action of oxygen, by the presence of aerobic bacteria and other substances which reduce oxygen tension.

Biochemical Properties. *Spherophorus necrophorus* produces acid and gas from glucose, maltose, and glycerol. Slight fermentation of lactose, galactose, fructose, arabinose, and mannitol has been reported by some investigators. It does not ferment xylose, rhamnose, mannose, raffinose, inulin, dulcitol, salicin, dextrin, erythritol, adonitol, sorbitol, inositol, or amygdalin. The organism is slightly proteolytic, causing the liquefaction of coagulated blood serum after ten days' incubation, but it does not liquefy gelatin or coagulated egg albumin. It produces indol but does not reduce nitrates. It produces hydrogen sulphide; gives a negative reaction to the Voges-Proskauer and methyl red tests; reduces methylene blue; produces a slight reaction for catalase. A small zone of beta hemolysis is formed around the colony on blood agar.

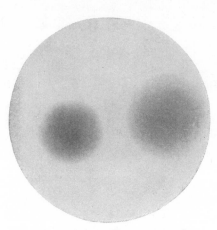

FIG. 28.3 — **Spherophorus necrophorus** colonies on agar plate, × 50. (From Nowak: Documenta Microbiologica, courtesy Gustav Fischer.)

Antigenic Structure and Toxins. Because of the wide variety of animals affected by this organism, the question of the antigenic relationships of various strains has been raised. Cesari found that horse strains were antigenically different from bovine strains, by the agglutination test. Harnach's study of horse, ox, and rabbit strains revealed that they were serologically identical. In the study of ten bovine strains Orcutt found that the cultures were serologically heterogeneous. Beveridge grouped the strains of his organisms into two serological groups; the first is composed of five bovine and one Macropus (kangaroo or wallaby) strain, and the second of three Macropus strains. Feldman, Hester, and Wherry revealed a marked antigenic heterogeneity in fourteen bovine strains of the organism; however, they found a definite relationship between the agglutinins in the blood sera of sheep, swine, horses, and adult cattle for *Spherophorus necrophorus.*

The organism produces a soluble exotoxin which produces an edema when inoculated intradermally in rabbits. Endotoxins and killed suspensions of the organism produce subcutaneous necrosis in the rabbit and guinea pig.

Pathogenicity. *Spherophorus necrophorus* is responsible for necrotic and gangrenous lesions in a variety of species of animals. In all of the animals affected the disease is characterized by a necrosis of tissue with the subsequent accumulation of cellular debris. The organisms do not progress far from the localized lesion, but in some cases metastasis occurs, and abscesses are formed within internal organs, such as the liver. In all of the animals the condition produced by this organism is called *necrobacillosis;* however, in some instances other names are in common use.

In horses *Spherophorus necrophorus* produces gangrenous dermatitis and necrotic processes about the lower extremities, known as "scratches." Ulceration of the intestines and a secondary necrotic pneumonia have been reported.

In cattle the organism has been recovered from numerous tissues of the body, but the most important condition is the necrosis in the mouth, larynx, and trachea of calves, commonly called "calf diphtheria." It produces liver abscesses in cattle of all ages and has been isolated from lesions in the intestinal tract, uterus, vulva, udder, teats, lungs, joints, and feet, either alone or as a secondary invader to other bacteria and traumatisms. Jensen, Flint, and Griner have clearly demonstrated that liver abscesses in cattle and sheep may be produced by the intraportal inoculation of a culture of the organism.

In sheep it is found in lip-and-leg ulceration, foot rot, necrotic hepatitis, necrotic vulvitis, and in a condition originating as necrosis of the ears due to fagopyrism.

In goats this bacillus has been isolated from ulcerative stomatitis and in reindeer from foot lesions.

In pigs *Spherophorus necrophorus* is found in the intestinal lesions of enteritis probably as a secondary invader, in necrosis around the nose and the teeth, and in stomatitis and pharyngitis.

In fowls the organism has been reported as present in avian diphtheria as a secondary invader. Emmel has described an infection in young chickens in which necrotic lesions were present on the head. These lesions yielded an organism which had all the cultural characteristics of *Spher. necrophorus.*

In rabbits it produces a natural infection characterized by necrotic ulcers about the lips and mouth and extending to the skin and subcutaneous tissues.

Spherophorus necrophorus has been found in a variety of zoological animals including kangaroos, monkeys, antelopes, snakes, and tortoises. It has been reported as present in Australian kangaroos and wallabies by Beveridge.

In man the organism has been found in a number of necrotic processes. Dack, Dragstedt, Johnson, and McCullough compared strains isolated from cases of ulcerative colitis with animal strains and found them so similar that they were all grouped as *Bacterium necrophorum.* They found their strains were typical of an organism commonly called *Bacterium funduliforme.*

The rabbit is particularly susceptible to experimental inoculation with *Spherophorus necrophorus*, especially to the infected tissues of animals. On subcutaneous inoculation the tissue around the point of injection becomes necrotic, and the process progressively spreads until the skin and adjoining muscle tissue become involved. The animal becomes emaciated and usually dies within a week. On intravenous inoculation, necrotic abscesses are formed throughout the body; the animal becomes emaciated and dies within a week or is destroyed before that time. Mice are susceptible, and the same type of lesion is produced. Guinea pigs are somewhat resistant. Abscesses form subsequent to subcutaneous inoculation, and necrosis of skin occurs. The contents of the abscesses discharge and the lesions heal, but in some cases the infection spreads and the animal dies. McCullough has reported that guinea pigs placed on a Vitamin C deficient ration until they were extremely scorbutic were more susceptible to *Spherophorus necrophorus* infection and that Vitamin C therapy produced prompt recovery in infected scorbutic guinea pigs.

Immunity. Agglutinating antibodies are produced in animals suffering with an infection produced by this organism. To what extent these antibodies protect the animal against more serious and fatal infection is not known. The presence of agglutinating antibodies in the serum of horses, cattle, sheep, and swine has been reported by Feldman, Hester, and Wherry; however, they found that the serum of cattle having hepatic abscesses did not show an appreciable increase in agglutinin.

Artificial immunizing agents have not been produced for this infection. Beveridge found that rabbits were not protected from experimental infection by two doses of formalinized culture injected subcutaneously. This, according to him, is not surprising since the main lesion of the disease, necrosis, is produced by endotoxins of the organism. Scrivner and Lee found that the injection of bacterins into the rabbit delayed the formation of typical lesions following the inoculation with live cultures.

Diagnosis. The presence of this organism in necrotic tissue is substantial evidence of infection; however, since it occurs so frequently as a secondary invader, the primary cause should always be sought. Rabbit inoculation is sometimes essential for definite diagnosis. The presence of agglutinins in the blood serum of animals is not considered significant enough for the diagnosis of the presence of internal lesions produced by *Spherophorus necrophorus*.

REFERENCES FOR FURTHER STUDY

Beveridge, W. I. B. Jour. Path. Bact., 38:467, 1934.

Emmel, M. W. Jour. Amer. Vet. Med. Assn., 113:169, 1948.

Feldman, W. H., Hester, H. R., and Wherry, F. P. Jour. Inf. Dis., 59:159–70, 1936.

Gay, F. P., and associates. Agents of Disease and Host Resistance, Chaps. 38, 39, 40: pp. 829–910. Charles C. Thomas, Baltimore, 1935.

Hagan, W. A. Jour. Inf. Dis., 35:390, 1924.

Harris, A. N. A. Aust. Vet. Jour., 23:152, 1947.

Jensen, Rue, Flint, J. C., and Griner, L. A. Amer. Jour. Vet. Res., 15:5, 1954.

McCullough, N. B. Jour. Inf. Dis., 63:34, 1938.

Ryff, J. F., and Lee, A. M. Amer. Jour. Vet. Res., 7:41, 1946.

Scrivner, L. H., and Lee, A. M. Jour. Amer. Vet. Med. Assn., 85:360–79, 1934.

Tunnicliff, E. A. Jour. Inf. Dis., 62:58, 1938.

29. The Genus Listeria

Students of veterinary bacteriology are apt to believe that all of the microorganisms of any consequence in animal diseases were discovered prior to 1910 and, moreover, that all of them have been isolated and described. It is true that the first quarter century of the life of bacteriology, beginning about 1880, represented the "heyday" of bacterial discovery. The organism described in this chapter, however, is evidence that all of the etiologic agents of disease were not discovered in the last part of the past century, which leads one to wonder what new paths of bacteriological research remain unexplored.

This group of organisms, or rather this species of an organism, for only one species is at present recognized, is composed of small, motile Gram-positive rods which are aerobic to microaerophilic, grow freely on ordinary media, ferment carbohydrates, and in a number of species of animals produce an infection which is characterized by a monocytosis; this species is *Listeria monocytogenes*.

Listeria monocytogenes

Synonyms and History. In 1926 Murray, Webb, and Swann, working in England, described an organism which produced a generalized infection characterized by a marked mononuclear leucocytosis in rabbits and occasionally in guinea pigs. They regarded the organism as one which had not been described previously and because of the effect on mononuclear cells, they coined the name *Bacterium monocytogenes*.

In 1927 Pirie, of South Africa, observed that an organism was the cause of a generalized infection known as "Tiger River Disease," in which focal necrosis of the liver was the pronounced lesion in the gerbille, a small ratlike animal living in burrows in the ground. He could find no other species of organism similar to the one he isolated nor could he find a suitable genus in which to classify it; consequently, he suggested a new genus for the organism in honor of Lord Lister and formed the name *Listerella hepatolytica*. He called attention to the similarity of his organism to the one isolated by Murray, Webb, and Swann and suggested that if they were identical the name *Listerella monocytogenes* be used. The name *Listerella monocytogenes* was used in Bergey's Manual in 1934. In 1937 Gill isolated the organism from sheep and suggested the name *Listerella ovis*.

The name Listerella has been used for other genera of plant life; consequently, Pirie suggested that the name Listeria would be more appropriate. In the 1948 edition of Bergey's Manual the genus name Listeria is adopted. This change automatically changes the name of the disease from listerellosis to listeriosis.

Distribution and Transmission. *Listeria monocytogenes* is found widely distributed in a number of different hosts in which it produces various types of diseases which are collectively called *Listeriosis*. In addition to the animals previously mentioned, the organism has been isolated from the following:

Sheep: Gill, 1931, 1933, 1937, in New Zealand; Ten Broeck, 1935, in New Jersey; Olafson, 1936, in New York; Jungherr, 1937, in Connecticut; Graham, Dunlap, and Brandly, 1938, in Illinois; Biester and Schwarte, 1939, in Iowa; Paterson, 1939, in England.

Cattle: Jones and Little, 1934, in New Jersey; Fincher, 1935, in New York; Olafson, 1936, in New York; Graham, Dunlap, and Brandly, 1938, in Illinois; Biester and Schwarte, 1938, 1941, in Iowa.

Chickens: Ten Broeck, 1932, in New Jersey; Seastone, 1935, in New Jersey; Paterson, 1937, in England.

Swine: Biester and Schwarte, 1939, in Iowa.

Foxes: Cromwell, Sweebe, and Camp, 1939, in Illinois.

Chinchillas: Shalkop, 1950, in Washington, D. C.

Ferrets: Morris and Norman, 1950, in Washington, D. C.

Raccoons: Gifford and Jungherr, 1950, in Connecticut.

Horses: Grini, 1943, in Norway; Krage, 1944, in Germany; Belin, 1947, in France; Svenkerud, 1948, in Norway.

Man: Burn, 1934, 1935. 1936, in Connecticut; Schultz, Terry, Brice, and Gebhardt, 1934, in California; Gibson, 1935, in Scotland; Carey, 1936, in Massachusetts; Macgregor and Wright, 1938, in Scotland; Pons and Julianelle, 1939.

The methods by which this organism is transmitted are unknown. Gill suggests that the larvae of *Oestrus ovis,* the "nasal
bot" of sheep, may be a means by which the organism is transmitted
among that species of animal. To what extent it is transmitted from
one animal species to another is not known. Some human cases
have revealed contact with sick animals; this indicates some degree
of contagiousness and emphasizes the importance of the public
health aspect of the disease.

Morphology and Staining. *Listeria monocytogenes* is a small
rod with rounded ends, 0.5μ in diameter by 1.0 to 2.0μ in length.
Filaments as long as 4μ are observed in some cultures. It occurs
singly, in V-shaped or parallel
pairs, and in short chains of
three to six organisms (Fig.
29.1). It is nonsporeforming
and noncapsule producing.

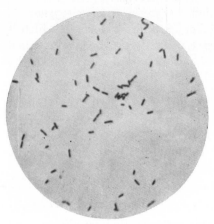

Griffin and Robbins have
demonstrated that *L. monocy-*
togenes is peritrichous with a
maximum of four flagella when
grown at room temperature,
but may produce no flagella at
37°C. with a small percentage
of the cells showing mono- and
a few bi- and tri-flagellated
forms.

FIG. 29.1 — **Listeria monocytogenes**
from sheep, agar culture, × 1,200.
(Photo by Schwarte.)

This organism is easily
stained by all of the aniline dyes
and is Gram-positive. Old cul-
tures are more easily decolorized, and many of the cells show typical
bipolar staining. It is not acid-fast.

Growth Requirements and Characteristics. The organism
is aerobic and facultative; grows well at any temperature between 20°C. and 40°C.; grows best at pH 7.0 to 7.2. Any of the
nutrient media which are used for the cultivation of pathogenic
bacteria can be used for the growth of this organism. In order to
obtain primary growth from infected tissue, it is essential to disperse
the tissue in a Waring blendor prior to inoculation of culture media;
even then, only a few colonies are found on the inoculated surface.
The presence of an inhibitory substance in fresh bovine brain tissue
which prevents the growth of the bacteria is strongly indicated by
the work of Gray and associates. These investigators found that
more abundant growth was obtained from brain tissue after it had
been refrigerated at 4°C. for a few weeks.

In another publication, Gray *et al.* found that the addition of 0.05 per cent potassium tellurite to tryptose agar was useful in isolating *L. monocytogenes.* This chemical inhibits the growth of most Gram-negative bacteria. Listeria colonies appear black with a green color at the periphery; micrococci are pinkish-yellow at the periphery and intensely black at the center; streptococci are small, pinkish-gray in color, with a dull surface.

On solid agar media, colonies of the organism are circular, smooth, and transparent; by reflected light they are gray in color.

In broth a slight turbidity is developed, and a fairly heavy granular sediment is formed.

On a semisolid medium the organism forms minute colonies surrounding the line of inoculation. In some cultures a clouding of the medium extends from the stab line (Fig. 29.2).

Resistance. The organism is destroyed by 58° to 59°C. in 10 minutes. It is easily killed by the usual disinfectants.

Biochemical Properties. *Listeria monocytogenes* produces acid from glucose, rhamnose, and salicin within 24 hours after inoculation;

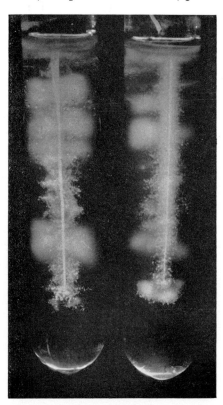

FIG. 29.2 — **Listeria monocytogenes** culture in semisolid medium. (From Seastone, courtesy Journal Experimental Medicine.)

produces acid in sucrose, maltose, lactose, glycerol, starch, and dextrin in seven to twelve days; is slow and somewhat variable in the fermentation of galactose, trehalose, sorbitol, and xylose. Jungherr, Paterson, and Peterson all reported the fermentation of fructose, but Burn obtained negative results with human strains. All of the investigators reported the absence of fermentation of mannitol, dulcitol, inulin, inositol, and arabinose. The organism does not produce indol, does not reduce nitrates or form H_2S. It does not liquefy gelatin. Litmus milk is decolorized, and a slight amount of acid is formed, but the medium is not coagulated. The organism produces beta type hemolysis on blood agar.

Antigenic Structure and Toxins. The limited amount of investigation of the antigenic structure of strains of this organism from various sources indicates that they are somewhat antigenically heterogenous although a group relationship appears to exist. In a study of the flagellar antigens of twenty-seven different strains of Listerella, Paterson concluded that they possess a common antigen and, in addition, that there are other antigens by which the organisms can be divided into three main groups, and possibly four, none of which adhere to any animal species grouping. The organism does not produce exotoxin.

Pathogenicity. *Listeria monocytogenes* is capable of producing natural infection in rabbits, guinea pigs, gerbilles, chickens, sheep, goats, cattle, foxes, swine, chinchillas, ferrets, raccoons, horses, and man.

The disease in all species of animals is somewhat varied as to type of tissue involved, but the underlying characteristics of the disease in all animals is a mononuclear leucocytosis. In the rabbit, chinchilla, guinea pig, and gerbille, liver necrosis is a pronounced lesion. In the sheep, ox, and pig, lesions are confined to the central nervous system where a marked meningitis is produced, and monocytic infiltration with focalization is apparent. Graham and associates have reported finding the organism in an aborted bovine fetus. In the chicken, the organism causes an extensive necrosis of the myocardium. The report of the organism from the fox was not conclusive concerning the etiological relationship to an acute, distemper-like infection which was present in the young animals. It was isolated from the heart blood of five of the eight foxes which were observed. Morris and Norman have found that the organism is harbored in apparently healthy ferrets. In the course of distemper studies colonies of *L. monocytogenes* appeared in the cultures inoculated with lung and spleen tissues from distemper infected ferrets. That the organism may be present in swine without causing symptoms of encephalitis is indicated by the report of Rhoades and Sutherland who isolated it from the liver, spleen, and kidney of a case of hog cholera. Bolin and Eveleth isolated the organism during the routine culturing of liver tissue from a pig which had died of lye poisoning. This organism has been isolated from meningitis in man.

Guinea pigs, rabbits, mice, and rats are all susceptible to experimental inoculation. The animals usually die within 48 hours and post-mortem examination reveals typical lesions of liver necrosis. Gray and co-workers have reported that abortion is produced in rabbits by ocular and oral inoculation with *L. monocytogenes*.

Immunity. Information concerning the immunity produced by this organism is not available. Olafson found that some sheep can be immunized to withstand subsequent injections of the organism, but just as many remain unprotected after the injection of 2.5 cc. of broth cultures two or three times a week for six weeks. The disease is so sporadic that wholesale immunization of flocks and herds is not indicated at the present time. In their experimental study of listeriosis, Olson, Cook, and Blore found that sheep were definitely more resistant after having received one injection of *L. monocytogenes.*

Diagnosis. The conditions which are produced by *Listeria monocytogenes* may be confused symptomatically with a number of diseases; consequently, the only certain method of diagnosis is the isolation and identification of the organism.

REFERENCES FOR FURTHER STUDY

Barber, M. Jour. Path. and Bact., 48:11–23, 1939.

Biester, H. E., and Schwarte, L. H. Jour. Amer. Vet. Med. Assn., 96:339–42, 1940.

———, ———. No. Amer. Vet., 22:729–34, 1941.

———, ———. Jour. Inf. Dis., 64:135–44, 1939.

Belin, M. Bull. Acad. Vet. Fr., 19:176, 1946.

Bolin, F. M., and Eveleth, D. F. Jour. Amer. Vet. Med. Assn., 118:7, 1951.

Burn, C. G. Proc. Soc. Exp. Biol. and Med., 31:1095, 1934.

———. Jour. Bact., 30:573–91, 1935.

———. Amer. Jour. Path., 12:341–48, 1936.

Carey, B. W., Jr. Jour. Pediatr., 8:626–29, 1936.

Cromwell, H. W., Sweebe, E. E., and Camp, T. C. Science, 89:293, 1939.

Ferguson, L. C., Bohl, E. H., and Ingalls, W. L. Jour. Amer. Vet. Med. Assn., 118:10, 1951.

Fincher, M. G. Cornell Vet., 25:61–63, 1935.

Gibson, H. J. Jour. Path. and Bact., 41:239, 1935.

Gifford, R., and Eveleth, D. F. Jour. Amer. Vet. Med. Assn., 101:413, 1942.

———, and Jungherr, E. Cornell Vet., 37:39, 1947.

Gill, D. A. "Circling Disease" of Sheep in New Zealand. Vet. Jour., 87:60–74, 1931.

———. Vet. Jour., 89:258–70, 1933.

———. Austral. Vet. Jour., 13:46, 1937.

Graham, R. Jour. Amer. Vet. Med. Assn., 95:289–92, 1939.

———, Dunlap, G. L., and Brandly, C. A. Science, 88:171–72, 1938.

———, Hester, H. R., and Levine, N. D. Science, 90:336–37, 1939.

———, Levine, N. D., and Morrill, C. C. Listerellosis in Domestic Animals. Bull. Agr. Exp. Sta. No. 499. Univ. of Illinois, Urbanna, Ill. 1943.

Gray, M. L., Singh, C., and Thorp, F. Proc. Soc. Exp. Biol. and Med., 89:163, 169, 1955.

———, Stafseth, H. J., and Thorp, F. Jour. Amer. Vet. Med. Assn., 118:242, 1951.

Gray, M. L., Stafseth, H. J., and Thorp, F. Jour. Amer. Vet. Med. Assn., 115: 171, 1949.

———, ———, ———, Sholl, L. B., and Riley, W. F. Jour. Bact., 55:471, 1948.

Griffin, A. M., and Robbins, M. L. Jour. Bact., 48:114, 1944.

Grini, O. Norsk Vet. Tidsskr. Nr. 3, 1943.

Hull, T. G. Diseases Transmitted from Animals to Man. 3rd edition. Charles C. Thomas, Springfield, 1947.

Jones, F. S., and Little, R. B. Arch. Path., 18:580–81, 1934.

Julianelle, L. A., and Pons, C. A. Proc. Soc. Exp. Biol. Med., 40:364–65, 1939.

Jungherr, E. Vet. Med. Assn., 91:73–87, 1937.

Krage, P. Berl. Münch. tierärztl. Wsch./Wien. tierärztl. Wschr. Jan. 21, 30–31, 1944.

Morris, J. A., and Norman, M. C. Jour. Bact., 59:313, 1950.

Murray, E. G. C., Webb, R. A., and Swann, M. B. R. Jour. Path. and Bact., 29:407–39, 1926.

Nyfeldt, A. C. R. Soc. Biol., 101:590–92, 1929.

Olafson, Peter. The Cornell Vet., 30:141–50, 1940.

Olson, C., Jr., Bagdonas, V., Rollins, C. L., and Blore, I. C. Amer. Jour. Vet. Res., 14:202, 1953.

———, ———, and Cook, R. H. Amer. Jour. Vet. Res., 12:306, 1951.

———, Cook, R. H., and Blore, I. C. Amer. Jour. Vet. Res., 11:29, 1950.

———, Dunn, L. A., and Rollins, C. L. Amer. Jour. Vet. Res., 14:82, 1953.

Paterson, J. S. Jour. Path. and Bact., 48:25–32, 1939.

———. Vet. Rec., 49:1533–34, 1937.

———. Vet. Rec., 51:873–76, 1939.

Pirie, J. H. H. Publ. So. African Inst. Med. Res., 3:163–86, 1927.

Pons, C. A., and Julianelle, L. A. Proc. Soc. Exp. Biol. Med., 40:360–61, 1939.

Pounden, W. D., Bell, D. S., and Mairs, R. E. Jour. Amer Vet. Med. Assn., 111: 128, 1947.

Rhoades, H. E., and Sutherland, A. K. Jour. Amer. Vet. Med. Assn, 112:451, 1948.

Ryff, J. F., and Lee, A. M. Amer. Jour. Vet. Res., 9:147, 1948.

Schultz, E. W., Terry, M. C., Brice, A. T., Jr., and Gebhardt, L. P. Proc. Soc. Exp. Biol. Med., 31:1021–23, 1934.

Schwarte, L. H., and Biester, H. E. Amer. Jour. Vet. Res., 3:165–76, 1942.

Seastone, C. V. Jour. Exp. Med., 62:203–12, 1935.

Shalkop, W. T. Jour. Amer. Vet. Med. Assn., 116:447, 1950.

Smith, H. C. Vet. Med., 48:294, 1953.

Stockton, J. J., Neu, Lisa, Carpenter, W. S., and Gray, J. L. Jour. Amer. Vet. Med. Assn., 124:102, 1954.

Svenkerud, R. R. Norsk Vet. Tidsskr. Nr. 9, 1948.

Webb, R. A., and Barber, M. Jour. Path. and Bact., 45:523–39, 1937.

Wright, H. A., and Macgregor, A. R. Jour. Path. and Bact., 48:470–72, 1939.

Zink, A., deMello, G. C., Burkhart, R. L. Amer. Jour. Vet. Res., 12:194, 1951.

30. The Genus Bacillus

The organisms which belong to the group of aerobic, spore-bearing bacilli are cylindrical, usually flagellated, grow in chains, and produce large, irregular colonies on solid media. Practically all of the species liquefy gelatin. Only one species, *Bacillus anthracis,* is pathogenic.

The aerobic bacilli are probably the most common type of microorganism in existence. They are found in the soil and on decaying vegetation where they are most active in bringing about the decomposition of organic substances, particularly those changes grouped together under the term ammonification. They are, therefore, of great importance in the maintenance of soil fertility. Because of the resistance of the spores to high temperatures and desiccation, these organisms are among those which most frequently contaminate culture media in the laboratory.

The various species are differentiated from each other by the size, shape, and position of the spores, the tendency to chain formation, motility, by differences in cultural and physiologic characteristics, and in pathogenicity. *Bacillus anthracis* can be separated, with certainty, from some of the common saprophytic soil species only by animal inoculation, by physiologic and serologic tests, or by careful observation of colony characteristics.

While it is true that the only definite pathogenic species is *Bacillus anthracis,* there are a few other species which have been known to produce pathologic conditions. *Bacillus subtilis* may cause iridocyclitis and panophthalmitis, and has been known to produce a fatal septicemia. It has been isolated in pure culture from liver and mandibular abscesses in cattle and sheep. *Bacillus megatherium* is capable of producing death in guinea pigs by virtue of a potent hemolysin which it liberates. Pseudoanthrax bacilli which are able to kill mice and guinea pigs, when used in large doses, also have been described. The exact identity of such bacilli is unknown, but many of these bacteria are confused with the anthrax bacillus. Topley and

[457]

Wilson enumerate the criteria which may be used to differentiate anthrax bacilli from pseudoanthrax bacilli as follows:

B. anthracis	*Pseudoanthrax bacilli*
1. Nonmotile	Generally motile
2. Capsulated	Noncapsulated
3. Grows in long chains	Grows in short chains
4. No turbidity in broth	Frequent turbidity in broth
5. Inverted fir-tree in gelatin	Fir-tree growth absent or atypical
6. Precipitin reaction strongly positive	Precipitin reaction weakly positive
7. Pathogenic for laboratory animals	Nonpathogenic for laboratory animals
8. Liquefaction of gelatin slow	Liquefaction of gelatin rapid

The student in veterinary bacteriology may study *B. subtilis* in lieu of *B. anthracis* in the laboratory since *B. subtilis* is not pathogenic to man. The virulence of *B. anthracis* to man makes the study of that organism in laboratory groups an unnecessary risk. *Bacillus subtilis* is used often to portray the general characteristics of bacilli, so it will be given a rather complete description. The only other species described in detail will be *B. anthracis*.

Bacillus subtilis

Synonyms and History. *B. subtilis* was first described by Ehrenberg as *Vibrio subtilis* in 1838 and is commonly known as the "hay bacillus."

Distribution and Transmission. The organism is found in the soil; hence it is on most vegetation. It is spread by water, wind, and normal traffic in feeds, and is present all over the world.

Morphology and Staining. The organisms occur as cylindrical rods, 1μ in diameter by 3 to 4μ in length, straight or slightly curved, with rounded ends, singly or in chains. They are actively motile by peritrichic flagella. Spores are oval and centrally located. The sporangium quickly disappears after the spore is formed. Spores germinate laterally. The organism is Gram-positive.

Growth Requirements and Characteristics. *B. subtilis* is easily cultured on any nutrient medium. Surface colonies on agar are small, grayish, amoeboid, with crenate margin and a curly edge. The surface is finely granular and dull. The growth is membranous. slightly sticky, and is emulsified with difficulty. A thick ring pellicle which usually sinks within 24 hours forms on broth. The pellicle swirls from the bottom of the tube in a twisted cone when the tube is rapidly rotated. On potato a luxuriant, warty, gray growth forms, which becomes pink with vesicles over the surface as the culture ages.

Resistance. The bacillus is extremely resistant to heat by virtue of the spores. Boiling kills it in 2 hours, or death may be brought about at 120°C. in 15 minutes. Spores remain viable for years in the dry state. Ordinary chemical disinfectants kill by prolonged contact.

Biochemical Properties. Acid is formed from glucose, sucrose, and maltose; indol is not formed; nitrates are reduced; H_2S is produced slightly. The organism is M. R. negative and V. P. positive. It reduces methylene blue; coagulates litmus milk which is then slowly peptonized from the top downward; forms NH_3; liquefies blood serum slowly.

Antigenic Structure. Nothing definite is known concerning the antigenic structure, and no toxins are produced.

The production of the antibiotic, subtilin, by this organism is discussed in the chapter on antibiotics. The action of a substance in the filtrate of cultures of *B. subtilis* against the toxin of *C. diphtheriae* was observed by Ramon and Richou. A similar but less marked effect was noted against *Clost. tetani* and *Clost. welchii* toxins.

Bacillus anthracis

History. Rayer and his assistant Davaine in 1850 were the first to observe nonmotile, filiform bodies in the blood of animals having died of anthrax. Pollender, however, reported in 1855 that he had observed rodlike cells as early as 1849 in the blood of cows having died of anthrax. Brauell, in 1857-58, reported the transmission of anthrax from man to a sheep in which he found small, motionless organisms after death. In 1859 Fuchs claimed to have seen "Vibrions" in the blood of animals as early as 1842. Delafond, 1860, found small bodies in the blood of numerous animals which had died of anthrax and in animals which had been artificially infected.

In a series of studies between the years 1863-1868, Davaine definitely established the presence of filiform bodies in the blood of animals which had died of anthrax. He gave the name "bacterides" to these bodies and found he could produce the disease in rabbits. He observed the bodies in man having "malignant pustule" and he killed guinea pigs by injecting the "bacterides." Tiegel in 1871, and Pasteur and Joubert in 1877, showed that anthrax was caused by the small "bacterides" of Davaine because filtrates from which the organisms had been removed did not produce disease. Absolute proof of the etiology of anthrax was established by Koch in 1876-77 when he cultured *Bacillus anthracis* and reproduced the disease in animals by injecting suspensions of the organism. He proved his postulates by isolating the organism from the infected animal.

Contributions to the immunity of anthrax were made in 1880 by Chauveau and in the same year by Toussaint. Final and undoubted proof of the value of vaccination, however, resulted from the famous experiments of Pasteur at Pouilly-le-Fort in 1881.

Distribution and Transmission. Anthrax is found all over the world. It is particularly prevalent in countries where no organized control of animal diseases exists. India, China, Asia, Siberia, Russia, Northern Africa, some parts of South America, and Mexico have anthrax as a major livestock problem. Germany, France, Italy, Great Britain, and the United States keep the disease well under control; however, in the United States anthrax is found in certain areas. The Mississippi and Missouri river valleys have endemic areas where anthrax is a problem. The disease has spread from the lower Mississippi region over the South where numerous sporadic cases occur. Other sections report cases from time to time. Such areas are strictly quarantined and have not developed into anthrax areas.

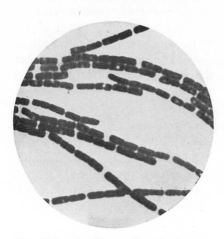

FIG. 30.1 — **Bacillus anthracis,** impression smear from a 48-hour-old agar plate colony, × 2,000. (From Nowak: Documenta Microbiologica, courtesy Gustav Fischer.)

The prevalence of anthrax in the United States in 1945–54 was summarized by Stein (1955). Most of the well-known anthrax districts remained endemic areas with isolated outbreaks of the disease occuring in many of the states. Numerous cases of the disease appeared in swine in the middle western states during 1951 and 1952. These isolated outbreaks were caused by raw bone meal which had been added to commercial feeds.

The organism is spread by the soil, infected feeds, and by water. Infected pasture lands remain contaminated for years. Hay taken from such land has been known to transmit the disease. The spores of the organism are spread by water which has flooded over contaminated ground. Tanneries, wool-sorting establishments, rendering plants, and fertilizer plants have also been incriminated as sources of anthrax which has been spread by stream flow.

Carnivorous animals, dogs, cats, and hogs may contract anthrax by feeding on dead carcasses. Pinkerton has reported the disease in mink which had been fed horse meat. Birds spread the infection by carrying bits of flesh or by eating infected meat and eliminating the spores in their feces. Blood-sucking flies have been incriminated in the spread of the organism among animals and in some cases from animals to man. Stiles has isolated the organism from colonies of spinose ear ticks (*Ornithodorus megnini*) which were attached to the ear of a cow dead with anthrax, thus indicating that ticks may be a vector of the organism.

Man contracts the disease by contact with infected animals, by handling infected hides, by sorting wool, from shaving brushes, and from contaminated furs and hair cushions.

Morphology and Staining. The bacilli are cylindrical rods, 1 to 1.2μ in diameter by 3 to 8μ in length (Fig. 30.1). The capsule is demonstrated by suitable stains, such as Räbiger (Fig. 30.2). Spores are ellipsoidal, situated centrally in the cell, and are 0.7 to 0.8μ by 1.5μ in size (Fig. 30.3). They are

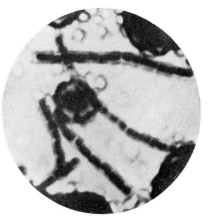

FIG. 30.2 — **Bacillus anthracis** in smear from spleen, showing capsules, × 2,000. (From Nowak: Documenta Microbiologica, courtesy Gustav Fischer.)

not formed in the animal body. Spores germinate at the pole. Young cells are Gram-positive, but old cells may decolorize easily.

Growth Requirements and Characteristics. *Bacillus anthracis* grows readily on meat infusion agar and is isolated easily from the blood or internal organs of an infected animal; it is aerobic, and the optimum temperature for growth is 37°C. A slightly alkaline medium, pH 7.5 to 7.8, is most conducive to good growth.

On the agar surface, colonies appear dull, opaque, grayish-white, with an irregular border from which long strands of cells are seen in parallel arrangement, giving the typical "medusa head" characteristic (Fig. 30.4). As the colony ages, "vesicles" may appear on the surface, giving it a contoured appearance. Broth is turbid with a floccular growth on the surface which sinks to the bottom of the tube within 24 hours. A thick, creamy growth occurs on potato; this growth later becomes granular, giving a mealy appearance. In a gelatin stab culture, filaments of growth radiate from the line of puncture and give the appearance of an inverted fir tree.

Aging and other treatment of stock laboratory cultures produce variants of different types. Pasteur was the first to note the loss of spore formation by exposure to 42°C. Chamberland and

Roux observed that asporogenous strains could be produced by contact with phenol, 1:800, and potassium bichromate, 1:2,000. Bormans reported that a permanent asporogenous type can be produced by growing the organism repeatedly in sheep, calf, horse, or dog sera. The organism loses its capsule when grown on artificial media. This loss causes colony variation. Contrary to the usual type of variation, rough (R) is normal and virulent, whereas smooth (S) is avirulent.

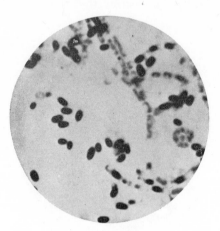

FIG. 30.3 — **Bacillus anthracis,** an old potato culture showing many spores, × 2,000. (From Nowak: Documenta Microbiologica, courtesy Gustav Fischer.)

Resistance. The vegetative cells of B. *anthracis* are not more resistant than similar cells of other bacteria; however, spores which are resistant are rapidly formed by this organism. All d i s i n f e c t i o n against anthrax must assume that the organism is in the spore state. Spores will remain viable for years and will be as virulent as the culture was proved to be when originally isolated. Pasteur showed that spores remained viable in a buried carcass for 12 years. Gaiger reported that spores could be germinated after 15 to 24 years' duration in the soil. Instances are reported where animals become infected on premises 25 years after the original cases of the disease. Hair, wool, bones, and hides not treated sufficiently to kill spores may remain infective for years.

The viability of B. *anthracis* in the tissues of artificially infected guinea pigs exposed to decomposition, temperature, and desiccation has been recorded by Stein (1947). The organism is rapidly destroyed by decomposition in unopened carcasses after the third day, except under temperatures of 5–10°C. when it survives at least four weeks. Repeated freezing, −72°C., and thawing, 37.5°C., may kill vegetative cells but probably not spores. Anthrax spore suspensions were viable for 90–124 days when kept at −60° to −70°C. and for nine to ten years at either −5° to −6°C. or at 5° to 10°C. Blood swabs from field cases of anthrax kept in the light at room temperature were still virulent up to nine years. The author (Merchant) has found agar slant cultures of B. *anthracis* isolated from a field case in 1928, kept sealed with paraffin and stored in the dark at room temperature, to be virulent at the end of 25 years.

In testing the resistance of anthrax spores to heat, Stein and Rogers (1945) tested 43 strains. All of these strains were killed by vigorous boiling within 3–5 minutes. Spores from 31 strains were killed in 5–15 minutes at 100°–101°C. in the steam sterilizer, but at 90°–91°C. only 6 out of 12 strains were destroyed in 60 minutes. In the autoclave, at 120°C., all of the 31 strains tested were destroyed in 5–15 minutes. In-

sistence that cultures of *B. anthracis* must not be sterilized in an open vessel or glass tube is supported by the work of Stein and Rogers (1946) who found that viable spores escape with the steam from such cultures.

The report of Saltys is of considerable importance to those engaged in laboratory studies of *B. anthracis.* Saltys observed that spores of the organism in films on slides may withstand the temperature of the Bunsen flame for 5–6 seconds; that none of the

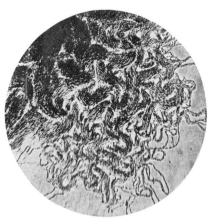

FIG. 30.4 — **Bacillus anthracis,** edge of agar plate colony, × 210. (From No-wak: Documenta Microbiologica, courtesy Gustav Fischer.)

common staining methods destroy all spores; that mercuric chloride 1:1,000 killed spores on slides in 5 minutes and did not alter the smear whereas a saturated solution of potassium permanganate ruined the smear for observation purposes. In view of these results it appears prudent to treat smears of *B. anthracis* with mercuric chloride 1:1,000 for 5 minutes and then proceed with the desired staining technic. Mercuric chloride 1:1,000 is more effective as a disinfectant when hydrochloric acid, 0.5 per cent, is added.

Ten per cent formalin at 40°C. will kill anthrax spores in 15 minutes, but when this chemical is used at lower temperatures more time must be allowed for disinfection. Freshly prepared sodium hydroxide in a 5 per cent solution is a satisfactory agent for disinfecting objects contaminated by the spores of this organism.

Biochemical Properties. *B. anthracis* forms acid but no gas from glucose, sucrose, maltose, fructose, trehalose, and dextrin. Some strains produce slight acid in glycerol and salicin. There is no fermentation of lactose, galactose, arabinose, rhamnose, mannose, raffinose, inulin, mannitol, dulcitol, sorbitol, inositol, and adonitol. Indol and H_2S are not produced; nitrates are reduced to nitrites; NH_3 is produced. Methylene blue is reduced by some of the more virulent strains, and some strains hemolize sheep blood. The organism is M.R. positive and V.P. variable. Litmus milk is coagulated, decolorized, and slowly peptonized.

Antigenic Structure and Toxins. There appears to be two antigenic substances in *B. anthracis.* One protein-like material is found in the capsule, and the other is a somatic polysaccharide antigen. Both antigens act specifically with precipitating sera. No antigenic groups have been reported for the organism. Workers in Germany have reported the purification of anthrax capsular antigens.

In a series of studies on the nature of the infection produced by *B. anthracis*, Cromartie, Bloom, Watson, and associates have contributed significant information which is of aid in understanding the disease. Two substances are present in crude extracts of lesions produced by the organism, one an inflammatory factor capable of damaging tissue and the other a protective antigen responsible for its immunizing property. The tissue-damaging factor is capable of interfering with the blood-clotting mechanism and inhibits an anthracidal substance produced by leucocytes and other cells. A disturbance in carbohydrate metabolism was observed in experimental cases of anthrax in rabbits producing a state of hyperglycemia. Bacterial counts in the blood of rabbits fatally infected showed that the majority contained large numbers of bacilli in their blood at the time of death. Some animals died with relatively few bacilli in the blood, which tends to disprove the mechanical obstruction theory which has been advanced to explain the mechanism of death from anthrax.

The protective antigen migrates in an invisible component intermediate between the gamma and beta globulins; it is destroyed by heating at 57°C. for 30 minutes and by trypsin; it is not destroyed by formalin in a final concentration of 1.0 per cent and is stable in the lyophilized state. This antigen has not been purified, but fractionation with ethanol in the cold suggests a method of concentration. The efficacy of the antigen in inducing active immunity in rabbits, sheep, guinea pigs, hamsters, and mice varies. The rabbit is protected against challenge doses of anthrax spores more than other animals. The protective antibodies present in hyperimmune rabbit serums fail to show any relationship to the antibody concerned in the precipitation and complement fixation tests.

The role of leucocytes in eliminating anthrax bacilli from the body of both immune and normal animals is explained by the presence of an anthracidal substance in leucocytes. This substance appears to be a basic polypeptide, contains lysine, and can be prepared from the thymus gland of the calf. It has been shown to protect mice against lethal doses of anthrax bacilli.

The results of the investigators, briefly described, substantiate the known facts concerning anthrax. The presence of edema and hemorrhage makes it evident that a tissue-damaging factor operates in the disease, but the effect of this specific substance upon leucocytes and their extracts explains why the infection progresses so rapidly in the highly susceptible animal. That the tissue-damaging factor and anthracidal factor in leucocytes are two contending forces in the disease appears evident. In those species of animals which are more resistant to anthrax the anthracidal factor in leucocytes appears to be in greater concentration, because the bacilli do develop in these species; but the capsule is soon lost and the bacilli disintegrate. The protective antigen appears to stimulate the production of a substance which does not allow the capsule to develop on the bacilli, but this substance does not seem to be allied with the antibody employed, or at least the usual effects noted, in the precipitation and complement fixation tests. Obviously, these studies should be continued and relationships noted to the various products of bacteria which are known to explain the different tissue reactions to infectious agents.

Pathogenicity. *Bacillus anthracis* is pathogenic for cattle, sheep (except Algerian), horses, mules, swine, dogs, and cats. Anthrax appears as a septicemia in the first four species of animals in an apoplectic form, an acute form, and in a subacute form. Massive hemorrhagic swellings may be present in the subacute type but are not so common in the apoplectic and acute types. In swine the disease is manifested by an acute pharyngitis with extensive swelling and hemorrhage of the throat region. Anthrax in dogs and cats is similar to that in hogs with the exception of a severe gastro-enteritis. The disease is rare in these animals, but cases have been reported.

On post-mortem examination anthrax is characterized by edematous infiltrations in the subcutis; hemorrhages in various parts of the body, especially in serous membranes; marked swelling of the spleen, which is dark red and soft (raspberry-jam consistency). This characteristic spleen has given rise to the terms "splenic fever" and "milzbrand" (German) by which the disease is often known. The blood is dark red, tarry, and does not clot; these facts have led the French to call the disease "charbon." Hemorrhage is often observed from the natural body openings; this is of sanitary significance, for such pools of blood leave countless numbers of bacilli in the ground.

The type of anthrax in man usually depends on the avenue of infection. Pulmonary anthrax, or wool-sorters' disease, is contracted by the inhalation of anthrax spores. The disease runs its course as an atypical pneumonia and is usually fatal. Cutaneous anthrax, or malignant carbuncle, results from skin infection through scratches or other breaks in the skin. The pustule starts as a small red pimple and gradually spreads, forming a large swelling with a dark center surrounded by small vesicles. Regional lymph nodes are swollen and painful. If the organisms enter the blood stream, septicemia results. Most cases of cutaneous anthrax recover. Intestinal anthrax results from the eating of uncooked meats of an anthrax carcass and is extremely rare in civilized countries.

Of the laboratory animals, the mouse is the most susceptible to B. anthracis. Guinea pigs are also highly susceptible and are universally used for diagnostic purposes. Rabbits are less susceptible but do succumb. Rats are more resistant than rabbits, and the white rat is more so than gray or brown rats. Some white rats live for weeks before they die and some survive in spite of comparatively large injections of living organisms. Birds generally are resistant; however, sparrows and young pigeons have been infected.

Immunity. Anthrax was one of the first diseases for which a definite immunity was produced by the use of bacteria. Chauveau, in 1879, noticed that sheep were more resistant after having survived a previous inoculation of blood heated to 55°C. from animals dead of anthrax. Toussaint, in 1880, first attempted artificial immunization. Pasteur, with Chamberland and Roux, in 1881, proved that immunity did exist after using two vaccines: *Vaccine I,* attenuated by growing at 42°C. for 12 days, killed mice, but not guinea pigs or rabbits; *Vaccine II,* attenuated for a shorter time, so it killed mice and guinea pigs, but not rabbits or sheep.

Sobernheim, in 1904, improved on Pasteur's method by using Pasteur Vaccine II simultaneously with immune serum. Cienkowsky, in 1884, employed a simultaneous method but used spores instead of Vaccine II with immune serum. In 1925 Eichhorn reported that satisfactory immunity could be produced against anthrax if a potent strain of the bacillus was used in preparing the vaccine and if an edematous reaction resulted in the area in which the vaccine was injected. Spore vaccines standardized to compare with Pasteur Vaccine II, along with hyperimmune anti-anthrax serum, have been used in the United States for prophylactic immunization. In certain districts where the strain of B. anthracis appears to be more virulent, vaccines of greater virulence, called "Vaccine III" and "Vaccine IV," are used simultaneously with immune serum.

Spore vaccines, generally attentuated to correspond to Pasteur Vaccine II, may be given intradermally. This method of vaccination against anthrax has particular virtue when the function of the skin in this disease is considered. Furthermore, the skin is recognized as tissue in which antibody is produced and it is so compact that the antigen is not quickly absorbed into the general circulation. Although the intradermal method of vaccination has merits, it has objectionable features, particularly the difficulty of making such an injection under field conditions into range animals. Subcutaneous and intramuscular methods of injection obviously are much easier to do.

The development of a special vaccine known as "carbozoo" by Mazzucchi in 1931 introduced a new anthrax vaccine. This vaccine was of No. II potency to which saponin was added. This glucoside has the property of causing tissue irritation, producing local edema, hence delaying the absorption of the vaccine. In addition to this reaction, Sterne of South Africa has observed that such an excipient as saponin or saturated sodium chloride decreases the virulence of virulent strains and increases the immunizing power of avirulent strains of anthrax bacilli. In many areas of the world saponized anthrax vaccine is used entirely.

Anthrax bacterins are prepared by using young, non-sporulated cultures attenuated with formalin. The duration of immunity produced by the bacterin is not as long as with spore vaccine but its use is recommended in those areas which have not been contaminated by successive outbreaks of anthrax. In many instances the promiscuous use of spore vaccines of too great potency has been actually found to cause endemic anthrax areas when such vaccines have been used without immune serum. In other instances too great reliance has been placed on spore vaccines alone. In some instances the spore vaccine has been too impotent to produce immunity, thus allowing natural outbreaks of the disease to occur.

In 1935 Gochenour, Schoening, Stein, and Mohler of the U.S.B.A.I. conducted a comprehensive comparative study of the efficacy of various anthrax vaccines and anti-anthrax serum. Their results indicated that spore vaccine produced a more satisfactory immunity than the bacterin and that immune serum was highly efficacious for a few days but its protective power was soon lost.

The use of capsule extracts and other purified antigenic fractions of *B. anthracis* appears to be promising according to Ivánovics. The new gélosé-alum vaccine of Ramon and Staub also indicates a new departure in the preparation of anthrax vaccine.

Serum therapy in anthrax has been demonstrated to be dependable. The exact nature of the protection, however, has not been ascertained. There are numerous evidences that it is not a bacteriolytic effect. Precipitation of the two antigenic fractions of the bacillus is obtainable by the use of immune serum. The destruction of the microorganism is usually brought about by the phagocytes; so it is plausible that the "leucocyte-repelling" action of capsulated B. anthracis is neutralized by precipitation which, at the same time, sensitizes the cells for more rapid engulfment by phagocytes.

Investigators of animal diseases in South Africa are constantly confronted with anthrax, hence have been most active in developing satisfactory immunizing agents for the disease. The keeping qualities of the vaccines is one of their problems, for it usually must be transported long distances. In 1937 Sterne described the isolation of non-capsulated, avirulent immunogenic variants from virulent strains of B. anthracis. This investigator (1939) was able to produce an immunity with these strains in domestic animals that far surpasses the results obtained with the Pasteur type of spore vaccine. Sutton (1947) described a special medium, tryptic digest of casein, Brewer's yeast extract buffered by phosphates, which was of value in the maintenance of the immunogenic capacity of the variant strain of B. anthracis. The value of this type of vaccine has been confirmed by Boor and Tresselt.

Diagnosis. In submitting material for anthrax diagnosis, great caution must be exercised. It is an unnecessary risk to autopsy a carcass which has obviously died of anthrax. In England such autopsies are forbidden by law. Sending an ear packed in a tight suitable container is a universal practice; this method is satisfactory, but the practice of sending blood smears, cotton swabs, a small vial of blood, or tissue is preferable if sufficient caution is taken.

Laboratory diagnosis of anthrax may be obtained by any of the following:

1. Direct microscopic smears from the suspected material.
2. Inoculation of culture media.
3. Animal inoculation, preferably a guinea pig or a mouse.
4. Precipitation test following the technic of Ascoli.

REFERENCES FOR FURTHER STUDY

Boor, A. K., and Tresselt, H. B. Amer. Jour. Vet. Res., 16:425, 1955.

Bullock, W. The History of Bacteriology. Oxford University Press, London, 1938.

Clark, Ada R. The Anthrax Bacillus. Chap. 35 in Gay, F. P. and Associates. Agents of Disease and Host Resistance. Charles C. Thomas, Baltimore, 1935.

Cromartie, W. J., Bloom, W. L., Watson, D. W., Heckly, R. J., Kegeles, G., Freed, M., McGhee, W. J. Weissman, N., and Graf, L. H. Jour. Inf. Dis., 80:1 through 153, 1947.

Eichhorn, A. Jour. Amer. Vet. Med. Assn., 68:276, 1925.

Eurich, F. W., and Hewlett, R. T. Bacillus anthracis. A System of Bacteriology. 5:439. Med. Res. Council, His Majesty's Stationery Office, London, 1929.

Gochenour, W. S., Schoening, H. W., Stein, C. D., and Mohler, W. M. Tech. Bull. No. 468, Apr. 1935, USDA, Washington, D. C.

Ivánovics, G. Ueber die Milzbrandimmunität Zeit. f. Immunit, etc., 94:436, 1938.

Ramon, G., and Staub, A. Sur une Nouvelle Méthode de Vaccination des Animaux Domestiques Contre le Charbon. Bull. Acad. de Méd., Ser. 3, 117, 299, 1937.

———, and Richou, R. Bull. Acad. Vet. Fr., 18:164, 1945.

Saltys, M. A. Jour. Path. and Bact., 60:253, 1948.

Schweiger, L. B., Trainer, D., and Eveleth, D. F. Isolation of *Bacillus subtilis* from Actinobacillus-like Lesions in Cattle and Sheep. Amer. Jour. Vet. Res., 4:127–33, 1943.

Stein, C. D. Differentiation of *B. anthracis* from Non-pathogenic Aerobic Spore-forming Bacilli. Amer. Jour. Vet. Res., 5:38–54, 1944.

———. Vet. Med., 40:340, 1945.

———. Vet. Med., 42:13, 1947.

———. Vet. Med., 43:340, 1948.

———. Vet. Med., 45:205, 1950.

———, and Rogers, H. Vet. Med., 40:406, 1945.

———, ———. Amer. Jour. Vet. Res., 7:481, 1946.

Sterne, M. Anderstepoort Jour. Vet. Sci. and Ani. Ind., 8:271, 1937.

———. Anderstepoort Jour. Vet. Sci. and Ani. Ind., 13:307, 313, 1939.

———. Anderstepoort Jour. Vet. Sci. and Ani. Ind., 21:41, 1946.

———. Jour. So. Afr. Vet. Med. Assn., 16:53, 1945.

Stein, C. D., and Van Ness, G. B. Vet. Med., 50:579, 1955.

Stiles, G. W. Isolation of *B. anthracis* from Spinose Ear Ticks (Ornithodorous megnini). Am. Jour. Vet. Res., 5:318–319, 1944.

Sutton, G. D. Jour. So. Afr. Vet. Med. Assn., 18:79, 1947.

Tomcsik, J., and Ivánovics, G. Die Schutzwirkung des Milzbrand—Antikopsel —Immunkörpers der Milzbrandinfektion. Zeit. f. Immunit, etc. 94:28, 1938.

Viljoen, P. R. Curson, H. H., and Fourie, P.J.J. Anthrax in South Africa Union of South Africa, 13th and 14th Rept., Dept. Agr., 429, 1928.

31. The Genus Clostridium

In this genus are placed those sporeforming rods which carry on their metabolic activities in an atmosphere devoid of oxygen; they are anaerobes. By virtue of the resistant spore which they produce, the natural habitat of the majority of the species in this genus is the soil in which they are active as agents in soil fertility. Some species are pathogenic to man and some to various animals in which they produce marked and distinct types of disease; some cause disease by the action of potent exotoxins produced either within or outside the animal body.

The spores of all the anaerobic bacilli are prevalent in the soil; consequently, the diseases which are caused by this group of bacteria are often called the soil-borne infections. This fact is best emphasized by the universal knowledge that the contamination of a wound by dirt may lead to tetanus or gas gangrene, both of which are caused by anaerobic bacilli.

The anaerobic bacilli are studied by specialized technic, the most fundamental of which is the maintenance of anaerobic conditions. These methods have been listed and briefly discussed in the chapter on technics and methods and should be reviewed by the student at this time.

A more thorough study of the "growth accessory substances" in the artificial cultivation of bacteria has revealed that the anaerobic bacteria may grow aerobically. For example, the addition of 0.025 per cent ascorbic acid powder or fluid to various fluid media will support the growth of anaerobes.

General Description of the Group. These bacilli are variable in size, measuring 0.4 to 1.2μ in diameter by 3 to 8μ in length. They are usually plump in shape with round ends, but some are long, slender rods. Sporulation occurs in all species with a variable position of spores—central, subterminal, and terminal. Most of the species are motile by peritrichic flagella. They are Gram-positive in young cultures but are easily decolorized when older. Granulation is noted in the cells of some species, giving variations in the depth of staining.

On solid media, the clostridia grow in thin, irregular colonies, but when the medium is moist, spreading occurs. Great variation in colony size and shape exists under different conditions. Fluid media are rendered uniformly turbid. In blood agar, hemolysis is first of the alpha type, which later develops into the beta type. Meat medium is reacted upon in two ways depending on the type of microorganism. It is digested and turned black by proteolytic varieties, whereas the saccharolytic types do not digest it, but they do turn the meat pink. Both of the above types of clostridia are capable of producing great quantities of gas in both protein and carbohydrate media. The gas (CO_2-H_2) ratio has been suggested by some workers as a means of differentiation.

Some of the common biochemical reactions of the Clostridia to be discussed in this chapter are given in Table 31.1.

TABLE 31.1

BIOCHEMICAL REACTIONS OF THE IMPORTANT CLOSTRIDIA

	Glu-cose	Mal-tose	Lac-tose	Sali-cin	H$_2$S	Gel. Liq.	Nit. Red.	In-dol	Milk
Clost. chauvoei..	+	+	+	−	+	+	−	−	Acid
Clost. septicum..	+	+	+	+	+	+	+	−	Acid
Clost. novyi.....	+	+	−	−	+	+	−	−	Acid
Clost. perfringens	+	+	+	−	+	+	+	−	Stormy
Clost. hemolyticum ..	+	−	−	−	+	+	−	+	Acid
Clost. tetani	−	−	−	−	+	±	−	+	No change
Clost. botulinum.	+	+	−	−	+	+	−	−	Acid
Clost. sordellii ..	+	+	−	±	+	+	−	+	Digested

Type specificity among the clostridia apparently depends on both O and H antigens. Some of the species, *Clost. chauvoei* and *Clost. septicum*, appear to be closely related. *Clost. tetani* and *Clost. botulinum* produce the most potent bacterial toxin known; in fact, they are disease-producing only by virtue of the toxin they generate. The gas gangrene group also produces toxin, but it is of a less potent nature.

The clostridia produce a variety of diseases in a number of species of animals. The diseases are manifested in two general ways; first, as an acute toxemia such as in botulism and tetanus where tissue changes are insignificant; and second, as a gas edema where edema is the general rule and gas formation is inconstant.

Antitoxin is prepared for use in immunizing against the toxin-producing species of anaerobes. Bacterial filtrates and antiserums are available for the less toxigenic types. Immunity against tetanus, botulism, and blackleg is widely and successfully practiced.

Only those members of the genus which are of significance to animal diseases will be discussed. There are many isolated and single reports of diseases produced by anaerobic, sporeforming bacilli, but the inclusion of all of them here is not feasible. The species given in the following list will be described in some detail:

Clostridium chauvoei   *Clostridium hemolyticum*
Clostridium septicum   *Clostridium tetani*
Clostridium novyi   *Clostridium botulinum*
Clostridium perfringens   *Clostridium sordellii*

Clostridium chauvoei (feseri)

Synonyms and History. *Bacillus chauvoei, Bacillus gangraenae emphysematosae*, blackleg bacillus.

Blackleg was differentiated from anthrax and named "charbon symptomatique" by Chabert on the basis of clinical symptoms and post-mortem lesions. Bollinger, in 1875, however, was the first to show that anthrax and blackleg had distinct etiologic agents. This conclusion was confirmed by Feser in 1876. Significant contributions were made to the literature concerning blackleg by Arloing, Cornevin, and Thomas in 1887, which accounts for the fact that they are often given the credit for the discovery of the organism. Even though they did contribute a great deal to the knowledge of blackleg, its cause and immunity, Roux is given the credit for being the first to cultivate the organism on artificial media in 1887. Improved methods for the cultivation of *Clostridium chauvoei* in pure cultures were contributed by Kitasato in 1889.

The name *Clostridium chauvoei* which has been used for this organism almost exclusively since its first isolation has been changed to *Clostridium feseri* in the 1948 edition of Bergey's Manual by Spray. This name is chosen because Feser is considered to be the first to describe the organism. It has been taken for granted that the species name *chauvoei* used by Arloing, Cornevin, and Thomas, in 1887, has had priority over any other. Changes in the names of bacteria, of which this is an example, serve no useful purpose in bacteriology. The name *Clost. chauvoei* will be continued in this text with the hope that in the next edition of Bergey's Manual it may be returned to its rightful status.

Distribution and Transmission. Blackleg in cattle is found in most parts of the world where animal husbandry is well established. In the United States the organism is scattered over the prairie states, being more prevalent in some areas than in others. The eastern Atlantic and southern gulf states seem to be free of the infection. The disease is a typical soil-borne infection. The organism gains entrance by the digestive tract or through breaks in the skin. It may be artificially introduced by traumatisms of various sorts and has been found to follow shearing, docking, and castration in sheep.

Morphology and Staining. *Clostridium chauvoei* is a rod 0.6μ in diameter by 3 to 8μ in length, with rounded ends, and occurs singly or in short chains, but long filaments are common (Fig. 31.1). Swollen cells are often found, navicular and lemon shapes being most common. The spores of the organism are elongated, oval, subterminal or terminal, and wider than the cell, giving it a typical pear-shaped appearance. The bacillus is motile by means of peritrichous flagella. The organism is Gram-positive but is easily decolorized in parts of the cell. Some cells show granular material in one or both poles. This is most apparent when stained with methylene blue. It does not form a capsule.

Growth Requirements and Characteristics. This organism is a strict anaerobe, and growth is improved by glucose and heart-meat infusion. Optimum temperature for growth is 37°C. The organism grows best in media which is slightly alkaline, although it has a rather wide pH range. It can be isolated in most instances in pure culture from deep muscle by seeding meat medium or brain medium.

On agar plates the organism forms a small, irregular colony, effuse, transparent, finely granular in the center, but becoming almost invisible toward the periphery (Fig. 31.2). The edges of the colony resemble wisps of hair. The colony is bluish-gray by transmitted light. In a glucose-gelatin shake-culture, the colonies appear toward the bottom of the tube, each usually with its gas bubble, and surrounded by a liquefied area. These colonies show numerous radiating threads, or papillae, giving the appearance of a chestnut burr. The organism produces a uniform turbidity in bouillon, produces gas, and forms a flaky, white deposit.

Resistance. The vegetative form of the organism is not resistant to heat or chemicals. In the spore form it is quite heat resistant, not being killed for 10 minutes at 120°C. The spores are resistant to desiccation, living in the soil for years. In dried, infected muscle the spores have remained virulent for eight years. Bichloride of mercury, 1:500, kills spores within 10 minutes. The spores are killed by 3 per cent formalin in 15 minutes. The coal-tar disinfectants, in the strength in which they are used on infected premises, are effective and kill the spores readily.

Biochemical Properties. *Clostridium chauvoei* produces acid and gas from glucose, fructose, maltose, lactose, and sucrose but not from mannitol, glycerol, dulcitol, salicin, or inulin. It coagulates milk into a flocculent curd but does not peptonize this medium. The organism turns meat medium more pink; acidifies but does not blacken Hibler's brain medium; produces a slight hemolysis on horse-blood-agar plates; does not produce indol; is M.R. negative and V.P. negative; does not reduce nitrates; does not form NH_3; produces H_2S; does not reduce methylene blue; does not form catalase.

Antigenic Structure and Toxins. *Clostridium chauvoei* is serologically homogenous. Differences in strains which some have found may have been due to the close relationship of this organism to *Clost. septicum.* By agglutination and complement fixation tests, some antigenic relationships b e t w e e n *Clost. chauvoei* and *Clost. septicum* have been observed, especially in the lower dilutions. No antigenic fractions of the organism have been described.

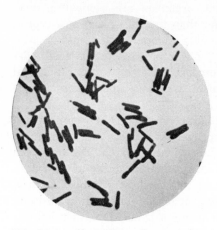

FIG. 31.1 — **Clostridium chauvoei** from a young agar culture, × 2,000. (From Nowak: Documenta Microbiologica, courtesy Gustav Fischer.)

That a true exotoxin is produced by *Clost. chauvoei* is open to question. Some strains undoubtedly do produce exotoxin, especially the more virulent ones. Grassberger and Schattenfroh claim to have succeeded in producing broth cultures containing a toxin that, in doses as small as those employed with diphtheria toxin, will kill laboratory animals. This toxin they have shown to be thermolabile. Kerrin, in 1934, also has shown that *Clost. chauvoei* produces toxin under suitable conditions. A dose of 0.025–0.5 cc. of toxin when injected intravenously into a mouse causes respiratory symptoms and death within a few minutes. Subcutaneous injection of the toxin into guinea pigs and mice is not fatal, but edema is produced. It is quite likely that this organism does produce exotoxin, but it is not as potent as that produced by other species of the gas-edema type, notably *Clost. septicum, Clost. perfringens,* and *Clost. novyi.*

Pathogenicity. Inoculation of pure cultures of this organism into laboratory animals results in death, with the production of many of the characteristic symptoms of blackleg. Guinea pigs, rabbits, white mice, and white rats can be infected. The guinea pig is the most susceptible and is commonly used as the experimental animal for the organism. Intramuscular injection of the guinea pig is followed by the first symptoms in about 14 hours; a soft inflamed swelling develops at the site of inoculation; in 24 to 30 hours the inflammation spreads to nearby muscles and these become emphysematous. Upon section, in typical cases, the tissues are found to be edematous and hemorrhagic, and the muscles contain many gas bubbles. Gas is also found in the subcutaneous fascia over the infected area.

Ryff and Lee have observed that the hamster is more susceptible to *Clost. chauvoei* than the guinea pig, succumbing to one-fifth the lethal dose required for the guinea pig.

Blackleg in cattle is characterized by a swelling, edema, and emphysema of the muscles and the subcutaneous tissues of the infected part. Infection occurs most commonly in the shoulder a n d hindquarters. The swelling increases rapidly in size, and the emphysema is soon detected by the crackling sound when the hand is drawn firmly across the affected part.

In sheep and deer the infection due to this organism usually follows traumatic injuries.

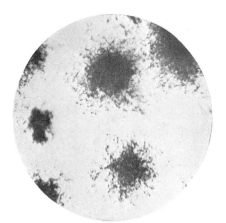

FIG. 31.2 — **Clostridium chauvoei** colony on agar plate, × 50. (From Nowak: Documenta Microbiologica, courtesy Gustav Fischer.)

The organisms, along with other anaerobes, continue to grow after death, and the body becomes distended with gas. The subcutaneous tissues of the infected part are edematous, even gelatinous, and are premeated with blood and gas bubbles. The underlying muscles are dark brown or even blackish, whence the name, blackleg. A very characteristic, sweetish-sour, pungent odor can be detected from the infected tissue. The disease usually results fatally in cattle in one to three days after the first appearance of the symptoms.

Immunity. Animals that have recovered from an attack of blackleg are immune during the remaining period of their lives. Very young cattle and aged cattle have a considerable degree of natural immunity. The reason for this immunity is not well understood; it probably is opsonic in nature in young animals, whereas in older cattle there is always the possibility that they have had a subinfection.

Active immunization by vaccination is extensively practiced, and blackleg is one of the diseases among animals for which immunizing agents are of real value. Many methods of attenuation of the organism for the vaccine have been developed. The method of Arloing, Cornevin, and Thomas has been modified by Preisz, by Kitt, and by Nörgaard. The latter modification was used extensively in the United States and is essentially as follows: Fresh material is secured by mashing the infected muscle in a mortar and squeezing the fluid through a linen cloth. This is spread in a thin layer and dried to a brown scale at a temperature of 37°C. This dried material retains its virulence for several years. The vaccine is prepared by mixing one part of this material with two parts of water and placing it in a hot-air oven containing a pan of water and heating to 93°–94°C. for 6 hours. This dries the material and attenuates the organism. This material is then pulverized and put in packages containing a definite number of doses. Before use, one cubic centimeter of water for each dose is added, and the material is mixed and then filtered.

Blackleg aggressin is used extensively in blackleg immunization. In 1912, Schobl showed that the edematous fluid taken from blackleg lesions, when made sterile by filtration, possessed remarkable immunizing properties. Following his method, Franklin and Haslam, in 1916, used aggressin on many thousands of cattle and found it highly efficient. In preparing blackleg aggressin, young cattle are injected with 20 to 30 ml. of virulent culture. Following death, the fluid and tissue from the infected part are carefully collected. The muscle is pressed until all the fluid is removed. A preservative is added, and all the fluid is then allowed to stand until most of the solid particles have settled. The supernatant fluid is then drawn off, filtered first through paper pulp and then through a Berkefeld or other filter of medium porosity. After suitable culture and guinea pig tests have been made, it is ready for use. The usual dose for young animals is 5 cc. Ryff and Lee believe that young animals should be given two injections of vaccine in order to produce secure immunity. Blackleg vaccine is commonly combined with Pasteurella bacterin for young calves.

An artificial aggressin is prepared by growing *Clost. chauvoei* in a meat-bouillon medium. After several days' incubation the fluid portion of the medium is collected, germ-free, by filtration. A preservative is added to the medium, and after sterility tests have been made, it is ready for use. It does not give as satisfactory results as the natural aggressin.

During recent years a whole culture bacterin has been prepared and has given satisfactory results. It has been shown by a number of workers that blackleg is often complicated by the presence of *Clost. septicum*. For that reason a filtrate composed of the end-products of the growth of both organisms is used. Scheuber described the preparation of the filtrate as follows: "A liver-glucose medium is inoculated with *Clost. chauvoei* and incubated. The medium is fortified with glucose, and a pH of 8 is maintained throughout the process. At the end of one week of incubation, the culture is seeded with *Clost. septicum* and incubated for 8–10 days. A 0.4 per cent formalin is added, the culture is shaken, and then is allowed to settle for 24 hours. The supernatant fluid is drawn off, incubated for a week, and then tested for sterility by inoculation into brain medium." Breed has modified this technic by adding brain and a few more buffer salts to the liver medium. He also used a 1 per cent formalin for attenuation. His results with the mixed whole-culture bacterin are quite satisfactory. Rodrigues in Brazil has substantiated the value of formolized vaccine in producing immunity.

Immune serum is of aid in treating blackleg as well as producing a passive immunity for a period of about two weeks. It is prepared by hyperimmunization of cattle with any of the above products.

Diagnosis. The symptoms and the post-mortem findings of blackleg are so characteristic that a laboratory diagnosis is often unnecessary. The organism is usually found in smears made directly from the infected muscle. Intramuscular inoculation of suspensions of infected tissue into guinea pigs produces characteristic lesions from which the organism can be isolated in pure culture. The differentiation of *Clost. chauvoei* and *Clost. septicum* is often necessary. *Clost. chauvoei* is shorter, more plump, and more ovoid than *Clost. septicum;* the former grows singly whereas the latter frequently forms long chains. When injected subcutaneously into guinea pigs, *Clost. chauvoei* produces edema and gas in the injected area.

Clostridium septicum

Synonyms and History. Pasteur and Joubert were the first to describe this organism in 1877, giving it the name *Vibrion septique.* Koch and Gaffky, in 1881, described it and originated the name *Bacillus oedematis maligni.* The organism has been called *Clostridium oedematis maligni* and *Clostridium oedematis* until recently, when there is a tendency to give the species name, *septique,* of Pasteur, the priority right after latinizing it to *septicum.* *Clostridium septicus* is found in some of the literature.

Distribution and Transmission. *Clostridium septicum* is widely distributed over the earth and, common to other anaerobic bacilli, it is found in the soil. Certain areas are more heavily contaminated than others, and it has been observed that certain premises may be infective for indefinite periods. The organism gains entrance into deeper tissues through cuts and abrasions of the skin. It may be unknowlingly injected into animals, and may gain entrance through the agency of various surgical procedures. Infection may follow castration in all susceptible animals. Docking and shearing sheep are means by which that animal becomes infected. Horses may become infected during operations in the field if aseptic technic is disregarded. Cows can become infected during parturition, especially when calf delivery is attempted by uninformed herdsmen whose knowledge of obstetrics embraces only forcible delivery. Since man is susceptible to the organism, care must be taken in the autopsy of infected animals as well as infected human beings. It is one of the organisms of the gas-edema group found particularly during wartimes.

In sheep the organism is one of the causes of bradsot or braxy. In such conditions the bacillus gains entrance through the mucous membrane of the abomasum due to penetration by sharp objects.

Morphology and Staining. *Clostridium septicum* closely resembles *Clostridium chauvoei* morphologically. It is a cylindrical rod 0.5μ by 2 to 6μ in size, with rounded ends, and arranged singly, although it may be found in long chains and filaments especially from serous surfaces (Fig. 31.3). Spores are oval, subterminal, and slightly larger in diameter than the bacillus, giving "navicular" or "snowshoe" shapes. It is motile by means of 4-16 peritrichic flagella. It does not produce a capsule. The organism is Gram-positive, although some parts of the cell may be decolorized. It does not stain uniformly, and with methylene blue, granules are observed in one end, or both ends, or in one-half of the cell.

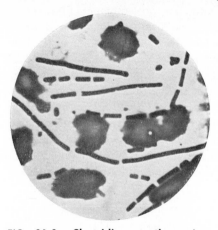

FIG. 31.3 — **Clostridium septicum,** impression smear from the surface of the liver of guinea pig, × 2,000. (From Nowak: Documenta Microbiologica, courtesy Gustav Fischer.)

Growth Requirements and Characteristics. *Clostridium septicum* is an obligate anaerobe; grows well on meat infusion media at an optimum temperature of 37°C., although fair growth occurs at room temperature. The optimum pH is 7.6. Growth of the organism is improved by 1 per cent glucose in the medium.

Agar surface colonies are small, irregular, effuse, finely granular, translucent, and have a filamentous edge (Fig. 31.4). Both S and R colonies have been described. Smooth colonies have an amoeboid edge, and the colonies are gray, bluish-gray, and opaque at the center. Colonies in agar-shake cultures are delicate, arborescent, and floccose. Gelatin-shake colonies are large and floccose, with filaments later permeating the medium. A slight turbidity and a light, powdery sediment is formed in broth.

Resistance. This organism is the same as those sporeforming bacilli which have been previously described.

Biochemical Properties. *Clostridium septicum* produces acid and gas from glucose, fructose, galactose, maltose, lactose, and salicin, but not from sucrose (thus differing from *Clost. chauvoei*), mannitol, dulcitol, glycerol, or inulin. Milk is slowly acidified, coagulated, and slightly digested, and some gas is formed. Gelatin is slowly liquefied. Coagulated blood serum is not liquefied. Blood-agar plates show alpha hemolysis followed in a few days by the beta type. Cooked meat medium is turned pink; gas is produced but there is no digestion. Hib-ler's brain medium is turned black. The organism is indol negative, NH_3 slight, H_2S positive, M. R. negative, and V. P. negative. Nitrates are reduced; methylene blue is not reduced; the catalase test is negative.

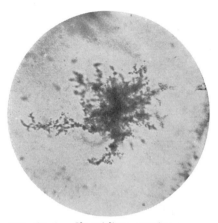

FIG. 31.4 — **Clostridium septicum** agar colony, × 100. (From Nowak: Documenta Microbiologica, courtesy Gustav Fischer.)

Antigenic Structure and Toxins. Both O and H antigens for the organism have been described. On the basis of O antigen it can be divided into four distinct agglutinative groups. Each of these groups in turn is divided into subgroups on the basis of H antigen. Some antigenic component is common to both *Clost. septicum* and *Clost. chauvoei,* because positive cross-agglutination and cross-complement-fixation tests are possible.

Exotoxin is produced by the organism. A 48-hour-old filtrate will produce death in guinea pigs within 30 minutes in doses as small as 0.5 ml. The exotoxin produced seems to be common to all four antigenic types.

Pathogenicity. Experimentally, the organism produces disease in guinea pigs, rabbits, mice, and pigeons. Species which are naturally infected are man, horse, sheep, cow, and the pig. Dogs and cats are susceptible but rarely are infected.

Malignant edema is usually an acute, febrile disease that terminates fatally in two or three days. In man it may be so acute that death occurs in 24 hours.

Gas may not be present in great quantities, although some gas bubbles are always found. The edema is blood-stained and usually gelatinized. Muscle underlying subcutaneous infection is dark red in color and soft in consistency. Hemoglobin-stained fluid may be found in the body cavities and in the pericardial sac. The action of the toxin of this bacillus on the circulation of the cat and rabbit has been described by Kellaway, Reid, and Trethewie. They found that toxin has a specific cardiac action causing a fall in systemic blood pressure and a rise in cardiac pressure; it has a direct action on the heart causing constriction of the coronary and pulmonary circulations, the latter more marked in the cat, leading to pulmonary edema. In the rabbit, but not in the cat, there is an initial peripheral vasoconstriction, causing a transient rise in systemic blood pressure. In the cat, but not in the rabbit, injection of toxin into the vessels supplying the adrenals causes the liberation of adrenalin, possibly as a result of the preliminary liberation of histamine.

Clostridium septicum is one of the causes of braxy, a disease which is found in sheep on the western coast of Norway, in Iceland, the Faroe Islands, and Scotland. In this disease the lesions are confined to the tissues adjacent to the fourth stomach and the mucosa and submucosa of that organ. Intense inflammation characterized by edema and hemorrhage with some necrosis is noted. Degenerative changes are found in the visceral organs.

Immunity. Animals which recover from malignant edema are soundly immune. The use of immunizing agents is of little practical value except in sheep. The relationship to blackleg, as well as the preparation of the whole-culture bacterin, has been discussed previously, and it is unnecessary to repeat it at this place.

Antiserum may be of some value in cases of *Clost. septicum* infection, especially if the case is diagnosed early. Otherwise, treatment is of little value.

Diagnosis. The isolation and identification of the organism is the only sure way to diagnose malignant edema. Guinea pig inoculation is commonly used to isolate the organism. Rabbits are more susceptible to *Clost. septicum* than to *Clost. chauvoei* and may be used to distinguish the two organisms. Serologic tests are of no value.

Clostridium novyi

Synonyms and History. This organism was first described by Novy in 1894 and named *B. oedematis maligni* II. Migula originated the name *B. novyi* in his classification in 1900. The organism was isolated and described by Weinberg and Seguin in 1915 and named *Bacillus oedematiens*. Bergey's Manual recognizes *Clost. novyi* as valid. *B. gigas* of Zeissler and Raszfeld (1929) apparently is identical with this organism. Although *Clost. oedematiens* is given as the name of the organism by English and European bacteriologists, it would seem that *Clost. novyi* has priority rights and for that reason will be used here.

Distribution and Transmission. The organism appears to be rather widely spread throughout the world, but it is brought to attention in those areas where sheep are raised, especially those areas where the liver fluke is prevalent. The organism has been found in Montana by Marsh. In Colorado, Newsom, Cross, and Dobbins found it twice in the examination of 200 spleens of normal and diseased sheep. Shaw, Muth, and Seghetti have found the organism of considerable significance in Oregon. It is prevalent in Australia, where Turner has contributed much valuable data concerning it and the disease it produces. It is also found in areas in Germany.

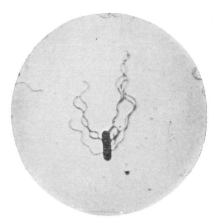

FIG. 31.5 — **Clostridium novyi,** showing flagella, × 2,000. (From Nowak: Documenta Microbiologica, courtesy Gustav Fischer.)

The spores of the bacillus are found in the soil, and, no doubt, commonly are present in the intestinal tract of animals and man. The spores of the organism are probably carried into the bile duct and into the liver by flukes and, stimulated by the necrosis produced by that parasite, the spores germinate, multiply rapidly, and produce the toxin which causes the disease. A type of disease known as "stall braxy" occurs in Germany after castration of young lambs.

Morphology and Staining. *Clostridium novyi* is one of the largest of the anaerobes, 0.8μ to 1.5μ in diameter and 5 to 10μ in length. The edges of the organism are parallel, and the ends are rounded. It occurs singly, in pairs, and in long, jointed filaments. The spores of this bacillus are oval and subterminal. It is motile by peritrichous flagella (Fig. 31.5). A capsule is not produced. The organism is stained easily and uniformly and is Gram-positive.

Growth Requirements and Characteristics. *Clostridium novyi* grows well on ordinary media, but glucose stimulates growth. Ferric salts, iron wire, and whole blood also aid growth. The optimum pH is 7.2 to 7.4 and the optimum temperature is 37.5°C. It is the most strictly anaerobic of the entire genus.

Agar plate colonies are small with irregular undulating borders and are finely granular in structure and grayish-blue in color (Fig. 31.6). On moist agar surfaces a thin scumlike colony is formed. Some strains have been described that form circumscribed mucoid colonies which are possibly due to dissociation.

In broth the organism forms slight turbidity during early hours of growth, but the cells form a light, loose, flocculent sediment within 24 hours. In glucose agar-shake cultures the colonies have a compact, yellowish center surrounded by a halo of fine filaments; the medium is shattered due to the evolution of gas.

FIG. 31.6 — **Clostridium novyi** colony on agar plate, × 80. (From Nowak: Documenta Microbiologica, courtesy Gustav Fischer.)

Resistance. This bacillus is typical of the group in resistance to destructive agents.

Biochemical Properties. *Clostridium novyi* forms acid and gas from glucose and maltose, and some strains from glycerol; does not attack lactose, sucrose, mannitol, salicin, or inulin. Litmus milk is slowly acidified with some gas production but no digestion. Gelatin is rapidly and completely liquefied. Cooked meat medium is bleached or turned slightly pink with no digestion. Coagulated serum and egg are not liquefied. Brain medium is neither blackened nor digested. The organism is NH_3 negative; H_2S slowly positive; indol negative; M.R. negative; and V.P. negative. Beta hemolysis, turning to alpha when exposed to the air, is produced on blood-agar plates under anaerobic conditions. The organism does not reduce nitrates.

Antigenic Structure and Toxins. Different types of antigens have not been described for this bacillus. Agglutinating antiserum has been found to act only on the homologous strain. The auto-agglutinating characteristic of the organism, however, makes it difficult to use the agglutination test with any degree of success for study.

A potent exotoxin is produced by some strains. The M.L.D. of toxin for a mouse has been set at 0.0002 cc.

Pathogenicity. *Clost. novyi* is pathogenic for guinea pigs, mice, and rabbits. When a 24-hour bouillon culture is injected intramuscularly into guinea pigs, death results within 24 to 48 hours. Experimentally, it has been found pathogenic for swine, cattle, and horses, producing rapid death and the formation of a pale, jelly-like edema of the subcutaneous and intramuscular connective tissue surrounding the point of inoculation. Degenerative changes are produced in visceral organs. The edema is not as hemorrhagic as in blackleg and malignant edema. The sheep is naturally susceptible and is the most commonly infected domestic animal. Parker has observed that the disease is most common in ewes more than 18 months old and rarely occurs in wethers.

Previous mention has been made of the relationship of the liver fluke, *Fasciola hepatica,* to infectious necrotic hepatitis of sheep. This disease is an extremely acute toxemia, the animal dying within 12 hours after symptoms have been noticed. Post-mortem examination reveals marked venous congestion, which gives the skin a dark color (black disease) and increased straw-colored fluid in the body cavities and pericardial sac. Greenish-colored areas of necrosis, about 1 cm. in size, in which immature liver flukes may be found, are found throughout the liver tissue. Larger, yellowish-white, necrotic foci, which are surrounded by a wide zone of venous congestion, may also be found in the liver.

Immunity. Antitoxin has a neutralizing effect on the toxin of *Clost. novyi.* The acute nature of the infection in which the organism is found, however, makes antitoxin therapy rather useless. However, Parker was able to control an outbreak of the disease in a flock of ewes with antiserum. Turner has prepared a formalinized broth vaccine which has shown encouraging results. More satisfactory results are obtained when at least three injections of the vaccine are given.

Diagnosis. The presence of *Clost. novyi* infection can be diagnosed correctly only by the isolation and identification of the organism. Lesions produced in the guinea pig are not sufficiently different from those caused by *Clost. chauvoei* and *Clost. septicum* to be of value.

Clostridium perfringens

Synonyms and History. *Bacillus aerogenes capsulatus, Bacillus welchii, Bacterium welchii, B. phlegmonis emphysematosae, B. enteritidis sporogenes, B. perfringens, Granulo bacillus saccharo butryicus immobilis, B. anaerobicus crytobutyricus, B. cadaveris butryicus, B. emphysematis vaginae, Clost. welchii.*

The organism was first isolated and adequately described by Welch and Nuttall in 1892 following its isolation from a cadaver. The following year E. Fraenkel isolated an organism which he named *B. phlegmonis emphysematosae* from four cases of gas gangrene. In 1898 Veillon and Zuber named this organism *Bacillus perfringens,* a name which is used in the 1948 edition of Bergey's Manual. In his classification of 1900, Migula referred to the organism as *Bacillus welchii.* Since Welch's description, in 1900, of forty-six cases from which the organism was isolated, it has been found in a wide variety of conditions affecting man in all parts of the world.

Clost. perfringens and bacilli similar to it have been isolated from a variety of animal infections. Although it is usually considered a secondary invader, becoming especially active after the death of the animal, it has been found to be the direct cause of a variety of conditions. Dalling (1926) isolated an organism from sheep which he called *Bacillus paludis.* Bennetts (1932) also isolated an anaerobe from sheep which he named *Clost. ovitoxicum.* Both of the above organisms are probably *Clost. perfringens,* differing only in the types of toxins produced.

Distribution and Transmission. This organism is the most ubiquitous of any of the anaerobic bacilli. It has been isolated from soil, feces, and the intestinal tracts of man and animals by numerous investigators.

Morphology and Staining. *Clostridium perfringens* is a rod, 0.8 to 1.5μ in diameter by 4 to 8μ in length, with usually rather square ends (Fig. 31.7). Short, almost coccal forms, and long filaments, may be found under certain growth conditions. Variant forms (club shapes, filaments, tadpole forms, granular types) are found frequently in old, coagulated serum cultures. It usually occurs singly, but may be found in pairs, short chains, and arranged in chains or filaments. It is absolutely nonmotile, differing from the other members of this genus. Spores are large and oval with slightly flattened ends, located subterminally or centrally. The spores are sometimes found in infected wounds, but are most readily formed in such media as casein broth, alkaline-egg broth, and coagulated serum free from fermentable carbohydrate. Capsules may be demonstrated in body fluids and in media containing serum.

The organism stains readily with the common aniline dyes and is Gram-positive in young cultures with the frequent occurrence of Gram-negative cells in old cultures.

Growth Requirements and Characteristics. The organism grows well in ordinary media. According to McCampbell it is best isolated from soil and other material by successive inoculations into milk, followed by intravenous injection into a rabbit which is killed immediately after inoculation and placed in an incubator at 37°C. for 8 or 10 hours. The thorax of the animal is then opened, and cultures are made from the heart blood into glucose broth and placed under anaerobic conditions. The optimum growth temperature is 37°C. The organism grows best in alkaline media, and spore formation is inhibited at pH 6.6.

The colonies upon agar and gelatin plates are round, grayish, semitranslucent, and smooth, with an entire edge. Two types of colonies have been observed upon blood agar, one hemolytic and the other non-hemolytic. Colony variants have also been described. One type is a thin, filmy growth which spreads rapidly and is composed of long filaments. Another type is an extremely viscid, mucoid colony which adheres firmly to the medium. Bouillon is uniformly clouded, followed by a heavy precipitate.

Resistance. The organism is not significantly different from the group in resistance.

Biochemical Properties. *Clostridium perfringens* forms acid and gas from glucose, fructose, galactose, maltose, lactose, and sucrose, but not from mannitol, dulcitol, or salicin. The aldehyde, acrolein, is produced from glycerol. Litmus milk is coagulated, and acid and gas are formed, giving a "stormy fermentation" within

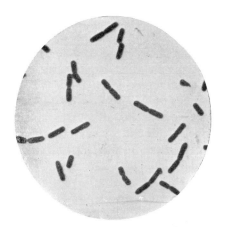

FIG. 31.7 — **Clostridium perfringens** × 2,000. (From Nowak: Documenta Microbiologica, courtesy Gustav Fischer.)

24 hours. Cooked meat medium with iron is blackened. The organism produces slight NH_3; is strongly positive to H_2S production; is indol negative; is M.R. negative; is V.P. negative; reduces nitrates slightly; is methylene blue negative; is catalase negative.

Antigenic Structure and Toxins. There is no evidence that any definite antigenic groups exist on the basis of the agglutination test. By toxin-antitoxin neutralization tests, however, four different types of the organism have been described but these types are not in agreement with any agglutination grouping.

In 1931, Wilsdon classified the various strains of *Clost. perfringens* on the basis of toxin-antitoxin neutralization into the following groups:

Type A strains produce Type A toxin; the homologous antitoxin neutralizes only Type A toxin.

Type B strains produce Type B toxin; the homologous antitoxin neutralizes Types A, B, C, and D toxins.

Type C strains produce Type C toxin; the homologous antitoxin neutralizes Types A, B, and C toxins.

Type D strains produce Type D toxin; the homologous antitoxin neutralizes Types A and D toxins.

The exotoxin produced by Type D strains of *Clost. perfringens* has been named epsilon toxin and appears to be potent. Shaw, Muth, and Seghetti found that 7 ml. of the toxin proved fatal to a sheep, and the minimum lethal dose for a mouse was 0.005 ml. These investigators report that the toxin is destroyed by a temperature of 70°C., but storing at 40°C. for two weeks does not diminish its potency.

Pathogenicity. *Clost. perfringens* is pathogenic for guinea pigs, mice, and pigeons, and to a less degree for rabbits. The organism is one of those most commonly found in gas gangrene in man. It is pathogenic for sheep, producing a variety of conditions. It has also been involved in an acute toxemia in calves and in horses. The organism has been shown to be widely distributed in soil and in the intestinal tracts of animals and man. It may invade tissues quickly after death and give rise to a mistaken diagnosis. It has been isolated from cattle dead of anthrax, swine that have succumbed to cholera, and isolated together with *Clost. chauvoei* from blackleg lesions in cattle and in sheep. Gas gangrene in a dog, following the subcutaneous injection of calcium gluconate by an owner, has been reported.

Experimental infection in the guinea pig is characterized by a large, crepitant swelling at the point of inoculation. The skin is dark red; subcutaneous tissue surrounding and some distance from the site of inoculation is emphysematous, edematous, and blood-tinged. The suprarenal glands are congested. The underlying muscle is pale pink in color and shows evidence of liquefaction necrosis.

The sheep appears to be the only domestic animal in which a definite disease is produced by more than one type of *Clost. perfringens*. A lamb dysentery which is characterized by an enteritis, ranging from a mild hyperemia to extensive necrosis and ulceration has been described by Gaiger and Dalling, of England. The organism associated with this disease produces a toxin which is classed at Type B. McEwen and Roberts have described a disease among sheep on the Romney Marsh in Kent, which occurs during the late winter and spring months. It is characterized by an acute toxemia with resulting enteritis and peritonitis, followed by typical lesions of gas gangrene after the animal has been dead for some time. The name *Clost. paludis* has been suggested for the organism found in this disease, but Topley and Wilson believe that it is best to refer to it as *Clost. perfringens* Type C. Griner and Bracken have observed that *Clost. perfringens* Type C can produce an acute toxemia in newborn calves. Bennetts (1932) described an infectious enterotoxemia found in sheep in Australia. The disease was due to the absorption of toxin which was liberated by the organism in the small intestine. The organism was identified as *Clost. perfringens* Type D of Wilsdon. This organism was found in lamb dysentery in Colorado by Newsom and Cross and in Montana by Marsh, Tunnicliff, and Jungherr. The condition known as pulpy kidney disease of lambs, which was observed in New Zealand by Gill (1932) and in Wales by Montgomerie and Dalling (1933) and by Montgomerie and Rowlands (1933, 1934), and in Oregon by Shaw, Muth, and Seghetti (1939) was caused by the same organism. An acute toxemia of lambs, sheep, and horses was found to be due to a toxin obtained from filtrates of intestinal contents of those animals by Gordon (1934). This toxin was neutralized by an antitoxin of *Clost. perfringens* Type D.

Immunity. British workers have found effective the use of a formalinized vaccine in immunizing pregnant ewes or the newborn lamb to prevent lamb dysentery. McEwen (1935) observed a formalinized vaccine useful in immunizing sheep against "struck." The infectious enterotoxemia found in sheep of western Australia has been treated successfully by the use of specific antitoxin prepared by using *Clost. perfringens* Type D as the incitant. This has been confirmed by Shaw, Muth, and Seghetti in Oregon.

The use of an alum-precipitated toxoid by Muth and Morrill for enterotoxemia in sheep was reported in 1946. The same year Bythell and Parker found that an anaculture was an effective immunizing agent. In 1947 Whitlock and Fabricant also obtained favorable results with an anaculture. In 1948 Baldwin, Frederick, and Ray reported that a formolized bacterin was of significant value in immunizing feeder lambs against enterotoxemia. DeMello and associates, in 1952, reported that formalin-treated, alum-precipitated epsilon toxoid is a satisfactory immunizing agent for the disease in sheep.

Diagnosis. *Clostridium perfringens* infection can be correctly diagnosed by the isolation and identification of the organism. This is best accomplished by the neutralization of the toxin by a known specific antitoxin. The diagnosis of enterotoxemia in sheep may be accomplished by mixing a quantity of the intestinal contents of the dead sheep with specific antitoxin and injecting into mice. Other mice are injected with intestinal contents not treated with antitoxin. If the former group of mice live and the latter group die, it is obvious that toxin is present in the intestine.

Humphreys has described a diagnostic culture test for the identification of *Clost. perfringens* which involves the detection of the formation of the aldehyde acrolein, from glycerol. He claims that in a large number of tests he has never known the test to mislead.

Clostridium hemolyticum

Synonyms and History. This organism was first isolated and described by Vawter and Records in 1926, from which the following description is freely taken. They gave it the name *Clostrid-*

ium hemolyticum-bovis. Hall studied strains of the organism and named it *Bacillus haemolyticus.*

Distribution and Transmission. In the United States, *Clost. hemolyticum* is apparently confined to the mountain valleys of the western states—Nevada, Idaho, southwestern Montana, eastern Washington, eastern Oregon, and eastern California. Brown has reported the isolation of the organism from a liver infarct of a steer in Kentucky, but the animal had come from Texas two months previously. Sordelli, Ferrari, and Prado (1933) have observed the organism in South America from the Andes region in Chile. The disease, bacillary hemoglobinuria, occurs most frequently in swampy, poorly drained areas and irrigated pastures. The fact that animals become infected in swampy places during the summer and early fall would indicate that the organism or its spores are taken in with the food or water while the susceptible animals are grazing on infected areas. The isolation of this organism, by Jasmin, from the bones of animals which had died of bacillary hemoglobinuria two years previously indicates a potential reservoir for the infection in range areas.

Morphology and Staining. The bacilli are rod-shaped, 1 to 1.3µ in diameter by 3 to 5.6µ in length, with rounded ends when organisms occur singly but truncate when in chains. Spores are heavily walled, globoid, oval, or slightly elongated and situated either terminally or subterminally. Spore formation decreases when the organism is grown on common artificial media, but this property is regained when the organism is grown on media containing serum or blood. This bacillus is sluggishly motile by means of six to sixteen long, peritrichous flagella. Capsules are not formed. The organism is Gram-positive during the first 24 hours of growth and then it is Gram-negative.

Growth Requirements and Characteristics. The organism is strictly anaerobic; it has an optimum temperature of 37°C. and an optimum pH of 7.5. Culture media which contain tryptophane or proteins, readily yielding this and other amino acids, are essential for growth and toxin production. Sulphur, likewise, appears to be utilized. Cooked liver medium containing sodium thioglycollate has proved to be satisfactory as a basic medium for routine culturing and toxin production.

On the surface of agar slants a light growth is present in 24 hours. In deep agar tubes growth is apparent after 24 hours' incubation; colonies at first are homogenous and lenticular but rapidly develop an eccentric fluff, later appearing as dense, woolly masses with short peripheral filaments. These masses vary from 0.25 to 0.5 mm. in diameter, according to the number in the tube. In broth a complete clouding is present in 8 to 12 hours followed by autoagglutination. An abundance of gas with a cheesy odor is produced.

Resistance. *Clost. hemolyticum* loses its viability quickly on some types of media, especially in peptic-digest broth plus raw rabbit liver, sealed with petrolatum. Viability is maintained for long periods, however, in beef-heart, peptic-digest broth. Although no definite data are available, the spores of the organism probably do not differ from those of other anaerobes in respect to resistance to heat, desiccation, light, and chemicals.

Biochemical Properties. *Clostridium hemolyticum* produces acid and gas from glucose and fructose. Records and Vawter previously had listed galactose as fermented, but their subsequent studies have proved this incorrect. Other carbohydrates not attacked are mannose, maltose, lactose, sucrose, mannite, raffinose, dulcitol, glycerin, arabinose, xylose, dextrin, inulin, and salicin. Blood agar shows diffuse hemolysis in 16 to 24 hours. Iron medium is blackened; gelatin is liquefied in two to six days; litmus milk is unchanged; coagulated serum is not liquefied; indol is produced in 16 to 18 hours; H_2S is produced in large amounts; methyl red and V. P. tests are negative; nitrates are not reduced.

Antigenic Structure and Toxins. Records and Vawter have shown that all strains of the organism studied by them are immunologically identical in respect to agglutination and toxin formation. They showed, also, by using specific antiserums in rabbits and then inoculating them with lethal doses of the organism, that no antigenic relationships exist between *Clost. hemolyticum* and *Clost. novyi*, *Clost. perfringens*, *Clost. chauvoei*, or *Clost. septicum*.

Two toxin fractions, which have not been separated in pure form, are produced in cultures and in the animal body. One fraction is markedly hemolytic but unstable. It is present in culture media at the eighth to tenth hour of incubation. Its maximum concentration is reached in 16 to 20 hours and disappears after 30 to 36 hours of incubation. The other fraction is recognized by its necrotizing action on tissues of rabbits and guinea pigs. It is present during the early stages of the growth of the culture but persists for a week longer.

The production of lecithinase by the *Clost. hemolyticum* has been reported by Jasmin who found that the production of opalescence in human serum and the flocculation of egg yolk solution by this enzyme paralleled the lethal and hemolytic action of the toxin produced by the organism.

Pathogenicity. *Clost. hemolyticum* is pathogenic to rabbits, guinea pigs, and white mice, but infection is dependent upon a high concentration of hemolytic toxin in the culture. The bovine is the most susceptible of the domestic animals. The disease has been observed in sheep and swine.

Guinea pigs weighing 300 to 500 gms. are killed in 18 to 36 hours by 0.1 to 0.5 ml. of toxic culture. Rabbits weighing 1.5 to 2 kg. die in 16 to 24 hours after receiving 0.5 to 1.5 ml. of toxic culture.

Mature white mice weighing 20 to 25 gm. die in 16 to 24 hours after inoculation with 0.1 ml. of culture. Upon autopsy an extensive, blood-stained edema without gas is found in the areolar tissue. The under-lying muscle tissue is usually light-colored but not so softened; blood-stained fluid is found in the body cavities; perivascular hemorrhages occur in the pleura and peritoneum; intestines are distended with gas, and the contents are bile-stained, and sometimes are blood-stained; single or multiple infarcts occur in the liver; hemoglobin-uria is a constant finding; the lungs are moderately congested.

The lesions produced by the natural infection in cattle, sheep, and swine are not unlike those described above. The most significant characteristics, however, may be repeated for emphasis. Light-colored infarcts are found in the liver from which the infection no doubt originates; extensive hemorrhages are found in the parietal peritoneum; subcutaneous connective tissue is icteric; pinhead-sized cortical hemorrhages are present in the kidneys; dark red-colored fluid accumulates in the urinary bladder.

Immunity. Records and Vawter (1945) have studied various types of vaccines and bacterins and have found that the aluminum hydroxide precipitated toxoid type of formalinized bacterin gives the best results.

A potent antitoxic serum is produced in horses and when given intravenously in 500 to 1,000 ml. doses to infected animals proves to be an adequate treatment.

Diagnosis. The symptoms of the disease, the animal involved, and the section of the country are most valuable in diagnosis. The organism must be isolated and identified for absolute proof, how-ever, because the disease may at times be confused with anthrax, hemorrhagic septicemia, and blackleg. *Clost. hemolyticum* resem-bles *Clost. novyi, Clost. sordellii* in some cultural characteristics as well as the effects produced in experimental animals. This organism is best identified by using a specific antiserum on young cultures obtaining a clear-cut agglutination reaction.

Clostridium sordellii

Synonyms and History. In 1922, Sordelli of Argentina isolated an organism which he called *Bacillus oedematiens sporogenes* from two fatal cases of gas gangrene in man. Meleney, Humphreys, and Carp, in 1927, unaware of Sordelli's work, described and named a similar organism *Clostridium oedematoides.* In 1927, Hall and Scott suggested the name *Bacillus sordellii* after studying cultures iso-lated from cases of gas gangrene in man. Hall, in 1929, identified two cultures isolated from cases of icterohemoglobinuria of cattle as identical with those from human beings, and in the same year, Hall, Rymer, and Jungherr found that cultures obtained from Meleney, from Sordelli, and from Nevada cattle were indistinguishable culturally and serologically. In 1931 Hall and Gray reported a fatal case of septic peritonitis in man due to this organism. The significance of *Clost. sordellii* as a pathogenic organism in animals was emphasized by Vawter in 1942 after his study of five cultures isolated from cattle and one from sheep in Nevada.

Distribution and Transmission. The geographical distribution of this organism is not known, but its isolation from such widely separated areas as Argentina and Nevada suggests that more detailed studies of anaerobes isolated from cases of gas gangrene in man and animals may reveal its presence elsewhere.

In common with other bacilli of this group, it is presumed that the organism gains entrance through wounds and abrasions of the skin and mucous membranes, and originates from the soil.

Morphology and Staining. *Clost. sordellii* is a nonmotile, sporeforming bacillus 1μ in diameter by $3.5–4.0\mu$ in length. Spores are located in a central or subterminal position. Capsules are not produced. Cultures 12 to 18 hours old are strongly Gram-positive.

Growth Requirements and Characteristics. This organism grows readily and luxuriantly in media such as cooked meat medium and sodium thioglycollate agar. In cooked meat media, the meat particles first become bright red, then blacken and become partially digested or gelatinized. White crystals, resembling tyrosin, appear in meat cultures after ten days at room temperature. A black, veil-like stratum develops in fluid media containing sodium thioglycollate.

Colonies of the organism in deep agar cultures are pleomorphic, appearing as biconvex discs, multiplane discs, disc types with eccentric fluffs, or dense feathery masses. The agar column is usually broken by gas. The proteolytic action of the organism is notable and the characteristic valeric odor of cultures 20–48 hours old is typical.

Resistance. No data have been recorded to indicate that the spores of *Clost. sordellii* are different than those of other bacilli in respect to resistance. Vawter observed that cultures 10 to 12 years old grew readily when revived with liver digest broth and were fully virulent.

Biochemical Properties. Glucose, fructose, and maltose are fermented; galactose, lactose, sucrose, mannite, arabinose, xylose, inulin, salicin, dulcitol, and glycerol are not fermented. Gelatin is liquefied in 24 hours; litmus milk is coagulated in 24 hours and is peptonized in 5 to 7 days. Coagulated serum is liquefied in 5 to 7 days with the residual clot turning black. Indol is formed in 18 to 24 hours; H_2S production is pronounced; methyl red test is positive; V.P. reaction is negative; nitrates are not reduced. Red blood cells are hemolyzed in 4 to 6 hours.

Antigenic Structure and Toxins. All studies of the organism indicate that it is antigenically homogenous.

A very potent, moderately stable, filtrable toxin is produced in 24 to 36 hours. This toxin is inactivated by 70° C. in 20 minutes and by 0.25 per cent formalin in 2 days at 37.5° C. The antigenic action of formalinized cultures is not destroyed.

Pathogenicity. Guinea pigs and rabbits are susceptible to *Clost. sordellii* and the lesions produced are typical of a gas edema. Bacteriemia is produced and death follows in 16 to 18 hours. Horses are killed by doses as small as 0.5 ml. of a toxic culture. Germ-free filtrates produce severe local reactions in horses when given subcutaneously. Cattle, likewise, are very susceptible.

Natural cases of the disease have been observed only in cattle and sheep by Vawter. Reference previously has been made to the strains isolated by him. Three of the cattle strains were isolated with either *Clost. hemolyticum* or *Clost. perfringens* from liver infarcts or other tissues of cattle which had died because of bacillary hemoglobinuria. One strain was isolated from a calf which showed atypical blackleg, and another strain from calves which had become infected by vaccination. An avirulent strain was isolated with *Clost. septicum* from a sheep.

Immunity. A highly potent antitoxic serum is produced in horses by the use of carefully attenuated cultures of the organism. Vawter has developed agglutinating antiserum in the rabbit by using formalinized cultures.

Diagnosis. The presence of *Clost. sordellii* in an infection can be detected only by the isolation and identification of the organism.

Clostridium tetani

Synonyms and History. Bacillus of Nicolaier; *Plectridium tetani; Bacillus tetani.*

Carle and Rattone, in 1884, produced tetanus in rabbits by injecting them with exudate taken from a wound of a man suffering with the disease. The description of the microorganism was contributed in 1884 by Nicolaier, who produced tetanus in rabbits by injecting garden earth. He observed long, slender bacilli in the lesions of rabbits suffering with tetanus. Rosenbach, in 1886, provided the connecting link between the work of Carle and Rattone and of Nicolaier when he produced tetanus in guinea pigs by injecting them with the material from a woman who had died of tetanus following severe frostbite. He noted the bacillus and was probably the first to call attention to the "drumstick" nature of it. In 1889 Kitasato succeeded in growing the organism in pure culture and in transmitting the disease experimentally. Von Behring and Kitasato, in 1890, showed the toxic nature of the bacillus and also demonstrated that rabbits could be immunized against the toxin by the injection of small doses. More important was the fact that the blood serum from such rabbits could neutralize the toxin in vivo and in vitro; thus, these investigators laid the foundation for serum therapy.

During the more recent years, *Clost. tetani* has been investigated with the view of obtaining more information concerning its distribution, antigenic relationships, and toxic action as well as toxin and antitoxin standardization and the manufacture of tetanus toxoid.

Distribution and Transmission. *Clostridium tetani* is widely distributed in nature. It has been isolated from the fecal material of humans and herbivorous animals, particularly horses. Ten Broeck and Bauer have shown that the bacilli undergo multiplication in the intestinal tract of guinea pigs. Soils from various parts of the world have revealed the presence of the organism. It is possible that under certain conditions the bacillus may maintain, for a time, a saprophytic existence and multiply in the soil.

The organism gains entrance through skin wounds caused by objects which carry dirt into the deeper tissues. Some cases of tetanus occur in which the infection atrium is unknown.

Morphology and Staining. *Clost. tetani* is a long slender rod, 0.5μ in diameter by 2 to 5μ in length, and long, filamentous forms occur which later break up into shorter rods. The ends of the organism are rounded. It occurs singly or in short chains which are sluggishly motile by means of peritrichic flagella (Fig. 31.8). The spores found in the organism are two or three times the diameter of the cell and are situated terminally, giving a "drumstick" appearance (Fig. 31.9). The organism stains readily by the ordinary aniline dyes and is Gram-positive.

Growth Requirements and Characterisitics. *Clost. tetani* is an obligate anaerobe and is isolated with difficulty in pure culture from soil or infected animals. Heating the material taken from animals to 80°C. and subsequently placing it in broth is often required for isolation. The organism grows well in liquid media to which finely divided particles, such as meat, steel, or cotton, are added. A temperature of 37°C. is best suited for growth. The optimum pH is 7.0 to 7.6.

Colonies on agar surfaces are irregular, often spreading from a denser center (effuse), have a filamentous edge, are glistening, and grayish-yellow becoming brownish with age. Broth is uniformly clouded, and a slight, finely granular sediment forms. In gelatin stabs, a typical "fir-tree" growth occurs. The gelatin is slowly liquefied. Alpha type of hemolysis first appears but is followed in a few days by complete hemolysis.

Resistance. Spores of the tetanus bacillus resist desiccation indefinitely. They also resist boiling for some time, over 1 hour, but are killed at 105°C. in from 3 to 25 minutes. The age of the spore appears to be an important factor. The temperature of the autoclave kills the spores in 15 to 20 minutes. It is resistant to ordinary disinfectants, surviving 5 per cent phenol for 15 hours.

Biochemical Properties. Carbohydrates are not fermented by *Clost. tetani,* although a small amount of glucose is utilized. Lit-

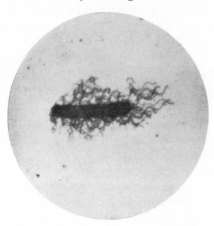

mus milk is usually unchanged, although some strains may cause coagulation upon prolonged incubation. This is probably due to a rennin-like enzyme. Peptonization is absent. In cooked meat medium some blackening occurs after a few weeks. Blackening occurs in brain medium especially if an iron wire is inserted into the tube. The organism also gives these reactions: indol negative, M.R. negative, V.P. negative, nitrates not reduced, NH_3 slight, H_2S slight, methylene blue not reduced, and phenol positive.

FIG. 31.8 — **Clostridium tetani** showing mass of flagella, Van Ermengen stain, × 2,000. (From Nowak: Documenta Microbiologica, courtesy Gustav Fischer.)

Antigenic Structure and Toxins. *Clost. tetani* has been divided into nine types on the basis of the agglutination test. Felix and Robertson indicate that there are at least two antigenic substances in the bacterial body: one, a flagellar H antigen; the other, a somatic O antigen. The latter is common to the species. Toxin produced by all strains is only of one antigenic type; that is, antitoxin produced by the injection of one strain of toxin will neutralize the toxins of all strains.

Tetanus toxin, however, is known to attack two different types of tissue. *Tetanospasmin* has an affinity for nerve tissue, and *tetanolysin* produces hemolysis. Tetanus toxin is not absorbed from the intact digestive tract, and there is some evidence that it is inactivated or destroyed by gastric juices. The toxin is destroyed by heat at 65°C. for 5 minutes but resists 120°C. for 1 hour when dry. A temperature of 55°C. for 1 hour destroys its toxicity but does not alter its combining power with antitoxin. Freezing and thawing does not materially alter the potency of toxin, according to Hartley. Direct sunlight for 15 hours destroys tetanus toxin if the temperature is 40°C. Daylight weakens toxin. One of the most effective means of preserving tetanus toxin is by precipitation with ammonium sulphate, drying over sulphuric acid, and storing in the dark at 5°C. in vacuum tubes under pento-phosphoric acid. The toxin is not resistant to acids or alkalies. Seventy per cent alcohol will destroy it in 1 hour. The potency of toxin may be decreased by certain chemicals, notably iodine trichloride, resulting in an anatoxin which may be used for immunization of horses in antitoxin production.

Pathogenicity. The injection of pure cultures of *Clost. tetani* or its toxin into experimental animals causes the development of typical tetanus. The mouse is one of the most susceptible of animals, although the horse, guinea pig, and monkey are more susceptible to toxin when dosage and body weight are considered. Rabbits, sheep, cattle, and goats are susceptible. The pig is next to the horse in susceptibility, although this is sometimes contrary to popular opinion. Cats, dogs, birds, and coldblooded animals are resistant.

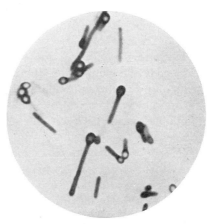

FIG. 31.9 — **Clostridium tetani** showing polar spores, × 2,000. (From Nowak: *Documenta Microbiologica,* courtesy Gustav Fischer.)

The organism usually gains entrance by means of traumatism, castration, harness galls, and parturition. Foreign material and other bacteria are conducive to the growth of *Clost. tetani* in tissues producing anaerobic conditions and necrosis, which apparently decreases the oxidation-reduction potential to a point conducive to the growth of the organism.

The absorption of the toxin and the mode by which it arrives at the central nervous system is controversial. Originally it was thought to be spread by the blood stream. The incubation period required for symptoms to appear after injection of toxin, however, made toxemia doubtful. Numerous workers have claimed that the toxin is absorbed by motor nerve endings and passes up the axis cylinders to the anterior horn cells, which explains why contractions are confined first to the affected limb or part. When the toxin becomes diffused through the cord and brain, the entire body may be affected. Abel and co-workers, however, contend that the toxin is absorbed by lymphatic vessels at the site of its liberation, then carried to the general circulation and distributed to the central nervous system by the arterial blood supply.

The period of incubation for the disease depends on the site of the injury. In man the average incubation period is seven days. In the horse the site of injury is more variable, and the incubation period varies from four to twenty days. The length of the incubation period is obviously hard to determine since so many factors seem to be responsible for the multiplication of the organism with subsequent toxin liberation.

The characteristic symptom of tetanus in all animals is a stiffening of muscles due to contraction. The muscles at the site of inoculation may be the first, and in mild cases they may be the only ones affected. In the horse the retraction of the eyes and protrusion of the nictitating membrane and spasmodic contraction of other parts of the body are diagnostic. Characteristic lesions are absent in tetanus upon post-mortem examination.

Immunity. Some animals have the ability to resist the action of tetanus toxin. In some cases this appears to be a natural immunity as in the dog, whereas in others, the cow, there is some evidence that the blood serum contains antitoxin. Most cattle show more than 1/500 unit of antitoxin per milliliter of blood serum. Sheep and goat serum likewise may contain small quantities. The presence of antitoxin in the blood of these animals has been explained by the assumption that tetanus bacilli may grow and multiply in the forestomachs, especially the rumen, and liberate enough toxin to stimulate antitoxin formation. The resistance of cows, sheep, and goats to tetanus, therefore, may be due to a slight immunity and not natural resistance. In this connection it is interesting to note that the blood of man, horses, pigs, guinea pigs, rabbits, and monkeys does not contain antitoxin.

When tetanus toxin becomes adsorbed to nerve tissue, it cannot be removed except by masceration of the tissue, and it cannot be neutralized by antitoxin unless the antitoxin is injected directly into the nerve sheath. The use of antitoxin, therefore, is mainly prophylactic.

The preparation of tetanus toxin and antitoxin is described in the chapter on toxin-antitoxin, to which the student can refer.

Diagnosis. The symptoms of tetanus are so characteristic that laboratory methods are rarely, if ever, used for diagnosis. The organism can be recognized in stained smears of exudate from the infected wound of an animal showing typical tetanus.

Clostridium botulinum

Synonyms and History. This organism was first isolated from brine-preserved ham in 1896 by Van Armengen who named it *Bacillus botulinus*. The following year Kempner was able to show that a potent antitoxin was produced in goats against the toxin liberated by the bacillus. The next most significant contribution was the recognition by Leuchs in 1910 that toxins of different strains were antigenically different. In 1915 Burke distinguished two distinct toxigenic strains which he designated A and B. A third strain, Type C, was discovered by Bengston in 1922 in fly larvae and was named *Clost. luciliae.* In 1923 Graham and Boughton isolated the same bacillus from chickens and ducks. In 1926 Thieler and his associates in South Africa cultivated an organism, which they designated *Clostridium parabotulinum* Type D, from cattle affected with lamziekte. Thieler and Robinson, in 1928, isolated an anaerobic bacillus, which they called *Clost. parabotulinum equi,* from horses and mules having died as a result of eating hay contaminated by decomposed rats. The name *Clostridium botulinum* Type E has been suggested for the last organism.

Distribution and Transmission. The detailed surveys of Meyer and co-workers have shown that the spores of *Clost. botulinum* are widely distributed in many parts of the world. The presence of most of the spores of anaerobic bacilli is attributed to the habitation of the area by people and animals. The spores of Type A of this organism, however, are more prevalent in virgin soil in the forests and mountains, especially in the western part of the United States. The spores of Type B are more prevalent in heavily manured soils and seem to be confined to the eastern United States and to Europe. Type C has been found in American and Australian soils. The other two types apparently are found only in South Africa. The spores of *Clost. botulinum* are rare throughout the middle-western part of the United States. Reported cases of botulism are often prone to be something else upon close analysis.

The persistence of botulism toxin in the bodies of animals which have died of botulism has been observed by many investigators. Reference is made above to decomposed rats in hay. Fourie has found toxin in the carcass of a hare after 54 days and in an iguana for 90 days. The toxin persisted in the body of a dead tortoise for over a year and Fourie believes that this is a most significant source of lamziekte which occurs in Bechuanaland, South Africa.

The organism is a saprophyte and under anaerobic conditions produces a potent toxin which is responsible for the disease botulism, which follows the consumption of contaminated food materials. Animal and vegetable foods are most commonly incriminated. In the United States, Meyer found vegetable foods incriminated in 72 per cent of the cases, animal products in 18 per cent, and the remaining of unknown origin. In Europe the greater percentage of cases of botulism is caused by contaminated animal products.

Morphology and Staining. *Clostridium botulinum* is a large bacillus, 0.9 to 1.2μ by 4 to 6μ, with rounded ends. It commonly occurs singly or in pairs, sometimes in short chains. Oval spores, usually greater than the cell in diameter, are situated terminally

(Fig. 31.10). The organism is sluggishly motile by means of four to eight peritrichic flagella. Capsules have not been demonstrated. Young cultures are Gram-positive, and some cells vary in depth of staining.

Growth Requirements and Characteristics. This bacillus is a strict anaerobe. It grows best at 25° to 30°C. and poorly at 37°C. Slightly alkaline medium is most suitable. The organism grows well on most common media, but growth is enhanced by 0.5 per cent glucose and 0.5 per cent K_2HPO_4 in beef heart and peptic-digest liver broth.

Colonies on agar surfaces are irregular, small, translucent, grayish-white to yellowish-brown, glistening, and have a fimbriate edge. Glucose agar-shake culture colonies vary in size, are opaque, and have a brown center with a less dense periphery. Types C, D, and E have woolly edges. Broth cultures are uniformly turbid with a moderate, powdery sediment. Types C, D, and E are lightly turbid and form a more flaky deposit in the tube.

FIG. 31.10 — **Clostridium botulinum** from agar culture, × 2,000. (From Nowak: Documenta Microbiologica, courtesy Gustav Fischer.)

Resistance. The spores of this bacillus are killed in 5 hours at 100°C., 2 hours at 105°C., 1½ hours at 110°C., 40 minutes at 115°C., and in 10 minutes at 120°C. It is apparent that boiling for a few hours will not kill the spores.

Biochemical Characteristics. The different strains of *Clost. botulinum* produce different types of changes in carbohydrate and protein media. Type A produces acid and gas from glucose, maltose, fructose, dextrin, and glycerol. Types B and C do not ferment salicin; C does not ferment glycerol. None of the strains ferments raffinose, inulin, mannitol, dulcitol, galactose, xylose, rhamnose, arabinose. Litmus milk is coagulated with resulting digestion and alkalinity. Blood medium is hemolyzed. Cooked meat medium is digested and blackened by Types A and B, but not changed by C, D, and E. The liquefaction of coagulated egg white medium is variable and has been suggested as a means of classifying the various types. Bengston suggests the designation of liquefying types as *Clost. parabotulinum* in which are placed all American Types A and B strains and all European Type A strains. European B strains and all C and D Types fail to liquefy coagulated egg white and are designated as *Clost. botulinum*. All types liquefy gelatin. Coagulated serum is liquefied by Types A and B, but not by C, D, and E. The organism is NH_3 positive, H_2S strongly positive, indol negative, nitrate reduction negative, M.R. negative, V.P. negative, methylene blue reduction negative, and catalase negative.

Antigenic Structure and Toxins. *Clost. botulinum* is divided into two main types on the basis of toxin produced. Antitoxin for A does not neutralize the toxin of B, nor does antitoxin for B neutralize the toxin of A. The other three types mentioned also produce specific toxins which are antigenically distinct. The two main types also can be distinguished on the basis of agglutination and complement fixation tests. The toxin is destroyed by heating 6 minutes at 80°C. Prolonged action of sunlight decreases potency in a few months. One of the most important characteristics of the toxin is that it is not affected by acidity equivalent to that of gastric juice or by peptic or tryptic digestion, thereby differing from other bacterial toxins.

Pathogenicity. Toxins of Types A and B *Clost. botulinum* produce botulism in man. Type A produces limberneck in chickens. Type C_a has been associated with botulism in wild ducks and limberneck in chickens. Type C_b produces forage poisoning in horses. Type D causes lamziekte in cattle. Type E is responsible for a forage poisoning in horses and mules. All toxins are capable of producing death in guinea pigs, rabbits, mice, mink, ferrets, and muskrats. Foxes, coyotes, and wildcats were found to be resistant by Quortrup and Gorham.

Botulism is produced only after the organism has grown in favorable food materials where the toxin has been eliminated. Although vegetable, fruit, and animal foods may be involved, the former has been found to be most important in the United States. Meyer has found that home-canned string beans are more commonly involved, followed by corn, olives, spinach, asparagus, beets, apricots, and pears. Of the animal products, pork has been most commonly incriminated. The above foods are of more significance to humans than to animals; however, cases of botulism (limberneck) in chickens have usually followed the feeding of spoiled foods primarily intended for human use. The condition in chickens is characterized by weakness, muscular incoordination, a drooping head, prostration, coma, and death.

Forage has been incriminated in the death of horses. Buckley and Shippen (1917) isolated a bacillus resembling *Clost. botulinum* from oat hay and ensilage which had caused symptoms suggestive of botulism in horses. Graham and Brueckner (1919) found corn ensilage caused botulism in horses. Experimental botulism could be produced by giving horses 2 ml. of a broth culture of the organism they isolated. The animals showed general muscular weakness, difficulty in mastication, pharyngeal paresis, inability to control the tongue, viscid discharge from the nostrils and mouth, inability to stand, emaciation, enuresis, and finally coma and death. Mention has been made previously of the observation by Theiler and Robinson (1928) of the cases of forage poisoning in equines following the eating of hay in which rats had decomposed, which certainly suggests a rather unusual source of the toxin.

Botulism in cattle, following the eating of corn ensilage, has been observed by Graham and Schwarze (1921). Although they did not suggest the organism was responsible for icterohemoglobinuria, Dubovsky and Meyer (1922) isolated *Clost. botulinum* from the livers and mesenteric lymph nodes of two cows with that disease. Seddon (1922) isolated a botulism organism from cattle in Australia afflicted with an impaction of the omasum (dry bible). The organism he isolated was very similar to the one found in South Africa by Theiler and co-workers in cattle suffering with lamziekte. The latter disease results from the eating of "green" skeletons by cattle afflicted with phosphorus starvation. The disease in cattle is characterized by paralysis of the locomotor system with difficult mastication and general weakness.

Botulism of wild ducks has been found in the western part of the United States. The birds obtain the toxin from feeding along the muddy shores of lakes. Whether the toxin is liberated by the growth of the organism in the mud or whether the ducks consume infected fly larvae in sufficient numbers to cause death is not known.

There are no significant lesions produced by botulism. General hyperemia is constant and microscopic thrombosis is found in some blood vessels; hemorrhages may be observed in the lungs.

Immunity. Antitoxin can be prepared which neutralizes *Clost. botulinum* toxin. The antitoxin is active for the homologous strain only, a fact which must be considered in treatment. Experimentally it has been found that antitoxin will prevent death when given immediately after the injection of toxin. No outstanding results have been obtained, however, by using antitoxin in treating field cases of botulism. In the human, large doses, 50 ml., given intravenously each day have proven to be of curative value. When the disease is diagnosed early in a food-poisoning epidemic, a prophylactic dose of 10 ml. of antitoxin should be given all those who have taken food and do not show symptoms.

Botulism antitoxin has been used extensively in all types of forage poisoning in horses, particularly in "cornstalk" poisoning. Its use in such conditions is not indicated and the benefit obtained is doubtful. No experimental evidence is available to show that this disease is due to botulism toxin nor have controlled experiments been performed to show the value of antitoxin in such cases.

Diagnosis. In man, botulism must be differentiated from other types of food poisoning. The only certain diagnosis of the disease is the demonstration of toxin by injecting a filtrate of the suspected food or forage into mice or guinea pigs simultaneously with protective doses of the various types of antitoxin. The organism may be isolated from the suspected food material and from the intestinal tract of those having died of the disease. The mere presence of *Clost. botulinum* in the intestinal tract of animals is not a safe diagnostic criterion, however, due to the prevalence of the organism in food materials consumed by animals in some regions. The symptoms observed in the animals before death and the food consumed must always enter into the diagnostic procedure.

Clostridium histolyticum

Clostridium histolyticum was first described by Weinberg and Seguin in 1916. It is not considered to be of great significance in animal infections but has been encountered as a secondary invader. The ability of the organism to produce extensive liquefaction necrosis in tissue is its outstanding characteristic. The organism is not significantly different from the other members of this group in regard to morphology and colony appearance. It does not ferment carbohydrates. Frank and Scott have reported two cases of *Clost. histolyticum* infection in the horse.

Clostridium sporogenes

This organism is another of the extremely active proteolytic species which is often encountered in wounds. It may be involved in *Clost. perfringens* and *Clost. septicum* infections in animals. It grows so easily and abundantly that other species are overgrown; consequently, it is difficult to isolate the true etiologic agent when contamination with this one is present. It is similar to other anaerobic bacilli in morphology and colony characteristics but is able to liquefy all protein materials with the production of a very offensive odor. Toxin production by the organism has never been proven. Although Weinberg has shown that some freshly isolated strains are capable of killing guinea pigs, most investigators claim that *Clost. sporogenes* is entirely nonpathogenic.

REFERENCES FOR FURTHER STUDY

Armstrong, H. L., and McNamee, J. K. Jour. Amer. Vet. Med. Assn., 117:212, 1950.

Baldwin, E. M., Frederick, L. D., and Ray, J. D. Amer. Jour. Vet. Res., 9:296, 1948.

Bergey, D. H., *et al.* Bergey's Manual of Determinative Bacteriology. The Williams & Wilkins Co., Baltimore, 1948.

Breed, Frank. Jour. Amer. Vet. Med. Assn., 90:521–28, 1937.

Brown, Russ. Jour. Amer. Vet. Med. Assn., 119:132, 1951.

Buer, A. W. Acta Pathologica, 23:21, 1946.

Bythell, D. W. P., and Parker, W. H. Vet. Rec., 58:367, 1946.

Cruickshank, J., and MacDonald, A. Mon. Bul. Emerg. Hlth. Lab. Ser. London, pp. 10–12, 1942.

DeMello, G. C., Clemente, J., Kiser, J. S., and Williams, J. H. Proc. 56th Ann. Mtg. U. S. Livestock San. Assn., p. 295, 1952.

Fildes, Paul. *Bacillus tetani.* A System of Bacteriology, 3:298–372. Med. Res. Council. His Majesty's Stationery Office, London, 1929.

Fourie, J. M. Jour. So. Afr. Vet. Med. Assn., 17:85, 1946.

Frank, E. R., and Scott, J. P. Cornell Vet., 26:252–57, 1936.

Friedmann, U., Hollander, A., and Traub, F. B. Jour. Immunol., 52:247, 1946.

Gay, F. P., and associates. Agents of Disease and Host Resistance, Chaps. 38, 39, 40. Charles C. Thomas, Baltimore, 1935.

Gill, D. A. New Zealand Jour. Sci. and Tech., 18:106–19, 1936.

Graham, Robt., and Schwarze, H. Jour. Inf. Dis., 28:317, 1921.

Griner, L. A., and Bracken, F. K. Jour. Amer. Vet. Med. Assn., 122:99, 1953.

———, and Johnson, H. W. Jour. Amer. Vet. Med. Assn., 125:125, 1954.

Gunnison, J. B. Jour. Immunol., 57:67, 1947.

———, and Coleman, G. E. Jour. Inf. Dis., 51:542–51, 1932.

Hartley, P. Quart. Jour. Pharm., 18:359, 1945.

Hewlett, R. T. *Bacillus botulinus.* A System of Bacteriology, 3:373–406. Med. Res. Council. His Majesty's Stationery Office, London, 1929.

Hottle, G. A., Mac, A., Nigg, C., and Lichty, J. A. Jour. Immunol., 55:255, 1947.

Jasmin, A. M. Am. Jour. Vet. Res., 8:289, 341, 1947.

Jungherr, E. Jour. Inf. Dis., 42:84, 1928.

Kellaway, C. H., Reid, G., and Trethewie, E. R. Austral. Jour. Exp. Biol. Med. Sci., 19:297, 1941.

Kerrin, J. C. Jour. Path. and Bact., 38:219, 1934.

Larsen, A. E., Nicholes, P. S., Gebhardt, L. P. Amer. Jour. Vet. Res., 16:573, 1955.

Mack, W. B., and Records, E. Jour. Amer. Vet. Med. Assn., 52:143–56, 1917.

Marsh, H., Tunnicliff, E., and Jungherr, E. Jour. Inf. Dis., 51:330–35, 1932.

Meyer, K. F., and Dubovsky, Bertha. Jour. Inf. Dis., 31:641, 1922.

Mueller, J. H., and Miller, P. A. Jour. Immunol., 56:143, 1947. Jour. Bact., 56:219, 1948.

Muth, O. H., and Morrill, D. R. Amer. Jour. Vet. Res., 7:355, 1946.

Newsom, I. E., Cross, F., and Dobbins, H. S. Jour. Inf. Dis., 45:386, 1929.

———, and Thorp, Frank, Jr. Jour. Amer. Vet. Med. Assn., 93:165–67, 1938.

Oakley, C. L. The Toxins of *Clost. welchii.* A Critical Review. Bull. Hyg. London, 18:781–806, 1943.

Parker, W. H. Vet. Rec., 60:497, 1948.

Percival, R. C., Burkhart, R. L., Cooper, M. S., and Martini, F. V. Amer. Jour. Vet. Res., 15:574, 1954.

Pillemer, L., and Warman, W. B. Jour. Immunol., 55:277, 1947.

Quortrup, E. R., and Gudheimer, R. L. Jour. Amer. Vet. Med. Assn., 102:264, 1943.

———, and Gorham, J. R. Amer. Jour. Vet. Res., 10:268, 1949.

Records, E., and Huber, M. Jour. Amer. Vet. Med. Assn., 78:863–65, 1931.

———, and Vawter, L. R. Nev. Agr. Exp. Sta., Bull. 113, 1928.

———, ———. Bacillary Hemoglobinuria of Cattle and Sheep. Bull. 173. Agr. Exp. Sta., Univ. of Nevada, Reno, 1945.

Robertson, M. The Organisms Associated With Gas Gangrene. A System of Bacteriology, 3:225–97. Med. Res. Council, His Majesty's Stationery Office, London, 1929.

Rodrigues, C. Arq. Inst. Biol., S. Paulo, 16:217, 243, 255, 265, 297, 1945.

Rose, A. L. Enzootic Botulism Among Wild Birds. Austral. Vet. Rec., 10:76, 1935.

Ryff, J. F., and Lee, A. M. Science, 101:361–62, 1945.

———, ———. Jour. Amer. Vet. Med. Assn., 111:283, 1947.

Schuchardt, L. F., Munoz, J., and Verwey, W. F. Amer. Jour. Vet. Res., 15:316, 1954.

Scott, J. P. Jour. Bact., 10:265, 1925.

———. Jour. Inf. Dis., 38:262, 1936.

———, Turner, A. W., and Vawter, L. R. Gas Edema Diseases. Rept. 12th Internat. Vet. Cong., II, 167–75, New York, 1934.

Shaw, J. N. Pulpy Kidney Disease in Oregon Lambs. Ore. Agr. Exp. Sta., Bull. 367, 1939.

———, Muth, O. H., and Seghetti, L. Ore. Agr. Exp. Sta., Bull. 360, 1939.

Smith, L. O. S., and Matsuoka, T. Amer. Jour. Vet. Res., 15:361, 1954.

Topley, W. W. C., and Wilson, G. S. The Principles of Bacteriology and Immunity, 3rd Ed. The Williams & Wilkins Co., Baltimore, 1946.

Turner, A. W. Black Disease (Infectious Necrotic Hepatitis) of Sheep in Australia. Austral. Council Sci. and Ind. Res., Bull. 46, 1930.

Tunnicliff, E. A. Jour. Inf. Dis., 52:407–12, 1933.

Vawter, L. R. Jour. Amer. Vet. Med. Assn., 75:201–15, 1929.

———. Amer. Jour. Vet. Res., 3:382–85, 1942.

———, and Records, E. Jour. Amer. Vet. Med. Assn., 68:494–514, 1926.

Weinberg, M., Nativelle, R., and Prévot, R. Les Microbes Anaerobies. Masson & Co., Paris, 1937.

Whitlock, J. H., and Fabricant, J. Cornell Vet., 37:211, 1947.

Wilsdon, A. J. Observations on the Classification of *Bacillus welchii*. Univ. Cambridge Inst. Ani. Path., 2nd Rept. Director. W. Heffer & Sons, Cambridge, 1931.

———. The Relationship of *Bacillus ovitoxicus* (Bennetts) to the *Clostridium welchii* Group. Univ. Cambridge Inst. Ani. Path., 3rd Rept. Director. W. Heffer & Sons, Cambridge, 1932–33.

32. | The Genus Corynebacterium

Diphtheria in man is produced by an organism which is rodlike and frequently filamentous with a tendency toward the development of branches. Many of the individual cells in a culture of this organism are swollen, clubbed, and irregular, and show a decided tendency to form in clumps and parallel lines. When grown upon certain types of media and stained with special stains the organism contains metachromatic granules in one or both poles. Numerous cells in a culture stain unevenly, giving a segmented or barred appearance. It is Gram-positive. This organism, known as *Corynebacterium diphtheriae,* represents the type species of the genus; consequently, all other bacteria which are similar to it are placed in this group. Because of the resemblance of many species to the diphtheria bacillus, the members of the group are commonly called the "diphtheroid" group.

The genus Corynebacterium is composed of species of bacteria which are found in man and animals. Many of them are nonpathogenic, being found on mucous membranes. A few are pathogenic and are associated with both acute and chronic diseases of man and animals. Only the most significant ones will be discussed in this text.

The most important member of the group, from the viewpoint of human health, is *Corynebacterium diphtheriae,* the cause of diphtheria. This organism is not of significance in animal health, but animals are frequently used in the production and standardization of diphtheria antitoxin and in the diagnosis of the disease; furthermore, methods which have been developed in the study of this organism are of value in the study of related forms from animals.

Among the strictly animal species, four have been found to be of greatest importance, *Corynebacterium pyogenes, Corynebacterium renale, Corynebacterium pseudotuberculosis,* and *Corynebacterium equi.* A few other species have been described and named, but since they are not of great importance to animal health, they will be referred to under the title *Miscellaneous Corynebacteria.*

There is usually no occasion to differentiate *Corynebacterium diphtheriae* from the four animal species; however, there are numerous instances when the animal strains may be found in the same species and in the same tissue. Differential laboratory methods can

TABLE 32.1

DIFFERENTIATION OF THE CORYNEBACTERIA

	C. diphtheriae	C. pyogenes	C. pseudo-tuberculosis	C. renale	C. equi
Hemolysis	—	+	±	—	—
Gelatin liq.	—	+	—	—	—
Litmus milk	no change	coag. acid. digestion	no change	alkaline digestion	no change
Nitrate rdc.	—	—	—	—	+
Dextrose	+	+	+	+	—
Maltose	+	+	+	—	—
Galactose	+	+	±	—	—
Lactose	—	+	—	—	—

be used for their identification. Some of the most valuable reactions are given in Table 32.1.

Corynebacterium diphtheriae

Synonyms and History. *Bacillus diphtheriae, Bacterium diphtheriae,* diphtheria bacillus, Klebs-Loeffler bacillus.

The diphtheria bacillus was first observed by Klebs in 1883 but was isolated and completely described by Loeffler in 1884. The discovery of the production of a potent toxin by the organism was made by Roux and Yersin in 1888. In 1890 von Behring demonstrated that recovery from the disease resulted in the formation of a specific antitoxic substance in the blood stream, thus paving the way for antitoxin therapy.

Distribution and Transmission. Diphtheria is world-wide in prevalence. Many countries, notably the United States, have controlled the disease by toxoid or toxin-antitoxin immunization, and as a consequence, widespread epidemics of the disease are rare where this procedure is followed.

The organism is transmitted by personal contact with infected individuals and by contact with fomites handled by infected individuals. Immune carriers of the organism are sometimes sources of epidemics of the disease.

Morphology and Staining. *Corynebacterium diphtheriae* is a pleomorphic rod, 0.3 to 0.8μ by 1.0 to 8.0μ in size. The rods are usually straight or slightly curved, and are frequently swollen on both ends (Fig. 32.1). Numerous cells show segmentation and the presence of metachromatic granules. The organism is nonmotile, noncapsulated, and nonspore-producing.

When stained with methylene blue, the barred characteristic is particularly apparent. It stains well with the ordinary dyes and is Gram-positive.

Growth Requirements and Characteristics. This organism is

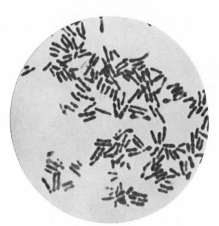

FIG. 32.1 — **Corynebacterium diphtheriae**, serum agar culture, × 2,000. (From Nowak: Documenta Microbiologica, courtesy Gustav Fischer.)

aerobic and facultatively anaerobic. It grows most abundantly at 37°C. in media which are adjusted to pH 7.0 to 7.2. It can be isolated from throat lesions of active cases of diphtheria by the use of media to which blood serum has been added. The most universally used medium for the primary growth of *C. diphtheriae* is Loeffler's coagulated blood serum. One of the difficulties encountered in the isolation of the organism is the growth of contaminating organisms. In order to overcome this objection, potassium tellurite may be added to the isolation medium. This salt prevents the growth of other organisms to some extent, but is valuable in that the colonies of *C. diphtheriae* are grayish-black which facilitates subculturing.

On serum agar this organism grows in small, finely granular, translucent colonies which have an irregular border. Old colonies frequently reveal a peripheral secondary growth; this gives the surfaces of such colonies a concentrically ringed appearance.

In broth a uniform turbidity is produced during the first 24 hours of growth, and then a thin pellicle is formed.

Resistance. The diphtheria bacillus is similar to the vegetative forms of other bacteria in resistance to heat and chemicals.

Biochemical Properties. *Corynebacterium diphtheriae* forms acid, but not gas, from glucose, maltose, arabinose, and galactose, and many strains ferment dextrin and glycerol; does not ferment sucrose, lactose, or mannitol; does not form indol, although some investigators report a color reaction with sulphuric acid and potassium nitrite as the test substances. Nitrates are not generally reduced to nitrites, although positive results have been obtained with some strains. Gelatin is not liquefied. The organism grows in litmus milk but does not alter that medium.

Antigenic Structure and Toxins. The antigenic structure of this organism is heterogenous, that is, the numerous strains are antigenically distinct. These strains, in turn, can be divided into antigenic subtypes by agglutination technic. This heterogenity of antigenic structure appears to be characteristic among many other species of Corynebacteria. The author noted a slight cross agglutination between one strain of *C. diphtheriae* (Park 8) and two strains of *C. renale* and one strain of *C. pseudotuberculosis*. It is quite probable that antigenic fractions are common to various species of the genus during certain phases of growth.

Corynebacterium diphtheriae is characterized, more than in any other way, by the toxin which it produces. The lesions which are produced in the disease are due to this powerful toxin. It diffuses through the body and produces lesions in numerous tissues far removed from the localized throat lesion of the primary disease. Different strains of the organism produce toxins of varying potency but not of different antigenic structure. The variation in the antigenic structure of the bacterial cells has no relationship to the toxins which are liberated by the different antigenic strains.

Diphtheria toxin is heat labile and is easily destroyed by chemicals. It can be attenuated, however, by formalin and precipitated by alum with the formation of toxoid which is of value in immunization.

Pathogenicity. The diphtheria bacillus is pathogenic primarily to man, and the disease is most frequent in the susceptible child population. In an infected individual the organism remains localized in the region of the tonsils, larynx, and upper part of the trachea. From this focus of infection the toxin is absorbed and spread throughout the body, producing degenerative changes such as albuminous and fatty degeneration in parenchymatous tissues. The disease is, in all respects, the most perfect example of a toxemia.

The toxin of the organism produces death in guinea pigs and rabbits, but mice and rats are resistant. Dogs and cats are moderately susceptible. The guinea pig is killed by doses as small as 0.002 ml. of a broth filtrate. In this animal the degenerative changes found in the actual disease are observed. The guinea pig is used universally as the test animal in the determination of the potency of diphtheria and in the standardization of antitoxin. The unit of measurement of toxin is called the M.L.D. (minimum lethal dose) and is defined as: *The least amount of toxin which, when injected subcutaneously, will cause the death of a 250-gram guinea pig in 96 hours.*

The pathogenicity of *C. diphtheriae* for animals has been a subject of considerable study. Many diphtheria-like organisms have been isolated from numerous animals. *C. diphtheriae* of the *mitis* variety has been reported from horses; this is considered significant in view of negative Schick reactions in that animal. Epidemics of diphtheria in man have been associated with milk supplies. Most often these epidemics have resulted from the contamination of the utensils or the milk by the dairyman or milk plant operators who are immune carriers of the organism. In some instances cows have been incriminated. Inasmuch as diphtheroid bacilli are commonly present in the bovine udder, any report incriminating *C. diphtheriae* must be substantiated by correct identification which must include toxicity tests. Pfeiffer and Viljoen in South Africa found that an epidemic of diphtheria in a localized community was associated with a diphtheritic mastitis in two cows, thus emphasizing that the bovine udder may become infected with this bacillus.

Immunity. Recovery from an attack of diphtheria results in durable immunity. Prophylactic treatment, however, is the modern method of combatting the disease. For this purpose a variety of immunizing products are used.

Fundamental to immunization is the determination of the susceptibility of the individual. Some persons may have had the disease and have not been aware of it. The *Schick Test* is used to detect diphtheria susceptibility. In this test a small amount of toxin, 1/50 M.L.D., is injected into the skin of the forearm. A positive test, that is, susceptibility, is characterized by a local area of erythema at the point of injection within 24 to 48 hours and is well marked at the end of the fourth day.

The products which are used in active diphtheria immunization are:

1. Toxin-antitoxin mixtures (T.A.T.) which are rarely used now but were the original method of von Behring.
2. Formol-toxoid (F.T.), which was originated by Ramon and is used extensively in France.
3. Alum-precipitated-toxoid (A.P.T.) is a precipitated toxin prepared by the addition of alum. The toxin in this preparation is liberated slowly into the tissues surrounding the point of injection, thereby producing a durable active immunity. It has an added value, in that only one dose is necessary.

In the treatment of an active case of diphtheria, antitoxin must be used. Antitoxin is usually prepared by the immunization of horses, but goats may be used by the injection of toxoid followed by toxin. The production of diphtheria antitoxin is basically the same as that of tetanus antitoxin, which has been described in the chapter on toxin-antitoxin. The student is referred to this chapter. More detailed information can be obtained in one of the various texts of medical bacteriology given in the reference list at the end of this chapter.

Diagnosis. Diphtheria is diagnosed by isolating and identifying the causal organism. The organism must be isolated in pure culture. Then 0.5 ml. of an emulsified growth is injected subcutaneously into each of two guinea pigs for a virulence test. One of these animals is given a protective dose of antitoxin. If the organism is *C. diphtheriae* the unprotected guinea pig will die in 96 hours and show typical lesions of the disease. The protected guinea pig remains alive.

Corynebacterium pyogenes

Synonyms and History. *Bacillus pyogenes, Bacterium pyogenes, Hemophilus pyogenes.*

Kitt, in 1890, was apparently the first to observe this organism in caseous pneumonia in the pig. It was isolated from the cow and described by Lucet in 1893. Poels, in 1897, called the organism *Bacillus polyarthritidis* because he found it in arthritis in calves. In 1902 Grips found the organism in swine pneumonia, and in 1903 Kunneman observed it in cases of suppuration in the cow. Glage studied bovine and swine strains of the organism in 1903, concluded that they were identical, and used the name *Bacillus pyogenes.* Since that time numerous studies of the organism, isolated chiefly from chronic suppurative lesions in the bovine and swine but occasionally from goats and sheep, have been made.

This organism had been considered to be pleomorphic and Gram-positive by most investigators; however, Priewe in 1911 considered it to be related to the influenza bacillus; in fact, he reported that antiserum of *Bacillus pyogenes* agglutinated suspensions of *Bacillus influenzae.* The organism was first included in the diphtheroid group and called *Corynebacterium pyogenes* (Glage) by Eberson in 1918.

Distribution and Transmission. Reports of this organism have been contributed from all quarters of the world where animals have been domesticated. In most cases the disease which it causes is chronic and occurs sporadically in the herd. Acute types of pneumonia in swine have been reported, however, which indicates that the organism may be of herd significance at times. In such cases transmission may be directly from one animal to another. In most cases it appears probable that the infection is due to the presence of the organism normally upon mucous membranes and skin. Hancock and Kelly have isolated *C. pyogenes* from the semen of apparently healthy bulls. Ruebke, and likewise Morgan, Johansson, and Emerson, have found it to be present in the sheath of normal bulls.

Morphology and Staining Characteristics. *Corynebacterium pyogenes* is a small, coccoid, pleomorphic bacillus varying from 0.2 to 0.3μ in breadth by 0.5 to 2.0μ in length. Cells with swollen ends and those with pointed ends are common (Fig. 32.2). The organisms are usually single but show a decided tendency to form clumps; palisade arrangements are frequently observed. It is nonmotile and noncapsule-producing.

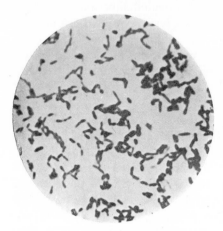

FIG. 32.2 — **Corynebacterium pyogenes,** serum agar culture, × 2,000. (From Nowak: Documenta Microbiologica, courtesy Gustav Fischer.)

Young cultures of this organism are decidely Grampositive, but old cultures are easily decolorized. It stains unevenly with methylene blue. Metachromatic granules are not found as frequently as in most of the other species of the group.

Growth Requirements and Characteristics. This bacillus is aerobic and microaerophilic. Growth is more abundant in an atmosphere of reduced oxygen tension. A neutral pH is more conducive to growth. The optimum temperature is 37°C.

The organism can be isolated from most tissue without much difficulty if serum media are used. Continued growth on artificial media is more difficult to obtain. Blood agar, blood bouillon, and milk are best suited for the maintenence of laboratory cultures. The incorporation of tellurium salts in the isolation medium is helpful in isolating pure cultures of the organism. When coagulated serum plus potassium tellurite is used, the organism forms small, black colonies which sink in a few days into a liquefied trough in the medium.

On serum agar *C. pyogenes* forms minute dewdrop-like colonies which resemble colonies of streptococci (Fig. 32.3). With age, however, the colonies become opaque and tend to become dry. In serum bouillon the organism forms a light, powdery sediment along the walls and in the bottom of the test tube. It does not form a pellicle.

Resistance. The organism is similar to other vegetative cells in resistance. The survival of the organism in heavy tenacious exudates from infected tissues has been noted by Roach. This author observed that iodine and lysol were the best disinfectants but it was difficult to rid contaminated instruments of the organism except by thorough cleaning and disinfection.

C. pyogenes is extremely sensitive to penicillin but the nature of the infectious process and the purulent exudate apparently prevent this antibiotic from coming in contact with the organism.

Biochemical P r o p e r t i e s. *Corynebacterium pyogenes* produces acid but no gas from glucose, maltose, galactose, lactose, fructose, mannose, sucrose, and dextrin, but none from arabinose, xylose, inulin, salicin, dulcitol, mannitol, or glycerol. Ryff and Browne have found that after cultures of *C. pyogenes* have become adjusted to unenriched media, they have greater saccharolytic properties. Many of their cultures fermented arabinose, xy-

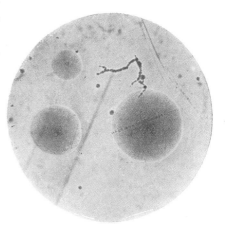

FIG. 32.3 — **Corynebacterium pyogenes,** colonies on serum agar, × 45. (From Nowak: Documenta Microbiologica, courtesy Gustav Fischer.)

lose, salicin, mannitol, and glycerol. Dulcitol was the only carbohydrate not being fermented. The organism does not form indol; does not reduce nitrates; does not form H_2S; is negative to the M.R. and V.P. tests. The reaction on milk is distinctive. Milk is first acidified and coagulated, and subsequently the clot is digested and within a week the medium is clear. Gelatin is slowly liquefied; coagulated blood serum is liquefied; a narrow zone of beta hemolysis is produced around the colony on blood agar.

Antigenic Structure and Toxins. This organism is antigenically homogenous by agglutination technic. Cross-agglutination with other diphtheroids has not been reported. A major and a minor antigen have been found in some strains.

An exotoxin lethal to rabbits and capable of hemolyzing red blood cells has been reported by Lovell. This exotoxin likewise produces necrosis of the skin in guinea pigs and is lethal to mice. The potency of the exotoxin may be determined by a hemolysin test. Antitoxin may be found in the serum of animals infected with this organism.

Pathogenicity. *Corynebacterium pyogenes* has been isolated from numerous tissues in swine, cattle, sheep, and goats. In swine it may cause pneumonia characterized by the formation of small focal, encapsulated abscesses followed by extensive caseous pneumonia. Polyarthritis is also due to the organism in many cases. In the bovine it has been found to be responsible for chronic, abscessing mastitis, suppurative pneumonia, actinomycosis-like lesions, abscesses in the peritoneal and thoracic cavities caused by traumatism, and arthritis. *Corynebacterium pyogenes* has been found associated with abortion in bovines by Maxwell and by Boyd and Kelly. In the calf it causes chronic suppurative pneumonia, umbilical infection, and arthritis. It has been isolated from mastitis and pneumonia in sheep and goats. The horse is rarely infected with the organism, but Karlsson has reported the isolation of it from a case of sinusitis. Fowls are likewise considered resistant but the above author isolated it from abscesses in the head of the chicken.

This organism produces subcutaneous abscesses in the rabbit and localizes in the joints, producing a deforming arthritis. Guinea pigs and rats are resistant. Abscesses are formed on the omentum and in the livers of mice following intraperitoneal inoculation. Morse and co-workers have found strains of the organism from calf pneumonia more pathogenic to mice than those from bovine mastitis.

Immunity. The sporadic nature of the conditions produced by the organism makes it difficult to observe immune animals. Bacterins and vaccines have been used in infected animals without influencing the course of the disease. Lovell has reported the presence of *C. pyogenes* antitoxin in the serum of infected animals, and Weitz has demonstrated the presence of antitoxin in dairy cows following the injection of alum-precipitated toxoid. Weitz and Langridge have reported that the injection of toxoid decreased the number of experimental udder infections in lactating ewes.

Diagnosis. *C. pyogenes* infection can be diagnosed correctly only by the isolation and identification of the organism. The characteristic morphology, colony size, and reaction on milk are significant in diagnosis.

Corynebacterium pseudotuberculosis

Synonyms and History. *Bacillus pseudotuberculosis ovis*, *Bacillus pseudotuberculosis*, *Corynebacterium ovis*. Preisz-Nocard bacillus.

In 1888 Nocard isolated an organism from bovine farcy which no doubt was *Corynebacterium pseudotuberculosis*. In 1891 Preisz and Guinard isolated a similar organism from the kidney of a sheep. Nocard, in 1893, observed his organism in equine pseudofarcy. Preisz, in 1894, was the first to describe the organism completely and to observe its resemblance to the diphtheria bacillus. At that time he called the organism *Bacillus pseudotuberculosis ovis*. Since then the organism has been found to be the cause of caseous lymphadenitis in sheep and deer and ulcerative lymphangitis in horses, and in various suppurative conditions in the bovine including skin lesions of a pseudotuberculosis.

In 1911 Buchanan called the organism *Bacillus pseudotuberculosis*. Eberson classified it with the diphtheroids in 1918 under the name *Corynebacterium pseudotuberculosis* (Preisz) Eberson.

Distribution and Transmission. *Corynebacterium pseudotuberculosis* is widely distributed but most prevalent in regions such as Australia, Argentina, New Zealand, South Africa, and the western United States where sheep are raised in large flocks. The organism appears to be a skin contaminant, for skin wounds caused by docking, castration, and shearing are predisposing to infection.

Among horses the organism is most prevalent in Europe; relatively few cases of ulcerative lymphangitis have been reported from the North American continent. The method of transmission among horses is not known, although the use of a currycomb and brush for a number of horses may well be questioned.

This organism has been found to be the cause of pseudotuberculosis of deer in the western mountain states of North America. It is believed to be transmitted to these animals from ground on which sheep are kept. Lacerations on the legs of deer due to brush offer an excellent avenue of infection for the organism.

Humphreys and Gibbons have shown that engorged female ticks (*Dermacentor albipictus*) harbored the organism and that by guinea pig inoculation larval ticks reared from such females were also shown to contain the organism.

Morphology and Staining. This bacillus is a coccoid to filamentous rod, 0.5 to 0.6μ by 1.0 to 3.0μ in size (Fig. 32.4). It shows a tendency to form in clumps and in a palisade formation. In natural lesions the organism is notably pleomorphic, but is uniformly coccoid on artificial media. Metachromatic granules are distinctly observed in the bacillary forms but are absent from coccoid cells. The organism is nonmotile and noncapsule-forming.

It is stained easily but unevenly by the ordinary dyes and is Gram-positive.

Growth Requirements and Characteristics. *C. pseudotuberculosis* is aerobic and facultatively anaerobic. It grows best at 37°C. and in a medium adjusted to pH 7.0 to 7.2. More abundant growth is obtained by the addition of serum to culture media. It can be isolated from primary lesions of the disease, but only a few colonies develop on the agar surface. When these are smeared over the surface of the medium a uniform and abundant growth results.

On the surface of serum agar this organism forms colonies which, when young, are typical of *C. diphtheriae*. As the colonies age they become opaque, concentrically ringed, dry, and crumbly (Fig. 32.5). Many of the colonies are rosette-like. Such colonies are cream- to orange-colored, depending on the strain. Variant smooth strains have been observed from cultures of the organism.

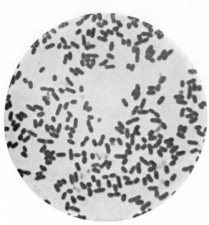

FIG. 32.4 — **Corynebacterium pseudotuberculosis**, agar culture, × 2,000. (From Nowak: Documenta Microbiologica, courtesy Gustav Fischer.)

These cultures are smooth and glistening and are bright pink to red in color.

The organism produces a thick, c r u m b l y pellicle in serum bouillon. The growth extends up on the sides of the tube a short distance from the surface of the medium. Some of the surface growth settles to the bottom of the tube, forming a coarsely granular sediment. The intervening medium remains clear.

Resistance. This organism is typical of the group in resistance.

Biochemical Properties.
Corynebacterium pseudotuberculosis is variable in fermenting ability. All strains produce acid but not gas from glucose, fructose, maltose, mannose, and sucrose; some strains ferment galactose, dextrin, and glycerol; none ferments arabinose, xylose, raffinose, lactose, rhamnose, inulin, salicin, dulcitol, adonitol, mannitol, or soluble starch. It does not produce indol; does not reduce nitrates, although a few positive strains are reported; forms H_2S slowly; is negative to the M.R. and V.P. tests. This organism is not proteolytic, consequently it does not liquefy gelatin, coagulated blood serum, or milk casein. It grows in milk but does not alter the medium. The organism is slightly hemolytic, producing a narrow zone of beta hemolysis. Carne reports that the red blood cells of animals decrease in sensitivity to the hemolytic activity of the organism in the following order: guinea pig, rabbit, horse, and sheep. The hemolysin does not have a relationship with the exotoxin formed by the organism.

Antigenic Structure and Toxins. The antigenic structure of the organism is not known but it appears to be somewhat heterogenous. This bacillus produces an exotoxin which is lethal for guinea pigs, rabbits, and sheep. The lesions produced in experimental animals are similar to those produced by diphtheria toxin. In 1907 Dassonville, who was one of the first to describe the toxin, reported that diphtheria antitoxin neutralized the toxin of the Preisz-Nocard bacillus. Toxin-neutralizing antibodies have been reported from the horse, showing lesions of ulcerative lymphangitis. It has also been shown that the blood serum from normal horses has this property. Some horses are negative to the Schick test, and it is intersting to specu-late concerning the rela-tionship between this fact, the presence of neutraliz-ing antitoxin for *C. Pseu-dotuberculosis* toxin in horses, and the means by which it is produced in horses free from apparent infection.

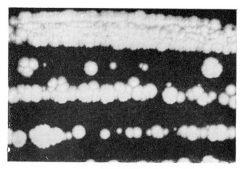

The presence of acid-fast variants of this bacil-lus in tuberculosis-like lesions of sheep and cattle

FIG. 32.5 — **Corynebacterium pseudotuber-culosis,** four-day growth on serum agar, × 2½.

has suggested that this type of infection may be responsible for no-lesion reactors to tuberculin. However, Larsen and Johnson could not detect any reaction to johnin and tuberculin in goats infected with *C. pseudotuberculosis.*

Pathogenicity. *Corynebacterium pseudotuberculosis* causes caseous lymphadenitis in sheep, a disease characterized by the presence of caseation necrosis in the lymph glands. The lesions are frequently confined to superficial glands, but generalized cases of the disease are not uncommon in which abscesses are distributed throughout the body. Marsh found that arthritis and bursitis present in lambs in Montana during July and August were due to this organ-ism.

In the horse the organism causes ulcerative lymphangitis, a disease which is confined to the lymph vessels of the extremities, particularly the hind legs. The lymph vessels and regional lymph nodes enlarge and ulceration occurs, producing a condition similar to the skin lesions of glanders.

The infection in goats is similar to that in sheep.

In deer the organism causes a disease similar in pathology to that in sheep with the exception of the presence of subcutaneous abscesses of the extremities.

Intravenous injection of the organism into the guinea pig causes death in four to ten days, with the formation of abscesses in the lungs and liver. Intraperitoneal injection of this bacillus into the male guinea pig produces the orchitis typical of the glanders bacillus.

The magpie (*Pica pica*), so common in the western mountain states of North America, is killed within 24 hours following intra-peritoneal injection of the organism.

Immunity. Bacterins and vaccines have been used to produce an immunity against this disease. In recent years formalinized toxin (toxoid) has been reported valuable in immunizing sheep.

Diagnosis. The conditions produced by the organism are so similar to many others that it is essential to isolate and identify the causal agent.

Corynebacterium renale

Synonyms and History. *Bacillus pyelonephritis boum, Bacillus renalis, Corynebacterium renalis, Bacillus renalis bovis.*

In 1877 Dammann observed small bacteria in lesions of typical pyelonephritis of the bovine, and in 1890 Hess observed a curved bacillus in the urine and kidneys of cows suffering with the disease. Bollinger reported an organism in 1890 under the name of *Bacillus renalis bovis*. Enderlen is given the credit for being the first to cultivate the organism upon artificial media and to describe it in detail in 1891. In the same year Höflich, independent of Enderlen, isolated and described the same organism. The most complete early description of pyelonephritis and of the organism was made by Ernst in 1905 and 1906. This investigator pointed out the relationship of the organism to the diphtheria bacillus and proposed the name *Corynebacterium renalis.*

Distribution and Transmission. The organism is widely distributed throughout the bovine population. It was first observed in the United States by Boyd, in Minnesota, in 1918. Jones and Little, in New Jersey, studied a number of cases of the disease and the organism in 1925 and 1926. Numerous cases of pyelonephritis have been observed in Iowa.

Jones and Little were able to isolate the organism from the vaginal mucous membrane of normal cattle. Ruebke, as well as Morgan, Johansson, and Emerson, have isolated it from the genital tracts of bulls. Ernst observed in his study that the infection was an ascending one. It is believed that certain predisposing factors, such as feeding and pregnancy, are responsible for the establishment of the organism in the pelvis of the kidney, the ureters, and urinary bladder where it produces pyelonephritis and cystitis. Most cases of the disease occur during the late winter and early spring months, which further substantiates the importance of predisposing factors.

Morphology and Staining. *Corynebacterium renale* is a pleo-morphic rod, 0.5 to 0.7μ by 1.5 to 3μ in size. This organism is more like the diphtheria bacillus than any of the animal diphtheroids, although it is slightly larger. It occurs singly, but clumps and palisade formations are common, especially in direct smears from kidney exudate (Fig. 32.6). Barred cells are usually observed, and large, distinct metachromatic granules are formed when the organism is grown on Loeffler's medium. The organism is non-motile a n d noncapsule-pro-ducing.

When smears of kidney exudate are stained with methylene blue the organisms are stained unevenly, and many cells with swollen ends are observed. The organism is Gram-positive, but the granules are more difficult to decolorize than the other part of the cell.

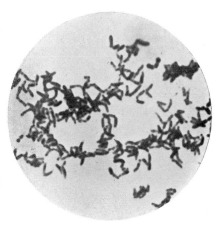

FIG. 32.6 — **Corynebacterium renale,** smear of kidney exudate, × 2,000. (From Nowak: Documenta Microbiologica, courtesy Gustav Fischer.)

Growth Requirements and Characteristics. This bacillus is aerobic and facultatively anaerobic and grows best in serum media adjusted to ph 7.0 to 7.2. The optimum temperature for growth is 37°C.

On primary isolation upon serum agar the organism forms small dewdrop-like colonies. These enlarge within two days and become opaque and ivory colored. They are moist at first and later become dry but never as dry as the colonies of *C. pseudotuberculosis.* The colonies are granular and have an uneven border (Fig. 32.7). Although the colonies of this bacillus cannot be considered smooth in the sense of the Gram-negative bacteria, some may be designated smooth as contrasted with those which are more rough. In a study of the colonial phase variant of the organism, Feenstra, Thorp, and Gray observed that the culture designated as "smooth" showed the weakest fermentation of glucose, the digestion of casein, the least resistance to the bactericidal action of bovine plasma, and was the least pathogenic to rabbits. Two cultures which they designated as "rough" showed the most resistance to the bactericidal action of bovine plasma and were the most pathogenic to rabbits.

In bouillon a fine powdery sediment collects on the walls and in the bottom of the test tube. Some strains form a thin pellicle.

Resistance. This organism is similar to the group in respect to resistance. *C. renale* is sensitive to penicillin, and this antibiotic would seem to be a most effective agent for treating cattle affected with pyelonephritis, inasmuch as it is eliminated through the renal circulation so rapidly. Morse has found that the drug is effective in those cases of the disease which are detected in the early stages.

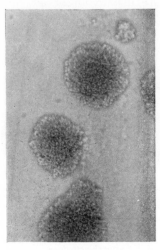

Biochemical Properties. *Corynebacterium renale* produces a slight amount of acid in glucose, and some strains are able to attack fructose and mannose. Many strains, however, appear to be devoid of saccharolytic ability. The organism does not form indol; does not reduce nitrates; does not form H_2S; is negative to the M.R. and V.P. tests. It does not hemolize red blood cells. Some strains do not alter litmus milk while others are able to digest casein with the formation of a subsequent alkalinity. It is able to split urea.

FIG. 32.7 — **Corynebacterium renale,** colony on serum agar, × 220.

Antigenic Structure and Toxins. The o r g a n i s m is antigenically heterogenous, and numerous strains cross-agglutinate with bovine strains of *C. pseudotuberculosis.*

Toxins are not produced.

Pathogenicity. *C. renale* causes pyelonephritis in cattle; it has been isolated from kidney abscesses in swine. The disease is not prevalent and is first manifested by hemoglobinuria and the voiding of blood clots. The infection is confined to the urinary bladder, the ureters, and the pelvis of the kidney. It may be unilateral or bilateral.

The pathogenicity of *C. renale* for rabbits was first reported by Enderlen, but the marked and typical renal pathology produced in that animal has since (1949) been described by Feenstra, Thorp, and Gray. By intravenous inoculation of the organism these investigators produced papillitis and pyelitis characterized by necrosis. Bacteria were found in the necrotic debris of the lesions and in the pelvis of the kidney.

Lovell and Cotchin were able to infect mice when extremely large doses (20 million per ml.) of the organism were inoculated intravenously. The bacillus showed an affinity for renal tissue where the greatest concentration was reached in three days with a gradual reduction in numbers up to the 16th day. Morse and Morgan have found that cystitis and pyelonephritis is produced in mice.

C. renale has not been found to be pathogenic for the guinea pig. Little or no growth is obtained in the chicken embryo.

Immunity. The disease caused by this organism is not a type which produces immunity or responds to immunizing treatment.

Diagnosis. Smears made from the exudate present in hemoglobin-stained urine from the cow reveal large numbers of this organism. Pure cultures of the organism can usually be obtained from such material. The fermentation of dextrose and the alkalinization of milk are considered differential characteristics.

Corynebacterium equi

Synonyms and History. In 1923 Magnusson, in Sweden, isolated this organism, to which he gave the name *Corynebacterium equi*, from suppurative pneumonia of a foal. The same year Lutje recovered an organism from suppurative pneumonia in three foals. He called his organism *Corynebacterium pyogenes (equi) roseum.*

Dimock and Edwards, in 1931, were the first to isolate the organism from cases of suppurative pneumonia of foals in the United States. Since that time they have found the organism frequently in Kentucky.

In 1936 Holth and Amundsen, of Denmark, observed a small coccobacillus in tuberculosis-like lesions of the cervical lymph nodes of swine. In 1938 Bendixen and Jepsen, of Denmark, found that the Holth bacilli were really *C. equi.* This has been confirmed by Karlson, Moses, and Feldman in Minnesota.

Distribution and Transmission. The distribution of *C. equi* is not known because the presence of the organism has undoubtedly been overlooked often in the past. In foals it is apparently confined to the Kentucky region and to eastern United States. The presence of the organism in swine is a new discovery. If the cervical lesions first described by Holth and Amundsen are any criterion, the organism is widely spread among American swine herds, for such lesions are extremely common. Karlson, Moses, and Feldman found it present in 23.2 per cent of 114 submaxillary lymph nodes of swine.

The transmission of *C. equi* is not known; presumably it gains entrance through the respiratory tract in foals, although hematogenous origin of the pulmonary infection is possible. Bruner, Dimock, and Edwards isolated the organism from the os uteri of barren mares and from aborted equine fetuses. This strongly suggests that prenatal infection of foals occurs. Bendixen and Jepsen isolated the organism from garden soil, which introduced a sanitation problem as far as swine were concerned.

Morphology and Staining. *C. equi* is a coccoid rod measuring 0.8 to 1.5μ. It is extremely pleomorphic, however, and different shapes are observed to be more common on different media. In exudate from a typical lesion of purulent pneumonia, *C. equi* is short and plump. On solid culture media it is coccoid, although bacillary forms are present (Fig. 32.8). In fluid media, large, swollen bacillary shapes are most common. The organism is capsule-producing, nonsporeforming, and nonmotile.

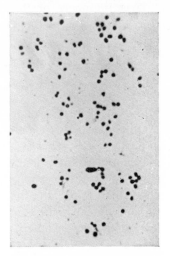

FIG. 32.8 — **Corynebacterium equi** from serum agar culture, × 1,400.

C. equi is stained easily with the common dyes and is Gram-positive. Metachromatic granules are demonstrated by a suitable stain, but they are not numerous. It is not acid-fast.

Growth Requirements and Characteristics. This organism is cultivated upon any of the nutrient medium which is used for pathogenic organisms; in fact, it grows quite readily upon any laboratory medium. It is aerobic and facultatively anaerobic; grows best at 37°C., although quite abundantly at 30°C. Ottosen has found that suppurative exudate from cervical abscesses of swine treated with 5 per cent sulfuric acid for 10–14 minutes and then inoculated onto agar plates was a satisfactory method of isolating *C. equi*.

Colonies on solid media are large, moist, and viscid with an entire edge. In 24 hours, growth is creamy-white, but as the culture ages it turns to pink, and in a few days' time the color is a salmon-pink. Pigmentation is accentuated when the organism is grown on coagulated egg-yolk medium and is incubated at room temperature. When the organism is grown on an agar slant, the growth is so viscid it flows from the surface of the medium and collects in the bottom of the tube. Growth on the inverted Petri dish is so abundant and viscid that some of the culture drops onto the dish below.

In bouillon the organism produces a heavy turbidity, and a scant viscid sediment collects in the tube.

Resistance. The organism is killed within 15 minutes at 60°C. and is readily destroyed by chemical disinfectants. It is resistant to 5 per cent oxalic acid for 60 minutes. This permits the use of oxalic acid in the isolation of the organism from less resistant bacteria.

Biochemical Properties. *Corynebacterium equi* is devoid of any ability to ferment carbohydrates although it is able to utilize glucose without producing an acid reaction. It differs from the other members of the group in being able to reduce nitrates to nitrites. The organism does not liquefy gelatin or coagulated blood serum; does not alter milk; does not form indol; H_2S forms in three to four days; does not react to the M.R. and V.P. tests; is catalase positive.

Antigenic Structure and Toxins. This organism does not reveal any antigenic relationship with other members of the diphtheroid group.

Bruner, Dimock, and Edwards demonstrated by complement fixation tests that the organism possesses species-specific and type-specific antigens. By using agglutination and precipitation tests, these investigators were able to divide the strains of *C. equi* into four main serologic types. Cultures from the genital tract of mares, from aborted equine fetuses, and from pneumonia of foals were found to belong to the same serologic type. In their studies of swine strains, Karlson, Moses, and Feldman observed antigenic heterogenity with the agglutination test; however, in the complement fixation test, with an antigen treated with acid and heat, the typical swine strains appeared antigenically homogenous. The type-specific component of the antigen is destroyed by acid and heat.

The antigenic heterogenity of the organism has also been emphasized by Ottosen who has reported six major groups in the study of 217 strains.

The organism is not toxin-producing.

Pathogenicity. *C. equi* is capable of producing bronchopneumonia in foals. The pneumonia is accompanied by the formation of small abscesses scattered throughout the lung tissue. Abscess formation is also observed in the mediastinal lymph glands, and in some cases lymph glands in the peritoneal cavity are involved. Subcutaneous injection of the organism produces an abscess filled with typical, thick, yellow pus. Installation of the organism into the upper air passages of the foal may not reproduce the disease, although Magnusson reports that it is possible to produce infection by intratracheal inoculation. Flatla has found that *C. equi* infection can be produced experimentally by feeding cultures of the organism to foals. In the infected animal extensive ulcerative enteritis was observed and abscesses were present in the mesenteric lymph nodes. This author considers the infection as primary in the intestinal tract with metastasis to the lungs. *C. equi* has been isolated from the os uteri of barren mares and from the fetuses of mares which have aborted.

In the pig, *C. equi* is associated with small, soft, encapsulated abscesses which are commonly found in the submaxillary lymph glands. Bendixen and Jepsen have been able to reproduce abscess formation by the subcutaneous inoculation of the organism into pigs. Plum has emphasized that the differentiation of *C. equi* infection in pigs from tuberculosis is only possible by microscopic examination.

Experimental animals, including the guinea pig, rabbit, and rat, are resistant to *C. equi*. Bruner and Edwards have found that this organism is able to kill 10-day-old chick embryos within 4 to 6 days; thus making available an experimental animal not hitherto available for the organism.

Immunity. No data are available concerning the immunity produced by the organism either naturally or artificially. The sporadic nature of the infection eliminates any great need of immunizing agents.

Diagnosis. Infection produced by *C. equi* can be accurately diagnosed only by the isolation and identification of the organism. Such characteristics as morphology, viscid pigmented growth, lack of carbohydrate fermentation, and marked nitrate reduction are considered outstanding and most valuable.

Miscellaneous Corynebacteria

The diphtheroid organisms form a large group of bacteria which are rather common on the mucous membranes and skin of man and animals. In man the identification of the various species is essential in order to arrive at a correct diagnosis of diphtheria. In animals the presence of other diphtheroids may confuse the diagnosis of the diseases which are known to be caused by certain species. The isolation of a diphtheroid organism may lead to a false diagnosis in some cases. The ubiquity of such bacteria emphasizes the need of the careful study of numerous strains of an organism before conclusions of etiologic relationships are made.

Corynebacteria have been isolated from pulmonary abscesses in mice, from throat lesions in chickens and other birds, from the conjunctiva of dogs and horses, and from abscesses in numerous animals. Many of these organisms have been considered the causes of the conditions from which they were isolated. It is apparent, therefore, that other species of Corynebacteria may be recognized in the future.

One organism which is not specifically identified as yet, although it appears to be identical with the *C. pseudodiphtheriticum* of man, has been found in the lungs of swine, cattle, and sheep by numerous investigators. It was first described by Ray who considered it to be the cause of pulmonary edema of cattle. Unpublished reports indicate that bacterins prepared with the organism are of definite value in treating infected herds.

Lesbouyries of France has reported the isolation of an organism he called *Corynebacterium metritis* from female rabbits. Chief symptoms were fever, loss of condition, unsteady gait, partial paralysis of the hind limbs, congestion of the vulva, and a muco-purulent discharge. Abortion occurred frequently. The significant lesions consisted of petechial hemorrhages of the vaginal mucous membrane and vulva, enlargement of the uterus and abdominal lymph nodes, and small multiple areas of abscessation and necrosis in the liver. Seventy-five per cent of the affected animals died or were destroyed.

REFERENCES FOR FURTHER STUDY

Andrews, F. W., *et al.* Diphtheria, Its Bacteriology, Pathology and Immunology. His Majesty's Stationery Office, London, 1923.

Boyd, W. L., and Kelly, M. D. Isolation of *Corynebacterium pyogenes* from a fetus and later from the mammary gland of the dam. Jour. Amer. Vet. Med. Assn., 103:24, 1943.

Brown, J. Howard, and Orcutt, Marion L. A study of *Bacillus pyogenes*. Jour. Exp. Med., 32:219–48, 1920.

Bruner, D. W., Dimock, W. W., and Edwards, P. R. The Serological Classification of *Corynebacterium equi*. Jour. Inf.. Dis., 65:92–96, 1939.

——, and Edwards, P. R. Classification of *Corynebacterium equi*. Ky. Agr. Exp. Sta., Bull. 414, Lexington, 1941.

Carne, H. R. A Bacteriological Study of 134 Strains of *Corynebacterium ovis*. Jour. Path. Bact., 49:313–26, 1939.

——, and Cramp, R. C. The Cause of Caseous Lymphadenitis of Sheep in Australia. The Austral. Vet. Jour., 8:28–33, 1932.

Daines, L. L., and Austin, Harold. A Study of So-called Skin-lesion and No-visible Lesion Tuberculin-reacting Cattle. Jour. Amer. Vet. Med. Assn., 80:414–36, 1932.

Dimock, W. W., and Edwards, P. R. *Corynebacterium equi* in Foals. Jour. Amer. Vet. Med. Assn., 79:809–12, 1931.

——, ——. Infections of Fetuses and Foals. Ky. Agr. Exp. Sta., Research Bull. 333, 1932.

Eberson, F. A Bacteriologic Study of the Diphtheroid Organisms with Special Reference to Hodgkin's Disease. Jour. Inf. Dis., 23:1–42, 1918.

Ernst, W. Ueber Pyelonephritis Diphtherica Bovis und die Pyelonephritis-bacillen. Centralbl. f. Bakteriol., L. Abt., Orig., 39:549, 1905; 40:79, 1906.

Feenstra, E. S., Clark, C. F., and Thorp, F., Jr. Mich. St. Coll. Vet., 5:147, 1945.

——, and Thorp, F., Jr. Amer. Jour. Vet. Res., 7:432, 1946.

——, ——, and Gray, M. L. Jour. Bact., 56:697, 1948.

——, ——, ——. Amer. Jour. Vet. Res., 10:12, 1949.

Flatla, John L. Infeksjon med *Corynebacterium equi* hos foll. Norsk. Veterinair-Tidsk., 6:249–91, 1942.

Hancock, J. L., and Kelly, W. R. Vet. Rec., 60:669, 1948.

Humphreys, F. A., and Gibbons, R. J. Some Observations on Corynebacterial Infections. Can. Jour. Comp. Med., 6:35–45, 1942.

Jewett, Walter. *Bacillus pyogenes* and Its Relation to Bovine Mastitis. Jour. Comp. Path. and Ther., 38:180, 1925.

——. Pyobacillosis in Sheep. Jour. Comp. Path. and Ther., 30:109, 1930.

Jones, F. S., and Little, R. B. Specific Infectious Cystitis and Pyelonephritis of Cows. Jour. Exp. Med., 42:593–607, 1925.

————, ————. The Organism Associated with Specific Infectious Cystitis and Pyelonephritis of Cows. Jour. Exp. Med., 43:11–20, 1926.

Karlson, A. G., Moses, H. E., and Feldman, W. H. Jour. Inf. Dis., 66:243, 1940.

Karlsson, K. F. Skand. Vet. tidskr., 35:129, 1945.

Krefft, R. A. Pseudotuberculosis Ovina: Estudio Bacteriologico de Procesos Caseosos do Lanares Magallanicos. Agriculture Tecnica, Chile, V:152–175, 1945.

Larsen, A. B., and Johnson, H. W. Amer. Jour. Vet. Res., 8:184, 1947.

Lesbouyries, G. Bull. Acad. Vet. Fr., 15:338, 1942.

Lovell, R. The *Corynebacterium pyogenes* Antitoxin Content of Animal Sera. Jour. Path. Bact., 49:329–38, 1939.

————. Studies on *Corynebacterium pyogenes* with Special Reference to Toxin Production. Jour. Path. Bact., 45:339–55, 1937.

————. Jour. Comp. Path., 56:196, 1946.

————, and Cotchin, E. Jour. Comp. Path., 56:205, 1946; 57:20, 1947.

Magnusson, H. Spezifische Infektiose Pneumonie beim Fohlen, In Neurer Eitererreger beim Pferde. Arch. f. Wiss. Prakt. Tier., 50:22–38, 1923.

Marsh, H. Amer. Jour. Vet. Res., 8:294, 1947.

Maxwell, H. The Occurrence, in Cattle, of Abortion, Macerated Fetuses and Acute Suppurative Mastitis Associated with *Corynebacterium pyogenes*. Cornell Vet., 33:315–18, 1943.

Merchant. I. A. The Corynebacteria Associated with Diseases of Domestic Animals. Jour. Bact., 30:95–117, 1935.

Minnett, F. C. Immunological Studies with the Preisz-Nocard Bacillus and their Application to Ulcerative Lymphangitis in the Horse. Jour. Comp. Path. and Ther., 35:71–197, 1922.

Morgan, B. B., Johansson, K. R., and Emerson, E. Z. Mich. St. Coll. Vet., 6:68 and 72, 1946.

Morse, E. V. Cornell Vet., 38:135, 1948.

————, and Morgan, B. B. Cornell Vet., 41:59, 1951.

————, Roberstad, L. W., and Glattli, H. R. Cornell Vet., 42:368, 1952.

Norgaard, V. A., and Mohler, John R. The Nature, Cause and Economic Importance of Ovine Caseous Lymphadenitis. U.S.D.A. 16th Ann. Rept. Bur. Ani. Ind., 1899.

Ochi, Y. and Zaisen, K. Studies on *Corynebacterium pyogenes*. Jour. Jap. Soc. Vet. Sci., 15:13, 1936; 16:8, 1937.

Ottosen, H. E. Abstr. Vet. Bull., XVII, p. 523, 1947.

————. Studies on Corynebacterium Magnusson-Holth with Special Reference to Serological Aspects, p. 119. Copenhagen, Carl F. Mortensen. 1945.

Pfeiffer, D. H., and Viljoen, N. F. Jour. So. Afr. Vet. Med. Assn., 16:148, 1945.

Phillips, C. E. Infectious Rhinitis (Bull Nose) in Swine. Can. Jour. Comp. Med., 10:33–40, 1946.

Plum, N. Maanedsskr. Dyrlaeger, 58:27, 1946.

Preisz, Hugo, and Guinard, M. L. Pseudo-tuberculose chez le Mouton. Jour. de Med. Vet., 42:563–72, 1891.

Ray, J. D. Specific Pulmonary Edema of Cattle, A Bacterial Infection Due to Unnamed Diphtheroids or Corynebacteria. Vet. Med., 23:490, 1928.

Roach, R. W. Vet. Rec., 58:169, 1946.

Rolle, M. Biology der *Bacterium pyogenes*. Inaug. Diss., Hannover. M. & H. Shaper, Hannover, 1929.

Ruebke, H. J. Bacterial Flora of the Bovine Male Genitalia. M. S. Thesis, Iowa State College Library, 1950.

Ryff, J. F., and Brown, J. Amer. Jour. Vet. Res., 15:617, 1954.

Thomson, David, and Thomson, Robert. The Corynebacteria (Diphtheria Bacillus and "Diphtheroids"). The Importance of Microphotography as an Aid to Their Classification and Identification. Annals, Pickett-Thomson Res. Lab., Vol. 2. Bailliere, Tindall and Cox, London. The Williams & Wilkins Co., Baltimore, 1929.

Vawter, L. R. The Study of Actinomycosis. Cornell Vet., 23:126–49, 1933.

Weitz, B. Jour. Comp. Path., 57:279, 1947.

——. Vet. Rec., 61:123, 1949.

——, and Langridge, R. Jour. Comp. Path., 57:286, 1947.

33. The Genus Mycobacterium*

One outstanding characteristic differentiates the organisms in the genus Mycobacterium from other bacteria. When any of the members of this group are stained with a suitable dye, such as carbol fuchsin, they are not decolorized by the action of acids diluted in alcohol. This property has led to the designation *acid fast* for this group of microorganisms. In addition to this characteristic, the Mycobacteria are recognized as slender rods which may be swollen, beaded, clavate, and branched. They are strictly aerobic and grow slowly on artificial media.

Acid-fast bacteria are widely distributed in nature; a few are pathogenic for man and animals; some are parasitic and pathogenic for cold-blooded animals, and others are saprophytes found in animal excretions and tissue and in the soil. The following species are conveniently listed in the three categories:

A. Species pathogenic for man and animals.

Mycobacterium tuberculosis is composed of two varieties or types. The human type causes tuberculosis in man, and the bovine type is pathogenic, primarily, for cattle.

Mycobacterium avium is the cause of tuberculosis in the avian family.

Mycobacterium paratuberculosis causes paratuberculosis, otherwise known as Johne's disease or chronic bacillary dysentery, in cattle and sheep.

Mycobacterium leprae is considered to be the cause of leprosy in man.

Mycobacterium lepraemurium is the cause of leprosy which occurs in wild rats.

Mycobacterium muris is a strain of an acid-fast organism found in the vole in which it produces lesions typical of tuberculosis.

---

* The author is indebted to William H. Feldman, Division of Experimental Medicine, Mayo Foundation, Rochester, Minn., for his aid in the revision of this chapter.

B. Species parasitic and pathogenic for cold-blooded animals.
   Mycobacterium piscium is pathogenic for frogs, toads, turtles, lizards, snakes, salamanders, and carp.
   Mycobacterium marinum has been isolated from necrotic areas in the livers of salt-water fish.
   Mycobacterium ranae is found in the livers of frogs.
   Mycobacterium cheloni is found in the lungs of turtles.
   Mycobacterium thamnopheos has been isolated from garter snakes and probably from other snakes.

C. Saprophytic species.
   Mycobacterium lacticola includes a number of strains of saprophytic bacteria which have been known under other species names (see Bergey's Manual, p. 888, 1948). The organism is found in butter, bovine manure, human and canine smegma, and in rat feces.
   Mycobacterium phlei is widely distributed in hay, grass, and in the soil and dust. It was originally isolated from timothy hay and is commonly called the timothy hay bacillus.

The student in veterinary bacteriology is primarily interested in the pathogenic species of Mycobacteria; however, it must be remembered that saprophytic species do exist, and that from the point of view of identification they may lead to confusion. The species which produce disease in cold-blooded animals are of especial interest to naturalists and others concerned with the diseases of zoological specimens.

Mycobacterium tuberculosis and Mycobacterium avium

Synonyms and History. *Bacillus tuberculosis, Mycobacterium tuberculosis* var. *hominis,* var. *bovis,* and var. *avium.*

The tubercle bacillus and tuberculosis of man and animals have been studied more than many of the other organisms and diseases combined. Entire books are written on the subject, and entire journals are devoted to past and current literature.

Tuberculosis is one of the oldest diseases of which there is any record. References are made of the disease in the earliest literature, and Egyptian mummies show lesions of the infection. The contagious nature of the disease was recognized by early peoples, and it was but natural that some confusion existed between tuberculosis and such diseases as syphilis during the middle ages.

The first successful transmission of the disease was obtained by Klencke in 1843 when he produced tuberculosis in rabbits by the intravenous inoculation of tuberculous tissue. Conclusive proof of the infectiousness of tuberculosis was contributed by Villemin in 1865 and more completely in 1868, when he produced the disease in the rabbit by inoculation with human and bovine tuberculous tissue. He was the first to demonstrate the difference in the resistance of the rabbit to the human and bovine organisms. Villemin concluded that (1) tuberculosis is a specific disease; (2) it is caused by an inoculable agent; (3) it can be transmitted from man to rabbit; (4) it is one of the virulent diseases.

The announcement of the discovery of the etiology of tuberculosis by Robert Koch in 1882 stands out as the most important contribution to the study of this disease. It was this discovery which opened the doors to others who have contributed to the subject since that time.

Robert Koch succeeded in staining the tubercle bacillus with alkaline methylene blue with vesuvin as a counter-stain. He was able to cultivate the organism on coagulated blood serum, and he proved the etiologic relationship of the organism to the disease by animal inoculation. During the early years of his work, Koch considered that the human and bovine organisms were identical. Ehrlich is given credit for having shown the acid-fast characteristics of this organism in 1882. His staining technic was later adopted by Koch. In 1890 Koch prepared a concentrated glycerin-broth extract of the tubercle bacillus. This he called tuberculin, and he hoped that it would serve as a protective and curative agent in the disease. Injection of tuberculin into infected animals, however, produced characteristic reactions, and it was soon realized that the substance was a valuable diagnostic agent instead of a curative one.

In 1872 Paulicki observed the similarity between avian tuberculosis and the human and bovine disease. Koch, however, considered that birds were infected with the human or bovine organism. Little significance was attached to the avian disease until Rivolta in 1899, Strauss and Gamaléia in 1891, and Maffucci in 1892 demonstrated that the avian organism was different from the human and bovine types.

In 1898 Theobald Smith revealed that the human and bovine strains of tubercle bacilli could be separated by growth on acidified glycerin broth. He showed that the bovine strains grew more slowly and decreased the acidity of the broth. This difference was not accepted by Koch and his school; consequently, considerable controversy over the subject existed until 1901 when Koch admitted that the human and bovine bacilli represented different types.

Mycobacterium tuberculosis can be considered to include two types of organisms, the mammalian and the avian. Present-day classification, however, uses the name *Mycobacterium tuberculosis* for the mammalian type and divides it into the human and bovine varieties, and uses the name *Mycobacterium avium* for the organism found in chickens and related animals. This distinction will be followed here, but for convenience of discussion the avian organism will be considered with the bovine and human types.

Distribution and Transmission. *Mycobacterium tuberculosis* is distributed throughout human and bovine populations in most parts of the world. The disease is one which is introduced by civilization. It is rarely found in native peoples of a country unless it has been introduced by those from the old world. Bovine herds are comparatively free of the disease in countries thinly populated by that animal. Crowding appears to be a definite factor in the prevalence of tuberculosis. In man the disease is most common in heavily populated cities and in people living in an insanitary environment and in close contact. In cattle the disease is most frequent in animals stabled together or kept in close contact in pens. This fact has been emphasized during recent years when it has been revealed that tuberculosis among cattle in the southern part of the United States is comparatively rare except in herds of work oxen which are stabled together. Avian tuberculosis is prevalent in chicken flocks of most countries of the world. In the United States the disease is most common in the middle western states surrounding the Great Lakes. It is a disease prevalent in temperate zones, probably because of the necessity of the housing of animals during unfavorable weather.

Among human beings, the organism is transmitted by sputum or other exudate containing the bacilli. This is illustrated by the prevalence of infection in families; in fact, the ease by which the infection becomes established in families has given rise to the belief that it is inherited. Tuberculosis is not inherited, but family predisposition and close contacts make it appear to be. It is obvious that coughing, sneezing, spitting, the contamination of the hands by mouth and nasal exudates, as well as the handling of food and cooking utensils by a person with open lung lesions of tuberculosis are means of transmitting the organism.

Among cattle the bacillus is transmitted through the feed and in some cases water. Pulmonary exudates in the bovine are usually swallowed; hence, the organism passes with the feces and contaminates the ground and feed. The organisms may be washed from the mouth while the animal is drinking and in this manner contaminate the water tank.

The bovine type of the organism is pathogenic to man. Cases of bovine tuberculosis in man may be caused by drinking milk from a cow with tuberculous mastitis or milk which has been contaminated with bovine fecal matter containing the organism. Swine may be infected with the bovine type of bacillus by feeding in the same lot with tuberculous cattle and with the human type by feeding on garbage from tuberculosis sanatoria or residences housing human cases.

Tuberculosis is spread through the avian family by the medium of feed and water contaminated with fecal material. Swine obtain the avian organisms by contact with infective droppings and by eating diseased chickens.

Morphology and Staining. *Mycobacterium tuberculosis* is a slender rod, 0.2 to 0.6μ in diameter by 1.5 to 4μ in length. The bovine type of the organism is considered to be shorter and thicker than the human forms, but this cannot be taken as a definite diagnostic criterion because strains of both types show variation in size (Figs. 33.1 and 33.2). The organism is uneven in size, and forms ranging from coccoid to filamentous are frequently observed in the same culture. *Mycobacterium avium* is similar to the human and bovine types, although it is considered more pleomorphic. It is usually uniform in size in smears made from infected tissue (Fig. 33.3), but on artificial media short coccoid cells and long, beaded filaments are common. The nature of these filaments was observed by Brieger and Fell by growing the avian tubercle bacilli in a hanging drop of dilute chicken embryo extract on a warm-stage. The colonies develop as follows: (a) The original rods elongate into filaments. (b) The filaments multiply by ordinary fission and also by forming fine, pin-like terminal sprouts which grow into independent bacilli. (c) After division the daughter filaments usually remain in contact at the site of fission; their terminal growth continues at an angle to the former cleavage plane and the colony thus acquires its characteristic structure. (d) The colony enlarges and ramification becomes increasingly complex until about the fifth day of incubation when growth declines. The bacilli remain filamentous. (e) When transferred to embryo extract of normal concentration, the pseudomycelial colonies pass through a phase of filamentous proliferation followed by disintegration of the filaments into short, discrete rods.

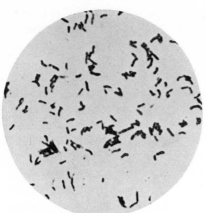

FIG. 33.1 — **Mycobacterium tuberculosis** variety bovis, glycerin bouillon culture, × 2,000. (From Nowak: Documenta Microbiologica, courtesy Gustav Fischer.)

Bloch has observed that tubercle bacilli grow in the depth and likewise on the surface of liquid media forming tight bundles or strands of bacilli in close parallel arrangement. Although Koch first described this characteristic, Bloch has associated it with the virulent strains of tubercle bacilli. When such cultures are treated with petroleum ether the strands of bacilli disrupt revealing the lipid nature of the substance which causes individual cells to adhere.

Tubercle bacilli are nonsporeforming and nonmotile. Extremely pleomorphic types of tubercle bacilli have been described. These forms range from small filtrable granules, diplococcoid shapes, diphtheroid shapes, to normal-sized bacilli. Such strains have led some investigators, such as Kahn and Mellon, to describe a complicated life cycle for this organism. Filtrable stages of the organism have been claimed on the basis of the production of disease by the injection of filtrates. The passage of a few bacterial cells through a filter is considered probable and at the present time an ultramicroscopic, filtrable stage of the organism is doubted.

In old cultures and in caseous lesions of the disease it is often possible to demonstrate large granules in many tubercle bacilli. Much, in 1908, was the first to describe these Gram-positive granules which he considered to be indicative of non-acid-fast tubercle bacilli, and for that reason they are known as "Much granules." Apparently they are a normal structure, but their significance is unknown. It has been suggested that they represent a collection of nuclear material, and Fontes believed that they extruded from the cell and gave rise to normal bacilli.

The most important staining characteristic of this organism is its resistance to acidified decolorizing agents. This resistance or acid-fast nature is due to the presence in the organism of a waxy and fatty substance which prevents the ready adsorption of dyes. In order to stain the bacillus, smears must be placed in hot staining solutions or remain in contact with the stain for several hours. The heated stain is quicker and therefore preferable. Numerous staining technics are available for staining this organism, but the Ziehl-Neelsen stain is one commonly used in most laboratories.

Yegian and Baisden have observed that the beaded characteristic of tubercle bacilli is more clearly portrayed by adding 10 per cent sodium chloride to the basic fuchsin.

The normal tubercle bacillus is commonly recorded as Gram-positive; however, during recent years Kretschmer has shown that tubercle bacilli devoid of waxy, lipoidal material are Gram-negative. It is apparent that the normal organism is Gram-positive by virtue of the waxy material it contains. This Gram-positive characteristic is altered by defatting substances. The reaction to the Gram stain is of little significance in the study of this group, and this staining technic is rarely, if ever, used.

Growth Requirements and Characteristics. *Mycobacterium tuberculosis* requires aerobic conditions for artificial growth.

The optimum temperature for growth is 37°C., although the organism does grow slowly at a temperature as low as 30°C. Avian tubercle bacilli grow well at temperatures between 25° and 45° The human and bovine strains of tubercle bacilli differ in the optimum pH for growth. Human strains grow best in a medium adjusted to pH 7.4 to 8.0 while bovine strains grow best at a pH of 5.8 to 6.9. Avian strains prefer a slightly alkaline medium.

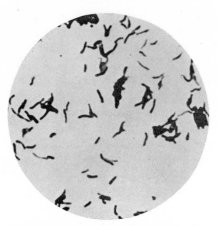

FIG. 33.2 — **Mycobacterium tuberculosis** variety hominis, glycerin potato culture, × 2,000. (From Nowak: Documenta Microbiologica, courtesy Gustav Fischer.)

Tubercle bacilli can be cultivated upon artificial media directly from infected tissues, but the organism frequently is not present in a pure culture. Various methods have been devised to overcome the presence of contaminants which grow more rapidly than tubercle. One of the methods which is commonly used is to add a 5 per cent solution of oxalic acid to the tissue or exudate, shake the tube vigorously and allow it to stand for about 30 minutes. Sterile water is added and the tube containing the specimen is centrifuged. The supernatant fluid is poured off without disturbing the sediment. This sediment is then "seeded" over the surface of four slants of suitable culture medium. Tubercle bacilli are usually numerous in the sediment which remains in the tube, for they are unaffected by the oxalic acid while other bacteria are destroyed.

Corper and Stoner believe that a 10 per cent solution of trisodium phosphate is as effective as sodium hydroxide or oxalic acid in destroying contaminating bacteria in samples to be examined for the presence of tubercle bacilli. The use of trisodium phosphate in routine isolations is also indicated by Van Vranken. Many of the bacteria which are present in tuberculous exudate are Gram-positive cocci. Petroff found that the incorporation of gentian violet in coagulated media, such as egg, prevented the growth of Gram-positive organisms but allowed the growth of tubercle bacilli. Gentian violet and malachite green are now commonly incorporated in media used for the isolation of tubercle bacilli.

The growths of the various types of tubercle bacilli on solid media have many characteristics in common. On a coagulated serum medium, for example, the human, bovine, and avian strains produce a dry, wrinkled, yellowish growth. On many specialized media, however, there are sufficient differences between the three types for identification. On egg-yolk agar medium, the human type produces a dry, rough, crumbly growth; the bovine type produces a scant, dry growth even after prolonged incubation; the avian type produces a smooth, moist, grayish-white growth (Fig. 33.4). Glycerin is commonly incorporated into many of the media used to cultivate these organisms. It was first used to prevent undue desiccation during long periods of incubation. This substance, however, is definitely stimulating to tubercle bacilli, especially the avian strains, which grow readily and abundantly in media to which it is added.

FIG. 33.3 — **Mycobacterium avium,** tissue smear, × 2,000. (From Nowak: Documenta Microbiologica, courtesy Gustav Fischer.)

The human strains grow well on glycerinated media but not as abundantly as do avian strains. The amount of glycerin ordinarily incorporated in media for the growth of human strains retards the growth of bovine strains. This chemical is usually omitted from media intended for the cultivation of bovine strains. Boissevain has shown that bovine strains grow abundantly on synthetic medium to which 0.1 per cent pyruvate is added.

Wohlers and Dehmel have found that Petragnani's medium and Besredka's bouillon are satisfactory media for the differentiation of the three varieties of tubercle bacilli, described below:

HUMAN TYPE

>*Petragnani medium:* luxuriant, dry, crumbly growth with yellow coloration of the medium.
>*Besredka bouillon:* crumbly deposit.

BOVINE TYPE

>*Petragnani medium:* delicate, light yellow, glistening growth, later green-colored.
>*Besredka bouillon:* crumbly deposit.

AVIAN TYPE

Petragnani medium: rapid, moist slimy growth with budlike elevations, sometimes yellow coloration of the culture.

Besredka bouillon: slimy, tuftlike growth.

The relative ease with which the growth of each of the three types of bacilli is miscible in salt solution is considered of differential significance. The avian type forms a uniform homogenous suspension in salt solution, but the human and bovine varieties are notoriously difficult to put into suspension.

In fluid media, such as 3 per cent glycerin bouillon, the three types present some differences. The avian culture forms a soft, viscid pellicle on this medium, and as the culture ages stalactites extend from the pellicle and a viscid sediment forms in the bottom of the flask. The bovine and human strains produce a thick, crumbly, yellowish pellicle, parts of which fall to the

FIG. 33.4 — The three types of tubercle bacilli on egg-yolk agar slant cultures; left to right, bovine, human, and avian. (From Feldman, Avian Tuberculosis Infections, courtesy Williams & Wilkins Co.)

bottom of the flask, forming a granular sediment. Slightly acidified, glycerin bouillon is rendered more acid in reaction by the growth of human strains, while an alkaline reaction is produced by the growth of bovine strains. The growth of strains of the tubercle bacillus used for the manufacture of tuberculin is quite abundant in a synthetic medium (see chapter on Technics and Methods). Certain batches of this medium were found to be unsatisfactory for tuberculin manufacture because of the variation in asparagine. After considerable study, Baisden found that, when trace quantities of various elements were added to the medium, satisfactory growth resulted. The minerals added were aluminum, barium, boron, calcium, cobalt, copper, lead, manganese, molybdenum, nickel, silver, sodium, strontium, and zinc.

Resistance. The presence of a lipid substance in *Myco. tuberculosis* increases its resistance to conditions which are detrimental to other nonsporeforming types of bacteria. When present in exudate which becomes thoroughly dried the organism may be viable for months. Although direct sunlight kills the bacillus after a few minutes exposure, much of the animal exudates and fecal matter in which the organism is present, usually protect it from the direct rays of the sun. The tubercle bacillus remains alive in putrefying material for months, consequently it is hazardous to spread manure on pasture land if such material has come from tuberculous animals. Well-rotted manure is considered free of the organism. Watering tanks may remain contaminated for months if the bacillus has been introduced into them by infected animals.

The necessity of thorough disinfection of barns and chicken houses following the removal of tuberculous individuals is a fundamental and difficult procedure in the eradication of tuberculosis. Previous to the application of a disinfectant all litter must be removed and burned. The tubercle bacillus is quite sensitive to high temperatures, so live steam is an effective sterilizing agent for solid surfaces. The cresol compounds in a 2 to 3 per cent solution are effective against this organism. Sodium hydroxide or lye in the 2 per cent solution which is so effective against some bacteria and viruses cannot be relied upon to kill tubercle bacilli. In fact, exudates to be examined for the presence of *Myco. tuberculosis* may be treated with 3 or 4 per cent sodium hydroxide in order to destroy contaminating bacteria but not tubercle bacilli.

Alcohol has been found to be an effective disinfectant against tubercle bacilli. Smith has demonstrated that these bacilli in water or sputum suspension are killed in 15–30 seconds in absolute, 95 per cent and also in 70 per cent alcohol. Bacilli in smears dried from sputum or water suspensions were usually killed by 50 and 70 per cent ethyl or 30 to 80 per cent isopropyl alcohol in 1 to 2 minutes, sometimes in 15 to 30 seconds. He concluded that 95 per cent alcohol is best for wet surfaces, 50 per cent for dry, and 70 per cent for wet or dry surfaces.

Laboratory cultures of tubercle bacilli under optimal conditions usually remain viable for at least six months, but it is advisable to transplant cultures at more frequent intervals to assure viability. Since these organisms must be incubated longer than more rapidly growing bacteria, the media which are used must be protected against desiccation. It has been noted that glycerin which has important nutrient qualities for human and avian types of tubercle bacilli reduces the rate of dissociation. Such media as coagulated egg yolk and blood serum do not dry out rapidly, and they are nutritionally adequate for cultivation purposes. This is especially true of Dorset's egg medium or modifications of it, one of which is given in the chapter on laboratory methods in this textbook. Laboratory media may be incubated in a chamber in which a high humidity is maintained. Screw cap tubes or small bottles that reduce evaporation to a minimum are commonly used. Culture tubes may be opened and a few drops of sterile water may be added in order to maintain a moist atmosphere. Sealing tubes with paraffin or with rubber caps to prevent evaporation although commonly done is not conducive to maximum growth of this organism because of the reduction in oxygen tension.

The value of chemical agents in the treatment of mammalian tuberculosis was first shown by Feldman, Hinshaw, and Moses in 1940, when the beneficial action of p, p'–diaminodiphenylsulfone–N, H'–didextrose sulfonate, otherwise known as promin, was observed in experimental tuberculosis in guinea pigs. Since that time other sulfone derivations have been proven to inhibit the development of tuberculous lesions in the guinea pig.

The discovery of streptomycin by Schatz, Bugie, and Waksman in 1944 and the demonstration of the bacteriostatic effect of this agent against experimental tuberculosis in guinea pigs by Feldman and Hinshaw, in 1944, are significant dates for students of tuberculosis to remember. Since that time streptomycin has been proven a valuable adjuvant in treating certain types of tuberculosis in man.

The usefulness of streptomycin in treating clinical tuberculosis in man is somewhat circumscribed due to the emergence during treatment of strains of tubercle bacilli resistant to different antibiotics. It seems to have been established that in tuberculous infections in man the tubercle bacilli are predominantly streptomycin-sensitive when treatment is begun. However, after the patient has received streptomycin for variable periods of time—from a few to several weeks—streptomycin-resistant variants may represent the majority of the tubercle bacilli present. This phenomenon can best be explained by the observations of Pyle that even in patients who have never received streptomycin a few streptomycin-resistant variants occur. Unless these resistant variants are suppressed by different effective drugs given concomitantly, there may emerge strains that may be resistant to streptomycin. The use of para-amino salicylic acid—mentioned below—in combination with streptomycin appears to have a considerable effect in curtailing the emergence of strains of tubercle bacilli resistant to streptomycin. The reader is referred to the chapter by Feldman and Karlson in the book, "Streptomycin, Nature and Practical Applications," edited by Waksman, for further reading on this subject.

Para-amino salicylic acid (PAS), first decribed by Lehmann, has been found to complement the action of streptomycin in the treatment of tuberculosis. This compound is effective on streptomycin-resistant strains of the organism and there is evidence that the two chemicals, when used together, are more effective in the treatment of tuberculosis than either one alone. Furthermore, the occurrence of streptomycin-resistant strains is prevented or delayed when the two compounds are used together. Although the occurrence of PAS-resistant strains has been observed, they occur less frequently than those which are resistant to streptomycin.

Numerous compounds have been discovered which inhibit the growth of *Myco. tuberculosis* in vitro, but are too toxic to be used in treatment. This organism is not sensitive to penicillin. Aureomycin has been found ineffective in the treatment of tuberculosis. Neomycin is active against *Myco. tuberculosis* in vitro and in animals. However, preliminary observations in the clinical use of this inadequately studied antibiotic indicate that in tuberculosis its toxic potential definitely circumscribes its use for any prolonged period of time. Its further use in clinical tuberculosis is problematic.

Biochemical Properties. Surprisingly little data are available concerning the biochemical activities of the tubercle bacilli. Human and avian strains have been known to produce a slight acid reaction in glucose, maltose, trehalose, and glycerol. Tubercle bacilli are catalase-positive, and some strains form a slight amount of H_2S. The methyl red and Voges-Proskauer tests are negative. Growth of the organisms occurs in milk, but the medium is not changed in appearance.

Antigenic Structure and Toxins. The acid-fast bacteria can be divided into the mammalian, avian, cold-blooded, and saprophytic types on the basis of agglutinin-absorption and complement-fixation tests. It has been found that the common agglutination reaction is not sufficient to separate the three types of tubercle bacilli. This indicates that they must share a common antigen. Agglutinin absorption, however, distinguishes the mammalian from the avian strains. The human and bovine varieties of *Mycobacterium tuberculosis* have been shown to be antigenically similar by cross-tuberculin reactions. The avian tubercle bacillus, *Mycobacterium avium*, however, is distinctly different. The avian organism can be subdivided into three groups on the basis of the complement-fixation reaction, but the human and bovine varieties are antigenically homogenous.

The nature of the toxic substances produced by tubercle bacilli in the natural disease remains unknown. The most important reaction produced by the end-products of bacterial growth is the allergic reaction observed in sensitized individuals following the injection of tuberculin. This reaction and its significance will be discussed later in the chapter.

Pathogenicity. The three types of tubercle bacilli are characterized by their pathogenicity for the three hosts—human, bovine, and avian. In addition to the primary host each type is able to produce disease in other species of animals. For the sake of clarity the pathogenicity of the three types will be considered separately.

Mycobacterium tuberculosis var. *hominis.*—The human type of tubercle bacilli is primarily pathogenic for man, anthropoid apes, monkeys, and certain of the parrots. It has been found to be pathogenic in naturally infected bovines by Feldman and Moses and by Tice. A rather extensive infection of cattle by the human type of the bacillus was reported by Hillermark, in Sweden, in which the organism was isolated from cattle which had been in close contact with persons having open lesions of tuberculosis. Although this is not considered to be a frequent occurrence in the United States, it is obvious that tuberculous people must be kept out of contact with cattle, for if this is not done, this may be one source of persistent tuberculin reactors in a herd.

The human type of the organism is also pathogenic for swine. The lesions produced in that animal are generally confined to the lymph nodes of the mesentery and the cervical region and are found, for the most part, in hogs which are fed uncooked garbage.

Tuberculosis of any type is rare in the horse and most cases are due to the bovine type of the organism. The human type has been recovered from horses (see Table 33.1). The same is true of sheep and goats. Birds, other than the parrot, are resistant to the human strain. Parrots are known to become infected after long years of close association with a tuberculous person. House dogs kept in close contact with human cases may become infected with the organism. Verge (Table 33.1) indicates that the human type is found more frequently than the bovine, due to greater possibility for infection with the human type of the organism, and not due to greater resistance of dogs for the bovine type than for the human type of the bacillus. This author found tuberculosis of dogs most prevalent around coffee stalls, wine shops, and restaurants in France where the pavement may be soiled with human sputum. Cats are generally considered highly resistant to the human strain by both experimental and natural infection but, according to Verge, a few cases due to this type do occur. Rabbits are but slightly susceptible to the human type and when infected they rarely succumb to the infection. The hamster, which has come into use in experimental procedures, has been found to be as susceptible as the guinea pig to the human type of the organism according to Glover.

Guinea pigs are highly susceptible to human tubercle bacilli, producing, even with extremely small doses, an irreversible, eventually fatal disease.

Extremely large doses of tubercle bacilli of the human type given subcutaneously to guinea pigs may result in a fulminating tuberculous infection within a relatively short time.

Mice can be infected with the human type of the organism, and by intravenous inoculation marked lesions are produced in the lungs. Susceptibility varies with the strain of mice used (Raleigh and Youmans). The albino rat is generally considered to be markedly resistant to this organism. Significant lesions have been produced, however, by injecting 5 mg. doses of bacilli intraperitoneally into that animal.

TABLE 33.1

PREVALENCE OF VARIOUS TYPES OF TUBERCLE BACILLI IN DOMESTIC ANIMALS—VERGE

Animal Species	Number of Strains Isolated	Type			
		Human	Bovine	Avian	Atypical
Horse	112	11	90	10	1
Sheep	270	1	269	......	....
Goat	54	1	52	1	....
Pig	3,418	98	1,196	2,061	63
Dog	606	392	200	2	12
Cat	132	6	126	......	....

Mycobacterium tuberculosis var. *bovis.*—This organism is primarily pathogenic for cattle, but swine are readily infected when in contact with tuberculous bovines. Cases of tuberculosis in horses and sheep have been reported as due to the bovine organism, but these animals are generally considered resistant to the organism. Cases of bovine tuberculosis also have been observed in dogs and cats. Chickens are resistant to the bovine bacillus, but parrots and related birds are highly susceptible.

The pathogenicity of the bovine tubercle bacillus for man has been recognized as a public health problem in all countries where milk and milk products are important articles of food. In the United States this danger to health has been reduced to a minimum, due to the eradication of tuberculosis from cattle herds and to the widespread pasteurization of milk. Children under sixteen years of age are most susceptible to bovine tubercle bacilli, and in them the organism usually produces lesions of a nonpulmonary nature. However, in sections of the world where infections due to the bovine type are common, a significant percentage of pulmonary tuberculosis is reported. The tissues most commonly involved are the cervical and abdominal lymph nodes and the bones, although generalized tuberculosis is by no means rare.

Bovine tubercle bacilli can produce generalized tuberculosis in the rabbit even when given in extremely small doses. The guinea pig is also very susceptible to the bovine oragnism. Mice are usually infected by intraperitoneal inoculations, but rats are resistant.

The hamster is susceptible to virulent strains of the bovine type of organism.

Mycobacterium avium. — The avian tubercle bacillus is primarily pathogenic to the domestic fowl, although the organism is capable of infecting all species of birds, and some species of mammals (see Table 33.2). It is quite likely that the factors which limit the prevalence of tuberculosis in many species of the avian family are the environmental conditions, crowding particularly, under which they live. The pheasant, in its wild state, is not often found to be infected, but the disease is apt to be quite severe in those which have access to and mingle freely with infected chicken flocks. The disease may be found in turkeys which are raised in contact with infected chickens. The pigeon, which is rather common on some farms, may become infected, the same being true of sparrows and crows. Water fowl, such as ducks, geese, and swans, even though living in close contact with infected chickens, rarely become infected. House birds such as canaries, parrots, and love birds are susceptible to the avian tubercle bacillus although they have rare opportunities to become infected. Ornamental birds, for example, the peacock and birds in zoological gardens, have been found to be infected, but such birds, also, are often isolated to the extent that the likelihood of the spread of the disease among them is diminished.

Among the mammals, swine and rabbits are the most susceptible. Tuberculosis in swine in the United States is predominately due to the avian bacillus. The prevalence of tuberculosis in swine is emphasized by the report of the United States Meat Inspection Division for the fiscal year 1948–49, which reported 8,655 total swine carcasses and 227,340 parts of swine carcasses condemned out of 49,062,663 inspected post mortem. Tuberculosis in swine due to avian tubercle bacilli is predominantly a disease of the lymph nodes and other lymphoid structures contiguous to the alimentary canal. However, generalization may occur, with lesions involving the liver, spleen, lungs, and kidneys. The rabbit may become infected with the avian type of the organism as a result of close contact with infected chickens. Intravenous inoculation with a suspension of avian tubercle bacilli usually produces an acute disease, the rabbit dying within 2 to 4 weeks. In this acute type of the disease macroscopic tubercles are usually absent but the spleen is enlarged and the animal has lost considerable weight. Stained smears of the splenic pulp reveal numerous acid-fast bacilli. Yersin first described this type of tuberculosis in the rabbit so it is commonly referred to as the *Yersin type.* The injection of tissue emulsions containing avian bacilli does not ordinarily produce this type of the disease, due, no doubt, to the smaller number of bacilli present.

The susceptibility of the bovine to *Mycobacterium avium* has been the subject of considerable research. In general it can be concluded that this animal is not readily infected with the avian organism under natural conditions to the extent that generalized macroscopic lesions are developed. Sensitization to avian tuberculin may occur but it is of transitory nature unless the animal is

TABLE 33.2

RELATIVE PATHOGENICITY OF THE AVIAN TUBERCLE BACILLUS FOR DIFFERENT ANIMALS

Animal	Degree of Susceptibility	Animal	Degree of Susceptibility
Chicken	Marked	Mouse	Slight
Pheasant	Marked	Rat	Slight
Turkey	Marked	Sheep	Moderate
Parrot	Moderate	Horse	Moderate
Duck	Moderate	Cow	Slight
Goose	Moderate	Guinea pig	Slight
Pigeon	Moderate	Dog	Not susceptible
Swine	Moderate	Cat	Not susceptible*
Rabbit	Marked	Goat	Slight

* One case of avian tuberculosis has been reported. (From Feldman, Avian Tuberculosis Infections, courtesy Williams & Wilkins Co.)

subjected to constant exposure. It is believed that natural infection with the avian type of the bacillus will rarely sensitize cattle sufficiently to cause them to react to mammalian tuberculin. Plum has observed, in Denmark, that the avian tubercle bacillus shows a marked affinity for the uterus of the cow. He has observed abortions caused by such an infection. Fincher, Evans, and Saunders observed a dairy cow which had become infected with the avian type after being pastured on an area which had been fertilized with chicken manure. Tuberculosis lesions were found in the cerebral and spinal meninges and in the uterus. The organism was isolated from the uterine exudate.

Cases of tuberculosis in the horse due to *Myco. avium* have been reported but this animal is considered quite refractory to the organism following natural exposure. Sheep may be infected but goats, dogs, and cats are considered quite resistant. Mice and rats possess slight susceptibility to the avian bacillus. Guinea pigs can be infected with inoculations of avian tubercle bacilli but the disease is mild and non-progressive. This fact is of great importance in the typing of an unknown tubercle bacillus.

The susceptibility of man to *Myco. avium* is a subject of considerable importance. Case histories are given in the literature which do show that man may be infected with the organism. When compared with the virulence of the human and bovine types of the organism, however, it is generally conceded that the avian type is of little consequence in human tuberculosis.

The reader is referred to "Avian Tuberculosis Infections" by Feldman for more details concerning the subject.

Differentiation of Types. The differentiation of the respective types of tubercle bacilli can only be accomplished with certainty by animal pathogenicity tests. The relative virulence for laboratory animals of the four types of *Myco. tuberculosis* responsible for tuberculosis in warm-blooded animals is shown in Table 33.3.

In distinguishing the various types of tubercle bacilli by animal pathogenicity tests, the relative susceptibility of the following

TABLE 33.3

RELATIVE VIRULENCE, IN LABORATORY ANIMALS, OF THE FOUR TYPES OF MYCOBACTERIA RESPONSIBLE FOR TUBERCULOSIS OF WARM-BLOODED ANIMALS*

Bacillary type	Animal			
	Guinea pig	Rabbit	Chicken	Vole
Human	+	∓	O	O
Bovine	+	+	O	+
Avian	∓	+	+	O
Vole	O	O	O	+

* Explanation of symbols: O = very resistant; ∓ = slightly susceptible; + = definitely susceptible. (From Feldman, W. H., Animal Tuberculosis and Its Relationship to the Disease in Man. Courtesy New York Academy of Science.)

animals must be determined for each bacterial strain studied—two guinea pigs, two rabbits, and two chickens. The latter should be previously tested with avian tuberculin and found negative. Guinea pigs should receive the infecting inoculum subcutaneously; rabbits and chickens are inoculated intravenously. If the vole bacillus is suspected, mice must be included in the typing series and given the inoculum intravenously. Guinea pigs living eight weeks after inoculation are killed for necropsy, while the rabbits and chickens are examined for lesions 90 days after inoculation. Reference to Table 33.3 should enable one to interpret with confidence the results of the tests and thus distinguish from each other the human, bovine, and avian types of tubercle bacilli.

Immunity. *Natural Resistance.*—It is obvious that many species of animals possess natural resistance to tuberculosis. According to Lourie this natural resistance may be of three types. First, there are those species in which the bacilli do not grow or do so to a limited degree. The inability of the bovine type to grow in the chicken, partly due to the high normal temperature, is an example. Second, in some animals the organisms grow without restriction but do not produce serious injury to the tissues. This has been found true of the growth of the human type of tubercle bacilli in the rat. Ordinarily this animal is considered resistant to tuberculosis, yet the symbiotic relationship of bacillus and animal is now recognized. Third, in most susceptible species there is evidence of natural resistance to the disease, manifested by the ability of the natural body defense mechanism to phagocytize the bacilli and to encapsulate and calcify the lesion they may have produced. However, it is not possible to eliminate the probability that resistance acquired during the active phases of the infection may be partly responsible for the fact that progressive tuberculosis does not develop in each animal infected with the disease.

Koch's phenomenon.—During the early years of his studies of tuberculosis, Koch found that guinea pigs already infected with tubercle bacilli reacted differently to subsequent injections of living bacilli than did normal animals. In a normal guinea pig the injection of living bacilli produces typical lesions of tuberculosis throughout the lymph system as well as in the lungs, liver, and spleen. Injection of tubercle bacilli into an animal known to have had tuberculosis for some time caused a marked necrosis and sloughing of the tissue at the point of injection, without any generalization or localization of the organism in the regional lymph nodes. Koch found that this reaction was also produced by the injection of dead tubercle bacilli, and he subsequently demonstrated a minor type of reaction to protein extracts of the organism. Koch's phenomenon revealed two things: first, that some degree of resistance to a second inoculation may be produced in the guinea pig by an active infection; second, that a hypersensitive condition to the organism, or the products of the organism, is produced in an infected animal. This last reaction, commonly known as a *tuberculin reaction,* is known to be an allergic phenomenon and is of value in the diagnosis of the disease.

Acquired Resistance.—The progressive nature of tuberculosis in animals and man indicates that immunity is not developed by the infection in quite the same degree as is observed in other diseases. But, as emphasized by Rich, a total acquired resistance is rarely developed in any disease and there is evidence that significant resistance is developed in tuberculosis. The total recovery of people who have had small pulmonary lesions, shown in later life by the X-ray, is considered to be due, at least partially, to acquired resistance.

Since the initial publications of Robert Koch, multitudinous attempts have been made to develop an immunizing agent which would be of value as a prophylactic in tuberculosis. In fact, Koch was searching for an immunizing agent when he discovered the effects produced by tuberculin. Numerous types of immunizing products have been used against tuberculosis, but it is not feasible to discuss them all here. The reader is referred to the book by Calmette for a complete list of such agents.

One product which has been prepared for artificial immunization is known as BCG meaning Bacille Calmette-Guérin; Calmette and Guérin were two French scientists who prepared the vaccine. This vaccine is composed of living organisms of a bovine strain which was attenuated by growth in potato-glycerin bile medium for several hundred transfers. It is claimed to be without harmful effect in calves and children and to produce an increased resistance to tuberculosis. While BCG may be a valuable aid in preventing tuberculosis in parts of the world where the disease is quite prevalent in human and bovine populations, it has never found favor in the United States.

Myers has called attention to the fact that BCG cultures of today do not meet Calmette's requirements and it is quite erroneous to have such cultures so labeled. Many of them are so virulent that tuberculous lesions are produced in lymph nodes adjacent to the point of inoculation.

The experimental results of Schroeder and Cotton; of Watson; of Haring, Traum, Hayes, and Henry; of Cotton and Crawford in cattle indicated that BCG should not be used as a possible means of controlling bovine tuberculosis in America. It is believed that the detection of infected animals, by the use of the tuberculin test, before the infection has developed to any great extent and the subsequent removal of reactors from the herd is the most satisfactory method to employ. At least this procedure has been found to be highly effective in the United States.

Mention should be made of the most recent immunizing agent advocated for tuberculosis. The vole bacillus, *Mycobacterium muris,* described by Wells in 1937, has been shown to produce resistance in guinea pigs against virulent human and bovine strains of tubercle bacilli. Subsequent experimentation with vaccine made of this organism has revealed that the resistance produced in the guinea pig is probably parallel to that produced by BCG.

Diagnosis. The diagnostic method employed for tuberculosis varies. In the packing plant the veterinarian engaged in post-mortem inspection of cattle, swine, and poultry detects the disease by the gross appearance of the lesions; in the laboratory direct smears, cultures, and animal inoculations are used; in the field the presence of the disease in the living animal is diagnosed by the tuberculin test, or in chickens by an agglutination test. Each of these methods will be discussed.

The description of the microscopic and macroscopic lesions of tuberculosis most appropriately lies in the field of pathology. It is considered expedient to give a brief review of the significant lesions of the disease here, however, in order to emphasize the importance of such lesions as an aid to diagnosis.

The unit lesion in tuberculosis is known as a *tubercle,* which may be microscopic in size or of macroscopic dimensions. The newly developing lesion is composed of tubercle bacilli intermingled with epithelioid cells. Many bacilli may be phagocytized by the epithelioid cells. As the lesion develops, necrosis of the initial concentration of epithelioid cells occurs and giant cells (concentrically arranged groups of histiocytes) appear around the area of necrosis. In the next stage the area of necrosis and the giant cell zone are surrounded by a loosely arranged zone of lymphocytes, monocytes, and fibrocytes which are supported in a newly formed reticulum of connective tissue derivation. As the central necrotic process progresses, this primary tubercle becomes larger, newly developed tubercles form in the adjacent tissue, and ultimately the tubercle is macroscopic in size. The macroscopic lesion of tuberculosis may be caseous or calcified. In some instances liquefaction necrosis results in large cavities, particularly in the lungs. In numerous cases healed lesions of long duration are evident by the presence of nodules composed of compact fibrous tissue and calcification.

With certain anatomical modifications the development of the tubercle in the avian species is the same as in mammals. The primary lesions are usually confined to the wall of the intestine from where the organism is spread to other parts of the body, forming massive lesions in the liver, spleen, bone marrow, and lungs, but not in the muscles. Lesions do not become calcified. However, lesions of tuberculosis in mammals, caused by the avian type of tubercle bacilli, do become calcified.

In mammals, tuberculosis is confined, usually, to the lymph system and the lungs in primary and localized tuberculosis. The escape of tubercle bacilli from a lesion in such tissues via the blood or lymph streams enables them to reach the general circulation, resulting in widely disseminated tuberculosis, with the formation of lesions in various parts of the body including the spleen, serous membranes, liver, kidney, mammary gland, bone marrow, ovaries, and testes. In mammals lesions of tuberculosis are rarely found in muscle and brain or in the thymus, thyroid, pancreatic or salivary glands. The presence of tubercles upon serous membranes of the thoracic and peritoneal cavities gave rise to the name *pearly disease,* because of the resemblance of the nodular lesions to pearls. In some cases of generalized tuberculosis the lesions are small and evenly distributed, resembling millet seeds, hence the term *miliary* tuberculosis.

While the presence of the previously described lesions are most suggestive of tuberculosis, other infectious agents produce caseation and calcification. Unrefuted diagnosis of tuberculosis is accomplished only by the detection of tubercle bacilli. In the laboratory this is accomplished by three procedures. *First,* smears of suspected tissue are stained with the Ziehl-Neelsen stain and examined for acid-fast bacilli. In some preparations organisms are few, so prolonged examination is often necessary. It may be necessary to treat the material with sodium hydroxide and centrifuge it so as to concentrate the bacilli before smears are made. *Second,* suitable media are inoculated in order to obtain a culture of the organism. The material to be cultured is usually treated with 3 per cent sodium hydroxide, 5 per cent oxalic acid, or 10 per cent trisodium phosphate solutions in order to kill other types of bacteria present. Cultures should be incubated at least eight weeks. *Third,* large guinea pigs (500 gms. or more) are injected subcutaneously with suspected material treated as described above. Those guinea pigs which are living at the end of eight weeks are killed, but this period may be shortened if the animal is given Old Tuberculin (0.5 ml.) subcutaneously at the end of the fourth week.

To identify the human and bovine types of tubercle bacilli, the production in the guinea pig of tuberculous lesions associated with acid-fast bacilli is essential.

If avian tuberculosis is suspected, chickens are used as the test animal.

The Tuberculin Test. In the field, the diagnosis of tuberculosis in the living animal is practically confined to the use of tuberculin. The value of this substance as a diagnostic agent has been proven by the successful eradication of tuberculosis from so many of the cattle herds of the United States that the percentage of tuberculin reactors was 0.19 in 1949. In 1918, the year marking the beginning of concerted testing of cattle, the per cent of reactors was 4.9.

Tuberculin as originally prepared by Koch is an extract of the soluble bacterial products of the bacilli which have been grown in glycerinated veal broth. After being allowed to grow for eight weeks, the bacilli are killed by streaming steam, removed from the broth by filtration, and the filtrate is evaporated to 1/10 its original volume. This represents Koch's Old Tuberculin commonly called K.O.T. This tuberculin contains proteins of the medium in addition to the proteins of the bacillus and for that reason has been objectionable as a diagnostic agent. In order to produce an extract of tubercle bacilli free from the proteins of the medium, Long and Seibert, in 1926, prepared a synthetic medium which was more satisfactory. The development of a synthetic medium for the production of tuberculin was a major project of the Biochemic Division (now a part of the Agricultural Research Service of the United States Department of Agriculture). Such a medium was developed in 1928 and was used experimentally in the production of tuberculin for a number of years. This medium (see chapter on Technics and Methods) was adopted as the official medium for tuberculin manufacture in 1934, at which time Dorset and Henley released their method of tuberculin manufacture. This method is recognized as the official A.R.S. method of preparing intradermal tuberculin which is followed by all laboratories engaged in the preparation of the product. Space does not permit the detailed description of the procedure here. It may be found in laboratory manuals devoted to detailed technics. In brief the procedure is described below:

1. The inoculated medium is incubated for eight weeks.
2. The cultures are heated in streaming steam for three hours, cooled, and filtered through fine-mesh copper gauze.
3. Glycerin is added to the filtrate 1.2 ml. for each 100 ml. of original culture medium and the mixture is evaporated to one-fifth the original volume.
4. Phenol, 0.5 per cent, is added as a preservative.
5. The tuberculin is centrifuged until perfectly clear and then filtered through a Mandler filter.
6. The finished product is tested for sterility, samples are centrifuged, and the sediment examined for the presence of dead tubercle bacilli. If any are found the tuberculin is refiltered.
7. The tuberculin is dispensed in 10 ml. vials and is ready to be used for intradermal testing.

The purification of tuberculin by precipitation with trichloracetic acid has been proposed for tuberculin testing by investigators in England. This purified protein precipitate commonly known as "Weybridge PPD" or P.P.D. has not been adopted for official testing of cattle in the United States. It is not considered to have any great advantage over the tuberculin commonly used.

Three different tuberculin tests can be used in the diagnosis of bovine tuberculosis; the *subcutaneous,* the *intradermal,* and the *ophthalmic.*

In the *subcutaneous* test, otherwise known as the thermal or temperature test, a dose equal to 0.5 gram of Koch's Old Tuberculin is injected subcutaneously. Previous to the injection, however, the temperature of the animal is taken three times at 2-hour intervals. If the temperature of the animal is normal, the tuberculin is injected. Eight hours after the injection, temperatures are again taken at 2-hour intervals through the eighteenth hour after injection. A positive reaction is noted by a rise in temperature of at least 2°F. during the interval between the eighth and eighteenth hour after injection.

In the *intradermal* test at least 0.1 ml. and not more than 0.2 ml. of tuberculin is injected into the dermal layer of the skin of the animal. In cattle the thin skin of the caudal fold or of the vulva is used. The skin of the cervical area has been found to give a more pronounced reaction but is not used in routine testing, except in a recheck of suspect reactors. A positive reaction is apparent by a small to large firm swelling at the point of injection within 72 hours. In the tuberculin test of chickens the wattle is used. A positive reaction is noted by the swelling of the wattle within 48 hours. Avian tuberculin must be used in detecting tuberculosis in chickens.

In the *ophthalmic* test, tuberculin is inserted into the conjunctival sac. Concentrated, especially prepared opthalmic tuberculin is placed into the eye with a soft camel's hair brush or with a medicine dropper. The concentrated tuberculin may be mixed with a suitable plastic substance, such as lactose, and molded into a small disc which dissolves readily in the eye. These ophthalmic-tuberculin discs are commonly used for the eye test. In the ophthalmic test, two applications of tuberculin are required. The first application is for the purpose of sensitization, for it has been shown that a more marked reaction is obtained by this procedure. The second application is given two or three days later for the purpose of diagnosis. The animal is kept under close observation for 8 hours after the installation of the diagnostic dose. A positive reaction is characterized by marked inflammation of the conjunctiva, profuse lachrymation, and by a mucopurulent exudate.

It is apparent that the intradermal tuberculin test is the most economical and practical for routine diagnosis. The other two tests are seldom used except in doubtful reactions to the intradermal test.

In 1946 Kerr, Lamont, and McGirr described a modification of the intradermal tuberculin test which they called the Stormont Test (named after the Stormont Experimental Laboratories near Belfast, Ireland). Essentially, this test consists of the injecton of 0.1 ml. P.P.D. tuberculin into the skin of the cervical region. On the seventh day the original site is reinoculated with 0.1 ml. of tuberculin. A positive reaction is based on an increase of 5 mm. or more in skin measurement between the seventh and eighth days following the "boost" injection. It is claimed that the Stormont Test detects more tuberculous animals than the routine intradermal test which consists of only one injection. This test has not come into use in the United States.

The Agglutination Test. The preparation of a suitable suspension of mammalian tubercle bacilli is a barrier which prevents the use of the agglutination test as a method of diagnosing tuberculosis in animals infected by those types of bacilli. Experimentally it has been shown that collodion particles and erythrocytes may be coated with tuberculin, thereby preparing an antigen suitable for agglutination purposes. Such a diagnostic test has not come into practical use.

In 1942 Moses, Feldman, and Mann demonstrated that a concentrated antigen may be used in a rapid agglutination test for the diagnosis of avian tuberculosis. *Mycobacterium avium* is readily miscible in salt solution so a stable suspension can be made for such a test. In 1950 Karlson, Zinober, and Feldman explored this test further and demonstrated that a whole blood, rapid agglutination test has real merits as a diagnostic test for avian tuberculosis.

Mycobacterium paratuberculosis

Synonyms and History. Johne's bacillus. *Bacillus paratuberculosis.*

During the study of a chronic dysentery of cattle in Germany, Johne and Frothingham, in 1895, demonstrated the presence of masses of acid-fast bacteria in the infected intestine. They considered these organisms were either avian tubercle bacilli or bovine tubercle bacilli which had become changed in some way so that infection in the intestinal tract was produced. In 1906 Bang, of Denmark, was the first to recognize the disease as an infection distinct from tuberculosis and to suggest the name paratuberculosis. The disease then came to the attention of investigators in England, and in 1907 McFadyean described it in some detail. The organism was first isolated in pure culture by Twort in 1910. In 1913 Twort and Ingram published a complete account of the disease.

Although primarily a bovine disease, paratuberculosis is also found in sheep, and McFadyean reported a case in a deer kept in captivity. Eveleth and Gifford have described, in their study of Johne's disease in Arkansas, that clinical cases of the disease are found only in cattle and sheep, but that swine, goats, horses, and mules may be found sensitive to the intradermal Johnin test.

Distribution and Transmission. *Myco. paratuberculosis* has been reported from most of the countries on the European continent, from the British Isles, and from neighboring islands. It is found in the United States, but the extent is not known. The disease does not spread rapidly through a herd; only a few animals show symptoms at a time. It has been observed that calves may become infected but do not show symptoms until they become adults. This chronic nature of the disease is a most outstanding characteristic and for this reason the infection is known to persist in a herd for years. Because of this, many cases probably pass unrecognized.

Johne's disease is characterized by a persistent diarrhea which may extend over a period of a year. The animal becomes progressively thin and emaciated. Lesions of the infection are confined to the ileum and the colon and in some cases extend posteriorly as far as the rectum. The intestinal mucous membrane is hyperemic and is so greatly thickened that it presents a corrugated appearance. The mesenteric lymph nodes are usually swollen and edematous. The organisms are present in the mucous membrane and, obviously, large numbers of them pass out with fecal material, thereby contaminating feed and water.

Morphology and Staining. *Mycobacterium paratuberculosis* is a short, think rod, 0.5μ in diameter by 1 to 2μ in length. In smears made from an infected intestinal mucous membrane the organism is found in clumps, although numerous single cells are scattered over the preparation (Fig. 33.5). The organism is comparable in size to the avian tubercle bacillus. It is stained with the usual acid-fast stains. Most of the cells are stained evenly, but an occasional beaded form may be seen. The organism is considered Gram-positive.

Growth Requirements and Characteristics. This bacillus is aerobic and grows best at a temperature of 39°C. It has a rather wide growth temperature range, however, since it will grow as low as 28°C. and as high as 43°C. The media which are used for the cultivation of the organism must be adjusted to pH 6.6.

An outstanding characteristic of *Myco. paratuberculosis* is the difficulty with which it is cultivated upon artificial media. Twort obtained growth only after he incorporated dead tubercle bacilli in his culture medium. Subsequently it was found that tuberculin supplied the essential growth factor and later that the extracts of saprophytic acid-fast bacteria were satisfactory. The nature of the growth factor which is needed by this organism is not known, but according to Twort and Ingram, it is found in various substances, such as grapes, figs, oats, and linseed. Johnson has described the following medium which he has found effective in producing satisfactory growth of the organism:

```
Asparagine  ..............................................  14.0 gm.
Dipotassium phosphate c.p. ...............................   1.8 gm.
Sodium citrate  ..........................................   0.9 gm.
Magnesium sulphate  ......................................   1.5 gm.
Ferric citrate  ..........................................   0.3 gm.
Dextrose  ................................................  10.0 gm.
Glycerine  ...............................................  40.0 gm.
Ground mesenteric lymph nodes of the calf ................ 100.0 gm.
Agar  ....................................................  20.0 gm.
Tap  water  to  make  ....................................1,000.0 ml.
```

On a suitable egg medium the organism produces tiny, dull-white colonies which are rarely visible in four weeks. As the culture ages, the colonies increase in size, form a central elevation, and become yellowish-white.

In glycerin broth containing extracts of *Myco. phlei,* the bacillus forms a thin pellicle which becomes thick and folded as the culture ages.

Resistance. *Myco. paratuberculosis* resembles the tubercle bacillus in resistance to heat and chemical disinfectants. Vardaman reports that cresylic compounds 1:64, phenol 1:40, sodium orthophenylphenate 1:100, alcohol 95 per cent, mercury bichloride 1:1,000, calcium hypochlorite 1:50, and methylene blue 1:500 prevent growth after 15 minutes' exposure. Lovell, Levi, and Francis have found this bacillus viable after nine months' exposure in tap water-mud suspension, 163 days in ditch water in open air, and 152–246 days in feces.

Biochemical Properties. The difficulty with which this organism is cultured artificially has retarded investigation concerning its biochemical properties. Presumably it is similar to the other acid-fast bacteria in not being able to produce changes in the various substances which are used in the study of bacteria.

Antigenic Structure and Toxins. Little is known concerning the antigenic structure of this organism. Positive reactions are obtained by the use of avian tuberculin in a large percentage of the cases of Johne's disease. This indicates an antigenic relationship with the avian tubercle bacillus. Some cases will also react to mammalian tuberculin.

Toxins are not produced by this organism.

Pathogenicity. *Myco. paratuberculosis* produces chronic bacillary dysentery in cattle and to some extent in sheep. The disease can be produced artificially in the bovine by injecting the organism intravenously, subcutaneously, or intraperitoneally.

Mohler has observed that guinea pigs, rabbits, mice, rats, chickens, and pigeons could be infected with the organism when it was thoroughly suspended in paraffin oil. Guinea pigs which had been given 2 ml. of inoculum intraperitoneally died in seven to thirty-two days. Mice were considered quite susceptible, dying in nine to twenty-four days after inoculation. Chickens had developed pin-point lesions on the liver and spleen when killed five months after inoculation. They were sensitive to Johnin which was injected in the wattle but not to avian tuberculin. Extensive lesions containing numerous acid-fast bacteria were found in the peritoneal cavity of pigeons killed 134 days after inoculation with 2 ml. of the suspended bacilli. In 1940 Olikaeva of Russia demonstrated that rabbits may be infected. In his experiments, groups of rabbits were inoculated intravenously and per os with 70-day-old cultures of *Myco. paratuberculosis.* Previous to injection they were fasted or given injections of bovine bile to reduce resistance. Twelve months after inoculation lesions were found in all groups of rabbits. These lesions consisted of multiple abscesses in the region of joints and the pleura. Hypertrophy and hyperemia of the parenchymatous organs were noted. Gastrointestinal lesions were rare. Cultures of the organism were obtained from the kidneys, liver, heart, and spleen of infected rabbits. Verlinde and Bekker have shown that the injection of a 5 mg. dose of living bacilli into a 40 gm. guinea pig subcutaneously, in the thigh, may produce tubercle-like lesions in the inguinal lymph nodes, the liver, the spleen, and the lungs. In some animals so inoculated, peritonitis accompanied by ascites was observed. None of the animals had lesions suggestive of Johne's disease in the intestinal tract.

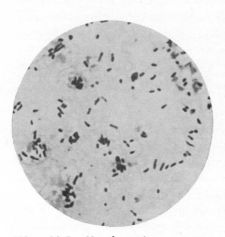

FIG. 33.5 — **Mycobacterium paratuberculosis,** smear of mucous membrane, × 2,000. (From Nowak: Documenta Microbiologica, courtesy Gustav Fischer.)

Immunity. The chronic nature of paratuberculosis indicates that any immunity which is formed by the disease is not significant. Very few animals ever recover from the infection; however, some reports of apparent recovery have been made.

Artificial immunizing agents for this disease are not in common use. French investigators have reported some resistance was produced in cattle, following the injection of organisms suspended in pumice and oil. This procedure is also used in England in certain problem herds, according to Doyle. Hagan in New York considered this type of vaccine worthy of more experimentation. Larsen, in 1950, reported on the use of a vaccine composed of moist living *Myco. paratuberculosis,* powdered pumice, mineral oil, and peanut oil. Calves were vaccinated at two weeks of age and challenged at 2 months of age by drenching with intestinal scrapings of an animal which had died of paratuberculosis. In this experiment 3 of the 7 vaccinated animals died of the disease. Animals which survived were positive to the Johnin test.

Inasmuch as the disease is not prevalent, the best method of control consists of testing all animals in problem herds, followed by the removal of all reacting animals.

Diagnosis. Paratuberculosis can be diagnosed by making smears from the intestinal mucosa. In the live animal a positive diagnosis may be obtained by pinching out a small piece of the rectum, washing the piece thoroughly with sterile saline solution, and then mashing it thoroughly between two slides. The smears thus made are stained with an acid-fast stain. This method is dependable only in cases in which lesions are present in the rectum. A possible source of error is the presence of saprophytic acid-fast bacilli in the feces.

Previous mention has been made of the positive reaction which may be obtained to the injection of avian tuberculin. In the use of tuberculin for this disease intravenous injection is made and a positive reaction is indicated by restlessness, shivering, diarrhea, and pyrexia. The temperature usually reaches its peak 4 to 8 hours after the injection of the tuberculin.

An extract of the bacillus called Johnin was produced in England and has been used to a limited extent in the United States as an intravenous temperature test, employing the same technic as was used with avian tuberculin. The production of intradermal Johnin was reported by Johnson and Cox in 1944, and since that time the intradermal test has become an accepted method for the diagnosis of paratuberculosis in cattle. A more specific intradermal Johnin, purified protein derivative (PPD), has been prepared by Larsen, Baisden, and Merkal by the precipitation of *Myco. paratuberculosis* culture filtrate with trichloroacetic acid.

Johnson observed that the skin of the neck region was more sensitive to Johnin than the caudal fold. This fact has been confirmed by numerous investigators; consequently, the intradermal test is applied in that region.

In applying the test, 0.2 ml. of intradermal Johnin is injected into the skin of a clipped area on the neck. After forty-eight hours the test is read. A positive reaction consists of a skin thickness of 3 mm.; a thickness of 3 to 2 mm. is considered suspicious; and under 2 mm. is negative. An injection of Johnin desensitizes the skin at that site so subsequent tests must be applied at other sites.

In a series of reports beginning in 1945 Sigurdsson and associates of Iceland have described an antigen, which is precipitated by ammonium sulfate and trichloracetic acid, which they isolated from the intestinal wall of sheep infected with Johne's disease. By using this antigen in the complement-fixation test, they found it of value in diagnosing the disease in sheep.

Mycobacterium leprae

Mycobacterium leprae is one of the important acid-fast organisms of significance to human health. This organism is considered to be the cause of leprosy, one of the diseases mentioned in the earliest history of mankind. Leprosy is a generalized disease of man which affects principally the skin and peripheral nerve trunks.

It is an exceedingly chronic disease having an incubation period as long as 20 years. As far as is known, it is transmitted only by close contact. However, with due caution physicians and nurses work among leprous patients for years without contracting the infection. The disease is still quite prevalent throughout the world. This infection is found in the United States where it is most prevalent in the Gulf states and California.

Myco. leprae was first observed by Hansen in 1874, and this discovery was definitely supported by Neisser in 1879. The morphological and acid-fast staining characteristics of the organism were not discovered, however, until after Koch had published his work on the tubercle bacillus. *Myco. leprae* is a small, slender organism, 0.3 to 0.5μ thick and 1 to 7μ long. It is often curved, and many cells present a beaded appearance. Like many acid-fast bacilli, this organism occurs in clumps and packets in the infected tissue. This organism is notoriously difficult to cultivate on artificial medium, and there is considerable doubt whether or not the organism has even been successfully cultivated. Although acid-fast bacilli have been cultured from leprosy lesions such cultures are probably saprophytes from the skin. No reaction is obtained with the sera of leprosy patients with cultures claimed to be *Myco. leprae*. Of much interest, however, is the fact that a high percentage (40 to 50 per cent) of leprosy patients give false positive serologic reactions for syphilis.

Leprosy is commonly diagnosed by the symptoms and lesions found in the patient. Of much importance in establishing the diagnosis definitely is the demonstration of acid-fast bacillary forms from tissue scrapings from the lobes of the ears or the alae nasi. Less dependable is the finding of acid-fast bacilli in smears from the nasal mucosa. Allergy tests have been extensively investigated, but at present none is specific for the disease. The complement-fixation test is also used, but this, too, is not considered specific enough for accurate diagnosis.

During recent years 4, 4′–diaminodiphenylsulfone and certain derivatives of this compound have been found to be quite effective against leprosy and their use is gradually being extended throughout the areas of the world where leprosy exists. The disease is best controlled by the separation of children from leprous parents and by the isolation of patients in leprosy colonies where modern treatment is often followed by marked resolution of the visible lesions and definite arrestment of the disease.

Mycobacterium lepraemurium

In 1901 Stefansky, in Odessa, observed a disease in rats which showed many lesions similar to human leprosy and which was caused by an acid-fast bacillus. The disease has been found in rats in London, Berlin, and in New South Wales. In the United States the disease has been reported from San Francisco by Wherry and by McCoy. Rat leprosy is characterized by swelling of lymph nodes, subcutaneous swelling and induration with ulceration, by falling of the hair, and by emaciation during the later stages of the disease. The condition is exceedingly chronic, extending as long as one year in some cases. Upon post-mortem examination the swollen lymph nodes are not suppurative. Increased numbers of epithelioid cells are present, among which the bacilli are found in large numbers. Subcutaneous swellings are similar to adipose tissue in appearance, but are also composed of epithelioid cells among which the bacilli are found. Nodules may be found in the liver and lungs.

The rat leprosy bacillus, to which the name *Mycobacterium lepraemurium* has been given, is 3 to 5μ long and is slender and curved. It is Gram-positive and is decidedly acid-fast. Numerous beaded or granular cells are observed in a tissue smear. The organism has not been cultivated artificially upon nonliving media. Zinsser and Carey report successful growth of the organism upon living rat spleen cells contained in plasma. The disease can be produced experimentally, often with difficulty, in rats by the injection of leprous tissue. Linhares has found that lice found on rats dying of leprosy were infected with acid-fast bacilli, but these could not be cultured on Lowenstein medium. Rats could be infected per os with a suspension of infected tissue, and both chicks and pigeons could be infected in inoculation in the chest muscle. Intraperitoneal and gastro-intestinal routes were successful in chicks but not in pigeons, which were infected by intravenous inoculation. In fowls, ducks, chicks, and pigeons the lesions were severe but were not as disseminated and numerous as in rats.

This disease has no etiological relationship with human leprosy.

Mycobacterium muris

In 1937, Wells reported the presence of lesions resembling those of tuberculosis in the vole, in England. An acid-fast bacillus was isolated from such lesions and the common name "the vole bacillus" was given to it. In an extensive report on the murine type of tubercle bacillus, in 1946, Wells pointed out the specific nature of the organism, leaving no doubt that a new organism had been discovered. On that basis it is quite appropriate to use the name *Mycobacterium muris*.

In the 1946 report Wells noted that the disease had been identified in more than 900 small animals in four different species, the wild vole (*Microtus agrestis*), the bank vole (*Clethrionomys glareolus*), the wood mouse (*Apodemus sylvaticus*), and the shrew (*Sorex araneus*). The disease had been observed in nineteen places in Great Britain.

Mycobacterium muris in infected lesions is an extremely pleomorphic rod ranging from 1 to 5μ in length and 0.5 to 0.6μ in width. No branching forms have been described. On culture media the organism is less pleomorphic and is shorter and thicker. It is nonmotile, noncapsulated and nonsporeforming. This bacillus is markedly acid-fast, resisting decolorization in 25 per cent H_2SO_4 for 24 hours. The typical beading of tubercle bacilli is observed in this organism in smears made from natural lesions and from artificial cultures.

Growth of *Myco. muris* is obtained on the types of media used for the cultivation of tubercle bacilli. Glycerin, 5 per cent or more, inhibits growth of the organism so it resembles the bovine type of the tubercle bacillus in that respect. The organism is difficult to grow on fluid media, forming a thin, unpigmented pellicle. Two types of colonies are formed on solid media. One is a round, smooth, white colony with an entire edge which becomes wartlike with a crateriform center. The other is irregular in shape with a fluted edge. This bacillus is killed by 60°C. in 20 minutes, 0.5 per cent phenol in 24 hours; by 5 per cent acetic acid. It is resistant to 6 per cent sulphuric acid, 5 per cent oxalic acid, and 3 per cent sodium hydroxide.

The appearance of the natural disease is typical of tuberculosis showing the presence of epithelioid cells, giant cells, caseation necrosis, and calcification. The majority of the lesions observed in captured animals are confined to the lymph nodes but the skin and subcutaneous tissue, the lungs, spleen, liver, suprarenal, and kidney are also affected. According to Robb-Smith scattered necrotic foci, rich in organisms, are found in the myocardium and there are also epicardial cellular foci in which concentric bodies are present. Artificial infection may be produced in the rabbit, guinea pig, white mouse, white rat, golden hamster, Orkney vole, Continental vole, wood mouse, and bank vole. Limited experimentation has shown that the vole bacillus is able to incite in susceptible animals a positive infection of a chronic nature which tends to disappear without leaving significant traces. It is not possible to separate the vole bacillus from the human and bovine types of tubercle bacilli by serological tests. Animals infected with the vole bacillus show a sensitivity to human and bovine tuberculin. Conversely, animals infected with the human or bovine tubercle bacillus are sensitive to tuberculin prepared from the vole bacillus. No significant antigenic relationships exist between this organism and the avian tubercle bacillus.

Previous mention has been made of the use of the vole bacillus as an immunizing agent against tuberculosis in guinea pigs, cattle, and man. Wells (1949) has concluded that there is evidence that the vole bacillus produces resistance to tuberculosis in man. It has also been shown that in the early stages of virulent infection in guinea pigs, vaccination with the vole bacillus leads to a greater retardation of the disease than does BCG; in the later stages, the degree of resistance is approximately equal. In cattle, the vole bacillus may confer more resistance that BCG.

Other Acid-fast Bacilli

In addition to the acid-fast bacilli which were listed at the beginning of the chapter as saprophytes, there have been others isolated from animal tissues. Their significance in the tissues from which they have been isolated is not known, but they do not appear to cause marked tissue destruction.

In 1930 Hastings, Beach, and Thompson reported saprophytic acid-fast bacilli from cattle that gave a positive tuberculin test. These animals did not show macroscopic lesions of tuberculosis upon post-mortem examinations, and these investigators concluded that the positive tuberculin reaction may have been due to the saprophytic bacteria. This assumption was shown to be improbable by Hagan, however, in 1931. Sensitization to tuberculin is considered to be possible only by specific tubercle bacilli.

Acid-fast bacilli have been found in skin lesions of cattle. Daines and Austin have shown that these bacilli are similar to tubercle bacilli but do not produce lesions in experimental animals. The exact identity of these bacilli is not known. They are often found in association with *Corynebacterium pseudotuberculosis*, and it may be possible for them to be acid-fast dissociants of that organism.

A saproyhytic acid-fast bacillus added to this group is an organism described by Karlson and Feldman in 1940. This bacillus was quite consistently isolated from swine tonsilar tissue. It resembles the avian bacillus in morphology and in many culture characteristics. Moreover, it sensitizes guinea pigs to avian tuberculin and gives a positive cross-agglutination reaction with avian tubercle bacilli. The bacillus is not pathogenic to chickens, mice, or calves and produces only a localized focal necrosis upon subcutaneous inoculation into guinea pigs and rabbits. In relationship to swine, infection is not known.

In 1948 a mycobacterium previously unrecorded was found by MacCallum *et al.* in ulcerated lesions of the skin in cases of human beings in a rural area of Australia. The organism was strongly acid-fast and the optimal temperature for artificial growth was 33°C.

It has been named *Myco. ulcerans*. In addition to man this bacillus was found to be pathogenic for rats and mice but not for guinea pigs. The nutritive requirements were comparable to those necessary for growing tubercle bacilli successfully.

REFERENCES FOR FURTHER STUDY

Anderson, W., Jansen, M. G. W., and Wicks, C. A. Can. Med. Assn. Jour., 62:231, 1950.

Anon. *Mycobacterium tuberculosis*, Isolation, Identification, and Sensitivity Testing. Difco Laboratories, Detroit, Michigan, Dec., 1954.

Baisden, L. A. Amer. Jour. Vet. Res., 12:254, 1951.

Block, H. Jour. Exp. Med., 91:197, 1950.

Brieger, E. M., and Fell, H. B. Jour. Hyg. Comb., 44:256, 1945–46.

Calmette, A. Tubercle Bacillus and Tuberculosis in Man and Animals. English translation by W. B. Soper and G. H. Smith. The Williams & Wilkins Co., Baltimore, 1923.

Corper, H. J., and Stoner, R. E. Jour. Lab. Clin. Med., 31:1364, 1946.

Cotton, W. E., and Crawford, A. B. Jour. Amer. Vet. Med. Assn., 80:18, 1932.

Council on Pharmacy and Chemistry. Current Status of the Chemotherapy of Tuberculosis in Man. Jour. Amer. Med. Assn., 142:650, 1950.

Daines, L. L. Amer. Assn. Adv. Sci., 66–68, 1938.

Dunner, E., Brown, W. B., and Wallace, Jour. Dis. Chest., 16:661, 1949.

Editorial. Immunization with the vole bacillus. Vet. Rec., 58:463, 1946.

Eveleth, D. F., and Gifford, Rebecca. Jour. Amer. Vet. Med. Assn., 102:27–34, 1943.

Feldman, W. H. Animal Tuberculosis and Its Relationship to the Disease in Man. Ann. New York Acad. Sciences. 48:469, 1947.

———. Avian Tuberculosis Infections. The Williams & Wilkins Co., Baltimore, 1938.

———, Hutchinson, D. W., Schwarting, V. M., and Karlson, A. G. Juvenile Tuberculosis Infection, Possibly of Avian Type. Amer. Jour. Path., 25:1183, 1949.

———, and Karlson, A. G., The Importance of the Isolation and Identification of Tubercle Bacilli. The Journal—Lancet, 67:239, 1947.

———, ———. Streptomycin in Experimental Tuberculosis. Chap. 9 in Waksman, S., Streptomycin, Nature and Practical Applications. The Williams and Wilkins Co., Baltimore, 1949.

Fincher, M. G., Evans, W. M., and Saunders, L. Z. Cornell Vet., 44:240, 1954.

Gay, F. P., and associates. Agents of Disease and Host Resistance. Charles C. Thomas, Baltimore, 1935.

Gervais, M. Le Bacille de Type Bovin dans la Tuberculose Humaine. L. Daniel, Lille, 1937.

Glover, R. E. Jour. Path. Bact., 58:107, 1946.

Hagan, W. A. The No-lesion Case Problem in the Tuberculosis Eradication Campaign. Cornell Vet., 21:163–76, 1931.

———. Cornell Vet., 25:345, 1955.

Haring, C. M., Traum, J., Hayes, F. M., and Henry, B. S. Vaccination of calves against tuberculosis with Calmette-Guerin Culture (B.C.G.) Hilgardia, 4:307, 1930.

Hillermark, K. Skund. Vet. Tidskr., 35:545, 1945.

Johnson, H. W. Studies on Johnin. Amer. Jour. Vet. Res., 5:320–28, 1944.

———, and Cox, B. F. Studies on Johnin. Amer. Jour. Vet. Res., 3:131–38, 1942.

Karlson, A. G., Delande, A., Carr, D. T., Pfuetze, K. H., and Feldman, W. H. Dis. Chest., 16:667, 1949.

———, and Feldman, W. H. Studies on an Acid-fast Bacterium Frequently Present in Tonsillar Tissue of Swine. Jour. Bact., 39:461–72, 1940.

———, Pfuetze, K. H., Carr, D. T., Feldman, W. H., and Hinshaw, H. C. Proc. Staff Meet., Mayo Clin., 24:85–88 1949.

———, Zinober, M. R., and Feldman, W. H. Amer. Jour. Vet. Res., 11:137, 1950.

Kerr, W. R., Lamont, H. G., McGirr, J. L. Studies on Tuberculin Sensitivity in the Bovine. Vet. Rec., 58:443, 451, 1946.

Koch, R. Die Etiologie der Tuberculose. Berl. klin. Wochenschr., 19:221, 1882.

Larsen, A. B. Proc. Book 87th Ann. Conv. A.V.M.A., 1950.

———, Baisden, L. A., and Merkal, R. S. Amer. Jour. Vet. Res., 16:35, 1955.

———, Groth, A. H., and Johnson, H. W. Amer. Jour. Vet. Res., 11:301, 1950.

Lehmann, J. Dis. Chest., 16:684, 1949.

Linhares, H. Transmissibility and inoculation routes of rat leprosy in rats and other animals. Mem. Inst. Asw. Cruz., 38:321, 1943.

Lourie, Max B. Immunology of Tuberculosis. The Cyclopedia of Medicine Surgery Specialties. F. A. Davis Co., Philadelphia, 1945.

Lovell, R., Levi, M., and Francis, J. Jour. Comp. Path., 54:120–29, 1944.

MacCullum, P., Tolhurst, J. C., Buckle, G., and Sissons, H. A. Jour. Path. and Bact., 60:93–122, 1948.

Mohler, W. H. Jour. Amer. Vet. Med. Assn., 94:590, 1939.

Moses, H. E., Feldman, W. F., and Mann, F. C. Amer. Jour. Vet. Res., 4:390–95, 1942.

Moulton, F. R., Editor. Tuberculosis and Leprosy. The Mycobacterial Diseases. Symposium Series, Vol. I, Amer. Assn. Adv. Sci., Science Press Printing Co., Lancaster, Pa., 1938.

Myers, J. Arthur. Invited and Conquered. Historical Sketch of Tuberculosis in Minnesota. Webb Pub. Co., St. Paul, 1949.

———. The Ever Continuing Search for Immunity in Tuberculosis. Postgrad. Med., 12:1–55, 1952.

Olikaeva, A. P. Experimental Johne's Disease in Rabbits. Veterinariya, Moscow, 2:26–32, 1940.

Pfuetze, K. H. Chair. Report of Committee on Chemotherapy and Antibiotics. Dis. Chest., 16:904, 1949.

Priestly, F. W. The Stormont Tuberculin Test: A Statistical Analysis. Vet. Rec., 58:455, 1946.

Pyle, M. M. Proc. Staff Meet., Mayo Clin., 22:465–73, 1947.

Raleigh, G. W., and Youmans, G. P. Jour. Inf. Dis., 82:197–204, 1948.

Rich, A. R. The Pathogenesis of Tuberculosis. Charles C. Thomas, Springfield, 1944.

Robb-Smith, A. H. T. Notes on the Morphology of Infection by the Vole Acid-fast Bacillus. Med. Res. Council Sp. Rpt. Ser. 259. His Majesty's Stationery Office, London, 1946.

Schroeder, E. C., and Crawford, A. B. Jour. Amer. Vet. Med. Assn. 74:773, 1929.

Schwalbe, J. Gesammelte Werke von Robert Koch. George Thieme, Leipzig, 1912.

Sigurdsson, B. Jour. Immunol., 51:279, 1945.

———. Jour. Immunol., 53:127, 1946.

———. Jour. Immunol., 55:131, 1947.

———. Jour. Immunol., 57:11, 1947.

———, Vigfusson, H., and Theodors, S. Jour. Comp. Path., 55:268, 1945.

Sikes, D. Amer. Jour. Vet. Res., 14:12, 1953.

———, and Groth, A. H. Amer. Jour. Vet. Res., 11:181, 1950.

———, Johnson, H. W., and Oglesby, W. T. Amer. Jour. Vet. Res., 12:302, 1951.

Smith, C. R. Public Hlth. Rpt., Wash., 62:1285, 1947.

Sweany, H. C., Turner, G. C., Lichtenstein, M., and Entin, S. Dis. Chest., 16:633, 1949.

Steele, J. H. The Present Status of Bovine Type Human Tuberculosis in the United States, p. 207. Proc. 58 Ann. Mtg. U. S. Livestock Sanitary Assn., 1954.

Thuringer, J. M., Butler H. W., and Wilber, Gertrude H. The Life Cycle of Mycobacterium Tuberculosis. University of Oklahoma Medical School, Oklahoma City, 1937.

Topley, W. W. C., and Wilson, G. S. Principles of Bacteriology and Immunity. 2nd Ed. The Williams & Wilkins Co., Baltimore, 1936.

Twort, E. W., and Ingram, G. L. Johne's Disease. Bailliére, Tindall and Cox, London, 1913.

Van Vranken, M. Amer. Rev. Tuberc., 55:374, 1947.

Vardaman, T. H. Amer. Jour. Vet. Res., 15:159, 1954.

Verge, J. Rev. Path. Comp., 44:65, 1944.

Verlinde, J. D., and Bekker, J. H. Tijdschr. Diergeneesk, 70:329, 1945.

Watson, E. A. Bovine Tuberculosis and B.C.G. Vaccination. 12th Internat. Vet. Cong. N. Y., U.S.A. 1934. Vol. II, p. 2. United States Printing Office, Washington, 1935.

Wells, A. Q. Lancet, May 22, 1:1221, 1937.

———. The murine type of tubercle bacillus. Med. Rec. Counc. Spec. Rpt. Series No. 259, His Majesty's Stationery Office, London, 1946.

———. Lancet, July 9, p. 53, 1949.

Yegian, Diran, and Boisden, L. Factors Affecting the Beading of the Tubercle Bacillus Stained by the Ziehl-Neelsen Technique. Jour. Bact., 44:667–72, 1942.

Yersin, A. Étude sur le développement du tubercule expérimental. Ann. de l' Inst. Pasteur, 2:245, 1888.

Youmans, G. P. The effect of para-aminoxalicylic acid in vitro and in vivo on virulent human type tubercle bacilli. Quart Bull. North. Univ. Med. School, 20:420, 1946.

———, Raleigh, G. W., and Youmans, Anne S. Jour. Bact., 54:409, 1947.

———, ———. Jour. Inf. Dis., 82:221–25, 1948.

34. The Genus Erysipelothrix *

Bacilli classified in the genus Erysipelothrix are slender rods, which may be curved or straight, and which show a marked tendency to form elongated filaments with only slight tendency toward branching. They are nonmotile, nonsporeforming, and do not form capsules. The organisms are Gram-positive and, when stained by Gram's method, many of the elongated filaments show granulation. They are micro-aerophilic and are not active biochemically under artificial conditions. These organisms are variable in size and shape, so for that reason they are classified in the family Corynebacteriaceae.

Within the last three decades the microorganism of this genus has become recognized as important to animal health in America. Previously, swine erysipelas was not thought to be of significance in the United States. It is now known, however, that the disease is widespread and constitutes a serious menace to the swine-raising industry; reports of its occurrence are increasing in the American literature. In addition to swine, *Erysipelothrix rhusiopathiae* has been isolated in cases of arthritis of lambs in the western sheep-raising areas. Infection in turkeys results in serious losses. Many cases of infection in man are reported in the literature of this country.

Topley and Wilson consider that *Listeria monocytogenes* and *Erysipelothrix rhusiopathiae* are sufficiently similar to warrant placing them in the same genus. These authors discuss the former under the name *Erysipelothrix monocytogenes*. However, Barber and also Julianelle have compared strains of these two microorganisms and have properly concluded that serologically they are separate and distinct, and that there are more cultural and metabolic differences than there are similarities. These latter workers agree that there is insufficient reason to place them in the same genus.

* The author is indebted to Alfred G. Karlson, Division of Experimental Medicine, Mayo Foundation, Rochester, Minnesota, for the original preparation and revision of this chapter.

The three species of this genus described in Bergey's Manual of Determinative Bacteriology, Ed. 1948, that is, *Erysipelothrix rhusiopathiae*, *Erysipelothrix muriseptica*, and *Erysipelothrix erysipeloides*, are generally considered to be identical. It is not possible to distinguish by bacteriologic or serologic procedures the strains isolated from such varied sources as swine, mice, rats, turkeys, sheep, fish, the soil, and from cases of erysipeloid in man. In this chapter they will be considered as a single species, *Erysipelothrix rhusiopathiae*.

Erysipelothrix rhusiopathiae

Synonyms and History. *Bacillus rhusiopathiae suis, Bacterium erysipelatos suum, Bacterium rhusiopathiae, Erysipelothrix porci.* The names *Bacterium murisepticus* and *Erysipelothrix murisepticus* were formerly used to designate the species when isolated from mice. The name *Erysipelothrix erysipeloides* was given to the microorganism when isolated from man.

In 1876 Robert Koch described a "mouse septicemia bacillus" obtained from mice which had been injected with putrid meat. No relationship to swine disease was then known for this bacillus. In 1882 Pasteur described a slender, curved rod which he isolated from swine showing symptoms of swine erysipelas. Vaccines made from this microorganism protected swine against natural infection, but from the descriptions of the bacillus it is assumed that Pasteur worked with impure cultures. Credit for the first accurate description of the swine erysipelas microorganism is given to Loeffler. In 1885 and 1886 he published the results of his work which demonstrated that the disease in swine is caused by a bacillus identical to, or closely resembling, the mouse septicemia bacillus of Koch. Loeffler repeatedly emphasized the similarity bewteen the two.

In 1909 Rosenback described a bacillus obtained in a case of erysipeloid of man as being almost identical to the one isolated by Koch from mice. On the basis of his studies on the causes of swine erysipelas, mouse septicemia, and erysipeloid in man, Rosenback concluded that there were three closely related species, *Erysipelothrix porci, Erysipelothrix murisepticus,* and *Erysipelothrix erysipeloides.* Studies that have since been made on the relationships of the microorganisms isolated from the above sources show that the strains are identical.

The history of swine erysipelas and of infections due to this microorganism in other animals in the United States is of some interest because, prior to 1930, it had been stated by many writers that the disease did not exist in America. In retrospect, however, it is likely that infections due to *Erysipelothrix rhusiopathiae* were not uncommon but were not recognized. As a matter of fact, in 1885, Smith reported the isolation from a sick pig of microorganisms which he said closely resembled the bacillus of swine erysipelas. In Minnesota, in 1894, there occurred a serious outbreak of a swine disease with mortality of 60 to 100 per cent, from which the swine erysipelas microorganism was isolated by Smith. There are at least five other reports of the occurrence of infections, due to microorganisms, we now call *Erysipelothrix rhusiopathiae,* in the United States prior to 1930.

Distribution and Transmission. Swine erysipelas and infections due to *Erysipelothrix rhusiopathiae* in other animals are known to occur in many parts of the world. In Europe the infection in swine appears in epizootic proportions in certain countries from spring until early fall, and sporadic outbreaks are observed during the colder months of the year. The disease has been reported from North Africa, China, and Japan. In Australia and New Zealand, as well as in America, polyarthritis in sheep due to *Erysipelothrix rhusiopathiae* is of some economic importance. The microorganism has been isolated from various species of fowl in Europe and, especially in America, it is known to cause serious losses among turkeys.

In North America the disease in swine is most commonly seen in the late summer months but the chronic forms of swine erysipelas have been recognized throughout the entire year. The infection in turkeys is most frequently seen in the late fall or early winter.

Natural infection in swine and perhaps in other animals occurs commonly via the alimentary tract. Soil, food, and water are readily contaminated by sick animals because the feces and urine contain the microorganism. Soil, which may retain viable and virulent microorganisms, serves as an excellent medium for conveying the infection to the animal body by way of the digestive tract. Surface waters may also be incriminated in transmitting the disease from one farm to another. *Erysipelothrix rhusiopathiae* has been isolated from fish meal used in the preparation of animal foods which are, therefore, potential sources of infection. Swine with subclinical infection and those that have the chronic form of swine erysipelas may live for a long time and be a constant source of infection. The role in the transmission of the disease, played by healthy animals which harbor *Erysipelothirx rhusiopathiae* in their tissues, has not been clarified but it has been repeatedly demonstrated that the microorganism can be isolated from swine that have no demonstrable disease.

Infections in man are largely limited to packing plant workers and others who handle animal products. The ubiquity of *Erysipelothrix rhusiopathiae* is demonstrated by the number of cases of erysipeloid among those who handle fish. In man, the disease is largely limited to the hands and arms where the microorganism has gained entrance via wounds. There are, however, several instances where the infection could be traced to the ingestion of pork. Of particular interest is the report that a group of veterinary students became infected with *Erysipelothrix rhusiopathiae* as the

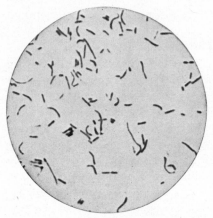

result of dissecting an improperly embalmed horse in an anatomy laboratory.

Morphology and Staining. *Erysipelothrix rhusiopathiae* is variable in form. In smears from blood and tissue it appears as a short, slender, straight or bent rod, 1 to 2 microns in length; it often appears in pairs or groups (Fig. 34.1). On culture media a mixture of short rods and elongated, thickened filaments, measuring 5 to 20 microns, may be found. In liquid media the filamentous forms of some cultures are bent and twisted

FIG. 34.1 — **Erysipelothrix rhusiopathiae,** agar culture, × 2,000. (From Nowak: Documenta Microbiologica, courtesy Gustav Fischer.)

into a mass resembling a mycelium. In young, actively growing cultures, pairs of rods often form an angle as though they had snapped off during fission. Branching is not common but has been observed. As has been noted, the microorganism is nonmotile and does not produce spores or capsules. Some investigators have demonstrated a waxlike covering. The microorganism stains well with ordinary dyes and is Gram-positive. Old cultures are easily decolorized by acetone alcohol. The thickened, elongated filaments are characteristically beaded when stained with Gram's stain. The organism has no metachromatic granules and is not acid-fast.

Growth Requirements and Characteristics. *Erysipelothrix rhusiopathiae* grows sparingly on ordinary culture media. The addition of serum to nutrient broth or agar enhances the growth. The presence of the amino acid, tryptophane, favors rapid and abundant development on solid or liquid media. It is micro-aerophilic, as shown by the tendency of recently isolated cultures to grow beneath the surface of solid media although older cultures grow well under atmospheric conditions. Growth occurs well at room temperature, as well as at 37°C. The optimal reaction of media is pH 7.4.

Two types of colonies are formed. The short rods, the so-called "S" or smooth types, form small, round, discrete, translucent colonies with entire edges, seldom more than 1 mm. in diameter. The elongated filamentous forms are found in colonies that are opaque, have uneven surfaces and edges, and tend to become confluent. They may measure 2 to 4 mm. in diameter. These large, irregular colonies are referred to as the "R" or rough forms. In broth the short rods, or the "smooth" type of the microorganism, form a uniform turbidity with no pellicle and very little sediment. The elongated, or "rough" type, produce a heavy, turbid growth with sediment in broth. In gelatin stabs the growth radiates from the line of inoculation to form a characteristic test-tube brush appearance.

Resistance. *Erysipelothrix rhusiopathiae* is remarkably resistant for a nonsporeforming microorganism. It resists drying at room temperature for several months. When kept moist, cultures will remain alive for six months or more. A broth culture has been reported to be viable and able to kill mice after standing for seventeen years. Exposure to sunlight destroys the organism in twelve to fourteen days. It is readily destroyed by boiling. A temperature of 70°C. kills the microorganisms in five to ten minutes, but the fact that they remain alive in smoked or pickled meat for several months is important. Pieces of pork 6 inches thick require cooking for two and a half hours to destroy the bacillus in the tissues. It has been found alive in cadavers seven months after death. In alkaline soil, which may be a source of infection, the organism lives and multiplies during the warmer months.

Certain strains have been found to survive, and even multiply, in concentrations of phenol that are destructive to many other microorganisms. Bichloride of mercury 1:100, formalin 2 per cent, cresol compound 3.5 per cent, and phenol 5 per cent will destroy the organism in five to fifteen minutes. The various sulfonamide preparations appear not to be effective in vivo against *Erysipelothrix rhusiopathiae.* The microorganisms are sensitive to penicillin and to streptomycin.

Biochemical Properties. *Erysipelothrix rhusiopathiae* is not active in producing changes on the differential media in common use. It does not form indol; does not reduce nitrates; is negative to the Voges-Proskauer, the methyl red, the methylene blue reduction, and the catalase tests; and does not hydrolyze esculin. The production of H_2S by this organism depends upon the type of medium under which it is cultured. No detectable H_2S is produced in some media, but when the culture is grown upon a medium containing lead acetate and serum, H_2S is apparent after four days' incubation. It forms acid but no gas from glucose, galatose, fructose, and lactose and produces a delayed reaction in mannose and cellobiose.

There is no surface growth or liquefaction of gelatin. Litmus milk may show a slight acid reaction, but there is usually no change. A narrow green zone of hemolysis occurs around deep colonies in blood agar.

Antigenic Structure. The results of cross-agglutination tests using unabsorbed serum indicate that all strains of *Erysipelothrix rhusiopathiae* have at least one common antigen. However, it has been possible to separate by cross-agglutination certain strains of the microorganisms into several serologic groups, depending on the quantitative differences in the amounts of the common factor or factors. Furthermore, by agglutinin-absorption procedures it can be demonstrated that there are separate serologic types of *Erysipelothrix rhusiopathiae* which may be due either to type-specific antigens or to quantitative differences in the antigens common to all. There appears to be no correlation between serologic differences and the source of the culture.

Pathogenicity. In Europe it is reported that the finer breeds of swine are more susceptible to infection than the coarse, more rugged breeds. In North America apparently all breeds are equally susceptible. Pigs from the age of three to eighteen months are more readily infected with the swine erysipelas bacillus, but the resistance shown by the very young is only a relative one, and many outbreaks of the disease among suckling pigs have been reported.

Swine erysipelas presents itself in three recognizable forms: the acute or septicemia type, the chronic form with endocarditis and arthritis, and the skin form or "diamond skin disease" which may be followed by gangrenous dermatitis.

The *acute* form is characterized by its sudden onset, high temperature, rapid course, and high mortality which varies from 25 to 75 per cent. Areas of hemorrhage may appear on the ventral portions of the animal which become dark red as the disease progresses. Accompanying symptoms are loss of appetite, general depression, and often discharge from the eyes. Post-mortem examination reveals hemorrhagic gastro-enteritis and marked enlargement of the spleen which has become dark red. The lymph nodes are swollen and hemorrhagic. Petechial hemorrhages may be found on the serous surfaces of the organs. The lungs are usually congested and edematous. If the course of the disease is prolonged, the organs and fat become icteric and this manifestation is accompanied by perirenal edema.

The *chronic* form of swine erysipelas is characterized by vegetative endocarditis of the heart valves, particularly the mitral.

This may also be accompanied by chronic arthritis, in which the joints of the limbs become enlarged, giving the swine a characteristic stilted walk. The arthritis occurs without the heart lesions in many instances. Chronic swine erysipelas is not often fatal, but the affected animals do not gain weight rapidly.

The *urticarial* form of swine erysipelas, called "diamond skin disease," is a mild infection characterized by the development on the skin of well-defined, diamond-shaped spots 1 to 5 cm. in diameter; these appear on the back and sides of the animal as dark red or purple areas which become raised. Extensive gangrene, with subsequent sloughing of the skin, often follows the "diamond skin disease."

The reproduction of the disease in swine by intravenous, intramuscular, or subcutaneous inoculation with virulent cultures is not routinely successful. In 1944 Fortner and Dinter demonstrated that cultures applied to skin scarifications resulted in a severe erythematous lesion along the scratch and in case of the virulent cultures in generalized infection. This technic has been confirmed by Shuman, who has found it valuable in the study of immunity. In 1955 Hughes reported that generalized swine erysipelas could be produced by the inoculation of a virulent culture into the ear vein.

In sheep the infection with *Erysipelothrix rhusiopathiae* is characterized by chronic polyarthritis. The infection is probably soil-borne and enters the body through the umbilicus at birth. Lambs up to 3 months of age appear to be most commonly stricken. In spite of the extensive polyarthritis that may occur, the parenchymal organs are not involved.

In addition to causing outbreaks of disease in swine and sheep, *Erysipelothrix rhusiopathiae* has been isolated in sporadic cases of infection of horses, cattle, dogs, reindeer, kangaroo, and wild boar.

Natural infections in turkeys, geese, ducks, chickens, and pigeons are of an acute nature. The postmortem appearance in birds is that of peracute septicemia. Attempts to infect poultry artificially are not always successful, however, and many authors conclude that fowls are relatively resistant to infection with the swine erysipelas bacillus.

Of the laboratory animals, mice and pigeons are highly susceptible to experimental infection. Both die in eighteen to ninety-six hours of acute septicemia. Rabbits are quite resistant. Subcutaneous injections into rabbits may give rise to local inflammation and edema, and highly virulent cultures may cause death in a period of from several days to a week. Intravenous injections are more often fatal to rabbits, and death often occurs in two or three days. Guinea pigs are markedly resistant to infection with the swine erysipelas bacillus. Horses, cattle, dogs, and cats are reactive to artificial inoculation of virulent strains.

Erysipeloid, as the disease is known in man, is characterized by a painful swelling at the point of inoculation in the skin. The area becomes reddened, turns purple, and some necrosis of the skin and subcutis occurs. The regional lymph nodes may become enlarged and painful. Arthritis may develop in the nearby joints. The disease is not often fatal and rarely becomes generalized.

Immunity. Animals that recover from swine erysipelas remain permanently immune although many may continue to harbor and disseminate the causative agent. Swine of more than eighteen months of age show a relative resistance which possibly may be attributed to early exposure.

Pasteur and Thuiller devised the first method of immunization in 1882, which is of historical interest only. They found that the swine erysipelas microorganism could be attenuated by passage through rabbits and that its virulence could be exalted by passage through pigeons. Their method of immunization consisted of injecting a live culture of an attenuated strain, followed in twelve days by injection of a virulent strain. The method has been abandoned because the injection of the virulent culture was found to be capable of actually causing the disease in some instances. Serious losses were known to result, and the disease actually was propagated in new localities by use of virulent cultures for vaccines.

The simultaneous method of vaccination against swine erysipelas is now commonly used in Europe. The method of Lorenz, who introduced the simultaneous, or serovaccination method, consists of, first, injecting a virulent culture, followed immediately by injection of immune serum. A modification of this method is to mix the vaccine with the immune serum immediately before use and to employ the mixture for inoculation in a single dose. In the swine-raising section of the middle western part of the United States, herds may be given two injections of vaccine along with immune serum after the disease has been found to be present on the premises. It has been observed by Shuman that the vaccination of gilts with culture and serum, just before breeding, will afford protection to the newborn pigs until weaning time. The immune serum made by hyperimmunizing horses is very effective in treating sick animals. Symptoms of acute swine erysipelas may be caused to abate in twenty-four hours or less by the use of immune serum.

The production of immunity against any disease by the use of a living culture has a number of disadvantages. This fact is true of swine erysipelas. The report of the value of a formalin-killed aluminum hydroxide adsorbed bacterin, by Traub in 1947, and by Dinter in 1948, was viewed with great interest. The application of this method experimentally by Cooper, Personeus, and Choman, and by Harvey *et al.*, has revealed that satisfactory immunity may be produced. Shuman has also shown that the use of this type of bacterin in swine produces an increased resistance to the disease.

Gray and Norden have reported a new immunizing agent called erysipelas vaccine avirulent (EVA) which is composed of a living avirulent but highly antigenic strain of *Ery. rhusiopathiae.* Experimental and field trials with this vaccine indicate that it is an effective immunizing agent. It may be used simultaneously with immune serum or used alone.

Prophylactic use of the immune serum is valuable in swine-raising but the passive immunity is of short duration and cannot be relied on for longer than two weeks. Specific immune serum has been used prophylactically and for treatment of turkeys and ducks, with some reported beneficial results, but there seems to be no agreement as to the practicability of such procedures.

Diagnosis. The diagnosis of infections due to *Erysipelothrix rhusiopathiae* may be made with certainty only by bacteriologic or serologic precedures. Swine erysipelas may readily be confused with other acute septicemic infections. The chronic forms of the disease, accompanied by valvular lesions, arthritis, or skin manifestations may also be caused by other microorganisms.

The slender, Gram-positive rods may sometimes be found in smears of tissue. Large clumps of the bacteria often are observed in smears of blood from pigeons (Fig. 34.2) and in smears from the spleen or kidneys of mice which have been inoculated with material obtained in cases of swine erysipelas. The microorganism can be demonstrated by inoculation of blood or serum agar. The tiny, smooth colonies, which may not be seen for several days, may then be transferred to suitable differential mediums for identification. Packer has shown that *Erysipelothrix rhusiopathiae* may be more easily isolated from contaminated tissues if sodium azide and crystal violet are incorporated in the medium.

Serologic tests are of value only in the chronic infections. The agglutination test has been found to be a useful procedure for detecting chronically infected animals in herds where, if allowed to remain, they may be constant sources of the infection.

The antigen for the laboratory tube test is made by centrifuging the microorganisms out of broth cultures and resuspending them in formolized physiologic saline solution. Serum dilutions are made in the ordinary manner with the antigen and incubated for four hours at 37°C. The tubes are then centrifuged for a short time before being read. In positive tests the supernatant fluid will be cleared, while in negative tests it will remain turbid. A rapid serum or whole blood test is made by mixing a drop of serum or blood with a drop of antigen 50 times heavier than that used for the tube test. A positive reaction is indicated in a few minutes by the formation of clumps. This rapid agglutination test which may be used in the field for chronic swine erysipelas is more commonly used than the laboratory tube test.

A rapid laboratory test may be made by using as the antigen a twelve-hour to twenty-four-hour broth culture of the smooth type of the organism. Hanging drops are made of serial dilutions of suspected serum and the broth cultures. After incubation for five to fifteen minutes the hanging drops are examined microscopically. A positive test is indicated by marked clumping of the microorganisms. In a negative test the bacilli remain evenly distributed throughout the field with no tendency to form clumps.

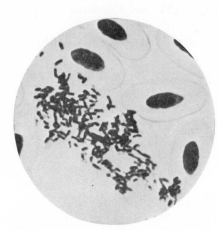

FIG. 34.2 — **Erysipelothrix rhusiopathiae,** smear of pigeon blood, × 2,000. (From Nowak: Documenta Microbiologica, courtesy Gustav Fischer.)

Care should be taken in making the hanging drops to prevent contamination of the hands.

REFERENCES FOR FURTHER STUDY

Barber, Mary. A Comparative Study of Listerella and Erysipelothrix. Jour. Path. and Bact., 48:11–23 (Jan.), 1939.

Callaway, H. P., Clark, R. S., Price, L. W., and Vezey, S. A. Vet. Med., 50:39, 1955.

Collins, D. H., and Goldie, William. Observations on Polyarthritis and on Experimental Erysipelothrix Infection of Swine. Jour. Path. and Bact., 50:323–53 (Mar.), 1940.

Cooper, M. S., Personeus, G. R., and Choman, B. R. Can. Jour. Comp. Med., 18:83, 1954.

———, ———, Harvey, M. J., and Percival, R. C. Amer. Jour. Vet. Res., 15:594, 1954.

Dougherty, E., and Bruner, D. W. Cornell Vet., 44:209, 1954.

Evans, W. M., and Narotsky, S. Cornell Vet., 44:32, 1954.

Fortner, J., and Dinter, Z. Ztschr. f. Infectionskr., 60:157, 1944.

Glendhill, A. W. The Antigenic Structure of Erysipelothrix. Jour. Path. and Bact., 57:179–89 (Apr.), 1945.

Gray, C. W., and Norden, C. J. Jour. A.V.M.A., 127:506, 1955.

Grey, C. G., Osteen, O. L., and Schoening, H. W. Swine Erysipelas, the Agglutination Test for its Diagnosis, and a Report on a Study of Arthritis in Swine. Amer. Jour. Vet. Res., 2:74–76 (Jan.), 1941.

Harvey, M. J., Burkhart, R. L., Cooper, M. S., Johnson, W. P., Percival, R. C., and Personeus, G. R. Clinical Observations Following Challenge of Swine Vaccinated with Adsorbed Erysipelas Bacterin. The Southwestern Veterinarian, Vol. 8, 1954.

Hughes, D. L. Brit. Vet. Jour., 111:183–92, 1955.

Julianelle, L. A. The Identification of Erysipelothrix and Its Relation to Listerella. Jour. Bact., 42:385–94 (Sept.), 1941.

Karlson, A. G., and Merchant, I. A. The Cultural and Biochemic Properties of *Erysipelothrix rhusiopathiae*. Amer. Jour. Vet. Res., 2:5–10 (Jan.), 1941.

Klauder, J. V. Swine Erysipelas. In: Hull, T. G.: Diseases Transmitted from Animals to Man. 3rd Ed., pp. 134–46, Charles C. Thomas, Springfield, 1947.

Levine, N. D. Erysipelothrix Septicemia. In: Biester, H. E., and Schwarte, L. H.: Diseases of Poultry, pp. 414–22. Iowa State College Press, Ames, 1952.

Moore, V. A. Mouse Septicaemia Bacilli in a Pig's Spleen, with Some Observations on Their Pathogenic Properties. Jour. Compt. Med. and Vet. Arch., 13:334–41, 1892.

Moulton, J. E., Rhode, E. R., and Wheat, J. D. Erysipelatous Arthritis in Calves. Jour. A.V.M.A., 123:335, 1953.

Packer, R. A. The Use of Sodium Azide (NaN$_3$) and Crystal Violet in a Selective Medium for Streptococci and *Erysipelothrix rhusiopathiae*. Jour. Bact., 46:343–49 (Oct.), 1943.

Shuman, R. D. Experimental Evaluation of Culture and Serum Vaccination for Control of Swine Erysipelas. IV. Gilts Vaccinated with Culture and and Serum before Breeding, and its Immunizing Effect on their Offspring. Jour. A.V.M.A., 123:431, 1953.

———. Experimental Evaluation of Swine Erysipelas Adsorbate Bacterin. Jour. A.V.M.A., 124:362, 1954.

———. Swine Erysipelas Induced by Skin Scarification. Proc. Book 88th Ann. Mtg. A.V.M.A., p. 153, 1951.

———, and Earl, F. L. Jour. A.V.M.A., 125:306, 1954.

Sikes, D. Amer. Jour. Vet. Res., 16:349, 1955.

Smith, Theobold. Investigations of Diseases of Domestic Animals. United States Department of Agriculture, United States Bureau of Animal Industry. Second Annual Report, p. 196, 1886.

———. Investigations of Diseases of Domestic Animals. Swine Erysipelas or Mouse Septicemia Bacilli From an Outbreak of Swine Disease. United States Department of Agriculture, United States Bureau of Animal Industry, Twelfth and Thirteenth Annual Reports, pp. 166–74, 1895–1896.

Taylor, J. B. Swine Erysipelas. Jour. Amer. Vet. Med. Assn., 79:813–14 (Dec.) 1931.

Ten Broeck, Carl. Studies on *Bacillus murisepticus*, or the Rotlauf Bacillus, Isolated From Swine in the United States. Jour. Exp. Med., 32:331–43 (Sept.) 1920.

Traub, E. Monatsh. f. Veterinäermedizin, 2:165, 1947.

Van Es, L. Swine Erysipelas Infection in Man. Nebraska Agriculture Experimental Station, Research Bulletin, 1942, p. 130.

———, and McGrath, C. G. Swine Erysipelas. Nebraska Agriculture Experimental Station, Research Bulletin, 1942, p. 128.

Watts, P. S. Studies on *Erysipelothrix rhusiopathiae*. Jour. Path. Bact., 50:355–69 (Mar.) 1940.

Wilson, G. S., and Miles, A. A. Topley and Wilson's Principles of Bacteriology and Immunity. 3rd Ed. The Williams & Wilkins Company, Baltimore, 1946. Vol. 1, pp. 395–403; Vol. 2, pp. 1283–88.

35. The Genera Actinomyces and Nocardia

These genera include the organisms which form a branched mycelium that may break up into small coccoid or bacillary segments that function as conidia. The filaments are often clubbed toward the ends and form in colonies radiating from a center. The greatest number of species are soil saprophytes, while a few are saprophytic and parasitic upon man and animals.

The most typical member of the genus Actinomyces is *Act. bovis*. The varied history of this organism is given later. It is significant to note here, however, that in addition to *Act. bovis*, the species *Act. israeli* is now recognized (Bergey's Manual 1948). In a recent study (1950) of strains of Actinomyces of both human and bovine origin Thompson has corroborated the work of others in concluding that there are two separate species which should be called *Actinomyces bovis* and *Actinomyces israeli*.

The genus Nocardia represents those actinomyces which are aerobic, differing from the anaerobic members of the genus Actinomyces. Two species of this genus, *Nocardia farcinica* and *Nocardia caprae* will be described briefly.

Actinomyces bovis

Synonyms and History. *Discomyces bovis, Nocardia actinomyces, Streptothrix actinomyces, Streptothrix bovis,* the "ray fungus."

Actinomycosis, as a disease, was reported long before the organism was known to exist; in fact, Moodie reported finding bone necrosis, simulating actinomycosis, in the fossil remains of a rhinoceros. In 1845 Langenbeck reported finding a ray fungus in a young man suffering with Pott's disease. The presence of sulphur granules in actinomycosis of the bovine was reported by Rivolta in 1868. He considered that such granules were organisms and coined the name *Discomyces bovis*. It must be noted that this organism might have been *Actinobacillus lignieresi*. The real significance of the organism as a specific agent of disease was determined in 1877 by Bollinger who called the disease actinomycosis. Bollinger took specimens containing the organism to Harz, a botanist who noted the ray fungus characteristic and suggested the name, *Actinomyces bovis*. In 1878 Israel observed a similar organism in a suppurative lesion in man, and in 1891 Wolf and Israel were able to culture it on artificial media under anaerobic conditions. These workers are credited, by some, as being the first to discover the organism. In 1891 considerable confusion was introduced by Bostroem, by the isolation of an aerobic organism from typical actinomycotic lesions in man and in cattle. He believed his organism was *Actinomyces bovis*. It was present upon various grasses as a saprophyte and was considered to be introduced into deeper tissues of the buccal cavity by the penetrating action of sharp awns. Bostroem's organism was not pathogenic for guinea pigs or rabbits and its relationship to actinomycosis was doubted first by Wright in 1905. Since then, the etiological relationship of the organism to actinomycosis has been completely disproven by many investigators. Bostroem's organism is considered under the name *Actinomyces hominis* (*Actinomyces graminis* of Topley and Wilson), a contaminating saprophyte which can be isolated frequently from actinomycotic lesions. *Actinomyces bovis* is considered to be the organism first observed by Bollinger, described and named by Harz, and isolated in pure culture by Wolf and Israel.

Distribution and Transmission. *Actinomyces bovis* is widely distributed throughout the world in regions devoted to the grazing of cattle herds. It is common in south Russia, the Scandinavian countries, England, Holland, and Italy, but uncommon in France and Germany. In the United States the organism is found in the north central states and in the western grazing states.

The organism is a normal inhabitant of the mucous membranes of the upper respiratory and digestive tracts. It has been found in the tartar of teeth and in decaying food material on the gums. The relationship of the awns of the bearded grasses to the infection is considered mechanical. Such sharp objects penetrate the tissues of the buccal cavity, afford a channel of entry, and produce primary necrosis of tissue which is essential to the development of the organism. In this respect the anaerobic conditions necessary for the multiplication of this organism are similar to those for the Clostridium group.

Morphology and Staining. *Actinomyces bovis* is a long, filamentous branching organism when grown under artificial conditions. Many of the filaments contain small coccoid forms which are considered to function as conidia (Fig. 35.1). In the infected tissues the organism forms typical "ray fungus" granules from 1 to 2 mm. in size. When an unstained preparation is examined under the microscope, these granules are found to be composed of a mass of clublike processes originating at the center of the granule. Many of the processes are well formed while others are small and ill defined (Fig. 35.2). The granules are compact, and many are calcified, but when placed between two slides they are easily crushed. If a smear which has been made in this manner is stained with the Gram stain, the long, slender, filamentous type of organism is found. The organism is Grampositive and nonacid-fast.

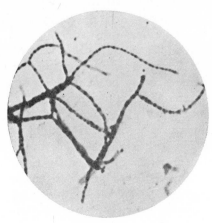

FIG. 35.1 — **Actinomyces bovis,** agar culture showing beaded filaments, × 2,000. (From Nowak: Documenta Microbiologica, courtesy Gustav Fischer.)

Growth Requirements and Characteristics. The organism grows best upon primary isolation under anaerobic conditions, but when adjusted to artificial media it will grow aerobically. The presence of 10 per cent CO_2 is stimulating to the organism. Original growth is slow, taking several days for a colony of any significant size to form. A favorable medium for the cultivation of the organism contains 1 per cent glycerin, 1 per cent blood serum, and 1 per cent dextrose added to a nutrient agar base and adjusted to pH 7.3 to 7.6. When a shake culture is made of the organism in this medium, numerous small colonies are formed about 1 cm. under the surface of the medium. Larger and scattered colonies which are irregular in shape and with a knobby surface are observed throughout the medium. The organism is frequently associated with numerous other species of bacteria which make the isolation of a pure culture difficult. A considerable number of contaminating bacteria are eliminated by placing the actinomycotic exudate in sterile water and washing the granules free from tissue cells. This may be repeated until only a thin layer of granules is left in the bottom of the tube. These granules are then crushed with a sterile rod, and cultures are made of this material.

Actinomyces bovis forms small, round, convex, opaque, amorphous colonies on the surface of the agar plate. As the colony ages, the center becomes elevated, the surface nodular, and the periphery lobular, giving the colony a rosette appearance.

A compact, white deposit of mulberry-like granules forms in broth medium. The granular sediment is not disintegrated upon shaking.

Coagulated serum medium and Dorset's egg medium support a moderate growth of the organism. The appearance of the cultures on these media is similar to that on agar but is usually more glistening; some strains may have a pink tinge of color. The media are not liquefied.

Resistance. The organism is killed at 60°C. in 10 minutes. It is not resistant to the mercurial disinfectants but is resistant to phenolic compounds. It is killed by a 1:1,000 solution of $HgCl_2$ in 5 minutes. Artifical cultures of the organism must be transferred often in order to maintain them. The granules are resistant to desiccation and more resistant to chemicals than the filamentous forms.

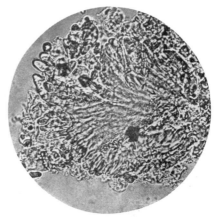

FIG. 35.2 — **Actinomyces bovis,** unstained granule in actinomycotic pus, × 110. (From Nowak: Documenta Microbiologica, courtesy Gustav Fischer.)

Biochemical Properties. *Actinomyces bovis* produces acid, but not gas, from glucose, maltose, lactose, and salicin under anaerobic conditions. It is able to reduce nitrates to nitrites and to produce ammonia, but gives a negative reaction for indol, to the M.R. and V.P. tests, and for H_2S and catalase production. The organism grows slowly in litmus milk which it peptonizes in about forty days. It liquefies gelatin slowly.

Antigenic Structure and Toxins. Little data are available concerning the antigenic structure of the organism. Colebrook found three strains of the organism antigenically different. Magnusson reported three serological types; Type A was found in cattle and Types B and C in swine. Exotoxins are not formed.

Pathogenicity. *Actinomyces bovis* is pathogenic for the bovine, swine, equine, and man.

The lesions produced by the organism in the bovine are most prevalent in the mandible and in the tongue, although they may be found in any of the tissues of the cervical region and on rare occasions are quite generalized throughout the internal organs. The organism is spread from localized lesions by continuity of tissue or by the blood stream. Lesions of actinomycosis in animals and in man are characterized by abscess formation with encapsulation. As the process advances, connective tissue increases, and the lesion becomes dense and compact. The affected part increases in size, which has given rise to common names for the disease, such as, "wooden tongue" and "lumpy jaw." Kimball, Twiehaus, and Frank have found the organism in orchitis of the bull.

Cases of actinomycosis due to *Actinomyces bovis* have been reported from swine, horses, and sheep. In swine it is considered most prevalent as a mammary infection of nursing sows, presumably due to the sharp teeth of suckling pigs.

Kimball and Frank report that this organism was recovered in 40 out of 55 typical, previously unopened cases of fistulous withers and poll evil in the horse. The relationship of the organism with *Br. abortus* and *Br. suis* in producing a bursitis in the supraspinous bursa of the horse has been shown by Roderick, Kimball, McLeod, and Frank. In a case of pulmonary actinomycosis in the dog, Menges, Larsh, and Habermann observed the organism and considered it to be the cause of the condition.

This organism is pathogenic for the rabbit and guinea pig, and when it is inoculated intraperitoneally into those animals, it produces encapsulated nodules similar to tubercles over the omentum.

Immunity. Actinomycosis is so chronic that it is apparent that some degree of resistance is possessed by the normal animal. The resistance is not increased by the infection, apparently, because the disease progresses continuously. Artificial immunization is not practical.

Diagnosis. The presence of *Actinomyces bovis* in the cervical region of cattle is detected only by the demonstration of Gram-positive filamentous cells. Other organisms, notably *Actinobacillus lignieresi, Staphylococcus aureus,* and *Corynebacterium pyogenes* may be found in cervical lesions.

It must be re-emphasized that the presence of sulphur granules is not diagnostic of actinomycosis, inasmuch as such bodies are also found in actinobacillosis.

Actinomyces israeli

Previous mention has been made of the history of this organism. While the majority of strains of Actinomyces which produce infection in man probably are *Act. israeli*, it is believed that *Act. bovis* is also found in typical cases of actinomycosis of the human family.

The morphology of *Act. bovis* and *Act. israeli* is not significantly different. The colonies of *Act. bovis* are usually smooth and soft in consistency as contrasted to those of *Act. israeli* which are rough and have a pebbled surface as the culture ages.

In brain broth *Act. bovis* grows slowly without producing any appreciable change in the medium. *Act. israeli* grows more abundantly in this medium, producing a slight acid reaction. *Act. bovis* produces a diffuse growth in thioglycollate medium but *Act. israeli* forms discrete, compact colonies, irregularly round, and variable in size.

The type of lesion produced by *Act. israeli* is not substantially different from that caused by *Act. bovis*, which has been described above.

Nocardia farcinicus

In 1888 Nocard isolated a filamentous organism from a disease in cattle that was commonly known as "bovine farcy." The disease caused by this organism is characterized by enlargement and ulceration of the lymph vessels of the inner surfaces of the legs. The regional lymph nodes are commonly involved, becoming enlarged and in some cases ulcerated. The disease is extremely chronic, continuing for one to one and one-half years before the general condition of the animal is unduly disturbed. Eventually, however, the animal dies with emaciation.

This organism is long and filamentous and breaks up into typical segments of small coccoid cells. It is stained easily by the aniline dyes and is Gram-positive. It is acid-fast, thereby differing from most of the pathogenic actinomyces but resembling certain soil actinomyces. The organism grows readily under aerobic conditions on agar, forming yellowish-white, granular colonies which later coalesce and form a heavy membrane. In broth it forms into irregular whitish masses, some of which sink to the bottom and others which remain on the surface and resemble flakes of paraffin.

Nocardia farcinicus produces natural disease in cattle only, but miliary lesions are produced in sheep by intravenous inoculation. Horses, mules, asses, dogs, and cats are resistant. Tubercle-like lesions are produced in guinea pigs and rabbits by intraperitoneal inoculation; miliary lesions are formed in the lungs, liver, and spleen by intravenous inoculation. The disease has been reported from the European continent but has never been found in the United States.

Nocardia caprae

In 1897 Silberschmidt isolated a streptothrix from the lungs of a goat affected with a disease similar to tuberculosis. The organism forms long filaments which segment into small bacillary and coccoid cells. It is Gram-positive and nonacid-fast. On agar this organism produces dry, irregular colonies which have a mealy, warty surface. Potato is a satisfactory medium for growth, and on this medium the colonies are rose-red in color, which later turns to chalky-white. Dry colonies form on the surface of broth. The organism produces tubercle-like lesions in the guinea pig, rabbit, and monkey.

REFERENCES FOR FURTHER STUDY

Cope, Zachary. Actinomycosis. Oxford University Press, New York, 1938.

Emmons, C. W. Pub. Hlth. Rep. Wash., 53:1967, 1938.

Erikson, D. Pathogenic Anaerobic Organisms of the Actinomyces Group. Med. Rec. Council Spec. Rep. Ser. 24D, 1940.

Kimball, Alice, and Frank, E. R. Amer. Jour. Vet. Res., 6:39, 1945.

———, Twiehaus, M. J., and Frank, E. R. Amer. Jour. Vet. Res., 15:551, 1954.

Menges, R. W., Larsh, H. W., and Habermann, R. T. Jour. Amer. Vet. Med. Assn., 122:73, 1953.

Naeslund, Carl. Acta Path. et Microb. Scand. Supp. 6, 1931.

Roderick, L. M., Kimball, Alice, McLeod, W. M., and Frank, E. R. Amer. Jour. Vet. Res., 9:5, 1948.

Rosebury, T. Bact. Rev. 8:189, 1944.

Thompson, L. Proceed. Staff Meet. Mayo Clinic, 25:81, 1950.

Topley, W. W. C., and Wilson, G. S. The Principles of Bacteriology and Immunity. 3rd Ed., The Williams & Wilkins Co., Baltimore, 1946.

Waksman, S. A. In Bergey's Manual of Determinative Bacteriology. 6th Ed. The Williams and Wilkins Co., Baltimore, 1948.

36. The Spirochetes

Spirochetes are microorganisms which are slender and spiral in shape, motile by means of a flexuous motion, and they multiply by transverse fission. Most of the forms which have been described are saprophytic upon plant and animal life; some are parasitic, and a few are pathogenic for man and animals.

The spirochetes were among the first types of microscopic life observed and described by Leeuwenhoek in 1681. The large forms which are representative of the group were seen in various types of plant infusions by the early microscopists, and as early as 1837, Donne observed spiral-shaped microorganisms in smears from genital lesions. In 1833 Ehrenberg used the name *Spirochaeta* for a large, free-living, spiral-shaped organism. The first spirochete of any pathogenic significance was described by Obermeir in 1873. This organism was found in the blood of patients suffering with relapsing fever. In 1891 Sakharoff found that a spirochete was the cause of a goose septicemia in Russia, and in 1902 Theiler observed a spiral-shaped organism in a febrile condition of cattle in South Africa.

The spirochetes were considered bacteria until 1905 when Schaudinn and Hoffmann concluded studies on the spiral organism of syphilis. They compared the organism with a flexuous protozoan parasite, a trypanosome of birds, and concluded that it, too, was a protozoan. As a result of their classical studies, the spirochetes were claimed by the protozoologists. During the past twenty years it has become obvious that these microorganisms are closely related to the bacteria and at the present time they are classified as bacteria in the order *Spirochaetales*. It is freely admitted, however, that the spirochetes show some of the characteristics of the flexuous protozoa.

The differentiation of the spirochetes is difficult because they are not cultivated with ease on artificial media and are devoid of marked biochemical activity. Present-day classifications are based upon the morphology of the different types, and on these characteristics two families are recognized.

These families are listed and described in Bergey's Manual, 1948, as follows:

FAMILY I.   *Spirochaetaceae*: spirals 30 to 500 microns in length, having definite protoplasmic structures.

FAMILY II.   *Treponemataceae*: spirals 4 to 16 microns in length, having no obvious protoplasmic structure.

None of the genera in the family *Spirochaetaceae* has species which are pathogenic for animals, although some have been isolated from oysters, shell-fish, and mollusks.

The family *Treponemataceae* contains three genera which do have species pathogenic for animals and man. These genera are differentiated as follows:

I.   Stains easily with aniline dyes.
Genus   I. *Borrelia.*

II.   Stain with difficulty except with Giemsa's stain or by silver impregnation.
Genus   II. *Treponema*, strict anaerobes.
Genus   III.   *Leptospira,* aerobes.

The species in each of these genera which are related to specific diseases in animals and man will be discussed.

THE GENUS BORRELIA

Borrelia anserina

Synonyms and History. *Spirochaeta gallinarum, Spironema gallinarum, Spirochaeta anserina, Treponema anserina, Borrelia gallinarum.*

In 1891 Sakharoff described a spirochete which he considered to be the cause of an acute septicemia in geese. He called the organism *Spirochaeta anserina*. In 1903 Marchoux and Salimbeni, in Brazil, reported a septicemia in domestic fowls. The disease was caused by a spirochete which they named *Spirochaeta gallinarum*. It is quite probable that the organism described by Sakharoff from geese and the one from fowls are identical.

Distribution and Transmission. *Borrelia anserina* is responsible for the disease commonly known as fowl spirochetosis. It has been observed in South America, Africa, Australia, Java, in parts of Asia, and to some extent in European Russia, the Balkan countries, and in Germany.

In the United States the organism has been found in Texas and California.

This organism is transmitted from one bird to another by the bite of ticks belonging to the genus Argas. The mechanical transmission of the spirochete by the chicken mite, *Dermanyssus gal-*

linae, and by the ingestion of fecal material from infected ticks has been considered probable. The organism can be transmitted by the contact of susceptible birds with the feces of those infected. Loomis observed in his study of the disease in turkeys in California that the infection was not transmitted by the tick *Argas persicus,* and concluded that the feces of infected turkeys constituted the chief source of infection.

Morphology and Staining. *Borrelia anserina* is a long, spiral organism, 10 to 20μ in length, with an average of one spiral per 1.5 micron (Fig. 36.1). The organism is not flagellated but does possess terminal filaments. It is actively motile. In old cultures small granules or coccoid bodies which are considered to be representative of pleomorphism have been found. These same bodies have been observed in ticks. The organism is stained readily with dilute

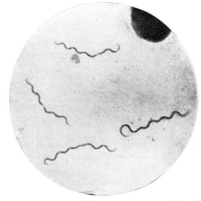

FIG. 36.1 — **Borrelia anserina** in blood of goose, Giemsa stain, × 2,000. (From Nowak: Documenta Microbiologica, courtesy Gustav Fischer.)

carbol fuchsin and Giemsa's stain. It is also easily demonstrated by the silver impregnation method of Levaditi and by the use of India ink. It is Gram-negative and nonacid-fast.

Growth Requirements and Characteristics. This spirochete is grown only under anaerobic conditions at a temperature of 37°C. It is cultivated with some difficulty, but the use of ascitic fluid containing pieces of rabbit kidney or heart muscle has been found satisfactory. It does not produce any characteristic type of growth, and nothing is known concerning its biochemical properties.

The organism is not resistant, and subcultures must be made weekly in order to maintain viability.

Pathogenicity. *Borrelia anserina* is found most often in chickens but has been reported in ducks, turkeys, and geese. The disease is characterized by an acute septicemia which is fatal within three or four days. The disease is most fatal to young birds. It is accompanied by a rise in temperature, drowsiness, diarrhea, and emaciation. Anemia and enlargement of the spleen are commonly observed, due to the destruction of red blood cells by the toxic products liberated by the disintegrating organisms.

Experimentally, the organism has been found to be pathogenic for ducks, geese, chickens, guinea fowls, turtledoves, sparrows, pheasants, pigeons, and canaries. It is not pathogenic for mammals.

Although it multiplies to some extent in rabbits after parenteral injection, it does not produce any significant disease. McNeil, Hinshaw, and Kissling were not able to infect rabbits, rats, lambs, or lizards with the organism.

Immunity. Fowls which have recovered from the disease are considered to be immune. Marchoux and Salimbeni showed in their original work that fresh blood heated to 55°C. for 5 minutes produced an immunity in suscepitible birds. Immune serum produced in horses and goats by the inoculation of blood from infected chickens has been found to be of value under experimental conditions; however, this procedure has not been employed as a practical means of controlling the disease in chicken flocks.

Diagnosis. The type of septicemia produced by *Borrelia anserina* in the avian family can be diagnosed accurately only by the demonstration of the organism in blood smears. Agglutinin is produced by the infection, but the agglutination test is not used as a method of diagnosis.

Borrelia theileri

Synonyms and History. *Spirochaeta theileri, Spironema theileri, Treponema theileri.*

In 1902 Theiler, in South Africa, found a long, spiral organism associated with a minor febrile disease of cattle. In some respects the disease was similar to piroplasmosis, or tick fever. This organism is transmitted from the infected host to susceptible animals by the bite of ticks, such as *Rhipicephalus decoloratus* and *Rhipicephalus evertsi*. A similar organism was found in the horse and in sheep by Theiler and in 1906 Stordy observed the organism in a horse. These organisms have been called *Spirochaeta ovis* and *Spirochaeta equi,* respectively, by Novy and Knapp. The cross-agglutination results obtained by Todd and others have indicated that the organism *Borrelia theileri* occurs in cattle, sheep, and horses.

This spirochete is a slender organism measuring 0.25 to 0.3µ in length. It is actively motile by means of polar filaments and a flexuous motion. It is stained by the Giemsa stain or other suitable blood stains.

Borrelia hyos

In 1913 King and Baeslack, by means of dark-field illumination, observed a spirochete in the blood of hogs with hog cholera. They considered the organism to be of some etiological significance to the disease. Later in the same year, King, Baeslack, and Hoffmann published another account emphasizing the constancy in which they found the spirochete in hog cholera virus blood and suggested the name *Spirochaeta suis.*

According to the above investigators *Borrelia hyos,* as named by Bergey, is a large spirochete 5 to 7μ in length by 1μ in width. It is flexible and round on its ends; however, a polar flagellum was observed on one cell by the India-ink method. In addition to the spirochete, these authors observed distinct, highly refractive bodies in hog cholera blood and suggested that these granular bodies may represent certain stages in the life cycle of the spirochete.

This organism was cultivated upon a medium composed of human ascitic fluid and fresh rabbit tissue by Hoskins. This investigator could find no etiological relationship of the organism with hog cholera.

THE GENUS TREPONEMA

None of the species in the genus Treponema is of any significance to animal health. One organism, *Treponema cuniculi,* has been isolated from rabbits but is not prevalent or of great importance. *Treponema pallidum,* the cause of syphilis in man, is of great health significance to the human race and warrants a brief consideration here.

Treponema pallidum

Synonyms and History. *Spirochaeta pallidum, Spirillum pallidum.*

In 1905 Schaudinn and Hoffman observed a spirochete in the primary chancres of syphilis and in enlarged regional lymph nodes. They considered the organism was the cause of the disease; this fact was subsequently proven by numerous investigators. Up to this time different agents were described as the cause of syphilis. These were, for the most part, the various bacteria which existed as saprophytes upon external genitalia.

Distribution and Transmission. *Treponema pallidum* is widely distributed throughout the civilized world. It is generally agreed that, quite contrary to other diseases, syphilis had its origin on the American continent, for it made its appearance in the old world after the return of Columbus from the discovery of this continent. The infection is transmitted readily by sexual contact and rarely by contaminated objects. Intra-uterine infection occurs in syphilitic mothers.

Morphology and Staining. This spirochete is 0.25 to 0.3μ in diameter and 8 to 15μ long. It is tightly coiled into eight to fifteen spirals which are rigid and with an amplitude of approximately 1μ. The organism is actively motile by means of an undulating and rotating motion. It is not flagellated, although long, polar filaments are often observed (Fig. 36.2). Granular forms of the organism have been described, but whether these forms are a part of a life cycle has not been determined. Multiplication occurs by transverse fission. No spores are formed.

Treponema pallidum is rendered visible in an unstained preparation by dark-field illumination. The brilliant, silvery appearance of the organism against the dark background is quite characteristic. A number of the more penetrating stains, such as Giemsa and Wright, are suitable to demonstrate the organism in smears. In tissue sections, s i l v e r impregnation methods are commonly employed. In such preparations the organism is stained a dense black color (Fig. 36.3).

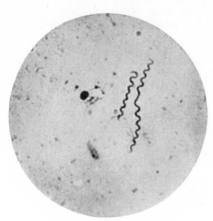

FIG. 36.2 — **Treponema pallidum** in primary chancre, Giemsa stain, × 2,000. (From Nowak: Documenta Microbiologica, courtesy Gustav Fischer.)

Growth Requirements and Characteristics. *Treponema pallidum* is cultivated with difficulty under artificial conditions. Reports of the growth of the organism on Noguchi's medium have been made, but it is doubtful if the organisms grown were actually the syphilis spirochete. It is commonly agreed, at the present time, that the organism has not been grown artificially.

Resistance. This spirochete is not resistant to heat, drying, or the action of chemicals.

The organism is susceptible to arsenical and bismuth compounds, which are extensively used in the treatment and cure of the disease. *T. pallidum* is sensitive to penicillin in vivo, and this drug is used extensively in treating syphilis. Some cases of the disease treated with penicillin relapse, however, and it is believed that resistance to this antibiotic is developed by some strains of the organism.

Pathogenicity. Under natural conditions man, only, is susceptible to *Treponema pallidum*. All races of mankind have been afflicted with the disease produced by the organism, but some individual and racial examples of resistance have been noted. The disease was particularly severe on the European continent after its first appearance, but resistance, apparently, has been developed since that time.

The organism is pathogenic to monkeys. Rabbits are susceptible and are used experimentally in the study of the organism and the disease. All types of the disease can be produced in rabbits by appropriate avenues of inoculation. Guinea pigs are susceptible to the organism, but they are not used to any great extent in experimental studies of the disease.

Immunity. Recovery from one attack of syphilis produces immunity, and persons suffering with an active case of the disease are refractive to a second inoculation. Artificial immunizing agents have never proven practical as a prophylaxis in the disease.

Diagnosis. Syphilis is diagnosed by two laboratory methods. Primary lesions of the disease are diagnosed by the use of dark-field illumination in the demonstration of the characteristic spirochete. Approximately two weeks after the first chancre, the presence of antibodies in the blood serum can be detected by appropriate serological tests. For this purpose the Wassermann test has been universally employed. During recent years the Kahn precipitation test has been used for routine diagnosis.

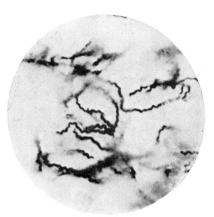

FIG. 36.3 — **Treponema pallidum** in lung of syphilitic fetus, silver impregnation stain, × 2,000. (From Nowak: Documenta Microbiologica, courtesy Gustav Fischer.)

Opinion is somewhat divided concerning the relative reliability of the complement-fixation (Wassermann) and the precipitation tests for the diagnosis of syphilis. Both tests are suitable but neither can be relied upon as absolutely accurate as diagnostic aids. They are used to supplement clinical observations. It must be emphasized that there are two periods when both reactions are negative: first, during the first two weeks of the developing chancre and, second, during the latent period of the disease following treatment. The student is referred to textbooks devoted to the human pathogens for additional information concerning these tests.

Treponema cuniculi

This organism was first observed by Ross in 1912 and by Bayon in 1913. Noguchi named it *Treponema cuniculi* in 1928.

It is practically the same size as *Treponema pallidum* and for this reason may lead to some confusion in experimental study. The organism produces about the genitalia of rabbits, superficial lesions which are characterized by slight elevation and desquamation. Generalization of the infection has not been observed. There is no antigenic relationship between this organism and the syphilis spirochete, and rabbits infected with *Treponema cuniculi* do not give a positive Wassermann reaction.

THE GENUS LEPTOSPIRA

In the genus Leptospira are found a number of species which are pathogenic for man and animals. Some of these species are world-wide in distribution, while others have been found only in isolated areas. In common with the other spirochetes, the Leptospira are cultured on especially prepared artificial media and are stained only by special technics.

They are recognized as species on the basis of pathogenicity and by serological tests. Wolff lists 36 antigenic types, and beyond doubt other strains will be added as more research is conducted.

Gsell has outlined 12 epidemiological principles concerning leptospirosis in man and animals with which the student should be familiar:

1. Leptospiral infections are zoonoses.
2. The number of animal species naturally infected by leptospires is less than the number which can be infected experimentally.
3. In a given area one animal species generally harbors predominantly one serotype of leptospire, or at most only a few serotypes which are weakly differentiated.
4. The intensity of the infection varies considerably in different animals.
5. The danger of infection from animals is due to the emission of leptospires in the urine.
6. The epidemiological importance of animal carriers of leptospirosis depends upon their collective mode of life.
7. Epidemics in man are possible under (a) natural conditions, and (b) artificial conditions created in animal husbandry.
8. Infection of man can occur either directly from an infected animal, or indirectly through water or soil contaminated by animals.
9. Infection attacks man chiefly through abrasions of the skin and mucous membranes.
10. Epidemiologically, human leptospirosis has characteristic features related to age, season, sex, and occupation.
11. Geographically, the leptospiroses are found throughout the world, but different types of leptospires occur in various areas.
12. The special conditions of domestic animal husbandry, practiced on a large scale only since 1900, account for the emergence of certain leptospiroses as new diseases.

Three species of Leptospira are known to be of significance to animal health in the United States: *L. icterohemorrhagiae, L. canicola,* and *L. pomona.*

From an animal disease point of view it is difficult to separate *L. icterohemorrhagiae* and *L. canicola* for the purpose of description and discussion; consequently, they will be treated under the one heading.

Leptospira icterohemorrhagiae and Leptospira canicola

Synonyms and History. A disease in man characterized by fever, jaundice, and petechial hemorrhages was observed as early as 1800 by Larrey. That this disease was different from other similar conditions was first noted in 1886 by Weil, after whom the disease has been named. The cause of Weil's disease was determined in 1914 by Inada and Ito to be an organism they called *Spirochaeta icterohemorrhagiae.* Subsequently, the organism was found in the kidneys of field mice and then in field rats which were considered to be the main reservoir of infection. This disease was confused with yellow fever as late as 1928 by Noguchi and his associates, who referred to their spirochete as *Spirochaeta icteroides.* This organism is considered identical with *Leptospira icterohemorrhagiae,* and yellow fever is now known to be caused by a filtrable virus.

A canine disease similar to the human infection was described as early as 1850 by Hofer. It became epidemic in Germany in 1898 when it was first called Stuttgart disease. This infection did not attract much attention until it was shown that *Leptospira icterohemorrhagiae* was the etiological agent. In 1917 Courmont and Durand found that puppies could be infected with the spirochetes which produced typical jaundice in man. Lukes, in 1924, and Krivacek, in the same year, observed, in the tissues of dogs which had died of Stuttgart disease, organisms which were morphologically identical to *L. icterohemorrhagiae.* In 1925 Okell, Dalling, and Pugh found the organism in epizootic jaundice in hunting dogs in England. The canine strain of the organism was studied in 1928 by Klarenbeek, of Holland, who referred to it as *Spirochaeta ictero-uraemia canis.* This organism was subsequently admitted to be the classical organism *Leptospira icterohemorrhagiae,* or, as called in German literature, *Spirochaeta icterogenes.*

In 1931 Klarenbeek and Schüffner recognized that another species, now called *Leptospira canicola,* was the cause of a considerable percentage of the leptospirosis of dogs. They found that this organism differed serologically from the classical strains. *Leptospira canicola* was isolated by Meyer and associates in 1937 in San Francisco and has been described by them in subsequent publications.

The entire subject of leptospirosis was reviewed in 1939 by Walch-Sorgdrager, to which article the student is referred.

Distribution and Transmission. Human leptospirosis has been found in Africa, America, Asia, Australia, and in most of the countries of Europe. Leptospirosis in dogs has been reported from many European countries, particularly Holland and Germany, and from the Netherlands Indies, the Federated Malay states, Madras, from North America, and from Great Britain.

The human disease, caused by *L. icterohemorrhagiae*, is contracted, for the most part, from infected rats. The great majority of the cases are obtained by contact with water into which infected rats are supposed to have eliminated the organism contained in urine. The rest of the cases result from direct contact with rats or their discharges. *L. canicola* infection in man is obtained from the dog. Leptospirosis in man is most prevalent in males and occurs more often during the late summer and early fall months of the year, presumably due to swimming.

FIG. 36.4 — **Leptospira icterohemor-rhagiae** from blood agar culture, Giemsa stain, × 2,000. (From Nowak: Documenta Microgiologica, courtesy Gustav Fischer.)

Canine leptospirosis due to *L. icterohemorrhagiae* is obtained from rats, while the disease due to *L. canicola* is always considered to be caused by contact with infective dog urine. It is probable that some cases result from sexual contact. In dogs the *L. canicola* disease is more prevalent among males, and, although puppies are susceptible, the greater percentage of cases occur in animals three to eight years of age. Meyer found the highest incidence of infection in San Francisco occurs during May and July and again in November and December; in Holland the peak in the cases of disease is reached during October and November.

Morphology and Staining. *Leptospira icterohemorrhagiae* and *Leptospira canicola* are indistinguishable morphologically. They are from 8 to 12µ long and vary from 0.1 to 0.2µ in thickness. They are closely spiraled and possess one or two wavy curves. The ends are commonly bent into the shape of a hook (Fig. 36.4). The organisms are actively motile by means of a serpentine, undulating motion. They are not flagellated. Some forms are capable of passing through the pores of Berkefeld N filters.

These organisms are stained with difficulty, but prolonged contact with Giemsa's stain will stain them a reddish color. Their morphology is best studied under dark-field illumination.

Growth Requirements. These Leptospirae are best obtained in pure culture by the inoculation of a suitable medium with the defibrinated blood taken from the suspected case. Meyer and coworkers have found that Schüffner's modification of Verwoort's medium is satisfactory for cultivation purposes. This medium is prepared as follows:

> Use 1.5 liters tap water (free from chlorine; rain water may be used instead of distilled water) and 1.5 gm. Witte peptone. Boil.
> Add 6 cc. phosphate mixture composed of 0.35 gm. monobasic potassium phosphate and 1.33 gm. dibasic sodium phosphate and 100 cc. distilled water. Boil.
> Add 300 cc. Ringer's solution composed of 0.8 gm. sodium chloride, 0.02 gm. potassium chloride, 0.02 gm. sodium bicarbonate, and 100 cc. distilled water. Continue boiling.
> Add 150 cc. Sorenson's buffer solution, pH 7.2. Boil until precipitation is complete (about 30 minutes). Cool in refrigerator overnight. Filter. Test pH, which should be 6.8 to 7.2. Bottle. Autoclave at 15 pounds for 15 minutes. The medium may be kept in this state in capped bottles until needed for use.
> Before use, add 8 to 10 per cent sterile rabbit serum, tube in 2.5 to 3 cc. quantities, and inactivate for 30 minutes in a 56°C. water bath. Test for sterility.

Various other modifications of the above medium are in use. It is important that the pH of any medium be maintained at 7.2–7.4 and that sterile serum contain no antileptospiral antibody.

The inoculated medium is incubated at 32° to 35°C. for as long as six weeks before growth may appear. Organisms adjusted to artificial conditions produce satisfactory growth within a week.

Resistance. These organisms are not resistant to heat and disinfectants. A temperature of 56°C. causes death in 20 minutes. They are able to survive a temperature of −27°C. for 9 months (Shigekawa). They do not survive long after elimination from the animal body, and for that reason transmission is considered to be rather direct from the infected to the susceptible animal. Specimens should be examined soon after collection if the organisms are to be observed on dark-field preparations, cultured, or inoculated into experimental animals.

Antigenic Structure. *L. icterohemorrhagiae* and *L. canicola* are antigenically different, although cross-agglutination does occur in very low dilutions. Numerous other strains of Leptospirae which are antigenically different have been isolated from human infections in various countries.

Pathogenicity. These two organisms show considerable difference in pathogenicity for experimental animals.

L. icterohemorrhagiae produces a typical and fatal icterus in the guinea pig, whereas *L. canicola* produces lesions only after the organism has been increased in virulence by passage through that animal. Larson has observed that the golden hamster (*Cricetus aceratus*) is susceptible to *L. canicola,* dying in 4–10 days after intraperitoneal inoculation with the organism. This information is of aid in the use of experimental animals for differential diagnosis. *L. icterohemorrhagiae* kills guinea pigs, mice, and hamsters, while *L. canicola* kills hamsters but only produces a febrile reaction with a loss of weight in guinea pigs, and fails to infect mice.

The water rat is recognized as being the reservoir for *L. icterohemorrhagiae* and is easily infected with the organism, which becomes localized in the kidneys and is eliminated in great numbers from the urine. This rat, however, is not susceptible to *L. canicola,* which persists for a short time in inoculated tissues but does not localize in kidney tissue and has never been recovered from rat urine. The reaction of the mouse to the two organisms is similar to that of the rat.

The dog is susceptible to both organisms which produce the natural disease. According to all reports *L. canicola* infection is much more prevalent in dogs than *L. icterohemorrhagiae.* The type of disease produced by each of the organisms is also somewhat different. *L. canicola* produces uremia but very little or no jaundice, whereas *L. icterohemorrhagiae* produces the typical jaundice of Weil's disease. Meyer and co-workers described a number of typical cases of *L. canicola* infection in which hemorrhage and faint icterus were found. Chronic types of canine leptospirosis have been described in which large numbers of the organisms are excreted with the urine.

In man, Weil's disease or epidemic jaundice is much more prevalent than the infection caused by *L. canicola;* in fact, relatively few cases of the latter infection have been reported. Meyer and co-workers, however, call attention to the fact that cases of canicola fever may be mild and difficult to diagnose clinically, since the majority of cases have no jaundice, resemble influenza or undulant fever, and are frequently accompanied by a meningitis.

Leptospirosis has been observed in cats and in silver foxes. Chamberland has reported a serious outbreak of the disease in Canadian foxes. It has been generally believed that neither of these species of Leptospira is associated with serious disease in swine, cattle, sheep, or horses. However, Rinehard has reported that positive serological reactions to both *L. icterohemorrhagiae* and *L. pomona* have been reported in testing bovine blood specimens. Yager has reported that serum samples from both cattle and swine were positive to *L. canicola,* upon investigation of an outbreak of leptospirosis in children who had bathed in a stream in Georgia. Serum samples from cattle are found to react in high titers to *L. pomona* in herds where cases of infertility are numerous.

Immunity. In their original work on the disease in man, Inada and Ito demonstrated that the disease responded favorably to the injection of blood from convalescent cases. Later they were able to produce in horses an antiserum which reduced the severity of the infection but did not prevent kidney lesions. Heat and phenol-killed cultures have been used successfully in Japan for the purpose of immunizing mine workers against the disease.

Meyer and associates reported the use of convalescent serum or serum from rabbits and horses immunized against specific strains for the treatment of the canine disease. Their results were very favorable when 10 to 50 ml. of serum were injected intranvenously. The use of monovalent *L. canicola* antiserum is always indicated in canine leptospirosis since the majority of cases are caused by that organism. Larson found that specific anti-*L. canicola* rabbit serum would protect hamsters against infection and proved of value as a therapeutic agent if used within three days after infection. The use of 10-day-old cultures to which 0.2 per cent formalin is added for attenuation gives satisfactory immunity in dogs, according to Alicata. In regions where both types of the organism are present, polyvalent antiserum should be used.

Diagnosis. Three methods are available for the diagnosis of canine leptospirosis. In the order of their value, Meyer and associates list (1) the agglutination-lysis test, (2) blood cultures and guinea pig inoculations with blood, and (3) urine examination by dark-field, serological procedures, cultures, and animal tests.

The rapid plate agglutination test in which heavy suspensions of leptospirae are used as antigens gives satisfactory results. The significant value of this test in detecting shedders of the organisms is emphasized by the study of war dogs by Jones, Roby, Davis, and Maurer. These investigators found 58 (1.33 per cent) positive reactors out of 4,368 dogs tested.

Leptospira pomona

Synonyms and History. The organism found in pigs in Argentina and called *L. suis* is considered to be identical to *L. pomona*.

L. pomona was namd after a village in Queensland, Australia, where the organism was isolated from dairy workers by Clayton and associates. Other strains found in Italy among rice field workers, and in Switzerland in swine, were found to be identical to the Australian strain.

Distribution and Transmission. *L. pomona* is known to be present throughout the world. In the United States it is the most common Leptospira found in cattle and swine.

The organism is eliminated in the urine of infected animals, consequently susceptible animals may become easily infected by the constant contacts they have with such excretion.

Morphology and Staining. *L. pomona* is similar to *L. icterohemorrhagiae* and *L. canicola* in morphology and staining characteristics.

Growth Requirements. The same basic media are required for *L. pomona* as for the two Leptospira described previously.

Resistance. *L. pomona* is susceptible to those disinfectants commonly employed against bacteria. The organism does not survive long outside the animal body. For that reason, laboratory tests and isolations must be conducted soon after the collection of the specimen.

Antigenic Structure. *L. pomona* shows some cross-agglutination with *L. autumnalis* and slight reactions with other Leptospirae.

Pathogenicity. This organism is pathogenic to cattle, in which it produces an acute fatal disease characterized by hemorrhage, hemoglobinuria, and icterus. Less acute cases of the disease in which anemia and icterus are the outstanding symptoms are also encountered. In some cases no visible symptoms are noted but the animal sheds the organism in the urine, and the serum gives a positive agglutination reaction. Abortions are frequently observed in cows affected, milk secretion is diminished or is completely absent, and the mammary gland becomes soft and pliable.

In swine, the disease caused by *L. pomona* is frequently associated with abortion or the pigs may be born dead or extremely weak. Swine may show no symptoms of the infection but may eliminate the organism in the urine and give a positive serum reaction.

In the horse, *L. pomona* is known to produce a rise in temperature following exposure. The eyes become involved, giving rise to the term "periodic ophthalmia or moon-blindness" which is considered to be the result of such infection.

L. pomona causes infection in man as a result of contact with infected cattle and swine. In Switzerland the term "swineherd's disease" is synonymous with leptospirosis.

Guinea pigs and hamsters are both susceptible to *L. pomona* and are useful as experimental animals in the study of the disease. Borg-Peterson and Fennestad have found that the striped field mouse (*Apodemus agrarius*) is susceptible to this organism and they believe it is of importance in the transmission of the disease.

Immunity. Animals which have recovered from leptospirosis are considered to be immune to the strain of organism producing the infection, but are susceptible to other non-antigenically related strains.

Vaccines are available for immunizing cattle and swine against the disease. When such vaccines are used in problem herds, the spread of the infection is immediately controlled. Whether widespread vaccination against leptospirosis will come into general use will depend upon the generalized spread of infection in livestock-raising areas.

Diagnosis. Leptospirosis due to L. *pomona* may by diagnosed by (1) agglutination-lysis test, (2) agglutination test, (3) isolation and cultivation of the organism, and (4) complement fixation.

REFERENCES FOR FURTHER STUDY

Alicata, J. E. Jour. Amer. Vet. Med. Assn., 102:472, 1943.

Baker, J. A., and Little, R. B. Jour. Exp. Med., 88:295, 1948.

Bergey, D. H., and associates. Bergey's Manual of Determinative Bacteriology. The Williams & Wilkins Co., Baltimore, 1948.

Bernkopf, H., Olitzki, L., and Stuczynski, L. A. Jour. Inf. Dis., 80:53, 1947.

Bohl, E. H. The incidence and clinical aspects of leptospirosis in cattle and swine in Ohio. Proc. Book, p. 167, Amer. Vet. Med. Assn., 92nd Ann. Meeting. 1955.

Borg-Peterson, C., and Fennestad, K. L. A field rodent (*Apodemus agrarius*) as a carrier of *Leptospira pomona* in Denmark. Jour. Amer. Vet. Med. Assn., 128:204, 1956.

Broom, J. C. Vet. Rec., 61:127, 1949.

———, and MacIntyre, A. B. Vet. Rec., 60:487, 1948.

Btesh, S. Trans. R. Soc. Trop. Med. Hyg., 41:419, 1947.

Chamberland, H. Can. Jour. Comp. Med., 7:39–46, 1943.

Esseveld, H., and Collier, W. A. Z. Immun. Forsch., 93:512–28, 1938.

Field, H. J., and Sellers, K. C. Vet. Rec., 62:313, 1950.

Freund, S. Jour. Comp. Path., 57:62, 1947.

Gay, F. P., and associates. Agents of Disease and Host Resistance. Chap. 44. Charles C. Thomas, Baltimore, 1935.

Gochenour, W. S. Jr., Yager, R. H., and Wetmore, P. W. Proc. Soc. Exp. Biol. Med., 74:201, 1950.

Gsell, O. R. Epidemiology of the Leptospiroses, p. 34. Symposium on the Leptospiroses, Med. Sci. Publ. No. 1, U.S. Govt. Printing Office, Washington, D. C., 1953.

Hindle, E. The Spirochaetes. A System of Bacteriology, 8:101–295. Med. Res. Council. His Majesty's Stationery Office, London, 1929.

Jones, T. C., Roby, T. O., Davis, C. L., and Maurer, F. D. Control of Leptospirosis in War Dogs. Amer. Jour. Vet. Res., 6:120–28, 1945.

Jungherr, E. Jour. Amer. Vet. Med. Assn., 91:661, 1937.

Jungherr, E. Jour. Amer. Vet. Med. Assn., 105:276, 1944.

Kaufmann, O. Z. Immun. Forsch., 93:354–67, 1938.

King, W. E., and Baeslack. Jour. Inf. Dis., 12:39–41, 206–35, 1913.

Larson, C. L. Pub. Health Rpt. Wash., 59:522–27, 1944.

Little, R. B., and Baker, J. A. Jour. Amer. Vet. Med. Assn., 116:105, 1950.

Loomis, E. C. Amer. Jour. Vet. Res., 14: 612, 1953.

Marsh, H. Jour. Amer. Vet. Med. Assn., 107:119–21, 1945.

Mathews, F. P. Amer. Jour. Vet. Res., 7:78–93, 1946.

McNeil, E., Hinshaw, W. R., and Kissling, R. E. Jour. Bact., 57:191, 1949.

Meyer, K. F., Stewart-Anderson, B., and Eddie, B. Canine Leptospirosis in the United States. Jour. Amer. Vet. Med. Assn., 95:710–29, 1939.

Mills, Susan. Vet. Rec., 60:267, 1948.

Molner, J. G., Meyer, K. F., and Raskin, H. A. Jour. Amer. Med. Assn., 136:814, 1948.

Monlux, W. S. Cornell Vet., 38:57, 1948.

Morcos, Z., Zaki, O. A., and Zaki, R. Jour. Amer. Vet. Med. Assn., 109: 112, 1946.

Morse, E. V. The economic significance of leptospirosis in domestic animals. Proc. Book, p. 162, Amer. Vet. Med. Assn., 92nd Ann. Meeting, 1955.

Novy, F. G., and Knapp, R. E. Jour. Inf. Dis., 3:291–393, 1906.

Rinehard, K. R. Epidemiology of the Leptospiroses, p. 126. Symposium on the Leptospiroses, Med. Sci. Publ. No. 1, U. S. Govt. Printing Office, Washington, D. C., 1953.

Roberts, S. J., York, C. J., and Robinson, J. W. Jour. Amer. Vet. Med. Assn., 121: 237, 1952.

Schmid, G., and Giovanella, R. Schweiz. Arch. Tierheilk., 89:1, 1947.

Savino, E., and Rennella, E. Abs. Vet. Bull., 16: 297, 1946.

Stoenner, H. G. Application of serology to the diagnosis of leptospirosis. Proc. Book, p. 172, Amer. Vet. Med. Assn., 92nd Ann. Meeting, 1955.

Sutherland A. K., and Morrill, C. C. Jour. Amer. Vet. Med. Assn., 113:468, 1948.

Theiler, A. Spirillosis of Cattle. Jour. Comp. Path. and Ther., 17:47–55, 1904.

Verge, J. Avian Spirochaetosis. Rec. Med. Vet., 112:257–70, 1936.

Walch-Sorgdrager, B. Leptospirosis, League of Nations Bull., Health Org., VIII. 1–2, 143–386, 1939.

Wolff, J. W. The Laboratory Diagnosis of Leptospirosis. Charles C. Thomas, Springfield, Ill., 1954.

Yager, R. H. Epidemiology of the Leptospiroses, p. 221. Symposium on Leptospiroses, Med. Sci. Publ. No. 1, U. S. Govt. Printing Office, Washington, D. C., 1953.

York, C. J., Johnston, R. V., and Robinson, V. B. The use of vaccine in the control of leptospirosis in cattle and swine. Proc. Book, p. 169, Amer. Vet. Med. Assn., 92nd Ann. Meeting, 1955.

37. | The Rickettsiales

Microorganisms classified in the Order Rickettsiales are pleo-morphic, either minute cocco-bacilli or coccoid, spherical, and ir-regular in shape (Fig. 37.1). They are stained lightly with the ordinary bacterial stains and are Gram-negative. They cannot be grown outside of tissue cells of the infected animal, the insect vec-tor, or in the chicken egg embryo.

In 1906 Ricketts transmitted Rocky Mountain spotted fever to guinea pigs and monkeys. In the same year he proved that the causal agent of the disease was transmitted by the wood tick, and in 1907 demonstrated that the infective agents were transmitted through the egg of the tick. In 1909 Ricketts found the microorgan-ism in blood smears of man, monkey, and guinea pig, and in the tissues of ticks. In 1910 Ricketts and Wilder proved that the louse was the transmitting agent in Mexican typhus and described an organism which was present in blood smears of humans infected with the disease and in smears of the intestinal contents of infected lice. These results were substantiated in 1916 by Da Rocha-Lima, who proposed the name *Rickettsia* for the newly-discovered micro-organisms in honor of the first discoverer.

Classification. The Rickettsiales are discussed in the majority of textbooks of bacteriology; however, their exact relationship to bacteria, to filtrable viruses, or to protozoa is not clear. They possess a number of basic characteristics, such as size, morphology, and method of division, which resemble bacteria. They differ from most bacteria in being difficult to stain and in their inability to grow on artificial media. They resemble some of the small bodies, known as inclusion bodies, which are produced within the cells of animals infected with certain of the filtrable viruses. They bear some re-semblance to those protozoa which are small, irregular, granule-like organisms found within the cells of infected animals.

The Order Rickettsiales is divided (Bergey's Manual 1948) into three families which are described as follows:

FAMILY I.   *Rickettsiaceae:* Intracellular parasites, or parasites intimately associated with tissue cells but
not occurring in erythrocytes. Frequently cause
diseases of vertebrates transmitted by arthropod
vectors.

FAMILY II.   *Bartonellaceae:* Facultative intracellular or extracellular parasites found characteristically in or
on erythrocytes of vertebrates. May be transmitted by arthropod vectors.

FAMILY III.   *Chlamydozoaceae:* Intracellular parasites found
in vertebrate tissues and not transmitted by
arthropod vectors.

Each of these families is divided into numerous genera, many
of which have species which are pathogenic to animals and to man.

Each family group will be described, and those species of particular significance will be discussed.

THE FAMILY RICKETTSIACEAE

This family is divided into the three genera Rickettsia, Coxiella, and Cowdria.

The Genus Rickettsia. There are six species in the genus Rickettsia which are identified by the type of disease each produces
and by the type of insect vector. *Rickettsia prowazekii* is louse-
borne, *Rickettsia typhi* is flea-borne, *Rickettsia rickettsii* and
Rickettsia conorii are tick-borne, and *Rickettsia tsutsugamushi* and
Rickettsia akari are mite-borne.

Those species which produce significant infections in animals
will be discussed in greater detail while those which are transmitted to man will be described briefly. The student is referred to
texts of Medical Bacteriology for more detailed discussions of these
latter species and the diseases they produce.

Rickettsia prowazekii

R. prowazekii is the cause of typhus fever, an acute infectious
disease of man characterized by high fever, severe headaches, and
a generalized macular or maculo-papular rash. The disease occurs
endemically in Korea, Japan, China, Indo-China, Serbia, Russia,
Central Europe, North Africa, Egypt, Ethiopia, South Africa, Mexico, Guatemala, Colombia, Peru, Bolivia, and Chile. The organism
has not become established upon the North American continent.

This organism is transmitted by the common body louse and the
head louse from an infected person to a susceptible one. Although
such lice neither fly nor jump they do crawl considerable distances,
hence may become lodged in clothing and crawl directly from person to person in close contact. Lice spend their life on the human

body, deriving nutrition from the blood of their host. The organism multiplies in the tissue cells lining the intestine of the louse (Fig. 37.2), causing a rupture of the infected cells and the liberation of masses of rickettsia. The feces of the louse contain large numbers of the organism by which other lice may become infected. The organism is transmitted to man by the infected lice at the time of feeding and, obviously, the lice become infected from man in the same process.

R. *prowazekii* is a minute, coccoid, ovoid rod although long rods and filamentous forms may be seen (Fig. 37.1). Single cells are 0.25 by 0.4μ in size. They are nonmotile. When stained with Giemsa stain the organism is light purple. It does not stain well by the Gram stain but is considered Gram-negative.

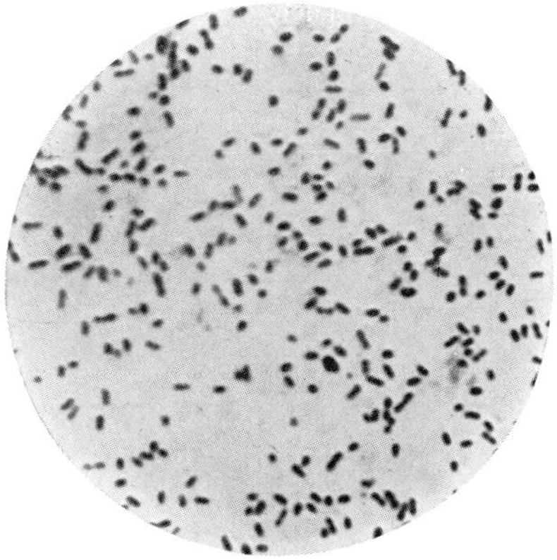

FIG. 37.1 — **Rickettsia prowazekii** in smear from louse intestine. Giemsa stain, × 2,000. (From Nowak: Documenta Microbiologica, courtesy Gustav Fischer.)

The organism can be cultivated artificially in tissue cultures of mammalian cells, in the intestine of the louse, in modified Maitland media with and without agar, on the chorioallantoic membrane, and in the yolk sac of the chicken embryo.

In addition to man and lice, the organism is pathogenic for apes, monkeys, guinea pigs, cotton rats, and the gerbille.

Immunity is produced in man by an attack of the disease. Killed vaccines, formerly produced from artificially infected lice, but now from infected yolk-sac material of the chicken embryo, are valuable immunizing agents. The disease is prevented in many areas of the world by prophylactic vaccination.

Antibodies are produced by the fifth or eighth day of illness, so agglutination and complement fixation tests may be used for diagnosis, using antigens composed of the organism. Serum from a patient with typhus fever agglutinates (Weil-Felix reaction) suspensions of *Proteus vulgaris*, strain OX19, revealing an antigenic component which is common to both organisms. Diagnosis is confirmed by the isolation of R. *prowazekii* from blood clots inoculated into guinea pigs or into embryonated chicken eggs.

Rickettsia typhi

R. *typhi* is the cause of murine typhus, a relatively mild, acute febrile disease of man, of 9 to 15 days' duration, characterized by headache and a macular rash. The disease is world-wide in distribution and occurs endemically throughout certain sections of the southern part of the United States and in Mexico. It has been frequently confused with epidemic typhus.

The organism produces a natural infection in rats and mice, among which it is transmitted by the rat flea and also the rat louse. It is transmitted to man from the rat by the rat flea, although the body louse of man is also known to be a transmitting agent.

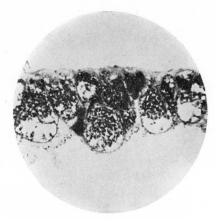

R. typhi does not differ from *R. prowazekii* in morphology and staining characteristics, and it can be cultivated on the same types of media. Growth has been obtained in the peritoneal cavity of X-rayed rats, in the lungs of white rats and white mice following intranasal inoculation, and in the lungs of rabbits following intratracheal inoculation.

FIG. 37.2 — **Rickettsia prowazekii** in epithelial cells of louse intestine, Giemsa stain, × 500. (From Nowak: Documenta Microbiologica, courtesy Gustav Fischer.)

In addition to rats, mice, fleas, lice, rabbits, and man, the following animals have been shown susceptible: ape, monkey, guinea pig, gerbille, woodchuck, flying squirrel, gray squirrel, fox squirrel, gopher, cottontail rabbit, swamp rabbit, chipmunk, skunk, opossum, and cat. In the guinea pig the organism produces, by intraperitoneal inoculation, a febrile reaction and testicular swelling without necrosis.

Immunity is produced by an infection caused by this organism. Antibodies developed are indistinguishable from those produced by *R. prowazekii* infection. The comparatively mild nature of the disease serves to differentiate murine typhus from epidemic typhus, otherwise accurate diagnosis is difficult.

Rickettsia rickettsii

R. rickettsii is the cause of Rocky Mountain spotted fever of man, an acute febrile disease characterized by marked prostration, chills, myalgia and arthralgia, and a distinctive rash which develops into rose-red maculopapular lesions from which the name was derived. The disease is found in most of the states of North America. In Brazil the disease is known as Sao Paulo typhus and Minas Gerais typhus and in Colombia it is called Tobia fever. The greatest number of cases in the United States occur in the western mountain states where the disease is endemic in the tick population.

The organism is present in numerous species of ticks. In the western mountain region the common wood tick *Dermacentor andersoni* is involved; the dog tick *D. variabilis* is found throughout the middle western and eastern states; the rabbit tick *Haemaphysalis leporis-palustris* is found throughout the United States, north into Canada and Alaska, and south into South America. Numerous other species of ticks are known to harbor the organism and are agents for its transmission among animal hosts from which it may be transmitted to those various ticks which attack man. *R. rickettsii* is transmitted through the life cycle of the tick from the ova to the adult. It is present in all the tissues of the tick and in the feces, hence man may become infected not only by the bite of the tick but also by crushing ticks or by handling tick-infested animals.

Morphologically, *R. rickettsii* is a small, lanceolate rod often occurring in pairs. It is 0.2 to 0.3μ in width by 1μ in length. When stained by the Giemsa method the organism is blue with purple polar granules. It occurs in the cytoplasm of infected cells in dense masses of coccoid forms. The organism can be cultivated in ticks, in tissue cells of mammalian origin, in Maitland media, on the chorio-allantoic membrane, and in the yolk sac of the chicken embryo.

In addition to man and the ticks themselves, the organism is known to infect various species of rabbits, squirrels, and mice. These animals are not considered to have a natural infection but serve as temporary passive carriers during the active life cycle of the tick. Mammalian blood does apparently contain an "activator" substance which serves to stimulate the growth of the organism in the tick. It is during this period of tick activity that man becomes accidentally infected. He does not enter into the cycle by which the organism is perpetuated. The large domestic animals are not susceptible to *R. rickettsii*. However, dogs and cats have been found susceptible to experimental infection. In Brazil dogs are found to be naturally infected and are considered to play a role in the transmission of the disease. The guinea pig is the best experimental animal, the organism producing fever, scrotal rash, necrosis of the tips of the ears and foot pads, and a markedly enlarged spleen. Monkeys and rabbits are susceptible and may be used as experimental animals in studying the disease.

A permanent immunity is developed in man by an attack of the disease. Vaccines prepared from infected ticks and from the yolk sacs of fertile chicken eggs are used for immunization. The disease is diagnosed by symptoms with the aid of the inoculation of guinea pigs and egg embryos, the Weil-Felix reaction, the virus-neutralization test, and the complement-fixation test.

Rickettsia conorii

R. *conorii* is the cause of Boutonneuse fever of man, a benign disease characterized by a maculopapular eruption on the palms and soles and a black, hemorrhagic area at the site of the tick bite. This disease is also known as Marseilles or Mediterranean typhus. It is found in various countries bordering on the Mediterranean Sea.

The organism is transmitted almost exclusively by the dog tick, R. *sanguinius,* in which it may live during the entire life cycle of the tick. Dogs do not show an apparent infection and are of significance in the disease only by serving as hosts for ticks. Rabbits, sheep, pigs, pigeons have been found resistant to the disease. The guinea pig is susceptible, and the same type of disease, except milder, is produced as by R. *rickettsii.*

R. *conorii* is similar to R. *rickettsii* in morphology and staining properties and may be cultivated upon the same types of media.

The disease is diagnosed by its peculiar symptomatology, by complement fixation, and by the Weil-Felix reaction. Vaccines are not used for the control of the infection.

Rickettsia tsutsugamushi

This organism causes tsutsugamushi fever and scrub typhus in man, an acute febrile disease characterized by exanthema and enlargement of the lymph nodes near the site of bite wounds. The disease is also known as Japanese flood fever, flood fever, and Kedani fever. In addition to Japan the disease is found in Formosa, Sumatra, the Malay States, and probably other regions of the Orient and the islands of the Southwest Pacific.

R. *tsutsugamushi* is transmitted by a mite, and there is evidence that the organism passes through the life cycle of the mite. It is a small bacterium-like organism 0.3 to 5μ in width by 0.8 to 2μ in length; it is non-motile and Gram-negative. Artificial growth is obtained upon tissue cultures, chicken egg embryo, in the rabbit testis, and the endothelial cells overlying Descemet's membrane of the rabbit eye.

In addition to man and the animals mentioned, the organism is pathogenic for monkeys, gibbons, guinea pigs, hamsters, rats, voles, mice, gerbilles.

The immunity produced in man is not as permanent as with the other rickettsia, and it is believed that different antigenic strains of the organism exist.

Rickettsia akari

R. akari is the cause of rickettsialpox of man, an acute but not fatal disease characterized by fever and a maculopapular rash which develops into vesicles with black scabs. The organism is transmitted by the mite, *Allodermanyssus sanguineus*. The disease has been found only in New York City.

The organism is a minute diplobacillus, found intracellularly and also intranuclearly in yolk sac cells. It is non-motile. Growth has been obtained only in the yolk sac of the chicken egg. Mice and guinea pigs have been infected experimentally but attempts to produce the disease in monkeys have been unsuccessful.

Miscellaneous Rickettsia

Rickettsia bovis was first described by Donatien and Lestoquard at Algiers, North Africa, in 1936 and subsequently by Moshkovsky in 1945. It is found as tightly massed irregular forms in monocytic cells of the bovine, in which it produces a slight febrile disease. It is transmitted by ticks of the genus Hyalomma.

Rickettsia canis was also described by Donatien and Lestoquard, 1935, being found in experimental dogs. They considered it to be transmitted by the dog tick. The organism occurred as spherical masses in the monocytic cells of the dog, in which it produced an acute fatal disease.

Rickettsia ovina was first described by Donatien and Lestoquard in 1936. It likewise was found in monocytes cells of sheep in Algeria. The tick *Rhipicephalus bursa* was considered to be the vector.

The Genus Coxiella. This genus has been created to include those microorganisms which are filterable, thereby differing from the Rickettsia, or as may be expressed, they represent those Rickettsia which are filterable. Only one species, *Coxiella burnetii*, has been described.

Coxiella burnetii

Coxiella burnetii is the cause of Q-fever in man — an acute, febrile, influenza-like disease characterized by sudden onset, malaise, headache, anorexia, weakness, and an interstitial pneumonitis.

This disease was first noted by Australian investigators in the province of Queensland in 1935, and the etiologic agent was observed and named *Rickettsia burneti* by Derrick of Australia in 1939. During the same period an organism was isolated from ticks, *Dermacentor andersoni*, by Davis in 1935, and described by Davis and Cox in Montana in 1938. This organism was named *Rickettsia diaporica* by Cox in 1939. Subsequently the two organisms were shown to be identical by Dyer and by Bengston, and the name *Coxiella burnetii* was given to it in honor of Cox and Burnet.

In addition to Australia and Montana, previously mentioned, the organism has been found to produce infection in western Europe, the Mediterranean area, the Balkans, the Near East, Spain, and Panama. In the United States Q-fever has been reported from numerous parts of the country. It was found to produce an infection in packing-house workers in Texas and Illinois. It is endemic in dairy cattle in southern California. The testing of serums from cattle and human beings in Washington has given positive results. Cases of the disease have occurred among laboratory workers in Washington, D.C., and Fort Bragg, So. Carolina, and two cases were reported among people who had contact with one of the workers in Washington, D.C. (Beeman). Undoubtedly, future surveys will reveal the presence of the organism in many other areas.

Coxiella burnetii is a small, bacterium-like, pleomorphic organism varying in size from coccoid shape to well-marked rods (Fig. 37.3). It occurs in large numbers in the cytoplasm of infected cells and particularly in the monocytes, pushing the nucleus of the cell over to one side. When observed extracellularly, diplobacillary, lanceolate, segmented bacillary forms and short chains are apparent. Sizes varying from 0.25 to 1.5 microns have been described. When stained with Giemsa stain it is reddish-purple and with Machiavello's stain it is bright red against a blue background. The organism is Gram-negative. Artificial culture is obtained in plasma tissue cultures, in modified Maitland media, in the yolk sac, and in all tissues of the chicken embryo. All strains are antigenically alike, although some are more antigenic than others.

C. burnetii is transmitted by numerous species of ticks to the various animals which serve as natural reservoirs. In Australia the tick, *Haemaphysalis humerosa,* is considered the most important vector. This tick is commonly found on the bandicoot (Smith, Derrick *et al.*), an animal which is found to be naturally infected, and also on cattle and rats. In the United States the ticks *Dermacentor andersoni, Amblyomena americanum, Haemophysalis leporis-palustris, Dermacentor occidentalis, Ixodes dentatus,* and *Otobius megnini* are recognized as transmitting agents. Many other species of ticks have been found to transmit *C. burnetii* experimentally, so it is quite likely that most ticks are vectors if the infection is present in an area. In common with other Rickettsia, ticks remain infected with *C. burnetii* for long periods of time and their feces contain the organism.

Mantovani and Benazzi have shown that ticks *(Rhipicephalus sanguineus)* which had fed on dogs suffering a natural infection of Q-fever harbored the organisms and were capable of transmitting them to susceptible hosts.

The cycle of transmission of Q-fever in the natural state involves many species of animals. The bandicoot in Australia has

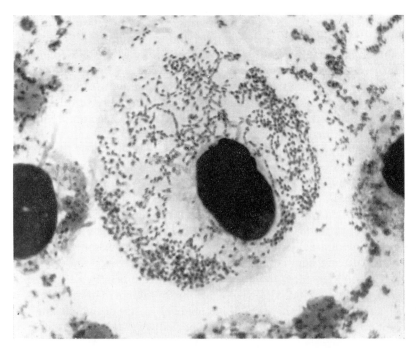

FIG. 37.3 — **Coxiella burnetii,** × 960. Subcutaneous exudate from guinea pig. Photo courtesy H. R. Cox.

been mentioned, and cattle have been persistently present in the picture in all areas where the disease exists. Experimentally, numerous species of rodents have been infected with the organism but the role they play in the natural disease is not known. Reports also indicate that goats, sheep, horses, mules, dogs, and cats may be hosts for the organism. Of the avian species, the chicken and parrakeet have been found susceptible experimentally. The transmission of *C. burnetii* to man may be made directly by the bite of ticks, by the handling of cattle whose hides have been contaminated by tick bites, and by contact with the flesh of cattle which are infected with the organism. The observation of Q-fever in southern California among dairy workers and the investigations of Huebner and his associates have revealed that the disease may be transmitted by milk. However, it has been demonstrated by Stoenner and

Lackman that the dairy cow cannot be infected by bathing the ends of the teats in infective material. This method of transmission is all the more important since it has been shown that C. *burnetii* is resistant to pasteurization at 143°F. 30 minutes. The discovery (Luoto and Huebner, 1950) of this organism in placental tissues of cows serologically positive to Q-fever antigen has revealed another potential source of infection.

In addition to the obvious methods of transmission just described, Parker, Bell, and Stoenner indicate that results with experimental animals suggest: " (1) that the eyes, nostrils, digestive tract, and the abraded or even the unabraded skin may be avenues of infection; (2) that the Rickettsia remains highly infectious for long periods in dry tick feces, in dry blood, and probably in other dried materials, and that dried infectious materials can contaminate the ground, inanimate objects, burrows, nests, etc., and can be in the air as dust particles; (3) that tissues of animals dead from Q-fever, or of live animals in which the Rickettsia has persisted following recovery, may be a source of infection for scavenger and predaceous animals; (4) that it is possible, as in the case of sheep, goats and cattle, that milk from infected animals may be infectious for their young; and (5) that there is at least a possibility that infected male animals may sometimes be able to transmit infection to females during copulation and perhaps vice versa."

The nature of Q-fever in man has been briefly described at the beginning of the discussion of the organism. Other details of the infection may be found in medical tests of which the description by Smadel is typical. The pathology of natural Q-fever in domestic animals, particularly cattle, is not thoroughly known. Allusions are made in the literature to a "slight illness." It has been apparent to all observers that the disease in the natural state is a very benign one and that the infected animal is best described as one having an "inapparent infection." Experimentally, Parker, Bell, and Stoenner obtained the following results in four cows following the inoculation via the milk ducts of 5 billion guinea pig doses of a yolk-sac culture of the organism: " (1) the blood of all 4 cows was infectious on two or more of the first five days (later on, all tests were negative); (2) the milk of each of the inoculated quarters of each cow was infectious from the first day to the date of sacrifice, or to such date as the tests were completed; (3) the systemic reaction was of brief duration preceding and accompanying an acute phase of mastitis and was characterized by marked pyrexia, slight serous nasal and lacrimal discharges, moderate to severe depression, partial inappetance, infrequent rumination and shallow rumen movements, moderate tachycardia, and a moderate polypnea accompanied only by a definite increase in vesicular murmur; (4) the disease produced temporary metabolic changes in the activity of the mammary gland as far as the constituents of milk were concerned; (5) the cows, except for the one sacrificed on the 5th day, all became positive serologically; (6) on autopsy, gross lesions were confined chiefly to the mammary gland and regional lymph nodes; (7) by titration of milk in guinea pigs, the milk was shown to be infective in dilutions of at least 10^{-5} and 10^{-4} on the 2nd and 7th day postinoculation, respectively, and thereafter at five-day intervals was infective at 10^{-1}; and (8) in the cow sacrificed on the 63rd day, the milk of the uninoculated right rear quarter became infectious on the 7th day and remained infectious until the cow was sacrificed." In addition to the experiment described above these authors were able to infect calves with infective milk. One calf became febrile on the 13th day while the other one did not develop symptoms.

The guinea pig is the experimental animal of choice in Q-fever studies. This animal is readily infected by subcutaneous or intradermal inoculation, and a marked inflammatory reaction occurs at the point of inoculation. Mortality is low in inoculated guinea pigs; those dying reveal a marked splenic enlargement. As previously mentioned, *C. burnetii* grews well in embryonated chicken eggs, and death of the embryo results four to five days after inoculation. Chicken embryo cultures are routinely used for infection experiments, cross immunity tests, and for experimental vaccine production.

The diagnosis of Q-fever in man is accomplished by the isolation of the organism and by serologic tests. The antigen used in serologic tests is prepared in chicken embryos. Either the agglutination test or the complement-fixation test may be used. Surveys of animal populations to obtain data relative to the presence of Q-fever in an area are made with the agglutination or complement-fixation tests.

The Genus Cowdria. The genus Cowdria is composed of one species which produces disease in animals, *Cowdria ruminantium.*

Cowdria ruminantium

In 1925 Cowdry described a small microorganism which he found in the endothelial cells of animals that had succumbed to "heartwater." He found the organism resembled those of typhus and Rocky Mountain spotted fever; consequently he named it *Rickettsia ruminantium*. The genus Cowdria was originated by Bengston in honor of Cowdry in 1948.

This organism is the cause of an acute septicemia which has

been observed in cattle, sheep, and goats in various parts of Africa. The name, "heartwater," is given to this disease because of the most characteristic lesion, hydropericardium, found on autopsy. The disease is further characterized by a high temperature and by nervous symptoms. The microorganisms are found in the endothelial cells of the capillaries of the renal glomeruli, in the endothelial cells of the large blood vessels, and in the superficial gray matter of the cerebral cortex. It is not found in blood smears from the infected animal.

Cowdria ruminantium is transmitted by ticks of the genus *Amblyomma*. If the ticks are infected during the larvae stage they remain infective after moulting to the nymph stage; if infected in the nymph stage they are infective in the adult stage. The organism multiplies within the cells of the intestine of the tick and probably to some extent in the lumen. It is not transmitted from one generation of ticks to another through the egg, thereby differing from the microorganism of Rocky Mountain spotted fever.

This organism is 0.2 to 0.3μ by 0.4 to 0.5μ in size. Diplococcoid forms are commonly observed. The organisms are usually contained within the cell, but a few scattered ones are occasionally seen in the surrounding tissue. It is stained a dark blue by Giemsa stain and is Gram-negative. It cannot be cultivated upon artificial media.

Cowdria ruminantium is not a resistant organism; in fact, it rarely survives more than 36 hours at laboratory temperatures. It will live as long as twelve days in brain tissue stored in a refrigerator.

The disease produced by this Rickettsia is most prevalent during the warm months of the year during the tick season. The goat is most susceptible, then the sheep and then cattle. In goats and sheep the death losses are often 100 per cent, while in cattle 60 per cent of the animals may die. Experimentally, the organism is infective for the guinea pig, the rabbit, the white rat, the ferret, and some of the species of antelope.

An animal which recovers from an attack of "heartwater" is resistant to further attacks, but the organism has been known to persist in recovered animals for as long as 105 days. The immunity is apparently cellular in nature, for the immune state cannot be transferred from an immune to a susceptible animal. Experimentally it has been found necessary to cause a reaction in order to produce an immunity against the disease.

The diagnosis of this disease is facilitated by the epizootic and the pathologic features of the infection. The organisms can be seen usually in the endothelial cells of the jugular vein and the vena cava. (Fig. 37.4.)

THE FAMILY BARTONELLACEAE

The family Bartonellaceae is composed of those microorganisms which are small and markedly pleomorphic, stain well with Giemsa's stain, lightly with aniline stains, and are Gram-negative. They are found in the erythrocytes of man and a number of species of animals. They are differentiated from protozoa found in erythrocytes by the absence of cytoplasm around the nucleus.

Four genera are classified by Bengston and Weinman as follows:

GENUS I.   *Bartonella*: parasites of the erythrocytes and of fixed tissues of man.

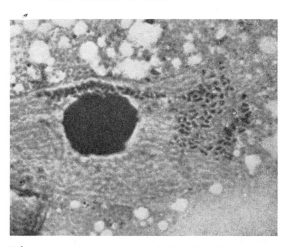

FIG. 37.4 — **Rickettsia ruminantium** in endothelial cell of vena cava of sheep, × 1,800. (From Donatien and Lestoquard, Arch. Inst. Past. d'Algérie.)

GENUS II.   *Haemobartonella*: parasites of the erythrocytes of lower mammals; increased in susceptible animals by splenectomy; sensitive to arsenicals.

GENUS III. *Grahamella*: parasites of the erythrocytes of lower mammals; not increased in susceptible animals by splenectomy; not sensitive to arsenicals.

GENUS IV.   *Eperythrozoon*: blood parasites found on erythrocytes and in plasma of lower mammals; appear as rings, coccoid cells, and short rods; splenectomy activates latent infection.

The Genus Bartonella. Only one species has been recognized.

Bartonella bacilliformis

This organism is the cause of Oroya fever in man, a condition characterized by anemia; an eruptive type of the disease in man is called verruga peruana; a third type is found which is a mixture of the first two.

The organism is a slender rod with granular swellings at the ends, producing club, dumbbell, or coccoid shapes. It measures 0.25 by 0.5 microns in width to 1 to 3 microns in length, but longer forms may be seen. Growth of the organism is obtained on semisolid rabbit-blood agar. It also grows on other artificial media and in the chicken embryo chorio-allantoic fluid and in the yolk sac. The ordinary aniline stains are not useful for staining this organism but it stains well with Giemsa's stain. The organism is found in the blood and endothelial cells of man and has been reported in sand flies.

The Genus Haemobartonella. This genus is composed of numerous species which are named and classified according to the animal they infect. These organisms cause haemobartonellosis and anemia in the various animals infected but do not cause eruption. As a group they are characterized as slender rods with rounded ends in which darker granules may be found producing club, dumbbell, or diplococcoid shapes. They vary in size from 0.1 to 0.25 by 0.7 to 4 microns in length. Short chains and filamentous, segmented forms are observed in some species. In an infection they are found distributed over the erythrocyte and have been observed within the cell. Some of them have been cultivated upon artificial media, especially semisolid, rabbit-blood agar. Artificial infection is difficult to produce in experimental animals without splenectomy. They are usually transmitted by insect vectors. They are sensitive to arsenicals.

The reader is referred to Bergey's Manual (1948) for greater details concerning the various species. The species names of Haemobartonella and their hosts are as follows: *H. muris,* the white rat; *H. canis,* the dog; *H. microtii,* the vole; *H. tyzzeri,* the guinea pig; *H. bovis,* cattle; *H. sturmanii,* buffalo; *H. peromyscii,* the deer mouse; *H. peromyscii* var. *maniculati,* the gray-backed deer mouse; *H. blarinae,* the short-tailed shrew; *H. sciurii,* the gray squirrel.

The Genus Grahamella. In this genus are found those bacteria-like parasites which occur within the erythrocytes of lower animals. The ends of the organism are enlarged giving dumbbell, wedge, and club-shaped forms which are arranged irregularly, 6 to 20 in number, in the erythrocyte. They are 0.1 to 1 micron in size. When stained by the Giemsa method they are light blue; the ends are darker blue. Only one species, *Grahamella talpae,* which is pathogenic for moles, is definitely recognized (Bergey 1948), although numerous other species have been recorded in the literature.

The Genus Eperythrozoon. The microorganisms classified in this genus are found in the plasma and on the erythrocytes of animals in which they produce anemia, eperythryzoonosis. These organisms are coccoid short rods, 1 to 2 microns long, often appearing in ring shapes. They stain bluish or pinkish violet by the Giemsa stain and are Gram-negative. Splenectomy of susceptible animals activates latent infections. They have not been grown on cell-free media. Six different species have been described: *E. coccoides*, in white mice; *E. ovis*, in sheep; *E. wenyoni*, in cattle; *E. suis*, in swine; *E. varians*, in gray-backed deer mice; *E. dispar*, in voles and dwarf mice.

Eperythrozoon suis has been found by Splitter in naturally occurring outbreaks of eperythrozoonosis among swine in Kansas. The disease is characterized by a severe ictero-anemia and marked debility. Swine which recover from the infection are considered to be permanent carriers.

THE FAMILY CHLAMYDOZOACEAE

The third family of the order Rickettsiales is composed of those microorganisms which are minute, pleomorphic, and coccoid. It is believed that they are obligate intracellular parasites; at least they have not been cultivated upon cell-free media. Three genera are placed in this family by Rake.

The Genus Chlamydozoon. The type species of this genus is *Ch. trachomatis*, the cause of trachoma in man. This disease is characterized by destructive lesions of the cornea and conjunctiva. The organism is small and coccoid, 200 to 350 millimicrons in diameter. It forms elementary bodies (groups of individual cells) and plaques up to 10 microns in diameter. Masses of the organism stain reddish-blue with the Giemsa stain. It has not been cultivated upon artificial media or in the chicken egg embryo. In addition to man it is pathogenic for apes and monkeys.

Another species of this genus, *Ch. oculogenitale*, causes an acute conjunctivitis and inflammation of the lower genito-urinary tract in man.

The Genus Miyagawanella. This genus is composed of those minute agents which are coccoid and pass through a development cycle from the individual cell stage to the formation of the elementary body. They are found in the cytoplasm of infected cells. Growth is obtained in the chicken egg embryo.

Miyagawanella psittacii

M. psittacii is the cause of psittacosis, a disease of man and numerous species of birds, characterized by acute pulmonary infection commonly called atypical pneumonia or pneumonitis.

The organism is widely distributed throughout the world, being most prevalent in those areas where parrots, parrakeets, and similar birds are found. It produces an acute infection with death in such birds but many birds harbor the organism without showing noticeable symptoms of disease. Transmission of the infectious agent occurs during close contact of birds with one another and in man by contact (feeding, handling, living in close quarters) with infected birds. In some instances infection is spread from person to person.

M. *psittacii* is a minute, coccoid organism 200 to 350 millimicrons in size. The organism is characterized by the formation of elementary bodies and inclusion bodies, within the invaded cells of the host. There may be more than one elementary body in each cell. The multiplication of the individual organisms within the elementary body then occurs, and the infected cell becomes packed with the microorganisms forming plaques or inclusion bodies. Upon the death of the cell the organisms are liberated. They then invade new cells where the cycle is repeated. This organism is cultivated upon tissue cultures and in the chorio-allantoic membrane and in the yolk sac of the chicken embryo. An endotoxin which is lethal to mice is formed in the yolk sac.

The occurrence of the natural disease among parrots and other psittacine birds has been mentioned. Most strains of the organism do not infect guinea pigs to any significant degree. Rabbits, pocket gophers, hamsters, cotton rats, and squirrels may be infected. Wild rats and white laboratory rats and deer mice are not infected by intraperitoneal inoculation.

The development of a fast immunity in human beings who have recovered from psittacosis is open to question. Antibodies are formed by an infection in man, naturally infected birds, and in experimental birds and animals. Complement-fixation and agglutination tests have been devised which are of aid in diagnosis as well as in the experimental study of this and closely related microorganisms.

Miyagawanella ornithosis

This organism is similar to M. *psittacii* in practically all of its characteristics, including the type of disease produced in man. Differentiation is provided by the use of toxin-antitoxin neutralization tests and the neutralization of infection in mice with chicken antisera.

This organism is commonly separated from M. *psittacii* on the basis of the species of the avian family infected. The latter organism infects psittacine birds, but M. *ornithosis* infects non-psittacine species, including pigeons, doves, pheasants, ducks, turkeys, and chickens. Numerous experimental animals are susceptible.

Miyagawanella felis

M. *felis* is an organism which was first described by Baker in 1942 as the cause of conjunctivitis, nasal catarrh, distemper, or pneumonitis in the cat. This organism is morphologically similar to other members of the genus and can be cultivated in chicken embryos. In addition to the cat, mice and hamsters are susceptible. This disease may be confused clinically with panleucopenia of cats caused by a virus which is discussed in the section on Virology.

In addition to the above species in the genus Miyagawanella, three species or strains of pneumonitis virus or virus pneumonia of man have been listed. These are: *M. pneumoniae* (the S-F strain of virus pneumonia), *M. louisianae* (the Louisiana strain of virus pneumonia) and *M. illini* (the Illinois strain of virus pneumonia). As far as is definitely known, animal or avian species have not been shown to be reservoirs of these organisms. *M. lymphogranuloma*, the cause of venereal lymphogranuloma of man, is another member of the genus which is pathogenic only for man. *M. bronchopneumoniae* has been isolated from laboratory mice in which it produces a pneumonitis.

The Genus Colesiota. This genus includes those organisms which are found in the conjunctiva and cornea. *C. conjunctivae* has been described by Coles, of South Africa, where it has been found in acute conjunctivitis and keratitis of sheep, cattle, and goats. This organism has not been found in cases of infectious conjunctivitis and keratitis in cattle in the United States. Another organism, *C. conjunctiva-gallii*, which was found by Coles and Anders in South Africa as the cause of conjunctivitis and keratitis in chickens, is classified in this genus.

REFERENCES FOR FURTHER STUDY

Baker, J. A. Science, 96:475, 1942.

———. Jour. Exp. Med., 79:159, 1944.

Beck, M. D., Bell, J. A., Shaw, E. W., and Huebner, R. J. Q-fever Studies in Southern California. II. An Epidemiological Study of 300 Cases. Pub. Hlth. Rep. Wash., 64:41, 1949.

Bengston, Ida A. Pub. Hlth. Rep. Wash., 59:402, 1944.

———. Bergey's Manual of Determinative Bacteriology. Williams and Wilkins Co., Baltimore, 1948.

Coles, J. D. W. A. 17th Rep. Div. Vet. Ser. Ani. Ind., Union So. Afr., 175, 1931.

———. Onderstepoort Jour., 4:389, 1935.

———. Jour. So. Afr. Vet. Med. Assn., 7, 1936.

Cowdry, E. V. Jour. Exp. Med., 42:231, 253, 1925.

Cox, H. R. Pub. Hlth. Rep. Wash., 54:1822, 1939.

———. Specific Complement-Fixing Antigens for Viral and Rickettsial Diseases. Amer. Jour. Pub. Hlth., 38:351, 1948.

———. The Spotted Fever Group, in Rivers, Viral and Rickettsial Infections of Man. J. B. Lippincott Co., Philadelphia, 1948.

Davis, G. E., and Cox, H. R. Pub. Hlth. Rep. Wash., 53:2259, 1938.

Derrick, E. H. Med. Jour. Aust., Aug. 21, p. 281, 1937.

———. Med. Jour. Aust., Jan. 7, p. 14, 1939.

Donatien, A., and Lestoquard, F. Arch. Inst. Past. d'Algérie, 15: 142, 1937.

Gillespie, J. H. Experimental Q-fever in cats. Amer. Jour. Vet. Res., 13: 91, 1952.

Huebner, R. J., Stamps, P., and Armstrong, C. Rickettsialpox—a Newly Recognized Rickettsial Disease. I. Isolation of the Etiological Agent. Pub. Hlth. Rep. Wash., 61:1605, 1946.

————, Jellison, W. L., Beck, M. D., Parker, R. R., and Shepard, C. C. Q-fever Studies in Southern California. I. Recovery of *Rickettsia burneti* from Raw Milk. Pub. Hlth. Rep. Wash., 63:214, 1948.

————, ————, ————, and Wilcox, F. P. Q-fever Studies in Southern California. III. Effects of Pasteurization on Survival of *C. burnetii* in Naturally Infected Milk. Pub. Hlth. Rep. Wash., 64:499, 1949.

Irons, J. V., and Cooper, J. M. Q-fever in the United States. II. Clinical Data on an Outbreak Among Stock Handlers and Slaughterhouse Workers. Jour. Amer. Med. Assn., 133:815, 1947.

————, Murphy, J. N., and Wolfe, D. M. Q-fever in the United States. III. Serologic Observations in an Outbreak Among Stock Handlers and Slaughterhouse Workers. Jour. Amer. Med. Assn., 133:819, 1947.

Jellison, W. L., Beck, E. J., Huebner, R. J., Parker, R. R., and Welsh, H. H. Q-fever Studies in Southern California. IV. Occurrence of *C. burnetii* in the Spinose ear tick, *Otobius megnini*. Pub. Hlth. Rep. Wash., 63:1483, 1948.

————, Ormsbee, R., Huebner, R. J., Parker, R. R., and Bell, E. J. Q-fever Studies in Southern California. V. Natural Infection in a Dairy Cow. Pub. Hlth. Rep. Wash., 63:1611, 1948.

————, Welsh, H. H., Elson, B. E., and Huebner, R. J. Q-fever Studies in Southern California. XI. Recovery of *C. burnetii* from Milk of Sheep. Pub. Hlth. Rep. Wash., 65:395, 1950.

Luoto, L., and Huebner, R. J. Q-fever Studies in Southern California. IX. Isolation of Q-fever organisms from Parturient Placentas of Naturally Infected Dairy Cows. Pub. Hlth. Rep. Wash., 65:541, 1950.

Mantovani, A., and Benazzi, P. The isolation of *Coxiella burnetii* from *Rhipicephalus sanguineus* on naturally infected dogs. Jour. Amer. Vet. Med. Assn., 122:117, 1953.

Meyer, K. F. Psittacosis-Lymphogranuloma Group, in Rivers, Viral and Rickettsial Infections of Man. J. B. Lippincott Co. Philadelphia, 1948.

Parker, R. R., Bell, E. J., and Stoenner, H. G. Jour. Amer. Vet. Med. Assn., 114:55, 124, 1949.

Rake, G. In Bergey's Manual of Determinative Bacteriology. Williams and Wilkins Co., Baltimore, 1948.

Smadel, J. E. Scrub Typhus and Q-fever in Rivers, Viral and Rickettsial Infections of Man. J. B. Lippincott Co., Philadelphia, 1948.

Smith, D. J. W., and Derrick, E. H., *et al.* Aust. Jour. Exp. Biol. Med. Sci., 18: 1, 99, 103, 119, 193, 1940.

Snyder, J. C. The Typhus Fevers in Rivers, Viral and Rickettsial Infections of Man. J. B. Lippincott Co., Philadelphia, 1948.

Splitter, E. J. *Eperythrozoon suis*, the etiologic agent of ictero-anemia or an anaplasmosis-like disease of swine. Amer. Jour. Vet. Res., 11: 324, 1950.

Steinhaus, E. A. Insect Microbiology. Comstock Co., Ithaca, 1946.

Stoenner, H. G., and Lackman, D. B. The role of the milking process in the intraherd transmission of Q-fever among dairy cattle. Amer. Jour. Vet. Res., 13: 458, 1952.

Topping, N. H., Shepard, C. C., and Irons, J. V. Q-fever in the United States. I. Epidemiologic Studies of an Outbreak Among Stock Handlers and Slaughterhouse Workers. Jour. Amer. Med. Assn., 133:813, 1947.

38. | The Pleuropneumonia Group[*]

The members of this group may be either parastic or sapro-phytic organisms. They appear to have a minimal cell wall. This results in the development of polymorphic forms including ring, globules, filaments, and small elementary bodies. Many of these forms pass bacteria-retaining filters. Most members of this group grow aerobically but an occasional strain may be stimulated by 10 per cent CO_2 atmosphere and one anaerobic species has been re-ported. The parasitic species of this group of organisms require a medium with a high protein content. This is customarily supplied by serum protein. This requirement probably reflects an inabil-ity of this group to synthesize certain protein complexes. Most members of the group that have been studied were found to be resistant to penicillin, thallium acetate, sulfathiazol, and sometimes crystal violet. Recent studies have suggested that certain of these organisms may require certain essential lipids for growth.

It is customary to exclude from this group those organisms that will revert to typical bacterial forms.

Members of the group may be cultivated either in suitable li-quid media or on solid media. On the latter, small glistening col-onies that often have a faint surface marking and some degree of either a central elevation or depression occur, usually after several days' incubation. These colonies are usually difficult to remove from the surface of the medium since they tend to grow into the medium. A few organisms of this group have been observed to form a film on the surface of suitable solid media.

Fluid medium is usually more satisfactory for the cultivation of members of this group. In some cases the organisms will pro-duce enough turbidity in the medium so that growth may be read-ily detected. However, in most instances only a faint turbidity is produced and control tubes should always be available for com-parison purposes. A more certain method of detecting growth is to

---

[*] The author is indebted to Dr. William P. Switzer for his aid in the re-vision of this chapter.

stain the sediment centrifuged from the culture and to observe typical organisms. In most cases Giemsa's stain has been used to stain these organisms since they stain very poorly with analine dyes.

Workers dealing with this group of organisms refer to them as pleuropneumonia or pleuropneumonia-like organisms (PPLO), since the first and only known member of this group for many years was the agent producing bovine pleuropneumonia.

Nocard and co-workers in 1898 were the first to cultivate the causal agent of bovine pleuropneumonia in a cell-free medium. This agent had been considered to be a filtrable virus up to that time. The studies of Bordet and of Borrel in 1910 disclosed the polymorphic characteristics of the organism. Elford demonstrated in 1929 that this organism possessed filtrable forms 125 to 150 mμ in size which were capable of developing into larger structures. It was for this reason, no doubt, that the agent of contagious pleuropneumonia was classified as a filtrable virus.

In 1923, Bridré and Donatien demonstrated that the causal agent of contagious agalactia of sheep and goats was quite similar to the cause of pleuropneumonia.

Shoetensack, in 1934, isolated an organism fulfilling the characteristics of this group from dogs suffering with distemper; however, he did not infer that the organism alone was the cause of distemper.

In 1935, Klieneberger reported that a pleuropneumonia-like organism (L$_1$) was present in all the cultures of *Streptobacillus moniliformis* which she had studied. The latter is a pleomorphic, Gram-negative organism found in the nasopharynx of rats and associated with at least one type of rat-bite fever in man. She was able to isolate the L$_1$ organism in pure culture and was able to maintain it in pure culture, although she considered it a symbiont of *S. moniliformis*. Other investigators, Dawson and Hobby, Dienes and Edsall, have suggested that the microorganism is a variant of *S. moniliformis*.

The discovery that organisms of this group are not confined to parasitic species was made by Laidlaw and Elford in 1936, upon the isolation of typical cultures from raw sewage. These observations were confirmed by Seiffert when he isolated similar microorganisms from soil, compost, manure, and decomposing leaves.

In 1938, Sabin and Findlay *et al.*, working independently, isolated pleuropneumonia-like organisms from mice which had developed nervous symptoms during the passage of lymphocytic choriomeningitis virus. It was subsequently discovered that the microorganisms had a special affinity for the mesenchymal cells of the pleura, peritoneum, and joints, but produced a neurotropic exotoxin which caused the choreiform symptoms. Other strains which localize in the mesenchymal cells of the joints of the mouse, producing a proliferative and chronic ankylosing arthritis, have been described by Sabin.

Nelson (1936a, b) described coccobacillary bodies associated with slowly developing coryza in poultry. These organisms were probably pleuropneumonia-like organisms. Van Herick and Eaton (1945) isolated a pleuropneumonia-like organism from chicken embryo material, which they believed to be a contaminant carried by the chicken embryo. It was not until 1952 that Markham and Wong showed that pleuropneumonia-like organisms would experimentally produce mild upper-respiratory-tract lesions in chickens and turkey sinusitis. Since that time, this group has been recognized as being of major importance to the poultry industry, and consequently, considerable research has been in progress on this group.

Edward et al. (1947) isolated pleuropneumonia-like organisms from the bovine genital tract and suggested that they caused an inflammation that predisposed to infertility. In 1953 Switzer isolated a pleuropneumonia-like organism from the nasal cavities of swine and later showed it to be the cause of certain fibrinous lesions on the serous membranes of swine, especially the pericardium, and to occur in pneumonic swine lungs (Switzer 1953a, b, and 1954a).

Carter (1954) demonstrated that members of this group of organisms occurred in certain cases of bovine bronchopneumonia.

Cordy et al. (1955) described a highly fatal disease due to a pleuropneumonia-like organism in a herd of dairy goats. This disease was characterized by septicemia and arthritis.

Greig (1955) reported the isolation of a pleuropneumonia-like organism from the respiratory tract of sheep.

At the present time this group of organisms is receiving an ever-increasing amount of consideration and there is little doubt that many new species will be reported.

Classification and Nomenclature

The classification and nomenclature of this group of organisms are not firmly established. The classification given here is based on that suggested by Freundt (1955) and Edward (1955).

Order *Mycoplasmatales*

Genus *Mycoplasma*

Individual species

1. *Mycoplasma mycoides* — organism causing contagious bovine pleuropneumonia

   M. mycoides var. *capri* — organism causing pleuropneumonia in goats

2. *M. agalactia* — organism causing contagious agalactiae of sheep and goats
3. *M. gallinarum* — organism associated with chronic respiratory disease, air sac infection, and sinusitis in poultry
4. *M. hyorhinis* — organism producing fibrinous pericarditis, pleuritis, peritonitis, and arthritis in swine
5. *M. bovigenitale* — frequent inhabitant of the bovine lower genital tract, both in males and females
6. *M. spumans, M. canis,* and *M. maculosum* — pleuropneumonia-like organisms isolated from dogs
7. *M. pulmonis* — organism from the respiratory tract of rats
8. *M. neurolyticum* — organism producing nervous symptoms in mice
9. *M. arthritidis* — organism producing arthritis in rats
10. *M. laidlawi* — sewage and other saprophytic strains
11. *M. hominis, M. fermentous, M. salivarium* — pleuropneumonia-like organisms isolated from humans

Other pleuropneumonia-like organisms not yet named from

(a) bovine pneumonia
(b) sheep respiratory tract
(c) acute septicemia and arthritis of goats

In this discussion of the pleuropneumonia-like organisms only those species that are of significance to domestic or laboratory animals will be considered.

Mycoplasma mycoides

The presence of this organism in bovine pleuropneumonia was first demonstrated by Nocard in 1898. The pleomorphic nature of the organism was recognized in 1910 by Bordet, who considered it allied to the spirochetes. The varied forms of the organism were recognized in 1910 by Borrell, who considered the coccal forms of the organism in coining the name *Asterococcus mycoides*. Other names which have been used for the organism are: *Coccobacillus mycoides peripneumoniae* (Martzinovski, 1911), *Micromyces peripneumoniae bovis contagiosae* (Frosch, 1923), *Mycoplasma peripneumoniae* (Nowak, 1929), *Asteromyces peripneumoniae bovis* (Wroblewski, 1931), and *Borrelomyces peripneumoniae* (Turner, Campbell, and Dick, 1935). In his classification of this group of organisms, Sabin first used the name *Bovimyces pleuropneumoniae* but subsequently suggested that *Asterococcus mycoides* had priority. Since the generic name *Asterococcus* had been used previously for a genus of algae, it now appears that the first valid generic name given to this organism was *Mycoplasma* (Nowak, 1929).

Bovine pleuropneumonia, the disease caused by *M. mycoides,* has been a well-recognized disease on the European continent for the past two centuries. In all countries where the disease has appeared, great losses of cattle have resulted. It has been eradicated in many of the sections of Europe, and before World War II was localized in Russia, Spain, and Poland. The condition is widespread

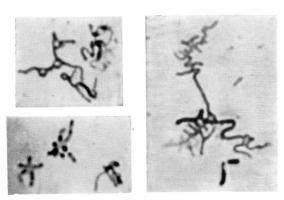

FIG. 38.1 — **Mycoplasma mycoides,** showing pleomorphism, × 3,000. (From Nowak: Documenta Microbiologica, courtesy Gustav Fischer.)

in Mongolia and Manchuria, and epizootics occur in Australia, India, and China. It is still present in Egypt and Central Africa. The disease is found in South American countries.

It was introduced into the United States as early as 1843 and by 1886 had spread as far west as Missouri. Stringent action was taken by the newly formed Bureau of Animal Industry and in March, 1892, a proclamation was issued stating that the country was free of the disease. The presence of this disease in various parts of the world, the marked infectiousness of it, and the postwar traffic are all factors which may result in the introduction of the infection again. All animal disease agencies must be alert constantly in order to prevent the establishment of the disease in the cattle herds of this country.

The microorganism is transmitted by direct contact and by water and feed recently contaminated by an infected animal. Chronic cases of the disease remain carriers because the organism is present in the exudate from healing lung lesions. Apparently healthy animals may remain infectious for 2 to 3 years.

At certain stages in the development of *M. mycoides* filtrable forms 125 mμ to 150 mμ in size are present. Large oval or rounded bodies 0.2μ to 0.8μ are seen in artificial cultures. These develop into a mycelium composed of hyphae up to 240μ in length which become curled and twisted, forming various shapes (Fig. 38.1). The organism can be stained with the commonly used bacterial stains and is Gram-negative. Deeper stained preparations are obtained with Giemsa's method. Masses of growth can be noted in tissue sections but it is essential to fix such sections with Zenker's fluid, for the organisms are not observed when formalin fixation is used. On solid medium, containing at least 10 per cent bovine serum, the organism produces minute colonies which are smooth and transparent with an entire edge. In well isolated colonies a nipple-like darker center is present (Fig. 38.2). The colonies are firmly adherent to the medium, due to the penetration of the organism below the surface. In serum bouillon, light turbidity is observed after the second day of incubation. Upon successive transplants the turbidity becomes more dense and forms filmy swirls when the tube is agitated. Optimum growth occurs at 37° to 38°C., with no growth below 27°C.

FIG. 38.2 — Colonies of **Mycoplasma mycoides** on serum agar, × 40. (From Nowak: Documenta Microbiologica, courtesy Gustav Fischer.)

Acid but no gas is produced from glucose, maltose, mannose, fructose, dextrin, and starch. Galactose, xylose, sucrose, and trehalose are slightly fermented. Arabinose, raffinose, rhamnose, lactose, adonitol, sorbitol, mannitol, glycerol, and aesculin are not attached. The organisms grow in milk but do not alter this medium. An olive-green color (alpha hemolysis) is produced in blood media.

M. mycoides remains virulent for only six to eight days when kept at incubator temperature, but is virulent for nearly a year when sealed in glass tubes and kept at 12°C. Lung tissue and exudate is infective for eight days if kept cool, but remains virulent for at least three months if kept at −5°C. The organism remains virulent in tissue kept in concentrated glycerin and 0.5 per cent phenol. A temperature of 58°C. kills the organism and it is easily destroyed by the various disinfecting chemicals. It is destroyed by exposure to air and sunlight.

The production of a toxin has been suggested by some investigators. The cachexia produced in cattle is given as evidence, and a similar condition is produced in rabbits following the installation of the organism contained in collodion sacs in the peritoneal cavity. It has been shown, also, that exudate contains a toxic principle which is precipitated by alcohol. It retains its activity at 80°C. and causes marked intoxication when injected intravenously into sheep and goats.

Under natural conditions this organism produces pleuro-pneumonia in cattle and related animals—the buffalo, yak, reindeer, and bison. Experimentally sheep and goats have been infected. Other animals and man are resistant.

Although in naturally occurring epizootics of the disease, cattle become easily infected, it has not been easy to produce the disease artificially. Subcutaneous inoculations produce a rise in temperature and edema at the site of inoculation. In calves such inoculations produce acute reactions characterized by localization in the joints. Injection of lung exudates into the udder cistern produces severe inflammation and the organism persists in the purulent viscid milk for two months. The intravenous injections of cultures contained in finely divided agar produce pulmonary emboli with resulting lesions typical of the disease. Sabin has suggested that pulmonary parasites may be factors in the establishment of infection in the lungs.

Animals which have recovered from pleuropneumonia are resistant to subsequent attacks. Artificial immunization was practiced long before the causal agent was discovered. This consisted of the inoculation of lung exudate subcutaneously, preferably in the tail, from which absorption was slow. Cultures kept in peptone-serum bouillon become attenuated after the twenty-fifth passage and may be used for vaccination. Hyperimmunization of cattle is produced by the injection of massive doses of culture and the resulting anti-serum is effective for passive immunization.

The type of lesion found in bovine pleuropneumonia is rather distinctive but cannot be depended upon for accurate diagnosis. Isolation of *Mycoplasma mycoides* is possible in the majority of cases of the disease if all of the precautions are taken to obtain the growth of the organism. The precipitation, agglutination and complement-fixation tests have been used with success for diagnosis.

Mycoplasma mycoides var. capri

This organism produces a highly fatal disease in goats. Following a 3- to 10-day incubation period there is usually a febrile reaction and copious nasal discharge which is catarrhal at first and becomes increasingly mucopurulent. Coughing increases in frequency and intensity as the disease progresses to the advanced stages, at which time the coughing may subside. Respiration is accelerated at first but becomes labored as the disease progresses and may become primarily abdominal. The affected animals may retain their appetites up to the terminal stages of the disease when they may collapse and die within an hour. Most of the animals affected with this disease die.

The lesions observed in cases of this disease are primarily pneumonia and pleuritis, with pericarditis present in some cases.

There are usually no other lesions except small hemorrhages on the mucous and serous surfaces.

Death of the animal usually occurs within 1 to 4 weeks after the onset of the symptoms.

This disease was thought to be caused by a virus until Longly (1951) isolated a pleuropneumonia-like organism and reproduced the disease with cultures of the organism. The disease is of considerable economic importance in parts of Europe, Asia, and Africa.

Workers dealing with this disease report that *M. mycoides* and *M. mycoides* var. *capri* have similiar properties except for host infected and antigenic structure. The possibility has been suggested that the disease in goats may be caused by a bovine organism which has become adapted to goats.

A pathogenic pleuropneumonia-like organism from goats was reported in the United States by Cordy *et al.* (1955). This organism was recovered from a herd of goats affected with a highly fatal septicemia and arthritis. They reproduced a similar disease syndrome in experimental goats by inoculation of the organism. This organism appeared to resemble that of goat pleuropneumonia in many biochemical reactions but had a different antigenic structure.

Mycoplasma agalactia

This organism, which is the cause of contagious agalactia of sheep and goats, was first reported by Bridré and Donatien in 1923. The disease is known to occur in the mountainous areas of Italy, France, Switzerland, and Algeria.

Mycoplasma agalactia is a minute pleomorphic microorganism possessing granules, globules, ring-structures, and filaments characteristic of the group. It stains faintly by the Gram method and is negative to that stain. The Giemsa stain gives a better preparation than the ordinarily used bacterial stains. The organism can be observed best by dark field illumination. Minute colonies, which are best observed under low power magnification of the microscope, develop along the needle path on solid medium.

This microorganism can be isolated from infected tissues by using fluid medium containing at least 10 per cent serum. Bridré and Donatien have shown that it grows in media containing up to 10 per cent serum, but undiluted serum will not promote growth.

Cows' and goats' milk may be used as culture media but no change is produced by the growth of the organism. Some of the carbohydrates—lactose, mannitol, and erythritol—promote growth but others—glucose, fructose, galactose, raffinose, arabinose, xylose, sucrose, and maltose—retard growth. Good growth occurs in the presence of staphylococci and other organisms and can be separated from them by filtration.

Mycoplasma agalactia produces natural infection in sheep and goats. These animals also can be infected artificially by intravenous inoculation and by feeding infected tissues. The disease in these animals is best known because of the effect on the mammary gland in which fibrosis and atrophy are produced. Arthritis, keratitis, and in some cases vesiculo-pustular skin lesions are also produced. The arthritis in many cases becomes chronic, resulting in deformity. The organism may localize in the testes and abortion has been observed.

Bridré and Donatien have demonstrated that this organism is antigenically distinct from the agent of bovine pleuropneumonia. Attempts to develop immunity have been unsuccessful with the exception of a transient resistance which is produced by immune serum.

Greig (1955) reported the occurrence of a pleuropneumonia-like organism in the respiratory tract of sheep. This organism produced a diffuse turbidity in enriched fluid medium. It grew on nutrient agar supplemented with 5 per cent rabbit or sheep blood. It fermented dextrose, sucrose, and maltose but not lactose, galactose, fructose, xylose, mannose, rhamnose, sorbitol, or mannitol. This organism was propagated in chicken embryos. It usually killed the embryos 3 or 4 days postinoculation when administered by way of the chorio-allantoic sac. This organism did not appear to have a pathogenic effect on sheep.

Mycoplasma gallinarum

Nelson (1936a, b) reported the cultivation in tissue culture of a small cocco-bacillary organism from coryza of chickens. This organism was probably a pleuropneumonia-like organism. Delaplane and Stuart (1943) isolated a pleuropneumonia-like organism in chicken embryos from a clinical condition they termed chronic respiratory disease of poultry.

Groupé et al. (1948) isolated a similar agent from cases of turkey sinusitis and reproduced the condition with it. Since that time numerous investigators have confirmed the role pleuropneumonia-like organisms play in the production of respiratory infections in poultry. However, in many cases there appear to be additional stress factors necessary to produce some of the severe clinical conditions observed in field flocks.

Exhaustive comparisons of various isolates of pleuropneumonia-like organisms from poultry have not yet been made but from the information now available it appears that they are closely related and therefore are included as a single species. On initial isolation this organism is a small coccoid, cocco-bacillary, or slightly filamentous object. Upon cultivation in artificial medium it frequently becomes more coccoid in shape. Some isolates have a distinct tendency to form clumps while others yield a more uniform growth. Hofstad (1950) found that Selas No. 03 filters would retain this organism but that Selas No. 02 filters allowed it to pass. It is most stable at a pH range of 6.1 to 8.6 and is rendered nonviable by a temperature of 45°C. for one hour and by 50°C. for 20 minutes. It will withstand lyophilization and can be stored at —35°C. for at least 2 years.

Rather high levels of penicillin fail to inhibit its growth although certain broad spectrum antibiotics do inhibit its growth in vitro.

Many strains of this organism have the ability to produce hemagglutination of chicken or turkey erythrocytes. This organism produces acid but no gas in enriched dextrose, maltose, and sucrose. No change occurs in lactose or mannitol. It is readily stained with Giemsa's stain.

One of the main means of transfer of this organism is by symptomless carrier birds. Treatment of some birds with broad spectrum antibiotics has temporarily eliminated clinical symptoms but resulted in production of the carrier state. Infected hens may in some cases transmit this organism through the egg to their offspring.

Nelson (1942) reported that the coccobacilliform bodies of rat infectious catarrh could be transferred to chickens with the production of a mild coryza. After the second transfer in chickens, the infection failed to transmit to other chickens.

Mycoplasma hyorhinis

This is a small coccoid organism that was first described by Switzer (1953a, b; 1954a). It frequently exhibits ring forms. It is common in the nasal cavities of swine, where it does not appear to cause any appreciable damage. However, when it gains entrance into the body it may produce an inflammation of various serous surfaces. The most severe lesion is usually pericarditis but pleuritis, peritonitis, and arthritis may occur. In many respects these lesions resemble the disease syndrome that occurs in Europe and is referred to as Glässer's disease. As yet no study of the possible role of this organism in cases of Glässer's disease in Europe has been reported. Clinical observations suggest that turbinate atrophy may predispose to invasion of this organism. The possibility of louse transmission of this agent has been suggestd by Willigan (1955).

This organism produces very small, smooth, glistening colonies on suitable solid medium. These colonies have an indefinite central elevation. This organism is slightly inhibited by the addition of lactose, sucrose, dextrose, maltose, or mannite to the medium. It is readily stained by Giemsa's stain. Satisfactory growth occurs in an ox heart-chicken serum medium described by Switzer (1955) or in a medium described by Edward (1947a). In addition, inoculation of this organism into the yolk sac of 6- or 7-day-old chicken embryos results in death of about half of the inoculated embryos during 4 to 13 days' postinoculation. Embryos succumbing from the seventh to thirteenth day postinoculation usually have pericarditis. Giemsa stained smears of this pericardial exudate are suitable for demonstration of the organism.

The primary mode of transmission of this organism is by inhalation of infective aerosols. It has been found that baby pigs may harbor the organism in their nasal cavities after remaining in contact with infected dams for only a few hours. The occurrence of visceral lesions due to this organism in the United States has not been adequately evaluated although in one survey it was found that as many as 8 per cent of the swine hearts were being condemned in one large Iowa packing plant because of pericarditis typical of that produced by this organism.

M. hyorhinis is frequently present in pneumonic swine lungs but does not appear to be capable of producing a primary pneumonia. It has not yet been determined whether it has a secondary role in the production of pneumonia.

Mycoplasma bovigenitale

Edward *et al.* (1947) reported the isolation of two different pleuropneumonia-like organisms from both male and female bovine genitalia. One of these organisms produced rather large colonies and did not require enrichment fluid for growth. This organism was considered to be a saprophyte and was designated as organism S. The second pleuropneumonia-like organism produced a film effect on horse serum agar with precipitation of portions of the serum. It developed very small colonies. This organism appeared to be parasitic and to be concerned in the production of infertility in the herd studied. Therefore the organism was given the name P. This latter organism is now named *M. bovigenitale.*

M. bovigenitale forms unstable, sparsely branching mycelium with very short filaments that may measure 2 to 5 microns in length. It produces an alpha hemolysis of horse red blood cells and does not attack any of the more commonly employed carbohydrates. Ten strains investigated serologically shared common antigens but at least three different serological types appear to exist.

Circumstantial evidence indicates it may be involved in the production of infertility in both male and female bovine, but experimental inoculation of cultures have not been completely convincing in this respect. It has been observed that isolates from cases where a diseased condition exists are often very difficult to subculture, and therefore the laboratory cultures employed may simply represent avirulent strains that are capable of growing in artificial medium. More study of this organism is necessary before its true significance as a pathogen can be determined. To date this organism has not been reported in the United States but there is no reason to suppose that it does not occur here.

Carter (1954) isolated a pleuropneumonia-like organism from cases of bovine bronchopneumonia. The published photographs of the colonies of this organism show a close resemblance to those of the S organism isolated by Edward from bovine genitalia. Carter used enrichment media to grow his organism. The possible significance of pleuropneumonia-like organisms in bovine bronchopneumonia has not been determined.

Mycoplasma pulmonis, M. neurolyticum, M. arthritidis

Several different pleuropneumonia-like organisms have been isolated from rats and mice. Many of these appear to be distinct species but at least one organism has been recovered from both rats and mice. Adequate comparisons of the various strains isolated in different laboratories have not been made in most cases. Therefore the number of species that should be recognized is largely a matter of opinion and will undoubtedly undergo considerable alteration as comparative studies are made.

The pleuropneumonia-like organisms of rats and mice are of very real importance to laboratory workers attempting to establish infectious agents in these animals by intranasal inoculation. Some members of this group will produce pneumonic lesions. In addition, members of this group have been isolated from material being serially passaged from brain to brain of mice. This group also produces natural occurring pneumonia, infectious catarrh, and otitis media.

M. pulmonis is defined as the organism isolated by Klieneberger and Steabben (1937) from the lungs of tame rats with bronchopneumonia and bronchiectasis. This organism was also isolated from normal appearing rat lungs. The organism was named L₃. It failed to produce lesions when inoculated into rats. In 1940, Klieneberger and Steabben reported additional studies on the lungs of 251 laboratory rats and 17 wild rats. Lung lesions were present in 108 of the laboratory rats but they recovered the organism from 138 lungs. Only 1 wild rat had lung lesions and it yielded the organism.

This organism fails to grow on serum free medium. On suitable solid medium the colonies tend to coalesce and form a filmlike growth. It grows better near the surface of semisolid agar medium with a granular growth. It produces hemolysis of horse blood agar and ferments glucose, maltose, mannose, dextrin, starch, and glycogen. It doesn't ferment fructose or galactose. The surface of the colony is somewhat rough with surface markings tending to obscure the central spot.

This organism also occurs in mice where it has been isolated from the brain and from the nasal cavity.

Other studies on bronchopneumonia of rats describe additional agents. Thus, Nelson (1940) described infectious catarrh and otitis media of rats due to small Gram-negative coccobacilliform bodies present in the cytoplasm of the leucocytes. He cultivated this organism in minced chicken embryo tissue suspensions and reproduced the disease with these cultures. His reason for thinking that this organism was different from the L₃ organism described by Klieneberger was that very little growth occurred in cell-free fluid medium, no growth occurred on solid medium, and the organism was stained by Gram's stain using dilute carbolfuchsin as the counterstain. He observed that elimination of this agent from a colony of rats markedly reduced the incidence of otitis media and also the severity of the naturally occurring bronchopneumonia. This coccobacilliform organism could be transferred to mice where it produced a rhinitis, otitis, and a fatal progressive pneumonia. It did not become established in chickens.

Nelson (1937a, b) also described natural occurrence of infectious catarrh of mice which was due to coccobacilliform bodies which closely resembled those from the rat and were transferrable to rats (Nelson, 1942). He found these bodies associated with a pleuropneumonia-like organism in the nasal cavities of some mice. This latter organism was localized primarily in the conjunctival sac where, in one inbred strain, it seemed to intensify a conjunctivitis (Nelson, 1950a, b).

Edward (1940) studied infectious catarrh of mice and also found it to be a transmissible disease. Edward (1947b) reproduced the disease with early subcultures of pleuropneumonia-like organisms isolated from the respiratory tract. He reported the occurrence of coccobacilliform bodies in the lesions produced by the cultures.

In addition to coccobacilliform bodies, Nelson (1946) described a virus-like agent present in laboratory rats with endemic pneumonia. This agent produced a reaction in susceptible mice very much like the coccobacilliform bodies of mouse and rat infectious catarrh. However, no coccobacilliform bodies were present in the cytoplasm of the leucocytes. This virus-like agent is regarded by Nelson as the cause of endemic pneumonia in laboratory rats and the rat coccobacilliform bodies are considered to be a separate disease entity commonly superimposed on the pneumonia. Rats under 8 months of age frequently carry the virus-like agent in their lungs but show no lesions. As the rat matures the virus-like agent produces pneumonia. Some commercial suppliers of laboratory animals are attempting to eliminate virus-like agent and coccobacilliform bodies from their stock by breaking the cycle of transmission. Young rats are delivered by caesarian section, placed on clean foster dams, and reared in isolation. This program has been referred to as "Nelson testing."

It appears that the organisms from chickens, mice, and rats, that Nelson termed coccobacilliform bodies, are members of the pleuropneumonia group but their requirements for growth in cell-free medium are not certain. Most workers contend they are the same as pleuropneumonia-like organisms already studied although some think they have not been grown in cell-free medium. Nelson (1954) reported that the intra-abdominal inoculation of 4 strains of murine pleuropneumonia-like organisms of the catarrhal type (or coccobacilliform bodies) regularly resulted in the production of oophoritis and salpingitis in weanling mice. No lesions occurred in the genital organs of male mice inoculated intraperitoneally.

Mycoplasma arthritidis

This organism was originally designated as L_4 when isolated by Klieneberger (1938) from the submaxillary gland of a rat. It was found to be serologically identical with a pleuropneumonia-like organism isolated by Findlay *et al.* (1939) and a filter-passing pyogenic agent isolated by Woglom and Warren (1938) from a transmissible sarcoma. This organism produces abscesses when inoculated into rats and mice. In the inoculated rats there is a tendency to localize in the joints. The intracerebral injection of mice causes encephalitis. The "Preston" strain of this organism examined by Edward did not grow on serum free medium, did not produce a film on solid medium, and grew throughout semisolid medium. It did not ferment glucose, fructose, galactose, maltose, or dextrin. It produced smooth growth in semisolid medium.

The natural habitat of this organism has not been determined but it has been recovered from abscesses, swollen submaxillary glands, and septicemias in rats. The mouse is even more susceptible to this organism than the rat but guinea pigs, pigs, rabbits, moles, hedgehogs, rhesus and cercapithecus monkeys were refractive.

This organism has been cultivated on the chorio-allantoic membrane of the chicken embryo. It is said to produce inclusions in the epithelial cells of the skin overlying the abscesses produced in the rat and mouse.

Mycoplasma neurolyticum

This organism was first encountered by Sabin (1938) and Findlay *et al.* (1938) in the brains of mice used for passaging other agents. It has since been found to be common in the nasal cavity, lungs, and especially the conjunctiva of mice where it is the usual pleuropneumonia-like organism recovered. On one occasion it has been recovered from a normal mouse brain. The relationship of this organism to the one recovered from conjunctivitis of mice by Nelson is not clear although Nelson believed the organisms were not the same. It is believed that newborn mice do not harbor this organism but become infected by contact. The eyes do not become infected until the lids open. Mice probably remain carriers of this organism throughout life but do not show any spontaneous disease.

Intracerebral inoculation of this organism into mice produces a very characteristic turning or rolling on the long axis of the body with or without other nervous signs. This usually occurs 2 or 3 days postinoculation. The majority of the mice recover but some nervous symptoms may persist for months.

Intra-abdominal or intrathoracic injection of this organism results in similar symptoms in 20 to 40 per cent of the inoculated mice. Glucose-serum broth cultures of this organism produce a true exotoxin that causes the same nervous symptoms following intravenous inoculation.

According to Sabin, fluid cultures of this organism consist chiefly of elementary bodies, minute rings, or ovals with condensed bodies at one or both poles and occasionally triangular or quadrangular structures in which the elementary bodies are linked by thinner bonds. The fully developed colonies range from 20 to 300μ and present central areas that are circumscribed, elevated, and darker than the rest of the colony. There appears to be a variation in the exotoxin producing ability of different isolates of this organism.

Edward (1954) studied a strain of this organism that had been maintained for several years in artificial medium and found that it did not form a film on solid medium, hemolysed horse blood agar, fermented glucose, maltose, and mannose, but not fructose or galactose. It gave a granular growth that was best near the surface of semisolid medium.

Mycoplasma spumans, M. canis, M. maculosum

Pleuropneumonia-like organisms were first isolated from dogs by Shoetensack (1934, 1936a, b). They were found in secretions of the upper respiratory tract and in lesions of the respiratory tract of dogs suffering from canine distemper. It was believed by this worker that they were the cause of canine distemper but it is now known that a virus is the primary cause of this disease. His isolates seemed to be of two distinct types and they were named *Asterococcus canis* I and II.

Edward and Fitzgerald (1951) undertook the investigation of sterility and epididymitis in a male dog and isolated a pleuropneumonia-like organism from his semen. A survey was made of the occurrence of this organism in the throats and genital tracts of the dogs in this breeding kennel. They isolated 3 distinct types of organisms from these sites. They called these organisms, α, β, and γ. When names for the three organisms from dogs were proposed by Edward (1955) there was no clear indication of which new name was to be applied to each of the previously described organisms. Therefore the three organisms will have to be considered by α, β, and γ designation until examination of type cultures has established their identity.

All three strains were recovered from the vagina. Only β and γ strains were recovered from the throat swabs. About one-half of the vaginal swabs and about three-fourths of the throat swabs were positive for pleuropneumonia-like organisms.

None of the three strains grew at room temperature or on media devoid of serum. They seemed to grow as well anaerobically as aerobically. The organisms had a slight granularity in semisolid medium that tended to disappear on repeated subculture. None of the strains fermented glucose and all three produced some degree of hemolysis of horse blood agar.

Identification of the three organisms was based on colony morphology, especially on primary isolation, and serological reactions. A close correlation was observed between these two criteria.

The α strain colonies were distinguished by having a coarse surface reticulum. In young colonies only the center had the heavy markings, leaving the periphery conspicuously translucent with a surface resembling a drop of water. All the α strains were isolated from the genitalia and were considered to warrant additional study as possible pathogens.

The β strains, which were the most common, were isolated from both the throat and genital tract. The colonies were large, flattened, and translucent. They had no center spot but had fine surface markings. On repeated subculture some strains of α and β colonies became more similar in appearance.

The γ strains were isolated from both the throat and vagina. They formed a film on the surface of horse serum enriched solid medium with precipitation of a portion of the medium to form small dark spots. This organism had a well-developed central tip.

These three organisms are distinct serologically. Their pathogencity has not been investigated.

Greig (1954) reported his observations on the pathogenicity of cultures of pleuropneumonia-like organisms isolated from the respiratory tracts of dogs. The cultural characteristics of the organisms were not described but were said to elicit at most only transient bouts of sneezing and occasional coughing in inoculated dogs.

Switzer (1954b) isolated pleuropneumonia-like organisms from pneumonic lungs of dogs clinically affected with canine distemper. This organism grew well in ox heart-chicken serum medium and produced distinct colonies on the surface of solid medium enriched with Difco serum fraction. Fluid cultures of this organism were composed primarily of small coccoid forms that stained well with Giemsa's stain and were faintly Gram-negative. Colonies of this organism had a well-marked central elevation. This organism passed a Selas No. 02 filter, grew with a uniform turbidity in fluid medium, produced no lesions or deaths in chicken embroys, and produced no lesions, when inoculated into the air sacs, sinus, nostril, or conjunctiva of turkeys.

This organism did not survive for an appreciable length of time at –40°C. or in the lyophilized state.

What appeared to be a completely distinct pleuropneumonia-like organism was isolated by Switzer (1954c) from the pneumonic lung of a 6-week-old kitten that had evidenced a chronic cough. This organism passed a Selas No. 02 filter but did not produce visible lesions in chicken embryos. It produced a very faint turbidity in ox heart-chicken serum medium and did not survive at –40°C. or in the lyophilized state. The individual organisms in fluid medium were stained rather lighly with Giemsa's stain and had numerous ring forms. On solid medium enriched with Difco serum fraction the colonies were very small and translucent without well-developed center spots. Fluid cultures of this organism produced no lesion in 7-week-old kittens when administered intranasally. The kittens were observed 3 weeks. The organism was not recovered from the respiratory tract of the inoculated kittens.

REFERENCES FOR FURTHER STUDY

Bordet, J. La Morphologie du Microbe de la Peripneumonie des Bovides. Ann. Inst. Past., 24–:161–67, 1910.

Borrell, Dujardin-Beaumetz, Jeantet et Jouan. Le Microbe de la Peripneumonie. Ann. Inst. Past., 24:168–79, 1910.

Bridré, J., et Donatien, A. Le Microbe de L'agalaxie Contagieuse du mouton et de la chevre. Ann. Inst. Past., 39:925–51, 1925.

Carter, G. R. Science, 120:113, 1954.

Cordy, D. R., Adler, H. E., and Yamamoto, R. Cornell Vet., 45: 50–68, 1955.

Daubney, R. Contagious Bovine Pleuropneumonia. Note on experimental reproduction and infection by contact. Jour. Comp. Path. Therap., 48:83–96, 1935.

Delaplane, J. P., and Stuart, H. O. Amer. Jour. Vet. Res., 4:325–32, 1943.

Dienes, L. Organisms of Klieneberger and *Streptobacillus moniliformis*. Jour. Inf. Dis., 65:24–42, 1939.

———. Cultivation of Pleuropneumonia-like Organisms from Female Genital Organs. Proc. Soc. Exptl. Biol. Med., 44:468–69, 1940.

Edward, D. G. Jour. Path. Bact., 50: 409–18, 1940.

———. Jour. Gen. Microbiol., 1:238–43, 1947a.

———. Jour. Path. Bact., 59:209–21, 1947b.

———. Jour. Gen. Microbiol., 10:27–64, 1954.

———. Internat'l Bul. Bact. Nomenclature and Taxonomy, 5: 85–93, 1955.

———, and Fitzgerald, W. A. Jour. Gen. Microbiol., 5: 566–75, 1951.

———, Hancock, J. L., and Hignett, S. L. Vet. Rec., 59: 329–30, 1947.

Findlay, G. M., Klieneberger, E., MacCallum, F. O., and Mackenzie, R. D. Lancet, 235:1511–13, 1938; 237:7–10, 1939.

Freundt, E. A. Internat'l Bul. Bact. Nomenclature and Taxonomy, 5: 67–78, 1955.

Greig, A. S. Canad. Jour. Comp. Med., 18: 275–78, 1954; 19: 265–71, 1955.

Groupé, V., Winn, J. D., and Jungherr, E. Proc. Soc. Exp. Biol. and Med., 67:397–98, 1948.

Hofstad, M. S. Unpublished observations, cited in discussion of "Chronic Respiratory Disease" by Hofstad, M.S. in Diseases of Poultry, p. 383, edited by Biester, H. E., and Schwarte, L. H., 3rd ed., The Iowa State College Press, Ames, Iowa, 1952.

Hutyra, F., Marek, J., and Manninger, R. Special Pathology and Therapeutics of the Diseases of Domestic Animals. Vol. 1, pp. 455–71. Alexander Eger. Chicago. 1938.

Klieneberger, E. The Colonial Development of the Organisms of Pleuropneumonia and Agalactia on Serum Agar, etc. Jour. Path. Bact., 39:409–20, 1934.

———. Jour. Hyg., 38: 458–76, 1938.

———. The Pleuropneumonia-like Organisms: Further Comparative Studies and a Descriptive Account of Recently Discovered Types. Jour. Hyg., 40:204–22, 1940.

———, and Steabben, D. B. Jour. Hyg., 37: 143–52, 1937; 40: 223–27, 1940.

Longly, E. O. Colonial Research Publications No. 7, London, His Majesty's Stationery Office, 1951.

Markham, F. S., and Wong, S. C. Poultry Sci., 31:902–4, 1952.

Nelson, J. B. Jour. Exp. Med., 63:515–22, 1936a; 64:749–58, 1936b; 65:843–49, 1937a; 65:851–60, 1937b; 72:655–62, 1940; 76:253–62, 1942; 84:15–23, 1946; 91: 309–20, 1950a; 92: 431–39, 1950b; 100: 311–20, 1954.

Nocard, Roux, Borrell, Salimbini et Dujardin-Beaumetz. Le Microbe de la Peripneumonie. Ann. Inst. Past., 12:240–62, 1898.

Nowak, J. Ann. Inst. Past., 43:1330–52, 1927.

Sabin, A. B. Science, 88: 575–76, 1938.

———. The Pleuropneumonia Group. Bact. Rev., 5:1–68, 331–35, 1941.

Shoetensack, H. M. Kitasato Arch. Exp. Med., 11: 277–90, 1934; 13: 269–80, 1936a; 13: 175–84, 1936b.

Switzer, W. P. Jour. Amer. Vet. Med. Assn., 123: 45–47, 1953a.

———. Vet. Med., 48:392–94, 1953b.

———. Iowa Veterinarian, 25: 9–11, 1954a.

———. Unpublished data, 1954b.

———. Unpublished data, 1954c.

———. Amer. Jour. Vet. Res., 16: 540–41, 1955.

Van Herick, W., and Monroe, D. E. Jour. Bact., 50: 47–55, 1945.

Willigan, D. A. Studies on a Transmissible Agent Isolated From Pericarditis of Swine. M.S. Thesis, Univ. of Illinois, Urbana, Ill., 1955.

Woglom, W. H., and Warren, J. Jour. Exp. Med., 68: 513–28, 1938.

39. The Pathogenic Fungi

A large group of plants lacking in chlorophyll are classified together under the general term, Fungi. In the majority of the forms placed in this group the individual vegetative filaments are known as *hyphae*. The entire plant usually forms in a tangled mass which is called a *mycelium*. Under optimum growth conditions the hyphae develop buds and branches, some of which separate from the mother cell, forming daughter cells. In the yeast this is the common method of division. In most of the fungi the newly formed parts remain attached even though the individual cells are divided by a wall, or septum. This type of morphology is common among septated molds. Some of the molds, however, do not develop separating walls in the vegetative hyphae; these are called nonseptated molds. For other details in regard to the morphology and reproduction of the fungi the student is referred to the discussion in Chapter 2.

The classification of this group of plants is in the process of revision, as is true of the bacteria. Most of the species which are classified as fungi have been isolated from nature. Many of them are pathogenic on plants, but the majority are considered free-living, that is, they grow on any natural medium which will furnish them nourishment. A number of the fungi have become parasitic on animal tissues, producing a variety of diseases. These conditions remain localized to the site affected in the majority of instances.

The classification of the plant kingdom given in Chapter 2 divides the fungi into six groups. One of these groups, the *Schizomycetes,* or Bacteria, obviously does not need further explanation. The other groups include those plants which are usually called fungi, or more commonly, yeasts, molds, mushrooms, rusts, etc.

Basidiomycetes. These plants are popularly known as the mushrooms, punks, rusts, and smuts. They reproduce by means of basidiospores which are formed in conspicuous reproductive structures. The members of this group are saprophytic on decaying vegetation, but some of them, rusts and smuts, are parasitic upon plants. None of the animal diseases are caused by members of this group.

Ascomycetes. These fungi are represented by the typical mold plant. The vegetative bodies, or hyphae, form into a mycelium and develop a characteristic reproductive organ, or ascus, in which the spores develop. These fungi are particularly numerous, but most of them are saprophytic or parasitic on the leaves and bark of plants.

Myxomycetes. The Myxomycetes are commonly known as the slime molds. In certain stages they resemble protozoa while in others they are more like plants. In consideration of their entire life cycle, they are classified as plants. Several of the members of the group have been associated with plant diseases, but they have not been proven to be the cause of any animal disease.

Phycomycetes. Most of the members of this group develop a vegetative mycelium. The great majority of them reproduce by a flagellated body, and some of the more primitive forms resemble the flagellated protozoa. Most of the individual species are saprophytic or parasitic upon plant life, but a few are found in fish and other invertebrates. Only one group, the Mucorales, contains species which are significant to animal health.

Fungi Imperfecti. Into this group are placed a large number of fungi which have not been thoroughly studied or for which no satisfactory classification has been adopted. Many of the pathogenic species of fungi which are found in animals are fungi imperfecti.

Classification. The classification of the fungi which are pathogenic to man and animals follows two procedures. One classification may be based upon the morphology of the fungi and the other classification is based upon the type of tissue (superficial or deep) involved. Any classification of an infectious agent, with the exception of the filtrable viruses, which is based upon animal species infected or upon types of tissue infected eventually leads to confusion. Furthermore, there is a danger in leading the student to believe that infectious agents are only found in one type of tissue. It is admitted that as far as the pathogenic fungi are concerned, such a classification is desirable from the medical point of view. The morphological variations among these organisms are so complex that a systematic classification is most difficult, and clinicians and pathologists are not as a rule primarily interested in taxonomy.

The basic classifications used by Swartz in his 1949 edition of Medical Mycology have merit. One classification based upon morphology is as follows:

I. Yeast and Yeastlike Fungi

    A. Perfect

    B. Imperfect

II. Ringworm Fungi

III. Other Pathogenic Imperfect Fungi

The second classification divides the fungi into the two categories:

I. Superficial

II. Deep

A third classification or list is based upon the relation of the fungi to disease: the tissues attacked and the disease produced.

The classification or arrangement followed in this chapter is as follows:

I. The Phycomycetes

II. The Blastomycetes (yeasts)

III. The Trichophytons (ringworm fungi)

IV. The Fungi Imperfecti (dimorphic organisms having a yeast and fungus phase)

This classification or order of discussion is used only for the convenience of discussion although it does have a morphological basis.

THE PHYCOMYCETES

The molds in this group are not known to be involved in any specific disease of animals, but species of the genera Mucor, Absidia, and Rhizopus have been found in disease processes.

THE GENUS MUCOR

The molds of the genus Mucor have been isolated from infected animal tissue. In 1880 Bollinger found *Mucor racemosus* in the respiratory tract of birds. A similar organism was isolated from the nasal cavity of sheep by Zurn and from a tumor in a horse by Frank. Gilman and Frank isolated a Mucor from the placental tissues of a cow, and Bendixen and Plum, in Denmark, also encountered it in the examination of bovine placental tissues. Jungherr, in Connecticut, found a species of this genus, *Mucor pusillus*, in cases of mycotic infections of placental tissues of the bovine.

The molds of the genus Mucor are widely distributed in nature. They are recognized by the cottony mycelium which they form on suitable media. The mycelium does not form stolons or rhizoids. Sporangiophores produced by these molds are single, erect, and are usually simple, although branching is sometimes observed (Fig. 39.1). Each branch terminates in a sporangium containing large numbers of sporangiospores.

THE GENUS ABSIDIA

One species, *Absidia ramosa*, has been reported from animals. Villemin found this mold in nasal lesions and submaxillary adenitis of the horse. Christiansen isolated it from a generalized, tumor-like condition in swine, and Bendixen and Plum found it in infected bovine placental membranes.

The members of the genera Absidia are similar to the Mucor's, but the mycelium forms stolons and rhizoids; the sporangiophores are erect but are in groups of two to five rising from the stolon; the sporangia are pyriform.

THE GENUS RHIZOPUS

In 1920 Theobald Smith isolated a mold from bovine fetal membranes and fetus. This mold was referred to as *Rhizopus rhizopodiformis,* but Dodge considers it *Rhizopus equinus.* The same type of mold was found by Christiansen in swine in 1922. *Rhizopus rhizopodiformis* (*R. Cohnii*) was found in bovine placental tissue by Jungherr.

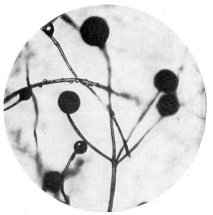

FIG. 39.1 — **Mucor racemosus,** mycelium showing sporangiophores, × 80. (From Nowak: Documenta Microbiologica, courtesy Gustav Fischer.)

The genus Rhizopus produces a mycelium which resembles the other two genera. The stolons of the aerial mycelium attach to the medium at the nodes. Sporangia arise in groups or singly at the nodes.

THE BLASTOMYCETES

The Blastomycetes or yeasts are round or oval cells which multiply by the process of budding. The newly developed bud remains attached to the parent cell until it is mature, at which time it, too, develops buds. In some instances the mature cells separate from the mother cells, but in some cases a number of cells remain attached, forming long chains.

THE GENUS CRYPTOCOCCUS

Cryptococcus neoformans

C. neoformans is the cause of a cryptococcosis in man and animals. The disease is often called "European blastomycosis" which is misleading because this infection is found world-wide in distribution.

Cryptococcosis of man is characterized by the development of lesions in the brain and meninges simulating brain tumors, abscesses, or tuberculosis. Localized tumor-like lesions are also found in man. In animals the disease appears most often in the nasal passage or lungs in the form of granulomatous lesions and abscesses. Meningitis and generalized lesions have been observed.

This organism was first noted by Busse (1894–95) in a generalized infection in man. A similar yeastlike organism was isolated from a hip tumor in man by Curtiss in 1896. San Felice, 1895 and 1898, found encapsulated yeastlike organisms in the lungs of swine and in the lymph nodes of an ox. A yeastlike organism was isolated from a myxomatous lesion in the lung of a horse by Frothingham in 1912 in Massachusetts. Meyer in 1912 also isolated the organism from a lesion in the nasal cavity of the horse. Other reports of the disease in the cow, a cheetah, horse, and pig are summarized by Saunders (1948).

In 1952, Pounden and associates reported that *Cryptococcus neoformans* caused mastitis in the bovine. This observation was confirmed by Innes *et al.*, and by Simon, Nichols, and Morse. Lesions in the meninges and the ventricular system of a dog were found to be due to *C. neoformans* by Seibold, Roberts, and Jordan (1953). The relationship of the organism to lesions of the nervous system and the world-wide prevalence of the disease are emphasized by Barron (1955).

Cryptococcus neoformans in both tissue and culture is a thick-walled, oval to spherical, budding cell, 5 to 15 microns in diameter. In tissues the cells are surrounded by a gelatinous capsule which may be as wide as the cell, and its presence serves to differentiate this organism from other yeastlike forms. Budding occurs in tissue and in artificial cultures. The newly formed bud forms a capsule and remains attached to the mother cell. The organism grows readily on the laboratory media used to cultivate pathogenic bacteria. Growth is slow on such media, not being visible for 10 to 14 days in some instances. On Sabouraud's agar, kept at room temperature, white, mucoid, glistening colonies appear which become brownish in color as the culture ages.

The organism is not resistant to disinfectants in common use. For example, Simon has found that it is killed by contact for 15 minutes by Roccal, 10 per cent; hydrogen peroxide, 3 per cent; ethyl alcohol, 70 and 95 per cent; sodium hydroxide, 1 normal.

Mice, guinea pigs, and rabbits may be infected with the organism. Intraperitoneal inoculation of a heavy suspension of the culture in mice results in meningeal and brain lesions in 10 to 20 days. Diagnosis of an infection produced by this organism is confirmed by the presence of the wide capsule surrounding the yeast-like cells when tissues are examined and by the isolation and identification of the organism on laboratory media.

THE GENUS CANDIDA

A great deal of confusion has centered around this genus in the literature by the description of many different species. Only one species, *C. albicans*, is recognized as pathogenic for animals.

Candida albicans

Candida albicans, often called *Monilia albicans*, is the cause of Moniliasis of man and animals, a disease characterized by persistent erosive lesions on the skin and mucous membranes, by pulmonary lesions, by meningitis, and by generalized systemic infection.

Moniliasis is commonly considered to be a disease of man but numerous reports of it in animals, especially the avian group, have been made (Saunders, 1948). In such cases the infection is usually confined to the mouth, the crop, the proventriculus, and the gizzard. Lesions consist of circular or elongated and at times confluent erosions involving the mucous membrane. They may invade the deeper tissues, producing extensive ulceration. The presence of thrush or mycotic stomatitis has been observed in calves, pigs, and colts but the etiological agent usually has not been adequately described. Future cases of this disease in animals should be authenticated by the isolation and description of the organism.

C. albicans, as observed in tissues, is a small, oval, budding, yeastlike organism, 3 to 6 microns in size. It can be cultivated easily on Sabouraud's glucose agar at 37°C. and at room temperature. The colonies are smooth and viscid, having a characteristic yeasty odor. As colonies enlarge they become rough and furrowed with a honeycomb-like center. This organism ferments glucose and maltose with the formation of acid and gas; acid is formed in sucrose but lactose is not fermented. The rabbit is quite susceptible to *C. albicans*. Intravenous inoculation of 1 ml. of a suspension of the organism produces death in 4 to 5 days with the formation of abscesses in the kidneys.

THE GENUS ZYMONEMA

Zymonema farciminosum (Blastomyces farciminosus, Cryptococcus farciminosus, Saccharomyces fariminosus)

Rivolta, in 1873, was the first to demonstrate this organism in the exudate from the lymph nodes of epizootic lymphangitis in the horse. Marcone, in 1895, was able to obtain a culture of the organism with which he reproduced the disease. In 1897 Tokoshige, in Japan, cultivated the organism in pure culture. Since then the disease has been reported from many countries. It occurs in France,

Italy, Egypt, South Africa, Russia, India, Japan, and the Philippine Islands. Epizootic lymphangitis is not prevalent in the United States although sporadic cases are observed.

In smears made of tissue exudate *Zymonema farciminosum* appears as spherical or ovoid cells 2.5 to 3.5µ in diameter and 3 to 5µ in length. Occasionally elongated and budding cells are observed. In cultures the organism forms irregular hyphae 2µ in diameter and septa about 10 to 20µ apart. The cells are finely granular or homogeneous. The organism can be studied in an unstained preparation just as well as when stained. A satisfactory stain for use is heated, dilute carbol fuchsin or the Gram stain, according to Kelser.

This organism is aerobic and grows best at 25° to 30°C. It grows slowly on artificial media. On Sabouraud agar the young colonies are small, round, grayish-white, and slightly velvety; old colonies are folded, yellowish-white, and sandy. Cultures grow more quickly on artificial media on successive transfers. On carrot and potato, colonies are moist, smooth, elevated, slightly folded, brownish-gray, and darken with age. Growth of the organism is slow on liquid media, but if 0.5 per cent agar is added to increase the viscosity, a thick, folded, snow-white pellicle composed of yeast cells and thick-walled hyphae is formed. The organism grows slowly on milk which is coagulated. It does not ferment any of the carbohydrates commonly used in the study of bacteria. Gelatin is liquefied.

Zymonema farciminosum is primarily pathogenic for the horse, but mules and donkeys are susceptible. The disease is characterized by a suppurative inflammation of the superficial lymph vessels in the regions where injuries produced by the saddle and harness may occur. The lymph vessels become enlarged and tortuous, and large nodules often develop along their course. The skin over these nodules often breaks, liberating purulent, yellowish exudate. These lesions then become ulcerous and heal slowly. The regional lymph nodes are commonly involved in epizootic lymphangitis. They become enlarged, abscesses develop, and when these rupture or are incised, a thick, yellowish-white pus is liberated.

Abscesses develop in the guinea pig and rabbit following subcutaneous inoculation. Man is considered resistant to the infection, but cases have been reported.

THE TRICHOPHYTONS

The fungi known as Trichophytons are parasitic on the epidermal layer or other keratinized tissues of mammals. The condition they produce is commonly referred to as *ringworm* because of the typical concentrically ringed lesion which is formed. The ancient Greek name *herpes* is often used for the disease, but this must not be confused with the term herpes of virus origin, such as, herpes febrilis. The Romans linked these diseases with those produced by lice and used the name *tinea*. This term is often used as a common name for ringworm.

THE GENUS TRICHOPHYTON

The members of this genus produce a dimorphic mycelium containing spirals, closterospores, chlamydospores, and aleurospores; produce giant colonies which are powdery, rarely velvety; produce suppurating lesions in mammalian epidermis, invading the hair follicle and often surrounding the hair with a sheath of mycelium and small spores; do not penetrate the hair.

Trichophyton mentagrophytes

This species is the most prevalent of any of the ringworm fungi, having been found in the horse, cat, cattle, dog, chinchilla, fox, guinea pig, mouse, monkey, muskrat, opossum, squirrel, and kangaroo. Man is also affected. The species produces a typical concentric lesion in the skin which increases in size, covering a large area and spreading to other parts of the body if allowed to go untreated.

Trichophyton gallinae

Turkeys and domestic fowls are most commonly affected by this organism. The disease it produces, known as favus, is confined to the head where typical lesions are found on the comb and wattles. In severe infections the organim may spread over the body causing a loss of feathers and leaving small, crusty, granular masses in the feather follicles.

The organism has been observed in man and in the dog. Guinea pigs and mice may be artificially infected.

Trichophyton equinum

This fungus is the cause of one of the types of ringworm in the horse and in man. In the horse the lesions which appear on the shoulder, back, and rump are characterized by small, shiny, bare areas without an inflammatory reaction. These areas are usually scattered, although many of them may coalesce to form larger ones.

Trichophyton schoenleini

In man this species is the most common cause of favus. It has been found in the rat, mouse, cat, dog, and rabbit, but is not thought to produce natural infection in those animals.

Trichophyton quickeanum

This species is found in mice and cats, usually causing lesions on the head. In mice the cornea may become involved, thereby causing blindness with resulting starvation. The organism produces lesions in man.

Trichophyton verrucosum

Cattle, dogs, horses, and sheep have been found to be affected by this organism. Man is also affected.

THE GENUS MICROSPORUM

This genus is recognized by the formation of closterospores and chlamydospores but the absence of aleurospores in most species. The majority of the species in the group produce ringworm in man, and a few are found in animals. In natural lesions the base of the hair is covered by a sheath of small arthrospores, not in chains, but arranged irregularly.

Microsporum felineum

The cat is the animal most susceptible to this organism. Large, denuded areas covered with a crusted exudate are produced. Extreme pruritis is caused by the infection, and the organism is spread by scratching. This fungus has been found in man and can be experimentally transmitted to the dog and guinea pig.

Microsporum canis

This organism is found in the dog and cat where it causes dry, scaly lesions without vesicles or pustules. It is easily transferred to the guinea pig on infected hairs. In man it produces tinea tonsurans microsporica and herpes circinatus.

Microsporum gypseum

This fungus is found in a number of animals including the cat, chicken, dog, horse, mouse, monkey, and tiger. It also is found in man.

Microsporum audouini

Man is considered to be more frequently infected with this organism than animals; however, it has been reported in the dog and monkey.

THE GENUS ASPERGILLUS

The genus Aspergillus includes numerous species which are widely distributed in nature, particularly in soil and on decaying vegetation. Each mold plant produces countless numbers of spores which are quickly disseminated by the wind and dust. This mold is one of the most common contaminants of laboratory media.

The Aspergillae are produced by two types of reproduction, sexual and asexual. In sexual reproduction two of the mold filaments twist together, forming a corkscrew-like body, the cell contents of each filament fuse, and fertilization takes place. This newly formed cell is then covered with a dense layer of threads forming an irregular, spherical body known as a *perithecium* (Fig. 39.2). The cell develops rapidly, forming eight ascospores. When liberated, these ascospores germinate and develop into the mold plant. In the asexual method of reproduction, a *conidiophore* is formed from hyphae differentiated for that purpose. The conidiophore becomes enlarged at the tip and becomes covered with a large number of papillae which develop into sterigmata (Fig. 39.3). In the typical

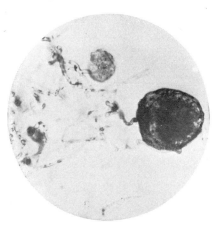

FIG. 39.2 — **Aspergillus** sp. showing perithecium, × 300. (From Nowak: Documenta Microbiologica, courtesy Gustav Fischer.)

Aspergillus mold the sterigmata remain single. The spores or *conidia* arise from the sterigmata and cling together in long chains. The spores are spherical or oval and may be green, black, brown, or yellow. It is to the color of the spores that the mold plant owes its color.

All of the molds of this genus are saprophytic except one, *Aspergillus fumigatus*.

Aspergillus fumigatus

This mold was first recognized as a factor in lung infections in 1815 by Mayer and Emmet who observed it in the lung tissue of a jay. Since then it has been found to be a rather common organism in various birds and mammals. The disease produced by *Aspergillus fumigatus* is known as aspergillosis or pneumomycosis. The disease has been found in the chicken, turkey, duck, goose, pigeon, canary, parrot, stork, raven, flamingo, hawk, bullfinch, plover, pheasant, ostrich, and swan. In mammals the organism has been observed in the horse, cow, sheep, dog, and skunk. It also has been found in man.

The spores of *Aspergillus fumigatus* are widely distributed, being especially numerous in moldy feeds. This is supposed to be the most common source of the infection for birds.

This organism does not differ from the general characteristics previously described for the group. It produces a blue-green spore which imparts a typical color to the mature mycelium. A portion of the mold colony, placed upon a glass slide, covered with a cover slip, and examined, will reveal interlacing hyphae and numerous conidiophores. The spores, or conidia, shatter from the head quite easily and are seen scattered throughout the field (Fig. 39.4).

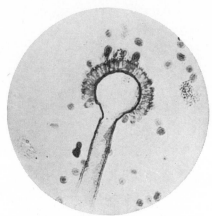

FIG. 39.3 — **Aspergillus fumigatus,** conidiophore, sterigmata, and conidia, × 340. (From Nowak: Documenta Microbiologica, courtesy Gustav Fischer.)

If injected intrathoracically into the pigeon or chicken, death is produced within a few days. Rabbits and guinea pigs are also susceptible to experimental inoculations.

Aspergillosis in birds involves the lungs and air sacks, and hyphae may penetrate into any of the organs of the abdominal cavity. The infection is found more frequently in young chicks which have become infected from moldy litter. Newly hatched chicks have been found infected, however, which makes it apparent that the organism has penetrated the egg shell prior to hatching. Pulmonary tissue is edematous, and blue-green patches of the mold growth are easily detected upon close examination. In mammals the infection is confined to the lungs.

FUNGI IMPERFECTI

All of the fungi whose life cycle is not completely known are placed in this group. The members of the group have become less numerous with the passing of years, and it is quite possible that in time all of those still classified as imperfect fungi will be reassigned. Dodge classifies the Actinomyces as fungi imperfecti. Inasmuch as this group has already been discussed in a previous chapter no description of it is necessary here. The genera to be discussed are fungi which have both a yeast phase and a mold phase in their complex morphological cycle.

THE GENUS SPOROTRICHUM

This genus is characterized by irregularly branched hyphae; conidiophores are not differentiated or may have only one conidium on a short branch which may be lateral or terminal.

The members of the genus which have been observed in animals have been confined to the horse. The exact identity of these organisms is not known. They are variably given *as Sporotrichum beurmanni, Sporotrichum equi,* and *Sporotrichum schencki.* Strains of this fungus from the horse apparently have not been subjected to complete comparative study. They are thought to be similar to, if not identical to, human strains now called *Sporotrichum schencki* var. *beurmanni.*

This sporothrix is responsible for a lymphangitis in the horse, which may be confused clinically with the epizootic lymphangitis produced by *Zymonema farciminosum (Blastomyces farciminosus).* In tissues this sporothrix produces yeastlike cells (Fig. 39.5), which are smaller than the blastomyces. On a suitable medium, such as Sabouraud's maltose agar, a small, grayish-w h i t e, fringed colony is

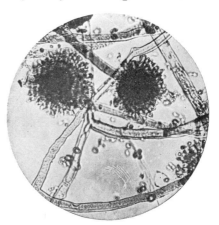

FIG. 39.4 — **Aspergillus fumigatus,** portion of mycelium showing hyphae and conidiophores, × 250. (From Nowak: Documenta Microbiologica, courtesy Gustav Fischer.)

formed. As it ages it becomes dark brown in color, wrinkled, and raised in the center. Upon microscopic examination the colony is found to be composed of mycelial threads. Conidia are attached to the sides and ends of the hyphae by short sterigmata.

THE GENUS BLASTOMYCES
Blastomyces dermatitidis

This organism is the cause of North American blastomycosis, a disease of man and animals characterized by pulmonary involvement and lesions resembling tuberculosis, the formation of cutaneous abscesses, and in some instances generalized infection with the formation of abscesses in various tissues. This disease was first observed in man by Gilchrist in 1896 and the fungus was isolated and named by Gilchrist and Stokes in 1898. Meyer was apparently the first to describe a natural case of the disease in the dog in 1912. Numerous reports of the disease in the dog have been summarized by Saunders. The first report of the organism in lesions of blastomycosis of the horse was made by Benbrook, Bryant, and Saunders in 1948.

Ramsey and Carter in 1952 published a summary of 16 reports of the disease in the dog, which concurred with their observations that suppurative granulomatous lesions are most commonly observed in the lungs and the skin.

The source of the infection in man is not known but it is assumed that it grows as a saprophyte in the soil and that infection of man and animals is accidental and quite rare. There are no reports of transmission occurring among animals or from animals to man. The nature of the disease, however, suggests that care must be taken by those handling tissue, either animal or human, infected with this organism.

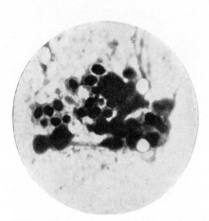

FIG. 39.5 — **Sporotrichum schencki,** yeastlike bodies in phagocyte, × 1,000. (From Nowak: Documenta Microbiologica, courtesy Gustav Fischer.)

B. *dermatitidis* occurs in infected tissue as large, round cells 5 to 15 microns in diameter, with a so-called "double-contoured" cell wall. Buds, similar to those in yeasts, may be observed and short chains of buds are often found. The organism can be cultured on Sabouraud agar at room temperature, where it grows slowly, forming a white colony which turns to brown as it ages. Branching, septate hyphae are found upon microscopic examination and lateral, oval conidia 2 to 8 microns in size are apparent. Reversion to the yeastlike type of growth is obtained by transfer to fresh media which are incubated at 37° C. Rabbits, guinea pigs, and mice can be artificially infected. Mice are the experimental animals of choice.

Blastomycosis is diagnosed by finding the double-contoured cell in a lesion of the disease. The organism is differentiated from *Cryptococcus neoformans* by the presence of a conspicuous capsule around the latter. The cells of *Coccidiosis immitis* which may be confused with B. *dermatitidis* do not show budding. The complement-fixation test and a skin test have been used to diagnose the disease in man but a report of the use of such tests in animals is not available. Positive diagnosis can be obtained by cultivation and identification of the organism.

THE GENUS HISTOPLASMA
Histoplasma capsulatum

This fungus is the cause of histoplasmosis, a disease of man and animals characterized by a wide range of clinical conditions. Internal lesions cause leukopenia, anemia, hepatomegaly, splenomegaly, vegetative endocarditis and ulcerative enteritis. Papular and ulcerative skin lesions have been observed but the disease is generally considered to be a systemic infection involving the reticulo-endothelial system. Recent studies of histoplasmosis have revealed that a mild type of the disease, causing nodular pulmonary lesions, exists in man. These lesions become calcified and obviously may be confused with tuberculous lesions in X-ray diagnosis.

The first case of histoplasmosis was described by Darling in 1906. He considered the organism to be a protozoan and gave it the name *Histoplasma capsulatum*. The fungus nature of the organism was noted by Da Rocha-Lima in 1912–13 but final proof that the organism was a fungus was contributed by Hausmann and Schenken in 1933–34 and by De Monbreun in 1934. De Monbreun was the first investigator to recover the organism from a natural case of the disease in the dog in 1939. Since that time the organism has been recovered from numerous dogs and other species of animals including rats, mice, skunks, cattle, sheep, swine, chickens, turkeys, pigeons, gophers, opossum, rabbits, raccoons, squirrels, cats and horses. Experimentally, the white mouse is considered superior to any other animal.

Histoplasma capsulatum is a typical example of a dimorphic organism, appearing as a yeast and also as a mold. In the lesions of the natural disease small, budding, oval, yeastlike bodies, 2–4μ in size, are found in the cytoplasm of endothelial and mononuclear cells. The yeastlike type of the organism is grown on sealed blood-agar slants at 37°C., forming colonies not unlike the staphylococci. On Sabouraud's glucose agar kept at room temperature white cottony colonies develop which become brown as they become older. In the young cultures definite branching septated hyphae are observed bearing small (2–5μ), round conidia called micro-conidia. In older cultures large (8–12μ), thick-walled conidia (macroconidia) are noted. These large conidia are surrounded with finger-like projections, which are considered quite diagnostic of the organism. The complete cycle by which the organism develops from the yeast form to the mold form or vice versa has not been explained.

Histoplasmosis is considered to be world-wide in distribution. At present it is known to be present in definite areas probably because those areas have been centers of investigation.

The discovery of *H. capsulatum* in the dog led to the supposition that this animal was the reservoir of the infection and that it was transmitted from the dog to man. Surveys of the incidence of histoplasmosis in human and dog populations do not indicate that there is any relationship of one to the other. The presence of the organism in suppurative skin exudates and the sputum indicate that infected animals should not be allowed in contact with human beings. It is likely that this organism is one whose natural habitat is the soil and plant life, but it has become parasitic on the cells of animals.

It is not possible to diagnose the disease by clinical observation; the similarity to tuberculosis has been mentioned as leading to confusion. The demonstration of the organism in tissues is considered the most satisfactory means of diagnosis, but this should be confirmed by the isolation and identification of the organism.

Histoplasmin, a product analogous to tuberculin and given intradermally, has been found valuable in detecting the incidence of histoplasmosis in human beings. The use of this diagnostic agent for dogs has been limited but in surveys where it has been used it is considered to be as reliable as when used for man (Cole, Prior, and Saslaw). An antigen composed of collodion particles sensitized with histoplasmin has been used in an agglutination test for the detection of the disease. The complement-fixation test has proven to be a reliable method of detecting infected animals in making field surveys.

THE GENUS COCCIDIOIDES
Coccidioides immitis

Wernicke, in South America, was the first to discover a case of coccidioidal granuloma in man in 1892. Rixford discovered a case of the disease in man in California in 1894. Giltner was the first to observe a case of the disease in cattle, also in California, in 1918. The relationship between coccidioidal granuloma and "San Joaquin Valley fever" was shown by Dickson and Gifford in 1936 when they showed that the two conditions were caused by *Coccidioides immitis.*

It has been believed that this organism is confined to California, particularly to the San Joaquin Valley. However, cases of the disease in man have been reported from Arizona, Colorado, Illinois, Kansas, Louisiana, Missouri, Nebraska, New Mexico, Pennsylvania, South Carolina, Tennessee, Texas, Washington, Alaska, and Hawaii. The disease has been found in South America, Old Mexico, and in Italy. This organism has been found in more cases of disease in cattle than any other animal. Cases of coccidioidal granuloma in the bovine have been reported in Arizona, California, Colorado, New Mexico, Old Mexico, and Texas. Maddy has observed that the infection is quite prevalent in dusty feed lots in the southwestern states. Cultures of the organism have been obtained from the dog in Arizona and in Canada and from the sheep in Arizona. Wild rodents which were trapped near San Carlos, Arizona, were found by Emmons to harbor the organism.

The presence of *Coccidioides immitis* in so many hosts has raised the question of their relationship to the disease in man. Stiles and Davis conclude that there is at present no evidence that the organism is transmitted from animal to animal, from animal to man, or from man to man under natural conditions. However, the transmission of the organism to laboratory animals from infected tissues has been reported and care must be observed in the handling of tissues taken from infected animals. Likewise, cultures of the organism in the laboratory must be handled with caution. It is believed that most of the cases of the disease are obtained from contact with the soil and from dust in which the spores of the organism are quite prevalent during rainy periods in the area of the southwestern United States. The organism may enter through skin abrasions and in rare instances through the gastro-intestinal tract.

Coccidioides immitis, in infected tissue, forms spherical, doubly contoured, thick-walled cells which are filled with a large number of ellipsoid spores. These cells or spherioles may be 30μ or more in size. In cultures of solid media, such as malt extract agar, the organism forms white cottony colonies. Examination of cultures by the hanging-drop technic reveals an extensive mycelium composed of interlacing hyphae. The hyphae are septate, but each cell has a number of nuclei. Numerous arthrospores form in the hyphae, which fragment as the culture ages freeing the arthrospores. These are highly infectious and infection results by their inhalation on dust particles.

In man, this organism produces a disease which is characterized by two different names. "Valley fever" is the name given to an acute influenza-like disease which is usually uncomplicated and rarely causes death. Coccidioidal granuloma is a highly fatal chronic form of the disease in which the lungs, skin, lymph nodes, bones, meninges, and thoracic viscera are involved.

In the bovine this organism produces abscesses in the lungs, pleural cavity, and in cervical lymph nodes. These lesions may be confused with those of tuberculosis, actinomycosis, actinobacillosis, and *C. pyogenes* abscesses. In fact, the only certain method of differentiation is the isolation and identification of the causal agent. Traum and Schalm have observed clublike radiations surrounding the coccidioidal spheriole in four cases of typical actinomycotic lesions in cattle. This further emphasizes the fact, previously mentioned, that actinomycosis cannot be diagnosed by the finding of stellate colonies in the purulent exudate.

The organism produces abscesses of the lymph nodes in sheep. These lesions are similar to those of caseous lymphadenitis.

Descriptions of the disease in dogs are limited; a few authentic cases have been recorded of which the one by Smith (1948) is typical.

A case of acute, generalized coccidioidomycosis has been observed in the mountain gorilla, *Gorilla beringeri*, by McKenny, Traum, and Bonestell.

In areas of the country where the disease is endemic it has been shown by Emmons that the wild rodents constitute the reservoir of infection. In order to determine whether coccidioides is present in a locality it is advisable to examine the pocket mice (Perognathus sp.), which are the rodents most frequently infected.

REFERENCES FOR FURTHER STUDY

Aksün, A. I. Jour. Amer. Vet. Med. Assn., 117:43, 1950.

Barron, C. N. Jour. Amer. Vet. Med. Assn., 127:125, 1955.

Benbrook, E. A., Bryant, J. B., and Saunders, L. Z. Jour. Amer. Vet. Med. Assn., 112:475, 1948.

Beurmann and Gougerot. Les Sporotrichoses. Felix Alcan, Paris, 1912.

Birge, R. F., and Riser, W. H. No. Amer. Vet., 26:281, 1945.

Castellani, Aldo. Fungi and Fungous Diseases. Amer. Med. Assn., Chicago, 1928.

Clark, D. S., Jones, E. E., Crowl, W. B., and Ross, F. K. Jour. Amer. Vet. Med. Assn., 124:116, 1954.

Cole, C. R., Farrell, R. L., Chamberlain, D. M., Prior, J. A., and Saslaw, S. Jour. Amer. Vet. Med. Assn., 122:471, 1953.

————, Prior, J. A., and Saslaw, S. Jour. Amer. Vet. Med. Assn., 116:135, 1950.

Conant, N. F. Medical Mycology—in Dubos, Bacterial and Mycotic Infections of Man. J. B. Lippincott Co., Philadelphia, 1948.

————, Martin, D. S., Smith, D. T., Baker, R. D., and Callaway, J. L. Manual of Clinical Mycology. W. B. Saunders, Philadelphia, 1944.

De Monbreun, W. A. Amer. Jour. Trop. Med., 19:565, 1939.

Dodge, C. W. Medical Mycology. The C. B. Mosby Co., St. Louis, 1935.

Dozier, H. L. Occurrence of Ringworm Disease and Lumpy Jaw in the Muskrat in Maryland. Jour. Amer. Vet. Med. Assn., 102:451, 1943.

Eggert, M. J., and Barnhart, J. V. Jour. Amer. Vet. Med. Assn., 122:225, 1953.

Emmons, C. W. Coccidioidomycosis in Wild Rodents. Pub. Hlth. Rep. Wash., 58:1–5, 1943.

————, Pub. Hlth. Rep. Wash., 64:892, 1949.

————, Bell, J. A., and Olson, B. J. Pub. Hlth. Rep. Wash., 62:1642, 1947.

————, Morlan, H. B., and Hill, E. L. Pub. Hlth. Rep. Wash., 64:1423, 1949.

Errington, P. L. Observations on a Fungus Skin Disease of Iowa Muskrats. Amer. Jour. Vet. Res., 3:195–201, 1942.

Furcolow, M. L. Pub. Hlth. Rep. Wash., 64:1363, 1949.

Hoerlein, A. B. Cornell Vet., 35:287, 299, 1945.

Howell, A., Kipkie, G. F., and Bruyere, P. T. Pub. Hlth. Rep. Wash., 65:722, 1950.

Innes, J. R. M., Seibold, H. R., and Arentzen, W. P. Amer. Jour Vet. Res., 12:469, 1952.

Jungherr, E., Mycotic Affections of the Bovine Reproductive System. Jour. Amer. Vet. Med. Assn., 86:64, 1935.

McKenny, F. D., Traum, J., and Bonestell, Aileen E. Acute Coccidiomycosis in a Mountain Gorilla (*Gorilla berengeri*), with Anatomical Notes. Jour. Amer. Vet. Med. Assn., 104:136, 1944.

Maddy, Keith T. Jour. Amer. Vet. Med. Assn., 124:456, 1954.

Menges, R. W. Jour. Amer. Vet. Med. Assn., 119:69, 1951.

———, Furcolow, M. L., and Habermann, R. T. Amer. Jour. Vet. Res., 15:520, 1954.

———, ———, and Hinton, Agnes. Amer. Jour. Hyg., 59:113–18, 1954.

———, and Georg, Lucille K. Vet. Med., 50:293, 1955.

———, and Habermann, R. T. Amer. Jour. Vet. Res., 16:314, 1955.

———, McClellan, J. T., and Ausherman, R. J. Jour. Amer. Vet. Med. Assn., 124:202–7, 1954.

Mosier, J. E., Barner, R. D., and Davis, J. C. Jour. Amer. Vet. Med. Assn., 116:128, 1950.

Newberne, J. W., Neal, J. E., and Heath, M. K. Jour. Amer. Vet. Med. Assn., 127:220, 1955.

Pounden, W. D., Amberson, J. M., and Jaeger, R. F. Amer. Jour. Vet. Res., 13:121, 1952.

Prior, J. A., Cole, C. R., and Torbet, V. Pub. Hlth. Rep. Wash., 64:1562, 1949.

Ramsey, F. K., and Carter, G. R. Jour. Amer. Vet. Med. Assn., 120:93, 1952.

Robinson, V. B., McVikar, D. L., and Peterson, J. C. Jour. Amer. Vet. Med. Assn., 119:195, 1951.

Ruhe, J. S., and Cazier, P. D. Jour. Amer. Vet. Med. Assn., 115:47, 1949.

Saunders, L. Z. Cornell Vet., 38:213, 1948.

Saslaw, S., and Campbell, C. C. Pub. Hlth. Rep. Wash., 64:290, 1949.

Seibold, H. R., Roberts, C. S., and Jordan, E. M. Jour. Amer. Vet. Med. Assn., 122:213, 1953.

Shaw, L. W., Howell, A., and Weiss, E. S. Pub. Hlth. Rep. Wash., 65:583, 1950.

Simon, J. Amer. Jour. Vet. Res., 16:394, 1955.

———, Nichols, R. E., and Morse, E. V. Jour. Amer. Vet. Med. Assn., 122:31, 1953.

Skinner, C. E. Bact. Reviews, 11:227, 1947.

———, Emmons, C. W., and Tsuchiya, H. M. Henrici's Molds, Yeasts and Actinomyces. John Wiley and Sons, New York, 1947.

Smith, C. E. Epidemiology of Acute Coccidioidomycosis with Erythema Nodosum. Amer. Jour. Pub. Hlth., 30:600, 1940.

Smith, H. A. Amer. Jour. Path., 24:223, 1948.

Stiles, G. W., and Davis, C. L. Coccidioidal Granuloma (Coccidioidomycosis) Its Incidence in Man and Animals and Its Diagnosis in Animals. Jour. Amer. Med. Assn., 119:765–69, 1942.

Swartz, J. H. Elements of Medical Mycology. 2nd edition. Greene and Stratton, New York, 1949.

Traum, J., and Schalm, O. W. Actinomycotic-like Clubs Associated with Coccidioidal Granuloma in Cattle. Proc. 6th Pacific Sci. Congr., 5:873–76, 1939.

PART IV

The Filtrable Viruses

40. General Characteristics of Viruses

The viruses constitute a group of infectious agents which are characterized by their exceedingly small size and that they are obligate parasites. They are the smallest living things known and are able to propagate only in the living cells of plants, animals, or bacteria. Many of the infectious diseases of animals and man are caused by members of the virus group.

The discovery of viruses was made by Iwanowski (1892) who first reported that the agent causing tobacco-mosaic disease would pass through filters which retained bacteria. Beijerinck (1898) also noted that tobacco-mosaic virus passed through filters and he referred to this agent as a *contagium vivum fluidum*. This same year Loeffler and Frosch discovered the virus of foot-and-mouth disease of cattle. Subsequently a large number of virus diseases have been described. Until recent years the diagnosis of virus infection was usually based on failure to demonstrate bacteria which would reproduce the disease while filtrates from the infected tissue would do so with regularity. Thus the etiological agent of many diseases was proved to be a virus many years before development of microscopes with which these small particles could be seen.

Elementary Bodies. The unit of a virus is referred to as an *elementary body* and may be thought of as analogous to a cell as the unit among the bacteria. The elementary bodies may be seen singly or in some cases they may be found in aggregates which are perhaps comparable to colonies of bacteria. An example is the Borrel bodies of fowl pox which are the unit particles of the virus. In the infected tissue they are commonly found in aggregates or "colonies" called Bollinger bodies. It has been shown conclusively that infectivity of a virus rests entirely within the *elementary body*.

Morphology. The general morphology of viruses is very similar to the bacteria. The usual shape of those viruses which have been seen are irregularly rounded, spherical, or rodlike particles.

Some appear as very short rods and a few have been shown to have a spermatozoa-like appearance having a rounded head and distinct tail (Fig. 40.1C). The morphology of at least one virus is dependent upon the character of the suspending medium. Bang has shown that Newcastle disease virus is plastic and undergoes changes in shape depending on the composition of the suspending medium. This virus is spherical in saline solution but it is either elongated or spermatozoa-shaped in distilled water.

Size. One of the important differences between bacteria and viruses is that of physical size. All of the viruses are smaller than bacteria; however, one of the large viruses, canary pox, is 260 by 310 mµ while the thickness of *H. influenzae* is 300 mµ. The viruses themselves vary considerably in size. The largest virus is approximately 300 mµ and the smallest, foot-and-mouth disease virus is only 10 mµ in diameter. Further comparison shows that the foot-and-mouth disease virus is nearly the same size as the largest protein molecule.

Estimates of the size of virus elementary bodies were first made by filtration studies. It was found that the pore diameter of filters could be altered by changing the proportion of materials used in their manufacture. By filtering virus-containing material through a number of filters of different pore size and testing the infectivity of the filtrates, fairly accurate determinations of the size of viruses have been obtained.

High speed centrifugation has also been useful in determining the physical size of viruses. Since the rate of sedimentation of a suspended particle is dependent upon its size, its density, and the viscosity of the liquid, it is possible to calculate fairly accurately the size of virus particles.

Comparative size of some viruses with Rickettsia,
bacteria, and mammalian cells

	mµ
Mammalian erythrocytes	7,500
Staphylococci	800–1,200
E. coli	500 × 1,000
H. influenzae	300 × 1,500
Rickettsiae	300
Fowl-pox virus	264 × 322
Rabies virus	160–240
Hog cholera virus	33
Foot-and-mouth disease virus	8–12
Large protein molecules	4–7

The development of the electron microscope (Fig. 40.2) has enabled investigators to determine the size of many viruses by direct

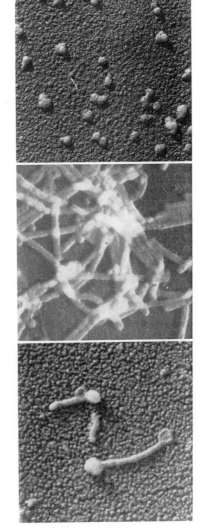

FIG. 40.1A — Equine encephalomyelitis virus (Western type), × 30,000. Electron Photo by Carr.

B — Influenza A virus, PR8 strain, showing filamentous and spherical forms, × 25,300. Courtesy Murphy, Karzon, and Bang, **Proc. Soc. Exp. Biol. Med.** 74:593, 1950.

C — Newcastle disease virus showing sperm-shaped elementary bodies, × 30,000. Electron Photo by Carr.

measurement. Although some of the larger virus particles can be seen under the ordinary light microscope, it was the development of the electron microscope which enabled virologists to view many of the viruses for the first time. However, not all of the known viruses have been seen or photographed by this method.

Chemical Composition. The chemical composition of a number of viruses has been determined. All of those which have been purified and chemically analyzed are composed chiefly of protein. Many of the plant viruses are pure nucleo-proteins. The animal viruses are in general more complex, but protein is the main constituent. Several of them are partly composed of lipids and polysaccharides. For example, equine encephalomyelitis virus contains 48 per cent lipids and Newcastle disease virus 27 per cent. Influenza virus contains a polysaccharide substance.

The amino acid content of viruses is variable. The amount of amino acids may be similar in closely related viruses or certain ones may be totally absent. These variations in virus composition may be of significance in determining their virulence, hosts, tissue specificity, and immunological differences.

Cultivation of Viruses. The viruses have, so far, never been successfully cultivated in a cell-free medium as one would cultivate bacteria. Living cells supply a vital factor which the virus itself does not possess. Some writers have visualized the virus particle as a mass of living nuclear material which depends upon the cytoplasm of a host cell to supply the necessary enzymes and nutrients to carry on virus multiplication. Such a concept may not be entirely correct, but in view of present knowledge some such arrangement probably exists.

Viruses may be propagated by one or more general methods:

1. Inoculation into a susceptible host.
2. Tissue cultures.
3. Inoculation into developing chicken embryos.

Propagation from one susceptible animal to another was the first method used to perpetuate a virus and still is the only successful method of cultivating certain ones. Tissue cultures have been devised which will support virus growth. There are many variations of this technic, but in general, tissue cultures consist of bits of living tissue which are removed aseptically from a living animal and are mixed with plasma, serum, or tissue extracts and suspended in a buffered saline solution. These materials are placed in flasks, test tubes, or on slide mounts. The virus is inoculated into the mixture and incubated for 2 to 5 days. Bacterial contamination, of course, must be avoided. The virus to be cultivated may determine the exact materials and technic necessary for successful propagation

FIG. 40.2 — Electron microscope. Courtesy Iowa State College Information Service. Photo by John Barry.

The discovery that the developing chicken embryo would support the growth of many species of animal viruses has been important in the study of viruses. The chicken embryo is the most useful experimental animal in virology, because of its accessibility, economy, convenience in handling, and susceptibility to a variety of virus agents. The chicken embryo can be infected with many viruses to which the adult bird is refractory. The fact that many viruses grow abundantly in the chicken embryo has made it possible to produce materials for vaccine manufacture on a large scale. In addition to furnishing a convenient means of virus propagation, the chicken embryo can be used in many other ways in virus studies. Virus assay, neutralization tests, materials for hemagglutination, complement fixation, heat survival and disinfection tests can all be satisfactorily conducted in embryos. The lesions which are produced or the lethal effects of the viruses can also be studied in embryos.

Physiology of Viruses. Little is known about the physiology of viruses. Attempts at measuring the respiration of a virus have not been successful. The technical difficulties encountered in measuring the metabolic activity of the virus which necessarily takes place within living cells have remained an obstacle. There is no doubt that chemical changes do take place in these parasitized cells, but methods are not yet sensitive enough to evaluate them.

Resistance of Viruses. In general, the viruses are more easily destroyed by physical and chemical agents than the bacteria, but there are exceptions.

The infectivity of most viruses is destroyed by heating at 56°C. for 30 minutes, some being destroyed at lower temperatures or in less than 30 minutes. Dried virus is more resistant to heat than virus suspended in a liquid.

Viruses are rapidly destroyed by direct sunlight and it is the rays in the ultraviolet range of the spectrum which are most lethal. Recently ultraviolet lamps have come in to use for the destruction of viruses in hospitals, resarch laboratories, and laboratories manufacturing biological products. Ultraviolet rays are used to inactivate viruses for vaccine production. Ultraviolet rays produce a minimum of change in the virus protein and the resulting vaccines are more effective in the production of active immunity.

Chemical destruction of viruses is usually not difficult, but viruses often resist concentration of chemicals which kill many of the nonsporeforming bacteria.

It must be borne in mind that, in order to destroy a virus chemically, it is necessary for the chemical to reach the virus. Since virus particles are so often contained within body cells where they have grown, they are protected by the coagulation of plasma and cell proteins. Therefore, those chemicals which coagulate protein materials are less efficient in destroying viruses which are contained in cells or in exudates than those substances which do not coagulate protein. A good example of this protection was found in the study of the effect of alcohol on the virus of foot-and-mouth disease. It was observed that the virus remained infective in tissue treated with 60 per cent alcohol for at least 26 hours, whereas virus which had passed through filters was killed within 20 minutes. It was further noted that the addition of sodium hydroxide in a concentration of 1:5,000 to the alcohol prevented the formation of protective coagula and the foot-and-mouth disease was then killed in 1 minute. The 1:5,000 concentration of sodium hydroxide alone was incapable of killing the virus.

The alkalies are probably the most efficient virucides. Sodium, potassium, or calcium hydroxides quickly destroy viruses upon contact. The use of sodium hydroxide in the form of "household lye" for disinfection of premises following outbreaks of foot-and-mouth disease or hog cholera is recommended procedure.

Phenols are effective in killing some viruses and not others. Hog cholera virus is routinely preserved with 0.5 per cent phenol in the production of virus for immunizing purposes. This concentration will not kill the virus even in several years. Other viruses such as foot-and-mouth disease and pseudorabies viruses have been found resistant to concentrations of phenol which kill most bacteria.

Salts of heavy metals such as the mercurials are lethal to many viruses but may require comparatively long exposure periods to inactivate them.

Chlorine compounds are effective against viruses if used in higher concentrations, but may fail to kill in low concentrations.

The glycols, propylene and triethylene, have been found useful as virucides. These substances have been used chiefly to destroy viruses in the air by spraying them into rooms in which the atmosphere has been contaminated with a virus of the respiratory group. The effects of such applications are only temporary if infective materials are soon reintroduced into the air.

Action of Sulfonamides. None of the sulfonamide drugs have been effective in treating virus infections. In fact, the sulfonamides have been used to aid in the isolation of viruses by controlling the growth of contaminating bacteria. In such cases sulfonamides are either added to the inoculum which is injected into an experimental animal or the animal receives the sulfonamide for a period after it has been injected with suspected virus material.

Action of Antibiotics. The various antibiotics which have been found quite effective against many species of bacteria have shown almost no effect upon viruses even in very high concentration. In fact, penicillin and streptomycin have proved very useful in the primary isolation of viruses. These agents will inhibit contaminating bacteria and allow the growth of the virus even from such materials as throat washings or intestinal contents. The addition of 1,000 to 10,000 O.U. of penicillin and 1 to 10 mg. of streptomycin per ml. of inoculum does not interfere with virus multiplication and is well tolerated by chicken embryos or experimental animals which may be inoculated for virus cultivation.

Variation of Viruses. As is the case with other biological material, the viruses show the characteristic of variability. Variation in virulence occurs in nature, since strains which are otherwise indistinguishable may be quite variable in the severity of the disease they produce. There are examples of antigenic variation in a single species of virus. Foot-and-mouth virus has three distinct antigenic types—A, O, and C, and immunity to one does not confer any protection against infection by another.

Many viruses have been shown to vary under artificial conditions. For example, serial passage of rabies virus through rabbits results in "fixed virus." The term "fixed" refers to the stabilization of the incubation period in the rabbit. Whereas the usual incubation period is about 21 days, after many passages the incubation period is reduced and becomes fixed at 6 to 8 days. In the process the virulence for the rabbit is increased, while it is decreased for other animals.

Cultivation of some viruses in chicken embryos or in tissue cultures results in decreased virulence. Certain viruses can be altered in their host specificity. Hog cholera virus has been considered the extreme of host specificity, being pathogenic only for one species of animal. However, by the technic of *alternate passage* this virus has been adapted to the rabbit. This is accomplished by first inoculating the virus into its natural host, then passing it into the rabbit The virus is passed back to swine, its natural host, and then back to rabbits. After several alternate passages the virus becomes adapted to the rabbit and loses its virulence for the original host. Some viruses can be changed in their tissue specificities. Herpes virus which usually infects the skin (dermotropic) can be made neurotropic by serial brain-to-brain passage through rabbits.

Induced variation in virulence has been useful in the production of immunizing agents such as in rabies or canine distemper products.

Another type of virus variation is that which has been described as *recombination*. This has been shown to occur in some instances in which two distinguishable strains of the same virus attack the same cell at the same time. A third strain is formed which possesses characteristics of both the original strains. Such a phenomenon has been observed among the bacterial viruses and in the influenza group.

Interference Phenomenon. The phenomenon of interference or cell blockade which has been observed with viruses is of interest. It has been found that a virus may be blocked from entering a cell which is already parasitized by another virus. This effect has been demonstrated by using closely related yet distinguishable strains of a virus showing that the virus which was inoculated first into the animal or chicken embryo prevented the multiplication of a second virus. It has also been observed that two unrelated viruses which attack the same tissue cells may interfere or that inactivated virus may block the entry of a live virulent one. Thus, a virus disease may be prevented in some instances by injecting avirulent or inactivated strains of a virus ahead of the entrance of the virulent strain.

REFERENCES FOR FURTHER STUDY

Beijerinck, M. W. Verh. Akad. Wetensch. Amsterdam. II, 6, No. 5:1–21, 1898.

Burnet, F. M. Principles of Animal Virology. Academic Press Inc., New York, 1955.

Iwanowski, D. Bull. Acad. Imp. Sci. St. Petersburg, 3:67, 1892.

Loeffler, F., and Frosch, P. Centralbt. f. Bakter. Abt. I. Orig., 23:371, 1898.

McCulloch, E. C. Sterilization and Disinfection. 5th edition. Lea and Febiger, Philadelphia, 1945.

Rivers, T. M. Viral and Rickettsial Diseases of Man. J. B. Lippincott Co., Philadelphia, 1952.

Van Rooyen, C. E., and Rhodes, A. J. Virus Diseases of Man. 2nd edition. Thomas Nelson and Sons, New York, 1948.

41. The General Characteristics of Virus Diseases

The general characteristics of virus diseases closely resemble those produced by bacteria, but may differ significantly in some respects. The viruses may be more host-specific and in some instances more tissue-specific than most pathogenic bacteria. Generalized infection by a virus may occur and lesions may be produced throughout the blood-vascular system, as is seen in hog cholera. Certain viruses may be found in the blood during early stages of infection without producing visible lesions of the blood-vascular system. Such a condition is referred to as a *viremia;* however, when there are lesions of the blood-vascular system, the term *septicemia* is often used. Many virus diseases are characterized by generalized infection.

Viruses, such as those of the pox group, have a predilection for epithelial tissue of the skin, while there are others which infect only the central nervous system producing encephalitis. Still other groups of viruses attack certain tissues causing the cell to proliferate and form tumors. The tendency to invade the surface epithelium or to stimulate tumor formation seldom occurs among bacteria.

The exudate resulting from virus invasion is ordinarily of a different character than that seen accompanying bacterial infection. In many instances there is little or no exudate. There is often infiltration of lymphocytes and mononuclear cells into the area of virus infection. Wound infection by a virus is almost never encountered, whereas a large number of bacterial species are capable of producing this condition.

A characteristic of certain virus infections is the production of *inclusion bodies.* Some of these are cytoplasmic while others are intranuclear bodies. The Negri body of rabies is so distinctive that it is used in the diagnosis of the infection. Whether these cell inclusions are aggregates of viruses or are merely a reaction product of virus parasitism has been debated. Some inclusion bodies have been shown to consist entirely of virus or at least contain it, while inclusions closely resembling those seen in virus diseases have occasionally been demonstrated in apparently healthy tissue. The fact remains, however, that the occurrence of these characteristic inclusions is of considerable diagnostic value in certain virus infections.

Transmission. Virus diseases are usually more contagious than bacterial diseases. A virus may escape in several ways from an infected host. It may escape from the infected host on moisture droplets from the respiratory tract. Diseases such as influenza are particularly apt to be spread in this manner. Rabies virus is eliminated in the salvia of an infected animal and is transferred by biting. Urine and feces from infected hosts may contain the viruses of some diseases. If food and water should be contaminated with these excrements, the disease may be transmitted. In many cases a viremia is present and biting or blood-sucking insects may be responsible for transmission of a virus disease. Virus diseases may also be spread by direct or indirect contact with infective material. The pox group of viruses may be spread in this manner. Since many viruses remain intracellular, they may be passed from one animal to another while in body cells such as desquamated epithelial cells. Many of the viruses are quite resistant to drying and may remain viable outside the host for weeks or months under favorable conditions.

The inapparent carrier is also important in virus transmission. Sometimes animals carry viruses without showing symptoms of the disease, yet they constitute a reservoir of infection for other susceptible species. Such a condition exists in the case of fowl harboring equine encephalomyelitis virus or in swine carrying the pseudorabies virus without showing clinical evidence of the disease.

Immunity. The fact that viruses are composed chiefly of comparatively simple proteins is probably responsible for their high antigenicity. In general, immunity produced by recovery from infection or by vaccination is usually more protective against an attack and is also more durable than that produced by bacterial agents. Thus, some of the most efficient immunizing agents are those prepared for use against virus diseases.

REFERENCES FOR FURTHER STUDY

Burnet, F. M. Principles of Animal Virology. Academic Press Inc., New York, 1955.

Rivers, T. M. Viral and Rickettsial Diseases of Man. J. B. Lippincott Co., Philadelphia, 1952.

Van Rooyen, C. E., and Rhodes, A. J. Virus Diseases of Man. 2nd edition. Thomas Nelson and Sons, New York, 1948.

42. | Methods Used in the Study of Viruses

Determination of Size and Morphology. Knowledge of the size and morphology of viruses has increased as the tools and technics have been discovered and developed. Scientists in the early part of this century were aware that living agents capable of inciting disease existed and that these agents were smaller than objects seen with the light microscope. However, in spite of this limitation, many of the physical properties of the various viruses were determined with remarkable accuracy.

Filters and Filtration. Filtration experiments were used by Iwanowski (1892) in his original work which proved the existence of a virus. He used filters having a pore size which retained bacteria yet an infectious agent passed through into the filtrate. This technic has been used since that time to separate viruses from bacteria and also as a criterion for the presence of a virus. If a filtrate proved infectious and no bacteria could be demonstrated, then a virus was presumed to be present. Filters of various porosities were manufactured and by passing a virus through a series of filters having pores of known size, the approximate size of the virus was determined by noting which filter allowed the passage of the virus and which one retained it.

There are several types of filters in use. The molded candle type includes the Berkefeld, Mandler, Selas, and Pasteur-Chamberland filters. These are made of porcelain or diatomaceous earth. Several types of asbestos pads are used, such as the Seitz, Boerner, and Swinney. Collodion and cellulose membranes are also used to advantage in many instances.

The *Berkefeld filter* is manufactured of diatomaceous earth and is graded into 3 porosities. The V (viel) grade is coarse and is used for preliminary filtration to remove some bacteria or large particles from a solution. The N (normal) grade is most useful since it retains most bacteria while nearly all viruses will pass through. The W (wenig) grade has very small pores and will retain all bacteria as well as some large viruses.

The *Mandler type* is also made of diatomaceous earth and is very similar to the Berkefeld. Three grades, preliminary, regular, and fine are manufactured.

The *Pasteur-Chamberland filter* is made of porcelain, molded into a candle form, and graded in porosities of L_1, coarse grade, to L_{13}, the finest grade.

Selas filters are a porcelain product made in 7 grades of porosity. They are graded from XF, XFF, No. 10, and No. 01 which are coarse grades to No. 015, No. 02, and No. 03 which retain bacteria.

Seitz filters are asbestos pads manufactured in 2 grades, K which are coarse and EK which retain bacteria. These pads are held in a metal holder and are discarded after being used once to eliminate cleaning.

Boerner filters are the same as the *Seitz* except that they are small and are fitted in a small metal receptacle which adapts onto a test tube and are centrifuged in order to force the liquid through them.

Swinney filters consists of a small *Seitz* pad placed in a metal receptacle which adapts onto a syringe and the material to be filtered is forced through the pad by positive pressure.

Collodion filters—The collodion filter is composed of nitrocellulose. The pore diameter may be varied by the addition of various amounts of alcohols, ether, acetone, and acetic acid. Filters of pore diameter ranging from 3μ to $10m\mu$ can be made. This type of filter has been most useful in determining the size of virus particles.

Cellulose filters—Filter membranes of pure cellulose or cellulose derivatives are manufactured in a variety of porosities. Those used in virology are: coarse with the pore diameter 3 to 0.75μ, medium 0.75 to 0.5μ, dense 0.5 to 0.2μ, and very dense below 0.2μ.

Preparation of Filters for Use. Before a filter is used, it must be clean, sterile, and free from leaks. New filters of the Berkefeld or Mandler type should be washed free of dust by passing distilled water through them from the outside to the inside of the filter and then reversing the flow. One method of testing for leaks is to apply air pressure to the inside of the filter candle while it is submerged in water. The air pressure should be started low and gradually increased. If there are cracks in the candle, air will pass through them on low pressure and the air bubbles will emerge from one spot. An actual test for the retention of small bacteria is sometimes used. A diluted broth culture of *Serratia marcescens* is filtered and the filtrate cultured. This organism is a small Gram-negative rod which produces a red pigment. It is also nonpathogenic, so it can be handled easily and detected on cultures of filtrates. Sterilization of filters of the molded candle type is usually accomplished by autoclaving for one and one-half hours at 121°C. after which they are gradually cooled and allowed to dry.

Sterilization of asbestos pad filters is done by autoclaving the pad assembled in its receptacle for 30 minutes at 121°C.

Collodion filters are sterilized by boiling or by treatment with ultraviolet light.

Technic of Filtration. The ideal condition of virus filtration is to remove bacteria but to allow the passage of all of the virus present in the solution. This condition is seldom reached.

The efficiency of filtration is dependent upon the following factors:

1. Size of virus to be passed.
2. Amount of virus present.
3. Diameter of the pores of the filter.
4. Electrical charge of the filter.
5. Electrical charge of the virus.
6. Amount of negative or positive pressure applied.
7. Viscosity and pH of the solution.
8. Duration of the filtering operation.

Successful filtration is to a great extent dependent upon knowledge of the properties of the various filters and of the virus to be filtered. Obviously, a filter must be chosen which has pores larger than the virus to be passed into the filtrate. On the other hand, the filter pores must be small enough to withhold bacteria which may be present.

Trouble is often encountered with certain virus-filter combinations because they are of the opposite electrical charge and the virus is adsorbed onto the filter. In this case little or no virus passes into the filtrate unless the concentration of virus is quite high. Filters made of diatomaceous earth are negatively charged while the asbestos pads have a positive charge. Most viruses are negatively charged. The application of negative pressure to the inside of the filter increases the rate of filtration. However, it should be measured by a mercury manometer or other suitable device and not allowed to become excessive or bacteria may be drawn through a filter which would otherwise withhold them. Ordinarily pressures of more than 5 cm. of mercury should not be used and if possible lower pressures are more desirable.

Cleaning of filters after their use varies. If the material being filtered is infectious, the sterilization or disinfection of the filter must precede the cleaning process. Boiling the filter in 2 per cent sodium carbonate is satisfactory. Immersion in 2 per cent phenol is used also. After bactericidal or virucidal treatment the filter should be washed with brushing and then distilled water used to wash out the pores by reversing the flow on the filter. The asbestos pads are not cleaned but are disinfected and then discarded.

Selas filters can be freed of organic material by firing in a furnace at around 1,200°F. Collodion membranes are more difficult to prepare but in many ways are more satisfactory than the other types because they absorb less virus and do not become clogged as soon.

Centrifugation. Centrifugation of virus-containing material may be done for two reasons: to concentrate the virus particles in the process of purification for detailed study and to determine the rate of sedimentation which will aid in estimating the size of the elementary body. If other constants are known, it is possible to calculate the size of a virus particle by its rate of sedimentation.

There are four types of centrifuges which are used in sedimentation of viruses. The *Sharples type* consists of a cylinder which is mounted in a vertical position and is driven by a high-speed electric motor. Fairly large amounts of solution may be passed through this type at speeds up to 50,000 r.p.m.

The *angle centrifuge* turns at a lower speed but will sediment many of the viruses. The tubes used to contain the virus material are narrow and flat so that any particle will have only a short distance to travel to be deposited on the wall of the tube. The head rotates at an angle of about 28° from the vertical. A small *air-driven type* is in the form of a turbine which has small vanes which compressed air strikes propelling the turbine at speeds up to 60,000 r.p.m. Only small amounts of material can be centrifuged in this apparatus.

The *bucket type* is driven directly by an electric motor or a geared motor. The material to be centrifuged is contained in plastic or hard glass test tubes of about 5 ml. capacity. Speeds of 40,000 r.p.m. are possible and will sediment many viruses in 1 hour.

Centrifuges have been modified to advantage in several ways such as the vacuum centrifuge in order to reduce air resistance, refrigeration of the chamber to protect the virus material from excessive heat, and the optical centrifuge in which the progress of sedimentation can be photographed at intervals during the operation.

Microscopy. *Light Microscope.* It is possible to observe the elementary bodies of some viruses under the ordinary light microscope. Technics have been devised for staining the larger viruses such as the pox group. As with the bacteria differential staining aids a great deal in distinguishing the virus particles from other small particles seen in tissue preparations. Although it is possible to see particles as small as 100 mμ, which is within the range of size of many viruses, it is very difficult to identify them with certainty. The practical limit of magnification for the light microscope is in the region of 1,200 to 1,500 diameters.

Dark-field illumination of virus specimens has some advantage over the ordinary application of light microscopy. By employing this technic, the limits of visibility and resolution are increased; however, its use has been limited.

A magnification of ×3,200 with good resolution has been obtained by using ultraviolet light. Instruments of this kind have not come into use because direct view of the object is not possible and photographic plates must be used.

Electron Microscope. The use of electron rays instead of visible light rays has made possible over-all magnifications up to ×100,000 with good definition. Microscopes of this type have been developed since the work of Marton in 1934.

The electron microscope is a very highly specialized instrument requiring considerable technical training and skill to operate it successfully. The basic principle of magnification of the electron microscope is similar to the light microscope except that electrons are used in place of light rays and the electron rays are focused by magnetic fields instead of the lens of glass in the light microscope. The source of electrons is a hot filament and they are accelerated by very high voltages of 50 kilovolts or more. This voltage must be controlled to within 1 to 2 volts, a technical achievement in itself. High vacuum is also necessary for successful operation of the electron microscope. By using specially designed pumps a vacuum of 10^{-5} mm. of mercury or below is maintained within the tube of the scope.

The objects to be observed are placed on a collodion membrane which is supported by a small disc of 200 mesh screen. This screen is then placed in a holder which is inserted into the microscope tube. A high vacuum is pumped in the tube and the electrons pass from the filament through the specimen and are focused on the fluorescent screen below. A shadow appears where the electrons strike an object in the specimen and are scattered so they do not reach the screen.

A process known as "shadow casting" has come into general use. Before the specimen is placed in the electron microscope, it is placed in a vacuum chamber and a metal, usually gold or chromium, is evaporated by heating it to incandescence so that a very thin layer of the metal coats the surface of particles, such as a virus. The coating on the surface of the object is not uniform since more of the metal is deposited on the side of the particle nearest the source of the metal vapor while very little is deposited on the opposite side. When such objects are observed in the electron microscope a third dimension can be determined.

In addition to viewing viruses on the flourescent screen of the electron microscope, photographs are usually taken and even more detail may be observed. Also pictures of viruses may be photographically enlarged several times. From such photographs the size may be calculated and the morphology can be observed.

Although the electron microscope is important as a virus research tool, it is too expensive and its successful operation too technical to be used in routine diagnosis of virus diseases.

Cultivation of Viruses. Viruses may be cultivated in three ways: animal inoculation, tissue cultures, and the inoculation of chicken embryos. Some viruses can be successfully propagated by any of the three methods while others can be grown only in the natural host animal.

Animal Inoculation. Animal inoculation was the first method of virus cultivation and for many years was the only means of virus propagation. This method is not as convenient and is also more expensive than embryo methods. Besides serving to propagate the virus, the inoculation of various animal hosts is important in the identification of an unknown virus. This procedure is used in distinguishing between viruses which produce similar lesions such as foot-and-mouth disease and vesicular stomatitis of cattle. In such cases calves and horses are inoculated. Calves are susceptible to both viruses while horses are insusceptible to foot-and-mouth virus but readily contract vesicular stomatitis.

Rabies diagnosis in some cases must be made by the inoculation of laboratory animals because Negri bodies cannot always be demonstrated in the brain tissue of the infected animal. There are many technics and routes of animal inoculation used for virus studies. The type of tissue attacked and the animal to be inoculated will determine the method employed.

Viruses which produce encephalitis are usually inoculated intracerebrally, the pox viruses intradermally and those of the respiratory group intranasally. Examples of other types of inoculation include inoculation into the scarified cornea of rabbits, scarified epithelium of the mouth and tongue in calves, or the foot pad of the guinea pig.

In poultry, inoculation of live virus vaccines is made into defeathered follicles on the legs, the web of the wing, or in the case of laryngotracheitis vaccine, into the cloacal bursa.

In addition to the above mentioned special methods of inoculation, the more common routes such as intravenous, subcutaneous, or intramuscular injections are used occasionally.

The materials used for animal inoculation may consist of filtered or unfiltered suspensions of organs or exudates. If the materials are unfiltered, it is important to add antibacterial substances, such as penicillin and streptomycin, to prevent contaminating or associated bacterial agents from becoming established. This is especially important in intracerebral inoculations. Some bacteria which are ordinarily considered nonpathogenic may cause infection when directly introduced into the brain tissue of the living animal.

A general procedure for preparation of inoculum is as follows: the infected tissue or exudate is removed from the animal with sterile instruments and placed in a sterile container. The tissue is cut into small pieces and placed in a sterile mortar. An abrasive such as sterile alundum (90 mesh) is sprinkled over the tissue which is ground to a paste and then suspended in tryptose phosphate broth or other buffered liquid to make a 10 to 20 per cent suspension. Centrifugation at 3,000 r.p.m. for 3 to 5 minutes will clarify the material so that the supernatant can be used in a syringe for injection. After centrifugation the supernatant fluid is transferred to another tube and the antibiotics are added. A period of 15 to 30 minutes' incubation at room temperature is allowed before the mixture is injected. However, if the material is collected relatively free of contamination, it can be inoculated immediately into animals and chicken embryos.

Cultivation of Viruses in Tissue Culture. There are many technics for the artificial cultivation of viruses. The virus to be grown and the materials available may modify the technic used. Most of the methods employ the following ingredients:

1. Tissue cells—avian or mammalian, embryonic, adult, or neoplastic.
2. Plasma—heparinized avian plasma is most satisfactory.
3. Serum—collected from the same species as the tissue cells used.
4. Tissue extracts—made from chicken embryos or adult tissue.
5. Balanced salt solution.

Other ingredients such as ascitic fluid, amniotic fluid, and serum ultra-filtrate are sometimes used. It is possible to cultivate certain tissue cells in a chemically defined medium composed of amino acids, vitamins, glucose, and inorganic salts. The addition of penicillin and streptomycin to control growth of any bacteria present is standard procedure.

The tissue culture technics which are most often used will be briefly described. For additional details of the procedures, the student is referred to one or more of the reference books listed at the end of this chapter.

It is of utmost importance that the glassware used in cultivating tissue cells be absolutely clean and free from film and toxic substances. The chemicals and the distilled water used must be free from toxic ions. The various manipulations of handling tissues and media should be carried out in a room which is free from dust and air currents. All instruments and other equipment must be sterile and handled in such a manner as to avoid contamination.

Slide Cultures. One of the simplest types of tissue culture is the slide culture. This type is recommended for the beginner because the culture can be observed frequently under the microscope and its progress noted. Tissue fragments cut with a sharp knife and no larger than 1 to 2 mm. in diameter are placed on a sterile coverglass and a drop each of heparinized plasma, serum, embryo extract, and balanced salt solution is added. The plasma will clot the entire mixture and thereby stabilize the tissue on the coverglass. A slide which has a deep depression in it is placed over the coverglass so that the plasma clot is in the center of the depression. The coverglass is sealed and held fast to the slide by a thin film of petrolatum applied around the edge of the hollow depression.

After a few hours in the 37°C. incubator, the culture will show evidence of growth (Fig. 42.1). Proliferation and migration of cells will be observed around the edge of the tissue fragment. Growth of the tissue cells will continue for 2 to 3 days, and then a portion of the tissue must be transferred to a fresh medium; if not, the

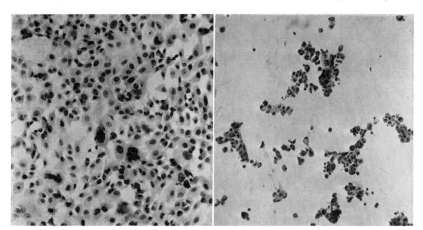

FIG. 42.1 — **Left.** Normal growth in tissue culture of human liver cells. **Right.** Same culture showing cytopathogenic effect after infection with poliomyelitis virus. (Courtesy J. T. Syverton, Univ. Minn.)

accumulation of waste products of cell metabolism will kill the tissue.

Flask Cultures. Various types of flasks have been used to contain cell cultures. Erlenmeyer, Carrel, and Porter flasks are most commonly used. A suspended cell culture is quite easily prepared by dropping small tissue fragments into a flask containing a suitable nutrient medium. Under such conditions the cells do not proliferate to any extent but survive long enough to support virus multiplication. Tissue fragments may be placed in flasks and then embedded in plasma clots if desired.

Another common method of tissue culture is the type in which the cells are grown on the glass surface of the inside of the flask. For this type of culture, trypsinized kidney cells may be used. Preparation of the cells consists of finely mincing the tissue with scissors, followed by treatment with trypsin. The action of the trypsin is to liberate the cells from the minced tissue particles so that uniform suspensions of cells can be prepared. In this way such suspensions can be standardized so that a uniform inoculum is available. The suspended cells are transferred into nutrient fluid contained in flasks. The cells will settle to the bottom and grow in a single layer forming a sheet of cells which adheres to the glass surface.

Roller-Tube Cultures. Tissue cultures may be grown in test tubes which are rotated during incubation. Tissue explants are first placed in the tube and a small amount of plasma or agar is distributed over the inside surface of the tube so that the fragments remain in place. A quantity of nutrient fluid is then added to the tube to fill it approximately 1/10 to 1/8 full. The culture is then placed in a horizontal position in a rotating drum at 37°C. As the tube is rotated 8 to 12 r.p.h., the tissue explants are submerged in the nutrient medium only a portion of the time. Some cells do not grow satisfactorily if they are entirely submerged. Other cells, especially those cultivated through many transfers, will stick to the glass surface and will grow when continuously submerged. In such instances rotation is unnecessary.

Monolayer Tissue Cultures. In 1952, Dulbecco devised a method of growth and titration of certain animal viruses which produces a cytopathogenic effect (see Fig. 42.1). Fibroblasts (other cells may be used) obtained from chicken embryos are first grown in a single layer on the glass surface of a flask. The nutrient fluid used for growth of the cells is then replaced with nutrient fluid containing virus. After a short period of incubation to allow attachment of the virus to the cells, the fluid is poured off and replaced with a layer of melted agar. Following an additional period of incubation, areas of necrotic cells will be found which are the result of virus growth in the tissue cells. If the virus has been sufficiently diluted, these areas of necrosis can be counted to determine the number of elementary bodies present in the original virus inoculum, since it is assumed that each area of necrosis results from one elementary body.

De-embryonated Eggs. A type of tissue culture which is made by the removal of the chicken embryo from the egg but leaves the chorio-allantoic membrane intact is referred to as a de-embryonated egg culture. To prepare this type of culture, eggs which contain 13- to 15-day embryos are selected. The shell which covers the natural air space is removed and the shell membrane over the embryo is broken and pulled to one side or removed. Sterile forceps are used to pull the embryo out of the shell and a pair of scissors to cut the umbilical stalk. The embryo and all other contents of the egg are discarded. Care must be taken to leave the chorio-allantoic membrane undisturbed in its natural position. Several rinsings with saline or balanced salt solution will remove small amounts of albumen and other materials which cannot be completely poured out. Nutrient fluid such as that used for other tissue cultures is then added in an amount to fill the egg shell about one-half full. The virus to be cultivated is then added and the open end of the egg covered. A paper cap can be cemented on or a small funnel can be dipped in melted paraffin and placed over the opening. The stem of the funnel should be plugged with cotton to prevent air contamination. The cells of the chorio-allantoic membrane will survive in the de-embryonated egg long enough for virus multiplication. Several viruses have been grown by this technic.

Tissue-Graft Cultures. Sometimes it is advantageous to graft bits of mammalian tissue onto the chorio-allantoic membrane of the chicken embryo. In this manner the tissue becomes implanted onto the membrane and is nourished by the embryo, but it retains its susceptibility for a particular virus. Viruses which do not propagate in the chicken embryo tissue may be grown in this way if the tissue graft is taken from a susceptible species of animal. Some of the pathologic changes produced by a virus can be studied in sections of the grafted tissue. The preparation of tissue-graft cultures consists of dropping small pieces of skin, amnion, or other tissues onto the chorio-allantoic membrane of a chicken embryo. The embryo is prepared by cutting out a section of the shell over the side of the egg and then "dropping" the membrane as described later in this chapter.

Virus Propagation in Chicken Embryos. The chicken embryo has been found susceptible to a great many viruses and has become most useful in virus diagnosis, research, and in vaccine production.

Eggs for the purpose of embryo inoculation should be procured from disease-free flocks since some infectious agents may pass from the infected hen into the egg. Antibodies may be present in eggs layed by recovered birds which will interfere with growth of certain avian viruses. Eggs from flocks in which the fertility rate is high are more satisfactory and economical.

Incubation of the eggs before inoculation is usually at 38° to 39°C. in a regular egg incubator. Humidity should be kept at 60 per cent. The eggs should be turned at least once or preferably twice a day. After inoculation the conditions of incubation may be varied. The temperature of incubation is usually 35° to 37°C. and the eggs are not turned. Incubation after inoculation may be done in an ordinary bacteriological incubator.

Eggs can be held for several days before starting incubation but should be kept at cool temperatures of about 10–12°C.

The length of incubation before inoculation depends upon the type of inoculation to be made and the virus to be cultivated. For example, inoculation into the yolk sac is usually made in 7- to 9-day old embryos while chorio-allantoic inoculation is made on 10- to 13-day embryos. The extreme range for inoculations is from 6- to 15-day embryos.

Before eggs are inoculated, they must be examined to determine that a viable embryo is present. This is done by candling in a darkened room. After 5 or 6 days of incubation, the blood vessels of the chorio-allantois are readily distinguishable in a fertile egg but none are found in an infertile egg which will be quite translucent.

Technics of Embryo Inoculation. The methods of inoculation are as follows:

1. Chorio-allantoic membrane.
2. Allantoic cavity.
3. Amniotic sac.
4. Yolk sac.
5. Intraembryonic.
6. Intracerebral.
7. Intravenous.

The first four methods are in common use and will be described briefly. The other three methods require considerable experience and skill to perform and are limited to special work.

Chorio-allantoic Inoculation. A number of viruses grow best on the chorio-allantois; the pox group is a good example. The chorio-allantoic membrane is useful not only for the isolation and propagation of many viruses but lesions are formed and can be studied.

It is possible to assay the quantity of virus present in unknown material by making dilutions of such material and inoculating onto the chorio-allantoic membrane. After a period of incubation the lesions or pocks are counted and the amount of virus in the original material is calculated. It is assumed that on membranes where the pocks are well separated each lesion originated from a single elementary body.

Embryos 10 to 14 days of age may be selected for chorio-allantoic membrane inoculation. In order to inoculate onto the membrane, a portion of it must be exposed. The technic of "dropping the membrane" is ordinarily used. This is accomplished by first candling the egg and a triangular area of 1 to 1.5 cm. is marked on the side, taking care to avoid the large blood vessels. A small electric drill with a suitable cutting disc is used to cut through the shell along the lines of the triangle. It is important to avoid cutting too deeply so that the delicate chorio-allantoic membrane is not injured. An inoculating needle can be used to remove the triangular piece of shell and then with a gentle downward pressure with the end of the needle a slit is made in the shell membrane. A small hole is then drilled in the end of the egg through the shell and shell membrane into the air cell. By using a rubber bulb, suction is applied to the opening in the end of the egg. As the air is exhausted from the natural air cell an artificial air cell is formed over the embryo by the air entering the slit in the shell membrane on the top of the egg, thereby separating the chorio-allantoic and shell membranes. The chorio-allantoic membrane is "dropped" and the contents of the egg displaced into the natural air cell (see Fig. 42.2).

The inoculum is placed directly onto the exposed membrane from a pipette or syringe and the openings sealed with melted paraffin, collodion, household cement, or cellulose tape. Eggs inoculated in this manner should be handled carefully and incubated in a horizontal position so the position of the membrane will not be disturbed.

Allantoic cavity inoculation is easily made by drilling a small hole through the shell into the air cell about 3 mm. from its border. The position and extent of the air cell is marked in the candler. A tuberculin syringe with a 25 gauge ⅝ inch needle is suitable for this type of inoculation. The needle is directed into the allantoic cavity by inserting it through the drilled hole and parallel to the long axis of the egg. Amounts of inoculum may vary from 0.05 to 0.5 ml. but 0.2 to 0.3 ml. are average for the allantoic cavity. If the larger amounts are injected, it is advisable to drill a second hole in the air cell near the first to allow for expansion or some of the inoculum may leak back past the needle.

Allantoic cavity inoculation may be made through a hole drilled on the side of the egg, but this may produce injury and hemorrhage. After inoculation the holes are closed and the eggs incubated in the same manner as described previously.

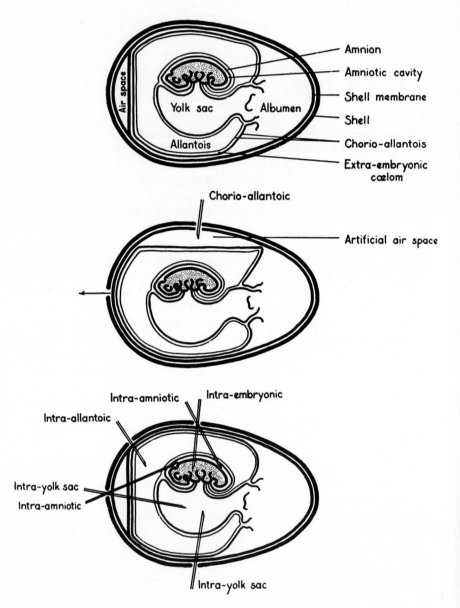

FIG. 42.2 — Sketch of chicken embryo showing position and relationship of structures to the various routes of inoculation.

Amniotic sac inoculation is more difficult and detailed than either of those already described. One method is to candle eggs with 10- to 12-day old embryos and mark the extent of the air cell. By using a drill, the entire top of the egg is cut off exposing the air cell. A small area of the shell membrane is made transparent by the application of sterile mineral oil so that the embryo can be viewed below. Sterile forceps are used to pierce the shell membrane and the chorio-allantoic membrane in order to pick up the amniotic membrane and pull it through the opening. The inoculation is made into the amniotic sac by injecting through the amniotic membrane as it is held in the forceps. Following inoculation, the membrane is released and allowed to go back to its normal position. The top of the egg is covered with a suitable cap of rubber or paper, or a small glass funnel which is cemented or paraffined onto the shell.

Another method is to approach the amniotic sac through a "window" cut as for chorio-allantoic inoculation. By using transillumination from below, so that the embryo can be viewed during the inoculation, the embryo is approached with the needle of the syringe. As the point of the needle reaches the embryo a short quick thrust will strike the embryo and it will move away from the end of the needle. The point of the needle is in the amniotic sac and the inoculation is then made. The normal swallowing movements of the embryo places part of the inoculum in contact with respiratory epithelium. Some viruses grow best when inoculated by this route.

Intraembryonic, intracranial, and *intravenous inoculation* of embryos are not widely used and will not be described here. For more detailed description of these and other methods of inoculation the student should refer to the work of Burnet.

Following inoculation, embryos are incubated for a period of one to six days during which they are observed twice daily for evidence of death of the embryo. Some viruses, such as equine encephalomyelitis, kill the embryo within 24 hours while others kill in 2 or 3 days. Still other viruses grow readily in the tissues of the embryo but seldom are they lethal.

Embryo death is accompanied by collapse of the large blood vessels of the chorio-allantois so that they are difficult to see upon candling the egg, whereas they are quite distinct while the embryo is alive. Normal movements of the embryo are no longer observed if the embryo is moribund or dead.

If the embryo is not dead after 5 or 6 days incubation, it is killed and examined for lesions.

Examination of the embryo should be done soon after death or certain lesions may be obscured by post-mortem changes.

Some of the lesions and changes which may be induced by virus growth are listed below.

1. Embryo death.
2. Hemorrhages of subcutaneous tissues, feather follicles, occipital region.
3. Congestion of vessels of the wings and feet or of entire embryo.
4. Growth of the embryo is stunted.
5. Tucking of the embryo.
6. Decreased amount of amniotic fluid.
7. Increased amount of allantoic fluid.
8. Thickening and edema of chorio-allantoic membrane.
9. Pocks or areas of leucocytic infiltration often with central necrosis (Fig. 42.3).
10. Microscopic lesions.
11. Formation of inclusion bodies.

It is desirable to refrigerate the embryos for four or five hours before examination. This will reduce hemorrhage into the fluids if the embryo is still alive. If materials are to be saved for further passage or for vaccine production, it is important to disinfect the shell with alcohol or tincture of iodine before opening the egg so as to avoid bacterial contamination. Allantoic fluid may be removed by a syringe or pipette directly from the egg by removing the shell over the air cell, then by breaking the shell membrane and the chorio-allantoic membrane beneath. Forceps or other suitable instruments are used to hold back the embryo and its membranes from obstructing the end of the pipette or syringe. Following the removal of fluids the embryo is removed from the shell in order to detect gross lesions. Various portions of the embryo or the extra-embryonic membranes may be collected for microscopic sections.

Observation of inoculated chorio-allantoic membranes is accomplished by cutting away the shell over the artificial air cell. The exposed membrane may be removed by cutting it at the border with a pair of scissors. Lesions in the membrane may be more clearly demonstrated by floating it on saline in a Petri dish which is placed over a black background.

If materials are to be held for a time before reinoculation, they should be stored in an ice chest. Although some viruses will remain viable for months when stored in the ordinary refrigerator, storage at temperatures of —35°C. or below is better. Lyophilization and storage *in vacuo* is also recommended for preservation of viruses.

Cultures, aerobic and anaerobic, should be made of all embryo materials harvested since many species of bacteria may produce lesions or death of embryos which may simulate those produced by viruses.

It should be pointed out that up to 10 per cent of the deaths in embryos may occur from nonspecific causes. Deaths due to such

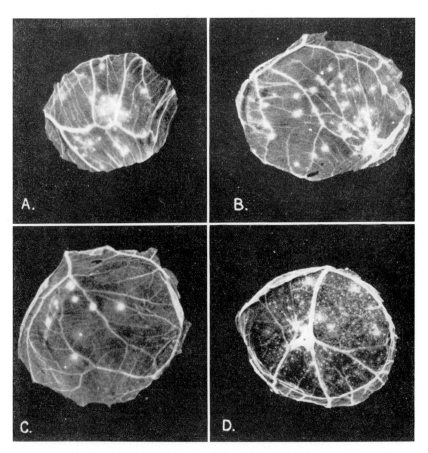

FIG. 42.3 — Chorio-allantoic membrane lesions, natural size. **A.** Herpes virus. **B.** Virus B. **C.** Pseudorabies virus, early passage. **D.** Late passage pseudorabies virus, showing primary and secondary foci. After Burnet, Lush, and Jackson, **Austral. Jour. Exp. Biol. Med. Sci.**, 17:35, 1939.

causes must not be confused with those produced by viruses. Passage of material from such embryos will fail to kill on second transfer.

Some viruses fail to produce lesions in the first passages so several "blind" passages must be made in order to establish them in embryos.

Serological Methods. The viruses are good antigens and readily stimulate the production of antibodies. The detection of specific antibody to a virus by various serological technics is useful not only for the diagnosis of virus infection but also for the identification of an unknown virus by reacting it with known immune serum. The discovery that a number of viruses will agglutinate erythrocytes in the absence of antibody has added a valuable tool in the study and identification of viruses.

The serological methods commonly employed in virus studies are as follows:

1. Agglutination and precipitation.
2. Complement-fixation.
3. Serum neutralization.
4. Virus neutralization.
5. Protection tests.
6. Hemagglutination and hemagglutination-inhibition.
7. Cytopathogenicity in tissue culture.

Agglutination and Precipitation. It has been shown that viruses may be sensitized by specific antibody and in the presence of an electrolyte the virus particles cling to each other forming aggregates which can be seen by either microscopic or macroscopic examination. The mechanism in this case is not different from that already described as occurring with bacteria (agglutination) or with protein molecules (precipitation). Since the size of viruses is intermediate between the bacteria and protein molecules, neither term will precisely fit the condition of virus flocculation in the presence of immune serum. The term flocculation which is more inclusive might be appropriate. The term agglutination is most often used, however, and is a valuable aid to the identification of certain viruses and for the detection of their antibodies. The preparation of the antigen for agglutination tests is often difficult because the viruses must be grown in the tissues of animals rather than on agar culture as for most bacterial antigens. The virus must be separated as completely as possible from the host cells in which it is grown. This is usually accomplished by centrifugation and washing in buffered solution followed by recentrifugation. The antigen is standardized and the agglutination technic carried out in a manner similar to agglutination testing with bacterial antigens. Suitable controls on the materials must be used in order to avoid error in conclusions.

The agglutination of virus elementary bodies is useful in two ways. If the virus is known, antibodies for it can be detected in an unknown serum. On the other hand, if known immune serum is available, an unknown virus can be identified by this technic.

So far only a few viruses such as vaccinia and varicella have been studied by using agglutination technic.

Soluble antigens of vaccinia and influenza have been identified by precipitation procedure.

Complement Fixation. There is little basic difference in the technic of complement fixation using viruses as antigens than that employed with bacterial antigens. Virus antigen for this test is obtained from infected animal tissues, such as lung or brain, or from the tissues or fluids of infected chicken embryos. The exact technics of preparation of viral antigens are too diverse to be described here. The complement-fixation procedure is otherwise the same as described in Chapter 11.

Complement-fixation tests are useful in detecting the presence of antibodies in serum by employing a known antigen or for the identification of an unknown virus by using known antibody.

Neutralization Tests. Neutralization tests are quite useful in virus studies and are more often applied than flocculation or complement-fixation procedures. There are two neutralization technics employed: serum neutralization (SN) and virus neutralization (VN).

Serum neutralization tests employ known virus to which unknown serum is added. If antibodies for the virus are present in the serum, the virus will be neutralized or rendered non-infective. The technic for neutralization tests will vary according to the virus to be used. The amounts of virus, the amount of serum, the test animal, and the route of inoculation employed must be modified to suit the conditions necessary for virus growth and to obtain satisfactory end-points. The basic principles of testing are in general the same and may be illustrated as follows:

1. Preliminary titration of the infectivity of the virus is necessary to determine dilutions to be used. A wide enough range of dilutions are used so that 100 per cent survival as well as 100 per cent mortality will be determined.
2. Equal volumes, usually 0.2 to 0.3 ml., of each virus dilution and known negative serum are mixed.
3. Equal volumes of each virus dilution and immune serum are mixed.
4. Incubate the mixtures 30 minutes at 37°C.
5. Inoculate 5 or 6 test animals or chicken embryos with a dose which should be infective as determined in the preliminary titration. Twice the volume of inoculum will be necessary to account for the dilution by the serum.
6. Inoculate an equal number of controls with each virus dilution which contains no serum.

7. Observe the animals or embryos for lesions or lethal effect and calculate the amount of virus neutralized by the serum after determining end-points of reaction.

For comparison purposes, end-points of 50 per cent death (LD 50) or 50 per cent infectivity (I.D. 50) are usually calculated. Reference to Table 42.1 shows the virus killed 50 per cent of the embryos or animals when diluted 10^{-7} or 1 to 10 million. In other

TABLE 42.1

HYPOTHETICAL SERUM NEUTRALIZATION TEST

	Virus Dilutions								LD_{50} per ml. of Inoculum
	10^{-2}	10^{-3}	10^{-4}	10^{-5}	10^{-6}	10^{-7}	10^{-8}	LD_{50}	
Virus + saline	6*	6	6	6	6	3	0	10^{-7}	10 million
Virus + normal serum	6	6	6	6	6	3	0	10^{-7}	10 million
Virus + immune serum	6	3	0	0	0	0	0	10^{-3}	1,000

* The number in each space indicates the number of deaths with each dilution. Six were inoculated.

words, the original virus suspension contained 10 million LD_{50} doses per ml. of inoculum. The virus and the normal serum mixture also killed 50 per cent in a dilution of 10^{-7}, showing that there were no antibodies in the normal serum for the virus. The virus mixed with serum from the immune animal showed a titer of only 10^{-3}, indicating a neutralization of the virus by the serum. In this case there was a reduction of 10 million LD_{50}'s to 1,000 LD_{50}'s by the immune serum; thus, 9,999,000 LD_{50}'s had been neutralized.

Virus neutralization tests may be conducted in a manner similar to the one described above for serum neutralization, except that the serum is known and the virus unknown.

Protection Tests. Protection tests, although not strictly sero-logical, are used in the study and identification of those viruses which can be used to produce a successful vaccine. This procedure is also employed for the testing of many commercial serum and vaccine products.

The protection test involves first the production of either active or passive immunity in an animal which is followed by a challenge dose of the virulent virus. It is, in a way, an *in vivo* neutralization test.

An example of the use of a protection test for the identification of a virus is to distinguish the three equine encephalomyelitis viruses.

In this instance vaccines are prepared from all three types and a series of guinea pigs immunized with each one. When satisfactory immunity is developed they are all challenged with the unknown virus which has been isolated from horse brain and is suspected of being one of the three.

In the example given in Table 42.2, the unknown virus would be identified as western equine encephalomyelitis since the animals immunized with vaccine prepared from known western virus were resistant to the challenge dose while the others, including the controls, were not.

Commercial products, such as rabies and hog cholera vaccines, are routinely tested for potency by using them to produce active

TABLE 42.2

A HYPOTHETICAL PROTECTION TEST FOR THE IDENTIFICATION OF EQUINE ENCEPHALOMYELITIS VIRUS

Immunized Guinea Pigs Given	Virus Dilution Used				
	10^{-3}	10^{-4}	10^{-5}	10^{-6}	10^{-7}
Eastern type vaccine	5*	5	2	1	0
Western type vaccine	1	0	0	0	0
Venezuelan type vaccine	5	5	3	0	0
Controls	5	5	3	1	0

* The number in each space represents the number of animals killed, five were inoculated.

immunity in test animals which are then given challenge doses of the living virus.

The passive immunizing property of anti-hog cholera serum is tested by injecting it in graded doses into a series of susceptible pigs simultaneously with a challenge dose of live hog cholera virus.

Virus Hemagglutination (HA Test). Hirst, in 1941, observed that agglutination of the chicken embryo erythrocytes occurred when they mixed with amniotic and allantoic fluids provided these fluids were high in influenza virus content. Subsequent research has shown that many viruses will agglutinate the erythrocytes of the adult fowl and certain mammals. Hemagglutination has become a valuable test for the presence of some viruses and also can be used to show the quantity present in a given fluid.

The mechanism by which a virus may agglutinate erythrocytes is not completely understood. It is known that virus hemagglutination differs from hemagglutination by antibody. It has been theorized that erythrocytes possess receptors which attract virus particles. The union of the virus with these receptors alters the properties of the erythrocytes so that they agglutinate. Hemagglutination by influenza virus has been studied in some detail, others to a lesser extent. A number of properties and characteristics of virus hemagglutination may be listed.

1. Ability to produce hemagglutination rests with the virus particle itself in most cases.
2. Hemagglutination by variola and vaccinia is produced by a product of the virus rather than the elementary body.
3. Union of virus and erythrocyte is not stable. After a period of time, the virus leaves the red blood cell and is again present in the suspending fluid. This is known as *elution* of a virus.
4. Following elution of the virus, the agglutinated cells fail to adhere to each other.
5. Red blood cells from which a virus has been eluted cannot be reagglutinated by the same virus, but may be agglutinated by an unrelated virus.
6. A virus killed by formalin retains its hemagglutinative property.
7. Heat inactivation reduces or completely destroys hemagglutination depending upon the temperature and duration of treatment.

TABLE 42.3

VIRUS HEMAGGLUTINATION OF ERYTHROCYTES OF VARIOUS ANIMALS

Source of R.B.C.	Newcastle of Fowl	Fowl Pest	Swine Influenza	Vaccinia
Chicken	+	+	+	±
Man	+	+	+	+
Cow	+	+	−	+
Sheep	+	+	−	±
Rabbit	±	....	+	±
Guinea pig	+	+	−	+

The quantity of a virus which will produce hemagglutination can be quite accurately titrated by HA test.

In the performance of the HA titration, doubling dilutions of the virus-containing material are made in saline using a separate pipette for each dilution. After the suspension of washed erythrocytes is added, the tubes are shaken and then allowed to stand at room temperature until sedimentation of the cells occurs and the results can be read. The period of incubation is usually 40 to 75 minutes. If agglutination is present, a granular mat, often with curling at the edges, will be observed in the bottom of the tube. Absence of agglutination is shown by the cells settling to the very bottom of the tube in a rather compact round "button."

Rapid HA tests are useful as a quick presumptive test for the presence of certain viruses in embryo fluids. The rapid test may be done on a slide or spot plate by adding equal volumes, 1 to 2 drops, of embryo fluids and a 4 per cent suspension of washed erythrocytes. If a fairly high concentration of virus is present, hemagglutination will be evident, usually within one minute.

TABLE 42.4
A Sample Hemagglutination Test

Dilution 1 to	10	20	40	80	160	320	640	1,280	2,560	5,120
ml. of each virus dilution	.5	.5	.5	.5	.5	.5	.5	.5	.5	.5
ml. of 0.25% washed chicken R.B.C.	.5	.5	.5	.5	.5	.5	.5	.5	.5	.5
hemagglutination	+	+	+	+	+	+	+	+	−	−

+ = hemagglutination; − = no hemagglutination. Hemagglutination titer is 1:1,280.

Hemagglutination Inhibition (*HI*). The discovery that certain viruses would agglutinate erythrocytes was promptly followed by the observation that antibodies to the virus would inhibit the reaction. HI tests have been a convenient method of detecting the presence of specific antibody in the serum of infected, or convalescent individuals. Furthermore, by diluting the serum, the comparative amount of antibody can be determined.

Although the serum from infected or recovered individuals will inhibit hemagglutination and also neutralize the virus, there is evidence that these reactions are the result of separate antibodies.

The virus antigen used in the above test must be titrated accurately by using the HA test previously described. A satisfactory amount of virus for the test is 20 hemagglutinating units to be contained in the .5 ml. which is added to tubes 3 to 10 inclusive. A *hemagglutinating unit* is the smallest amount of virus contained in .5 ml. of saline which will completely agglutinate the erythrocytes in .5 ml. of .25 per cent of suspension. Reference to Table 42.4 shows .5 ml. of the 1:1,280 dilution to contain 1 hemagglutinating unit of virus. Therefore .5 ml. of 1:64 dilution of the original virus will be used in the test.

Forty units of virus should be added to tube 2 to keep the amount of virus constant in each tube. Tube 1 is a serum control to check the red blood cell suspension. If agglutination should occur in tube 1, the serum should be absorbed first by the erythrocyes to remove the natural hemagglutinins and then retested. Tube 10 and 11 are controls on the virus and red blood cell suspension respectively.

It should be noted that interference with hemagglutation may occur which may be due to one of several factors:

1. Chemical contamination of tubes or ingredients, acids for example.
2. Inhibitory substances in tissue extracts.
3. Peculiarities of R.B.C.'s from certain individuals.

4. Heat-labile components of serum.
5. Bacterial enzymes and toxins.
6. Species incompatability between R.B.C. used and serum tested.

TABLE 42.5
A Sample Hemagglutination–Inhibition Test

	1	2	3	4	5	6	7	8	9	10	11
Serum ml.	.2	——— doubling dilutions are made ———								0	
Saline ml.	.8	0.5 ml. taken from tube 1 and								0	.5
		mixed with tube 2 etc.									
Virus ml.		.5	.5	.5	.5	.5	.5	.5	.5	.5	
0.25% washed R.B.C. ml.	.5	.5	.5	.5	.5	.5	.5	.5	.5	.5	.5
Final dilution of serum. 1 to...	10	20	40	80	160	320	640	1,280	2,560		
Positive serum	—	—	—	—	—	—	+	+	+	+	—
Negative serum	—	+	+	+	+	+	+	+	+	+	—

$+$ = hemagglutination; $-$ = no hemagglutination.

REFERENCES FOR FURTHER STUDY

Beard, J. W. Jour. Immunol., 58:49, 1948.

———. Physiol. Rev., 28:349, 1948.

Beveridge, W. I. B., and Burnet, F. M. Med. Res. Council Spec. Rept. No. 256. His Majesty's Stationery Office, London, 1946.

Burnet, F. M. Med. Res. Council Spec. Rept. No. 220. His Majesty's Stationery Office, London, 1936.

———. Brit. Jour. Exp. Path., 21:147, 1940.

Cameron, Gladys. Tissue Culture Technique. Academic Press Inc., New York, 1950.

Dubecco, R. Proc. Natl. Acad. Sci., 38:747, 1952.

Henle, W. Jour. Immunol., 64:203, 1950.

Hirst, G. K. Science, 94:22, 1941.

———. Jour. Exp. Med., 87:301, 1948.

Parker, R. C. Methods of Tissue Culture. 2nd edition. Paul B. Hoeber, Inc., New York, 1950.

Reed, L. J., and Muench, H. Amer. Jour. Hyg., 27:493, 1938.

Rivers, T. M. Viral and Rickettsial Diseases of Man. J. B. Lippincott Co., Philadelphia, 1952.

Scherer, W. F., et al. An Introduction to Cell and Tissue Culture. Burgess Publ. Co., Minneapolis, 1955.

Van Rooyen, C. E., and Rhodes, A. J. Virus Diseases of Man. Thomas Nelson & Sons, New York, 1948.

White, P. R. The Cultivation of Animal and Plant Cells. The Ronald Press, New York, 1954.

Woodruff, A. M., and Goodpasture, E. W. Amer. Jour. Path., 7:209, 1931.

43. | Classification of Viruses

Progress in the systematic classification of viruses has been limited by the technical difficulties encountered in their study. Specific morphological and physiological characteristics which could be used to determine the relationship of one virus to another have been more difficult to obtain than with the bacteria, and it is unlikely they will ever be obtained to the extent of the bacteria.

A system which has been of limited value in the classification of animal viruses is based on their tissue specificity or the pathological changes they produce. The one generally used is as follows:

I. Dermotropic viruses—those infecting the superficial epithelium.

II. Neurotropic viruses—those infecting the nervous system.

III. Organotropic viruses—those infecting particular organs or systems.

IV. Viruses inciting tumor formation.

In the past, the common names of viruses, such as hog cholera virus, have been taken from the diseases with which they are associated. Few proposals of family, generic, or species names had been made until Holmes published, in 1939, a classification and nomenclature of the phytopathogenic viruses or plant viruses. This system was extended by Holmes to include all viruses and was published in Bergey's Manual of Determinative Bacteriology in 1948. Although this classification is not yet complete and will be modified as new data are determined, nevertheless it is the first real attempt at virus taxonomy.

The animal viruses as classified by Holmes are in many cases incomplete, and important references which contain essential characteristics are missing. Some of the well-established animal viruses such as equine influenza, vesicular exanthema of swine, and contagious ecthyma of sheep are not classified. Infectious bronchitis of chickens is a disease which is not classified separately, this name appearing under laryngotracheitis. At one time, the name infectious bronchitis was applied to the disease later known as laryngotracheitis, as well as to the disease now known as infectious bronchitis. In the early 1930's the two diseases were distinguished from each other. Recent work on fox encephalitis and canine hepatitis has shown these diseases are caused by the same virus. Sompolinsky has suggested that since this virus infects more than one organ of the body, it should be transferred from the genus *Tarpeia* to *Tortor,* and Holmes (personal communication) has agreed. This would seem to be a step in the right direction if the classification is to be generally adopted and useful. If those who are actively studying the viruses and those interested in their classification will constructively criticize and suggest changes and additions to Holmes' work, a more satisfactory classification will be forthcoming.

There are those who predict that considerable opposition to Holmes' classification will prevent its acceptance. Some virologists feel that it is yet too soon to attempt classification because of inadequate knowledge of the viruses themselves.

On the other hand, there are many others, including some workers in the field of plant and insect viruses, who are in general accord with the genus and species classification of these agents of disease.

The adoption of Holmes' classification of the animal viruses for the organization and relation of material for this text is not without some hesitancy, and some criticism is anticipated. It should be pointed out that this classification is the first attempt at virus taxonomy and will have precedent over succeeding ones.

The fundamental basis of this classification is pathogenicity—the most obvious characteristic of the viruses. It is only through their pathogenicity that they are ordinarily recognized. This is in contrast to the bacteria, of which only a few of the total species known are parasitic, so characteristics other than disease production are used for classification. Since the viruses will remain as obligate parasites, pathogenicity will undoubtedly remain as a fundamental criterion for their recognition.

It is the usual custom of those writing in periodical literature and textbooks of bacteriology to use the nomenclature of the latest edition of Bergey's Manual of Determinative Bacteriology although it is not binding to do so. Any author of a modern textbook on virology would certainly be remiss if he did not recognize this classification and nomenclature.

The Holmes classification as revised by Packer and with suggestions by Van Rooyen is presented below.

In the discussion of the various viruses in the succeeding

chapters, the scientific as well as the common names will be used but the use of the common names will predominate.

ORDER VIRALES

Suborders

I. Infecting bacteria *Phagineae*
II. Infecting plants *Phytophagineae*
III. Infecting animals *Zoophagineae*

Family of
1. Diseases of insects only *Borrelinaceae*
2. Diseases of pox group *Borreliotaceae*
3. Diseases of encephalitis group *Erronaceae*
4. Diseases of yellow fever group *Charonaceae*
5. Diseases of infectious anemia group *Trifuraceae*
6. Diseases of mumps group *Rabulaceae*

Genera and Species of Family *Borreliotaceae*

Genus *Borreliota* — pox group

Borreliota avium ....fowl pox
Borreliota variolae ....smallpox
Borreliota suis ....swine pox
Borreliota ecthymatis .....contagious ecthyma — sheep
Borreliota marmorans ..... ectromelia — mice

Genus *Scelus* — herpes group

Scelus recurrens ....herpes febrilis
Scelus suillum ....pseudorabies
Scelus beta ....virus B
Scelus tertium ....virus III — rabbits
Scelus ulceris ....ulcerative dermatosis — sheep
Scelus bovinum .... erosive stomatitis — cattle

Genus *Hostis* — foot-and-mouth disease group

Hostis pecoris ....foot-and-mouth disease
Hostis equinus ....equine vesicular stomatitis
Hostis exanthematis ....vesicular exanthema — swine

Genus *Molitor* — wart group

Molitor verrucae ....common warts (human)
Molitor hominis ....molluscum contagiosum (human)
Molitor bovis ....cattle warts
Molitor buccalis ....canine oral papillomatosis
Molitor tumoris ....rous sarcoma — chicken
Molitor gingivalis ....rabbit oral papillomatosis
Molitor sylvilagi ....rabbit papilloma
Molitor myxomae ....rabbit myxomatosis

Genera and Species of Family *Erronaceae*

Genus *Erro* — typical encephalitis group

Erro scoticus	louping ill — sheep
Erro silvestris	spring-summer encephalitis
Erro incognitus	Australian X-disease
Erro japonicus	Japanese B encephalitis
Erro scelestus	St. Louis encephalitis
Erro nili	West Nile encephalitis
Erro equinus	western equine encephalomyelitis
Erro tenbroeckii	eastern equine encephalomyelitis
Erro venezuelensis	Venezuelan encephalomyelitis
Erro bornensis	Borna disease — horse
Erro gallinae	avian encephalomyelitis

Genus *Legio* — poliomyelitis group

Legio debilitans	poliomyelitis — man

Genus *Theilerella*

Theilerella muris	mouse encephalitis
Theilerella tescheni	Teschen disease — swine

Genus *Armlillia*

Armlillia erebea	lymphocytic choriomeningitis
Armlillia simulans	pseudo-lymphocytic choriomeningitis

Genus *Formido* — rabies group

Formido inexorabilis	rabies

Genera and Species of Family *Charonaceae*

Genus *Reedella* — yellow fever group

Reedella evagatus	yellow fever
Reedella vallis	Rift valley fever

Genus *Tarpeia* — influenza group

Tarpeia alpha	influenza A
Tarpeia beta	influenza B
Tarpeia premens	common cold
Tarpeia felis	feline distemper
Tarpeia vitulae	pneumoenteritis — cattle
Tarpeia canis	canine distemper
Tarpeia viverrae	ferret distemper
Tarpeia avium	laryngotracheitis
Tarpeia pulli	infectious bronchitis — chickens

Genus *Tortor* — generalized-infection group

Tortor suis .... hog cholera
Tortor bovis .... rinderpest — cattle
Tortor equorum .... African horse sickness
Tortor equae .... equine influenza and abortion
Tortor ovis .... blue tongue — sheep
Tortor felis .... panleucopenia — cat
Tortor galli .... fowl pest
Tortor furens .... Newcastle disease
Tortor vulpis .... fox encephalitis-canine hepatitis

Genera and Species of Family *Trifuraceae*

Genus *Trifur* — infectious anemia group

Trifur equorum .... equine infectious anemia
Trifur gallinarum........ fowl leucosis

Genera and Species of Family *Rabulaceae*

Genus *Rabula* — mumps group

Rabula inflans .... mumps
Rabula levis .... guinea pig salivary disease
Rabula innocuus .... hamster salivary disease
Rabula exiguus .... rat salivary disease
Rabula latens .... mouse salivary disease

REFERENCES FOR FURTHER STUDY

Crawford, M. Vet. Bull., 20:57, 1950.

Holmes, F. O. Handbook of Phytopathogenic Viruses. Burgess Co., Minneapolis, 1939.

———. Order Virales. *In* Bergey's Manual of Determinative Bacteriology. 6th ed. Williams and Wilkins Co., Baltimore, 1948.

Sompolinsky, D. Maanedsskrift for Dyrlaeger, 50:24, 1949.

Steinhaus, E. A. Bact. Rev., 13:203, 1949.

Van Rooyen, C. E. Canad. Jour. Microbiol., 1:227, 1954.

44. The Genus Borreliota—
the Pox Group

The generic name Borreliota is derived from the name *Borrel*, the name of the man who discovered the elementary bodies of fowl pox, and *iota* meaning the smallest thing.

Members of this group infect the surface epithelial layers of the skin producing lesions which progress from papule to pustule to scab formation followed by healing.

RELATIONSHIPS OF ANIMAL AND HUMAN POX VIRUSES

The occurrence of pox lesions in various animals, similar in every way to the lesions of smallpox of man, has stimulated considerable research to determine the relationship of pox in animals to pox in man. This might seem an easy problem to solve but many complicating factors have been found and there are some contradictory data published throughout the years of study on this subject. Most of the confusion which has resulted concerns the following observations: the virus from smallpox lesions of man can be transferred to animals in which it will produce a similar lesion but the infection does not spread to other animals; the serial passage of either human or animal pox virus in animals, except the natural host, results in a modification of its pathogenic properties to form vaccinia; the pox viruses of animals and man are closely related immunologically. From the evolutionary standpoint, the theory has been advanced that all of the pox viruses may have originated from one virus, perhaps vaccina, which became particularly adapted for various animal hosts and man. There are other investigators who suggest that variola is the more primitive virus because vaccinia can be developed from variola by passage. A number of characteristics of the pox viruses may be listed on which there is rather general agreement.

1. Variola, smallpox virus, is primarily a pathogen of man.
2. Variola is readily transferable to the skin of monkeys or the cornea of a rabbit.

3. Variola may be transferred to various animals such as the cow, horse, sheep, and pig but usually is difficult to establish at first. Adaptation is more certain in these hosts if one or more primary transfers are made in rabbits or monkeys.
4. After serial passage of variola in animals it is converted to vaccinia.
5. It is possible to convert sheep-pox and horse-pox virus to vaccinia by passage in other species of animal.
6. Vaccinia is readily transferable from animal to animal by artificial inoculation but usually does not spread under natural conditions.
7. Naturally occurring sheep pox, horse pox, and cow pox are caused by a distinct strain of virus in each case although they share antigens in common with vaccinia.
8. Vaccinia is quite easily transferable to man in whom it produces localized infection whereas variola is usually generalized.
9. Both fowl and swine are susceptible to vaccinia.
10. Fowl-pox virus bears no antigenic relationship to vaccinia or variola.
11. Certain strains of swine pox are antigenically distinct from vaccinia.

In summary, it appears that under natural conditions each animal species is infected by a separate strain of pox virus. By artificial inoculation these strains are intertransmissible to all hosts. Vaccinia is a "laboratory virus" converted from certain of the naturally occurring strains by animal pasage. Cross-immunity occurs among all strains. Fowl-pox and swine-pox viruses, however, are distinct from those found in other animals and cannot be converted to vaccinia.

Borreliota avium

Common Name. Fowl-pox virus, also turkey pox, pigeon pox, and canary pox.

Disease Produced. Fowl pox, avian diphtheria.

Hosts Affected. Chicken, turkey, pigeon, canary, duck, goose, guinea fowl, pheasant, and sparrow.

Properties of the Virus. The elementary bodies, which are coccoid-shaped, are approximately 250 mμ in diameter (see Fig. 44.1). They often are referred to as *Borrel bodies*. Aggregates of Borrel bodies often occur in the lesions and are called *Bollinger bodies*. Digestion of the Bollinger body with 1 per cent trypsin releases the elementary bodies.

The fowl pox virus will pass through the coarser grade filters, such as Berkefeld V, but fails to pass finer grades. It is killed by 60°C. in 8 minutes or 56°C. in 30 minutes. Storage of the virus at 0 to 4°C. in dried material retains its viability for 2 years.

The following chemicals are reported to inactivate the virus in 10 minutes' exposure: 1:500 sodium hydroxide, 1:1,000 crystal violet, 70 per cent ethyl alcohol, and 1:400 cresol.

Phenol in 3 per cent concentration kills in 30 minutes but not in 10 minutes. Formaldehyde, 3 per cent, does not kill by exposure for 20 minutes; 50 P.P.M. of chlorine and 1:400 tincture of iodine are reported effective against fowl pox.

Three or more strains of fowl pox virus are responsible for natural outbreaks of the disease among various species of fowl. Fowl pox virus is found in chickens and is probably the same in turkeys. Pigeon pox and canary pox are strains which produce disease in pigeons and canaries respectively. All three strains are immunologically related and are intertransmissible by artificial inoculation.

Cultivation. Fowl pox can be readily passed from one bird to another by inoculation onto the scarified epithelium of the comb or wattles or defeathered feather follicles. It can also be grown on the chorio-allantoic membrane of chicken embryos where it produces thickening, edema, and necrosis of the membrane, but the virus usually is not lethal to the embryo. Tissue cultures can also be used to propagate the virus of fowl pox.

Transmission. Contact with infected birds or objects contaminated by them may transmit the disease. Injury to the epithelium predisposes to infection, in fact, it has been reported essential for the initiation of fowl pox. Insects such as mosquitoes and biting flies have been shown to transmit the virus. Artificial inoculation, intramuscularly or intravenously, will result in infection. Droplet transmission is possible from cases of pox infection of the mouth and pharynx.

Characteristics of the Disease. Fowl pox occurs widely throughout the world, attacking adult or young adult birds. The disease is more prevalent in fall and winter months. Mortality rates are usually low, but may be as high as 50 per cent. However, losses from decreased egg production and loss in weight may be considerable. Deaths most often occur in birds having lesions in the mouth, pharynx, orbit, and sinuses. Infection of this type is called avian diphtheria. Occasionally lesions will be seen on the feet. The course of the disease usually runs 3 to 4 weeks.

Pathological Changes. The lesions are characterized by the proliferation of the surface epithelial structures followed by

FIG. 44.1 — Elementary bodies of fowl pox, shadow cast with chromium, × 80,000. (Courtesy Van Rooyen and Rhodes, Virus Diseases of Man. Thomas Nelson Sons, New York, 1948.)

degeneration. The basal layer of epithelium is usually undamaged unless secondary bacterial invasion occurs. Cells of the infected area become swollen and exhibit vacuoles in which Bollinger bodies can be demonstrated. Healing takes place usually without scar formation.

Immunity. Recovery from an attack of fowl pox results in immunity. Artificial immunization is practiced in certain areas, especially those in which the disease appears quite regularly each year. There are two products in general use, pigeon-pox vaccine and fowl-pox vaccine.

Pigeon-pox vaccine is prepared by inoculating the virus into defeathered follicles in young pigeons or by propagating it on the chorio-allantoic membrane of chicken embryos. The material harvested for vaccine is either preserved in 20 per cent glycerin or is dried. The dried vaccine can be kept viable several months and is diluted just before use.

Fowl-pox vaccine may be prepared by growing the virus on the comb of young cockerels or on the chorio-allantoic membrane of chicken embryos. These materials are harvested, then dried and stored. They are prepared for use by diluting in water.

Pigeon-pox vaccine produces less reaction in vaccinated birds, so is usually recommended for use in laying flocks. Fowl-pox vaccine is used in young birds before they come into production and it is considered to produce better immunity than pigeon-pox vaccine. The vaccines are applied by subcutaneous inoculation into the shank (stick method), by brushing the vaccine into defeathered follicles, or by piercing the web of the wing with a needle dipped in the vaccine.

Diagnosis. The lesions on the comb and wattles are usually so characteristic that they alone are diagnostic. However, when lesions are present in the mouth, pharynx, or orbit diagnosis may be more difficult. In these cases transmission of material from the lesions to susceptible birds or chicken embryos will produce typical lesions if the disease is fowl pox. Bollinger and Borrel bodies in the infected tissue may be demonstrated microscopically. Agglutination of Borrel bodies is occasionally used as an aid to the identification of the virus.

Borreliota variolae

Common Name. Smallpox virus, variola, vaccinia, and especially adapted varieties which naturally infect the cow, sheep, horse, goat, camel, and swine.

Disease Produced. Smallpox, alastrim, cow pox, sheep pox, horse pox, goat pox, camel pox, and swine pox.

Hosts Affected. Man, cow, horse, sheep, goat, camel, monkey, swine, and experimentally the rabbit, guinea pig, dog, buffalo, and chicken.

Properties of Virus. The elementary bodies measure approximately 225 mμ and are coccoid in shape. Smallpox elementary bodies are often termed *Paschen bodies*. Inclusions consisting of collections of elementary bodies are found in abundance in infected tissue. These have been termed *Guarnieri bodies*. Various stains such as Giemsa, methylene blue, or carbol fuchsin, and many special stains can be used to demonstrate these bodies. The variola virus is filterable through Berkefeld V, N, and W, and Chamberland L₃ but not through the Mandler type. There is considerable absorption of the virus by most filters. Filtration of vaccinia material through Seitz pads allows the passage of soluble antigen into the filtrate. The soluble antigen is not infective but is flocculated by antivaccinial serum. Two portions of the soluble antigen are distinguishable, "L" which is labile at 56°C. and "S" which is stable at 95°C.

Thermal inactivation of the virus occurs by exposure to 55°C. for 20 minutes. The virus is preserved at freezing temperatures for prolonged periods. It has been known to survive in dried crusts for over one year. Ultraviolet rays rapidly destroy the virus. Both vaccinia and variola may agglutinate chicken erythrocytes; however, the erythrocytes from different individual chickens may vary in their agglutinability. Hemagglutination occurs best at 37°C.

Cultivation. Animal inoculation is one of the methods of cultivation. Monkeys are quite susceptible to variola. Inoculation of the scarified cornea of the rabbit (Paul's test) is used. Repeated transfer will adapt variola to other animals such as calves. Vaccinia can be propagated in nearly all animals, but calves are commonly used for vaccine production.

Vaccinia can be cultivated by intratesticular inoculation. Certain strains of vaccinia have been converted to neurovaccinia by brain to brain passage in rabbits.

The chorio-allantoic membrane of the chicken embryo will support a good growth of either variola or vaccinia. Growth of the virus on the membrane produces thickening, edema, leucocytic infiltration, and necrosis, and may or may not be lethal to the embryo.

The virus can be grown successfully in tissue cultures.

Transmission. Smallpox is transmitted usually by contact with infected individuals or contaminated fomites, but also by droplets from the respiratory tract.

Characteristics of the Disease. Smallpox has occurred in all parts of the world and has been known throughout the ages, often in serious epidemics causing many deaths. General use of vaccine has reduced the incidence to a very low figure in the United States and European countries.

The animal pox viruses and diseases, as far as known, are not significantly different from variola to warrant complete separate descriptions of the virus. Some of the characteristics of the common animal pox diseases will be given.

Cow pox. This disease is world-wide in distribution and occurs enzootically mostly in dairy cattle. Cow pox is always a local infection on the udder and teats. It may be caused by either cow pox or vaccinia strains which have been shown to differ antigenically by Downie. Lesions are indistinguishable, but the cow pox is believed to be the naturally occurring strain. Pox in cows has been observed shortly after the vaccination of persons milking them. Cow-pox virus is transmissible to man and produces immunity against smallpox as has been shown by the classical work of Jenner. Cow-pox lesions usually heal leaving no scar. Ordinarily the disease is considered quite benign but occasionally predisposes the teat to the entrance of mastitis organisms. Immunization against cow pox is not practiced in cattle.

A disease condition in man, known variously as "milker's nodules," "milker's warts," or paravaccinia, which occurs on the hands and arms of people who milk cows, has been described. The disease resembles cow pox and vaccinia but has been distinguished from these by Bonnevie and also Findlay and Haig, who isolated a virus by chicken embryo inoculation which is distinct from vaccinia.

Horse pox. Horse pox is also known under the names contagious pustular dermatitis, and "grease heel." The virus attacks the buccal mucous membrane, skin of the lips and nares, producing vesicles, papules, and pustules. The virus also attacks the skin in the pastern-fetlock region and occasionally over the back where the saddle or harness may abrade it. Ulcers and pustules are produced in these regions. The virus may be transmitted by contaminated brushes, combs, saddles, and harness as well as other contaminated materials. Horses are susceptible to inoculation with vaccinia, but the natural cases are believed due to a specially adapted equine virus.

Sheep pox. Pox in sheep is a more severe disease than cow pox or horse pox. Sheep pox is accompanied by fever and generalized symptoms in addition to eruptions of the skin. In these respects the disease more closely resembles human smallpox than do the other animal poxes. Although sheep are susceptible to vaccinia, and sheep are used in some countries for vaccine production, sheep pox is caused by a distinct strain of virus. In some instances substantial death losses have been recorded. The disease does not occur in the United States. Transmission is by contact and has been shown to be air-borne. Lesions appear mostly on the skin areas devoid of wool such as the udder, teats, scrotum, and around the eyes. Immunization is practiced in some countries.

Goat pox. A pox disease occurs in goats which closely resembles sheep pox. It is found chiefly in Norway.

Swine pox. Two viruses which produce pox lesions in swine are described. One is closely related to the vaccinia-variola group, the other is apparently unrelated antigenically and has a limited host range.

The vaccinia-like swine-pox virus has been described in outbreaks of the disease in Europe and Japan. The relationship of the virus in these reports is indicated by its transmissibility to rabbits and immunity to it which is conferred by vaccinia. It is seen more frequently in young pigs. The lesions produced are typical of the pox diseases starting with a small red papule followed by vesicle and pustule formation. The eruptions may involve the mouth and pharynx and occasionally the lungs which may account for some deaths. Skin lesions become black and encrusted followed by healing if uncomplicated by bacterial infection.

Transmission is by contact and by the hog louse. The distinct swine-pox virus is described below.

Borreliota suis

Common Name. Swine-pox virus.

Disease Produced. Swine pox.

Hosts Affected. Only swine are naturally susceptible to this virus. The rabbit, horse, calf, sheep, dog, cat, mouse, fowl, guinea pig, rat, and man are insusceptible by direct inoculation.

Properties of the Virus. Little is known of the characteristics of this virus. It is reported to pass Berkefeld V and N candles.

Cultivation. The virus can be cultivated in pigs. Primary isolation can be made by inoculation onto the chorio-allantoic membrane of chicken embryos. Lesions produced are typical of the pox group of viruses. The embryo is not killed.

Transmission. Swine pox is transmitted by contact and possibly by flies, mosquitoes, and hog lice.

Characteristics of the Disease. Outbreaks of swine pox due to this virus have been reported in Europe and in the United States (Iowa). It occurs in young pigs and is usually limited to occasional outbreaks. Lesions are found in the skin of the abdomen and over the sides and back. There is usually hemorrhage into the lesion, producing a dark center. The infection may spread to many pigs in a group which are in close contact. The infection is usually not severe enough to produce death losses unless complicated by other infections, but may account for reduced weight gains for a short period.

Pathological Changes. Lesions on the underline are typical of the pox diseases passing successively through papule, vesicle, and pustule formation. The lesions on the back are not as characteristic. These develop into small, hard, smooth elevations which become encrusted and soon drop off.

Immunity. Immunity results from having recovered from the disease. Artificial inmmunization is not practiced. No cross-immunity is produced against the vaccinia-like swine-pox virus.

Diagnosis. The disease is usually diagnosed by the characteristic lesions. It is differentiated from pox produced by vaccinia-like virus by cross-immunity tests and by determining the host range.

Borreliota ecthymatis

Common Name. Ecthyma virus.

Disease Produced. Contagious ecthyma, contagious pustular dermatitis, and sore-mouth.

Hosts Affected. Sheep, goats, man, and possibly the rabbit.

History and Distribution. Although contagious ecthyma of sheep had been known many years previous, Aynaud was the first to describe the virus in 1923. The disease is widely distributed in the sheep-raising areas of the United States, Australia, Europe, Great Britain, and Africa.

Properties of the Virus. The ecthyma virus is comparatively large, probably being nearly the size of vaccinia. Elementary bodies have been observed with the light microscope by staining as for Paschen bodies of variola.

The virus will pass the Berkefeld V filter with difficulty, but is retained by Berkefeld N and W, Chamberland L_2, and Seitz types. It will pass through the Mandler (6–9 lb.) if the diluent used is adjusted to pH 7.6 but it is retained by this filter if the pH is 8.2.

As with vaccinia, the digestion of ecthyma-infected tissue with trypsin is often necessary to liberate the elementary bodies from the tissue cells before filtration of the virus is accomplished. Ecthyma virus is quite resistant to desiccation. Observations are recorded in which the virus remained viable for 4 years, 8 months in one instance and for 15½ years in another. A temperature of 56°C. for 30 minutes kills the virus, but material held at 55° for 20 minutes remains infective.

Cultivation. The virus of ecthyma has been transmitted to the sheep, goat, man, and possibly the rabbit. Guinea pigs, dogs, and calves are not susceptible. Attempts to cultivate the virus on the chorio-allantoic membrane of chicken embryos have been unsuccessful.

Transmission. Ecthyma is spread by contact with infected sheep. Transmission from the ewes' udder to the mouth of suckling lambs and vice versa may occur.

Characteristics of the Disease. Lesions of ecthyma of sheep usually appear on the lips but are also frequent on the coronary band of the feet. Occasionally lesions are observed on other parts of the body such as the udder, teats, eyes, ears, nostrils, and vulva. Young animals are most susceptible and suffer most from the disease because they cannot eat or nurse without great difficulty and this results in severe loss of weight and thriftiness. Foot lesions cause lameness in infected animals. Older animals show a milder form of the disease. Death losses are low unless secondary bacterial infection is serious or screw worms attack the infected area. *Spher. necrophorus* or *Staph. aureus* are usually found in cases of bacterial complications. There are no generalized symptoms noted in uncomplicated cases of ecthyma differing from sheep pox in this respect. The duration of the disease is usually about 25 days.

Man is susceptible to ecthyma virus, and a number of proven cases of the disease have been reported. The lesions are usually on the hands, arms, or fingers, occurring in cuts or abrasions. The disease is not serious and complete recovery occurs in about 6 weeks.

Pathological Changes. The successive pathological stages observed in ecthyma are papule, vesicle, pustule, and scab formation. These changes are analogous to the changes seen in the pox diseases. In some cases there are proliferative changes in the infected areas of the lips giving rise to pseudo-papillomas or wartlike lesions.

Immunity. Recovery from ecthyma is accompanied by permanent immunity. Artificial immunity is successful and is used in many sheep-raising areas. Live vaccine prepared from the scab material of artificially infected sheep is used. The vaccine is applied to the scarified skin of the medial aspect of the thigh. Lesions indicating a "take" of the vaccine should appear in 6 to 7 days after vaccination.

Cross-immunity tests show that strains of ecthyma virus from various countries are antigenically homologous and no relationship to vaccinia, sheep pox, or ulcerative dermatosis can be demonstrated. Complement-fixing and neutralizing antibodies have been demonstrated in the serum of immune animals.

Diagnosis. A diagnosis of ecthyma is based on the appearance of typical lesions on the lips and feet or lips alone and differentiation of the virus from *Scelus ulceris* by cross-immunity tests.

Elementary bodies have been demonstrated in some cases of ecthyma in stained preparations of exudate.

Borreliota marmorans

Common Name. Ectromelia virus.

Disease Produced. Mouse ectromelia. Mouse pox.

Hosts Affected. White mouse. Experimentally the rat and chicken embryo.

History and Distribution. Ectromelia is a disease of laboratory mice which has been described in England. The first descriptions of the disease and the virus were by Marchal in 1930.

Properties of the Virus. Direct measurements from electron photographs of the virus show it is 130 to 140 mμ in size. It is filterable through Berkefeld N, Chamberland L₂, and Mandler filters. The virus is inactivated if heated to 55°C. for 30 minutes. It remains viable for 6 months in a dried state, for 2 months if frozen at —10°C. and for at least 5 months if stored in 50 per cent glycerin. *Borreliota marmorans* is resistant to 1 per cent phenol for 20 days but is killed by 40 days' exposure.

Ectromelia virus will produce hemagglutination of fowl erythrocytes. The hemagglutinin in this case is a soluble substance which can be removed from the elementary bodies. The hemagglutination occurs best at 37°C. and there is no evidence of elution of the virus from the erythrocytes. In these respects ectromelia closely resembles the hemagglutinating properties of vaccinia. Sera from mice which have recovered from ectromelia will inhibit hemagglutination by vaccinia virus.

Cultivation. *Borreliota marmorans* has been successfully propagated in tissue cultures which employ mouse embryonic tissue. The virus can also be grown on the chorio-allantoic membrane of chicken embryos on which it produces small opaque foci. If the embryos are incubated at 36 to 37°C. death occurs in 3 to 4 days, whereas the embryos survive if incubated at higher temperatures. Inclusion bodies can be demonstrated from the lesions of the membrane.

Transmission. The virus of ectromelia is transferred by contact with infected mice.

Characteristics of the Disease. The infection is characterized by lesions in the skin usually on the feet. They begin as localized swellings which become moist then dry with scab formation and separation of the skin by a line of demarcation between the infected and noninfected areas. There is also mottling of the liver and spleen. Inclusion bodies can be demonstrated in skin lesions. Young mice are most susceptible.

Immunity. Specific immunity follows recovery. Mice which have been vaccinated with vaccinia virus are refractory to ectromelia virus.

Diagnosis. A diagnosis of ectromelia is made by the appearance of the typical lesions and by transmission of the virus to other mice and to chicken embryos. Demonstration of hemagglutinins for avian erythrocytes and agglutinins for elementary bodies is also used.

REFERENCES FOR FURTHER STUDY

Borreliota avium (Fowl pox)

Cunningham, Chas. H. Fowl Pox. *In* Diseases of Poultry. 3rd edition. Edited by Biester, H. E., and Schwarte, L. H. Iowa State College Press. Ames, Iowa, 1952.

Goodpasture, E. W. Virus Diseases of Fowl. *In* Filterable Viruses. Rivers, T. M. The Williams and Wilkins Co., Baltimore, 1928.

Hutyra, F., Marek, J., and Manninger, R. Special Pathology and Therapeutics of the Diseases of Domestic Animals. Alex. Eger, Chicago, 1946.

Borreliota variola (Smallpox and Animal pox)

Blaxall, F. R. Animal Pock Diseases. *In* A System of Bacteriology. Vol. 7. His Majesty's Stationery Office, London, 1930.

Bonnevie, P. Brit. Jour. Derm., 49:164, 1937.

Borrel, A. Ann. Inst. Past., 17:81, 1903.

Cathie, D. M. Brit. Med. Jour., 1:99, 1932.

Craigie, J. Brit. Jour. Exp. Path., 13:259, 1932.

Downie, A. W. Brit. Jour. Exp. Path., 20:158, 1939.

———, and Dumbell, K. R. Jour. Path. and Bact., 59:189, 1947.

Findlay, G. M. Jour. Roy. Micro. Soc., 56:213, 1936.

———, and Haig, D. A. Brit. Jour. Derm., 64:451, 1952.

Gordon, M. H. Med. Res. Council Rept. No. 98. His Majesty's Stationery Office. London, 1925.

Green, R. H., Anderson, T. F., and Smadel, J. E. Jour. Exp. Med., 75:651, 1942.

Hutyra, F., Marek, J., and Manninger, R. Special Pathology and Therapeutics of the Diseases of Domestic Animals. Alex. Eger., Chicago, 1946.

Nagler, F. P. O. Med. Jour. Aust., 1:281, 1942.

Paschen, E. Munch. med. Wschr., 53:2,391, 1906.

Paul, G. Berl. Klin. Wschr., 53:874, 1916.

Smadel, J. E. Smallpox and Vaccinia. *In* Viral and Rickettsial Diseases of Man. Edited by Rivers, T. M. J. B. Lippincott Co., Philadelphia, 1952.

Borreliota suis (Swine pox)

McNutt, S. H., Murray, C., and Purwin, P. Jour. Amer. Vet. Med. Assn., 74:752, 1929.

Murray, C. Jour. Amer. Vet. Med. Assn., 90:326, 1937.

Schwarte, L. H., and Biester, H. E. Amer. Jour. Vet. Res., 2:136, 1941.

Borreliota ecthymatis (Contagious ecthyma of sheep)

Aynaud, M. Ann. Inst. Past., 37:498, 1923.

Blackmore, F., Abduss-alam, F., and Goldsmith, W. N. Brit. Jour. Derm. and Syph., 60:404, 1948.

Bosworth, I. J., and Glover, R. E. Proc. Forty-ninth Ann. Cong. Nat. Vet. Med. Assn. Gr. Brit. and Ireland, 1931.

Boughton, I. B., and Hardy, W. T. Jour. Amer. Vet. Med. Assn., 85:150, 1934.

Glover, R. E. Jour. Comp. Path. Therap., 41:318, 1928.

———. Rep. Inst. Anim. Path. Univ. Camb., p. 17, 1929–30; p. 1, 1932–33.

Hart, L., Hayston, J. T., and Keast, J. C. Australian Vet. Jour., 25:40, 1949.

Newsom, I. E., and Cross, F. Jour. Amer. Vet. Med. Assn., 84:233, 1934.

Seddon, H. R., and Belschner, H. G. Vet. Res. Rept. N. S. W. No. 5, 36, 1929.

———, and McGrath, T. T. Vet. Res. Rept. N. S. W. No. 6, 109, 1933.

Borreliota marmorans (Mouse pox)

Barnard, J. E., and Elford, W. J. Proc. Roy. Soc. London Ser. B., 109:360, 1931.

Burnet, F. M. Nature, 158:119, 1946.

Marchal, J. Jour. Path. and Bact., 33:713, 1930.

45. The Genus Scelus— the Herpes Group

The genus name *Scelus* comes from the Latin word which means rascal. Members of the herpes group induce lesions of skin which are vesicular in character, but involvement of the central nervous system may occur.

Scelus recurrens

Common Name. Herpes simplex.

The virus *Scelus recurrens* causes "fever blisters" or "cold sores" of man. It does not cause natural disease in animals, but rabbits, guinea pigs, mice, and cats have been experimentally infected. The virus can be grown on the chorio-allantoic membrane of chicken embryos and in tissue cultures.

Scelus suillum

Common Name. Pseudorabies virus.

Disease Produced. Pseudorabies, Aujeszky's disease, mad-itch, infectious bulbar paralysis.

Hosts Affected. Cattle, swine, brown rats, dog, cat, horse, sheep, and, rarely, man. Experimentally the rabbit, guinea pig, mouse, monkey, chicken and chicken embryo may be infected.

History and Distribution. Pseudorabies was first described by Aujeszky in Hungary in 1902. The etiological agent was shown to be a virus by the work of Schmeidhoffer in 1910. The disease occurs sporadically in many parts of the world. It has been reported in Europe, British Isles, South America, and the United States.

Properties of the Virus. The elementary bodies are recorded as being 100 to 150 mμ in size. No information is available regarding the morphology of the virus. It is preserved in 50 per cent glycerin stored at 0°C. for several years. In fluid from pulmonary edema it is viable after 797 days' storage in a refrigerator. Heating at 55–60°C. for 30 to 50 minutes, 70° for 10 minutes, 80° for 3 minutes destroys the virus, and at 100° the virus is killed instantly. Phenol in a 5 per cent concentration will destroy the virus in 2 hours, 1 per cent in 15 hours, and 0.3 per cent in 61 days. One per cent sodium hydroxide destroys the virus immediately. Putrefaction destroys the virus in 11 days.

Cultivation. Animal passage in rabbits by skin or cerebral inoculation can be used to propagate the virus. Tissue cultures which employ rabbit or guinea pig testicular tissue will support growth of pseudorabies virus. Chicken embryos can be infected by various routes of inoculation and pock lesions are produced when the virus is inoculated onto the chorio-allantoic membrane (see Fig. 42.3). The egg-adapted virus may be lethal to the embryo, killing it in 3 to 5 days after inoculation, but recently isolated strains may fail to kill or do so irregularly.

Transmission. Transmission of pseudorabies in cattle usually takes place when the virus is introduced into the injured skin or mucous membrane. Shope and others have called attention to rats and swine as disseminators of the virus, these hosts being readily infected by feeding. Shope has also drawn particular attention to the presence of pseudorabies virus in the nasal secretions of swine and to the fact that the secretions are the usual source of the virus for other swine and cattle. Dogs and cats have been known to contract the disease following the consumption of infected tissues of cattle. Commercial hog-cholera virus used for immunization purposes has been contaminated with pseudorabies virus, and transmission to swine has occurred through the use of such a product.

Characteristics of the Disease. Pseudorabies is a highly fatal, relatively noncontagious disease of cattle and laboratory animals and a highly contagious, mild disease of swine. Its occurrence in swine, according to Shope, is quite widespread and is usually not detected. The disease is seldom fatal in swine, but in artificially infected hogs a definite temperature increase and inappetence is observed. Local paralysis may result if the virus is injected intramuscularly. In other animals, there is intense itching at the point of skin infection which is accompanied by self-mutilation by gnawing or rubbing. These symptoms are so characteristic in cattle and laboratory animals that they are considered diagnostic of the disease. Mania is often observed in cattle and sometimes other animals so it is confused with rabies, hence the name pseudorabies has been used. In the final stages of the disease the virus involves the brain and the animal becomes paralyzed. This is followed by coma and death. The virus has been isolated from human infection in laboratory workers. However, the disease is mild and of short duration.

Pathological Changes. There are no characteristic pathological lesions in pseudorabies. The kind and extent of lesions depend upon the animal species infected and the duration of the disease. In animals with skin infection, the lesions may include hyperemia, edema and necrosis which are usually accompanied by severe traumatic lesions. Depending upon the duration of the disease, there may be meningitis and perivascular, leucocytic infiltration of the brain tissue. In sheep and swine pulmonary edema may be observed.

Immunity. Resistance apparently follows recovery in swine. Neutralizing antibodies have been demonstrated in the serum of large numbers of swine. A majority of the samples of commercial anti-hog cholera serum tested by Shope showed the presence of neutralizing antibodies for pseudorabies.

Artificial immunizing agents are not used for the prevention of this disease.

Diagnosis. The diagnosis can be made in cattle and sheep and laboratory animals from the symptoms of intense itching of the skin. In swine, and as confirmation in other hosts, subcutaneous inoculation into rabbits is employed. Rabbits which are inoculated subcutaneously with pseudorabies material should exhibit characteristic symptoms of intense pruritus in 3 to 7 days if the virus is present.

Scelus beta

Common Name. Virus B.

Disease Produced. Encephalitis.

Hosts Affected. Man, captive monkeys, and, experimentally, guinea pigs, mice, rabbits, and chicken embryos.

History and Distribution. Virus B was first isolated from a fatal case of encephalitis, patient B, a laboratory worker who had been bitten by a monkey. Only 3 human cases of this disease have been reported, all of them fatal. Isolations of the virus from the central nervous system and from kidney tissue of monkeys have been reported. So far the disease is found only in the United States.

Properties of the Virus. B virus is approximately 125 mμ in size and is filterable through Berkefeld V and N candles, Seitz and Chamberland L$_3$ filters. The virus can be preserved in 50 per cent glycerin, by storing in dry ice at $-70°C.$ or by lyophilization. *Scelus beta* is antigenically related to herpes and pseudorabies viruses.

Cultivation. *Scelus beta* can be cultivated on the chorio-allantoic membrane of the chicken embryo where it produces pocks similar to those of *Scelus recurrens* and *Scelus suillum*.

The virus can also be propagated in tissue cultures, and will produce a cytopathogenic effect in the cells of the culture.

Transmission. The virus occurs in the saliva of some monkeys and is transferred to man by biting. Other hosts are infected only by artificial inoculation.

Pathological Changes and Characteristics of the Disease. Vesiculopustular lesions appear at the site of the monkey bites, followed by lymphangitis and lymphadenitis. A week later meningoencephalitis develops followed by death. There is also focal necrotic lesions in the spleen, adrenals, and lymph nodes. Intranuclear inclusions are described in experimental infections.

Immunity. Neutralizing antibodies can be demonstrated from the sera of some normal monkeys. Artificially infected monkeys are immune following recovery from the infection.

Diagnosis. A diagnosis of virus B infection would necessitate isolation of the virus and its differentiation from other viruses.

Scelus tertium

Common Name. Virus III.

Disease Produced. Virus III infection.

Host Affected. Domestic rabbit.

History and Distribution. Virus III was first described by Rivers and Tillet in connection with attempts to infect rabbits with chicken-pox virus of man. At first these investigators thought they had transferred the chicken-pox virus to rabbits, but later found they were propagating a virus which was latent in the rabbits and did not produce lesions until it had been concentrated by successive passages.

Properties of the Virus. *Scelus tertium* is filterable through Berkefeld V and N and Chamberland L₂ candles. It is inactivated at 55°C. in 10 minutes. The virus is preserved for 6 weeks in 50 per cent glycerin and for 16 months when frozen and dried.

Cultivation. Cultivation of virus III is by inoculation of rabbits or in tissue cultures employing rabbit testicular tissue.

Transmission. The injection of filtrates of diseased tissues or in some cases blood and tissues from apparently normal rabbits is the source of the virus.

Characteristics of the Disease. After 4 to 6 days' incubation, anorexia, emaciation, diarrhea, and fever result. Reddened spots and papules appear in the skin. Recovery occurs in a few days, the disease being non-fatal.

Immunity. Specific neutralizing antibodies are present in the blood serum after recovery.

Diagnosis. Diagnosis of Virus III infection is possible only by transmission to susceptible rabbits and differentiation from other viruses by cross-immunity experiments.

Scelus ulceris

Common Name. Ulcerative-dermatosis virus, lip-and-leg ulceration, balano-posthitis, posthitis, and ulcerative vulvitis.

Host Affected. Sheep.

History and Distribution. Ulcerative dermatosis has been known to occur in sheep in England since 1894 and was described in Montana by Knowles in 1907. In these early publications the term "lip and leg ulceration" was used to denote the condition and *Spher. necrophorus* was believed to be the causative agent. Tunicliff and Matisheck in 1941 proved the etiological agent to be a virus.

Properties of Virus. The size and shape of the virus are not known, but it is fllterable through Berkefeld V and N filters.

Cultivation. This virus is cultivated artificially only by passage in sheep.

Transmission. It is transmitted by contact with infected tissues and from the ram to ewes by breeding.

Characteristics of the Disease. The *Scelus ulceris* infects only the surface epithelial structures producing ulcerations of the lips, interdigital space and pastern area, vulva, and prepuce. Erosion and destruction of the epithelium occur. The ulcers which are produced often require several weeks to heal. The disease is not fatal but lameness, unthriftiness, and breeding difficulties may result.

Pathological Changes. The basic pathological changes are those of tissue destruction and ulceration followed by surface scab formation and slow healing.

Immunity. If immunity follows recovery, it is temporary since the disease has been observed more than once in the same animals. Artificial immunizing agents are not used for the prevention of this disease.

Diagnosis. Usually a clinical diagnosis of ulcerative dermatosis is made. This condition must be differentiated from contagious ecthyma of sheep, which it closely resembles, by conducing protection tests using ecthyma vaccine in one group and leaving another group unvaccinated. If *Scelus ulceris* is inoculated into both groups, both will show infection. On the other hand, if those given ecthyma vaccine show no lesions following inoculation and the control group becomes infected, the virus in question is that of contagious ecthyma.

Scelus bovinum

Common Name. Erosive-stomatitis virus.

Disease Produced. Erosive stomatitis of cattle.

Hosts Affected. Cattle. Insusceptible: guinea pigs, rabbits, mice, and sheep.

History and Distribution. Erosive stomatitis of cattle was first described in South Africa by Mason and Neitz. This disease was encountered in 1938 immediately following an outbreak of foot-and-mouth disease while cattle of the area surrounding the outbreak were subjected to frequent mouth inspection. Erosive stomatitis is apparently localized in the original South African area of Natal. However, a similar disease described in Ireland is called Armagh disease, but there have been no direct comparisons of these two viruses.

Properties of the Virus. The size of the erosive stomatitis virus has not been determined, but it is known to pass filters which retain common bacteria. The virus will remain viable for 21 days in a refrigerator or 6 weeks if frozen.

Cultivation. *Scelus bovinum* has been carried through 4 passages on the chorio-allantoic membrane of chicken embryos.

Transmission. The erosive stomatitis virus is probably transmitted by contact. Experimentally it is transmissible by inoculation into the tongue or dental pad of calves.

Characteristics of the Disease. Erosive stomatitis of cattle is a very mild disease of young cattle. The infection is localized in the mouth, there being no foot lesions or generalized symptoms as seen in foot-and-mouth disease of cattle. Infected animals show no excessive salivation and the disease would not ordinarily be observed unless the cattle were carefully and frequently examined.

Pathological Changes. The lesions on the dental pad, tongue, and lips are at first pearl-like. The area becomes elevated with a reddened border and contains a grayish material. Within a day or so these areas become eroded and then quickly heal.

Immunity. Immunity to the erosive stomatitis virus has not been studied to any extent. However, calves which have recovered from experimental inoculation are susceptible to a second exposure.

Diagnosis. Ulcerative stomatitis is diagnosed by proving the presence of a virus in the lesions by inoculation of calves and by its differentiation from other stomatitis viruses by animal inoculation.

REFERENCES FOR FURTHER STUDY

Scelus suillum (Pseudorabies)

Aujeszky, A. Centr. f. Bakt. Abt. 1. Orig., 32:353, 1902.

Burnet, F. M., Lush, D., and Jackson, A. V. Austral. Jour. Exp. Biol. Med. Sci., 17:41, 1939.

Galloway, I. A. Vet. Rec., 50:745, 1938.

Remlinger, P., and Bailly, J. La Maladie d' Aujeszky. Masson and Co., Paris, 1938.

Schmeidhoffer, J., Z. Infektionskranheit. Haustiere, 8:383, 1910.

Shope, R. E. Jour. Exp. Med., 54:233, 1931.

————. Jour. Exp. Med., 62:85, 1935.

————. Jour. Exp. Med., 62:101, 1935.

Scelus beta (B virus encephalitis)

Sabin, A., and Wright, A. M. Jour. Exp. Med., 59:115, 1934.

Scelus tertium (Virus III infection)

Holmes, F. O. Order Virales. Supplement No. 2. *In* Bergey's Manual of Determinative Bacteriology. The Williams and Wilkins Co., Baltimore, 1948.

Rivers, T. M., and Tillet, W. S. Jour. Exp. Med., 38:673, 1923.

————, ————. Jour. Exp. Med., 39:777, 1924.

Scelus ulceris (Ulcerative dermatosis of sheep)

Filmer, J. F. Austral. Vet. Jour., 14:47, 1938.

Tunicliff, E. A. Amer. Jour. Vet. Res., 10:240, 1949.

————, and Matisheck, P. H. Science, 94:283, 1941.

Scelus bovinum (Erosive stomatitis of cattle)

Mason, J. H., and Neitz, W. O. Onderstepoort Jour. Vet. Sci., 15:159, 1940.

46.

The Genus Hostis—
the Foot-and-Mouth Disease Group

The generic name *Hostis* comes from the Latin, meaning enemy or stranger. Members of the genus produce lesions of the skin and mucous membrane which are characteristically vesicular in nature.

Hostis pecoris

Common Name. Foot-and-mouth disease virus.

Disease Produced. Foot-and-mouth disease, aphthous fever.

Hosts Affected. Cattle, swine, sheep, goat, deer, buffalo, and rarely man. Experimentally the guinea pig, rabbit, hedgehog, rat, and young mice may be infected. The guinea pig and white mouse are used in experimental studies of this disease.

History and Distribution. The first disease of animals proved to be of virus etiology was foot-and-mouth disease and was determined by Loeffler and Frosch. In 1897 these investigators showed that bacteria-free lymph collected from infected animals could be used to transmit the infection and, in the following year, that the causative agent of foot-and-mouth disease could be passed through filters which retained bacteria. The disease has occurred in all parts of the world and is still endemic in many countries. It is completely controlled in the United States and Canada by vigorous eradication methods. Nine outbreaks of the disease were recorded in the United States between the years 1870 and 1932. A serious outbreak occurred in Mexico in 1946 and a limited one in Canada in 1951. Australia and New Zealand have remained free of the disease.

Properties of the Virus. The elementary bodies of foot-and-mouth disease are the smallest of the animal viruses. They are approximately 10 mμ in size.

Michelsen has reported that the virus of foot-and-mouth disease will agglutinate the erythrocytes of the rat and that this reaction is inhibited by specific immune serum.

The virus is killed by exposure to 85°C. for 1 minute and 70°C. for 15 minutes but not at 60°C. for 15 minutes.

Foot-and-mouth disease virus remains viable for long periods of time in frozen meat products. It it quite resistant to aging and drying. It will remain infective one month on infected hair, 4 to 5 months on hay and grains, and for one month or more in the soil. In one instance the survival of the virus was demonstrated on a farm 345 days after an outbreak.

Hostis pecoris is comparatively resistant to chemical disinfection. Exposure of the virus to mercuric chloride 1 to 1,000 or 3 per cent cresol solution fails to kill the virus in 6 hours. It also resists 1 per cent phenol for 5 months and 70 per cent alcohol for 2 to 3 days. Although the virus is resistant to these chemicals, it is easily destroyed by alkalies, 1 per cent sodium hydroxide killing it within one minute. Therefore, sodium hydroxide is commonly used for disinfection following outbreaks of the disease.

There are three classical types of the virus: A, O, and C which are immunologically distinct. Several strains within these types have been described. In South Africa, types S.A.T. 1, 2, and 3 have been identified.

Cultivation. The cultivation of *Hostis pecoris* is usually accomplished by the inoculation of scarified areas of the buccal mucosa and tongue of calves or by foot-pad inoculation of guinea pigs. Suckling white mice are quite susceptible and are very useful in conducting titrations of foot-and-mouth disease virus and for serum neutralization tests. It is also possible to cultivate the virus in tissue cultures which employ bovine kidney cells or epithelial tissues taken from either bovine or guinea pig embryos.

A cytopathogenic effect is produced in the cells of the tissue culture as a result of the growth of the virus. Gillespie has shown that all three strains of foot-and-mouth disease virus can be adapted to grow in chicken embryos if they are first adapted to grow in tissue cultures and day-old chicks. Type O virus has been adapted to chicken embryos directly from bovine tissue cultures without first adapting it to day-old chicks. Virus in the 25th embryo passage was found to be nonpathogenic for cattle but did stimulate immunity.

Transmission. Foot-and-mouth disease is quite highly contagious, especially among cattle. Dilutions of 1 to 10 million of virus-containing material have been found infective. Vesicular fluid and saliva contain the most virus, but during febrile stages, the blood, milk, urine, and feces also contain it. Contact with infected animals and especially the ingestion of contaminated food and water transmits the disease. Indirect infection may take place by contact with inanimate objects of various kinds. The virus can penetrate the intact mucous membrane, but its entrance is facilitated by abrasions. Artificial inoculation by almost any route will result in infection.

Transmission of the disease is complicated by the fact that some clinically recovered animals may harbor the virus for some time and act as reservoirs of the infection.

The sources of the virus in the outbreaks of foot-and-mouth disease in the United States include imported cattle, ships' garbage, containing meat scraps, which was brought ashore and fed to hogs, contaminated straw and hay brought from foreign countries, and imported smallpox vaccine in the form of calf lymph.

Characteristics of the Disease. Foot-and-mouth disease infects all cloven-hoofed animals and occasionally other animals, but it rarely infects man. The disease is characterized by the formation of vesicular lesions in the mouth, on the muzzle, in the interdigital space and coronary band of the feet, on the udder and teats of cows, and the snout of swine. The virus may also infect the parenchyma of the mammary gland resulting in complete loss of function.

Upon entry of the virus into the body, one or more primary vesicles are formed and often they are not observed. The virus gains entrance to the blood stream from these primary vesicles and is distributed to all parts of the body, localizing chiefly in the skin and mucous membranes, producing a large number of secondary vesicles.

Losses due to foot-and-mouth disease may be quite high in young animals, but in older animals deaths are usually 5 per cent or less. However, losses due to emaciation, debility, reduced milk flow, and complicating conditions may be considerable.

Pathological Changes. The formation of vesicles on the buccal mucous membrane and tongue is followed by ulceration, erosion, and healing. Lesions of the feet are similar to those in the mouth, being first vesicular and then ulcerative. The lesions of both the mouth and feet are accompanied by swelling, redness, and pain which account for lameness and reluctance of the animal to eat and move about. In the malignant form of the disease there is marked myocardial degeneration which results in many deaths in young animals.

Immunity. Immunity begins to develop in about 6 days following the onset of infection, and plays a definite role in recovery. Such immunity is variable in duration, but usually lasts for at least a year. However, the fact that there are three antigenic types of the virus means that recovery from an attack by one type confers no protection against another. Monovalent, bivalent, or trivalent vaccines are used to produce active immunity in cattle, depending upon the type or types of the virus which prevail in the locality. The virus for vaccine production is propagated by inoculation of the tongue of susceptible cattle. Vesicular fluid and epithelium are collected from the infected areas and mixed with formalin to kill the virus, and with aluminum hydroxide which adsorbs the virus. The vaccine must be carefully prepared and handled up to the time it is used. It is ordinarily administered subcutaneously, but an intradermal product is in use in Argentina.

Convalescent and hyperimmune serum have proved valuable in treating the malignant form of foot-and-mouth disease and are also useful in exposed animals to prevent a generalized infection, although local vesicle formation occurs in animals so treated.

Diagnosis. The characteristic appearance of vesicles in the mouth and feet usually narrows the possibilities to two or three viruses. In the United States three viruses must be differentiated in a vesicular disease of swine and in cattle two viruses must be considered. Determination of the host range in three or four species of animals is the first step in diagnosis. Those species used in such a test and their susceptibility to the three viruses are presented in Table 46.1.

TABLE 46.1
HOST RANGE OF THE VIRUSES PRODUCING VESICULAR LESIONS*

	Cattle	Swine	Horses	Guinea pigs
Foot-and-mouth	+++	++	−	++
Vesicular stomatitis	++	++	+++	++
Vesicular exanthema	−	+++	±	−

* Confirmatory tests may include protection tests in guinea pigs immunized with a known virus.

Complement-fixation tests have been shown by Brooksby and by Bankowski and Kummer to be useful in the rapid differentiation of the vesicular viruses.

Differential filtration may aid in distinguishing foot-and-mouth and vesicular stomatitis viruses since elementary bodies of the latter are about 10 times the size of the foot-and-mouth disease virus. The fact that vesicular stomatitis virus can be cultivated in chicken embryos and the foot-and-mouth disease virus cannot is useful in diagnosis.

It has been shown that the virus of foot-and-mouth disease will regularly produce typical lesions following intramuscular inoculation into a susceptible calf while the virus of vesicular stomatitis fails to do so. This fact, also, must be considered of importance in diagnosis.

Cross immunity or complement-fixation tests must be made in order to determine whether the outbreak in question is due to strain A, O, or C.

Hostis equinus

Common Name. Vesicular-stomatitis virus.

Disease Produced. Vesicular stomatitis, pseudo-foot-and-mouth disease.

Hosts Affected. Horses, mules, cattle, and swine. Experimentally sheep, goats, guinea pigs, and man. Occasionally cats, rats, and rabbits.

History and Distribution. Vesicular stomatitis was first observed in South Africa in 1884 by Hutcheon. It was first recognized as occurring in the United States by French veterinarians who examined horses imported to France from the United States and Canada during World War I (1915). It was diagnosed in horses in Colorado in 1916. Occasional outbreaks in horses and in swine have occurred in various parts of the country since that time. Cotton and Olitsky, Traum and Schoening reported simultaneously, in 1926, on the filterability of the agent of vesicular stomatitis proving the existence of the virus. An outbreak which was confined to swine occurred in the area of Kansas City in 1944.

Properties of the Virus. The elementary bodies of vesicular stomatitis are rod-shaped 60 by 210 mμ in size, and are filterable through Seitz and Berkefeld filters. *Hostis equinus* is inactivated at 58°C. for 30 minutes.

The virus resists 0.5 per cent phenol for 23 days, but is rendered noninfective by 0.05 per cent crystal violet as used in hog cholera vaccine production.

There are two antigenic types of vesicular-stomatis virus recognized: the New Jersey and Indiana types. Complement-fixation tests using hyperimmune serum to each of the two antigenic types have been found useful in their differentiation from each other and from foot-and-mouth disease virus.

Cultivation. The virus can be cultivated in guinea pigs by foot-pad inoculation. Tissue cultures have also been used for cultivation. Inoculation of vesicular-stomatitis virus onto the chorio-allantoic membrane of the chicken embryo results in growth of the virus and death of some embryos. The infected membrane becomes thickened, and hemorrhages may be observed in the embryo itself.

Transmission. Vesicular-stomatitis virus is transmitted by contact with contaminated objects such as eating from common feed boxes, troughs, and mangers, or by drinking water contaminated with saliva from a case of the disease. Abrasions of the mucous membranes of the mouth greatly favor the entry of the virus. Ferris, Hanson, Dicke, and Roberts have presented evidence that the virus can be transmitted by biting flies and mosquitoes.

Characteristics of the Disease. Vesicular stomatitis is primarily pathogenic for horses and mules, but may occasionally be found in cattle and swine. It occurs chiefly in the United States although it was first described in South Africa. In cattle and swine the disease closely resembles foot-and-mouth disease from which it must be differentiated. Vesicular stomatitis is usually quite benign. Complete recovery results in one to two weeks after the onset of symptoms except in an occasional case in which there is secondary bacterial infection of the vesicles. The vesicles are usually confined to the mouth, but they may appear on the feet and udder.

Olitsky and Sabin have demonstrated the neurotropic properties of *Hostis equinus* in guinea pigs and mice, but these tendencies are not known to occur in other animals.

Pathological Changes. Vesicle formation is the first change noted. The vesicles rupture and erosion of the surface epithelium follows. These eroded areas are covered with new epithelium in three to four days.

Immunity. Recovered animals are immune to reinfection by the same type of virus. Artificial immunization is not practiced.

Diagnosis. Since the horse is not susceptible to foot-and-mouth disease, the diagnosis of vesicular stomatitis is usually not difficult in the equine, although it has been confused with horse pox.

If the disease is confined to cattle or swine it is essential that it be accurately identified. In such instances host range, differential filtration, and embryo inoculation procedures may be used. The realkalinization technic of Pyl which consists of acidification of the virus material to pH 3 and return to pH 7.5 kills *Hostis pecoris* but not *Hostis equinus.*

Hostis exanthematis

Common Name. Vesicular-exanthema virus.

Disease Produced. Vesicular exanthema.

Hosts Affected. Swine. Horses are susceptible to A and C types. Some strains have been shown to be pathogenic for hamsters. Cattle, sheep, and guinea pigs are not susceptible.

History and Distribution. Vesicular exanthema was first observed in California in garbage-fed swine in the years 1932–33. At first, 1932, it was diagnosed as foot-and-mouth disease and treated as such. The following year it was recognized as a different virus disease by Traum and the name vesicular exanthema was suggested. Six years after the first outbreak of the disease it reappeared and spread in California infecting approximately one-fourth of the swine of that state. Other outbreaks have been recorded since 1939–40, but none occurred outside the state of California until 1952 when the disease spread to many states.

Properties of the Virus. The virus will pass Berkefeld N filters. Four types of the virus are differentiated immunologically: A, B, C, and D.

According to Madin and Traum, the vesicular-exanthema virus is approximately 14 to 22 mμ in size. The virus is also reported by them to remain viable at ordinary refrigerator temperatures for two years but not for three years. Virus remains viable for six weeks, stored at room temperature, and for twenty-four hours at 37°C. The virus is non-infective after fifty-four hours at 37°C.

Cultivation. Cultivation of vesicular-exanthema virus has usually been carried out by the inoculation of swine. Some strains have been grown in hamsters by intradermal inoculation. Tissue cultures composed of swine embryo tissue cells have supported the growth of the virus and a cytopathogenic effect is produced by the virus.

Transmission. Vesicular exanthema is transmitted by contact with or by consumption of food and water contaminated with the virus. Uncooked garbage which contains pork trimmings has often been the source of the virus. It is also thought to be carried by inanimate objects and by persons going directly from farm to farm.

Characteristics of the Disease. Lesions of vesicular exanthema are almost identical to those of foot-and-mouth disease. The vesicles appear on the snout, in the nostrils, around the coronary band, interdigital space and digital pads of the feet, also on the udder of nursing sows. Animals become lame and the hoofs are sometimes shed. Death losses are low except in suckling pigs. Recovery follows after the vesicles rupture and heal, but gains in weight are retarded for some time afterward. Sows in advanced pregnancy may abort.

Immunity. Hogs are resistant after recovery from an attack but for only a few months' duration. An experimental vaccine has been used by Madin and Traum with encouraging results.

Diagnosis. Animal inoculation is necessary for accurate diagnosis. Swine and horses are usually inoculated with vesicular fluid from suspected cases, and if the virus is present the swine should show lesions within 48 hours. Horses may develop lesions if type A or C strain of vesicular exanthema is present. Since calves and guinea pigs are insusceptible to vesicular exanthema, but are easily infected with *Hostis pecoris* or *Hostis equinus*, they should be used also as test animals.

REFERENCES FOR FURTHER STUDY

Hostis pecoris (Foot-and-mouth disease)

Brooksby, J. B. Proc. Soc. Exp. Biol. Med., 67:254, 1948.

Gillespie, J. H. Cornell Vet., 45:170, 1955.

Hutyra, F., Marek, J., and Manninger, R. Special Pathology and Therapeutics of the Diseases of Domestic Animals. Alexander Eger Inc., Chicago, 1946.

Loeffler, F., and Frosch, P. Centralb. f. Bakt., 22:257. 1897.

——, and ——. Centralb. f. Bakt., 23:371, 1898.

Michelsen, E. Nord. Vet. Med., 1:905, 1949.

Mohler, J. R. U.S.D.A. Cir. 400, p. 82, 1925.

——, and Snyder, R. U.S.D.A. Miscell. Pub. No. 163, 1933.

Olitsky, P. K., Traum, J., and Schoening, H. W. U.S.D.A. Tech. Bull. 76, 1928.

Proceedings 51st Annual Meeting of U. S. Livestock Sanitary Assn. pp. 13–20, 1947.

Rosenbusch, C., DeCamps, A., and Gelormini, N. Jour. Amer. Vet. Med. Assn., 112:45, 1948.

Skinner, H. H. Proc. Roy. Soc. Med., 44:1041, 1951.

Traum, J. Proc. 12th Internat. Vet. Congress, 2:87, 1934.

Waldman, O., Pyl, G., Hobohm, K. O., and Mohlman, H. Centralb f. Bakt., 148:1, 1941.

Hostis equinus (Vesicular stomatitis)

Cotton, W. E. Jour. Amer. Vet. Med. Assn., 69:313, 1926.

——. Jour. Amer. Vet. Med. Assn., 70:168, 1926.

Eichhorn, E. A., and Manthei, C. A. Jour. Amer. Vet. Med. Assn., 94:608, 1939.

Frank, A. H., Appleby, A, and Seibold, H. R. Amer. Jour. Vet. Res., 16:28, 1945.

Ferris, D. H., Hanson, R. P., Dicke, R. J., and Roberts, R. H. Jour. Inf. Dis., 96:184, 1955.

Hanson, R. P. Jour. Bact., 68:724, 1954.

Hutcheon, D. Vet. Jour., 47:54, 1898.

Mohler, J. R. Jour. Amer. Vet. Med. Assn., 52:410, 1918.

Olitsky, P. K., Traum, J., and Schoening, H. W. Jour. Amer. Vet. Med. Assn., 70:147, 1926.

Pyl, G. Hoppe-Seyler's Zeit. f. Physiol. Chemie, 226:18, 1934.

Sanders, E. F., and Quinn, A. H. N. Amer. Vet., 25:413, 1944.

Shahan, M. S. Amer. Jour. Vet. Res., 7:27, 1946.

——, Frank, A. H., and Mott, L. O. Jour. Amer. Vet. Med. Assn., 108:5, 1946.

Hostis exanthematis (Vesicular exanthema)

Bankowski, R. A., and Kummer, M. B. Amer. Jour. Vet. Res., 16:374, 1955.

Crawford, A. B. Jour. Amer. Vet. Med. Assn., 90:380, 1937.

Hurt, L. M. Rep. Los Angeles Livestock Dept. 1939–40, 1941–42, 1946–47.

Madin, S. H., and Traum, J. Vet. Med., 48:395, 1953.

——, ——. Vet. Med., 48:443, 1953.

McClain, M. E., Madin, S. H., and Andriese, P. C. Proc. Soc. Exp. Biol. Med., 86:771, 1954.

Traum, J. Rep. 12th Internat. Vet. Cong., 2:91, 1934.

——. Jour. Amer. Vet. Med. Assn., 88:316, 1936.

White, B. B. Jour. Amer. Vet. Med. Assn., 97:230, 1940.

47.

The Genus Molitor—
the Wart Group

The generic name *Molitor* comes from the Latin, meaning contriver. Members of this group produce lesions of the epithelium characterized by proliferation without vesicle or pustule formation.

Molitor verrucae

Common Name. Common-wart virus.
Disease Produced. Warts.
Hosts Affected. Man.

The common warts of man are transmissible but have a long incubation period of one to twenty months. They are usually quite benign and usually disappear spontaneously. Acquired immunity to the virus is thought to play a part in recovery. Vaccines have been tried but unsuccessfully. Attempts to transmit warts of man to animals are usually unsuccessful. Laryngeal warts of man have been reported transferable to the vagina of dogs, but this has not been confirmed.

Molitor hominis

Common Name. Molluscum-contagiosum virus.
Disease Produced. Molluscum contagiosum.
Hosts Affected. Man.

Molitor hominis produces tumorlike growths in skin which disappear spontaneously. Elementary bodies measuring 300 mμ are contained in large molluscum bodies which are 10 to 30μ in size.

The virus is not transmissible to animals.

Molitor bovis

Common Name. Cattle-wart virus.
Disease Produced. Cattle warts.
Hosts Affected. Cattle. The horse is susceptible but rabbits, mice, guinea pigs, and man are insusceptible to experimental inoculation.

History and Distribution. Cattle warts apparently occur in all countries. Royère, in 1902, was able to transmit experimentally the warts of cattle, horses, and dogs. Magalhães, in 1920, was able to transmit cattle warts by using Berkefeld filtrates of wart material.

Properties of the Virus. The virus has not been studied to any extent. It is known to pass through Berkefeld N filters.

Cultivation. *Molitor bovis* is artificially transferable in calves and horses. The virus has been adapted to grow in chicken embryos.

Transmission. It is believed that warts are spread by contact with infected animals or objects contaminated by them. Injuries to the skin favor the establishment of the infection.

Characteristics of the Disease. Warts are more common in young cattle, especially in calves under one year. Affected areas are usually on the head, neck, and shoulder regions, often near or surrounding the eyes. They may also occur on the udder and teats or on other parts of the body. The infected skin first becomes thickened, then rough and nodular, with the loss of hair. Sometimes the warts become large, pendular, and cauliflower-like in appearance. In such cases the growth and development of the host may be retarded. Frequently, spontaneous recovery occurs.

Immunity. Acquired immunity probably plays a part in spontaneous recovery. Vaccines are commercially available which are made by grinding fresh wart tissue in saline and then treating it with formalin to kill the virus. A wart vaccine of chicken embryo origin is also available. Although spontaneous recoveries often occur, the use of these vaccines is claimed to result in rapid disappearance of the warts.

Diagnosis. A clinical diagnosis of warts is ordinarily sufficient.

Molitor buccalis

Common Name. Canine oral-papillomatosis virus.

Disease Produced. Canine oral papillomatosis.

Hosts Affected. Dog.

History and Distribution. Canine warts probably occur in all countries. Their contagiousness was recognized by McFadyean and Hobday and also Penberthy in 1898. Findlay, in 1930, reported the transmission of canine warts by Berkefeld filtrates of wart material.

Properties of the Virus. *Molitor buccalis* will pass through Berkefeld N filters. It is inactivated by a temperature of 45° to 58°C. in one hour. The virus remains viable upon storage in the refrigerator either in dried material or in 50 per cent glycerin for 63 days.

Cultivation. The virus is transmissible to young dogs by inoculation into the scarified mucous membrane.

Transmission. Transmission of *Molitor buccalis* is presumed to occur through contact with infected dogs.

Characteristics of the Disease. In experimentally inoculated dogs, the lesions appear in the mouth after one month's incubation. Areas which were inoculated become blanched and raised, then become roughened, finally resulting in a mass of closely packed papillae. In naturally occurring cases the warts may appear on the lips, tongue, palate, or buccal mucosa. The warts are quite benign and recovery with immunity results. Secondary warts often appear in other parts of the mouth after the primary ones have appeared.

Immunity. Dogs which have recovered from infection with *Molitor buccalis* are resistant to reinfection; therefore, immunity probably is concerned with the disappearance of the papillomas. Artificial immunizing agents are not used to any extent. Wart vaccines prepared as for bovine use have been suggested for use in dogs.

Diagnosis. A clinical diagnosis is ordinarily made in canine oral papillomatosis.

Molitor tumoris

Common Name. Rous-sarcoma virus.

Disease Produced. Rous sarcoma.

Hosts Affected. Chicken. Experimentally the pheasant and duck can be infected, with difficulty.

History and Distribution. The original virus was described by Rous in 1911 from an adult hen. Since its discovery this virus has been studied in considerable detail. Although the disease is of no economical importance as far as poultry are concerned, the extensive research which has been done on the virus has been a valuable contribution to the study of viruses and to the fundamental knowledge of certain neoplasms. The virus occurs in the United States, and similar strains have been isolated in England and Japan.

Properties of the Virus. *Molitor tumoris* is reported as being 60 to 100 mμ in size. It will pass Berkefeld V filters. Heating the virus to 54°C. for 30 minutes will inactivate it. At 37°C. the virus becomes inactive in about 48 hours. Spontaneous degradation occurs at refrigerator temperatures due to oxidation; therefore, the addition of reducing substances has a preserving effect upon the virus.

Cultivation. *Molitor tumoris* can be cultivated on the chorioallantoic membrane of the chicken embryo, with the production of focal lesions.

Transmission. The injection of tissue cells or a filtrate of the infected tissue will transmit the disease. Transmission by contact does not ordinarily occur.

Characteristics of the Disease. Rous-sarcoma virus induces tumor formation of connective tissue which metastasizes readily to various organs of the body. Death may result in 2 to 5 weeks following inoculation of the virus. All birds which are artificially exposed do not develop tumors, and it has been shown that resistance to infection is sometimes attributable to genetic factors.

Pathological Changes. The parent cell of the sarcoma is the normal histiocyte. At the point of infection a nodule is formed which enlarges and becomes necrotic or cystic and often contains a brownish sanguinous fluid mixed with mucoid exudate. Metastatic lesions occur in the heart, liver, and lungs, and the infected bird becomes emaciated, weak, and depressed, and finally dies.

Immunity. *M. tumoris* is antigenic, and antibodies have been demonstrated which will neutralize the virus. Antigenic relationships have been shown between *M. tumoris* and other sarcoma viruses such as the Fujinami, Mill Hill 1 and 2 strains which have been isolated from fowl tumors.

Diagnosis. A diagnosis of transmissible tumor of fowl depends upon reproduction of the condition by the injection of cell-free filtrates of infected tissue.

Molitor gingivalis

Common Name. Rabbit oral-papillomatosis virus.

Disease Produced. Rabbit mouth warts.

Hosts Affected. Rabbits.

History and Distribution. The virus of oral papillomatosis of rabbits was discovered by Kidd and Parsons in 1936 in a rabbit with induced Vitamin A deficiency. Later these investigators found similar papillomas in the oral mucous membranes of "normal" domestic rabbits.

Properties of the Virus. *M. gingivalis* passes Berkefeld V and N filters.

Transmission. Usually transmission accompanies injury of the mucous membrane and simultaneous exposure to the virus. Older animals are more resistant to exposure.

Characteristics of the Disease. Benign papillomas occur on the lower surface of the tongue and occasionally on the gums or floor of the mouth.

Immunity. Resistance to the *Molitor gingivalis* results after recovery from the infection.

Diagnosis. A diagnosis of oral papillomatosis of rabbits would consist of the appearance of the typical lesions of the mouth and the demonstration of their transmissibility to other rabbits.

Molitor sylvilagi

Common Name. Rabbit-wart virus. Rabbit-papilloma virus.

Disease Produced. Rabbit warts.

Hosts Affected. Cottontail rabbit and experimentally the domestic rabbit.

History and Distribution. Rabbit-papilloma virus was isolated from cottontail rabbits by Shope in 1932. The specimens which yielded the virus were collected from rabbits in northwestern Iowa and later from some in southern Kansas. The disease is apparently confined to the middle western United States.

Properties of the Virus. The elementary bodies of *Molitor sylvilagi* are nearly spherical in shape and are approximately 44 mμ in diameter. They will pass all grades of the Berkefeld type filter. The virus withstands a temperature of 65° to 67°C. for 30 minutes but it is killed at 70° exposure.

Cultivation. *M. sylvilagi* can be passed serially in wild cottontail rabbits. It will produce lesions in domestic rabbits, but cannot be passed serially in that species.

Transmission. Transmission of rabbit-papilloma virus can be accomplished by intradermal inoculation in rabbits. Scarification or application of benzene to the skin increases its susceptibility to the virus.

Characteristics of the Disease. *M. sylvilagi* is specific for the skin epithelium of the rabbit. At first there are minute elevations in the skin which becomes keratinized and wrinkled, followed by cornification, forming large "horns" in some cases. Some papillomas become malignant and metastasize to internal organs.

Immunity. Specific immunity can be produced by intraperitoneal injection of the virus. No antigenic relationships have been noted with other viruses such as vaccinia, fibroma, or myxoma.

Diagnosis. The appearance of the cornified warts are characteristic and need little confirmation. Transmission experiments to rabbits may confirm a diagnosis of rabbit papilloma.

Molitor myxomae

Common Name. Rabbit-myxoma virus.

Disease Produced. Rabbit myxomatosis.

Hosts Affected. Domestic rabbit. Experimentally the cottontail and jack rabbit.

History and Distribution. Sanarelli, in 1898, reported on myxomatosis of rabbits and showed that the disease was transmissible and suggested that the causative agent was too small to be seen by ordinary methods. Myxomatosis has been reported in South America, United States, Great Britain, Europe, and Australia. The disease has been deliberately introduced into wild rabbits of Australia in order to aid in the control of the "rabbit plague" of that country.

Properties of the Virus. *M. myxomae* passes Berkefeld V and N filters, but not Chamberland L_5 or L_7 types. The size of fibroma strains is 125 to 175 mμ. Thermal inactivation takes place at 55°C. in 10 minutes or at 50° for 1 hour. Strains of the virus which produce fibromas have been transformed to myxoma types by the addition of a thermostable substance derived from myxoma strains.

Cultivation. The rabbit-myxoma virus can be cultivated in tissue cultures which contain rabbit tissues such as mononuclear cells, testicular tissue, or lymphoid tissue. It is also readily cultivated by chorio-allantoic inoculation of chicken embryos. Discrete foci of ectodermal proliferation appear in the chorio-allantoic membrane 3 days after inoculation. No changes are noted in the embryo itself.

Transmission. *M. myxomae* can be transmitted by contact with infected rabbits or their discharges. The virus has been recovered from flies. In some cases the disease has been transmitted by fleas. In Australia, the successful use of myxomatosis as a rabbit control measure is due to the spread of the virus by mosquitoes.

Characteristics of the Disease. Myxomatosis is characterized by tumors which appear in the skin around the eyes, mouth, nose, and genitalia. There is conjunctivitis, edema of the eyelids, nasal discharge, and dyspnea. The central nervous system is invaded by extension of the virus from the blood stream. The disease is fatal in 1 to 2 weeks. However, if the animals are kept in a room which is held at a temperature of 36° to 42°C., there are few deaths, and there is retrogression of the lesions. Fibroma strains do not produce fatal infection.

Pathological Changes. The tumor masses produced by the myxoma virus are gelatinous in appearance and consist largely of loosely arranged connective tissue cells. Infected epithelial cells in or adjacent to the tumor contain cytoplasmic inclusions.

Immunity. Rabbits which recover from myxomatosis are immune to the disease. Neutralizing antibodies are produced which are effective against both the myxoma and fibroma strains. If a fibroma strain is injected 48 to 96 hours before the myxoma strain, protection against fatal myxomatosis results. This may be explained by the phenomenon of virus interference.

Diagnosis. The appearance of soft tumors in the skin of rabbits suggests myxomatosis. Transmission experiments to rabbits and to chicken embryos are confirmatory. Demonstration of cytoplasmic inclusions in the infected tissue cells may also be used.

REFERENCES FOR FURTHER STUDY

Molitor verrucae (Common warts)

Molitor hominis (Molluscum contagiosum)

Van Rooyen, C. E., and Rhodes, A. J. Virus Diseases of Man. 2nd edition. Thomas Nelson and Sons, New York, 1948.

Molitor bovis (Cattle warts)

Creech, G. T. Jour. Agr. Res., 39:723, 1929.

Findlay, G. M. A System of Bacteriology, 7:252. His Majesty's Stationery Office, London, 1930.

Magalhães, A. Brazil Med., 34:431, 1920.

Royère, J. Des Verrues Chez l'Homme et Chez les Animaux. Thesis. Lyons, No. 56, 1902.

Segre, D., Olson, C., and Hoerlein, A. B. Amer. Jour. Vet. Res., 16:517, 1955.

Molitor buccalis (Canine oral papillomatosis)

De Monbreun, W. A., and Goodpasture, E. W. Amer. Jour. Path., 8:43, 1932.

Findlay, G. M. A System of Bacteriology, 7:252. His Majesty's Stationery Office, London, 1930.

McFadyean, J., and Hobday, F. Jour. Comp. Path. Therap., 11:341, 1898.

Penberthy, J. Jour. Comp. Path. Therap., 11:363, 1898.

Molitor tumoris (Rous sarcoma)

Amies, C. R. Jour. Path. Bact., 44:141, 1937.

Andrews, C. A. Jour. Path. Bact., 34:91, 1931.

Claude, A. Physiol. Rev., 13:246, 1933.

———. Jour. Exp. Med., 66:59, 1937.

Keogh, E. V. Brit. Jour. Exp. Path., 19:1, 1938.

Rous, P. Jour. Exp. Med., 13:397, 1911.

Molitor gingivalis (Rabbit oral papillomatosis)

Kidd, J. G. Jour. Exp. Med., 70:583, 1939.

Parson, R. J., and Kidd, J. G. Jour. Exp. Med., 77:233, 1943.

Shope, R. E. Jour. Exp. Med., 58:607, 1933.

———. Jour. Exp. Med., 65:219, 1937.

Molitor sylvilagi (Rabbit papilloma)

Kidd, J G. Jour. Exp. Med., 70:583, 1939.

Shope, R. E. Jour. Exp. Med., 58:607, 1933.

———. Jour. Exp. Med., 65:219, 1937.

Molitor myxomae (Rabbit myxomatosis)

Berry, G. P., Lichty, J. A., and Dedrick, H. M. 2nd Internat. Cong. for Microbiol. Proc., London, 1936. (Abst.) p. 96.

Bull, L. B., Ratcliffe, F. N., and Edgar, G. Vet. Rec., 66:61, 1954.

Lush, D. Aust. Jour. Exp. Biol. and Med. Sci., 15:131, 1937.

Rivers, T. M., and Ward, S. M. Jour. Exp. Med., 66:1, 1937.

Sanarelli, G. Centralb. f. Bakt. Abt. I., 23:865, 1898.

Shope, R. E. Jour. Exp. Med., 56:803, 1932.

48. The Genus Erro— the Encephalitis Group

The genus *Erro* is composed of those viruses which produce disease which is characterized chiefly by injury to cells of the brain. The genus name *Erro* is the Latin name meaning a vagrant.

Erro scoticus

Common Name. Louping-ill virus.

Disease Produced. Louping-ill.

Hosts Affected. Sheep, cattle, and man. Experimentally horses, swine, mice, dogs, monkeys, rats (inapparent), and chicken embryos.

History and Distribution. Louping-ill was described in Scotland in 1807 by Duncan, but the etiology was discovered to be a virus only after many years of controversy and experimental work. Pool, Brownlee, and Wilson in 1931 were the first to reproduce the disease in sheep by injecting Berkefeld filtrates. Louping-ill occurs in Scotland, Northern England, and some areas of Russia.

Properties of the Virus. *Erro scoticus* is comparatively small, measuring approximately 20 to 27 mμ in size. The virus passes all grades of Berkefeld filters and the Chamberland L_2 and L_3 candles. The virus is heat sensitive being destroyed at 58°C. in 10 minutes, at 60°C. in 2 to 5 minutes, and at 80°C. in 30 seconds.

E. scoticus may not survive more than 2 weeks in the refrigerator, but will live for 4 to 6 months in glycerin.

An antigenic relationship has been shown between *Erro scoticus* and *Erro silvestris*.

Cultivation. Louping-ill virus can be cultivated in tissue cultures which employ minced chicken embryo in Tyrode's solution. Inoculation of the virus onto the chorio-allantoic membrane results in the growth of the virus and the death of the embryo within 6 days. Lesions of the embryo include liver necrosis, generalized edema, and jaundice.

Transmission. Under natural conditions the virus of louping-ill is transmitted only by the bite of ticks (*Ixodes ricinus*). Experimentally the virus can be transferred in sheep by intracerebral, ocular, intravenous, and subcutaneous inoculation.

Characteristics of the Disease. Louping-ill occurs in the spring and fall among lambs and yearlings and occasionally in older sheep. The disease exhibits a diphasic febrile reaction in most cases. At first, the infected sheep shows depression and increased temperature, followed by a second temperature increase which is accompanied by symptoms of encephalitis. The mortality of this type of the disease is high. However, the disease may be abortive in some cases and only the first phase is noted; no nervous symptoms occur.

The disease has been described in man. It has been most frequently diagnosed in laboratory workers and seldom among people who have contact with sheep. The disease in man is not serious. There is fever, malaise, headache, and mild nervous symptoms.

Pathological Changes. Most of the pathological changes occur in the central nervous system. These changes include congestion and leucocytic infiltration of the meninges, perivascular cuffing, and degeneration of the cells in the cerebrum, cerebellum, and medulla. Inclusion bodies have been demonstrated in the central nervous tissue of infected mice.

Immunity. Animals which have recovered from louping-ill are resistant to reinoculation. Complement-fixing and neutralizing antibodies are demonstrable in the serum of recovered and immunized animals. Formolized chicken embryo vaccine is used to produce artificial immunity to the disease. Tick eradication is very important in control.

Diagnosis. In addition to symptoms of the disease, the diagnosis of louping-ill is based on isolation of the virus by intracerebral inoculation in mice or by chicken embryo inoculation. Serologic reactions are helpful in the differentiation of *Erro scoticus* from Russian Far Eastern encephalitis virus.

Erro silvestris

Common Name. Russian spring-summer virus. Far Eastern encephalitis virus.

Disease Produced. Russian Far Eastern encephalitis.

Hosts Affected. Man, cattle, horses, sheep, goats, dogs, wild carnivora, wild rodents, also grouse and other birds. Rabbits and pigeons are insusceptible.

History and Distribution. *Erro silvestris* is apparently confined to various parts of the U.S.S.R. The disease it produces was known about 1914, but did not become a problem until about 1935. It has been found in many animals—man is only an accidental host. Men who work in the forests as lumbermen are among the most frequently infected.

Properties of the Virus. The Russian spring-summer virus will pass all three grades of Berkefeld filter, Seitz and Chamberland L_2, L_3, and L_5 candles. The elementary bodies of the virus are 15 to 25 mμ in size. A temperature of 60°C. for 10 minutes will kill the virus. There are definite antigenic relationships between louping-ill and Russian virus. St. Louis, Japanese, and West Nile viruses show some relationships but are less pronounced.

Cultivation. *Erro silvestris* can be grown in tissue cultures employing minced chicken embryo and Tyrode's solution as well as in chicken embryos.

Transmission. Ticks (*Ixodes ricinus*) are the vectors of Russian virus. Transovarial transmission of the virus in ticks from one generation to another has been shown.

Characteristics of the Disease. The disease in animals is usually of the inapparent type and is not diagnosed clinically. Evidence of the disease is most often based on serological tests, but the virus has been isolated from the brain of cattle. Intracerebral inoculations of the virus in white mice result in convulsions and paralysis in 5 to 13 days and death.

The infection in man is manifest after a 10- to 14-day incubation period. Symptoms include fever, nausea, and headache which are followed by flaccid paralysis and other signs of encephalitis.

Some infections are abortive, ending in complete recovery within a few days. Others terminate in death or permanent neurologic injury.

Immunity. Formolized virus is used for the production of artificial immunity. The control of ticks is an important control measure.

Diagnosis. Isolation and identification of *Erro silvestris* constitutes a diagnosis of infection. Serological differentiation of the virus from louping-ill is necessary.

Erro incognitus

Common Name. Australian X virus.

Disease Produced. Australian X disease.

Hosts Affected. Man. Experimentally the monkey, horse, sheep, and calf. Australian X disease appeared in 1917 in Australia as an epidemic of encephalomyelitis. A total of 134 people were infected with a mortality of 70 per cent. The disease was also noted in 1922, 1925, and 1926 but was more mild in character. It has not been diagnosed since 1926. The virus was isolated in the early outbreak, but was lost and has not been available for complete study or comparison with other viruses. From the available data, it is now believed that Australian X is identical to Japanese B virus.

Erro japonicus

Common Name. Japanese B virus.

Disease Produced. Japanese B encephalitis.

Hosts Affected. Man and horse. Experimentally cattle, sheep, swine, rabbits, hamsters, monkeys, mice, chickens, and chicken embryos.

History and Distribution. A "summer encephalitis" which had been described as occurring among the Japanese population for the last 100 years was not accurately identified as of virus etiology until 1936. The virus is widely spread over Japan and has also occurred in Korea, Okinawa, China, and far eastern Russia. The disease is known to occur in horses and there is considerable evidence of the existence of the virus in cattle, sheep, hogs, and goats. The virus has not been found in North or South America, Europe, or Africa.

Properties of the Virus. The elementary bodies of *Erro japonicus* are reported as 20 to 30 mμ in size by filtration studies. The virus is filterable through Berkefeld N, W, Seitz and Mandler filters. Exposure to 56°C. for 30 minutes inactivates the virus. It is preserved for long periods by freezing at −70°C. and by lyophilization, but it is less stable at ordinary refrigerator temperatures. At 0°C. it lives for about 3 weeks. It is more stable in 10 per cent serum or skim milk than in saline suspension. Antigenic relationship between Japanese B, West Nile, and St. Louis viruses has been demonstrated.

Sabin has reported that Japanese B virus will agglutinate the erythrocytes of chickens, pigeons, and sheep, if the conditions of the test are carefully controlled.

Cultivation. *Erro japonicus* can be cultivated in either tissue cultures or chicken embryos. Chorio-allantoic inoculation of the embryo is preferable but the yolk sac route is satisfactory. Embryos die within 2 to 3 days following inoculation. The greatest concentration of the virus occurs in the embryo itself.

Transmission. Japanese encephalitis virus is presumably transmitted by mosquitoes. Epidemiological and experimental studies strongly suggest this mode of transmission. It has been possible to experimentally transmit the disease to mice by bites of infected mosquitoes. Viremia occurs in many animals and fowl following inoculation.

Characteristics of the Disease. Japanese B encephalitis in man may show a few days of prodromal symptoms or the onset may be sudden. The symptoms include high fever, general impairment of mental faculties, and often paralysis. Death occurs in many cases. Mortality rates range from 40 to 90 per cent with the highest rate among the aged. Japanese B and St. Louis encephalitis are closely related both epidemiologically and clinically. In the horse, there is evidence that inapparent infection is widespread in Japan. However, there are reports of outbreaks of encephalomyelitis in Japanese horses in which the mortality rate reaches 50 per cent in those horses clinically affected with the disease. The symptoms in the horse include high temperature, excitement followed by apathy, depression, and spastic or flaccid paralysis of the legs.

Pathological Changes. The pathological changes are those of meningitis and encephalitis. The meninges are edematous and congested. The brain proper is congested, and microscopically there is cellular infiltration and perivascular cuffing of the blood vessels.

Immunity. Animals which recover from experimental inoculation or vaccination are resistant to reinoculation.

Neutralizing and complement-fixing antibodies are formed following infection or vaccination.

Vaccines may be produced from virus propagated in chicken embryos or from formolized mouse brain. These vaccines have been used to some extent in man and experimentally in mice. Neutralizing antibodies are produced by the use of vaccines, but the value of such vaccines has not been determined.

Diagnosis. A diagnosis of *Erro japonicus* infection is made by isolation and identification of the virus. Isolation can be made by intracerebral inoculation of rabbits and young mice or by yolk sac or chorio-allantoic inoculation of chicken embryos. Serological and immunological differentiation from related viruses must be done.

Erro scelestus

Common Name. St. Louis encephalitis virus.

Disease Produced. St. Louis encephalitis.

Hosts Affected. Man and horse. Experimentally mice, hamsters, monkeys, and chicken embryos. Rabbits and guinea pigs, and wild and domestic fowl show no symptoms, but a viremia may be present for a time after inoculation.

History and Distribution. An outbreak of encephalitis of man occurred in 1932 in the vicinity of Paris, Ill. The following year over 1,100 cases of the disease were diagnosed in the St. Louis area, and the virus was isolated from brain material by Webster and Fite. Since 1933, the disease has remained endemic but it has spread widely throughout the United States. A probable reservoir of the virus has been shown to exist in many wild and domestic animals and fowl.

Properties of the Virus. The virus, *Erro scelestus,* measures 20 to 30 mμ in size. It is filterable through Berkefeld V, N, and Seitz filters. The virus is killed by 56°C. for 30 minutes, 0.1 per cent formalin in 10–18 hours, but resists 1 per cent phenol for 25 days and 0.5 per cent for 50 days. The infectivity is rapidly lost in the refrigerator. However, it is preserved by lyophilization or if stored at −70°C. The virus will live longer in serum or skimmed milk than in saline suspension. Penicillin does not affect the virus.

St. Louis encephalitis virus will produce the agglutination of chicken, pigeon, or sheep erythrocytes if tested under proper conditions.

Cultivation. *Erro scelestus* multiplies in tissue cultures which employ either chicken or mouse embryonic tissues. Chicken embryos can be readily infected by any of the usual routes of inoculation. Inoculation of the virus onto the chorio-allantoic membrane results in edema, opacity, diffuse proliferation, and necrosis of the membrane after 3 to 4 days' incubation. The embryo itself is usually little affected by the virus.

Transmission. St. Louis encephalitis is seasonal in occurrence, most of the cases occurring in summer and early fall. This period coincides with greatest insect activity. It has been shown that mosquitoes, especially *Culex tarsalis* and *Culex pipiens,* can transmit the virus and are considered the chief vectors. Nine species of mosquitoes have transmitted the infection under experimental conditions. Repeated isolations of the virus have been made from *Culex tarsalis* mosquitoes trapped in nature. The virus has been isolated from chicken mites, *Dermanyssus gallinae,* which have been collected in nature and so may play a part in spread of the disease. Transovarian infection has been demonstrated in the mites.

Characteristics of the Disease. The incubation period in man ranges from 9 to 21 days. Onset of the illness is sudden with headache, high fever, neck rigidity, mental confusion, and tremors. This is usually followed by encephalitis, with the symptoms of apathy and sleepiness in some patients or sleeplessness and excitement in others.

Some cases are abortive and the encephalitic symptoms do not appear. Mortality rates in the early epidemics of 1932–33 and 1937 were 37, 20, and 23.7 per cent respectively. In the horse, *Erro scelestus* produces a disease characterized by high temperature, depression, sleepiness, incoordination, and paralysis, and in some cases death. Many horses, however, develop neutralizing antibodies to the virus without showing any signs of illness.

Pathological Changes. The pathological changes are almost entirely confined to the brain and cord. The outstanding changes are those of congestion with occasional petechial hemorrhage, of leucocytic infiltration, and perivascular cuffing of the blood vessels.

Immunity. Complement-fixing and neutralizing antibodies are produced following infection and recovery, and remain in high titer for several years. Horses which have developed neutralizing antibodies are refractory to the virus. Mice can be successfully immunized by the inoculation of formolized or ultra-violet-treated virus. Neutralizing antibodies are readily produced by vaccination of mice or hamsters, but resistance to intracerebral challenge does not always parallel the appearance and disappearance of these antibodies.

Convalescent serum has been used for treatment of St. Louis encephalitis in man.

Vaccines are not commercially available for the immunization of animals or man.

Diagnosis. Accurate diagnosis of St. Louis encephalitis depends upon isolation and identification of the virus. Isolation of the virus may be accomplished by intracerebral inoculation of mice or chorio-allantoic inoculation of chicken embryos with brain material from the infected host.

Complement-fixation or serum neutralization tests are often used in diagnosis of the nonfatal case as well as inapparent infections in many hosts.

It is important to differentiate St. Louis encephalitis from the equine encephalitis viruses which may be encountered in clinically identical cases in man or animals. (See *Erro equinus.*)

Erro nili

Common Name. West Nile virus.

Disease Produced. Encephalitis.

Hosts Affected. Man. Experimentally monkeys, mice, and hamsters are susceptible. Rabbits and guinea pigs are insusceptible.

West Nile virus was isolated in 1937 by Smithburn from the blood of a human patient in Africa. No further isolations of the virus have been reported, but epidemiological surveys show considerable serological evidence of the existence of West Nile virus in many parts of Africa. The virus has neurotropic tendencies when injected into mice, monkeys, or hamsters.

Erro nili is 21 to 31 mμ in size and is antigenically related to Japanese B and St. Louis viruses. There is also some similarity to louping-ill and Russian Far Eastern viruses. The virus will produce hemagglutination if placed under proper conditions.

The West Nile virus can be grown in tissue culture or in chicken embryos.

Erro equinus (Western type)
Erro tenbroeckii (Eastern type)
Erro venezuelensis (Venezuelan type)

Common Name. Equine encephalomyelitis viruses.

Disease Produced. Equine encephalomyelitis, sleeping sickness.

Hosts Affected. Horse, man, rarely pheasant and pigeon. Experimental hosts include the guinea pig, white mouse, hamster, rat, domestic and wild rabbit, monkey, squirrel, gopher, wild mouse, deer, sheep, calf, pig, goat, dog, and prairie chicken. Domestic fowl and some wild birds show only a viremia following inoculation, with no symptoms. Cats are resistant.

History and Distribution. Epizootics of encephalitis in horses have been known in the United States for many years previous to 1931, but it was in that year Meyer, Haring, and Howitt were able to recover a filter-passing virus from the brain of infected horses involved in a California outbreak. The incidence of encephalitis increased sharply in the western states in the next few years and spread eastward to the middle west until, in 1937 and 1938, 173,889 and 184,662 cases, respectively, were reported. In 1939 a sharp drop to 8,008 cases was attributable to resistance developed by earlier attacks and especially to widespread vaccination with chicken embryo vaccine.

In 1933, Ten Broeck and Merrill, also Giltner and Shahan, reported on a virus responsible for equine encephalitis which occurred in New Jersey, Virginia, Delaware, and Maryland. Ten Broeck and Merrill demonstrated distinct antigenic differences between the eastern and western strains of the virus. The eastern type spread over the eastern and southern states and in 1939 it spread westward to some extent.

The western type virus has occurred in at least 20 states which include nearly all of those west of the Mississippi River and a few east of it. The eastern type has been found in 14 eastern and southern states. Both viruses have been identified from five states.

Coincident with the disease in the horse, both viruses have been isolated from cases of encephalitis in man. In 1941, an epidemic of human encephalitis due to the western type virus occurred in the Dakotas, Minnesota, and adjacent areas of Canada. Over 3,000 cases were diagnosed, with a mortality rate of 8 to 15 per cent. These viruses have spread widely among wild and domestic animals and fowl, and so a reservoir of the virus remains and the disease is enzootic in many areas.

A third type of equine encephalomyelitis has been reported from Venezuela, S. A., which is caused by a virus with similar properties to those of the eastern strain, but it is antigenically distinct.

Equine encephalomyelitis occurs in the United States, Canada, Panama, and South America.

Properties of the Virus. The elementary bodies of *Erro equinus* have been reported as being 20 to 35 mμ in diameter by collodion membrane filter studies. Measurements made from photographs taken in the electron microscope show the eastern type is 40 to 47 mμ in diameter and the western type 40 to 53 mμ. Both viruses are spherical in shape. The general chemical composition of the western strain is reported by Beard as 54 per cent lipoid, 4 per cent carbohydrate, and the remainder ribonucleoprotein. The equine encephalitis virus is comparatively resistant. The virus withstands a temperature of 70°C. for 10 minutes when in suspension. It resists undiluted ether, 0.2 per cent chloroform, 2 per cent phenol, 0.05 per cent mercuric chloride, and 1:500 merthiolate. Formalin in a concentration of 0.4 or 0.2 per cent will inactivate the virus in three to four days. The virus is preserved by refrigeration for at least one year in chicken embryo fluids. It is also preserved in 50 per cent buffered glycerin or by lyophilization.

Chanock and Sabin have reported that *Erro equinus* will agglutinate the erythrocytes of the chickens if the pH of the suspending liquid is 6.1. The age of the chicken used for the donor of the erythrocytes is also important. Erythrocytes from newly hatched chicks are considered more suitable than from adult chickens.

Three antigenic types of equine encephalitis virus are recognized: eastern, western, and Venezuelan. Several substrains of the western type have been distinguished on the basis of virulence.

Equine encephalomyelitis occurs in Argentina and Brazil. The Argentine strains of the virus closely resemble the western type while the Brazilian strains are of the eastern variety.

Cultivation of the Virus. *Erro equinus* can be cultivated in tissue cultures of the Maitland type which employs rabbit testicular tissue. The virus is readily cultivated in chicken embryos by any method of inoculation. The virus grows rapidly, and uniformly kills the embryo in 18 to 24 hours. This rapid lethal effect is a distinguishing characteristic of the virus. Hemorrhage, thrombosis, and necrosis are observed in the dead embryos.

Transmission. The virus *Erro equinus* is eliminated in nasal secretions of infected horses and contact with such secretions may result in transmission of the virus. However, the disease is usually thought to be transmitted by blood-sucking arthropods in a majority of cases. *Erro equinus* has been isolated repeatedly from mosquitoes trapped in endemic areas. Species of mosquitoes of the genera

Aedes, Anopheles, Culex, and *Culiseta* have yielded the virus. In addition to mosquitoes, ticks such as *Dermacentor andersoni* and mites *Dermanyssus americanus, Dermanyssus gallinae* have also yielded the virus. Experimental transmission has been proved with these arthropods. Mosquitoes become infective 7 to 20 days after feeding on an animal which shows viremia. There is evidence of multiplication of the equine encephalitis virus in the mosquito and the insect remains infected for life. Transovarial transmission of the virus occurs in ticks, but probably does not in mosquitoes. The virus may be transmitted from chicken to chicken by infected mites.

The "reservoir" of the virus which appears to exist in mosquitoes and other insects and inapparent hosts constitutes a problem in control.

Characteristics of the Disease. Equine encephalomyelitis is seasonal, occurring in the summer and early fall months. In the horse, there is at first high temperature accompanied by viremia which is followed by typical symptoms of encephalomyelitis. These include depression, sleepiness, pharyngeal paralysis, incoordination, paralysis of the lips and legs. Death may occur in 3 to 8 days after onset. Complete recovery or survival with nervous sequelae may occur. Some cases are mild and of short duration with rapid recovery. Infection by the eastern type is more severe and rapid than that produced by western strains. Mortality rates are about 90 per cent with eastern type and approximately 27 per cent with western type infection.

Experimental infections in mice and guinea pigs have been studied extensively. The induced disease in these hosts is evidenced by depression, paralysis, rapid dehydration, and death.

Human infection has been contracted under natural conditions as well as by laboratory accidents.

Typical symptoms of encephalitis occur in man. Headache, sweating, drowsiness, mental confusion, and paralysis are usually observed. The mortality rate is about 10 per cent. The eastern type infection in man is usually more severe and intense than the western type. The Venezuelan type in man is usually mild. The infection of fowl is usually of the mild inapparent type.

Pathological Changes. The pathological changes which occur in equine encephalomyelitis are chiefly microscopic and confined to the brain and meninges. In the brain there is mononuclear infiltration and leucocytic perivascular cuffing. There is congestion and edema of the meninges.

Immunity. Antibodies which fix complement or neutralize the virus appear with recovery from the disease or by vaccination. In many hosts such as fowl, serological demonstration of these antibodies is the only evidence of virus invasion. Active immunization by chicken embryo-propagated virus has been widely used and with success. Monovalent eastern, monovalent western, or polyvalent vaccines are available. The type of vaccine chosen depends upon the type or types of the virus which occur in the area where it is to be used. Formalinized chicken embryo vaccine was at first prepared from the whole embryo and its fluids which included allantoic, amniotic, and yolk sac contents. This practice was abandoned because of the development of hypersensitivity to egg proteins in some vaccinated horses. The vaccine was otherwise successful, however.

The whole embryo vaccine was succeeded by a purified intradermal vaccine. This vaccine is formalinized, 0.4 per cent, and the virus protein is recovered from the infected embryo contents by high speed differential centrifugation.

The immunity produced by the killed vaccine is considered durable for only one season and so animals in enzootic or epizootic areas must be vaccinated each year.

The same vaccine which is used in horses is useful in immunizing laboratory workers who work in research or in vaccine production laboratories.

Animals which recover from natural infection are resistant to reinfection.

Diagnosis. A diagnosis of equine encephalomyelitis depends upon isolation and identification of the virus or by satisfactory serological evidence. Actual isolation of the virus is usually made from the central nervous tissue at post-mortem. Isolation of the virus from the blood of naturally infected animals is rare because the stage of viremia is transient and usually precedes the onset of symptoms. White mice or guinea pigs are the most suitable test animals for isolation of the virus and are inoculated intracerebrally with brain tissue from the suspected case. These animals should show symptoms in about 4 days following inoculation. Chicken embryos may be inoculated directly with the brain of the infected animal and should die in about 24 hours, if the virus is present.

A virus isolated from the nervous tissue of an animal with encephalitis, should be identified and specifically differentiated from other viruses by cross-immunity, complement-fixation, and serum neutralization tests.

Serological tests are used in the diagnosis of nonfatal or inapparent infections. However, the mere demonstration of antibodies does not constitute a diagnosis of present infection, but may in some cases reflect a past contact with the virus and a persistence of antibody. If possible, sera collected early in the disease should be compared with the antibody content of that collected in convalescence. A distinct increase in the titer of anti-bodies in the latter would carry significance. However, a positive serological test indicates contact with the virus at some time and is useful in epidemiological surveys.

Erro bornensis

Common Name. Borna-disease virus.

Disease Produced. Borna disease.

Hosts Affected. Horses, sheep, and possibly cattle and deer. Rabbits, guinea pigs, mice, monkeys, rats, and possibly fowl are susceptible to experimental inoculation.

History and Distribution. Borna disease is so named because of a particularly severe outbreak of the disease near the town of Borna in Germany in 1894. The disease was known in Germany for many years before but under different names. It is a disease primarily of the equine species, but also may occur in sheep. Cases of the infection have been reported in cattle and deer but are not well substantiated. The etiology of the disease was suggested to be a virus by Joest in 1911 and was confirmed by Zwick, Seinfried, and Witte in 1926. The disease occurs in central European countries.

Borna disease and equine encephalomyelitis are so similar that cases of the latter disease which occurred in the United States were thought at first to be Borna disease, but the two were soon differentiated.

Properties of the Virus. The elementary bodies of *Erro bornensis* are 85 to 125 mμ in size. They will pass collodion filters and also Berkefeld, Mandler, and Chamberland filters, but only with irregularity. The virus is inactivated by exposure to 57°C. for 30 minutes or 70°C. for 10 minutes.

It is killed by 1 per cent phenol in 4 weeks, but not in 2 weeks. It is resistant to drying and survives in the dried state or in glycerin for 6 months to 1 year.

Erro bornensis is antigenically distinct from *Erro equinus* and *Erro scoticus.*

Cultivation. No data regarding tissue culture or chicken embryo cultivation of the virus is available. The virus for most experimental work is propagated by intracerebral inoculation of rabbits.

Transmission. The Borna disease virus is eliminated from the infected animal in the saliva, nasal secretions, milk, and urine. The saliva and nasal secretions are considered most important in transmission. Contamination of food and water with these secretions has transmitted the disease. The incubation period is about 30 days.

Characteristics of the Disease. The onset of definite symptoms of the disease may be preceded by a slight fever and other mild signs of illness. These are followed by typical symptoms of meningitis and encephalomyelitis such as dullness, incoordination, paralysis, and altered behavior. The course of the disease is usually 1 to 3 weeks and death occurs in 90 per cent of the cases.

Pathological Changes. The lesions of Borna disease are confined to the central nervous system. Gross lesions are not marked nor characteristic. Microscopic lesions of the brain and meninges consist of areas of leucocytic infiltration and degeneration of nerve cells.

Intracytoplasmic inclusion bodies can be demonstrated in some of the ganglion cells of the hippocampus major.

Immunity. Recovery from an attack of Borna disease confers temporary immunity. A brain tissue vaccine prepared from rabbits has been of some value in immunizing horses. Such immunity may last for 6 months to 1 year.

Diagnosis. Accurate diagnosis of Borna disease depends upon the isolation of the virus by rabbit or guinea pig inoculation and differentiation from other viruses. The demonstration of intracytoplasmic inclusion bodies from the brain tissue is of value.

Erro gallinae

Common Name. Avian encephalomyelitis virus. Epidemic tremor virus.

Disease Produced. Avian encephalomyelitis, epidemic tremor.

Host Affected. Chicken. Experimentally turkey poults, ducklings, and young pigeons are susceptible.

History and Distribution. Avian encephalomyelitis was first observed in the New England states in 1930 by Jones who later described the disease and the virus causing it, in 1932. Since this first description, the disease has spread and has been diagnosed in many states. The disease has also been reported in Australia.

Properties of the Virus. The elementary bodies of *E. gallinae* are 20 to 30 mμ in size and will pass Berkefeld V and N as well as Seitz filters.

The virus survives for at least 88 days in 50 per cent glycerin and for 68 days in lyophilized material.

No relationship between the avian and equine encephalomyelitis viruses has been shown.

Cultivation. *Erro gallinae* can be cultivated in tissue cultures composed of minced whole embryo tissue and chicken serum. Newly-hatched chicks are uniformly susceptible to the virus by intracerebral inoculation, whereas chicken embryos are infected irregularly by the usual technics of inoculation. This fact has been pointed out by Olitsky as a striking reversal of the general rule, since many viruses will grow readily in the developing embryo, but will not affect the newly-hatched chick or adult bird.

Transmission. The mechanism of transmission of avian encephalomyelitis is not definitely known. Transmission by contact with infected birds has been thought to be of importance by some investigators, but is discounted by others. Van Roekel, also Jungherr and Minard suggest that the virus is egg-borne. The virus was found in the unabsorbed yolk of naturally infected chicks. Jungherr and Minard also report the production of typical lesions in the brain of chicks inoculated with saline suspensions of feces collected from infected flocks. However, clinical symptoms were not observed, nor was the virus isolated in these cases.

Characteristics of the Disease. Avian encephalomyelitis is a disease of young chicks which occurs within the first six weeks of life. Most of the clinical cases are noted in chicks between one and three weeks of age. Older birds are refractory even to artificial inoculation.

Tremor of the head is one of the most often noted symptoms. Incoordination and leg weakness are frequently observed. General debility, prostration, and death may follow. Mortality rates range from 0 to 50 per cent with an average of about 17 per cent.

Many cases of the disease are asymptomatic but will show histopathological evidence of infection if the brain is carefully examined.

Pathological Changes. The only lesions observed in avian encephalomyelitis are microscopic lesions of the brain. There is marked degeneration of the neuron cells of the brain proper and of the cord. There is also perivascular cuffing of the blood vessels of the meninges and the brain.

Immunity. Neutralizing antibodies have been demonstrated in the serum of birds which are vaccinated with killed virus. However, no protection to intracerebral challenge is demonstrable in such birds.

No immunizing agents are used for the prevention of avian encephalomyelitis.

Diagnosis. A diagnosis of avian encephalomyelitis is based on the appearance of characteristic symptoms, typical histopathological lesions of the brain and demonstration of the presence of the virus by intracerebral inoculation of susceptible chicks.

REFERENCES FOR FURTHER STUDY

Erro scoticus (Louping-ill)

Burnet, F. A. Brit. Jour. Exp. Path., 17:294, 1936.

Gordon, W. S., Brownlee, A., Wilson, D. R., MacLeod, J. Jour. Comp. Path. and Therap., 45:106, 1932.

Hurst, E. W. Jour. Comp. Path. and Therap., 44:231, 1931.

Pool, W. A., Vet. Jour., 87:177, 1931.

――――. Vet. Jour., 87:222, 1931.

――――, Brownlee, A., and Wilson, D. R. Jour. Comp. Path. and Therap., 43:253, 1930.

Schwentker, F. F., Rivers, T. M., and Finkelstein, M. H. Jour. Med., 57:955, 1933.

Van Rooyen, C. E., and Rhodes, A. J. Virus Diseases of Man. Thomas Nelson and Sons, New York, 1948.

Erro silvestris (Russian spring-summer encephalitis)

Holmes, F. O. Order Virales Supplement No. 2. *In* Bergey's Manual of Determinative Bacteriology. p. 1249. Williams and Wilkins, Baltimore, 1948.

Van Rooyen, C. E., and Rhods, A. J. Virus Disases of Man. Thomas Nelson and Sons, New York, 1948.

Erro incognitus (Australian X disease)

Kneebone, J. LeM., and Cleland, J. B. Aust. Jour. Exp. Biol. Med. Sci., 3: 119, 1926.

Perdrau, J. R. Jour. Path. Bact., 42:59, 1936.

Van Rooyen, C. E., and Rhodes, A. J. Virus Diseases of Man. Thomas Nelson and Sons, New York, 1948.

Erro japonicus (Japanese B)

Burns, K. F., and Matumoto, M. Amer. Jour. Vet. Res., 10:146, 1949.

――――, ――――. Jour. Amer. Vet. Med. Assn., 115: 112, 1949.

――――, ――――. Jour. Amer. Vet. Med. Assn., 115: 167, 1949.

Kasahara, S., *et al.* Kitasato Arch. Exp. Med., 13:248, 1936.

Sabin, A. B. Fed. Proc., 10:573, 1951.

――――, Ginder, D. R., and Matumoto, M. Amer. Jour. Hyg., 46:341, 1947.

Taniguchi, T., Hosokawa, M., and Kuga, S. Jap. Jour. Exp. Med., 14:185, 1936.

Van Rooyen, C. E., and Rhodes, A. J. Virus Diseases of Man. Thomas Nelson and Sons, New York, 1948.

Erro scelestus (St. Louis encephalitis)

Cox, H. R., Philip, C. B., and Kilpatrick, J. W. Pub. Health Rep., 56:1391, 1931.

Hammon, W. M., Jour. Amer. Med. Assn., 117:161, 1941.

――――, *et al.* Science, 94:305. 1941.

――――, *et al.* Science, 94:328. 1941.

――――, Carle, B. N., and Izumi, E. M. Proc. Soc. Exp. Biol., N. Y., 49:335, 1942.

Leake, J. P. Jour. Amer. Med. Assn., 101:1933.

――――, Musson, E. K., and Chope, H. D. Jour. Amer. Med. Assn., 103:728, 1934.

Webster, L. T., and Fite, G. L. Science, 78:463, 1933.

Erro nili (West Nile encephalitis)

Smithburn, K. C., Mahaffy, A. F., and Paul, J. H. Amer. Jour. Trop. Med., 21:75, 1940.

Erro equinus, Erro tenbroeckii, Erro venezuelensis (Equine encephalomyelitis)

Beck, C. E., and Wycoff, R. W. G. Science, 88:530, 1938.

Chanock, R. M., and Sabin, A. B. Jour. Immunol., 73: 337, 1954.

Giltner, L. T., and Shahan, M. S. Science, 78: 63, 1933.

————, ————. Science, 78: 587, 1933.

————, ————. N. Amer. Vet., 14:25, 1933.

Hammon, W. M., Reeves, W. C., and Galinda, P. Amer. Jour. Vet. Res., 6:145, 1945.

Kelser, R. A. Jour. Amer. Vet. Med. Assn., 82: 767, 1933.

Kubes, V., and Rios, F. A. Science, 90: 20, 1939.

Meyer, K. F., Haring, C. M., and Howitt, B. Science, 74: 227, 1931.

Olitsky, P. K., and Casals, J. "Viral Encephalitides," In Viral and Rickettsial Infections of Man. Edited by T. M. Rivers. J. B. Lippincott Co., Philadelphia, 1952.

Reeves, W. C. Proc. U. S. Livestock San. Assn., p. 150, 1945.

Sharp, D. G., Taylor, A. R., Beard, D. I., and Beard, J. W. Arch. Path., 36: 167, 1943.

Ten Broeck, C., and Merrill, M. H. Proc. Soc. Exp. Biol. and Med., 31:217, 1933.

Erro bornensis (Borna disease)

Beck, A., and Frohbose, H. Arch. f. wissensch. prakt. Tierh., 54:84, 1926.

Elford, W. J., and Galloway, I. A. Brit. Jour. Exp. Path., 14: 196, 1933.

Hutyra, F., Marek, J., and Manninger, R. Special Pathology and Therapeutics of the Diseases of Domestic Animals. Vol. III. 5th edition. Alex. Eger, Chicago, 1946.

Joest, E. Zeit. f. Infktionskt. Haust., 10:293, 1911.

Moussu, R. Rec. de Med. Vet. Paris., 98:499, 1922.

Nicolau, S. Comp. Rend. Acad. Sci., 186: 655, 1928.

————, and Galloway, I. A. Brit. Jour. Exp. Path., 8: 336, 1927.

————, ————. Med. Res. Counc. Spec. Rep. No. 121. His Majesty's Stationery Office, London, 1928.

Zwick, W., and Seifried, O. Berl. Tierarztl. Waschr., 40:465, 1924.

————, ————. Infektiose Gehirn-Ruckenmarks-Entzundung (Bornasche Krankheit) des Pferdes. In Handbuch der Pathogenen Mikroorganismen. Vol. 9. Kolle, W. and Wasserman, A. V. Gustav Fischer und Urban Schwarzenberg. Jena and Berlin, 1929.

————, ————, and Witte, J. Zeit. f. Infktionskt. Haust., 30: 42, 1926.

————, ————, ————. Zeit. f. Infktionskt. Haust., 32: 150, 1927.

Erro gallinae (Avian encephalomyelitis)

Jones, E. E. Science, 76:331, 1932.

————. Jour. Exp. Med., 59:781, 1934.

Jungherr, E., and Minard, E. L. Jour. Amer. Vet. Med. Assn., 100:38, 1942.

Kligler, I. J., and Olitsky, P. K. Proc. Soc. Exp. Biol. and Med., 43: 680, 1940.

Olitsky, P. K. Jour. Exp. Med., 70:565, 1939.

————. Avian Encephalomyelitis. Chapter 23. In Diseases of Poultry. 3rd Edition. Edited by Biester and Schwarte. Iowa State College Press, Ames, 1952.

Van Roekel, H. Vet. Med., 34:754, 1939.

————, Bullis, K. L., and Clarke, M. K. Jour. Amer. Vet. Med. Assn., 93:372, 1938.

49.

The Genera Legio, Armlillia, and Theilerella— the Poliomyelitis Group

THE GENUS LEGIO

Viruses of the genus *Legio* induce disease characterized by involvement of the nervous system and usually involve the cells of the alimentary tract so that the virus is recoverable from the feces. The generic name is from the Latin, meaning army or legion.

Legio debilitans

Common Name. Poliomyelitis virus, infantile paralysis virus.
Disease Produced. Poliomyelitis.
Hosts Affected. Man and monkey. Experimentally certain strains have been adapted to cotton rats, mice, and guinea pigs.

Poliomyelitis virus is spherical in shape and measures 20 to 28 mµ in diameter. It grows readily in tissue cultures composed of human fibroblasts, neoplastic epithelial (HeLa) cells, or kidney cells. It produces a cytopathogenic effect when grown in tissue culture. This effect can be prevented by immune serum.

Three antigenic types are distinguished: the Brunhilde, Lansing, and Leon.

Poliomyelitis is widespread in man and each year takes its toll. The virus at first attacks the pharyngeal region and probably some parts of the intestinal tract, producing mild influenza-like symptoms in most cases, but in some, central nervous involvement with paralysis and occasionally death occurs. Many infected individuals completely recover, but others suffer from paralysis which may permanently disable.

Poliomyelitis does not naturally infect animals and it is difficult to experimentally transmit the disease in animals except monkeys.

A number of surveys have been conducted to ascertain whether or not wild or domestic animals or fowl might harbor the virus of poliomyelitis, but so far no positive evidence has been found. There is evidence of transmission of the virus through the medium of milk contaminated from human cases or carriers.

THE GENUS ARMLILLIA

Viruses in the genus *Armlillia* are those affecting the central nervous system of lower animals and occasionally man. The genus name *Armlillia* is derived from Armstrong and Lillie, who first isolated lymphocytic choriomeningitis.

Armlillia erebea

Common Name. Lymphocytic choriomeningitis virus.

Disease Produced. Lymphocytic choriomeningitis.

Hosts Affected. Mouse and man. Experimentally guinea pig, rat, monkey, and hamster. Inapparent infection results from inoculation of the dog and ferret. Insusceptible hosts include the pig, chicken, rabbit, canary, parakeet, and the vole.

History and Distribution. Armstrong and Lillie, in 1934, while working with material from a fatal human case of St. Louis encephalitis discovered a new virus. This virus, which was found in the 5th monkey passage, had previously been thought to be the St. Louis virus, since the original case was clinically typical and occurred during the 1933 epidemic of St. Louis encephalitis. A virus was isolated in 1935 from mice by Traub and from a case of meningitis in man by Rivers and Scott and shown to be identical with that isolated by Armstrong and Lillie. Numerous isolations of the virus have been made from laboratory and wild mice. One isolation from a cow's brain is reported by Alice and McNutt. The virus is widely distributed. It has been isolated from many parts of the United States, also from England, France, Japan, and North Africa.

Properties of the Virus. The elementary bodies of *Armlillia erebea* are calculated to be between 40 and 60 mμ in size. They will pass Berkefeld V, N, W, Chamberland L$_1$, L$_2$, L$_3$, and Seitz filters.

The virus is inactivated by exposure to 55°C. for 20 minutes, also by ultra violet light, and by various detergents.

Armlillia erebea is preserved in 50 per cent glycerin for 7 months and in the frozen state for 1 year.

Cultivation. *Armlillia erebea* can be grown in tissues cultures which employ either mouse or chicken embryo tissues in Tyrode's solution. It can also be grown on the chorio-allantoic membrane. The virus may kill the embryo in 8 to 9 days but without the formation of pocks or specific lesions.

Transmission. It has been suggested that the mouse is the primary host for the virus of lymphocytic choriomeningitis and is thought to be the usual source of the virus. *A. erebea* has been isolated from house mice trapped in homes where human infection has been diagnosed. The virus escapes from the infected mouse in the nasal secretions, semen, urine, and feces. It is believed that these infected materials, especially urine, become dried and that they are carried into the air and inhaled by man or enter the eye. *In utero* infection of mice has been shown to occur. The virus can also be transmitted by arthropods such as lice, bedbugs, ticks, and possibly mosquitoes, since the virus circulates in the blood for a time after an animal becomes infected. Transovarial transmission of the virus from one tick to another has been reported.

The virus has also been found as a contaminant in canine distemper virus, which was passed in dogs and ferrets, and from cultures of rabies virus which employed mouse brain or monkey serum.

Characteristics of the Disease. The virus of lymphocytic choriomeningitis is widely distributed in mice and is quite often transferred to man and other hosts. The disease in mice is usually not noted, but many mice carry the virus. Young mice are more susceptible than old ones. Experimental intracerebral inoculation of the virus in mice results in illness characterized by emaciation, dullness, tremors, and spasms of the legs, and by death. Naturally infected mice are often symptomless but may harbor the virus for some time. Usually losses in infected stocks are not over 2 per cent.

In man, there are usually prodromal symptoms such as sore throat, tonsilitis, bronchitis, and cough, which simulate influenza. These symptoms are followed by meningeal symptoms of headache, vomiting, and neck rigidity. Recovery usually occurs in a few weeks. In some cases there are recurrent attacks. Neutralizing antibodies for the virus of lymphocytic choriomeningitis have been demonstrated in the blood of about 12 per cent of normal people in the U. S., indicating widespread subclinical infection.

Pathological Changes. The outstanding pathological changes are observed in the meninges and choroid plexuses which show lymphocytic infiltration. The brain may show perivascular cuffing and degeneration of nerve cells.

Naturally infected mice often show mild leucocytic infiltrations of the meninges and focal liver necrosis.

Immunity. Mice which have recoverd from an attack of lymphocytic choriomeningitis are usually refractory to a second inoculation. Complement-fixing and neutralizing antibodies are formed in response to the virus. Artificial immunity can be produced in mice with live virus, but immunity is less durable in guinea pigs which receive formalinized virus.

Diagnosis. The diagnosis of *A. erebea* infection depends upon isolation and identification of the virus in susceptible mice or guinea pigs. It is very important to determine the absence of latent *A. erebea* infection in any mouse stock used for diagnostic purposes. Intracerebral inoculation of ordinary nutrient broth into mice with latent choriomeningitis will give rise to meningeal symptoms and lesions. The possibilities of the presence of this virus in laboratory mice stocks must be considered when any intracerebral inoculations are to be made.

Armlillia simulans

Common Name. Pseudo-lymphocytic choriomeningitis.

Disease Produced. Meningitis.

Host Affected. Man. Experimentally the mouse, guinea pig, rat, monkey, and chicken embryo are susceptible.

MacCallum, Findlay, and Scott reported in 1939 the isolation of a virus from two patients with acute meningitis. The disease is similar in most every respect to lymphocytic choriomeningitis except that the incubation period is shorter, 5 days instead of 5 to 12 days, and that the symptoms and the lesions are less pronounced in the case of pseudo-lymphocytic choriomeningitis. The virus, *A. simulans,* is larger, 150 to 225 mμ in size as compared to 40 to 60 mμ for *A. erebea.* These two viruses are immunologically distinct.

A. simulans has not been isolated from natural disease in animals.

THE GENUS THEILERELLA

Viruses of the genus *Theilerella* cause spontaneous encephalomyelitis in animals. Lesions and character of the disease closely simulate human poliomyelitis but the virus bears no immunological relationship to the poliomyelitis virus.

Theilerella muris

Common Name. Mouse-poliomyelitis or Theiler's encephalomyelitis virus.

Disease Produced. Mouse poliomyelitis. Theiler's encephalomyelitis.

Hosts Affected. White mouse. Wild gray mouse may be an intestinal carrier.

History and Distribution. Mouse encephalomyelitis was first noted in the United States by Theiler in 1934 who reported that the etiology of the disease was a virus. The virus is widespread, probably occurring wherever white mice are raised. It has been identified in the United States, South America, Europe, and Japan.

Properties of the Virus. By filtration studies *T. muris* is reported to be 9 to 13 mμ in diameter. Gard, on the basis of electron microscope photographs, describes the virus as being filamentous, 15 mμ in width and 115 mμ in length. It passes all grades of the Berkefeld type filter and the Chamberland L$_3$ type. The virus retains its viability for 14 months at —78°C., and at least 150 days in 50 per cent glycerin stored at 2° to 4°C. It is readily inactivated by 1 per cent hydrogen peroxide and by heating to 55°C. for 30 minutes.

Cultivation. *T. muris* can be cultivated in tissue cultures of mouse embryo brain or in the chicken embryo by allantoic, yolk sac, or chorio-allantoic membrane inoculation.

Transmission. The virus is eliminated in the feces and this constitutes the usual source of the virus which is spread to other susceptible mice. It has been reported that the virus is present mainly in the small intestine and that the virus content of the ingesta is about 10 times greater than that of the adjacent intestinal wall. The virus is found in the central nervous system of paralytic cases but not in the "carrier" animal.

Characteristics of the Disease. Encephalomyelitis or poliomyelitis of mice closely parallels human poliomyelitis in many respects, and so has been fairly well studied for that reason. As in human poliomyelitis, this disease of mice is characterized by intestinal infection, with a few individuals exhibiting nervous symptoms. In infected stocks of mice, a high per cent of the animals become intestinal carriers with about one in a thousand becoming paralytic. The paralysis observed in this disease is a flaccid type involving the hind legs. However, young mice may die without showing paralysis. The virus has been found in wild gray mice and kangaroo rats housed near white mice which were carriers.

Pathological Changes. The pathological changes are similar to human poliomyelitis. There is necrosis of ganglionic cells of the anterior horn. There may be inflammatory changes with perivascular and focal leucocytic infiltration in the central nervous system.

Immunity. Recovery from mouse poliomyelitis usually confers immunity to the disease, but the virus may persist in the animal for at least one year.

Diagnosis. *T. muris* infection is diagnosed by isolation and identification of the virus. It must be differentiated from other viruses which infect the central nervous system of mice.

Theilerella tescheni

Common Name. Teschen disease virus.

Disease Produced. Teschen disease of swine. Encephalomyelitis of swine.

Hosts Affected. Domestic and wild swine. Mice, rats, guinea pigs, rabbits, monkeys, and hamsters are insusceptible.

History and Distribution. The first report of Teschen disease was published by Trefney in 1930 and it occurred near the town of

Teschen in Czechoslovakia. Klobouk, in 1931, was the first to artificially transmit the disease and demonstrate the etiology as a virus. The disease is reported to have spread rapidly throughout Czechoslovakia and in 1938 it spread to Germany, Austria, Hungary, Yugoslavia, Switzerland, and France. The disease is not known to occur in the western hemisphere.

Properties of the Virus. Horstmann reports the virus to be 10–15 mµ as determined by filtration studies. It is resistant to the effects of penicillin and streptomycin, to ether and to drying. It is destroyed by exposure to a temperature of 70°C. for 30 minutes.

Cultivation. Teschen disease virus has been propagated only in susceptible swine. Attempts to adapt the virus to experimental animals, chicken embryos, and tissue cultures of minced chicken embryo tissues have been unsuccessful.

Transmission. The virus is transmitted by contact. Experimentally the virus will reproduce the disease if inoculated intracerebrally, intranasally, or orally. The virus is shed in the feces.

Characteristics of the Disease. Teschen disease most often attacks young pigs. An incubation period of 4 to 28 days is noted in artificially infected pigs. If the virus content is high in the inoculum, the incubation period is short — 6 days — and becomes longer as the virus is diluted. First evidence of the disease is a temperature increase, 104°–106°F., followed by stiffness, ataxia, tremors, convulsions, and prostration. Death follows in 3 to 4 days in many cases. The mortality rate ranges from 50 to 70 per cent but may reach 90 to 100 per cent in some outbreaks.

Pathological Changes. There are no macroscopic lesions characteristic of Teschen disease. Microscopic changes are found only in the central nervous system. A striking resemblance between the histopathological changes of Teschen disease and those seen in human poliomyelitis has been reported. Degeneration of nerve cells, perivascular infiltration, and glial proliferation are most common. Cells of the anterior horn, particularly of the lumbar region, are markedly affected.

Immunity. Many of the animals infected with Teschen disease and which do not die may fully recover, although convalescence is prolonged. Immunity results from such an attack. A live vaccine has been used for the prevention of the disease with good results. It is made from brain tissue of an artificially infected pig and is administered intramuscularly. Limited work on the comparison of a few strains has not revealed any pronounced antigenic differences.

Diagnosis. Teschen disease may be confused with hog cholera, pseudo-rabies, and certain nutritional deficiencies. The isolation of an encephalitic virus which is not neutralized by anti-hog cholera serum and which does not infect any host except swine, should be suspected as being Teschen disease virus. Further comparison with known strains of Teschen disease would be necessary in order to positively identify it.

REFERENCES FOR FURTHER STUDY

Legio debilitans (Poliomyelitis)

Aycock, W. L. Amer. Jour. Hyg., 7:791, 1927.

Goldstein, D. M., Hammon, W. M., and Veits, H. R. Jour. Amer. Med. Assn., 131:569, 1946.

Howe, H. A. Poliomyelitis. *In* Viral and Rickettsial Diseases of Man. Edited by Thomas M. Rivers. J. B. Lippincott Co., Philadelphia, 1952.

Knapp, A. C., Godfrey, E. S., Jr., and Aycock, W. L. Jour. Amer. Med. Assn., 87: 635, 1926.

Rosenow, E. C. Jour. Inf. Dis., 50 377, 1932.

Van Rooyen, C. E., and Rhodes, A. J. Virus Diseases of Man. Thomas Nelson and Sons, New York, 1948.

Armlillia erebea (Lymphocytic choriomeningitis)

Alice, F., and McNutt, S. H. Amer. Jour. Vet. Res., 6:54, 1945.

Armstrong, C. Harvey Lectures, 36: 39, 1940–41.

———, and Lillie, R. D. Pub. Health Rep., 49: 1019. 1934.

Casals-Ariet, J., and Webster, L. T. Jour. Exp. Med., 71: 147, 1940.

Dalldorf, G. Jour. Exp. Med., 70: 19, 1939.

Rivers, T. M., and Scott, T. F. M. Science, 81:439, 1935.

Traub, E. Science, 81: 298, 1935.

Van Rooyen, C. E., and Rhodes, A. J. Virus Diseases of Man. Thomas Nelson and Sons, Philadelphia, 1948.

Armlillia simulans (Meningitis)

MacCallum, F. O., Findlay, G. M., and Scott, T. M. Brit. Jour. Exp. Path., 20:260, 1939.

Theilerella muris (Mouse poliomyelitis)

Gard, S. Acta Med. Scand., Supp. 143, 1943.

Olitsky, P. K. Jour. Exp. Med., 72:113, 1940.

Theiler, M. Jour. Exp. Med., 65:705, 1937.

———. Science, 80:122, 1934.

———, and Gard, S. Jour. Exp. Med., 72:49, 1940.

———, ———. Jour. Exp. Med., 72:79, 1940.

———, ———. Jour. Exp. Med., 72: 69, 1940.

Theilerella tescheni (Swine encephalomyelitis)

Dobberstein, J. Zeit. Infektkr. Haust., 59:54, 1942.

Fortner, J. Dtsch. Tierärztl. Wschr., 49:43, 1941.

———. Zeit. Infektkr. Haust., 59:81, 1942.

Horstmann, D. H. Jour. Immunol., 69: 379, 1952.

Kaplan, M. M., and Meranze, D. R. Vet. Med., 43: 330, 1948.

Klobouk, A. Zverol. Rozpravy., 5:95, 1931.

Shafer, W., and Heynen, K. Cent. f. Bakt. Abt. I. Orig., 147:25, 1941.

50. The Genus Formido— the Rabies Group

The Genus *Formido* is composed of viruses which involve the nervous system only. The generic name *Formido* is from the Latin meaning a frightful thing.

Formido inexorabilis

Common Name. Rabies virus.

Disease Produced. Rabies.

Hosts Affected. All mammals. Fowl can be experimentally infected. Reptiles and fish are insusceptible.

History and Distribution. Rabies is a disease which has been recognized since ancient times. The disease was described as early as 500 B.C. in dogs. The relationship of rabies in animals to human rabies was recognized in A.D. 100 and cauterization of dog-bite wounds was recommended.

Zinke in 1804 reported the transmission of rabies to a normal dog by the inoculation of saliva from a rabid one. Thus the infectiousness of the disease was proved and quarantine measures on dogs were instituted in the Scandinavian countries as early as 1826. Consequently, these countries have been free of the disease for over 100 years.

The classical work of Pasteur, in the 1880's, which showed that the virus could be modified so that it would produce immunity without the hazard of producing the disease is one of the milestones in medicine.

Although Pasteur had theorized that the etiological agent of rabies was smaller than bacteria, Remlinger, in 1903, showed that Berkefeld filtrates of brain tissue were infective. Also in 1903, Negri described intracytoplasmic inclusion bodies in the nerve cells of rabid animals, which are of diagnostic significance. These inclusion bodies known as *Negri bodies* are found only in rabies. There have been periods in history when rabies became epizootic in European areas, but the disease usually is enzootic or sporadic in occurrence. Rabies is distributed generally throughout the world, but the British Isles and the Scandinavian countries have been free of the disease for many years.

Properties of the Virus. Rabies virus measures 100 to 150 mμ in diameter. It will pass all grades of Berkefeld filters, also Mandler and Chamberland types, but the virus is retained by Seitz pads. The virus is killed by exposure to 70°C. for 15 minutes, but if dried it may withstand 100°C. for 2 to 3 minutes. The virus is preserved in 50 per cent glycerin for about one year and by freezing for more than one year. Quick freezing followed by desiccation preserves the virus, but it is attenuated by slow drying.

Ultra-violet radiation rapidly destroys rabies virus. Mercuric chloride, formalin, acids, and bases readily inactivate the virus. Phenol, chloroform, and ether are effective but require considerable time to kill.

Sulfonamides, penicillin, and streptomycin do not affect the virus and are frequently used in its isolation from contaminated materials.

Various strains of the rabies virus have been shown to vary in their pathogenic properties and in the amounts of antigenic constituents, but distinct antigenic types have not been described.

There are two types of the virus which are well-known. *Street virus* is the rabies virus as it occurs in nature. *Fixed virus* is a laboratory adapted virus which is developed by continued passage of a street strain by brain to brain inoculation in an animal such as the rabbit. Street virus in the rabbit usually has an incubation period of 15 to 21 days. As fixation occurs through passage, the incubation period becomes progressively shorter until it becomes "fixed" at 6 to 8 days. Strains of street virus vary considerably in their ability to become fixed. Some become fixed in 20 passages, while others require 50 or more and still others do not become fixed at all. Ordinarily, the more virulent street strains are more apt to become fixed in a few passages.

Fixed virus is also modified in other ways than a shortened incubation period. It multiplies faster and a greater quantity of virus is found in the brain tissue. It also loses most of its ability to form Negri bodies and becomes less virulent for hosts other than the one in which it has become fixed.

Fixed virus is quite stable and it is very difficult to effect a change back to a street form. Fixed virus is used almost exclusively for vaccine production.

Cultivation. Rabies virus can be cultivated in tissue cultures composed of brain from the embryo rabbit, mouse, rat, or chicken suspended in Tyrode's solution, serum, and plasma.

Chicken embryos are infected irregularly, but the virus can be adapted to grow successfully though no specific lesions are produced. Infectivity for animals is reduced by cultivation in chicken embryos.

Transmission. The transmission of rabies is almost invariably through the bite of an infected animal. The fact that the virus is eliminated in the saliva is of great significance, and unless saliva is introduced beneath the skin, the disease is seldom transmitted. The virus has been demonstrated in the saliva of dogs 3 to 8 days before the onset of symptoms. However, it has also been reported that only about 50 to 60 per cent of the infected dogs shed the virus in the saliva. Rare cases of rabies have been reported where only clawing and scratching occurred, or where the skin was contaminated with saliva.

The virus is most concentrated in the central nervous system and saliva, but it has also been demonstrated in various organs of the body as well as in the blood and milk from infected animals.

The dog is by far the most important animal as a disseminator of rabies virus, not only to man but to other animals as well. Wild carnivora may be infected and transmit the disease. In the United States foxes and skunks are the most commonly involved. These animals are sometimes responsible for infecting domestic farm animals.

On the island of Trinidad, a paralytic form of rabies in domestic animals and man is transmitted by blood-lapping vampire bats which carry the virus in their saliva and prey on animals and man, especially children. This same situation has also been described in Brazil and Mexico.

In the United States, rabies virus has been isolated from the brain of insectivorus bats. These animals have been known to attack human beings on a number of occasions.

The incubation period in natural cases of rabies is variable. In general, the greater the quantity of virus introduced into the wound the shorter is the incubation period. The location of the wound is also correlated with the length of incubation before symptoms occur. Virus introduced into wounds on the legs is less dangerous and requires a longer incubation period. In dogs, the minimum period is 10 days, the average 21 to 60 days, but may be as long as six months. In man, the period of incubation varies between 1 and 3 months, with the minimum of 10 days.

Characteristics of the Disease. In animals rabies may be manifest in one of two forms: furious, and dumb or paralytic types.

Furious rabies in animals, especially in the dog, is characterized by altered behavior such as restlessness, hiding, depraved appetite, excitement, unprovoked biting, aimless wandering sometimes for many miles, excessive salivation, altered voice, pharyngeal paralysis, staggering, general paralysis, and finally death.

Death usually occurs within 3 to 4 days after the onset of symptoms. There are probably no recoveries in natural cases of rabies, although some experimentally inoculated animals may show an abortive type of illness and recover. The dumb or paralytic form of rabies is frequently observed in animals inoculated with fixed virus, and is occasionally observed in other animals with street virus contracted under natural conditions. Animals showing this type usually show a short period of excitement which is followed by incoordination, ataxia, paralysis, dehydration, and loss of weight, followed by death.

Pathological Changes. The pathological changes are not marked in rabies. There are degenerative changes in the cells of the brain, accompanied by hyperemia and edema of the meninges. There are also leucocytic infiltration and "cuffing" of the blood vessels of the brain tissue.

The *Negri body* (see Fig. 50.1) is an eosinophilic cytoplasmic inclusion body found only in rabies and is of great significance in diagnosis. Although the Negri body is pathognomonic of the disease, its precise nature is not yet established. It varies in size from 0.25 to 20μ, is round in form, and typically has an internal granular structure.

Various investigators have described the Negri body as a protozoan parasite, colonies of the virus, and a reaction product of the cell. Although the composition of these bodies is not known, their significance in rabies is undisputed.

Immunity. The fact that there are virtually no recoveries from rabies has no doubt been an important driving force in the large amount of research on this disease and particularly with respect to immunization procedures. Pasteur, with the assistance of Chamberland and Roux, in 1884, showed that dogs could be protected against rabies by injecting suspensions of dried spinal cord of the rabbit infected with the disease. In the next year, Pasteur made the historic injections of his vaccine into a 9-year-old boy who had been exposed by the bite of a rabid dog, and the vaccine was given credit for saving the boy's life.

In the years following, thousands of exposed persons have received antirabies vaccine, and the results have been quite satisfactory. Although several modifications of Pasteur's rabies vaccine have been made, the name "Pasteur treatment" is still usually applied to any human antirabic vaccine treatment. Many rabies vaccines have been prepared for use in the prevention of this disease, some of which are as follows:

Desiccated cord or Pasteur type vaccine. Rabbits are injected subdurally with fixed virus and in 6 to 7 days they are killed and the cords are harvested intact. They are cut into 2 or 3 pieces and placed in jars with potassium hydroxide for the required desiccation and incubated at 23°C. The loss of virulence parallels loss of moisture from the cord.

Originally, Pasteur started with injections of cord dried 14 days and gave daily injections with progressively less attenuation until 1-day cord was given on the 11th day. In recent years 7- to 8-day cord is used at the beginning and 2-day cord at the end. The number of injections varies with the exposure. Cases with least risk may be treated for 14 days while those more severely exposed are treated 21 to 25 days.

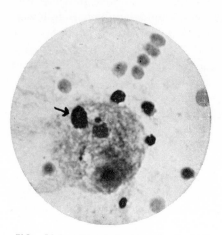

FIG. 50.1 — Negri bodies in Purkinje cell of bovine cerebellum, × 540. (Photo by Benbrook.)

Phenolized type. Examples of this type are the Fermi, Semple, and Umeno-Doi vaccines. The phenolized type of vaccine has been widely used in both human and veterinary medicine. In the preparation of this vaccine fixed virus is inoculated intracerebrally into animals such as horses, rabbits, or goats and their brain and cord is removed when they have reached the last stages of the disease. Technics of processing vary, but ordinarily this type of product contains 20 per cent brain suspension with 0.5 per cent phenol added. A period of 30 days at 37°C. is allowed for the phenol to kill the virus. Depending on the risk involved, the frequency, duration, and dose may be varied in the human treatment. In animals a prophylactic dose of 5 ml. is administered yearly in dogs. If animals are exposed the dose is increased.

Chloroform-treated type. Kelser has prepared a killed vaccine for "single injection" immunization of animals. This vaccine is prepared by the subdural infection of fixed virus into rabbits. The brain and cord are harvested and emulsified in saline, 1 gram of tissue to 2 ml. saline, and then chloroform is added to make 1 per cent by volume. The mixture is stored in a refrigerator for 2 weeks and is thoroughly shaken each day.

Better absorption and higher antigenicity of this type vaccine has been reported.

Ultraviolet-treated vaccine. Webster and his co-workers found that rabies virus was readily killed by exposure to ultraviolet light, yet retained its immunizing properties. The technic of preparation of this type vaccine has been modified by Habel and others to produce a highly antigenic vaccine which is superior to other types of killed vaccines.

Ultraviolet rabies vaccine is prepared from the brains of animals which have been inoculated intracerebrally with fixed virus. Vaccines of this type have been found suitable for "single dose" immunization procedures.

Live vaccines. In some of the early work with rabies vaccines, it was found that live fixed virus could be peripherally injected into an animal without producing the disease. It was also observed that the live vaccines were superior in stimulating immunity. Several methods for the use of live, fixed virus vaccines have been devised. One of these is the Hoegyes vaccine which uses dilutions of the virus to keep it below the infective level as the series of injections begin. Usually a 1:10,000 dilution of the virus is used first, and as the treatment is continued, progressively lower dilutions are injected until 1:100 dilution is administered at the end of 14 to 20 days.

The Harris method employs fixed virus in the form of rabbit brain which is frozen, quickly dried, and powdered. The minimum infective dose for rabbits is determined, and in large animals 500 doses are injected on the first day of treatment and then gradually increased to 5,000 doses at the end of 15 days. In dogs, the dose is 100 minimum infective doses in the beginning and increased to 1,500. Live vaccines are quite antigenic and for that reason are preferred by some over killed virus products. However, there have been some cases of fixed virus rabies which occur following treatment, and this danger, though somewhat remote, has been a point against the use of this type of vaccine.

Avianized vaccine. The adaptation of rabies virus to growth in the chicken embryo by Koprowski and Cox led to the development of a live virus vaccine. It was found that a strain of the virus, designated as the Flury strain, was altered in its pathogenicity after its adaptation to the chicken embryo. After 40 to 50 embryo passages the virus was no longer pathogenic for rabbits and dogs if introduced extraneurally. However, it would still produce rabies if injected intracerebrally. After 180 or more embryo passages the virus is further reduced in pathogenicity, being nonpathogenic when injected intracranially, except in suckling mice.

Avianized rabies vaccine is reported to be completely safe when injected intramuscularly into dogs. It has the following advantages: It possesses high antigenic properties in common with other live vaccines. There is no danger from neuro-paralytic accident, which occasionally occurs with vaccines prepared from nervous tissues. Also, an immunity of longer duration is claimed.

Vaccine Potency Tests. For many years no satisfactory test for potency of rabies vaccines was available. In 1940, the Habel mouse test was adopted by the U. S. Bureau of Animal Industry as the official test to be applied to all rabies vaccine products to be used in Veterinary Medicine. In 1948 this test was adopted by the National Institute of Health for official testing of antirabic vaccines for human use. Habel considered that a satisfactory vaccine should stimulate immunity which would protect against a challenge dose of at least 1,000 lethal doses.

To conduct the test, a standard challenge virus is essential. Killed vaccine to be tested is diluted so that the inoculum contains 0.5 per cent of the original brain tissue. A 0.25 ml. dose of the diluted vaccine is given every second day for 6 doses. At the end of 14 days the vaccinated mice and an equal number of controls are inoculated intracerebrally with the challenge virus. The number of deaths are recorded and LD_{50} end points are calculated for the vaccinated mice and the controls. The number of protective doses are determined by comparison of the LD_{50} end points of the two groups. Live vaccines may be tested with the same technic except that graded doses of the vaccine under test are injected instead of the uniform 0.25 ml. as for killed products.

Neuro-Paralytic Accident. The use of vaccines in exposed persons and animals has generally been successful—however, there have been failures. In cases of severe exposure, especially about the face, occasional deaths occur despite prompt and intensive treatment. In those fatal cases, death usually occurs after a relatively short incubation period. Vaccine treatment almost never fails in cases in which the incubation period would be over 30 days.

Occasionally, death results during vaccine treatment of dogs and human beings, due to an ascending paralysis, and the rabies virus cannot be recovered from the tissues. Several explanations have been advanced to explain these neuro-paralytic accidents. Some believe they are the result of incomplete killing of the virus in the vaccine—and there is an actual case of fixed virus rabies. Others suggest that they are *autosterilizing infections* in which the live virus is present at first and starts the degenerative process which continues after antibodies destroy the virus. However, the view usually taken is that of hypersensitivity, which develops from the repeated injection of brain tissue. The nervous tissue, which is tissue specific rather than host specific, stimulates in certain individuals antibodies to its own nerve tissue. These antibodies, then, are thought to be responsible for the demyelinization of the nerves and paralysis and death results.

These accidents occur more often in persons receiving more than one series of antirabic treatment and in those who have allergic tendencies. The allergic theory has been strengthened by research which has shown that the substances responsible for the paralysis can be removed from vaccines by various calcium salts, by extraction with benzene, or by differential centrifugation.

Immune Serum. It has been shown that antibodies to rabies virus appear in the serum of animals following vaccination. These antibodies are able to precipitate, to fix complement, and also to neutralize the rabies virus. Tests employing these antigen-antibody reactions have been useful in following response of animals to vaccination. Several investigators have reported beneficial results of immune serum in the prophylaxis of rabies.

Habel and Koprowski and Cox have reported favorably upon the protection of animals inoculated with rabies by the injection of hyper-immune serum.

Diagnosis. Accurate diagnosis of rabies is important especially in instances where human beings are definitely exposed by animal bites.

Demonstration of Negri bodies in the cells of the hippocampus major constitutes a diagnosis of the disease. The demonstration of Negri bodies is more successful if the animal is confined and allowed to die. Smears are made of the hippocampus and cerebellum of the brain and stained with a differential stain such as Lenz, Sellers, or Giemsa (see chapter on *Technics and Methods*). The Negri bodies can also be demonstrated in paraffin sections stained with hemotoxylin and eosin.

It is not always possible to demonstrate Negri bodies in the brain tissue of rabid animals. It is reported that 10 to 12 per cent of infected animals fail to show microscopic evidence of the disease. In these cases mouse inoculation is used. A small amount of the brain tissue is emulsified in a mortar and a mixture of streptomycin and penicillin is added to inhibit any bacteria present. The amounts of antibiotic used varies between 1,000 and 5,000 units of each per ml. of material. Following centrifugation of the material, .02 to .03 ml. of the supernatant is inoculated intracerebrally into 5 or 6 Swiss albino mice. If rabies virus is present in the inoculum, the mise will usually show symptoms of paralysis, depression, and dehydration in 6 to 16 days, with death occurring in 1 or 2 days following the appearance of symptoms. Occasionally symptoms may not appear until 17 to 25 days, and inoculated mice should be observed for 21 days before reporting them as negative.

Negri bodies can be demonstrated usually at 5 to 15 days in mice, if the virus is present. In cases where early diagnosis is important, 1 or 2 mice are sacrificed at 5 days and their brains examined for Negri bodies.

REFERENCES FOR FURTHER STUDY

Habel, K. Pub. Hlth. Rep., 55:1473, 1940.

————. Pub. Hlth. Rep., 60:545, 1945.

————. Pub. Hlth. Rep., 62:791, 1947.

————, and Wright, J. T. Pub. Hlth. Rep., 63:44, 1948.

Harris, D. L. Jour. Inf. Dis., 11:397, 1912.

Hodes, H. L., Webster, L. T., and Lavin, G. I. Jour. Exp. Med., 72:437, 1940.

Kelser, R. A. Jour. Amer. Vet. Med. Assn., 77:595, 1930.

Koprowski, H., and Black, J. Jour. Immunol., 64:185, 1950.

————, ————, and Nelsen, D. J. Jour. Immunol., 72:94, 1954.

————, and Cox, H. R. Jour. Immunol., 60:533, 1948.

————, and Van Der Scheer, J. Amer. Jour. Med., 8:412, 1950.

Kough, R. H. Jour. Amer. Med. Assn., 155:441, 1954.

McKendrick, A. G. Bull. Health Org. League of Nations, 9:31, 1940.

Negri, A. Zeit. für Hyg. Infections Krankh., 43:507, 1903.

Pasteur, L. Ann. Inst. Pasteur, 1:1, 1887.

Remlinger, P. Ann. Inst. Pasteur, 17:834, 1903.

Webster, L. T. Rabies. The Macmillan Co., New York, 1942.

51.

The Genus Reedella—
the Yellow Fever Group

Viruses of the genus *Reedella* or the typical yellow fever group produce disease which is characterized by fever and necrosis of tissue cells without vesicle, papule, or pustule formation, or conspicuous nervous involvement. These viruses exhibit a high degree of affinity for liver parenchyma.

The generic name is *Reedella*, from Walter Reed, commemorating the historic studies on yellow fever.

Reedella evagatus

Common Name. Yellow fever virus.

Disease Produced. Yellow fever.

Hosts Affected. Man. Mice and members of the monkey family can be experimentally infected.

Yellow fever occurs only in man under natural conditions. Its occurrence is usually limited to the warmer climates of the tropical and subtropical regions, but at times it has been spread into southern United States and, during summer months, northward into the middle Atlantic regions. The virus is transmitted by mosquitoes. This fact was dramatically demonstrated by the U.S. Army Medical Commission to Cuba in 1901 under the direction of Walter Reed. Certain members of this Commission allowed themselves to be used in experiments to prove that the mosquitoes which fed on yellow fever patients could transmit the disease.

The virus is relatively small in size, measuring 17 to 25 mμ in size. It can be isolated from the blood of patients by intracerebral inoculations of mice. Strains of the virus which have been adapted to mice can be successfully transferred to the chicken embryo for propagation. Chicken embryo vaccine was used extensively for immunization purposes during World War II.

Reedella vallis

Common Name. Rift valley fever virus.

Disease Produced. Rift valley fever.

Hosts Affected. Man, sheep, cattle, and goats. Experimentally, the monkey, mouse, ferret, white rat, and hamster are susceptible. The horse, pig, guinea pig, and chicken have been found insusceptible.

History and Distribution. The disease Rift valley fever and the virus were described in 1931 by Daubney, Hudson, and Garnham. A disease of sheep which occurred in the Rift valley, East Africa, became epizootic in that area. A similar disease to that in the sheep was contracted by those who investigated the outbreak as well as among the sheepherders who tended the infected flocks.

So far the disease has not been identified outside British East or Central Africa.

Properties of the Virus. *Reedella vallis* is approximately 23 to 35 mμ in diameter. It is able to pass all grades of Berkefeld and Chamberland candles.

Thermal inactivation of the virus occurs at 56° for 40 minutes.

The virus remains viable for 8 months in glycerin when stored at 4°C., 1 month in dried tissue, or 6 months in 0.5 per cent phenol.

Cultivation. Rift valley fever virus can be cultivated in tissue cultures of minced chicken embryo in Tyrode's solution. It can be readily cultivated on the chorio-allantoic membrane of the chicken embryo. In the embryo the virus produces hyperplasia and necrosis of the membrane. Liver necrosis is noted in the embryo.

Transmission. *Reedella vallis* is transmitted in naturally occurring cases by mosquitoes, and the virus has been isolated from these insects which have been caught in nature. Infection has been reported in laboratory workers but the mode of transmission was unkown. It is not transmitted among animals by contact.

Characteristics of the Disease. The disease in sheep is characterized by listlessness, anorexia, and prostration. In the newborn lamb, the death rate may be high due to extensive liver necrosis. Abortion occurs in pregnant ewes. In man, the onset may be sudden after an incubation period of 5 to 6 days. Symptoms are malaise, chilling, headache, and fever. There may be extreme pain in the arms, legs, and joints. The temperature curve is of the saddle-back type. Leucopenia is characteristic. The disease runs a benign course with complete recovery in a few days.

Pathological Changes. In animals, the chief pathological changes are in the liver. Necrosis of the liver is most outstanding with scattered petechial hemorrhages. The kidneys, spleen, and lymph nodes may show minor degenerative changes.

Immunity. Antibodies are produced as a result of infection and are capable of neutralizing the virus. There is no antigenic relationship between Rift valley fever virus and yellow fever or dengue. A vaccine produced in chicken embryos is used to prevent the disease. Immune serum is used to some extent in this disease.

Diagnosis. A diagnosis of Rift valley fever depends upon isolation and identification of the virus by mouse inoculation and serum neutralization tests, using known immune serum.

REFERENCES FOR FURTHER STUDY

Reedella evagatus (Yellow fever of man)

Reed, W., Carroll, J., Agramonte, A., and Lazear, J. W. U. S. 61st. Cong. 3rd sess. Senate Doc. #822, Washington, D. C., 1911.

Theiler, M. Yellow Fever. *In* Viral and Rickettsial Infections of Man. Edited by T. M. Rivers. J. B. Lippincott Co., Philadelphia, 1948.

Van Rooyen, C. E., and Rhodes, A. J. Virus Diseases of Man. Thomas Nelson and Sons, New York, 1948.

Reedella vallis (Rift valley fever)

Daubney, R., Hudson, J. R., and Garnham, P. C. Jour. Path. and Bact., 34: 545, 1931.

Mackenzie, R. D., Findlay, G. M., and Stern, R. O. Brit. Jour. Exp. Path., 17: 352, 1936.

Schwentko, F. F., and Rivers, T. M. Jour. Exp. Med., 59: 305, 1934.

52. The Genus Tarpeia— the Influenza Group

Viruses of the influenza group induce disease primarily of the respiratory system. The generic name *Tarpeia* is the name of a Roman maiden who treacherously opened a citadel to an enemy.

Tarpeia alpha

Common Name. Influenza A virus.

Disease Produced. Influenza, "flu."

Hosts Affected. Man and swine. The monkey, ferret, mouse, and hamster can be experimentally infected. Rabbits, guinea pigs, and rats show inapparent infection.

History and Distribution. Human influenza has been recognized as a disease entity for many centuries. The etiology was thought by Pfeiffer to be *Hemophilus influenzae;* he first described this organism in 1893. However, this organism could not be isolated from many typical cases of influenza, and much doubt arose as to its role in the disease. In 1931, Shope reported on the isolation of the virus of swine influenza, and showed that a virus and a hemophilic organism were responsible for the disease in swine, which was clinically similar to human influenza. Smith, Andrewes, and Laidlaw, in 1933, were the first to isolate influenza virus from a human source. These workers produced a respiratory infection in ferrets by injecting throat washings from human cases of influenza. Since the first isolation and description of the influenza virus, an immense amount of work has been published on the virus and the disease.

Influenza is world-wide in occurrence. While it is usually endemic, it has been known to produce several pandemics, that of 1918 being the most severe. It has been estimated that up to half the world's population was attacked in that outbreak, with the death of some 20 million persons. In the United States 550,000 deaths occurred during the 1918 pandemic.

Properties of the Virus. The elementary bodies of *Tarpeia alpha* have been reported as 80–100 mu in diameter. Most of the elementary bodies are ovoid or spherical, but elongated forms have been photographed (Fig. 52.1) which appear to break up or segment to form spheres. Influenza virus will pass Berkefeld V and N, and also Chamberland L_2 and L_5, filter candles.

The virus is inactivated by exposure for 30 minutes at 56°C. It may be preserved by freezing and drying or freezing alone at low

FIG. 52.1 — Influenza A virus, PR8 strain, filamentous forms showing segmentation, × 41,000. Courtesy Murphy, Karzon and Bang. **Proc. Soc. Exp. Biol. Med.** 74:596, 1950.

temperatures. Simple drying of the virus does not preserve it for more than several days unless it is kept cool and in a dark place, in which case it may survive for weeks.

The common chemical disinfectants are able to destroy influenza virus in the commonly used concentrations.

Penicillin, streptomycin, or tyrothricin have no effect upon the virus, so the first two mentioned are used to aid in its isolation in pure culture from bacteria-contaminated materials.

An important discovery that certain viruses would cause hemagglutination was made by Hirst during his work on influenza virus. It was also observed that specific immune serum would completely inhibit the hemagglutination reaction. Influenza virus will agglutinate the erythrocytes of several species of animals; however, chicken or human cells are used in most cases. Hemagglutinating properties of the virus are not destroyed by temperatures which will kill the virus. Formalin-killed virus also will produce hemagglutination. The combination of virus and erythrocytes is not stable, and elution of the virus results upon standing. The virus has been concentrated by absorption-elution methods.

Certain biological materials, such as egg white, have been shown to inhibit virus hemagglutination.

A soluble solution (SS) has been described in influenza preparations. It has the following properties: the particles are about 10 mμ in size; they are derived from the elementary body; they are not associated with infectivity; they will not agglutinate erythrocytes or be absorbed by them. SS produces toxic lesions when injected into mice. Antibodies to it develop after infection but not after vaccination, and it acts as an antigen in the complement-fixation test.

Toxic symptoms have been described following injection of influenza virus into mice. This is believed to be due to a "toxin" rather than to mere virus multiplication.

Cultivation. Chicken embryos are most often used for cultivation of the virus. The most sensitive method is amniotic sac inoculation and it is recommended for primary isolation. Allantoic cavity and chorio-allantoic membrane inoculation are also used. Incubation at 35°–36°C. after inoculation is preferable to 37°C. Influenza virus may be lethal to the embryo in 3 to 5 days, but may fail to kill. Some embryos will show retarded development, and microscopic lesions are pronounced in the epithelial cells of the respiratory tract. Certain strains of influenza virus produce typical pocks when inoculated in the chorio-allantoic membrane. Hemagglutination tests of the amniotic or allantoic fluid are the usual methods of detecting virus multiplication in the embryo.

Tarpeia alpha can also be cultivated in tissue cultures composed of chicken embryo tissue, human embryonic lung or kidney, or monkey kidney cells. Tissue cultures can be used for the primary isolation of influenza virus. It is also possible to cultivate the virus in de-embryonated eggs.

Transmission. Influenza is essentially a droplet-spread infection. The virus is expelled into the air by persons in late incubation period or early stages of the disease. Direct contact with contaminated clothing or eating utensils may also spread the infection. The disease is most prevalent in the winter and it is thought that weather conditions are a predisposing factor. The incubation period is 24 to 48 hours.

Characteristics of the Disease. Human influenza usually begins with headache, chills, "ache all over" feeling, and temperature increases, and there may be dizziness and vomition. Cough develops which may last for many days. There is a distinct leucopenia. The fever lasts 3 to 5 days, and recovery usually takes place in a week or ten days. Bacterial complications sometimes occur. Secondary bacteria include *H. influenzae*, *Dip. pneumoniae*, hemolytic streptococci and *Staphylococcus aureus*.

Immunity. Resistance to influenza follows recovery from the disease but it is often of short duration.

A number of vaccines have been prepared and used for active immunization, but embryo-propagated virus has been used most extensively for vaccine manufacture.

Various methods of vaccine preparation include formalinized allantoic fluid, alum-precipitated products, and vaccines prepared by concentration methods such as freezing and thawing, high speed centrifugation, and red cell absorption and elution. Some vaccines employ only influenza A, but bivalent A and B vaccines have been used in others. The PR8 strain of influenza A and the Lee strain of influenza B are commonly employed. The results of the use of vaccines have been varied. Some workers report negative results, but more recent work with more concentrated vaccines has generally shown a significant reduction in the attack rate.

Diagnosis. A diagnosis of influenza is based on clinical symptoms. More accurately it must include isolation of the virus in chicken embryos and its identification by hemagglutination and hemagglutination-inhibition procedures.

Serum neutralization and complement-fixation tests are of some value in determining recent contacts or in following the immune response to vaccination or infection.

Swine influenza

Van Rooyen has suggested the name *Tarpeia shopei* as appropriate for the swine influenza virus in honor of Dr. R. E. Shope, the discoverer. However, there remains some doubt that the swine influenza virus is sufficiently different from *T. alpha* to warrant a species designation.

History and Distribution. Coincident with the 1918 pandemic of influenza in man, a similar disease was recognized in swine in Iowa by Koen and the name "hog flu" was ascribed to it. Several investigators attempted unsuccessfully to determine the etiology of the disease. In 1931 Shope studied the disease and recovered a virus. This virus was unable to produce typical swine influenza when inoculated alone in the form of a filtrate. A mild indefinite illness, "filtrate disease," was produced. In the same year Lewis and Shope reported the isolation of a hemophilic organism, *Hemophilus suis,* which occurred consistently along with the virus and that these two agents together were responsible for the clinical swine flu. *Hemophilus suis* alone was found incapable of producing the disease.

Swine influenza is widely distributed among swine in the United States. It also occurs in swine in Europe, Great Britain, and in Ireland.

Properties of the Virus. The general properties of swine influenza virus are identical to influenza A (see *Tarpeia alpha*).

The only difference between swine influenza and influenza A is on the basis of antigenicity and pathogenicity; however, even these differences are not always clear-cut.

COMPARISON OF SWINE INFLUENZA AND INFLUENZA A VIRUSES

1. They are closely related antigenically. They share antigenic components, and more difference may be in quantity of these components than in kind.

2. Antibodies which react serologically with swine virus are widely prevalent in man.

3. Antibodies which react serologically with influenza A have been demonstrated in swine sera, and a natural infection due to influenza A virus is presumed.

4. Influenza A virus isolated from human cases is pathogenic for swine by inoculation, but does not spread by contact to other swine.

5. Immunization of animals with swine virus gives protection against the swine virus, but does not regularly protect against influenza A.

Swine influenza virus possibly represents specially adapted strains of human influenza A virus which are epizootic in swine. Koen in his original description of swine influenza called particular attention to the occurrence of influenza in the farm families and swine on the same farm during the 1918 pandemic. Shope and others have suggested that swine influenza virus is a persistence of the 1918 pandemic virus in swine. It has been suggested that swine may be a source of influenza virus to man, but this has not been proved.

Cultivation. Swine influenza virus can be cultivated in the same manner as influenza A. Chicken embryo propagation is the most often employed. A higher proportion of deaths of embryos occurs if *H. suis* and the virus are inoculated together.

The virus alone can be transmitted to mice or ferrets without difficulty. In these animals typical respiratory infection is produced.

Transmission. Droplet infection is the most common method of transmission of swine influenza. An unusual method of transmission in this disease has been carefully studied by Shope. He found that the virus was latent in some swine and that the disease could be "precipitated" by intramuscular injections of *H. suis*. This was possible only in the fall and winter months. More extended investigation found that the lungworm of swine may act as a carrier of the virus and perpetuate the disease from one year to another. The virus has been isolated from lungworm ova and also lungworm larvae found in earthworms in the vicinity of hog lots. Hogs which may feed on earthworms then become infested with lungworms, and at the same time they are exposed to the swine influenza virus carried directly to the lungs by the lungworms.

Characteristics of the Disease. Swine influenza is prevalent in the fall and winter months. It is quite contagious; usually close to 100 per cent of the susceptible swine become infected. Morbidity is high, but the mortality is low, usually 2 per cent or less. The symptoms appear suddenly and there is fever, anorexia, extreme prostration, cough, rapid respiration, and a peculiar abdominal breathing. The course of the disease is usually 2 to 6 days with rapid recovery except in complicated cases. There is some loss in fattening hogs and also reduced fertility in sows which are bred near the time of the outbreak.

Although Shope has emphasized the synergistic action of *H. suis* in producing swine influenza, Scott showed that a Pasteurella could act in a similar manner but the disease produced did not spread among swine. British workers have also suggested that organisms other than *H. suis* could act in the same role.

Pathological Changes. The pathological changes in uncomplicated swine influenza are confined to the respiratory tract. Exudative bronchitis and bronchiectasis with extensive pulmonary consolidation and atelectasis are characteristic. Leucopenia is a constant finding early in the disease.

Immunity. Animals which recover from swine influenza are resistant to reinfection. Antibodies can be demonstrated in their serum.

Artificial immunization with chicken-embryo propagated virus has been tried experimentally, but has not yet come into general use.

Diagnosis. Clinical diagnosis of swine influenza is ordinarily made. For accuracy, isolation and identification of the virus by embryo inoculation, by hemagglutination, and hemagglutination-inhibition tests should be done.

Tarpeia beta

Common Name. Influenza B virus.

Disease Produced. Influenza B.

Hosts Affected. Man. Mice and ferrets can be experimentally infected.

History and Distribution. In 1940, Francis isolated an influenza virus which proved to be immunologically distinct from influenza A. In addition to its occurrence in the United States, it has been identified in England.

Characteristics of Influenza B. *Tarpeia beta* is similar in every respect to *Tarpeia alpha* in its properties. It is not as widely distributed nor is the disease produced as severe. Otherwise, the two viruses can not be differentiated except on immunological bases.

Influenza B has been incorporated in many of the recent influenza vaccines.

An influenza virus isolated by Taylor, also by Francis, Quilligan, and Minuse, differs from either A or B types. This virus has been designated as influenza C. Van Rooyen has suggested the *Tarpeia alpha* subspecies *taylori* for influenza C virus.

Tarpeia premens

Common Name. Common cold virus.
Disease Produced. Common cold.
Hosts Affected. Man and chimpanzee.

The common cold in man is initiated by a virus, with various secondary bacteria being responsible for many of the symptoms. The virus, which will pass all grades of Berkefeld filters, is capable of reproducing the disease in a majority of susceptible human volunteers. The virus has been grown in tissue culture, and its propagation in chicken embryos has also been reported.

The transmission of the common cold is believed to be the contact and droplet transfer.

The disease is quite benign unless secondary bacterial infections of the tonsils, sinuses, or middle ear result. Pneumococci, staphylococci, streptococci, or influenza organisms are most frequent secondary invaders.

Recently, allergic phenomena have been associated with the production of some of the symptoms of a cold.

Vaccines in which the common secondary bacteria are incorporated have been used with varying claims of success or failure.

Cold virus does not affect animals, except the chimpanzee.

Tarpeia felis

Common Name. Feline distemper virus.
Disease Produced. Feline distemper.
Hosts Affected. Domestic cat. Other members of the cat family, such as tiger, lion, ocelot, leopard, lynx, puma, are relatively susceptible. Insusceptible hosts include the rabbit, guinea pig, mouse, rat, dog, ferret, and man.

History and Distribution. The virus of *Tarpeia felis* was first described by Hindle and Findlay in 1932. Verge and Christoforoni had suggested a virus etiology in 1928 but their results were not clear-cut. The disease is wide-spread, occurring in Great Britain,

Europe, South America, and the United States. In addition to losses in domestic cats, heavy losses have been suffered in zoological gardens in wild animals of the feline family.

Properties of the Virus. The virus of feline distemper will pass Berkefeld N and Chamberland L_3 filters. Storage of the virus in 50 per cent glycerin will preserve it for 3 weeks.

Critical studies to compare feline distemper virus and panleucopenia virus have not been made. Blood studies by Hindle and Findlay failed to show any characteristic blood changes in feline distemper, while an outstanding characteristic of panleucopenia is the marked reduction in circulating leucocytes.

Several authors consider these two diseases to be identical, however.

Cultivation. *Tarpeia felis* has not been cultivated in any host except the susceptible members of the cat family.

Transmission. Feline distemper is a highly contagious disease of cats, the infection being easily transmitted by droplets or by fomites.

Characteristics of the Disease. The symptoms of feline distemper are high temperature, eye and nasal discharges, weakness, loss of appetite, diarrhea, and respiratory distress.

Mortality rates are high especially in young animals. Some animals may die suddenly without showing any pronounced symptoms.

Pathological Changes. Lesions of the respiratory system are not marked, but there may be congestion of some areas. There is always some involvement of the intestinal tract. Catarrhal exudate is present in parts or all of the small intestine. In severe cases hemorrhage and sloughing of the mucosa is observed.

No characteristic blood changes or cell inclusions have been described.

Immunity. Recovered animals are immune to feline distemper for life. Immune serum is helpful in protecting exposed cats but it is of less value in treating sick animals.

Diagnosis. A diagnosis of feline distemper should be based on clinical symptoms, blood studies, and cross immunity tests to differentiate this disease from panleucopenia of cats. The presence of respiratory symptoms in feline distemper is considered a differential characteristic.

Tarpeia vitulae

Common Name. Pneumoenteritis virus.
Disease Produced. Pneumoenteritis.
Hosts Affected. Calves. Experimentally mice.

History and Distribution. Although the pneumoenteritis syndrome had been recognized clinically for several years and a number of bacteria ascribed as the causal agent, Baker, in 1943, was the first to isolate a virus. The isolations made by Baker are apparently the only ones reported in this country and there have been none outside the United States.

Properties of the Virus. The virus of pneumoenteritis will pass Berkefeld N filters. It can be preserved by freezing for 1 week but does not survive more than 4 weeks. Lyophilization preserves the virus for about 4 months.

Cultivation. The virus can be maintained by passage in mice, but has not been cultivated by any other means.

Transmission. The pneumoenteritis virus is present in the lungs and intestines, and contact with excretions from these sources is probably the means of natural transmission. Artificial inoculation intranasally into susceptible calves and mice will reproduce the disease.

Characteristics of the Disease. The first symptoms of disease appear 2 to 4 days after inoculation. Increased temperature is the first to be noted. This is followed by malaise and anorexia. Diarrhea and respiratory distress appear a day or so after the initial temperature rise.

Recovery follows in a few days if secondary bacterial infection is avoided.

Pathological Changes. Gross lesions consist of consolidation of portions of the anterior lobes of the lungs, and a catarrhal exudate is found in the small intestine, especially the ileum. The mesenteric lymph nodes are swollen and edematous.

Immunity. Calves which have recovered from an attack are refractory to artificial inoculation. Serum from recovered animals neutralizes the virus but is not always complete.

Diagnosis. A diagnosis of pneumoenteritis is made by demonstration of the virus by mouse inoculation with bacteria-free material.

Tarpeia canis

Common Name. Canine distemper virus.

Disease Produced. Canine distemper. "Hardpad" disease.

Hosts Affected. Dog, fox, mink, ferret, wolf, coyote, raccoon, weasel, skunk, binturong, and the dingo.

History and Distribution. Canine distemper has been recognized as a disease of dogs in Europe since the 18th century, having been introduced from Asia or Peru. Its distribution is worldwide. For many years, the cause of the disease was ascribed to several different bacteria. Carré in 1905 found that filtrates of nasal discharges would reproduce the disease and proposed that the etiological agent was a virus. The role of the virus as the primary agent has been well established for many years. However, secondary bacteria may be a factor in the natural disease.

Properties of the Virus. The virus of canine distemper has not been studied to any extent with regard to its specific properties. Canine distemper virus is not resistant, being killed by exposure to 58°C. for 20 minutes, and by common disinfectants. Bindrich and Garlheer state that the canine distemper virus ranges in size between 70 and 105 mμ as determined by filtration through Gradacol membranes. It will pass Mandler and Chamberland L₂ filters. Field strains of the virus are preserved for at least a year when stored at 7°C. in oxygen-free nitrogen, for a year and a half by lyophilization and for 2 years when stored at —24°C. At 10°C. it will remain viable for a month or two.

Celiker and Gillespie, using egg-adapted distemper virus, report the following effects of pH, chemicals, and heat. Exposure to 50°C. for 60 minutes or 55°C. for 10 minutes destroys the infectivity. Virus held at 25°C. is inactivated in 7 to 8 days, and at 4°C. 7 to 8 weeks are required to inactivate it.

The virus remains viable for 24 hours when the pH of the suspending liquid is 4.4 to 10.4, whereas a pH of 4.2 or 10.9 inactivates it in 2 hours. The virus is destroyed by 0.1 per cent formalin in 1 to 2 hours, 0.5 per cent phenol in 48 to 72 hours, 0.3 per cent chloroform in 10 minutes, and Roccal 0.2 per cent in 30 minutes.

Cultivation. Canine distemper virus is ordinarily kept viable by passage in susceptible dogs or ferrets. Haig, also Cabasso and Cox, have reported that ferret-passaged strains can be adapted to grow in the chorio-allantoic membrane of chicken embryos. No significant lesions are noted until 9 or 10 "blind" passages are made. Subsequent passages show increased thickening and whitish areas in the chorio-allantoic membranes. Material beyond the 28th passage fails to produce illness in ferrets but does produce immunity to the virulent virus.

Transmission. The disease is quite contagious, with transmission occurring by droplet transfer and by contact. The average incubation period is four days.

Characteristics of the Disease. Canine distemper is an acute, highly infectious disease of dogs, foxes, mink, and occasionally other carnivora. It more often infects young animals.

The symptoms include fever, inappetence, diarrhea, loss of appetite, purulent conjunctivitis, and rhinitis. A diphasic temperature curve is characteristic. At the onset of the disease there is a sharp rise in temperature and a watery discharge from the eyes and nose. This phase is of 1 to 2 days' duration and is often not observed. A second and sustained fever occurs about 2 or 3 days following the first, and it is during this period that symptoms are most pronounced. Secondary becterial invasion may contribute to the symptoms and lesions observed. *Brucella bronchiseptica* and *Past. multocida* are organisms which may assume this role in some cases.

Some infected animals will show skin eruptions which occur usually on the posterior abdomen and inner aspect of the thighs.

In other cases, the skin of the foot pads and the nose become very thick and hard. This condition is called "hard pad disease." A feature of hard pad disease is a demyelinating encephalitis with a high mortality. This type of the disease was first thought to be due to a virus other than canine distemper. However, Cabasso has compared the hard pad strains with those from a typical case of canine distemper and found them to be closely related, immunologically.

Some cases are abortive and mild, lasting only a few days, with complete recovery.

Pathological Changes. The pathological changes may vary, depending on whether or not secondary bacterial invasion occurs. In uncomplicated cases the lesions are less pronounced. Most animals show involvement of the respiratory system. The mucous membranes are red, swollen, and covered with muco-purulent exudate. There is often bronchitis and occasionally pneumonia. Purulent conjunctivitis is a rather constant finding. Catarrhal enteritis is usually present. Occasionally there are encephalitis and meningitis.

Inclusion bodies were described in canine distemper by Lenz in 1908 and were considered at that time to be diagnostic of the disease. Demonstration of inclusions is still an important aid to the diagnosis of distemper. These inclusion bodies are most often found in epithelial cells and may be either intranuclear or cytoplasmic. Epithelial cells of the urinary bladder, kidney, renal pelvis, and the lining membrane of the gall bladder or bile ducts are the usual sites, although they may occur in other tissues. Goss *et al.* describes their occurrence in the epithelium of the tongue and conjunctiva and suggests the use of stained smears as an aid to diagnosis of canine distemper in the sick animal. The inclusion bodies of distemper may be confused with those of fox encephalitis *(Tortor vulpis)* or occasionally rabies if only the brain is examined.

Immunity. Animals which recover from canine distemper are immune for life.

Artificial immunization is widely practiced, and a variety of products and procedures are available.

Passive immunity. Serum from dogs which have been hyperimmunized by repeated injections of distemper virus is useful in preventing the disease in exposed animals and to some extent for the treatment of the sick. It is injected with live virus for active immunization by the serum-virus method. Many serum producers also hyperimmunize their dogs used for serum production against the common secondary bacteria.

Active immunization. The method of Laidlaw and Dunkin has been used with success. This method consists of the subcutaneous injection of formalinized virus of canine origin followed by intradermal injection of living virus of ferret origin two weeks later.

Another method which has been widely used is the injection of live virus followed by immune serum 24 to 48 hours later.

Others recommend two or three doses of killed vaccine spaced at 2 week intervals for active immunization.

A live virus modified by continued ferret passage is also used. This vaccine, called Distemperoid Vaccine, prepared by the method of Green, is ferret virus of 60 or more continuous passages. The distemper virus so modified is called distemperoid. It is highly pathogenic for ferrets and will also produce severe disease in mink and skunks, but is avirulent when injected into dogs and foxes. The injection of distemperoid virus in dogs or foxes produces active immunity to canine distemper. It has been further observed that the administration of distemperoid vaccine is of value in preventing distemper in exposed animals as well as apparent curative properties in sick animals. The effects of distemperoid virus are explained by the phenomenon of virus interference. It is theorized that all of the susceptible cells of the animal body are not affected at once, and if the modified virus can be injected and absorbed by these cells before the virulent distemper virus reaches them, these cells are "blocked" by the avirulent distemperoid virus and the virulent strain does not enter.

Distemper virus of blood origin is also used in the live state and will confer active immunity. In this case the dose is graded according to the size of the animal, with no antiserum being used.

Avianized vaccine. The adaptation of the canine distemper virus to growth in the chicken embryo has made possible the development of a live vaccine for use in the prevention of the disease. Since its introduction in 1951, it has been accepted as a useful immunizing agent.

Diagnosis. Canine distemper is diagnosed by the correlation of clinical symptoms and microscopic demonstration of inclusion bodies in the epithelial cells of the urinary or gall bladder. It must be differentiated from fox encephalitis, *Tortor vulpis,* infection in foxes or dogs.

Tarpeia viverrae

Common Name. Ferret distemper virus.

Disease Produced. Ferret distemper.

Hosts Affected. Ferret. Dog, rat, mouse, guinea pig, and rabbit are not susceptible.

History and Distribution. In 1934 an epizootic respiratory disease destroyed the entire stock of ferrets in the laboratories of Columbia University, N.Y., in the course of two months. Slanetz, Smetana, and Dochez isolated a virus and studied the experimental disease.

Properties of the Virus. *Tarpeia viverrae* will pass the Berkefeld type N filter. It is inactivated by exposure to 60°C. for 30 minutes. It remains viable for at least 4 months when lyophilized or for 3 months in 50 per cent glycerin. No antigenic relationships between ferret distemper and canine distemper viruses have been shown.

Cultivation. The virus of ferret distemper has not been cultivated under artificial conditions.

Transmission. Transmission of ferret distemper occurs by pen contact and through contaminated food.

Parenteral inoculation of the virus will result in infection of ferrets. The incubation period is 4 days.

Characteristics of the Disease. Ferret distemper is an acute febrile disease with depression, anorexia, conjunctivitis, and purulent rhinitis. In some cases there are convulsions and other evidence of nervous involvement.

Mortality is usually high, 70 to 100 per cent. Secondary bacterial infection often accompanies ferret distemper.

Pathological Changes. Congestion of the turbinates accompanied by mucopurulent exudate and consolidation of some areas of the lungs are the usual gross lesions. The most outstanding microscopic changes are the cytoplasmic and intranuclear inclusion bodies seen in the epithelial cells of the respiratory tract, mucous glands, salivary glands, kidney, renal pelvis, bladder, bile ducts, and intestinal tract.

Immunity. A vaccine prepared of formalinized lung tissue from infected ferrets will produce effective immunity for at least one year.

Diagnosis. A diagnosis of ferret distemper depends upon isolation of the virus and its differentiation from canine distemper virus by cross immunity tests.

Tarpeia avium

Common Name. Laryngotracheitis virus.

Disease Produced. Laryngotracheitis.

Hosts Affected. Chickens and pheasants. Other birds and laboratory animals are refractory to inoculation.

History and Distribution. Laryngotracheitis was first recognized as a disease entity in 1925 by Beach, who reported in 1930 that the disease was produced by a filtrable virus.

The disease is widespread in poultry throughout the United States and Canada. It also has been identified in Australia and European countries.

Properties of the Virus. The size and morphology of *Tarpeia avium* have not been determined. It will pass through Berkefeld V and N filter candles.

Heat inactivation of the virus occurs by exposure to 55°C. for 15 minutes and to 75°C. for 30 seconds.

Five per cent phenol kills in 1 minute and 3 per cent cresol and 1 per cent sodium hydroxide are lethal in 30 seconds.

The virus remains viable at 4° to 10°C. for 217 days and in the dried state for 661 days. It does not survive in the carcass of dead birds long after decomposition is evident.

Cultivation. The virus of laryngotracheitis can be cultivated in chicken embryos. Chorio-allantoic inoculation is best since the virus produces pock lesions and this fact is an aid in its differentiation from other viruses which attack the respiratory system of chickens.

Transmission. The transmission of laryngotracheitis is by droplets from the respiratory tract which contain the virus and are inhaled by susceptible chickens. Contaminated food and water also play a part in transmission. Recovered birds have been shown to harbor the virus for as long as 16 months, and are capable of transmitting the disease to susceptible birds.

Characteristics of the Disease. Laryngotracheitis is a disease of adult and young adult birds. More outbreaks occur in the fall and winter months. Symptoms of gasping and coughing are outstanding. Infected birds are depressed, and in laying flocks egg production is sharply reduced and ceases entirely in some cases. The disease usually spreads rapidly and the morbidity rate is high, but death rates average about 15 per cent. Death results from occlusion of the lumen of the larynx or trachea with blood and exudate.

Pathological Changes. Lesions of laryngotracheitis are limited to the larynx and trachea. There is marked hyperemia and congestion of the mucous membrane of these organs. These changes are accompanied by hemorrhage, excessive mucous secretion, and caseous exudation. Intranuclear inclusion bodies are described as occurring in tracheal epithelium.

Immunity. Recovery from laryngotracheitis confers immunity.

Artificial immunity is practiced. Live virus, usually embryo propagated, is inoculated onto the cloacal mucous membrane. The virus produces an infection at this site but does not involve the respiratory system. Birds so vaccinated are immune to tracheal infection.

Diagnosis. Laryngotracheitis must be distinguished from infectious bronchitis and Newcastle disease, with which it may be confused at times. Isolation and identification of the virus in chicken embryos is most accurate (see Table 52.1).

Tarpeia pulli

Common Name. Infectious bronchitis virus.

Disease Produced. Infectious bronchitis.

Hosts Affected. Chickens.

History and Distribution. Infectious bronchitis was first recognized by Schalk and Hawn in North Dakota in 1931.

There was some confusion in nomenclature of the early 1930's because laryngotracheitis was also being referred to as infectious bronchitis by some investigators. A few years later laryngotracheitis was found not to involve the bronchi but was confined to the larynx and trachea, and was distinct from infectious bronchitis. So the name infectious bronchitis as originally suggested by Schalk and Hawn is applied to the disease which they described.

Infectious bronchitis is widely distributed in the poultry-raising areas of the United States and Canada but has not been described elsewhere.

The disease was originally thought to be confined to baby chicks, but it is also of considerable importance in adult chickens.

Properties of the Virus. The virus of infectious bronchitis is between 65 and 135 mμ in size, with the average about 90mμ. The elementary bodies are spherical and are filterable through all grades of Berkefeld candles as well as Seitz pads. The virus is not resistant to heat and dies in a short time at 37°C. The following chemicals are lethal in 3 minutes or less: one per cent phenol, cresol, formalin, Lugol's solution, or metaphen, also mercuric chloride, 1 to 1,000, or potassium permanganate 1 to 10,000 concentration, and 5 per cent NaOH.

Cultivation. *Tarpeia pulli* can be readily cultivated in chicken embryos. Allantoic cavity inoculation is preferable. Outstanding changes in the infected embryo are stunting or dwarfing and tucking of the embryo. These changes may not be evident in the first passage but are almost always present by second or third passage. Embryo adapted strains become increasingly virulent for embryos on passage and the virus may consistently kill in 3 to 4 days after inoculation.

Transmission. Infectious bronchitis is usually transmitted by infective droplets from the respiratory system which are expelled by the coughing of sick birds. Food and water which may be contaminated with nasal secretions may also play a part in transmission. The incubation period in artificially exposed birds is about 24 hours.

Characteristics of the Disease. Infectious bronchitis is of sudden onset and spreads rapidly, affecting the entire flock in a short time. Gasping, wheezing, nasal discharge, and distinct bronchial rales are characteristic. In older birds, the symptoms may be less distinct, but rales are definite, and in laying flocks egg production is reduced to one-half or more. Mortality may be high in baby chicks, but is negligible in older birds. The greatest loss in older birds is in lowered egg yield and quality.

Pathological Changes. Lesions are confined to the respiratory system. Usually there is a clear mucoid exudate in the trachea, congestion of the lungs, with bronchi entirely filled with exudate, and the air sacs show a definite "cloudiness."

Immunity. Birds which have recovered from infectious bronchitis are immune. Chicks hatched from eggs laid by immune stock are passively immune for at least 2 weeks but are usually susceptible at 5 weeks.

Neutralizing antibodies can be readily demonstrated in the serum of immune chickens.

Artificial immunization is used to some extent in the prevention of infectious bronchitis. Live virus is sometimes introduced into a flock of young adult birds before they begin egg production, usually at 6 to 10 weeks of age. About 5 per cent of the flock is inoculated and the remainder of the flock contracts the disease by contact. Immunity is produced with only a few losses in this age of bird.

Live virus which has been modified by many chicken embryo passages is also employed as an immunizing agent. It may be ad-

TABLE 52.1
DIFFERENTIATION OF AVIAN RESPIRATORY VIRUSES IN CHICKEN EMBRYOS

Virus	Chorio-allantoic Membrane	Effect on Embryo	Agglutination of Avian R.B.C. by Allantoic Fluid
Newcastle	No lesions	Lethal 48–72 hrs.	+
Bronchitis	No lesions	Dwarfed	—
Laryngotracheitis ...	Thickened with pock lesions	No gross changes	—

ministered by spraying the birds with dried virus in the form of dust, or it may be sprayed as an aerosol or added to drinking water.

Diagnosis. Accurate diagnosis of infectious bronchitis depends upon the isolation of the virus and its differentiation from Newcastle and laryngotracheitis viruses. Trachea and lungs from suspected cases should be removed and an emulsion prepared and, after adding antibiotics, inoculated into embryos. Allantoic cavity inoculation is preferable for bronchitis or Newcastle viruses but chorio-allantoic inoculation should be done in case laryngotracheitis virus is present. If susceptible chicks are available, a portion of the inoculum introduced into the trachea will produce bronchial rales and other symptoms in about 24 hours if bronchitis virus is present. If Newcastle or laryngotracheitis virus is present the incubation period is longer.

REFERENCES FOR FURTHER STUDY

Tarpeia alpha (Influenza of man)

Burnet, F. M. Brit. Jour. Exp. Path., 17:282, 1936.

———. Austral. Jour. Exp. Biol. and Med., 19:292, 1941.

———, and Clark, E. Influenza. Macmillan Co. Ltd., Melbourne, 1942.

Henle, G., and Henle, W. Jour. Exp. Med., 84:623, 1946.

Hirst, G. K. Science, 94:22, 1941.

———. Jour. Exp. Med., 75:49, 1942.

Salk, J. E. Jour. Immunol., 49:87, 1944.

Smith, W., Andrews, C. H., and Laidlaw, P. P. Lancet, 2:66, 1933.

Thomsen, D., and Thomsen, R. Ann. Pick.-Thom. Res. Lab., 9:1, 1933.

———, ———. Ann. Pick.-Thom. Res. Lab., 10: 641, 1934.

Van Rooyen, C. F., and Rhodes, A. J. Virus Diseases of Man. Thomas Nelson and Sons, New York, 1948.

Swine influenza

Glover, R. E., and Andrewes, C. H. Jour. Comp. Path. and Therap., 53:329, 1943.

Koen, J. S. Amer. Jour. Vet. Med., 14:468, 1919.

Lewis, P. A., and Shope, R. E. Jour. Exp. Med., 54:361, 1931.

Magill, T. P., and Francis, T., Jr. Brit. Jour. Exp. Path., 19: 273, 1938.

Scott, J. P. U. S. Livestock San. Assn. Proc., 1941.

Shope, R. E. Jour. Exp. Med., 54:349, 373, 1931; 56:575, 1932; 63:669,1936; 66:151, 1937; 67:739, 1938; 69:847, 1939; 77:111, 127, 1943.

Young, G. A., Jr., and Underdahl, N. R. Amer. Jour. Vet. Res., 16:545, 1955.

Tarpeia beta (Influenza of man)

Francis, T., Jr., Quilligan, J. J., Jr., and Minuse, E. Science, 112:495, 1950.

———. Science, 92:405, 1940.

———. Proc. Soc. Exp. Biol. and Med., 45:861, 1940.

Hirst, G. K. Jour. Exp. Med., 76:195, 1942.

Taylor, R. M. Amer. Jour. Pub. Hlth., 39: 171, 1949.

Tarpeia premens (Common cold of man)

Van Rooyen, C. E., and Rhodes, A. J. Virus Diseases of Man. Thomas Nelson and Sons, New York, 1948.

Tarpeia felis (Feline distemper)

Findlay, G. M. Vet. Jour., 89:17, 1933.

Hindle, E., and Findlay, G. M. Jour. Comp. Path. and Therap., 45:11, 1932.

Verge, J., and Christoforoni, N. Compt. Rend. Soc. Biol., 99:312, 1928.

Tarpeia vitulae (Pneumoenteritis of calves)

Baker, J. A. Cornell Vet., 32:202, 1942.

———. Jour. Exp. Med., 78:435, 1943.

Gilmore, H. D. Vet. Rec., 51:674, 1939.

Lamont, H. G., and Kerr, W. R. Vet. Rec., 51:672, 1939.

Tarpeia canis (Canine distemper)

Cabasso, V. J. Vet. Med., 47:417, 1952.

———, and Cox, H. R. Proc. Soc. Exp. Biol. Med., 71: 246, 1949.

Carré, H. Compt. Rend. Acad. Sci., 140:689, 1905.

Celiker, A., and Gillespie, J. H. Cornell Vet., 44:276, 1954.

Dunkin, G. W., and Laidlaw, P. P. Jour. Comp. Path. and Therap., 39:201, 213, 222, 1926.

Goss, L. J. Amer. Jour. Vet. Res., 9:65, 1948.

Goss, L. W., Cole, C. R., and Engel, H. Jour. Amer. Vet. Med. Assn., 112:236, 1948.

Green, F. G. Vet. Rec., 61:163, 1949.

Innes, J. R. M. Vet. Rec., 61:73, 1949.

Laidlaw, P. P., and Dunkin, G. W. Jour. Comp. Path. and Therap., 44:1, 1931.

MacIntyre, A. B., Trevan, D. J., and Montgomerie, R. F. Vet. Rec., 60:635, 1948.

Stader, O., and Slaughenhaupt, R. R. N. Amer. Vet., 23:782, 1942.

Wharton, D. R. A., and Wharton, M. W. Amer. Jour. Hyg., 19:189, 1934.

Tarpeia viverrae (Ferret distemper)

Slanetz, C. A., Smetana, H., and Dochez, A. R. Jour. Bact., 31:48, 1936.

———, ———. Jour. Exp. Med., 66: 653, 1937.

Tarpeia avium (Laryngotracheitis of chickens)

Beach J. R. Jour. Amer. Vet. Med. Assn., 68:570, 1925.

———. Science, 72:633, 1930.

———. Jour. Exp. Med., 54:801, 1931.

———. Infectious Laryngotracheitis, *in* Diseases of Poultry. Edited by Biester, H. E., and Schwarte, L. H. 3rd edition. Iowa State College Press, Ames, 1952.

Brandly, C. A. Jour. Inf. Dis., 57:201, 1935.

Burnet, F. M. Brit. Jour. Exp. Path., 15:52, 1934.

Gibbs, C. S. Jour. Amer. Vet. Med. Assn., 81:651, 1932.

Schalm, O. W., and Beach, J. R. Jour. Inf. Dis., 56:210, 1935.

Seifried, O. Jour. Exp. Med., 54:817, 1931.

Tarpeia pulli (Infectious bronchitis)

Beach, J. R., and Schalm, O. W. Poult. Sci., 15:199, 1936.

——. Infectious Bronchitis, *in* Diseases of Poultry. Edited by Biester, H. E., and Schwarte, L. H. 3rd edition. Iowa State College Press, Ames, 1952.

Delaplane, J. P., and Stuart, H. O. Rhode Island Agr. Exp. Sta. Bull., 273, 1939. 284, 1941.

Hofstad, M. S. Cornell Vet., 37:29, 1947.

Jungherr, E. L., and Terrell, N. L. Amer. Jour. Vet. Res., 9:201, 1948.

Loomis, L. N., Cunningham, C. H., Gray, M. L., and Thorp, F., Jr. Amer. Jour. Vet. Res., 11:245, 1950.

Reagan, R. L., Hauser, J. E., Lillie, M. G., and Craige, A. H., Jr. Cornell Vet., 38:191, 1948.

Schalk, A. F., and Hawn, M. C. Jour. Amer. Vet. Med. Assn., 78:413, 1931.

53. The Genus Tortor—
the Generalized Infection Group

Viruses of the generalized infection group produce diseases characterized by involvement of many tissues. The generic name *Tortor* is from the Latin meaning tormentor.

Tortor suis

Common Name. Hog cholera virus.

Disease Produced. Hog cholera, swine fever (Europe).

Hosts Affected. Swine. Wild hogs are susceptible to some extent and sometimes are inapparent carriers.

History and Distribution. Hog cholera was first recognized as a disease in the United States in 1833 in Ohio, but the exact origin of the disease in that state is not known. The first accounts of the disease in England were in 1862, and from England the disease spread over Europe and then to Africa. The etiological agent was first thought to be *Salmonella choleraesuis* or possibly *Pasteurella multocida,* since cultures of these organisms were recovered from many typical cases and injection of them into other hogs would frequently produce a disease with similar lesions. However, immunity experiments which employed bacterins made from these organisms showed that their use afforded no protection against hog cholera. In 1903, de Schweinitz and Dorset in their investigations of the disease in southwestern Iowa found that filtrates made of swine body fluids would consistently reproduce the disease. They also proved that such filtrates were free of any bacteria by cultural and by laboratory animal inoculation. This discovery was of great significance and quickly led to an entirely new concept of the disease. The following months witnessed the production of the first successful antiserum, and by 1908 the process of anti-hog cholera serum manufacture and simultaneous serum-virus immunization procedure were established.

Hog cholera is still most prevalent in the chief swine-raising area, the midwestern United States. It has spread world-wide in all areas where swine are kept. Certain countries, notably Canada, have been quite successful in controlling it by vigorous quarantine measures.

Properties of the Virus. The virus of hog cholera is usually reported as 30–35 mμ or less in size. The virus readily passes Berkefeld and Chamberland filters. Thermal inactivation occurs by exposure to 55°C. for 30 minutes, 60°C. for 10 minutes, or in dried blood, 72°C., for one hour. The virus is destroyed in one hour by 2 per cent cresol, but solutions of sodium hydroxide are considered the most effective disinfectant. Hog cholera virus is quite resistant to phenol. The virus will survive long periods in contact with 0.5 per cent phenol and it is routinely preserved in this manner when it is produced for immunization purposes.

The virus is resistant to aging if the temperature is low. In saline-glycerin solution at −15°C., it will live for 5 years. It will survive in meat products for months, and it is also resistant to pickling, salting, and smoking for at least 6 months. Putrefactive processes destroy the virus in a few days, except in the bone marrow where it has been known to survive for 15 days.

Variation in virulence of the virus is well known. The American strains are considerably more virulent than the European. Variation among American strains has been reported by Dale *et al.* However, definite antigenic types of the virus have not been distinguished.

Cultivation. Hog cholera virus has been cultivated in tissue cultures which employ various swine tissues such as lymph node, spleen, kidney, testicle, and chorioid plexus. Propagation is reported in swine tissues implanted on the chorio-allantoic membranes of chicken embryos.

Transmission. Hog cholera is a highly contagious disease of swine and it spreads rapidly and easily among them. Eye and nasal secretions, blood, urine, and feces all contain the virus during the disease and for a period before symptoms are shown. Under natural conditions contact with these secretions or excretions may result in transmission. Very minute quantities of the virus will reproduce the disease in susceptible pigs. Blood from hog cholera pigs can be diluted to 1:1,000,000 and regularly produce the disease when injected, and dilutions of 1:50,000,000 occasionally are infective.

Birds, such as pigeons, also insects, have been suspected of playing some role in the transmission of hog cholera, but experimental evidence has so far failed to incriminate any of these.

Pigs which have recovered from clinical hog cholera or serumvirus vaccination are possible disseminators of the virus. The urine of such animals may remain infective for other swine for 20 to 30 days after inoculation with the virus, and the blood has been found to contain the hog cholera virus for some time after injection — in one instance, up to 10 months.

Wild pigs are often inapparent carriers of the virus and so are a distinct menace to domestic swine.

Other farm animals have been suspected of transmitting the virus of hog cholera. Jacotot, in France, has reported that hog cholera virus can be transmitted to sheep, goats, horses, dogs, rabbits, pigeons, and calves by injection and by contact, and that the virus could be recovered from these animals and would produce the disease in swine. Zichis, in this country, also reported the passage of hog cholera virus through sheep and calves and back to swine with evidence of its multiplication in these hosts. However, neither of these investigators noted any symptoms of disease in animals used except swine.

Transmission of hog cholera is not infrequently by way of infected scraps of pork in garbage which is fed to susceptible pigs. Introduction of the virus into hog-cholera-free areas has occurred in this manner.

Characteristics of the Disease. Hog cholera begins with a rise in temperature which reaches 106° to 107°F. and remains high until just before death. Depression, loss of appetite, stilted gait, incoordination, purulent conjunctivitis, and diarrhea are usually characteristics of the disease. Mortality rates are usually around 90 per cent in the United States and in Africa. In European countries the death loss is often lower.

Hog cholera is frequently complicated by secondary bacterial infection. *Salmonella choleraesuis* is most common, but other organisms such as *Past. multocida, Ery. rhusiopathiae,* or *S. necrophorus* may be found. These bacteria may also complicate the "reaction period" of serum-virus immunization.

Pathological Changes. The outstanding pathological change in hog cholera is the appearance of hemorrhages, usually petechial, but also ecchymotic in some cases. These may appear on any or nearly all serous surfaces. Hemorrhages of the bladder, kidney, epiglottis, and epicardium are commonly noted. Hemorrhagic lymphadenitis and a leucopenia are usual findings.

Cases with secondary bacterial invasions may show severe enteritis, and even more extensive hemorrhages.

Inclusion bodies have been described by Boynton *et al.,* in the epithelial cells of the duct of the gall bladder of cholera hogs. The demonstration of these inclusion bodies has been proposed as constituting a diagnosis of the disease.

Immunity. The development and use of successful immunizing agents for hog cholera has been of inestimable value to the swine-raising industry. The production of anti-hog cholera products is in itself a very large industry.

Active immunization is produced by the simultaneous administration of live virus and serum from hyperimmunized hogs. This method is widely used and confers lasting immunity.

Simultaneous virus. The *virus* is prepared by inoculating pigs of approximately 80 pounds with the live hog cholera virus. After 5 to 7 days, when the temperature of the pigs is at its highest point, they are bled to death from the anterior vena cava. The blood is collected aseptically, defibrinated, and preserved with 0.5 per cent phenol. After satisfactory tests for purity, it is released as an immunizing agent to be used along with antiserum. An expiration date of 90 days from the date of bleeding is allowed on the virus.

Hyperimmune serum. Immune serum is produced from healthy hogs usually weighing 250–300 lbs., which are first vaccinated by the simultaneous method. Following a lapse of time to allow the development of immunity, the hogs are hyperimmunized by the intravenous injection of 5 ml. of virus blood per pound of body weight. After 11 days they may be bled for serum. One to three tail bleedings may be taken at intervals of 7 days and the final bleeding is from the throat. All of the bleeding is with strict attention to asepsis. The blood is collected and mechanically defibrinated. A small amount of castor bean extract is then added to produce hemagglutination, which facilitates removal of the erythrocytes. The clear serum is obtained by passing the defibrinated blood through a separator similar to the ordinary cream separator. The serum is then pasteurized at 58.5°C. for 30 minutes. Phenol in a quantity to make 0.5 per cent final concentration is added as a preservative. The serum is tested for potency and purity as provided by the U. S. Department of Agriculture. After satisfactory tests have been completed, the serum is bottled and labeled and is ready for use. An expiration date of 3 years from the date of the first bleeding is allowed on the serum.

Crystal-violet vaccine. Cole and McBryde found that crystal-violet would attenuate the hog cholera virus without destroying its antigenic properties. Their method consists of preparing a 0.5 per cent solution of crystal-violet and a 3 per cent solution of disodium phosphate; 100 ml. of each solution is added to 800 ml. of defibrinated virus blood. The mixture is incubated at 37°C. for 14 days, with agitation once daily. At the end of 14 days the virus no longer produces the disease and is given alone for the production of immunity. Two doses are recommended, to be given about 2 weeks apart.

Tissue vaccine. B.T.V. Boynton devised a vaccine for hog

cholera patterned after his anti-rinderpest vaccine for cattle. This vaccine is prepared from lymphoid tissues of cholera-infected pigs, and the virus is attenuated by 1 per cent oil of eucalyptol. The period required for attenuation varies but generally takes about 8 weeks at refrigerator temperatures.

Crystal-violet and tissue vaccines are used in about the same manner. They are used in unexposed hogs and two doses are recommended, to be given without serum. The cost is lower and there is less tendency to "light up" secondary infections than with the serum-virus method. An additional advantage is that these vaccines do not perpetuate the disease as does the serum-virus method.

On the other hand, the hogs must remain unexposed to the disease during the period of immunity production, since no passive immunity is provided. The use of serum with these vaccines has generally been unsatisfactory. The immunity produced by the vaccines is not considered as durable, and breeding stock should receive additional injections of the vaccine every 10 to 12 months.

Lapinized hog cholera virus. Baker, in 1947, succeeded in adapting the hog cholera virus to the rabbit by the alternate passage technic. It was observed that after many such passages the virulence of the virus for swine was lost while the immunogenic properties were retained. Swine inoculated with the lapinized virus showed no symptoms following the injection and were later resistant to challenge by the fully virulent hog cholera virus. This rabbit-adapted strain of the virus has been successfully used as an immunizing agent for the disease. It is produced in rabbits and can be used with or without immune serum.

Although the lapinized hog cholera virus is non-pathogenic for young and adult swine, it has been reported by Sautter *et al.* that it can infect the fetal pig causing edema, ascites, and congenital malformations.

Modified live virus vaccine. The lapinized virus has also been used in a similar immunizing product that employs virus which has gone through fewer rabbit passages, thus retaining some pathogenicity. This product is produced in swine and is harvested in the form of blood and spleen emulsion. This emulsion is lyophilized and then reconstituted with distilled water just before use. An administration of immune serum is necessary when modified live virus is used.

Passive immunity. Hyperimmune serum is used chiefly for active immunization procedures, but is also administered as a therapeutic agent to sick animals or occasionally alone to confer passive immunity for a short period.

Passive immunity is usually conferred on suckling pigs by

transfer of antibodies through the milk of immune sows. This has been shown by experimental trials as well as field observations.

Diagnosis. The diagnosis of hog cholera depends upon the demonstration of the presence of the virus. This can be accomplished only by injection of blood or tissues from suspected cases into known susceptible pigs. It is necessary to protect other pigs with known anti-hog cholera serum and inject a similar amount of the suspected material into them. The suspected blood and tissue suspensions must be rendered bacteria-free by filtration or by the addition of antibiotics such as penicillin and streptomycin. If the pigs which received no antiserum die with lesions typical of hog cholera and those given immune serum live, a diagnosis of the disease is made. Cultures of the inoculum and of the dead pigs should be made to exclude any role bacteria might play in the results. Although this procedure is the only accurate method of diagnosis, it is obviously too expensive to be used as a routine procedure.

Demonstration of inclusion bodies as described by Boynton has not come into use. Blood counts which show distinct leucopenia and are accompanied by other features of the disease are helpful in diagnosis.

African Swine Fever

An acute infectious disease, closely resembling American hog cholera, occurs in East and South Africa. The disease was recognized by Montgomery in 1910 as differing from ordinary swine fever (hog cholera), and he determined the etiological agent to be a filtrable virus in 1911.

Properties of the Virus. The properties of the virus are similar to those of hog cholera. It is pathogenic only for swine and produces a generalized infection. The virus will pass through Berkefeld, Chamberland, and Seitz filters. The dried virus is not destroyed by exposure to 40°C. in 15 days or 50°C. in 3½ hours. It is preserved in 0.5 per cent phenol — 50 per cent glycerin mixture at room temperature for 536 days. The virus has been found viable after 6 years' storage in the refrigerator. African swine fever virus bears little or no antigenic relationship to either European swine fever or American hog cholera viruses.

Cultivation. McIntosh has reported the successful cultivation of the virus in chicken embryos. He used virus which was partially rabbit adapted for the work. The embryos used were 8 days old and were incubated at 33°C. following inoculation.

Transmission. The transmission of the virus is considered to be through ingestion. Montgomery muzzled healthy pigs and placed them in contact with pigs sick with African swine fever, and they did not contract the disease. Most of the outbreaks of African swine fever can be related to contact with either the African wart hog or brush pig which have been proved inapparent carriers of the virus.

Characteristics of the Disease. African swine fever is characterized as an acute generalized infection accompanied by high temperature, dullness, loss of appetite, cyanosis, and incoordination of the hind legs. The incubation period is three to four days and the duration of the disease three to four days. Mortality is usually 100 per cent, with only an occasional animal surviving. The lesions are most pronounced in the blood vascular system which shows extensive hemorrhage.

Immunity. Immunity production has been attempted but has not been successful. Anti-hog cholera serum and vaccine from the United States and from European countries have been of no value in the prevention of African swine fever. Swine hyperimmunized against European strains of swine fever are not immune to African swine fever. Attempts to immunize swine by any means, using the African swine fever virus, have not been successful.

Tortor bovis

Common Name. Rinderpest virus, cattle plague virus.

Disease Produced. Rinderpest.

Hosts Affected. Cattle, sheep, goats, deer, camel, buffalo, and swine.

History and Distribution. Rinderpest of cattle has been one of the most devastating of all diseases in certain areas of the world. It apparently had its origin in Asia, and with the migration of peoples and cattle during the middle ages, the disease was carried into Europe. In the 18th and 19th centuries it ravaged the cattle population of Europe, and great losses from the disease were reported. In the years 1711 to 1714, Holland lost nearly all its cattle. In 1865, rinderpest was reintroduced into Great Britain after 20 years' freedom from the disease, and within 2 years' time 500,000 cattle died. The disease spread to Africa in the 1890's and millions of cattle were destroyed. The institution of successful immunity procedures, in about 1900, and of strict quarantine measures brought the disease under control in most areas. The disease still is enzootic in many areas of Asia and Africa. European areas have been free of the disease since shortly after the end of World War I.

Rinderpest has been introduced into Brazil and Australia but it has been promptly eliminated. It has not occurred in the United States.

The virus of rinderpest was discovered in 1902 by Nicolle and Adil-Bey.

Properties of the Virus. Rinderpest virus will pass Berkefeld V and the coarser grades of Chamberland filters. However, filtration is difficult since much of the virus is apparently absorbed into the filter.

Heating of the virus to 60°C. quickly destroys it. The virus is fairly resistant to phenol. In 2 per cent concentration, phenol fails to kill in 5 days, but if glycerin is added to the mixture, the virus is destroyed in 48 hours. One per cent phenol does not destroy the virus in 21 days and in 0.5 per cent concentration the virus may live at least 271 days. *Tortor bovis* is killed by formalin and by chloroform. The virus apparently does not survive long in nature after it leaves the host. It is quickly destroyed by putrefaction.

Cultivation. Rinderpest virus has been adapted to grow on the chorio-allantoic membrane of chicken embryos. No specific lesions are produced though some deaths occur.

The virus can also be grown in the yolk sac of 6- to 7-day-old embryos, if the virus is first adapted to eggs by chorio-allantoic passage.

Transmission. Rinderpest is usually transmitted through the medium of food and water which are contaminated with eye and nasal secretions, urine or feces of sick animals. The urine contains large amounts of the virus. The virus may be disseminated in meat products from infected animals.

Characteristics of the Disease. Rinderpest is an acute, highly fatal disease of cattle. It is also a disease of sheep, goats, buffalo, and other ruminants and swine, but infection of these animals is less severe and occurs less frequently than in cattle.

A sharp rise in temperature precedes the appearance of other symptoms by a day or two. The symptoms are usually marked depression, stupor, loss of appetite, emaciation, conjunctivitis, muco-purulent nasal discharge, and diarrhea. Mucous membranes are hyperemic and show necrotic areas.

The course of the disease runs from 4 to 8 days, with occasional cases running a prolonged course. Mortality rates are usually high, up to 90 per cent, but some animals recover.

Pathological Changes. The most pronounced change occurs in the mucous membranes throughout the body. There is general congestion, hemorrhages, and areas of erosion and ulceration. Ulcers of the abomasum and in the mouth are characteristic.

Immunity. Immunity to rinderpest has been studied for many years and many immunizing agents have been tried.

Recovered animals are usually immune to second attacks.

Active immunity was first produced by the injection of immune serum and the virus simultaneously. Although this method was successful, it was later abandoned because of the high cost of serum, because the use of live virus spread the infection to new areas, and because of the losses which occurred from protozoan diseases spread by injecting virus blood which was frequently contaminated with protozoa.

Chemically killed vaccines have been used with success. Boynton's tissue vaccine is prepared by the addition of phenol and glycerin to lymphoid tissues of cattle which have been inoculated with the virus. The mixture is heated to 42°C. and held for 3 hours to accomplish attenuation. The final concentration of phenol is 0.5 per cent.

Chloroform-inactivated vaccine prepared according to Kelser's method has been useful in producing active immunity. Cattle which have been inoculated with virulent rinderpest virus are sacrificed during the acute stages of the disease and the lymphoid tissues removed and finely ground. Chloroform is added to the tissue emulsion to make 0.75 per cent concentration. After 48 hours the vaccine is ready to use.

Formalin-treated vaccine has been useful in some areas, especially in Africa.

A number of specially adapted live vaccines are used for immunization against rinderpest. Desiccated goat spleen given in graded doses is effective as long as the virus in it remains alive.

Lapinized and avianized rinderpest vaccines were a result of adaptation of the virus to rabbits and to chicken embryos by Shope, Griffiths, and Jenkins of the American-Canadian Commission working at Gross Isle during World War II. These vaccines have been used and proved successful.

Diagnosis. In localities where the disease is known to exist, rinderpest is diagnosed largely upon the clinical and post-mortem manifestations.

Accurate diagnosis depends upon transmission of the disease to susceptible animals and specific protection of similar animals by rinderpest vaccine.

Tortor equorum

Common Name. African horse-sickness virus.

Disease Produced. African horse sickness.

Hosts Affected. Horse. Mules are somewhat resistant. Mice, rats, and guinea pigs can be infected by intracerebral inoculation. Dogs and goats can be infected.

History and Distribution. African horse sickness causes serious losses in horses and mules in Africa. It has been known for several centuries in that region. The virus which is the etiological agent in the disease was first described by M'Fadyean in 1900. The disease does not ordinarily occur except in southern Africa. However, it has been known in Egypt, and in 1944 it was identified in horses in Palestine.

Properties of the Virus. Polson has studied the virus of horse sickness and described it as spherical in shape and measuring 46 mμ in diameter. It is filterable through Berkefeld, Seitz EK, and Chamberland filters.

The virus is destroyed by a temperature of 70°C. for 5 minutes or 50°C. for 10 minutes. Slow drying at room temperature also is destructive, but rapid drying at low temperatures has no effect on viablity.

Plurality of the virus has been established and must be considered in immunity production. Eight strains have been identified.

Cultivation. *Tortor equorum* has been adapted to guinea pigs and mice by intracerebral passage. Such neurotropic strains have been cultivated in chicken embryos. Neurotropic tendencies of the virus are retained in the embryo since nearly all of the multiplication takes place in the brain of the embryo. No deaths or specific lesions are noted in the infected embryo.

Transmission. African horse sickness is not spread by contact. It is readily transmissible by injection of blood or nasal discharges from an infected animal. Insect vectors have long been suspected, since the occurrence of the disease coincides with the coming of the summer season, and it promptly disappears after the first frost. Mosquitoes trapped in the wild state have been shown to harbor the virus, and a few successful transmissions by artificially fed mosquitoes have been reported.

Characteristics of the Disease. African horse sickness is an acute or subacute febrile disease, which is classified as one of four forms. The pulmonary form begins with temperature increase to 105° to 106°F., depression, dyspnea, profuse sweating, and a large amount of serous discharge from the nose. The cardiac form is the subacute type with edema of the subcutaneous tissues about the head and neck. Sometimes a combined attack of the pulmonary and cardiac forms occurs. In others the disease is mild with only a short period of fever and recovery. Death rates and complications are higher in the pulmonary type of the disease. In some outbreaks mortality may be 90 to 95 per cent while in others it may be only 25 per cent.

Pathological Changes. The most common changes in horse sickness are severe pulmonary edema, subcutaneous edema, and cardiac hemorrhage.

Immunity. Animals which have recovered from the disease are immune to the homologous strain but may contract the disease as a result of exposure to a strain of different antigenic type. Foals receive passive immunity to the homologous virus through colostrum from immune mares.

A number of immunization procedures have been used.

Serum-virus method of active immunization has been used but has been discarded in favor of other methods.

Killed vaccines produced by heat inactivation or formalin-treated have been tried.

Live vaccine attenuated by intracerebral inoculation of mice and guinea pigs has been used. Mice are ordinarily used for this purpose and a polyvalent vaccine is produced. This neurovaccine is reported safe and effective.

Diagnosis. A diagnosis of African horse sickness is made upon clinical symptoms, lesions, and the absence of other agents such as *B. anthracis* or protozoan parasites. In cases suspected in areas where the disease has been identified previously, isolation of the virus by transmission to other horses and identification by protection tests are necessary.

Tortor equae

Synonym. *Tarpeia caballi.*

Common Names. Equine influenza virus. Mare abortion virus.

Disease Produced. Equine influenza, "Shipping fever." Abortion.

Hosts Affected. Horse. Experimentally, newborn hamster and chicken embryo.

History and Distribution. Equine influenza has been recognized as a disease for several centuries. At times it has been confused with other diseases, such as strangles in years past. The disease was proven to be transmissible by Diekerhoff, in 1882, by transferring blood from one horse to another. Poels in 1908 reproduced the disease by intravenous injection of semen filtrate from a stallion. Filtration experiments by Basset in 1911 confirmed the existence of the virus.

Equine influenza is widespread, occurring especially in horses which are shipped and concentrated at sales, shows, or for military purposes.

Dimock and Edwards in 1922 suggested that equine abortions could be caused by a virus since no bacteria could be cultured from some aborted fetuses. In 1933 they succeeded in transmitting the infection by injecting filtered material from abortions. Virus abortion in mares has been reported in several states of the United States but more of the cases have occurred in Kentucky. Reports of equine abortion have also appeared in literature from South Africa and Central Europe.

Until 1949 the virus of equine abortion was thought to be a

distinct virus. However, Manninger in that year presented evidence to show that the mare abortion virus and equine influenza virus were the same. In 1954 Doll, Wallace, and Richards, also Doll and Kintner confirmed the findings of Manninger and concluded that the two viruses were either identical or very similar.

Properties of the Virus. *Tortor equae* will pass through Berkefeld V and N candles. The virus is not resistant to heat or disinfection. Infectivity is reduced by fluctuations in pH of diluents or temperature. It is preserved at —70°C. for at least 31 months. In dried splenic tissue it is infective after 29 days at 4°C., 119 days at room temperature, and 457 days at —18°C.

There is no antigenic relationship between the equine and human and swine influenza viruses.

Cultivation. Artificial cultivation of equine influenza virus is possible in suckling hamsters. The virus can also be propagated in the chorio-allantoic membrane of the chicken embryo if first adapted to the hamster.

Transmission. The virus of equine influenza occurs regularly in the blood and nasal discharges during the disease. In some cases, the virus has been detected in the semen of stallions as long as six years after an attack of influenza. Food and water which are contaminated with nasal discharges may transmit the infection. Artificial installations of the virus into the nasal cavities result in infection and so droplet transmission possibly occurs. There are proven cases of transmission from stallion to mares during breeding.

Predisposing factors such as fatigue and excitement of shipping are important in initiating attacks.

Characteristics of the Disease. The incubation period in equine influenza ranges from 4 to 11 days but is usually 5 to 6 days. The disease is acute, with high temperature, loss of appetite, depression, increased respiratory and pulse rate, and nasal discharge. Not infrequently there is edema of the legs or of the subcutis. Tendonitis and tendovaginitis may occur. The mucous membrane of the eye may become icteric and often shows marked hyperemia. Secondary bacterial infection may occur with either *Past. multocida* or hemolytic streptococci. Most of the therapy of equine influenza is directed toward these secondary bacteria. In adult animals recovery usually results in a week or ten days if there are no complications. In young animals the disease is more severe, with some death losses. Purpura hemorrhagica may follow an attack of influenza.

Abortion in mares is sometimes preceded by an attack of influenza. Experimentally, infected mares show mild influenza followed by abortion in 28 to 33 days.

Pathological Changes. Most of the lesions of equine influenza are found in the respiratory tract. The mucosa of the upper respiratory tract is congested, covered by excessive mucus, and may show petechial hemorrhages. The lung tissue becomes edematous, and some areas show consolidation. Adjacent lymph nodes are edematous and hyperemic.

Aborted fetuses show gross changes of liver necrosis and hemorrhages on the heart and in the lungs. Microscopically, acidophilic intranuclear inclusion bodies can be demonstrated in the hepatic cells and epithelium of the bronchi.

Immunity. Horses which have recovered from influenza are resistant to reinfection.

Artificial immunization has been successful on an experimental basis by injecting spleen suspensions containing a strain of equine influenza virus of low virulence into colts, but commercial vaccine is not available.

Neutralization of the virus by immune serum can be demonstrated. Complement-fixing antibodies are formed as a result of infection. Mares which have aborted are resistant to respiratory inoculation and to abortion although some have aborted a second time several years after the first.

Diagnosis. A diagnosis of equine influenza is usually made on clinical observations. The diagnosis of virus abortion is made on the finding of the intranuclear inclusions in the liver cells of the aborted fetus and the absence of the bacterial causes of equine abortion.

Tortor ovis

Common Name. Blue tongue virus.

Disease Produced. Blue tongue, pseudo foot-and-mouth disease.

Hosts Affected. Sheep and cattle. Experimentally suckling mice and hamsters, also chicken embryos.

History and Distribution. Blue tongue of sheep has been known in South Africa since 1876 and probably for some years before. The virus was discovered in 1905 by Theiler. The disease is most prevalent during wet years and during the summer months. Until 1932 it was thought that under natural conditions blue tongue occurred only in sheep, but Bekker, De Kock, and Quinlan reported its occurrence in cattle over a wide area of South Africa. Blue tongue has also been reported in East Africa, the island of Cyprus, Syria, Turkey, Israel, and in southwestern and western United States.

Properties of the Virus. The elementary bodies of *Tortor ovis* are reported as being approximately 100 mμ in size. The virus is quite resistant to aging. Blood which contains the virus will remain infective for at least two years when kept at room temperature, and Neitz has reported it viable after 25 years.

Cultivation. Blue tongue virus has been adapted to grow in chicken embryos. McKercher reports that the blue tongue virus adapts more readily to the chicken embryo if chorio-allantoic inoculation is used. However, satisfactory growth has been obtained by the yolk sac route. After inoculation the eggs are incubated at 35°C. for 24 hours and then at 32°C. A majority of the embryos will die in 3 to 4 days. The virus is difficult to adapt to embryos, however, and it was only after eggs from riboflavin-deficient hens were used that adaptation was successful. After adaptation is accomplished, eggs from normal hens can be used.

Transmission. Blue tongue is not spread by contact. Susceptible sheep which drink from the same trough as infected ones do not contract the disease. Drenching a susceptible sheep with virulent blood does not transmit it. Field observations as long ago as 1905 suggested insect transmission. Several species of mosquitoes are thought to be capable of transmitting the infection, and mosquitoes trapped in nature have been shown to contain the virus. However, in Africa and the United States species of the genus *Culicoides* are considered the most common vectors. The fact that some sheep and cattle and also the wild blesbuck may carry the virus without showing symptoms presents a problem. Cattle have been shown to retain the virus in their blood for at least 22 days after inoculation and sheep for 60 days. Goats also may harbor the virus for some time following inoculation.

Characteristics of the Disease. Blue tongue of sheep begins with a temperature rise 2 to 4 days after exposure. Some animals show only the temperature increase and then quickly recover. Others will develop the typical disease. Symptoms include sore mouth and reluctance to eat, swelling and cyanosis of the tongue, lips, and gums, eye and nasal discharge, diarrhea, and loss of weight. Lameness is observed, caused by swelling and tenderness about the coronary area. Mortality rates may reach 30 per cent among infected sheep.

The symptoms in cattle are similar to those of sheep. Depression, salivation, chewing movements of the mouth, and rapid loss of weight predominate. Nasal discharge with erosion around the nostrils with dried encrustations are observed. In some cases hyperkeratosis of the skin areas about the neck, shoulders, and tail is observed. Swelling and inflammation of the coronary area of the feet and the teats of the udder are noted, but Mason and Neitz were unable to reproduce these lesions by experimental inoculation of cattle. Death may occur in some severely infected cases but most cattle recover.

Pathological Changes. The principal lesions of blue tongue are found in the mouth and tongue. They are characterized by hyperemia of the mucous membranes followed by loss of epithelium. Ulcers appear on the inside of the lips, dental pad, and tongue. The tongue may lose most of its epithelium and becomes blue and occasionally gangrenous. The mucous membranes of the gastro-intestinal tract may be hyperemic, edematous, with occasional small hemorrhages.

Immunity. Early investigations of blue tongue showed that immunity resulted from a recovery from a natural case of the disease.

Serum-virus injections were the first means of immunization. Serum alone was found to be of some value as a therapeutic agent. Live virus which was attenuated by several passages through sheep was used successfully for many years. Occasional animals will suffer mild reactions to the injection of the vaccine and these reactions are more severe in animals exposed to intense sunlight. Immunity induced by the vaccine is not effective for more than a season, and annual or semi-annual vaccination is recommended.

Modification of the blue tongue virus by serial passage in chicken embryos has made possible a live virus vaccine. In Africa a quadrivalent vaccine is used extensively, while in the United States only one antigenic type apparently exists and so a monovalent vaccine is used. Schultz and DeLay have reported losses in newborn lambs in instances where the chicken embryo vaccine was used to vaccinate pregnant ewes. The fetal lamb is most susceptible at 5 to 6 weeks' gestation.

Diagnosis. A diagnosis of blue tongue depends upon isolation and identification of the virus by transmission to susceptible sheep and protection tests in immunized sheep. Blue tongue is sometimes confused with foot-and-mouth disease or rinderpest. However, both of these diseases spread rapidly by contact while blue tongue does not.

Tortor felis

Common Name. Panleucopenia, feline agranulocytosis, feline enteritis virus.

Disease Produced. Panleucopenia, agranulocytosis, infectious enteritis of mink.

Hosts Affected. Domestic cat, mink, and raccoon. The guinea pig, ferret, rabbit, and mouse are insusceptible.

History and Distribution. Lawrence and Syverton, in 1938, described a disease of cats characterized by leucopenia and also a virus as its etiological agent. Others in this country have described epizootics of panleucopenia in cats. Kikuth *et al.* report an identical disease in Germany. Some writers regard panleuco- penia (*Tortor felis*) and cat distemper (*Tarpeia felis*) as the same disease. Failure of Hindle and Findlay to find any significant blood changes in distemper cats and the marked fibrinous enteritis described by Leasure leaves some doubt as to the identity of these two conditions of cats. Until careful comparisons are made they should be regarded as different diseases.

Wills has shown that the etiological agent of infectious enter- itis of mink appears to be identical to the panleucopenia virus of cats.

Properties of the Virus. *Tortor felis* passes all grades of the Berkefeld type filter as well as Seitz EK Pads. Its size has been estimated to be 35 mμ or less.

The virus can be preserved for 138 days in 50 per cent glycer- in and also by desiccation at −80°C.

Cultivation. The virus of panleucopenia has not been culti- vated except in susceptible cats. Limited attempts to cultivate it on the chorio-allantoic membrane of chicken embryos have been unsuccessful.

Transmission. The disease is highly contagious and is prob- ably spread by respiratory droplets and contaminated food. The virus is present in blood, nasal secretions, feces, and irregularly in the urine of infected cats.

Characteristics of the Disease. After a period of 5 to 6 days of incubation, infected animals becomes listless, refuse food, and may show vomition, diarrhea, nasal and eye discharge. Tempera- ture increase is usually noted but not marked. Death occurs in 50 to 90 per cent of those cats infected. Some animals recover after a mild illness of 2 to 4 days.

Pathological Changes. Most pronounced changes occur in the blood picture. Leucopenia, especially neutropenia, is characteristic. Leucocyte counts of the circulating blood drop sharply from 10,000 to 13,000 down to as low as 1,000 or less in 3 to 4 days.

Bone marrow changes are marked by a change from a fairly firm red marrow to a nearly fluid, hemorrhagic type. Intranuclear inclusion bodies in the epithelial cells of the mucosa of the intes- tinal tract can be found in a majority of cases.

Immunity. Cats which recover from panleucopenia are immune.

Immune serum is commercially available for prophylactic and therapeutic uses. This serum is effective in many cases if given 3 days before symptoms begin, but if given later it is less effective.

Formalinized tissue vaccine is available for the active immunization of cats against the disease. Two doses given 7 to 10 days apart are recommended.

Diagnosis. The diagnosis of panleucopenia of cats is usually based on leucocyte counts associated with clinical features of the disease.

The panleucopenia virus has not been specifically differentiated from *Tarpeia felis*, the cat distemper virus described in Great Britain.

Tortor galli

Common Name. Fowl pest virus, fowl plague virus.

Disease Produced. Fowl pest, fowl plague.

Hosts Affected. Chickens and turkeys are most commonly infected. Water fowl such as ducks and geese are susceptible, as are guinea fowl, sparrows, owls, blackbirds, canaries, and pigeons. Some mammals can be experimentally infected. These include mice, rats, rabbits, ferrets, monkeys, and hedgehogs.

History and Distribution. Fowl pest was first recognized in Italy in 1878. The virus was described by Centanni in 1901 and 1902 in reports on the disease and on experiments which proved that the etiological agent would pass Chamberland filters.

Fowl pest has spread world-wide, occurring in many countries at some time during the last 50 years. The disease made its first appearance in the United States in 1924–25 and again in 1929. It was first recognized in New York, New Jersey, and Pennsylvania, and spread westward to Michigan, Illinois, and Indiana. The disease was brought under control in all instances by eradication methods, and no occurrences have been recorded since 1929.

Fowl pest remains enzootic in countries of Europe, in the Mediterranean and Danube areas, and also in many areas of Asia.

Properties of the Virus. The elementary bodies of *Tortor galli* may be round or filamentous in shape and are reported to vary between 60 and 140 mμ in size, the average particle being about 101 mμ in diameter. They will pass through Berkefeld, Chamberland, and Seitz filters.

Thermal inactivation of the virus occurs at 60°C. in 5 minutes but at 55°C. it remains viable after 15 minutes exposure.

The virus is preserved at -70°C. for at least 242 days. Infectivity is lost at storage temperatures of 6°C. and 37°C. within 85 and 92 days respectively. One per cent phenol or 0.02 per cent merthiolate does not kill the virus in 1 hour. Five per cent phenol is lethal in 10 minutes' exposure. Formalin, 0.1 per cent, inactivates the virus in 18 to 24 hours and 0.2 and 0.4 per cent concentrations within 6 hours.

Exposure to 10,000 Oxford units of penicillin for 1 hour is without effect.

Fowl pest virus will produce hemagglutination of erythrocytes of the following animals: chicken, chicken embryo, turkey, duck, man, dog, cat, rabbit, swine, horse, ox, sheep, guinea pig, and monkey. The cells of the rabbit and swine are least satisfactory. Hemagglutination is specifically inhibited by immune sera.

Variant strains have been described on the basis of antigenicity and virulence. No antigenic relationship to Newcastle or other viruses has been proved.

Cultivation. *Tortor galli* can be readily grown in chicken embryos by the usual methods of inoculation. The virus multiplies very rapidly and high concentrations are present in the fluids and tissue of the embryo. The virus is uniformly lethal to the embryo within 24 to 48 hours. Hemorrhage is the most common lesion observed in the dead embryo.

Transmission. Fowl pest is usually transmitted by contact with infected birds. The virus is present in eye and nasal secretions as well as in blood, urine, and feces. Contaminated food and water are common sources of the virus. Insect vectors have been suspected of transmission in some cases. Immune carriers also play a part in the dissemination of fowl pest. Wild birds such as owls, sparrows, and blackbirds may spread the virus.

Characteristics of the Disease. Fowl pest is an acute infection with sudden onset. Some birds may die before definite symptoms are noted. A majority of the infected birds will show depression, anorexia, loss of egg production, diarrhea, ruffled feathers, and an unsteady gait. The comb and wattles become cyanotic. Edema of the head region and gasping and coughing are common. Nervous symptoms are sometimes observed, especially in the less susceptible species of birds. Mortality rates in chickens are very high and deaths occur in 24 to 48 hours after onset of the disease.

Pathological Changes. A post-mortem examination of birds dying of fowl pest will show lesions of a septicemia. Petechial hemorrhages may be found in organs such as the lungs, heart, proventriculus intestines, and in the fat around the gizzard and in the mesentery. Subcutaneous edema of the head region is usually observed.

Immunity. The few birds that recover from fowl pest are immune.

Serum-neutralizing and hemagglutination-inhibiting antibodies are readily demonstrated in immune birds. Several methods of active immunization have been studied. Live virus and immune serum injected simultaneously confer immunity, but the method is not considered practical because of the expense and the losses of birds following the inoculation.

Killed vaccines of various kinds have been of limited value. Formalinized virus confers some protection against the disease but it is not highly effective. Other vaccines which have been heat killed, ultra-violet killed or chemically killed have been even less successful.

Living virus vaccine produced from a variant of a Dutch East Indies strain of fowl pest virus has been studied by Moses, Brandly, Jones, and Jungherr. Under experimental conditions, this virus appeared to produce satisfactory resistance to challenge with highly virulent virus.

Diagnosis. A diagnosis of fowl pest requires isolation and identification of the virus. Chicken embryo inoculation with blood and tissue material will isolate the virus. The addition of suitable antibiotics such as penicillin and streptomycin to the inoculum is desirable if not always required. If fowl pest virus is present in the inoculum it should produce death of the embryos in 24 to 48 hours. Hemagglutination tests of allantoic fluid should be positive if fowl pest is present. However, Newcastle disease virus may be isolated from birds showing similar symptoms and under the same conditions of isolation. Since both fowl pest and Newcastle viruses will produce hemagglutination, it is necessary to differentiate them by serum neutralization and hemagglutination-inhibition tests using known immune sera.

It is also necessary to eliminate bacteria as a cause of rapid deaths among fowl, since fowl pest and fowl cholera are sometimes confused clinically.

Tortor furens

Common Name. Newcastle disease virus.

Disease Produced. Newcastle disease, avian pneumoencephalitis.

Hosts Affected. Chickens chiefly, also turkeys, pheasants, quail, pigeons, parakeets, doves, ducks, geese, sparrows, starlings, and chukar partridge are susceptible. The virus has been reported to attack some mammals such as man and experimentally has been transferred to hamsters, sheep, swine, monkeys, and mice.

History and Distribution. The close clinical similarity between Newcastle disease and fowl pest probably prevented the recognition of Newcastle disease as a separate entity for several years. It was recognized in the Dutch East Indies and in England almost simultaneously, but Doyle in 1927 was the first to identify the disease, and to describe the virus as it occurred on a farm near Newcastle,

England. Since the first description, Newcastle disease has been recognized in many countries including the United States, Canada, South Africa, China, Japan, most European countries, the Philippine Islands, Australia, and throughout the East Indies.

Newcastle disease was first reported by Beach in 1940 in California. Beach further proved the relationship of the virus isolated from the California outbreak to Newcastle virus isolated in England. Since 1940, Newcastle disease has spread widely over the United States and each year accounts for considerable losses in poultry.

Properties of the Virus. The morphology of Newcastle virus may vary, depending upon the conditions of preparation and perhaps also with the strain used. Bang, also Cunha *et al.,* using American strains, show definite pleomorphism. Spherical as well as sperm-shaped particles are observed in electron micrographs (Fig. 40.1C). The sperm-like particles measure about 70 x 180 mμ for the head piece and the tail part up to 500 mμ in length. Dawson and Elford photographed an English strain of the virus and found the particle size to vary between 140 and 270 mμ with the average about 193 mμ. These workers did not observe any sperm-like forms; however, their preparations were not made in the same manner as were those made by Bang. The virus will pass Berkefeld V and N candles as well as Chamberland L₃ and Seitz filters. *Tortor furens* is more resistant to heat than many other viruses. A majority of strains resist 56°C. for 30 minutes, and occasional strains have been found viable after 180 minutes.

The Newcastle virus has been found by Moses, Brandly, and Jones to be quite stable to comparatively wide pH ranges. After 1 hour's exposure at pH values of 2 to 12, the virus was unaffected. This is contrasted with the fowl pest virus which was found to remain viable only within the range of pH 6 to 11.

The following chemicals are reported to kill the virus in 3 minutes: ethyl alcohol 70 and 95 per cent, phenol 3 per cent, cresol 3 per cent, and tincture of iodine 1 per cent. Sodium hydroxide in 2 per cent concentration is reported as effective by some investigators but not by others.

Fumigation with formaldehyde at 100 per cent humidity destroys the virus under incubator conditions and triethylene glycol is effective in destroying it in the air.

The virus will remain viable in embryo fluids stored at 5°C. for at least a year and for longer periods at —70°C. It has remained alive in fecal material for 5½ months kept at 40°F.

Newcastle virus will remain alive in the carcasses of slaughtered birds for 300 days when held at —4°F. When dried on various materials and held at room temperature, the virus lives

30 days, and if temperatures are lowered to freezing, it remains alive for as long as a year.

Penicillin and streptomycin are without effect on *Tortor furens.*

A hemolysin which is capable of lysing chicken erythrocytes has been described by Kilham. The amount of hemolysin activity of the virus is found to parallel its concentration.

An important property of the Newcastle disease virus is that of hemagglutination. Avian, usually chicken, erythrocytes are commonly used for hemagglutinating work, although turkey and other avian species can be used. Certain mammalian erythrocytes are also agglutinated by the virus. In this case, hemagglutination is variable depending on the strain of virus tested and the individual animal used. Man, guinea pig, and mouse erythrocytes are most satisfactory. Cow, bison, elk, horse, dog, goat, and sheep erythrocytes are quite irregular, while those of the fox are not agglutinated by the virus.

Hemagglutination by Newcastle virus is quantitative, and under standardized conditions the amount of virus present in a fluid can be determined. Furthermore, the hemagglutination reaction is inhibited by specific immune serum which is also quantitative. See Table 42.5.

Various strains of *Tortor furens* have been shown to vary in virulence, hemagglutinating activity against various mammalian erythrocytes, and heat stability of the hemagglutinating property. Asiatic and European strains of the virus are more virulent than the American ones. No significant antigenic difference among strains has been reported.

Cultivation. Newcastle virus is readily cultivated in chicken embryos. The conditions of growth of this virus are not critical. It can be grown by any route of inoculation, at a fairly wide range of temperatures of incubation, and requires no adaptation to the embryo. The usual method of inoculation is into the allantoic cavity. The virus is usually lethal to the embryo in 48 to 72 hours, and hemorrhages of the feather follicles, subcutaneous tissues, occipital region, yolk sac membrane, and general congestion of the embryo are common lesions.

The virus has been grown in tissue cultures composed of plasma and embryonic tissues in Tyrode's solution, and also in de-embryonated eggs.

Transmission. Under natural conditions Newcastle spreads rapidly by airborne droplets coughed or sneezed from the respiratory system. Beach has succeeded in isolating the virus from the air of a chicken house.

The virus may be introduced into a flock and also spread by means of contaminated food. Outbreaks of Newcastle disease in

England have been initiated by feeding the offal from dressed chickens imported from the Continent to other poultry.

Poultry culling and testing personnel who travel from farm to farm may transfer the virus on clothing and equipment.

Newcastle virus has been recovered from eggs laid by hens during the early stages of the disease. However, the virus usually kills the embryo and so these eggs seldom hatch. Even though the eggs do not hatch they may spread the infection if they are accidentally broken in the incubator or if the shell of the egg is contaminated by the virus.

Attempts to isolate the virus from the eggs produced by recovered birds have been unsuccessful.

Carriers of Newcastle disease seldom are found but are believed to exist. Although the carrier rate is very low it still must be considered as a method of spread of the disease.

Characteristics of the Disease. Newcastle disease is an acute, highly contagious disease of chickens and occasionally of other fowl. It begins with sudden onset after an incubation period of about 5 days. The first symptoms noted are dullness, coughing, sneezing, and gasping. In laying flocks, egg production drops sharply in two or three days' time. The infection spreads rapidly to all susceptible contact birds. Nervous symptoms occur in some birds, especially young ones, within a few days after onset of the disease. Paralysis of the legs or wings or often torticollis resulting in a complete twisting of the neck is observed. Morbidity rates are usually near 100 per cent and mortality rates are variable, ranging from 5 to 50 per cent. Death losses are ordinarily higher in baby chicks than in adult or young adult birds.

In European and Asiatic countries the mortality rates are much higher than those in the United States, 70 to 100 per cent, and there is more tendency for the virus to produce lesions of a generalized nature in outbreaks which occur in those countries.

Several reports of Newcastle infection in man have been substantiated by the isolation of the virus. So far the conjunctiva is apparently the tissue most often involved. Although the disease is mild and usually localized, Quin *et al.* have reported evidence of generalized infection since Newcastle virus has been isolated from blood, saliva, and urine in some instances. Spontaneous recovery results in a few days.

Infection of other animals by Newcastle virus does not occur under natural conditions but has been produced by experimental inoculation. Intracerebral inoculation of hamsters, mice, monkeys, swine, and sheep has produced fatal infection. The virus has been adapted to hamsters and mice and has been passed in series in these animals until it produces a rapidly fatal disease.

The virus produces death in sheep and swine after intracerebral inoculation, but the virus can not always be recovered from the brain tissue, and serial passage has not been accomplished in these animals.

Pathological Changes. The most marked pathological changes occur in the respiratory system. There is hyperemia and congestion throughout, with much mucus in the trachea. In European and Asiatic outbreaks the lesions are much more pronounced and in addition to the respiratory lesions, hemorrhages, especially of the lymph follicles of the intestinal tract, will be observed. Cloudiness of the air sac membranes is a usual finding, and petechial hemorrhages may be seen in the respiratory tract on the epicardium and in the digestive tract. Catarrhal enteritis is also observed.

The brain shows microscopic cellular infiltration of lymphocytes and hemorrhage.

Immunity. Birds which recover from a natural case of Newcastle disease are solidly immune. HI and SN antibodies are demonstrable in the serums of recovered birds for several months after recovery. The eggs from recovered hens contain antibodies and can be demonstrated by the HI test as described by Schmittle and Millen. Chicks which are hatched from these eggs may show antibodies in their serum for a period of 3 or 4 weeks.

Active immunization to Newcastle disease is widely used. Both live and killed types are available and have their particular advantages and disadvantages.

Killed vaccines are made from infected tissues or embryo propagated virus. A variety of chemicals such as formalin or phenol, as well as physical methods, have been employed to kill the virus.

Killed vaccines have the advantage of being completely safe to use, but immunity is apparently not as effective or as lasting as is desirable unless 2 doses are given, spaced 2 to 3 months apart. Formalin-inactivated vaccine is in common use.

Live vaccines include avirulent strains and modified virus.

Two types of live virus vaccine are used, one more virulent than the other. The more virulent type is administered by application to the web of the wing. The other type is quite avirulent and may be administered intranasally or by mass inoculation methods such as aerosol, dusting with the dried virus, or in the drinking water. Immunity conferred by the wing-web vaccine is more durable than the intranasal type. Losses from the infection by the vaccine strain occur, especially in unthrifty flocks. Egg production is substantially lowered in laying flocks and the disease is perpetuated and in some cases introduced into new flocks through vaccination.

Combination of live Newcastle vaccine and other live vaccines such as fowl pox, laryngotracheitis or bronchitis has been tried.

Diagnosis. The most dependable diagnosis of Newcastle disease is the isolation and identification of the virus. The virus is abundant in the respiratory tissues during the initial stages of the disease. It is also present in the blood, spleen, brain, and liver during the early stages but is in less concentration than in the respiratory tract. Inoculation of chicken embryos with emulsions of pooled organs will isolate the virus. The addition of penicillin and streptomycin is necessary in most cases to prevent bacterial contamination of the embryos. Presumptive evidence of the presence of the virus can usually be obtained in about 48 hours by conducting a hemagglutination test on the allantoic fluid. In areas where fowl pest does not occur, a positive diagnosis of Newcastle disease is made on the basis of the isolation of a virus from poultry which produces hemagglutination.

Confirmatory tests for identification of Newcastle virus should include HI and SN tests, using known immune serum or protection tests with immune birds.

It is difficult to isolate the virus from the tissues of infected birds after antibodies are detectable in the serum. The virus is not often isolated from birds showing advanced nervous symptoms.

Serological evidence of the disease can be obtained by HI or SN tests upon serum of sick, convalescent, or recovered birds. However, such evidence must be carefully interpreted only after other findings and history are considered. The presence of antibodies in the serum may result from previous infection in older birds, vaccination, or passive egg transfer in chicks.

Newcastle disease may be confused with fowl pest, infectious bronchitis, or laryngotracheitis. See Table 52.1.

Tortor vulpis

Common Name. Fox encephalitis virus, canine hepatitis virus.

Disease Produced. Fox encephalitis, canine hepatitis.

Hosts Affected. Fox (silver and red), dog, and coyote. The raccoon, gray fox, and black bear are slightly susceptible by intraocular inoculation. Cats, ferrets, white rats, gray squirrels, mink, sheep, monkeys, and rabbits are insusceptible.

History and Distribution. An epizootic disease of the silver fox was reported by Green in 1925 in which there were symptoms of encephalitis. An organism of the genus *Salmonella* and later a streptococcus were suggested as causes of the disease. In 1930, Green described a filtrable virus as the etiological agent. Three years later Green reported the transmissibility of fox encephalitis to dogs and described focal liver necrosis and intranuclear inclusions, in various endothelial cells. Cowdry and Scott had reported, in 1930, inclusions in the hepatic cells of two dogs but no transmission experiments were tried. Rubarth of Sweden published an extensive study of canine hepatitis as found in that country and suggested that the viruses of fox encephalitis and canine hepatitis were the same. Siedentopf and Carlson have compared the viruses of these two diseases in this country and concluded that they are identical.

Canine hepatitis has also been recognized in Great Britain.

Properties of the Virus. *Tortor vulpis* will pass Berkefeld N and Seitz EK filters. It can be preserved in 50 per cent glycerin for several years and it retains its virulence under storage.

Cultivation. *Tortor vulpis* can be cultivated in tissue cultures composed of canine kidney cells. Cabasso *et al.* report that the virus produces a cytopathogenic effect when grown in tissue culture. Fieldsteel and Emery have shown that serial transfer of the virus loses its pathogenicity for the canine after 51 passages, but it retains its immunogenic properties.

Miles *et al.* have reported the successful cultivation of canine hepatitis virus in the chicken embryo.

Transmission. The virus is probably transmitted by discharges from the respiratory tract. Blood and nasal secretions are consistently infectious during the disease.

Characteristics of the Disease. *Tortor vulpis* infection in the fox is of sudden onset. Some foxes are found dead without having shown symptoms, since wild animals in general do not readily exhibit signs of sickness until disease is well advanced. Those animals which are noted sick may show loss of appetite, lethargy, weakness, and finally coma. Nervous symptoms include hyperexcitability, paralysis, convulsions, and muscular twitchings. Nasal discharge and diarrhea are frequently observed. Mortality rates are usually within 10 to 25 per cent.

The disease in dogs runs an acute, rapid, fatal course within a week. There is apathy, vomition, diarrhea, nasal and eye discharges which are often copious and become purulent. Nervous symptoms include spasms, excitability, and "running fits." Respiratory symptoms with acute tonsillitis have been described by Coffin.

Pathological Changes. A post mortem of animals dying of fox encephalitis may not show a definite pathological picture. There is general congestion of many tissues, and hemorrhages, especially in the brain, will be observed.

In the dog outstanding changes will be found in the liver,

which is grossly enlarged, with a lighter color and a distinct lobular design. Tissues of the nervous system show cellular infiltration. Acute tonsillitis is usually observed.

Green has described intranuclear inclusions which regularly appear in both dogs and foxes as well as other infected species. These inclusion bodies are found in the vascular endothelium, meningeal, and hepatic cells. Their demonstration is of value in diagnosis of the disease.

Immunity. Animals which recover from fox encephalitis or canine hepatitis are immune.

Siedentopf and Carlson report reciprocal neutralization of virus from cases of fox encephalitis and canine hepatitis by their respective antisera. There is no immunological relationship between *Tortor vulpis* and canine distemper. Hyperimmune serum is available and it is recommended for use both as a prophylactic and a therapeutic agent for fox encephalitis or canine hepatitis.

Simultaneous serum-virus vaccination has been attempted but many delayed cases of the disease followed this method.

Formalin-inactivated virus is widely used for the prevention of infectious canine hepatitis. This type of vaccine is produced from the tissues of dogs artificially infected with the virus.

Diagnosis. Since both foxes and dogs are susceptible to *Tortor vulpis* and to canine distemper, differential diagnosis is important. Ferrets are highly susceptible to canine distemper virus but are insusceptible to fox encephalitis-canine hepatitis virus. If ferrets are available, the inoculation of this animal is helpful in the differential diagnosis.

Green has pointed out that the inclusion bodies of canine distemper may be either intracytoplasmic or intranuclear, while those of fox encephalitis-canine hepatitis are only intranuclear. He further notes that distemper inclusions are not found in hepatic cells, but those of canine hepatitis and fox encephalitis are usually abundant in those cells.

REFERENCES FOR FURTHER STUDY

Tortor suis (Hog cholera)

Baker, J. A. Jour. Amer. Vet. Med. Assn., 111:503, 1947.
Birch, R. R. Hog Cholera. The Macmillan Co., New York, 1922.
Boynton, W. H. Jour. Amer. Vet. Med. Assn., 83:747, 1933.
————. Jour. Amer. Vet. Med. Assn., 87:650, 1935.
————, Takahashi, W. N., Woods, G. M., and Walker, W. W. Vet. Med., 43:403, 1948.
————, Woods, G. M., Wood, F. M., and Casselberry, N. H. Proc. U. S. Livestock San. Assn., 1941.
————, ————, ————. Vet. Med., 37:214, 1942.
Cole, C. G., Henley, R. R., and Hubbard, E. D. Jour. Amer. Vet. Med. Assn., 108:193, 1946.

Dale, C. N., Schoening, H. W., Henley, R. R., and Zinober, M. R. Jour. Amer. Vet. Med. Assn., 118:279, 1951.

De Kock, G., Robinson, E. M., and Keppel, J. J. G. Onderstepoort Jour. Vet. Sci., 14:31, 1940.

De Schweinitz, E. A., and Dorset, M. U.S.D.A. Cir. 41 (B.A.I.) 1903.

Dorset, M., Bolton, B. M., and McBryde, C. N. U.S.D.A. Cir. 72 (B.A.I.) 1905.

———, McBryde, C. N., and Niles, W. B. U.S.D.A. Cir. 102 (B.A.I.) 1908.

———, ———, ———, and Rietz, J. H. Jour. Agr. Res., 13:101, 1918.

Hutyra, F., Marek, J., and Manninger, R. Special Pathology and Therapeutics of the Diseases of Domestic Animals. Vol. 1, 5th ed. Alex. Eger Inc., Chicago, 1946.

Jacotot, H. Ann. Inst. Past., 62:516, 1939.

Kernkamp, H.C.H. Jour. Amer. Vet. Med. Assn., 74:844, 1929.

McArthur, C. L. Jour. Inf. Dis., 24:44, 1919.

McBryde, C. N., and Cole, C. G. Jour. Amer. Vet. Med. Assn., 89:652, 1936.

———, ———. Jour. Amer. Vet. Med. Assn., 98:454, 1941.

McIntosh, B. M. Jour. So. African Vet. Med. Assn., 23:217, 1952.

Montgomery, R. E. Jour. Comp. Path. Therap., 34:159, 1921.

Salmon, D. E. U.S.D.A. Cir. 43 (B.A.I.) 1904.

Sautter, J. H., Young, G. A., Luedke, A. J., and Kitchell, R. L. Proc. 90th Ann. Meeting, Amer. Vet. Med. Assn., p. 147, 1953.

Shope, R. E., and Lewis, P. A. Jour. Exp. Med. 50:719, 1929.

Ten Broeck, C. Jour. Exp. Med., 74:427, 1941.

Zichis, I. Jour. Amer. Vet. Med. Assn. 95:272, 1939.

Tortor bovis (Rinderpest)

Boynton, W. H. Philippine Jour. Sci., 36:1, 1928.

Daubney, R. Jour. Comp. Path. Therap., 41:228, 1928.

Hornby, H. E. Jour. Comp. Path. Therap., 41:17, 1928.

Hutyra, F., Marek, J., and Manninger, R. Special Pathology and Therapeutics of the Diseases of Domestic Animals. Vol. I. 5th ed. Alex. Eger Inc., Chicago, 1946.

Joint United States-Canadian Comm. and Chem. Warfare Service, U. S. Army. Amer. Jour. Vet. Res., 7:133, 1946.

Kelser, R. A. Philippine Jour. Sci., 36:373, 1928.

Nicolle, M., and Adil-Bey. Ann. Inst. Past., 16:56, 1902.

Weston, E. A. Jour. Amer. Vet. Med. Assn., 66:337, 1925.

Tortor equorum (African horse sickness)

Alexander, R. A., and Du Toit, P. J. Onderstepoort Jour. Vet. Sci., 2:375, 1934; 4:291, 323, 349, 379, 1935; 7:11, 1936; 11:9, 1938.

———, and Mason, J. H. Onderstepoort Jour. Vet. Sci., 16:19, 1941.

———, Neitz, W. O., and Du Toit, P. J. Onderstepoort Jour. Vet. Sci., 7:17, 1936.

Du Toit, P. J., Alexander, R. A., and Neitz, W. O. Onderstepoort Jour. Vet. Sci., 1:21, 25, 1933.

———. Onderstepoort Jour. Vet. Sci., 19:7, 1944.

Henning, M. W. Animal Diseases in South Africa. Central News Agency, Ltd., South Africa, 1932.

M'Fadyean, J. Jour. Comp. Path. Therap., 13:1, 1900.

———. Jour. Comp. Path. Therap., 23:315, 1910.

Nieschulz, O., and Du Toit, R. M. Onderstepoort Jour. Vet. Sci., 8:213, 1937.

Polson, A. Nature, 148:593, 1941.

Tortor equae (Equine influenza and abortion)

Basset, J. Comp. Rend. Acad. Sci., 153:485, 1911.

Dale, C. N., and Dollahite, J. W. Jour. Amer. Vet. Med. Assn., 95:534, 1939.

Diekerhoff, W. Die Pferdestaupe, Berlin, 1882.

Dimock, W. W. Jour. Amer. Vet. Med. Assn., 96:665, 1940.

———, and Edwards, P. R. Ky. Agr. Exp. Sta. Bull. Supp. 333, p. 297, 1933.

———, ———. Cornell Vet. 26:231, 1936.

———, ———, and Bruner, D. W. Ky. Agr. Exp. Sta. Bull. No. 426, 1942.

Doll, E. R., and Kintner, J. H. Cornell Vet., 44:355, 1954.

———, Richards, M. G., and Wallace, M. E. Cornell Vet., 44:133, 1954.

———, and Wallace, M. E. Cornell Vet., 44:453, 1954.

———, ———, and Richards, M. G. Cornell Vet., 44:181, 1954.

Goodpasture, E. W., and Anderson, K. Amer. Jour. Path., 18:563, 1942.

Henning, M. W. Onderstepoort Jour. Vet. Sci., 21:17, 1946.

Jones, T. C., and Maurer, F. D. Amer. Jour. Vet. Res., 3:179, 1942.

———, ———. Amer. Jour. Vet. Res., 4:15, 1943.

———, Gleiser, C. A., Maurer, F. D., Hale, M. W., and Roby, T. O. Amer. Jour. Vet. Res., 9:243, 1948.

Manninger, R. Acta Vet. Hungarica, 1:62, 1949. (In English.)

Maurer, F. D., and Jones, T. C. Amer. Jour. Vet. Res., 4:257, 1943.

Tortor ovis (Blue tongue of sheep and cattle)

Alexander, R. A., Haig, D. A., and Adelaar, T. F. Onderstepoort Jour. Vet. Sci., 21:231, 1947.

Bekker, J. G., De Kock, G. W., and Quinlan, J. B. Onderstepoort Jour. Vet. Sci., 2:393, 1934.

Cox, H. R. Bact. Rev., 18:239, 1954.

De Kock, G., Du Toit, R., and Neitz, W. O. Onderstepoort Jour. Vet. Sci., 8:129, 1937.

Hardy, W. T., and Price, D. A. Jour. Amer. Vet. Med. Assn., 120:23, 1952.

Henning, M. W. Animal Diseases in South Africa. Vol. II. Central News Agency, Ltd., South Africa, 1932.

Mason, J. H., and Neitz, W. O. Onderstepoort Jour. Vet. Sci., 15:159, 1940.

McKercher, D. G., McGowan, B., and Saito, J. K. Proc. 91st Ann. Meeting Amer. Vet. Med. Assn., p. 167, 1954.

Neitz, W. O. Onderstepoort Jour. Vet. Sci., 23:77, 1948.

Nieschulz, O., Bedford, G. A. H., and Du Toit, R. M. Onderstepoort Jour. Vet. Sci., 2:509, 1934.

Polson, A. Nature, 148:593, 1941.

Schultz, G., and DeLay, P. D. Jour. Amer. Vet. Med. Assn., 127:224, 1955.

Spreull, J. Jour. Comp. Path. Therap., 18:321, 1905.

Tortor felis (Panleucopenia of cats)

Bentnick-Smith, J. N. Amer. Vet., 30:379, 1949.

Hammon, W. D., and Enders, J. F. Jour. Exp. Med., 69:327, 1939.

———, ———. Jour. Exp. Med., 70:557, 1939.

Kirkuth, W., Gonnert, R., and Schweickert, M. Centralb. f. Bakt. Abt. I Orig., 146:1, 1940.

Lawrence, J. S., and Syverton, J. T. Proc. Soc. Exp. Biol. Med., 38:914, 1938

———, ———, Shaw, J. S., and Smith, F. P. Amer. Jour. Path. 16:333, 1940.

Leasure, E. E., Lienhardt, H. F., and Taberner, F. R. No. Amer. Vet., 15, No. 7, 30, 1934.

Lucas, A. M., and Riser, W. H. Amer. Jour. Path., 21:435, 1945.

Riser, W. H. No. Amer. Vet., 24:293, 1943.

Syverton, J. T., et al. Jour. Exp. Med., 77:41, 57, 1943.

Wills, C. G. Canad. Jour. Comp. Med., 16:419, 1952.

Tortor furens (Newcastle disease)

Bang, F. B. Proc. Soc. Exp. Biol. Med., 71:54, 1949.

Beach, J. R. Proc. U. S. Livestock San. Assn., 46:203, 1942.

———. Science, 100:361, 1944.

———. Jour. Amer. Vet. Med. Assn., 112:85, 1948.

———. Avian Pneumoencephalitis, *in* Diseases of Poultry. Edited by Biester, H. E., and Schwarte, L. H. 3rd ed. Iowa State College Press, Ames, 1952.

Beamer, P. D., Sutherland, A. K., and Schmittle, S. C. Amer. Jour. Vet. Res., 10:384, 1949.

———, and Prier, J. E. Cornell Vet., 40:56, 1950.

Beaudette, F. R. Proc. U. S. Livestock San. Assn., 47:122, 1944; 52:254, 1948; 53:202, 1949.

Brandly, C. A. Jour. Amer. Vet. Med. Assn., 116:139, 1950.

———, Moses, H. E., Jones, E. E., and Jungherr, E. L. Amer. Jour. Vet. Res., 7:250, 1946.

Cunha, R., Weil, M. L., Beard, D., Taylor, A. R., Sharp, D. G., and Beard, J. W. Jour. Immunol., 55:69, 1947.

Cunningham, C. H. Amer. Jour. Vet. Res., 9:195, 1948.

Dawson, I. M., and Elford, W. J. Jour. Gen. Microbiol., 3:298, 1949.

Doyle, T. M. Jour. Comp. Path. Therap., 40:144, 1927.

Freyman, M. W., and Bang, F. B. Johns Hopkins Hosp. Bull., 84:409, 1949.

Hofstad, M. S. Poul. Sci., 28:530, 1949.

———. Cornell Vet., 40:190, 1950.

Ingalls, W. L., and Mahoney, A. Amer. Jour. Pub. Hlth., 39:737, 1949.

Jungherr, E. L., Tyzzer, E. E., Brandly, C. A., and Moses, H. E. Amer. Jour. Vet. Res., 7:250, 1946.

Kilham, L. Proc. Soc. Exp. Biol. Med., 71:63, 1949.

Lush, D. Jour. Comp. Path. Therap., 53:157, 1943.

Moses, H. E., Brandly, C. A., and Jones, E. E. Science, 105:477, 1947.

Quinn, R. W., Hanson, R. P., Brown, J. W., and Brandly, C. A. Jour. Lab. Clin. Med., 40:1, 1952.

Schmittle, S. C., and Millen, T. W. Cornell Vet., 38:306, 1948.

Stover, D. E. Amer. Jour. Vet. Res., 3:207, 1942.

Van Roekel, H., Sperling, F. G., Bullis, K. L., and Olesiuk, O. M. Jour. Amer. Vet. Med. Assn., 112:131, 1948.

Winslow, N., Hanson, R. P., Upton, E., and Brandly, C. A. Proc. Soc. Exp. Biol. Med., 74:174, 1950.

Zargar, S. L., and Pomeroy, B. S. Amer. Jour. Vet. Res., 11:272, 1950.

Tortor vulpis (Fox encephalitis, canine hepatitis)

Cabasso, U. J., Stebbins, M. R., Norton, T. W., and Cox, H. R. Proc. Soc. Exp. Biol. Med., 85:239, 1954.

Coffin, D. L. Jour. Amer. Vet. Med. Assn., 112:355, 1948.

Cowdry, E. V., and Scott, G. H. Arch. Path., 9:1184, 1930.

Evans, C. A., Dowell, M., and Green, R. G. Jour. Inf. Dis., 86:1, 1950.

Fieldsteel, A. H., and Emery, J. B. Proc. Soc. Exp. Biol. Med., 86:819, 1954.

Green, R. G. Proc. Soc. Exp. Biol. Med., 22:546, 1925.

———. Amer. Jour. Hyg., 13:201, 1931.

———. Jour. Amer. Vet. Med. Assn., 99:45, 1941.

———, and Evans, C. E. Amer. Jour. Hyg. 29(B):73, 1939.

———, Katter, M. S., Shillinger, J. E., and Hanson, K. B. Amer. Jour. Hyg., 18:462, 1933.

———, and Shillinger, J. E. Amer. Jour. Hyg., 19:362, 1934.

———, Ziegler, B. B., and Dewey, E. T. Amer. Jour. Hyg., 12:109, 1930.

Green, R. G., Ziegler, N. R., Carlson, W. E., Shillinger, J. E., Tyler, S. H., and Dewey, E. T. Amer. Jour. Hyg., 19:343, 1934.

————, ————, Green, B. B., Shillinger, J. E., Dewey, E. T., and Carlson, W. E. Amer. Jour. Hyg., 21:366, 1935.

————, Green, B. B., Carlson, W. E., and Shillinger, J. E. Amer. Jour. Hyg., 24:57, 1936.

Innes, J. R. M. Vet. Rec., 61:173, 1949.

Miles, J. A. R., Parry, H. B., Larin, N. M., and Platt, H. Nature, 168:699, 1951.

Riser, W. H. No. Amer. Vet., 49:568, 1948.

Rubarth, S. Acta Path. et Microbiol. Scand. Suppl. No. 69, 1947. (In English.)

Siedentopf, H. A., and Carlson, W. E. Jour. Amer. Vet. Med. Assn., 115: 109, 1949.

Tortor galli (Fowl pest)

Burnett, F. M., and Ferry, J. D. Brit. Jour. Exp. Path., 15:56, 1934.

Centanni, E. Centralb. f. Bakt. Abt. I. Orig., 31:182, 1902.

————, and Savonuggi, E. La Clin. Vet., 24:292, 1901.

Elford, W. J., Chu, C. M., Dudgeon, J. A., Fulton, F., and Smiles, J. Brit. Jour. Exp. Path., 29:590, 1948.

Gerlach, F. Geflugepest, *in* Handbuch der Pathogenen Mickroorganismen. Kolle, W., and Wasserman, A. Vol. 9. 1929.

Hutyra, F., Marek, J., and Manninger, R. Special Pathology and Therapeutics of the Diseases of Domestic Animals. Alex. Eger Inc., Chicago, 1946.

Johnson, S. R. Jour. Amer. Vet. Med. Assn., 67:195, 1925.

Julein, R. C. Jour. Amer. Vet. Med. Assn, 67:168, 1925.

Jungherr, E. L., Tyzzer, E. E., Brandly, C. A., and Moses, H. E. Amer. Jour. Vet. Res., 7:250, 1946.

Lush, D. Jour. Comp. Path. Therap., 53:157, 1943.

Mohler, J. R. Jour. Amer. Vet. Med. Assn., 68:549, 1926.

Moses, H. E., Brandly, C. A., Jones, E., and Jungherr, E. L. Amer. Jour. Vet. Res., 9:314, 421, 1948.

Stubbs, E. L. Jour. Amer. Vet. Med. Assn., 67:180, 1925.

————. Jour. Amer. Vet. Med. Assn., 68:650, 1926.

————. Fowl Plague, *in* Diseases of Poultry. 3rd ed. Edited by Biester, H. E., and Schwarte, L. H. Iowa State College Press, Ames, 1952.

54.

The Genus Trifur—
the Infectious Anemia Group

Viruses of the genus *Trifur* induce disease characterized by disturbances in balance of blood cells. The genus name, *Trifur*, is from the Latin, meaning an arrant thief.

Trifur equorum

Common Name. Equine infectious anemia virus.

Disease Produced. Equine infectious anemia, "swamp fever."

Hosts Affected. Horse, mule, donkey, and, rarely, man. Experimentally, the guinea pig and rabbit can be infected but show only mild reactions.

History and Distribution. Equine infectious anemia has been recognized in Europe for a little over 100 years and for at least 50 years in the United States. It has been recognized in at least 34 states and in Canada. The disease has spread widely throughout Europe and also occurs in Africa and Japan.

The infectious nature of the disease was recognized for many years before Carré and Vallée reported that the etiological agent was a filtrable virus in 1904.

Properties of the Virus. The elementary bodies of *Trifur equorum* are reported by Reagan *et al.* as rounded particles and measure from 11 to 59 mμ with the average being 30 mμ in diameter.

Using filtration methods, Mohlmann and Gralheer have determined the size of the virus as 60 to 95 mμ in diameter. The virus will pass the Chamberland and Berkefeld V filters.

Equine anemia virus is comparatively resistant. A temperature of 58°C. for one hour is necessary to inactivate it. An exposure of 30 days in 0.5 per cent phenol will inactivate the virus, while 0.1 or 0.2 per cent formalin is lethal after 33 days.

The virus survives at 5°C. for 3 months or if 20 per cent glycerin is added it is viable after 15 months' storage. Freezing at low temperatures followed by desiccation is not detrimental to the virus and it is preserved for at least 16 months in this condition.

Cultivation. Equine anemia virus has not been cultivated in chicken embryos or tissue cultures. The virus has been carried through 20 rabbit passages by Reagan and his co-workers.

Transmission. It is believed that under natural conditions equine anemia is spread by insect vectors and by ingestion, but insect vectors or other means of introducing infectious material beneath the skin are most important. It is known that the virus escapes from the infected host by the blood, urine, feces, milk, spermatic fluid, saliva, and nasal secretions. Transfer of the virus by blood may occur by biting flies, mosquitoes, lice, or by bleeding needles or surgical instruments which have been used on infected animals. Transfer of the virus from mare to foal may occur through the milk or *in utero*. Secretions and excretions may contaminate food or water with resulting transmission. The chronic carrier of the virus is of great importance in the dissemination of the disease because it may show no definite symptoms of the disease and there is no reliable test for its detection except horse inoculation.

Characteristics of the Disease. Equine anemia may be an acute, subacute, or chronic disease of horses, mules, or donkeys. The incubation period is usually from 12 to 15 days but in some cases may be as long as 2 months. The acute form begins with a temperature increase, which is followed by weakness, incoordination, rapid respiration, with loss in weight, anemia, and subcutaneous edema. Pregnant mares may abort during a period of febrile reaction. Death may result in 15 to 30 days or the animal may develop a subacute form of the disease. In such cases the anemia may be marked; the other symptoms continue. Some animals show the chronic forms with or without acute flare-ups of the disease. However, chronic cases have been shown to carry the virus in their blood for periods of 11 to 14 years. Such animals are a menace to other horses and if found should be destroyed.

In rabbits infected by artificial exposure a temperature rise is the only manifestation of the disease. Guinea pigs, which have been inoculated with the virus, may show a febrile reaction, loss in weight, and death in some cases. A Japanese commission reported that swine are susceptible to the virus but this was not confirmed by Stein.

A few cases of equine anemia in man are reported. The symptoms include headache, fever, anemia, edema, general debility, and loss of weight. A case of infection in a veterinarian, proved by horse inoculation, is reported by Peters.

Pathological Changes. The pathological changes which are seen at post-mortem of acute or subacute cases include general emaciation and edema, hemorrhages of mucous membranes, enlarged spleen and liver. The liver may be quite friable and will be a yellowish-brown color.

Gross changes in chronic cases are not marked or are entirely absent.

Immunity. A degree of resistance to equine anemia apparently exists in the chronic cases of the disease but such resistance does not enable the animal to rid itself of the virus.

Numerous attempts to produce immunity by a variety of common methods have all been unsuccessful.

Diagnosis. The only reliable diagnosis of equine infectious anemia is by horse inoculation. This is not an economical procedure, so temperature curves, clinical symptoms, blood counts, sedimentation rates of erythrocytes are used in areas where the disease has been proved to exist or as presumptive evidence of the disease.

Trifur gallinarum

Common Name. Avian-leucosis virus, fowl leucosis virus.

Disease Produced. Avian leucosis complex, fowl leucosis.

Hosts Affected. Chicken, also pheasant, and possibly turkey.

History and Distribution. Avian leucosis was described by Marek in 1907, and Ellerman and Bang in 1908 reported that the disease was transmissible and that the etiological agent was a virus. The filterability of the agent of avian leucosis has been repeatedly confirmed by other workers.

The fact that the word *complex* is retained in the designation of this disease is appropriate, and there is still much to be clarified with respect to the virus as the etiological agent as well as the relationship of the pathological manifestations to each other. It is not within the scope of this text to present the mass of data regarding the disease or the pathology. However, some of the characteristics of the virus are known and there is fairly general agreement on some phases of the disease which can be presented.

Avian leucosis is widespread among flocks of chickens in the United States and European countries. Death losses, unthriftiness, and lowered egg production as the result of this disease take a heavy annual toll from the income of poultry flocks.

Properties of the Virus. The particle size of leucosis virus is reported as about 72 mμ by Stern and Kirschbaum. It will pass all grades of Berkefeld and Seitz filters.

The virus is inactivated by a temperature of 56°C. applied for 30 minutes. It is preserved for at least 54 days in the dried state and for 104 days in glycerin at 4°C. or at −60°C. for 6 months or more. Viability is lost after 14 days at 37°C.

Cultivation. Avian leucosis virus has been cultivated or at least survives in chicken embryos if inoculated intravenously.

Transmission. Higher incidence of leucosis has been shown among chickens reared on premises in contact with infected birds. Progeny of infected stock show a high incidence of leucosis. Transmission through the egg occurs and the virus has been identified from eggs.

Characteristics of the Disease. The general types of the leucosis complex are:

1. Neural lymphomatosis—with cellular infiltration of the nerves and paralysis.

2. Ocular lymphomatosis—infiltration of the iris.

3. Visceral lymphomatosis—cellular infiltration involving visceral organs, especially the liver, spleen, kidney, and ovary.

4. Osteopetrotic lymphomatosis—involving the bones, especially the shanks.

5. Erythroblastic form—characterized by anemia.

6. Granuloblastic form—characterized by increase in leucocytes of the granuloblastic type in the circulating blood.

7. Myelocytomatosis—characterized by the formation of tumor masses in various organs.

According to the "unitarian theory," the same virus is the etiological agent of all the various types of the disease listed above, and there is much evidence to support this theory. On the other hand, some investigators have been able to isolate "pure virus" which will consistently reproduce one type of lesion. Whether there may be more than one virus or a single virus which rapidly undergoes variation or whether the host itself influences the type of pathological change produced is not clear. Much of the work on leucosis is hampered by the extreme difficulty in securing and maintaining leucosis-free experimental birds.

Pathological Changes. Briefly stated, the outstanding character of leucosis is the growth of cells of leucocytic types which infiltrate the various tissues of the infected bird, giving rise to various symptoms and lesions depending upon the site of infection.

Immunity. Little or no immunity results from natural infection and no immunizing agents are of value in the disease.

Diagnosis. A diagnosis of leucosis depends upon the finding of characteristic lesions and by blood studies.

REFERENCES FOR FURTHER STUDY

Trifur equorum (Equine infectious anemia)

Carré, H. J., and Vallée, H. P. Comp. Rend. Acad. Sci., 139:331, 1904.

Dreguss, M. N., and Lombard, L. S. Equine Infectious Anemia. University of Pennsylvania Press, Phila., Pa., 1954.

Horse Adm. Bureau Tokyo. Vet. Jour., 70:604, 1914.

Mohler, W. M. Jour. Amer. Vet. Med. Assn., 88:624, 1936.

Mohlmann, H., and Gralheer, H. Arch. Exp. Vet. Med., 8:204, 1954.

Peters, J. T. Ann. Int. Med., 23:271, 1945.

Reagen, R. L., Lillie, M. G., Hickman, J. W., and Brueckner, A. L. Amer. Jour. Vet. Res., 11:157, 1950.

Stein, C. D. Jour. Amer. Vet. Med. Assn., 87:312, 1935.

———. Vet. Med., 36:410, 1941.

———, Lotze, J. C., and Mott, L. O. Amer. Jour. Vet. Res., 3:183, 1942.

———, Lucker, J. T., Osteen, O. L., and Gochenour, W. S. Jour. Amer. Vet. Med. Assn., 95:536, 1939.

———, and Mott, L. O. Vet. Med., 37:9, 1942.

———, ———. Vet. Med., 39:408, 1944.

———, ———. Proc. U. S. Livestock San. Assn., 47:37, 1947.

———, and Osteen, O. L. Amer. Jour. Vet. Res., 2:344, 1941.

———, ———, Mott, L. O., and Shahan, M. S. Amer. Jour. Vet. Res., 5:291, 1944.

———, ———, ———, ———. Vet. Med., 39:46, 1944.

Trifur gallinarum (Avian leucosis)

Ellerman, E., and Bang, O. Centralb. f. Bakt. Abt. I. Orig., 46:4, 595, 1938.

Furth, J. Jour. Exp. Med., 53:243, 1931; 55:465, 495, 1932; 58:253, 1933; 59:501, 1934.

Hall, W. J., Bean, C. W., and Pollard, M. Amer. Jour. Vet. Res., 2:272, 1941.

Jungherr, E. L. The Avian Leucosis Complex, *in* Diseases of Poultry. 3rd ed. Edited by Biester, H. E., and Schwarte, L. H. Iowa State College Press, Ames, 1952.

Lee, C. D., Wilcke, H. L., Murray, C., and Henderson, E. W. Jour. Inf. Dis., 61:1, 1937.

———, ———. Amer. Jour. Vet. Res., 2:292, 1941.

Ratcliffe, H. L., and Stubbs, E. L. Jour. Inf. Dis., 56:301, 1935.

Stern, G., and Kirschbaum, A. Science, 89:610, 1939.

55. | The Genus Rabula and Unclassified Viruses

THE GENUS RABULA — The Mumps Group

Viruses of the mumps group induce disease characterized by changes in the salivary glands.

Rabula inflans

Mumps virus produces epidemic parotitis in man, with infections involving the testes, ovaries, and meninges in some cases. It does not produce natural disease in animals, although there are reports of reactions in monkeys, rabbits, and cats after experimental inoculation. The monkey is the most susceptible, and the virus can be passed serially in the animal.

Mumps virus can be grown in chicken embryos, and hemagglutination is an important characteristic which aids in experimental studies and diagnosis.

Rabula levis

Common Name. Guinea pig salivary gland virus.

Disease Produced. Guinea pig salivary gland disease.

Host Affected. Guinea pig.

Properties of the Virus. The virus will pass the Berkefeld N filter. It is inactivated by 54°C. for 1 hour. It will remain viable in glycerin for several weeks.

Transmission. Transmission is probably by contact with saliva of infected animals.

Characteristics of the Disease. The natural disease is not serious; however, intracerebral inoculation of the virus results in meningitis.

Pathological Changes. Acidophilic intracytoplasmic inclusions occur in the epithelium of salivary ducts. Intranuclear bodies are also found.

Immunity. Neutralizing antibodies are found in the serum of infected guinea pigs.

Diagnosis. A diagnosis of guinea pig salivary gland disease is based on the demonstration of inclusion bodies from the salivary glands and ducts and by intracerebral inoculations of saliva or salivary gland material into susceptible guinea pigs.

Rabula innocuus

This virus is known as the hamster salivary gland virus. It is not pathogenic except to the extent of producing inclusion bodies in the salivary glands of that animal.

Rabula exiguus

This is a virus causing intranuclear inclusions in the salivary glands of rats.

Rabula latens

Inclusion bodies in mice have been found in the salivary glands and this virus is described as the etiological agent.

UNCLASSIFIED VIRUSES

There are a number of viruses which are unclassified, including those which are newly discovered and those on which the data is incomplete.

Diseases of Cattle

Malignant Catarrhal Fever. The etiology of this disease is thought to be a virus but the evidence is doubted by some. The disease occurs throughout Europe, in South Africa, the United States and has been identified in Brazil. It is ordinarily sporadic in occurrence and does not spread to any extent through a herd. The most pronounced lesions are found in the upper respiratory tract and in the oral cavity, consisting of marked congestion and necrosis in these areas with much muco-purulent exudate covering the mucous membranes and discharging from the nostrils. Involvement of the brain, intestinal tract and lungs usually results in a more serious form of the disease and most of the animals die.

The disease has been difficult to transmit with regularity. Sheep and goats are thought to harbor the virus.

Malignant catarrhal fever is confused in some countries with Rinderpest and according to some authorities in South Africa with the disease designated there as snotsiekte.

Virus Diarrhea of Cattle. Olafson, MacCallum, and Fox, in 1946, described a disease of cattle occurring in New York which is characterized by diarrhea and lesions in areas throughout the digestive tract. The disease has been reproduced in cattle by the inoculation of bacteria-free filtrates. A disease of cattle which is clinically similar has been described by Pritchard *et al.* in Indiana. This disease has been designated as Indiana virus diarrhea and as erosive gastroenteritis.

Neither the New York nor the Indiana viruses have been studied to any extent. Pritchard has shown them to be antigenically distinct. Olafson has reported that the New York type is not antigenically related to the rinderpest virus. The Indiana type will pass through a Berkefeld N filter. Attempts to infect other animals and chicken embryos have been unsuccessful. Cattle infected with virus diarrhea show leucopenia, high temperature, diarrhea, salivation, nasal discharge, and dehydration. Varying degrees of erosion and of ulceration of the mucous membranes of the mouth, tongue, pharynx, and esophagus occur. Hemorrhages may be seen in various mucous surfaces. Laminitis and a nonproductive cough are often seen in the Indiana type of the disease. Morbidity is higher in the Indiana type, with nearly 100 per cent of the cattle in some herds becoming affected, while morbidity many range from 33 to 88 per cent in the New York type. Mortality is reported as 0 to 50 per cent in both types.

Virus diarrhea in many respects resembles rinderpest, mucosal disease as described by Ramsey, malignant catarrhal fever, and infectious rhinotracheitis, and therefore presents a problem in differential diagnosis.

Ephemeral Fever. A virus disease of cattle called ephemeral fever, "three day sickness," or "stiff sickness," was originally reported by Bevan in 1907 from Africa. The disease also occurs in Australia, India, and countries of the Middle East.

Very little information is available regarding the virus. Although artificial inoculations of blood from an infected animal will transmit the disease with regularity, filtrates of laked blood have usually failed.

The bovine is apparently the only animal which is susceptible to the disease. It does not spread from one animal to another by contact, but is spread by biting insects. It is most prevalent during wet seasons.

The disease is acute with sudden onset. There is observed high temperature, nasal discharge, muscular stiffness, lameness, and depression. Reluctance to swallow is especially evident in the sick animal. Recovery usually occurs in 3 to 5 days. Mortality rates are low.

Infectious Infertility of Cattle. In 1938, Daubney, Hudson, and Anderson described a disease of cattle in Kenya, East Africa, which accounted for considerable sterility. It is believed to be caused by a virus. Vaginitis of the cows and epididymitis in the bull are the outstanding features of the condition. The disease is transmitted by the bull in breeding.

A similar if not identical condition has been described by Mc-Intosh, Haig, and Alexander in the Union of South Africa. These investigators report that the virus which they isolated in suckling mice and chicken embryos from cases of vaginitis in cattle is less than 100 mμ in size. Upon adaptation to mice, the virus produces lethal effects in that host. Edema and pocks were produced on the chorio-allantoic membrane of the chicken embryos.

Lumpy Skin Disease. A disease of cattle called lumpy skin disease was first reported by McDonald, in 1931, under the name of pseudo-urticaria. It occurs only in various parts of Africa.

A virus thought to be the etiological agent has been reported by Van Den Ende *et al.* This virus was isolated from the skin of cattle with lesions of lumpy skin disease by chicken embryo inoculation. It produces edema of the chorio-allantoic membrane, stunting of the embryo, and hemorrhages of the feather follicles. Filtrates from a Gradacol membrane with A.P.D. of 52 mμ or larger are infective while those having an A.P.D. of 21 mμ retained the virus. However, difficulty has been encountered in the reproduction of lesions of lumpy skin disease by the inoculation of the chicken embryo virus into cattle. Insect transmission is suggested by some of the characteristics of the epizootiology. The virus can be demonstrated in the blood in the early stages of the disease and has also been demonstrated in the saliva.

The disease is of sudden onset, with high temperature followed by the development of skin nodules in 7 to 10 days. The center of the skin nodule may become necrotic, but not in all cases. The entire skin surface as well as the mucous membranes may develop the nodules. The losses from the disease are in lowered milk production, loss of weight, and occasional deaths.

Diseases of Sheep

Scrapie. A virus disease of sheep known in Europe since the early 1700's has been called scrapie because the outstanding symptom is that of scratching or scraping the skin. The virus is neurotropic and produces characteristic degenerative changes in the central nervous system, causing incoordination, paralysis, and death of the infected animal.

Adult sheep are the chief hosts, but goats are susceptible.

The virus has not been studied to any extent because of the difficulties in growing it. It has not been cultivated artificially in any host except sheep or goats. Furthermore, it is most difficult to investigate because of the extremely long incubation period of 18 months to over 2 years.

The disease was reported in North America for the first time by Schofield of Ontario, Canada, in 1939. It was reported in Michigan in 1947 and in California in 1952. Several other states have reported the occurrence of scrapie, but the numbers of sheep that have been infected has been small.

All of the symptoms exhibited by the infected animal are referable to damage to the nervous system. The affected sheep will rub the skin on various objects such as fences and will show the attitude of the "scratch reflex" when rubbed. They may become excitable, with the head carried higher than normal. Convulsions may occur in some animals. The disease usually lasts for several weeks to 6 months, becoming progressively more severe until death ensues.

Histopathological examination of the central nervous system will show marked vacuolation of the neuron cells which is diagnostic of the disease. More of the cells of the medulla show this change than those from other parts of the brain. Apparently no immunity results from having the disease, since there are no recoveries.

Diseases of Swine

Transmissible Gastroenteritis of Pigs. A virus disease of swine, especially of the newborn, characterized by diarrhea, vomition, dehydration, and high mortality, was described by Doyle and Hutchings in 1946. Since that time the disease has been recognized throughout swine-raising areas of the United States.

According to Young *et al.* the virus will pass through a Gradacol membrane having a pore diameter of 230 mμ, but fails to pass through one of 170 mμ average pore diameter.

The virus has been cultivated in tissue cultures composed of swine kidney and produces a cytopathogenic effect.

Attempts to transmit the disease to other animals have been unsuccessful. Transmission of the virus is by ingestion or by inhalation. Newborn pigs are highly susceptible by intranasal inoculation, and air-borne transmission is believed to be important in the rapid spread of the disease in this age of pig. It is believed that the virus is introduced into some herds by inapparent carrier swine.

The disease is most severe in pigs under five days of age. Diarrhea, vomition, and rapid dehydration are characterisitc. Mortality ranges from 80 to 100 per cent. The severity and mortality rates progressively decrease as the pigs become older. Older swine may show mild symptoms, while some infections are of the inapparent type.

Immunity to transmissible gastroenteritis virus follows an attack and recovery. Neutralizing antibodies can be demonstrated in the serum of convalescent swine. Serum from immune swine will protect pigs from fatal infection.

Diseases of Fowl

Navel Infection. A disease described in 1947 by Eveleth, Bolin, and Goldsby, in North Dakota, was responsible for considerable losses in turkey poults and baby chicks at the college farm at Fargo. The outstanding lesions occur in the umbilical region and are characterized by necrosis. The disease is transmissible by bacteria-free filtrates and the etiology is concluded to be a virus. The agent has been grown in chicken embryos and it is lethal to a high percentage of them.

The offspring of certain hens were observed to die from the infection while those of others did not.

Injection of the virus into mature hens produced no disease in most individuals but the death of some birds occurred, with severe inflammation of the ovary and oviduct.

ADDITIONAL VIRUSES WHICH INFECT ANIMALS

SCIENTIFIC NAME	COMMON NAME	DISEASE
Jungablutia columbia	Columbia SK-MM	Encephalomyocarditis of rodents
Rocacea alpha	Anopheles A virus	Isolated from mosquitoes in South America
Rocacea beta	Anopheles B virus	Isolated from mosquitoes in South America
Rocacea wyeomyia	Wyeomyia virus	Isolated from mosquitoes in South America
Rocacea hammonii	California virus	Isolated from mosquitoes in California
Rocacea semliki	Semliki forest virus	Isolated from mosquitoes in Africa
Rocacae dickii	Uganda S virus	Isolated from mosquitoes in Africa
Rocacea zika	Zika forest virus	Isolated from mosquitoes in Africa
Rocacea ntaya	Ntaya swamp virus	Isolated from mosquitoes in Africa
	Nairobi sheep disease	Tick-borne gastroenteritis of sheep and goats
	Mouse hepatitis virus	Hepatitis of mice

ADDITIONAL VIRUSES WHICH INFECT HUMAN BEINGS

SCIENTIFIC NAME	COMMON NAME	DISEASE
Briareus varicellae	Chicken pox virus	Chicken pox
Morbillifex morbillorum	Measles virus	Classical measles
Morbillifex embryorum	German measles virus	German measles
Morbillifex subitus	Roseola subitum virus	Roseola subitum
Smithburnia bunyamwera	Bunyamwera encephalitis virus	Bunyamwera encephalitis
Smithburnia bwamba	Bwamba fever virus	Bwamba fever
Dalldorfia coxsackie	Coxsackie virus	Encephalitis
Reedella triginta	Infectious hepatitis virus	Hepatitis
Reedella centum	Serum hepatitis virus	Hepatitis
Sabina doerrii	Sandfly fever virus	Sandfly fever
Sabina ashburnii	Dengue fever virus	Dengue fever
Sabina coloradensis	Colorado tick fever virus	Colorado tick fever

REFERENCES FOR FURTHER STUDY

Rabula inflans (Mumps)

Van Rooyen, C. E., and Rhodes, A. J. Virus Diseases of Man. Thomas Nelson and Sons, New York, 1948.

Animal salivary gland viruses

Cole, R., and Kuttner, A. Jour. Exp. Med., 44:855, 1926.

Kuttner, A., and Wang, S. Jour. Exp. Med., 60:773, 1934.

McCordock, H. A., and Smith, M. Jour. Exp. Med., 63:303, 1936.

Malignant catarrhal fever

Henning, M. W. Animal Diseases in South Africa. Central News Agency Ltd., 1932.

Hutyra, F., Marek, J., and Manninger, R. Special Pathology and Therapeutics of the Diseases of Domestic Animals. Vol. I. Alex. Eger, Chicago, 1946.

Virus diarrhea of cattle

Olafson, P., MacCallum, A. D., and Fox, F. H. Cornell Vet., 36:205, 1946.

————, and Rickard, C. G. Cornell Vet., 37:104, 1947.

Pritchard, W. R., Taylor, D. B., Moses, H. E., and Doyle, L. P. Jour. Amer. Vet. Med. Assn., 128:1, 1956.

Ramsey, F K., and Chivers, W. H. North Amer. Vet., 34:629, 1953.

Walker, R. V. L., and Olafson, P. Cornell Vet., 37:107, 1947.

Ephemeral fever

Bevan, L. E. W. Jour. Comp. Path. Therap., 20:104, 1907.

Seddon, H. R. Aust. Vet. Jour., 14:90, 1938.

Infectious infertility of cattle

Daubney, R., Hudson, J. R., and Anderson, J. East Afr. Agr. Jour., 4:31, 1938.

McIntosh, B. M., Haig, D. A., and Alexander, R. A. Onderstepoort Jour. Vet. Res., 26:479, 1954.

Lumpy skin disease

McDonald, R. A. S. Dept. Animal Health Annual Rpt., Northern Rhodesia, 1931.

Polson, A., and Turner, G. S. Jour. Gen. Microbiol., 11:228, 1954.

Thomas, A. D., and More, C. E. Jour. So. Afr. Vet. Med. Assn., 16:36, 1945.

Van Den Ende, M., Don, P., and Kipps, A. Jour. Gen. Microbiol., 3:174, 1949.

————, ————, ————, and Alexander, R. A. Nature, 161:526, 1948.

Von Backstrom, U. Jour. So. Afr. Vet. Med. Assn., 16:29, 1945.

Scrapie

Cuille, J., and Chelle, P. L. Rev. Path. Comp., 38:1358, 1938.

Editorial, Jour. Amer. Vet. Med. Assn., 121:455, 1952.

Gaiger, S. H. Jour. Comp. Path. Therap., 37:259, 1924.

Holman, H. H., and Pattison, I. H. Jour. Comp. Path. Therap., 53:231, 1943.

Plummer, P. J. G. Canad. Jour. Comp. Med., 10:49, 1946.

Schofield, F. W. Rpt. Ontario Vet. Coll. for 1938. P. 34, 1939.

Thorp, F., Judd, A. W., Gray, M. L., and Scholl, L. B. Michigan State College Vet., 13:36, 1952.

Transmissible gastroenteritis of pigs

Bay, W. W. Jour. Amer. Vet. Med. Assn., 120:283, 1952.

————, Doyle, L. P., and Hutchings, L. M. Jour. Amer. Vet. Med. Assn., 122:200, 1953.

Doyle, L. P., and Hutchings, L. M. Jour. Amer. Vet. Med. Assn., 108:257, 1946.
Young, G. A., Hinz, R. W., and Underdahl, N. R. Amer. Jour. Vet. Res., 16:259, 1955.
————, Underdahl, N. R., and Hinz, R. W. Cornell Vet., 43:561, 1953.

Navel infection

Bolin, F. M., Schlamb, K. F., Bryant, R. L., and Eveleth, D. F. Amer. Jour. Vet. Res., 10:391, 1949.
Eveleth, D. F., Bolin, F. M., and Goldsby, A. I. No. Dak. Agr. Exp. Sta. Bimonth. Bull., 9:160, 1947.

Additional viruses infecting animals

Daubney, R., and Hudson, J. R. Parasitology, 23:507, 1931.
Gledhill, A. W., and Andrewes, C. H. Brit. Jour. Exp. Path., 32:559, 1951.
Montgomery, R. E. Jour. Comp. Path. Therap., 30:28, 1917.
Van Rooyen, C. E. Canad. Jour. Microbiol., 1:227, 1954.

Additional viruses infecting human beings

Van Rooyen, C. E. Canad. Jour. Microbiol., 1:227, 1954.

56.

The Genus Phagus—

the Bacteriophages or Bacterial Viruses

Under the genus *Phagus,* family *Phagaceae* of the suborder *Phagineae,* are placed those viruses which attack bacteria.

History

An interesting phenomenon was reported in 1915 by Twort who was working with a staphylococcus isolated from calf-lymph vaccine. He observed a visible change in some of the colonies which was found to be transmissible and it suggested a "disease of bacteria." Furthermore, it was found that filtrates of the changed cultures would also initiate the "disease" of the staphylococcus.

D'Herelle, working independently, made similar observations on colonies of a cocco-bacillus isolated from an intestinal disease of locusts. In areas of confluent growth of this organism on agar, there would occasionally be small areas where no growth would occur.

In another experiment D'Herelle was searching for a virus in dysentery and typhoid fever of man. He thought a virus might be associated with these diseases in the same way as the hog cholera virus had a few years earlier been found to be associated with *Sal. choleraesuis* as the cause of hog cholera. To test his hypothesis, D'Herelle injected *Shig. dysenteriae* and *Sal. typhosa* together with filtrates of fecal materials collected from cases of the disease into laboratory animals to try to reproduce the disease. He also tried mixtures of these organisms and the filtrates on agar plates. It was found that filtrates from patients recovering from the disease would produce the same phenomena as seen with the organisms from the locusts. The addition of filtrates at the time of inoculation of broth cultures resulted in failure of growth and, furthermore, if the filtrates were added in the early stages of growth, the bacterial cells were observed to undergo lysis with consequent clearing of the tubes. This was the beginning of many years' work in which D'Herelle found bacteriophages from many sources. The name *bacteriophage* was proposed by D'Herelle because of the disappearance of the bacterial cells in the presence of these viruses.

Since the work of Twort and D'Herelle, much work has been done on the bacterial viruses which has contributed significantly to the knowledge of viruses in general as well as having many practical applications.

Properties of the Bacterial Viruses (Bacteriophages)

Size and Morphology. The size of the bacterial viruses varies from those which are 10 to 20 mµ to some nearly 100 mµ. Most of those which have been photographed under the electron microscope have a "tadpole" or sperm-shaped particle (Fig. 56.1). The body of the particles in Figure 56.1 is spherical, 70 mµ in diameter, and a distinct tail is observed which is 30 mµ wide and 150 mµ in length.

Cultivation. The bacterial viruses can not be cultivated except in the presence of living susceptible bacteria. Growth rates are quite rapid upon the addition of a virus to a culture of its host organism. Apparently a virus particle enters a host cell and multiplies until it bursts the cell and liberates the newly formed particles. The *burst times* vary with various viruses, but may be from 13 to 40 minutes, and the yield of virus per cell varies from 120 to 400 particles.

Resistance. The bacterial viruses are in general more resistant to heat than the animal viruses. Whereas a majority of the animal viruses are killed by exposure to a temperature of 56°C. for 30 minutes, many of the bacterial viruses require 60°C. for 30 minutes or even higher temperatures. *Strep. lactis* phages, for example, resist milk pasteurization temperatures, 62°C., for 30 minutes.

A majority of bacteriophages are resistant to aging and to drying.

Antigenic Structure. Like most viruses, the bacteriophages are antigenic when injected into the animal body. Antiphage serum is specific and neutralizes the action of the phage against its host bacteria. Different strains of phage which attack the same bacterial species have been distinguished by means of serological tests.

Specificity of the Bacterial Viruses. Among the bacterial viruses are examples of the extreme in host specificity. Certain phages are able to distinguish strains of bacteria within a species which cannot be distinguished by any other means. On the other hand, some phages attack different species of bacteria within the same genus, especially if the bacteria are antigenically similar.

Interference Phenomena of Bacterial Viruses. It has been shown that the phenomena of virus interference occurs among the bacterial viruses. If two serologically distinguishable viruses which are capable of attacking the same species of bacteria are added together, one may predominate in some cases to the complete exclusion of the other. It appears that when one particle of the virus enters the bacterial cell it prevents in some manner the entry of other virus particles. The mechanism is analogous to cell

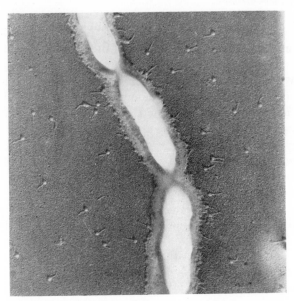

FIG. 56.1 — **Strep. lactis** and bacteriophage, × 15,000. Courtesy Parmellee, Carr and Nelson. **Jour. Bact.**, 57:391, 1949.

blockade and virus interference as described for several animal viruses.

It has also been observed that in some instances interference does not occur and more than one virus multiplies in the same organism.

Genetic Variation of Bacterial Viruses. The observations of Hershey regarding the genetics of bacteriophages are of interest and pose some intriguing possibilities in virus study. This investigator observed that two related but distinguishable viruses of *E. coli* will grow in the same cell at the same time, and among the viral progeny appear types different from either "parent" virus.

Pathological Changes. The effect of a bacterial virus on a susceptible bacterial cell is lysis. The virus grows and multiplies until the cell bursts, expelling the cell contents and the newly developed virus particles. Electron micrographs have clearly shown bacterial cell disintegration as the result of phage attacks.

Broth cultures which show turbidity may be seen to clear in a matter of hours as a result of lytic action. Lysis may occur in agar colonies, and variation in colony characteristics is sometimes observed.

The appearance of resistant mutants among susceptible strains of bacteria is frequently noted.

Enumeration of Bacterial Viruses

The usual method of determining the amount of virus present in a solution is the plaque counting technic. A *plaque* is the clear area showing no growth on an agar plate which is seeded with the host organism and the virus which will attack it. By making appropriate dilutions of materials, the plaques can be counted in a manner similar to a bacterial plate count.

It is presumed that each plaque counted is from a single particle of virus in the original inoculum.

The size and other characteristics of the plaques are useful in classification and recognition of the phages. Some of the species of bacteria associated with animals and man for which bacteriophages have been demonstrated are *E. coli, Sal. typhosa, Sal. pullorum, Sal. paratyphi, Sal. enteritidis, Sal. choleraesuis, Shig. dysenteriae, Aerob. aerogenes, Klebs. pneumoniae, Past. multocida, Past. pestis, Past. pseudotuberculosis, Vibrio comma, Bacillus subtilis, Bacillus anthracis, Coryn. diphtheriae, Strep. pyogenes, Strep. equisimilis, Strep. lactis, Micrococcus aureus,* and *Myco. tuberculosis.* There are many plant bacteria for which phages have been isolated.

Habitat of Bacterial Viruses

As with other viruses, the habitat of the bacterial viruses is found to be essentially the same as their hosts. Undoubtedly the richest source of phages for the bacteria associated with animals and animal disease is sewage and intestinal contents. However, if one were to isolate a phage active against *Strep. lactis,* a creamery, cheese factory, or milk-processing plant would be the obvious place to examine, since it is in these places that the organism and likewise its phage are most likely to be concentrated.

Practical Considerations

D'Herelle conceived the idea from his early work that a bacteriophage would be a great weapon in the fight against diseases of man and animals. He investigated outbreaks of animal disease and held the view that recovery from infection and cessation of the outbreak were related to the occurrence of a bacteriophage which was active against the organism producing the disease. D'Herelle further reported resistance to infection by the injection of phage into susceptible animals. In spite of the encouraging work of D'Herelle, the use of bacteriophage for the treatment of disease has been quite limited. One of the difficulties has been the high host specificity of the phages, and the fact that a phage may act only on a single strain of the disease-producing organism. This would necessitate typing of the organism causing each outbreak and the maintenance of many phage strains.

Bacteriophage has been used successfully in typhoid fever in man, but the difficulties mentioned above, as well as other factors, have prevented its general use in the treatment of the disease. The problem of bacteriophage activity against *Strep. lactis* is very important to the dairy industry which uses this organism to ripen cream, for butter-making and in cheese-making.

In some milk plants, phage prevents proper development of the cultures and as a result considerable economic loss is suffered from inferior products.

Phage studies have aided in the classification of several species of bacteria. Differences in phage susceptibility have been shown in strains of bacteria which are otherwise indistinguishable as well as showing relationships among others which may vary in other respects, such as biochemical activity.

Classification of Bacterial Viruses

The first systematic classification of the bacteriophages appears in the 6th edition of Bergey's Manual of Determinative Bacteriology. In this classification, F. O. Holmes has placed the phages in one genus *Phagus* and has described 46 species. The bases for separation of these viruses is host specificity, size of virus particle, size of plaque produced, and thermal inactivation. All of the known bacteriophages are not described in this classification but most of the common ones are listed. For the complete classification refer to Bergey's Manual.

REFERENCES FOR FURTHER STUDY

Bacterial viruses

D'Herelle, F. Comp. Rend. Acad. Sci., 165:373, 1917.

———. The Bacteriophage and its Behavior. English translation by Smith, G. H. The Williams & Wilkins Co., Baltimore, 1926.

Hershey, A. D. Genetics., 31:620, 1946.

———, and Bronfenbrenner, J. Bacterial Viruses: Bacteriophages *in* Viral and Rickettsial Diseases of Man. Edited by T. M. Rivers. J. B. Lippincott Co., Philadelphia, 1948.

Holmes, F. O. Filterable Viruses *in* Bergey's Manual of Determinative Bacteriology. 6th edition. The Williams & Wilkins Co., Baltimore, 1948.

Knouf, E. G., Ward, W. E., Reichle, P. A., Bower, A. G., and Hamilton, P. M. Jour. Amer. Vet. Med. Assn., 132:134, 1946.

Parmellee, C. E., Carr, P. H., and Nelson, F. E. Jour. Bact., 57:391, 1949.

Twort, F. W. Lancet, 2:1241, 1915.

Wilson, G. S., and Miles, A. A. The Bacteriophage *in* Topley and Wilson's Principles of Bacteriology and Immunity. 3rd edition. The Williams & Wilkins Co., Baltimore, 1946.

Index

Index

A antigen, 328
Abbe condenser, 10, 72
Abortion
  due to Brucella abortus, 385
  due to Brucella suis, 386
  due to Leptospira pomona, 592
  due to Vibrio fetus, 317
  of equines, 354, 691, 791
Abortus-Bang Ring (ABR) test, 391
Absidia, 634
  ramosa, 634
Achromobacteriaceae, 250
Acid agglutination, 193
Acid fast, 526
Acid-fast organisms
  stains for, 80
    Gabbett's method, 81
    Ziehl-Neelsen method, 80
Acid milk, 276
Acidophiles, 122
Acids, 122
  as preservatives, 122
Actinobacillosis, 439
Actinobacillus, 250
  actinoides, 441
  lignieresi, 439, 572
Actinomyces, 250, 572
  antibioticus, 137
  bovis, 441, 572
  graminis, 573
  griseus, 138
  hominis, 573
  israeli, 572, 576
  lavendulae, 131, 138
Actinomycetaceae, 250
Actinomycetales, 250
Actinomycin A, 137
Actinomycin B, 137
Actinomycosis, 572
Acute bloody diarrhea in newborn
  puppies, 339
Adenine, 55
Aerobacter, 250, 324, 332
  aerogenes, 332
Aerobes, 49
African horse sickness, 691, 789
African swine fever, 786

Agar cup-plate method, 119
Agar plate method, 118
Agents, decolorizing, 75
Agglutination, 190, 680
  in bacterial differentiation, 194
  macroscopic plate test, 197
  macroscopic tube test, 197
  microscopic test, 196
  test in avian tuberculosis, 549
  test for brucellosis, 391
  test for glanders, 436
Agglutinin, 190, 191
  absorption test, 194
  method of action of, 192
  significance of in immunity, 195
Aggressin, 168
Agricultural bacteriology, definition
  of, 4
Alcaligenes, 250
Alcohol, 125
Alexin, 205
Algacide, 100
Alimentary allergy, 236
Alkalies, 123
Allergen, 236
Allergin, 236
Allergy, 228, 229, 235
  and anaphylaxis, differences be-
    tween, 231
  in animals, 236
  bacterial, 236
  terminology of, 236
Allicin, 144
Alpha globulin, 173
Alpha hemolysin, 291
Alpha-hydroxy-phenazine, 307
Alternate passage, 660
Alum-precipitated toxoid (APT), 508
Amino acids, 58
Ammonia, oxidation of by bacteria,
  59
Ammonification, 58
Amphitrichous bacteria, 26
Anaerobes, 49
Anaerobic methods, 68
Anamnestic reaction, 178
Anaphylactin, 231

*Composed in Linotype Textype by the
Iowa State College Press.*

Chapter headings in Ludlow Tempo Bold.

*Running heads and subheadings in Linotype
Spartan Heavy.*

Paper stock: Warren's 60-pound Westbrook Gloss.

*Cover cloth: Holliston Roxite Record Buckram
No. 63292.*

*Printed at the Iowa State
College Press, Ames, Iowa.*